[1]

The Norwegian Kvaerner-Fjellstrand Foil Cat research craft, a precursor for economical and comfortable ferries over 50 knots.

JANE'S HIGH-SPEED MARINE CRAFT
1990

Twenty-Third Edition

Edited by
Eur Ing Robert L Trillo
CEng, FIMechE, FRAeS, AFAIAA, AFCASI

JANE'S TRANSPORT DATA

Part of the Jane's Information Group

ISBN 0 7106 0903 5

ADMINISTRATION
Publisher: Ken Harris

Managing Editor: Philip Butterworth-Hayes

Product Group Manager: Alida Macchietto

Research: Wendy Adamson

EDITORIAL OFFICES
Jane's Information Group Limited, Sentinel House, 163 Brighton Road, Coulsdon, Surrey CR5 2NH, United Kingdom. Tel: 081 763 1030. International 4481 763 1030. Telex 916907 Janes G. Fax: 081 763 1005. International 4481 763 1005.

Typesetting, origination and printing in the United Kingdom by Butler and Tanner Ltd.

SALES OFFICES
Send enquiries to: Iain Duncan Smith, Sales Director, Jane's Information Group Limited, UK address as above. Or in the USA to: Joe McHale, Vice-President Sales, Jane's Information Group Inc., 1340 Braddock Place, Suite 300, Alexandria, VA 22314-1651. Tel: (703) 683 3700. Fax: (703) 836 0029.

ADVERTISEMENT SALES OFFICES

Group Advertisement Sales Director: Simon Kay

Australia: Stephen Goddard, Stephen M.K. Goddard Representation, Suite 17, 118 Queen Street, Woolahra, NSW 2025. Tel: (02) 327 8577. Telex: 177816; Fax (02) 327 8357.

Austria: Tony Currow, see United Kingdom.

Benelux: Sandie Palmer, see United Kingdom.

Brazil: L. Bilyk, Brazmedia International s/c Ltda, Alameda Gabriel Monteiro da Silva 366, CEP, 01442 São Paulo, Brazil. Tel: (011) 853 4133. Telex: 32836 BMED BR. Fax: (011) 852 6485.

Canada: Monika Cornell, see USA.

France: Marie Hélène Causse, Agence MHC, 20-22 rue Valadon, 75007 Paris. Tel. 01 45 55 63 43. Telex. SELEX F 642138 MHC 171. Fax (01) 45 55 99 34.

Germany: Tony Currow, See United Kingdom

Israel: Tony Currow, see United Kingdom.

Italy and Switzerland: Dott Vittorio Negrone, Ediconsult Internazionale Srl, Piazza Fontane Marose 3, 16123 Genoa. Tel. (010) 268278, 268334, 268513. Fax (010) 56 65 78. Telex 281197 EDINT 1.

Korea: Young-Seoh Chinn, JES Media International, KPO Box 576, Seoul. Tel (02) 545 8001, (02) 549 5561.

Scandinavia: Denise Woodhatch, see United Kingdom.

Singapore, Indonesia, Malaysia, Philippines, Taiwan and Thailand: Hoo Siew Sai, Ad Media Pte Ltd, 3 Philipp Street, No 0902 Matterhorn Building, Singapore 0104. Tel 532 4026. Telex RS 43370. Fax 532 4027.

Spain: Angel Macho Diaz, Varenga JA, Modesto Lafuente, 428010, Madrid. Tel. (01) 4460214. Fax. (01) 4460198.

United States: Monika Cornell, Jane's Information Group Inc, 1340 Braddock Place, Suite 300, Alexandria, VA 22314-1651. Tel. (703) 683 3700. Fax (703) 836 0029.

United Kingdom/Rest of World: Tony Currow, Denise Woodhatch, Sandie Palmer, Jane's Information Group, Sentinel House, 163 Brighton Road, Coulsdon, Surrey CR5 2NH. Tel. (081) 763 1030. Telex 916907 JANES G. Fax (081) 763 1005.

Administration Manager: Jenny Collen, Jane's Information Group. See United Kingdom.

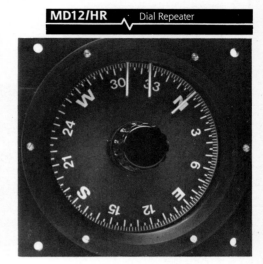

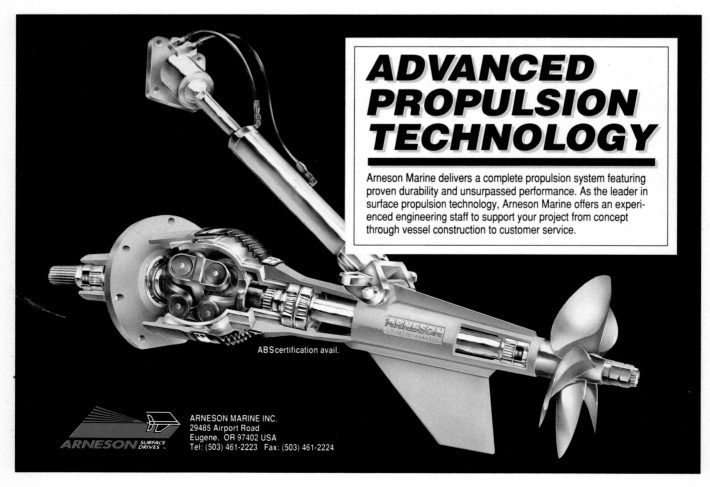

Contents

Alphabetical list of advertisers

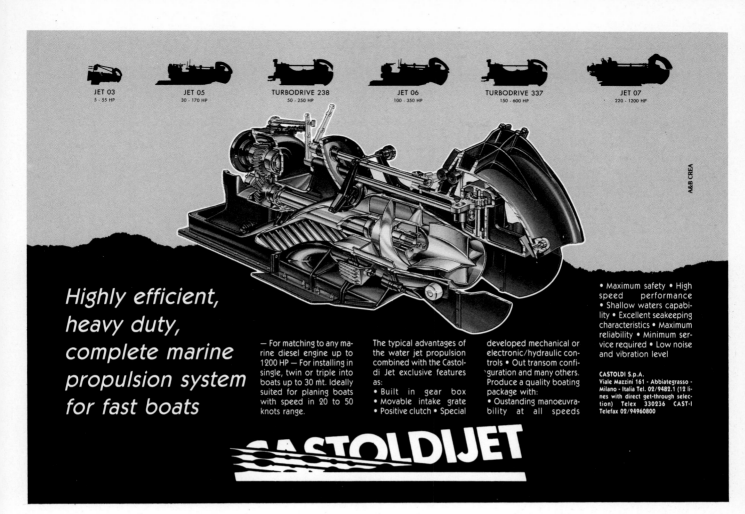

Classified list of advertisers

The companies advertising in this publication have informed us that they are involved in the fields of manufacture indicated below:

Air-boats and hydrofoils
Royal Schelde

Air cushion skirt systems
Northern Rubber

Controllable pitch propellers
KaMeWa

Design, Consultancy and Tank Testing
BMT Fluid Mechanics

Engines
Cummins Engine Company
MTU
Ruston Diesels
SACM
Turbomeca

High-speed catamaran vessels
Atlantic Marine
Fjellstrand
Hike Metal Products
Mitsui Engineering & Shipbuilding
Royal Schelde

High-speed mono-hull craft
Atlantic Marine
Crestitalia
Hike Metal Products
Rodriquez
Smuggler Marine AB Sweden
Smuggler Marine UK

Hydrofoils
Rodriquez

Navigation system
Marine Data

On-board generating sets
SACM
MTU

Propulsion systems
Arneson Marine
Cummins Engine Company
FIAT Aviazione
SACM

Surface Drives
Arneson Marine

Surface Piercing Propulsion
Arneson Marine

Surface Propellers
Arneson Marine

Waterjet propulsion systems
Castoldi
CWF Hamilton
KaMeWa
Riva Calzoni
SACM

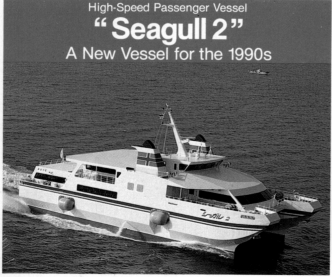

HM Customs and Excise needed low speed manoeuvrability,

the Royal Hong Kong Marine Police wanted no unscheduled downtime,

the New York State Police Department required high propulsion efficiency,

and the West German Customs demanded high speed.

Hamilton Jet gave them everything.

No matter what the application, Hamilton Jet marine propulsion systems can deliver propulsion efficiency with reliability and without unscheduled downtime.

That's why Defence Forces and Government Agencies around the world specify Hamilton Jet. Proven in the most demanding conditions, Hamilton Jets are found wherever a tough job needs doing.

From patrol and assault craft through to passenger and fishing vessels, Hamilton power them all.

The pioneers of marine jet propulsion over 30 years ago, Hamilton Jet are still at the forefront of technology with millions of dollars spent on advanced research and development, and special features no other unit can match.

Highly Specified. Hamilton Jet

Manufactured in New Zealand by CWF Hamilton and Co Ltd, P O Box 709, Christchurch, New Zealand, Ph: (3) 484-179, Fax: (3) 486-969.
Worldwide Distributors — Italy, Spain, UK, USA, Canada, India, France, Germany, Holland, Australia,
Finland, Hong Kong, Indonesia, Korea, Norway, Singapore, Sweden, Taiwan, Japan and Malaysia.

CWF0001C

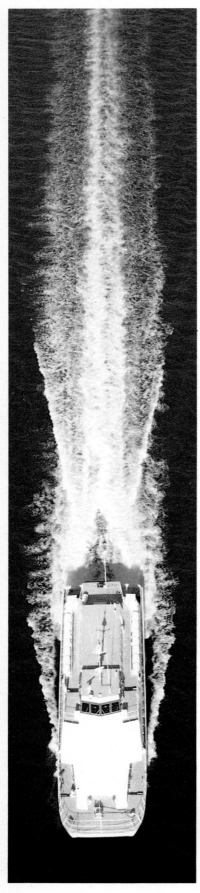

Fly the sea - with special quality

Only the best is good enough for Fjellstrand passenger catamarans, which are tailor- made to achieve the optimum combination of speed, comfort and reliability.

Backed by long experience and comprehensive research, the quality achieved by these ultra- fast, ultra-smooth vessels guarantees top technical and economic performance.

Fjellstrand's sea-skimming designs emphasise operational reliability and high regularity in any appropriate type of traffic, with maintenance kept to a minimum.

At service speed, the noise level in the upper saloon is a mere 62 db(A), and only 68 db(A) amidship in the lower saloon.

All-indoor production using modern machinery and systems is backed by continuous testing and a fully developed quality assurance system.

As world leader in catamaran construction, Fjellstrand offers a total transport concept - including market and economic analyses, financing, crew training and technical/ operational management.

Get in touch today - and learn how to FLY THE SEA.

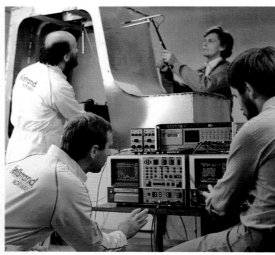

fjellstrand

Fjellstrand a.s - N-5632 Omastrand, Norway - Tel. + 47 5 55 41 00 - Telefax + 47 5 55 42 44 - Telex 42 148 fboat n

FOREWORD

The 1990s are going to see a rapid surge forward in the application of the high-speed craft technologies that have been so dynamically developed and commercially exploited by world leaders Australia and Norway over the past ten years. Though ill-defined, the terms boat, craft, vessel and ship do convey in people's minds some general ideas as to size and there is now no doubt that fast ships are coming. This year we shall see the first two 74m, 35 knot passenger/car Wave-Piercing-Catamaran ferries (built by International Catamarans (Tasmania) Pty. Ltd) operated by Hoverspeed Ltd. from Portsmouth to Cherbourg, with a payload capability of 450 passengers and over 80 cars. A further two have been ordered by Sea Containers for Hoverspeed Ltd., probably for the shorter English Channel crossing and a fifth ship for 1991 service with Tasmanian Ferry Services, the latter designed to carry 350 passengers plus 70 cars across the Bass Strait in 4 hours 10 minutes. The previous largest high-speed craft in commercial use have been the two BHC SRN4 Mk.3 hovercraft at 56.40m length (424 passengers plus 55 cars) which have provided an effective but rather bumpy crossing of the English Channel, starting as the shorter Mk.1 version some 22 years ago. The catamaran will not possess the very high speed potential of the hovercraft but neither will it suffer the marked fall-off in speed that can be experienced by hovercraft in the English Channel sea states. The comparison of these two very different craft types will be extremely interesting; it has been a very long time to wait (12 years) for a vessel to appear that is larger than the SRN4. It will appear at Portsmouth after a Blue Riband attempt during a trans-Atlantic crossing on its delivery from Tasmania, which is in itself another bold step forward.

that schedules have to be set to allow for this characteristic. We seem to be back to Sir Christopher Cockerell's starting point: how to make ships go faster. The 35 knot service speed of Sea Containers catamarans is only 11 knots faster than ferries that crossed between Britain and France in the 1930s and half the speed of the SRN2 70-passenger hovercraft of 28 years ago. Certainly 35 knots is a very useful and significant increase above the common 18 to 22 knots of current conventional ferries and will make a welcome difference to journey times. It is also a speed level which can begin to offer attractive competition against road traffic. In a number of countries a difficult coastline with consequently difficult road conditions combine already to make 'going by sea' an attractive alternative, Norway, Italy, Japan and Greece provide examples. Road traffic congestion is another factor encouraging alternative means of travel and a growing menace to the lives of millions of people and their environment. It is really rather astonishing to hear in the United Kingdom of suggestions for a new motorway to run from Dover to Southampton to help relieve congestion that will follow the opening of the Channel Tunnel. How much better would be the institution of high-speed multiple ferry services from the Calais/Boulogne area to Portsmouth, Southampton and other points west to relieve this expected congestion.

From Britain, the FBM Marine 32-Knot FDC 400 Seamaster *Patria* a precursor for much smoother travel at speeds of 30 knots plus.

From Australia, the International Catamarans Ltd Pty Ltd 74m, 35 knot Wave−Piercing Catamaran, (superstructure not fitted) a precursor for significant increases in size for high-speed passenger/car ferries.

The Australians are not alone in the provision of large high-speed vessels for the ferry industry. Ulstein International A/S in Norway, through their Eikefjord Marine A/S yard, have received the first order for 1991 delivery for a 60m CIRR-200 surface-effect-ship (SES) designed to carry 364 passengers and 56 cars, while further SES designs are now on offer from The Netherlands, Royal Schelde (436 passengers, 62 cars) and Italy, Societa Esercizio Cantieri (300 passengers, 70 cars) and Fincantieri Cantieri Navali Italiani SpA. (350 passengers, 80 cars). These SES projects have calm water speeds in the 42 to 45 knot range but comparable speeds to the 74m InCats in sea states likely to be encountered on routes up to 100 nautical miles.

The leap to the arrival of these larger vessels has stimulated the rather conservative conventional ferry operators, and design studies are now in hand in both Australia and Norway for high-speed ferries of over 100m length. There is no obvious technical reason why size increases should not continue, giving increased vessel work capacities in keeping with traffic growth, while at the same time greatly improving comfort at sea. It is interesting to note that steel is coming in as a preferred hull material for some of the larger SES projects, an indication of the improving economics of these vessels as size increases. Also, gas turbine engines will be used for the Norwegian Ulstein and Italian SEC SES passenger/car ferries.

The dramatic increase in carrying capacity of these larger craft now under construction is not being accompanied by such a dramatic increase in block speed (terminal to terminal). The large catamarans are displacement vessels and as such show a steep rise of resistance with speed, hence bringing in an early limit to really high speed for this type. The large surface-effect ships are basically planing craft (as is the amphibious hovercraft) and show a steep rise of resistance in waves, so

Governments should not abrogate their responsibility to provide effective planning in transport and this must mean the integration of all transport systems and included in that integration must be environmental aspects and safety. It is astonishing that road and rail links for the Channel Tunnel are only now being considered. It may well come about that high-speed ferries, 35 to 60 knots, will dominate cross-Channel traffic in the not too distant future. With such use of coastal waters, marine traffic control would become essential and having eliminated pollution by carrying the road vehicles the carrying vessels themselves must not pollute; government legislation and integrated planning are essential for these developments are fast approaching.

The technology for high-speed displacement vessels in the immediate future, carrying loads of several hundreds of vehicles at 35 to 45 knots and higher, is within reach. To achieve higher speeds requires research and development for the evolution of new craft forms. While such work is now proceeding in Norway and Japan, regrettably in Britain the government has turned off almost all support for research and development for the shipping industry, implying that we are pulling out for the long term and has by its policies allowed some of the finest marine research facilities in the world, the ship towing tank and cavitation tunnel, at what was the National Physical Laboratory, Feltham, to be literally scrapped and destroyed.

The opportunity exists now for revitalising shipbuilding , based on taking up the new ideas for marine transport now firmly established and, at the same time, discarding bad management, bad union and bad government practices. This cannot happen, however, without the intelligent application of government funds. It is essential that funds are provided for research and development and for further specialised start-up support to develop new ideas and inventions that can exploit market opportunities. The Norwegian and Japanese high-speed shipping developments are supported by effective government research programmes. The idea of proceeding very far without such programmes in some form for the shipping industry in Britain is naive at best and at worst positively destructive as we have already seen. An added deterrent

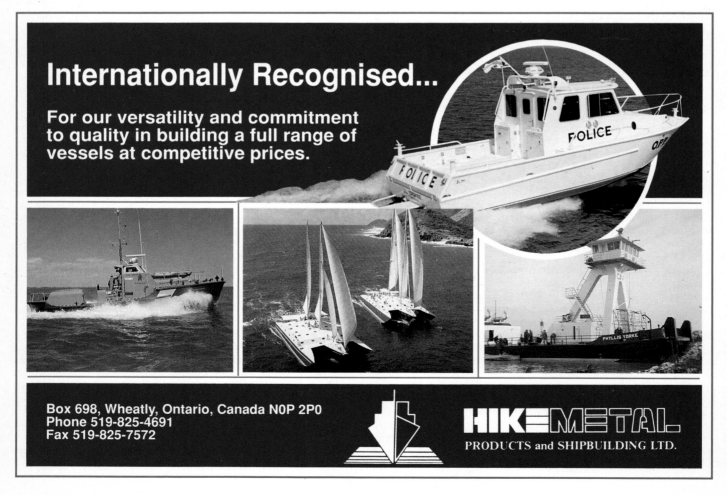

to a successful shipbuilding industry in Britain has been the continuing neglect in the education of the country, so that even if the government *should* do anything towards assisting in the creation of a future shipbuilding industry, we would be desperately short of well-educated and well-trained people to manage and staff that industry.

At the present time the Australians, Norwegians and Japanese seem likely to provide the vessels that will be needed for future ferry systems, the Australians already leading in pure size, the Norwegians taking the practical speeds up above the 50 knot level and the Japanese (as discussed in the Foreword to the 1989 edition of this book) pursuing the development of high-speed ocean-going freight vessels and advances in propulsion for future ships. World deliveries of high-speed craft (mostly ferries of over 25m in length combined with speeds of over 30 knots) are now running at well over 100 per year and continuing a long-established growth rate (in numbers) of over 20$ per annum.

The export potential for advanced ships is excellent. A single company in Norway, Kvaerner Fjellstrand has already sold 52 of its high-speed catamarans to 18 countries, including the USSR and South Korea, and this same company, along with Westamarin in Norway, is heading for successfully entering the 50-knot ship market with its Foil Cat project. This concept involves part hydrofoil support and part displacement support, the hydrofoil lift not only reducing overall resistance at the higher speeds and hence reducing fuel consumption too, but also by providing a dynamic ride control system, very considerably improving comfort in waves. A further Norwegian export success has been the sale by the Brodrene Aa yard of Ulstein International of a CIRR 120 SES for delivery this year to the Yasuda Ocean Line of Japan for the Nagasaki to Kayoshima route.

Some new high-speed developments are occurring in Britain. FBM Marine on the Isle of Wight has developed its own form of small-water-plane-area-twin-hull (SWATH) vessel, a 32 knot Fast Displacement Catamaran (FDC).Though close to the original SWATH concept, the FBM Marine 400-seat FDC Seamaster has rather greater area at the water plane and this makes it less sensitive to changes in deadweight while at the same time enhancing pitch stability. This vessel has achieved a full-load service speed of 31.7 knots at a quite economical power level, which is a record for a SWATH type vessel and, like the much higher-speed Foil Cat type, will have the advantage of showing very little speed loss in waves, as well as offering greatly improved ride. At the time of writing (early March 1990) the first 31.7m Seamaster 400 is due to leave for Madeira where it will enter service on a 44 nautical mile Atlantic route. Like the more advanced catamarans, the FDC 400 type is a displacement vessel and its

transport efficiency will increase substantially with size, enabling some growth in speed to be achieved while still maintaining acceptable overall economics. Where only moderately high speeds are required and deeper draught is not a problem, the FDC 400 type and the SWATH type in general stand to gain a useful part of the market.

The writing is on the wall and it says that a revolution in the world shipping industry has started; the old ideas of what a ship is are being left behind. There are no longer barriers to increase in speed, there are many vessel configurations and concepts now evolving which can fit the various speed regimes with greater comfort and improving economics; there is positive concern in the more enlightened countries that future craft shall not pollute our seas and atmosphere and a rapidly arising awareness that transport by sea can alleviate many congestion problems.

Acknowledgements. In compiling the content of this book I depend very much on the material sent in by the very large number of contributors who update their entries each year. For this input I give my sincere thanks. There are also many correspondents who write to me during the year and contribute background as well as detailed information and data, which is most helpful and for which I am most grateful. Of these many I would particularly like to thank Alan Bliault, Michael Daley, Howard Daniel, Graham Gifford, Paul Kerr, Nabuo Masuda, Ronald Sim, Ronald Wade and Yun Liang.

Moving this year to the computer production of copy, I want above all to thank my youngest son Robert without whose expert and enthusiastic help I would have encountered great difficulty in the most expedient use of a computer in this transition stage. In addition, I am considerably indebted to him for his invaluable assistance in the preparation of copy. Again this year, as ever, my grateful thanks go to my assistant Ann Alexander for helping to keep me 'on cushion' and the work on schedule, as well as producing the indexes. A big thank-you also to Annette Ridout and Mary-Anne Martin for their vital input on the computer. At Jane's, Wendy Adamson and Jackie Clarke have patiently handled the flow of problems that come with the work, for which I am most appreciative, and once again I thank Butler and Tanner, the printers, for their very considerable effort in the production of this book.

Robert L. Trillo,
Brockenhurst,
Hampshire,
England.

April 1990.

[15]

PREFACE

SPEED/LENGTH COMBINATIONS

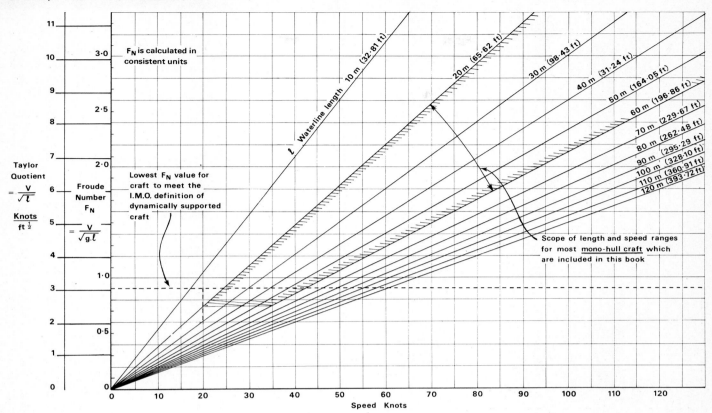

A NOTE ON HIGH SPEED

The accompanying chart is provided in order to help clarify the general term 'high-speed' in relation to water-borne craft. The basic plot shown is of Froude Number versus speed, Froude Number being the non-dimensional parameter which governs the ratio of the length of the wave made by the hull to the length of the hull, with this ratio determining the proportions of the major resistance components, skin friction and wave-making resistance.

$$F_N = \text{Froude Number} = \frac{V}{\sqrt{gl}}$$

where V = speed of craft relative to water
       g = acceleration due to gravity
       l = length of craft at the waterline

Since Froude Number is non-dimensional, it may be calculated in metric or English units.

Alongside the F_N scale on the chart there is a scale for the dimensional Taylor Quotient, $\frac{V}{\sqrt{l}}$, more commonly referred to as the 'speed-length ratio'. This is expressed in units of knots and feet, so has the dimensions $\frac{\text{knots}}{\text{ft}^{1/2}}$.

There is no precise definition for what constitutes high-speed but it is generally agreed to be around the condition where for a planing hull planing support takes over significantly from buoyancy support and that this is in the region of Froude Numbers equal to 0·9 to 1·0. The International Maritime Organisation has set the minimum Froude Number for 'dynamically supported' craft at 0·9 though the displacement and engine power conditions (eg continuous or maximum) are left undefined by IMO.

The chart shows the area of speed and length combinations for which mono-hull craft are included in this book. A minimum length of 20 metres is set simply to avoid attempting to cover the vast number of small high-speed mono-hull craft that exist in the world. A minimum speed of 20 knots is set and this then covers Froude Numbers down to 0·73.

It is apparent that the rather loose understanding of what constitutes 'high-speed', i.e. that based on the conditions for planing of a planing hull, should perhaps give way to a rather more simple basis applicable to all types of vessel. With a few exceptions, this book excludes craft with speeds below 20 knots and so this figure is taken as the beginning of 'high-speed', regardless of the hydrodynamic conditions occurring. It may well be that as the development of higher-speed craft continues, a higher level than 20 knots should be set.

NOTE ON CONTENT OF BOOK

There is no charge made for entries in the editorial section of this book.

To start the 1990s the title of this book has been changed to Jane's High-Speed Marine Craft; the section covering low-speed air cushion platforms will be included for the time being as there is continuing interest in some of the technologies involved which can be applied to high-speed air cushion craft.

The Sections dealing with sailing hydrofoil craft and operators of low-speed air-cushion platforms have been deleted due to reduced activity in these areas.

The Section dealing with high-speed catamarans has been re-titled 'High-Speed Catamaran and Multi-hull Vessels' to reflect the anticipated growth in multi-hull types.

The Section dealing with high-speed mono-hull craft covers only those above 20m in length combined with speeds of over 20 knots.

Every effort is made to establish the highest accuracy for all information and figures quoted but this does of course depend on the accuracy of the information received and up-dating by all contributors. If no up-dating reply is sent in, the entry may be deleted.

The definitions of quantities are those given by the craft builders, operators and engineering component manufacturers. There is, however, a lack of uniformity in data presentation in the shipping business and until reasonably uniform standards are agreed and established worldwide (as for the aircraft industry) the figures presented in this book will be as offered by the various contributors. In general no attempt is made to alter the data sent in, hence the wide variety of terms used and differences in format in information presented.

Details of craft that are no longer in production but are still in service are included.

TELEPHONE AND TELEFAX

Telephone and telefax numbers are given with national (internal) codes but some amendments are still outstanding.

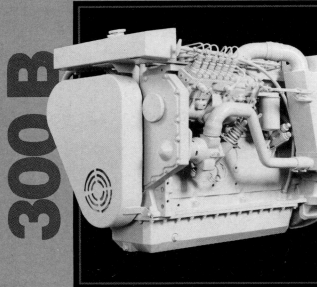

Definitions of Sea Conditions: Wind and Sea for Fully Arisen Sea

Sea State	Description	(Beaufort) Wind force	Description	Range (knots)	Wind Velocity (knots)	Wave Height (ft) Average	Wave Height (ft) Significant	Wave Height (ft) Average of One-Tenth Highest	Significant Range Periods (sec)	Periods of Maximum Energy of Spectra $T_{max}=T_c$	Average Period T_z	Average Wave Length L_w (ft unless otherwise indicated)	Minimum Fetch (nautical miles)	Minimum Duration (hr unless otherwise indicated)
	Sea like a mirror	U	Calm	1	0	0	0	0	—	—	—	—	—	—
0	Ripples with the appearance of scales are formed, but without foam crests	1	Light airs	1-3	2	0.04	0.01	0.09	1.2	0.75	0.5	10 in	5	18 min
1	Small wavelets; short but pronounced crests have a glossy appearance, but do not break.	2	Light breeze	4-6	5	0.3	0.5	0.6	0.4-2.8	1.9	1.3	6.7	8	39 min
	Large wavelets; crests begin to break. Foam of glossy	3	Gentle	7-10	8.5	0.8	1.3	1.6	0.8-5.0	3.2	2.3	20	9.8	1.7
	appearance. Perhaps scattered with horses.		breeze		10	1.1	1.8	2.3	1.0-6.0	3.2	2.7	27	10	2.4
2	Small waves, becoming larger;	4	Moderate		12	1.6	2.6	3.3	1.0-7.0	4.5	3.2	40	18	3.8
					13.5	2.1	3.3	4.2	1.4-7.6	5.1	3.6	52	24	4.8
	fairly frequent white horses.		breeze	11-16	14	2.3	3.6	4.6	1.5-7.8	5.3	3.8	59	28	5.2
3					16	2.9	4.7	6.0	2.0-8.8	6.0	4.3	71	40	6.6
4	Moderate waves, taking a more	5	Fresh	17-21	18	3.7	5.9	7.5	2.5-10.0	6.8	4.8	90	55	8.3
					19	4.1	6.6	8.4	2.8-10.6	7.2	5.1	99	65	9.2
	pronounced long form; many white horses are formed (chance of some spray).		breeze		20	4.6	7.3	9.3	3.0-11.1	7.5	5.4	111	75	10
5	Large waves begin to form;	6	Strong	22-27	22	5.5	8.8	11.2	3.4-12.2	8.3	5.9	134	100	12
					24	6.6	10.5	13.3	3.7-13.5	9.0	6.4	160	130	14
	white crests are more extensive everywhere (probably some spray).		breeze		24.5	6.8	10.9	13.8	3.8-13.6	9.2	6.6	164	140	15
6					26	7.7	12.3	15.6	4.0-14.5	9.8	7.0	188	180	17
	Sea heaps up, and white foam from breaking waves begins to be blown in streaks along the direction of the wind (Spindrift begins to be seen).	7	Moderate gale	28-33	28	8.9	14.3	18.2	4.5-15.5	10.6	7.5	212	230	20
					30	10.3	16.4	20.8	4.7-16.7	11.3	8.0	250	280	23
7					30.5	10.6	16.9	21.5	4.8-17.0	11.5	8.2	258	290	24
					32	11.6	18.6	23.6	5.0-17.5	12.1	8.6	285	340	27
7					34	13.1	21.0	26.7	5.5-18.5	12.8	9.1	322	420	30
					36	14.8	23.6	30.0	5.8-19.7	13.6	9.6	363	500	34
	Moderate high waves of greater length; edges of crests break into spindrift. The foam is blown in well-marked streaks along the direction of the wind. Spray affects visibility.	8	Fresh gale	34-40	37	15.6	24.9	31.6	6-20.5	13.9	9.9	376	530	37
					38	16.4	26.3	33.4	6.2-20.8	14.3	10.2	392	600	38
					40	18.2	29.1	37.0	6.5-21.7	15.1	10.7	444	710	42
8					42	20.1	32.1	40.8	7-23	15.8	11.3	492	830	47
	High waves. Dense streaks of foam along the direction of the wind. Sea begins to roll. Visibility affected.	9	Strong gale	41-37	44	22.0	35.2	44.7	7-24.2	16.6	11.8	534	960	52
					46	24.1	38.5	48.9	7-25	17.3	12.3	590	1110	57
	Very high waves with long overhanging crests. The resulting foam is in great patches and is blown in dense white streaks along the direction of the wind. On the whole, the surface of the sea takes on a white appearance. The rolling of the sea becomes heavy and shocklike. Visibility is affected.	10	Whole* gale	48-55	40	26.2	41.9	53.2	7.5-26	18.1	12.9	650	1250	63
					50	28.4	45.5	57.8	7.5-27	18.8	13.4	700	1420	69
					51.5	30.2	48.3	61.3	8-28.2	19.4	13.8	736	1560	73
9					52	30.8	49.2	62.5	8-28.5	19.6	13.9	750	1610	75
					54	33.2	53.1	67.4	8-29.5	20.4	14.5	810	1800	81
	Exceptionally high waves. Sea completely covered with long white patches of foam lying in direction of wind. Everywhere edges of wave crests are blown into froth. Visibility affected.	11	Storm*	56-63	56	35.7	57.1	72.5	8.5-31	21.1	15	910	2100	88
					59.5	40.3	64.4	81.8	10-32	22.4	15.9	985	2500	101
	Air filled with foam and spray. Sea white with driving spray. Visibility very seriously affected.	12	Hurricane*	64-71	>64 / >46.6	74.5	94.6		10-35	24.1	17.2	—	—	—

* For hurricane winds (and often whole gale and storm winds) required durations and reports are barely attained. Seas are therefore not fully arisen.

DEFINITIONS OF SYMBOLS AND UNITS

Four of the seven base units of the SI (Système International d'Unités) which are used in this book are:

length	metre	m
mass	kilogram	kg
time	second	s
electric current	ampere	A

Decimal unit	Quantity	Formula
Pa (Pascal)	pressure or stress	N/m^2
N (Newton)	force	$kg.m/s^2$
W (Watt)	power	J/s
Hz (Hertz)	frequency	1/s (1 Hertz = 1 cycle per second in previous British practice)
V (Volt)	electric potential difference	W/A

Other units		Quantity
dB	(decibel)	sound pressure level, re 0.0002 microbar
dBA	(decibel)	sound level, A-weighted, re 0.0002 microbar

CONVERSIONS

Length
1 km = 0.6214 statute mile = 0.540 nautical mile
1 m = 3.281 ft
1 cm = 0.3937 in
1 mm = 0.0394 in

Area
1 ha (hectare = 10 000 m²) = 2.471 acres
1 m² = 10.764 ft²

Volume
1 m³ = 35.315 ft³
1 litre = 0.220 Imperial gallon = 0.264 US gallon

Velocity

1 km/h = 0·621 statute mile/h = 0·540 knots
1 m/s = 3·281 ft/s

Acceleration

1 m/s² = 3·281 ft/s²

Mass

1 t (tonne)   = 1000 kg = 0·9842 long ton = 2204·62 lb
                = 1·1023 short tons
1 kg (kilogram) = 2·205 lb
1 g (gram)   = 0·002205 lb

Force

1 MN (meganewton)   = 100·36 long ton force
1 kgf   = 2·205 lbf
1 kp (kilopond)   = 2·205 lbf
1 N   (newton)   = 0·2248 lbf (The Newton is that force which, applied to a mass of 1 kilogram, gives it an acceleration of 1 m/s².)

Moment of force (torque)

1 Nm   = 0·7376 lbf.ft

Pressure, stress

1 atm (standard atmosphere)   = 14·696 lbf/in²
1 bar (10⁵ pascal)   = 14·504 lbf/in²
1 kPa (kN/m²)   = 20·885 lbf/ft²
1 Pa   (N/m²)   = 0·020885 lbf/ft²

Power

1 metric horsepower (ch, ps) = 0·7355 kW = 1·014 horsepower (550 ft lb/s)
1 kW = 1·341 horsepower (1 horsepower = 550 ft lb/s) = 1·360 metric horsepower

Nautical mile

The International Nautical Mile is equivalent to the average length of a minute of latitude and corresponds to a latitude of 45° and a distance of 1852 m = 6076·12 ft.

Fuel consumption

Specific fuel consumption, 1·0 g/kWh = 0·001644 lb/hph (hp = 550 ft lb/s)
    1·0 litre/h = 0·220 Imperial gallon/h
                = 0·264 US gallon/h

BUILDERS

AIR CUSHION VEHICLES

AUSTRALIA

AIR CUSHION ENTERPRISES PTY LTD

Assets purchased by Delta Hover Pty Ltd in September 1988.

Ranger 2000

DELTA HOVER PTY LTD

25 Sara Street, Toronto NSW 2282, Australia

Telephone: (049) 504144
Telex: 177816
Telefax: (049) 596846

B A Wilson, *General Manager*
K Matthews, *Sales Director*
L McLeod, *Manager of Design and Development*
Phillip Heyne, *Production Manager*

Delta Hover Pty Ltd was established to undertake design, manufacture, marketing and operation of commercial and military hovercraft for the world market.The company operates from a small but well equipped factory in Toronto on the shores of Lake Macquarie.

RANGER 2000

The base model hovercraft marketed by Delta Hover is the Ranger 2000, an enhanced capability development of the earlier Surveyor 12D hovercraft. The Ranger carries 19 or 21 passengers economically at 35 to 40 knots and is capable of speeds in excess of 48 knots. It is a fibreglass craft of advanced design, powered by a 300hp supercharged diesel engine and is simple and reliable to operate. The selling price on the Australian market FOB Newcastle was A\$425,000 in early 1989.

SURVEYOR 1500

Externally the Surveyor 1500 is the same as the earlier Surveyor 12D craft. The Surveyor 1500 has improved ergonomics in the control system, and has other production changes which improve maintainability, and may be fitted with a 220hp Cummins diesel engine. The craft can be built in survey in NSW for carriage of 13 to 15 passengers in the USL Code Class 1D (operation in partially smooth waters). The FOB Newcastle price was A\$350,000 in early 1989.

NQEA AUSTRALIA PTY LTD

60–92 Cook Street, PO Box 1105, Portsmith, Cairns, Queensland 4870, Australia

Telephone: (070) 52 7222
Telex: 48087AUS AA
Telefax: (070) 51 5520/31 1812

D G Fry, *Chief Executive*
S C Grimley, *Managing Director*
G M Steene, *Executive Director, Marketing*
A Rankine, *Executive Director, Production*
R D Rookwood, *Senior Design Engineer*
A E G Mill, *Company Secretary*

NQEA started activities in 1948 with the operation of general engineering agencies and later general engineering manufacture. In 1964 it entered the shipbuilding industry with the construction of dumb barges. This activity was followed by work on many types of vessels, including Australia's 'Attack Class' patrol boats, and the construction of several medium-sized craft, including tug boats, fishing trawlers and 22 workboats for the Australian Defence Department.

In 1977, NQEA was the successful tenderer for 14 (of a total of 15) 42m 'Fremantle Class' patrol craft for the Australian Navy, the lead vessel being built in the UK by Brooke Marine. Taking 85 weeks to construct the craft, NQEA were delivering at a rate of one every 14 weeks.

More recently NQEA have been building a number of high-speed wavepiercer catamarans (International Catamarans type) and are building the British-designed AP1–88 under licence from British Hovercraft Corporation, the first order having been received in February 1986. With six craft now completed Australia's NQEA claims to be at the forefront of the high-speed vessel industry, offering prospective buyers in the ferry, patrol boat and general workboat fields the choice of mono-hull, catamaran and amphibious hovercraft.

Details of the AP1–88 hovercraft are given in the British Hovercraft Corporation entry.

Craft built	Name	Seats	Launched	Operator
BHC AP1–88	*Benidorm* (ex *Courier**)	81	7 December 1986	Real Maritima de Cruceros
BHC AP1–88	*Hover Mirage*	70	March 1987	Hover Mirage Pty Ltd
BHC AP1–88	*Hover Mirage II*	70	April 1987	Hover Mirage Pty Ltd
BHC AP1–88	*Tienpengyang I*	94	November 1989	Tien Peng Yang Hovertravel Corporation
BHC AP1–88	*Tienpengyang II*	101	May 1990	Tien Peng Yang Hovertravel Corporation
BHC AP1–88	*Tienpengyang III*	101	July 1990	Tien Peng Yang Hovertravel Corporation

*Arrived UK Dec 1988 from Australia, GH 2108, fitted with 100 seats and later sold to Real Maritima de Cruceros, Spain.
The *Tienpengyang* series I, II and III are Yard No's 142, 166, 167 respectively.

The 24m InCat *Taupo Cat* with *Hover Mirage* both built by NQEA Australia Pty Ltd

NQEA AP1–88 *Hover Mirage* in service with Hover Mirage Pty Ltd, Australia

BELGIUM

The Eurosense BEASAC SR.N6 Mk 1S

EUROSENSE TECHNOLOGIES
[OPERATOR]
New-Yorklaan, B-8380, Zeebrugge, Belgium

Telephone: (02) 50/54 64 38
Telex: 26687
Telefax: (02) 50/54 74 86

E Maes, *Managing Director*
J Van Rensbergen, *Project Manager*

BEASAC (Belfotop Eurosense Acoustic Sounding Air Cushion-platform)
Since 1983, Eurosense has been under contract with the Belgian Ministry of Public Works, Coastal Services, for the constant monitoring of the access channels to the major Belgian seaports, and for the study of the coastal morphology. For this purpose, Eurosense has used aerial remote sensing as well as hydrographic survey techniques. The latter technique is based on the use of a fully amphibious, air-propeller driven hovercraft.

The hovercraft can reach regions inaccessible to classic hydrographic vessels, eg the nearshore areas. Nearshore bathymetric surveys by hovercraft ensure an overlap with beach observations (executed by aerial or terrestrial survey) thus enabling a complete coverage of the coast and nearshore seabottom to be achieved. Furthermore, the manoeuvrability of the hovercraft and the high survey speed (up to 55km/h, or 30 knots) result in measurements being obtained up to 4 times faster than those with classic hydrographic vessels. This enables large areas to be covered in a very short time period, which is essential when studying a rapidly changing sea bottom.

This new concept in the field of hydrography was developed by Eurosense and called BEASAC (Belfotop Eurosense Acoustic Sounding Air Cushion-platform). The first version was developed under the name BEASAC using the SR.N6 Mk 1S. Subsequently, the diesel powered BEASAC II was designed and is under further evaluation. In the interim, a third version, the twin-propellored SR.N6 Mk 6, has been operational and named BESAC III.

BEASAC

The first BEASAC hovercraft is a modified SR.N6 Mk 1S (British Hovercraft Corporation).

Two 10kVA diesel generators provide the electrical power supply for the onboard computers, sensors, hydrographic instruments, air-conditioning, etc. The generators are mounted inside the raised side decks.

Two hydraulically-operated arms are mounted on each side deck to bring acoustic transducers in and out of the water. A mechanical weak link construction prevents damage to the craft structure in case of collision with floating objects. Eurosense developed an automatic retraction and deployment system especially for acquisition in shallow waters, allowing the measurements to be performed up to the last available metre of water-depth.

In front of the pilot, near the instrument panel, a navigation screen shows the predefined tracks and harbour planimetry and is continuously updated with the position of the craft, its speed and direction and the distance off-track.

Other modifications are servo-controlled rudders, air-conditioned computer-room, survey monitoring table (main cabin), long-range fuel tanks (endurance: 7 hours), antennas, etc.

BEASAC TWIN

The second BEASAC hovercraft is based on the SR.N6 Mk 6 (British Hovercraft Corporation). This hovercraft has twin propellers, a more powerful engine and a tapered skirt, offering an increased manoeuvrability and all-weather performance.

In the centre of the craft a pressure cabin is constructed. In this cabin, a hydraulically-operated arm lowers the acoustic transducers through a moonpool in the floor of the craft. The longitudinal and transversal keels of the skirt are modified to allow for this movement. As for BEASAC, a mechanical weak link construction and an automatic retraction and deployment system are installed.

Other modifications, such as auxiliary power supply units, long range fuel tanks, surveyor cabin, pilot navigation screen, etc are similar to the above mentioned BEASAC modifications.

HYDROGRAPHIC EQUIPMENT OF BEASAC

Positioning systems: Several options are possible (eg Trisponder, Syledis, Toran, Motorola, GPS).

DEPTH MEASUREMENT: Two acoustic transducers (210 and 33kHz) are installed in a streamlined housing, called 'fish'. This 'fish' is mounted on a hydraulically-retractable arm. Other sensors include a flux gate compass, gyroscope, heave compensator and air-cushion height detectors, permitting the simultaneous registration of all craft movements (eg roll, pitch, heading, etc).

ACQUISITION SYSTEM: A powerful computer system is extended with interfacing networks to gather all sensor registration. Adapted driver software interrogates, synchronises and memorises all sensor data together with depth and position. Special graphical navigation screens inform the pilot and surveyor of track, planimetry and quality control of the data.

SHORE-BASED DATA-PROCESSING: Special computer hardware and software, developed by Eurosense, enable easy and continuous chart production, as well as further data processing (eg Digital Terrain Modelling, differential map production, volume computation, refraction calculation, etc.)

CANADA

ACV SALES INC

This company has ceased trading. Details of its craft *Amphibian* can be found in the 1989 edition of this book.

CANADA HOVERCRAFT INC

Marine Technology Centre, 99–9865 West Saanich Road, Sidney, British Columbia, V8L 3S1, Canada

Telephone: (604) 656 2326

Craig R Darling, *President*

Canada Hovercraft Inc (CHI) is licensed by Westland Aerospace to manufacture and market the API-88 air cushion vehicle in Canada. In early 1988 CHI was in the process of developing a Canadian manufacturing infrastructure to support its market development programme.

JONES KIRWAN & ASSOCIATES

Box 4406, Station 'D', Hamilton, Ontario L8V 4L8, Canada

Telephone: (416) 388 2929

D Jones, *President*

Jones Kirwan & Associates was responsible for the design of the Air Trek 140, as well as a number of other Canadian hovercraft. The company also designs air-cushion supported agricultural spray booms.

AIR TREK 140

Designed by Jones Kirwan & Associates for use in arctic conditions, this utility hovercraft carries up to 16 passengers or freight weighing up to 1360kg (3000lb). The main structure is built in marine-grade aluminium and is stressed to operate at 61km/h (38mph) in 0.9m (3ft) high seas. The craft received full certification from the Canadian Coast Guard in early 1984.

For several years the Air Trek 140 has been in use as an icebreaker capable of breaking ice 0.45m to 0.70m thick, in such applications as river mouth ice-clearing. Development of an ice-grooving tool to improve further the icebreaking capability of hovercraft is being undertaken by Jones Kirwan & Associates. In early 1987 the Air Trek 140 was damaged in road transit and was not operational as at November 1988.

LIFT AND PROPULSION: Integrated system powered by a single 10.4-litre Caterpillar 3208 turbocharged, after-cooled, diesel rated at 360hp for 5 minutes and 350hp continuous. Thrust is supplied by a ducted, six-blade wooden propeller. Power is transmitted to two centrifugal lift fans behind the driver's and crewman's seats via an infinitely variable Eaton Hydrostatic drive system. The operator can select the fan speed to suit the terrain or wave conditions; the fans will then remain at that speed constantly irrespective of the main engine rpms.

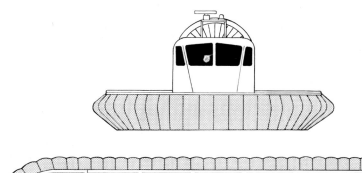

CONTROLS: Multiple rudders operating in the propeller slipstream provide directional control and act as shut-off doors to modulate thrust. Louvres in the duct wall between the propeller and the rudders give reverse thrust.

SKIRT: HDL 'kneed' segments (96) in 542g/m^2 (16oz/yd^2) neoprene coated fabric. Skirt may be reset from the craft deck while the craft is floating on water.

HULL: Marine-grade aluminium.

ACCOMMODATION: Cabin with independent diesel heater and heavily insulated for arctic conditions. Dual operating position.

DIMENSIONS
Length: 11.2m
Width: 5.73m
Cabin length: 3.93m
    width: 2.08m
    height: 1.83m
Freight area: 11.90m^2

WEIGHTS
Max load: 1360kg
Fuel capacity: 363kg
Crew of two: 145kg
Craft weight: 4832kg
Max weight: 6700kg

PERFORMANCE
Cruising speed, ice and water: 61km/h (38mph)
Cruising speed, ice: 72km/h (45mph)
Fuel duration at max cruising speed: 8 hours
Fuel consumption at max cruising speed: 45kg/h (100lb/h)

SIX-SEAT HOVERCRAFT (DESIGN)

Design of a new six-seat hovercraft commenced in the summer of 1987.

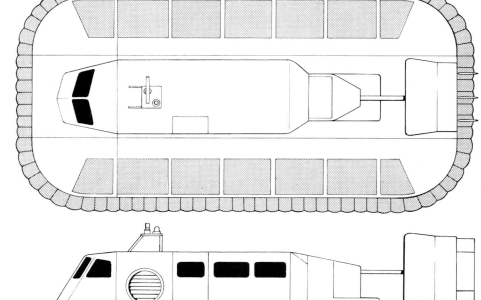

Air Trek 140 (early configuration)

TRANSPORT CANADA
Transportation Development Centre (TDC)
[RESEARCH AND DEVELOPMENT ORGANISATION]
Complexe Guy Favreau, 200 René-Lévesque West, Suite 601, West Tower, Montreal, Quebec H2Z 1X4, Canada

Founded in Montreal in 1970, the Transportation Development Centre (TDC) is the research and development group within Transport Canada. TDC studies, promotes and directs the application of science and technology towards a more efficient and effective national transport system. Working in co-operation with the Canadian transport community, TDC conducts and commissions research projects covering all modes of transport.

AIR CUSHION TECHNOLOGY

TDC has investigated the application of air cushion technology to Canadian transportation since the early 1970s, having acquired for evaluation the Bell Aerospace Textron Voyageur 002, since handed over to the Canadian Coast Guard.

TDC was also involved in a ship-to-shore supply operation in 1974–75 on the Quebec North Shore when Voyageur 004 was used to supply land-locked villages during the winter.

A number of research contracts dealing with air cushion stability and modelling were also granted by TDC to the Air Cushion Group of the University of Toronto Institute of Aerospace Studies (UTIAS).

AEROBAC CONCEPT

As the major part of Canada consists of sparsely settled regions, with a prevalence of muskeg and other water-logged terrains, one of the domains of interest to TDC is off-road transportation. The Aerobac concept was developed following trials in the Canadian hinterland with air cushion trailers. These showed that while the air cushion itself was satisfactory over marshes and flat surfaces, it became a hindrance when dealing with hilly paths or rocky surfaces. Hence a vehicle was needed that could deal effectively with all surfaces, using air cushion for lift but able to revert to wheels or to tracks, as local conditions dictated. Initially Aerobac trailers were considered, permitting the

conventional off-road vehicles, to which they are coupled, to operate at their unladen foot-print pressure. Later amphibious self-propelled versions were developed. Tandem operation of the two versions is possible for increased payloads.

Commercial development of Aerobac vehicles does not come within the scope of TDC. A technology transfer agreement has been made between the Canadian government and VITRI Robots and Vehicles Inc (VRV) to market this vehicle concept. For description of the Aerobac family of vehicles see the VRV entry.

RECENT PROGRESS

No major projects have been pursued in the air cushion domain by TDC in the past year. Its current role consists in maintaining a watching brief over air cushion technology developments and in providing technical information to the public.

In this guise TDC has supported the yearly Canadian Air Cushion Technology Society (CACTS) conferences, and has provided consultations on a number of proposed ferry projects and icebreaking operations in Canada.

VITRI ROBOTS AND VEHICLES INC (VRV)
[DESIGN, DEVELOPMENT AND MARKETING ORGANISATION]
238 De Brullon Street, Boucherville, Quebec J4B 2J8, Canada

Telephone: (514) 641 3914
Telex: (VIA USA) 750 846
Telefax: (514) 397 9494

Pierre F Alepin, *President*

VRV is involved in the development of products requiring the integration of diverse technologies. VRV works in conjunction with large organisations, providing them with needed entrepreneurial creativity developing from small organisations, and brings together individuals having the most appropriate background and experience for the task in hand.

The Aerobac concept, integrating air cushion technology with that of off-road vehicles, is being promoted by VRV for Canadian and world-wide applications.

VRV has acquired rights from Canadian Patents and Development Ltd, a Canadian Crown Corporation, for designs of the Aerobac family of vehicles developed by the Transportation Development Centre (TDC), of Transport Canada. VRV has also obtained a licence from Institut Français de Recherche pour l'Exploitation de la Mer (IFREMER) for the use of Bertin and SEDAM air cushion systems on hybrid vehicles using surface contacting propulsion and able to operate with or without the air cushion system.

VRV AEROBAC (DESIGNS)
VRV vehicles are based on the designs licenced from TDC, comprising air cushion trailers and tracked self-propelled vehicles (AB-7), and on its own designs, based on a proposal to the US Air Force for an air cushion-assisted crash rescue vehicle (ACCRV), and developed as a family of wheeled cargo or passenger vehicles.

The designs are characterised by relatively high cushion pressures, 4 to 7kPa, and by a variable stiffness suspension system. A high stiffness is used for off cushion stability; when on cushion a low stiffness is desired in order to reduce shock load transfer to the structure. When on cushion the load on the wheels, or tracks, is kept at the minimum value compatible with guidance and traction requirements.

Model of VRV proposed ACCRV design to a US Air Force requirement

AEROBAC PCE (DESIGN)
In order to support a TDC evaluation programme, VRV has carried out a production cost evaluation (PCE) of an Aerobac AB-7 design (see Transport Canada entry in the 1986 edition), modified to a two-engine configuration, using cabin layout, transmission and tracks of a Bombardier B-10 muskeg vehicle. The air cushion fans are separately driven so that a breakdown of either engine systems still permits the vehicle to move off cushion, or to be towed, on cushion, to a repair depot.

As the TDC evaluation programme would

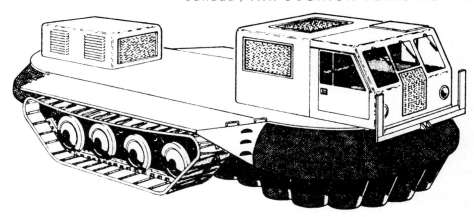

Aerobac PCE: design of prototype of tracked hybrid ACV with 7-tonne payload capability

involve testing as an airport rescue vehicle, a foam package can be installed on the PCE, with a capacity of 4500 litres. The transmission fitted on the PCE allows a speed of 60km/h to be attained, conditions permitting. The fire pump is driven by a power take-off from this transmission.

LIFT AND PROPULSION
Traction system: Detroit 6V-92TA
  Power: 230kW
  Transmission: Clarke 28661
  Differential: Levy M-24
  Tracks: Muskeg 1m width
  Suspension: Oleo-pneumatic
Cushion system: Detroit 6V-92TA
  Power: 230kW
  Fans: Two VIM HCHB-040
  Total flow (at 7.5kPa): 20m³/s
SKIRT: SEDAM multicell.
DIMENSIONS
Length: 11.5m
Width: 6.2m
Height: 3.4m
Loading area: 20m²
WEIGHTS
Payload: 7 tonnes
Max weight: 21 tonnes
PERFORMANCE
Fuel capacity: 800 litres
Max speed: 60km/h
Max slope: 40%
Endurance (70% power): 8 hours
Ground pressure
  cushion only: 6.3kPa
  tracks only: 35.6kPa

AEROBAC CRV
FIRE PACKAGE
Water reservoir: 4500 litres
Foam agent: 600 litres
Fire pump: Hale 50FB
Power take-off: 75kW
Flow at 1.0MPa: 2500 litres/min
Roof turret: 2000 litres/min

Protection nozzles: 3 at 150 litres/min
Hose reel: 5cm, 50m

ACCRV (DESIGN)
In 1985 the US Air Force issued a request for proposals for a crash rescue vehicle with air cushion assist. In addition to a 4000-litre water capacity fire package this vehicle has to carry a rescue platform, extensible to 15m, and have a triage area able to receive three victims. It must be fully amphibious, protected against exploding ammunition on the ground, able to travel at 100km/h over smooth surfaces and able to negotiate rubble to 30cm height. As applicable to other US Air Force CRVs it must be made air transportable in a Lockheed C-130, within 15 minutes preparation time.

A VRV design study made use of a multicell air cushion, (in order to provide high lateral stability), installed between the axles of the vehicle. Folding side bodies are fitted in order to meet the width requirement of the C-130. This design, with a max weight of 13.5 tonnes is illustrated in model form (for design data see VRV entry in 1987 edition).

AR-5 (DESIGN)
The basic vehicle design, without the ACCRV components, was transformed into a wheeled hybrid ACV, the AR-5. The use of air cushion vehicles over inland trails has been proposed at various times as a means of providing reasonably

Aerobac AR-5 design for an air cushion-assisted wheeled cargo vehicle with a 5-tonne payload capability

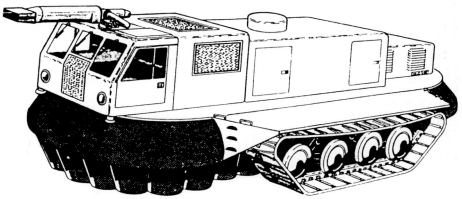

Aerobac CRV: design for a crash rescue vehicle PCE with a 4500-litre water capacity

fast ground transportation in regions where population and traffic densities are too low to justify the cost of a conventional road. The Terraplane BC-7 was developed by Bertin in 1965 for such a use (see *Jane's Surface Skimmers 1967–68*). If the trail, or hoverway, is relatively flat, wheeled propulsion is adequate resulting in a lighter vehicle. The AR-5, adapted from the ACCRV design retains removable side bodies to permit travel without restriction over public roads.

LIFT AND PROPULSION
Engine: Deutz BF12L 413F
Power: 350kW (hydrostatic transfer to transmission and fans)
Fuel capacity: 600 litres
Fans: Two VIM HCHB 040
Total flow: 20m³/s (at 7.5kPa)
Max cushion pressure: 6kPa
DIMENSIONS
Length: 12.2m

Width: 4m (2.6m on road)
WEIGHTS
Max weight: 14 tonnes
Payload: 5 tonnes
PERFORMANCE
Max speed: 100km/h
Speed, off road: 60km/h (roughness under 30cm)
   in water: 12km/h
Endurance: 8 hours

CHINA, PEOPLE'S REPUBLIC

MARINE DESIGN AND RESEARCH INSTITUTE OF CHINA (MARIC)

[DESIGN, RESEARCH AND DEVELOPMENT ORGANISATION]
346 Sichuan Road, Central, PO Box 002–053, Shang-hai, People's Republic of China

Telephone: Shanghai 3215044
Telex: 33029MARIC CN
Cable: Shanghai 5456

Su Ba-Ying, *Director*
Yun Liang, *Deputy Chief Naval Architect*

The Marine Design and Research Institute of China (MARIC) has been responsible for much of the ACV research, development and design programmes on both amphibious and sidewall (SES) hovercraft which have been built in China. The following table summarises the more recent developments in ACVs in China.

MARIC 89–7110

(Name of building yard not available)
This amphibious hovercraft announced in 1989 is designed to operate on inland rivers, sea beaches, and shallow water areas for short-range passenger transportation or touring.
DIMENSIONS
Length overall (rigid structure):13.60m
Beam overall (rigid structure):5.50m

MARIC 89–7110 33-passenger hovercraft

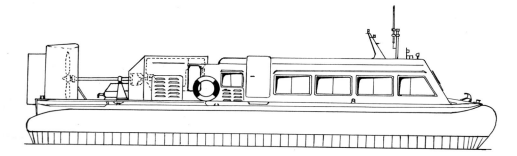
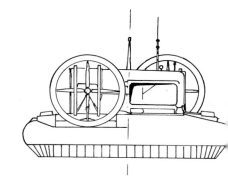

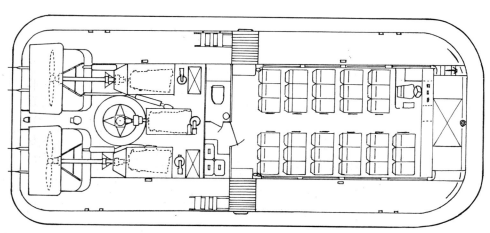

General arrangement of MARIC 89–7110

Height overall (from landing pad to the top of air duct):2.70m
Skirt height:0.50m
Length of cabin:6.00m
Width of cabin:3.50m
Height of cabin:1.95m
Weight,max:10.50 tonnes
Accommodation:33 passengers
Max calm water speed:28.1 knots
Sea keeping capability: The craft can operate safely in Beaufort 6 wind force
HULL
Built in medium strength sea-water-resistant aluminium alloy, riveted construction.
ENGINES
Propulsion: Two Deutz DF6L913C air-cooled diesels.
Lift: One Deutz BF6L913C air-cooled diesel.
PROPULSION
Two fixed-pitch ducted propellers, 1.80m diameter, driven via flexible coupling and clutch.
LIFT FAN
Centrifugal type, 1.50m diameter, driving via flexible coupling and gear box.

Summary of craft built

Builder & craft	Designer	Seats/payload	Launched
Dagu Shipyard			
Type 722 (Amphibious)	MARIC	15-ton payload	August 1979
Type 7203 (Sidewall)		81 seats	September 1982
Jinxiang (Sidewall)	MARIC	80 seats	1983
MARIC			
Shanghai			
Jing-Sah (Amphibious)	MARIC	0.84-ton payload	
Three-engined craft (Amphibious)	MARIC	(development craft, details in *Jane's Surface Skimmers 1985* and earlier editions)	
Shipbuilding and Marine Engineering Establishment			
Shanghai			
—(Amphibious)		2.8-ton payload	
Dong Feng Shipyard			
Type 717 II (Sidewall) *Ming Jiang*	MARIC	54–60 seats	October 1984
Type 717 III (Sidewall) *Chongqing*	MARIC	70 seats	September 1984
Type 7210 (Amphibious) two built	MARIC	0.8 tonnes	May 1985
Chaohu Shipyard			
Auhui Province			
Type WR 901 (Sidewall) four built	Shanghai Ship and Shipping Research Institute	40 seats	December 1980 (pre-production prototype)
Wuhu Shipyard			
5-ton expl. craft (Sidewall)			1975
Type 719 (Sidewall)	MARIC	186 seats	1984
Type 719 II	MARIC	257 seats	1988
Hudong Shipyard			
Type 716 II (Amphibious)	MARIC	32 seats or 2.5 tonnes	1985
Type 716 III (Amphibious)	MARIC	70 seats or 6.0 tonnes	1988

CHINA AIR CUSHION TECHNOLOGY DEVELOPMENT CORPORATION (CACTEC)
[DESIGN, RESEARCH, DEVELOPMENT AND PRODUCTION ASSISTANCE ORGANISATION]
Head Office: 41 Changdi Road, Tianjin, People's Republic of China

Telephone: Tianjin 311984, 313544
Cable: Tianjin 3333

Hu Wenliang, *Manager*

Branch office: 132 Jichang Road, Shanghai, People's Republic of China

Zhu Bi Yu *General Manager*

Telephone: 3770539
Telex: 33157 CSQXS CN

Formed in 1984, CACTEC is a subsidiary of the China State Shipbuilding Corporation (CSSC) and is a specialised business corporation working jointly with MARIC on a wide variety of applications of the air cushion principle with emphasis on the research, development, design and production of amphibious and sidewall (SES) hovercraft. Craft operated by CACTEC are given in the *Operators* section of this edition.

DAGU SHIPYARD
Yangzhabei, Xigu, Tanggu, Tianjin, People's Republic of China

Telephone: Tanggu 3901 Ext 98
Cable: Tanggu 3128

Tong Fuchang, *Director*

Building of various types of hovercraft (amphibious and sidewall) design and building of medium and small size steel vessels.

TYPE 722
Please see 1989 edition of this book for details of this craft.

TYPE 7203
Derived from Types 713 and 717 (built in the 1970s), Type 7203 is a high-speed passenger ferry for use on coastal and sheltered waters. Alternative applications include coastguard patrol and port/harbour firefighting duties.

Built at the Dagu Shipyard, Tianjin, the prototype was launched in September 1982 and underwent trials on the Hai river and in Tang-Gu in late 1982.
LIFT AND PROPULSION: A multi-fan system improves seakeeping performance. Three centrifugal fans of different diameters are separately fitted in the bow, amidship and stern. Each feeds air to the bow and stern skirts and the air cushion at different volumes and pressures. Diameters of the bow, amidship and stern fans are 800mm, 1200mm and 450mm respectively. The lift system is powered by a single 12150C high-speed diesel rated at 300hp at 1500rpm. The lift engine directly drives the amidship and stern fans. The bow fan is driven via a hydraulic pump and motor. Total lift power is about 250hp. Disengaging the bow fan reduces lift power consumption to about 100hp in calm waters. When operating in waves the bow fan is required since it affects the craft's trim. Propulsive power is supplied by two 12150CZ water-cooled, turbocharged, high-speed marine diesels, each rated at 450hp at 1450rpm. Each drives a three-bladed propeller via a V-type transmission.
CONTROLS: Craft direction controlled by twin rudders and by differential use of water propellers.
ACCOMMODATION: In standard configuration passenger cabin seats 81 passengers. If required, seating capacity can be increased to 100. Two aisles between seats are 800mm wide.
SKIRT: Loop and segment type in bonded natural rubber coated fabric.
DIMENSIONS
Length overall: 22.2m
Beam overall: 6.9m
Height overall: 5.2m
Height sidewalls: 1.1m
Draught, hullborne: 2.06m
Draught, on cushion: 1.22m

Type 7203 fast ferry

MARIC-designed Type 7210 built by Dong Feng Shipyard

WEIGHT
Max: 35 tonnes
PERFORMANCE
Max speed: 30 knots
Cruising speed: 26 knots
Range: 180n miles

JINXIANG

An 80-seat sidewall passenger ferry, Jinxiang is a joint project of the Marine Design and Research Institute of China and the Dagu Shipyard, Tianjin. In July 1983 it successfully completed a 128km maiden voyage along the Yangtze river from Shanghai to Vantong in under three hours. The craft is diesel-powered and has a maximum speed of 55km/h.
HULL: High strength, corrosion-resistant aluminium alloy.
DIMENSIONS
Length: 22.2m
Beam: 6.9m
Height: 5.2m

DONG FENG SHIPYARD

Jiuxi, Hangzhou, Zhejiang, People's Republic of China

Telephone: Hangzhou 62904
Cable: Hangzhou 0009

TYPE 7210

Two fully amphibious utility hovercraft type

'7210' were completed in May 1985. They were designed by MARIC and constructed by Dong Feng Shipyard, Hangzhou. Built in medium-strength sea-water resistant aluminium alloy with riveted construction, the craft is powered by air-cooled marine diesels. Lift is provided by a Deutz BF6L 912 diesel engine driving via a gearbox a centrifugal aluminium fan. Thrust is supplied by another diesel, a Deutz BF6L 913 driving via a transmission shaft and elastic coupling, a 1.8m, five-blade, ducted air propeller built in grp. The skirt is of the bag-finger type in rubberised fabric, low-temperature resistant down to −20°C. The total skirt height is 500mm.
DIMENSIONS
Length overall: 9.85m
Beam overall: 3.40m

MARIC Type 717 II

Overall height on landing pads: 2.80m
WEIGHTS
Max weight: 4.7 tons
Payload: 800kg
PERFORMANCE
Max water speed over calm water: 45km/h
Range: 250km

The first two craft were delivered to units of the oil industry for transporting people and equipment in offshore areas and marshes.

TYPE 717 II & III

This craft is a waterjet-propelled, rigid sidewall air cushion vehicle, designed by MARIC as a high-speed inland water passenger ferry for use on shallow water. The '717' series of the 1970s has been developed. The Type 717 II *Ming Jiang* pass-

MARIC Type 717 III

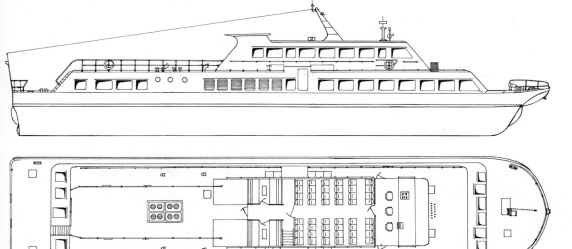
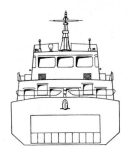

Layout of MARIC 717 III SES

MARIC Type 716 II 32-passenger ACV

enger ferry hovercraft was completed in October 1984, and was delivered to the Chongqing ship transportation company as a high-speed passenger ferry. The Type 717 *Chongqing* sidewall hovercraft was also completed in Dong Feng Shipyard, in September 1984, and was delivered to the Chongqing ferry boat company as a high-speed passenger craft operating on the rapids of the Yangtze river. A further type 717 III was delivered in September 1989

LIFT AND PROPULSION: Integrated system powered by two 12V 150C marine diesels rated at 224kW continuous. Two engines are mounted aft and each drives a 600mm diameter centrifugal fan, Type 4–72 for lift, and via an elastic coupling, universal joint and transmission shaft, a mixed flow waterjet pump. Another bow fan is driven via a hydraulic pump and motor by the integrated power system. The type 717 III is powered by two Cummins high speed diesel NTA-855-M engines of 298kW (Max) each.

STRUCTURE: The sidewalls are built in grp, but other parts of hull and superstructure are built in riveted, high-strength aluminium alloy.

DIMENSIONS	717 II	717 III
Length overall:	20.40m	21.40m
Beam overall:	4.54m	4.54m
Height overall:	3.80m	5.40m
WEIGHTS		
Max weight:	21.20 tons	23.00 tons
Payload:	54–60 passengers	70 passengers

PERFORMANCE
Speed, max, calm water:	45km/h	42km/h
Range:	400km	250km

HUDONG SHIPYARD
Bahaoqiao, Pudong Dadao, Shanghai, People's Republic of China

Telephone: Shanghai 840951
Telex: 33025SHDSY CN
Cable: 1675 Shanghai

TYPE 716 II
Designed by MARIC, the amphibious hovercraft type 716 II was completed in Hudong Shipyard in 1985. Now the craft is undergoing evaluation by the China Air Cushion Technology Development Corporation (CACTEC). The craft operates in offshore areas, shallow water and marshes for transporting people and equipment.
HULL: Riveted skin and stringer structure employing high-strength aluminium alloy sheet. Main hull forms a buoyancy raft based on a grid of longitudinal and transverse frames which form a number of flotation compartments.
LIFT AND PROPULSION: One Deutz BF12L 413FC air-cooled marine diesel (428hp at 2300rpm) via a gearbox and transmission shaft drives a 2m diameter centrifugal fan. Two identical engines, via transmission shafts, drive directly two 4-blade 2.3m diameter ducted air propellers.
CONTROLS: Directional control is by two sets of twin vertical aerodynamic rudders mounted on the rear of the propeller ducts.
DIMENSIONS
Length overall: 18.44m
Beam overall: 7.72m
Height on landing pads: 4.55m
Cushion width: 6.90m
WEIGHTS
Max weight: 19.4 tons

Payload: 4.0 tons (or 32 passengers)
PERFORMANCE
Max calm water speed: 39 knots
Range: 120n miles

WUHU SHIPYARD
Wuhu, Anhui, People's Republic of China

Telephone: Wuhu 5971
Cable: Wuhu 5307

TYPE 719
Designed by MARIC, and completed at Wuhu Shipyard in 1984, the Type 719 sidewall hovercraft is undergoing evaluation by the China Air Cushion Technology Development Corporation (CACTEC).
HULL: Main hull and sidewall are built in marine steel with welded construction, but superstructure is of grp construction.
LIFT AND PROPULSION: A 12180 four-stroke, water-cooled, turbocharged marine diesel rated at 900hp, via gearbox and transmission shaft, drives two 1.2m diameter twin air inlet type centrifugal fans. Two identical diesels, via gearboxes and transmission shafts, drive two three-blade marine propellers.
CONTROLS: Craft direction controlled by twin rudders and by differential use of marine propellers.
SKIRT: Loop and segment type in bonded rubberised fabric.
DIMENSIONS
Length overall: 35.5m
Beam overall: 7.6m
Height overall: 8.5m

MARIC Type 719G, 186-passenger sidewall hovercraft

WEIGHTS
Max weight: 95 tons
Payload: 186 passengers
PERFORMANCE
Max calm water speed: 30 knots
Service water speed: 25 knots
Range: 500n miles

TYPE 719 II

The 719 II sidewall hovercraft is the second such craft to be built with a steel hull.

This SES is constructed mainly of marine grade steel, and the superstructure is of aluminium. The vessel is powered by three MWM TBD234V16 high-speed diesel engines. One engine drives three centrifugal fans for cushion lift and each of the others drive a 1.0 diameter marine propeller.

The vessel can carry 257 passengers and meets the requirements of ships operating in class A area of Yangtze River.

PRINCIPAL PARTICULARS
Length overall: 40.00m
Beam overall: 8.28m
Height overall (mast included): 9.55m
Height, moulded: 3.26m
Displacement, max: 123.5 tonnes
Speed, maximum (achieved during delivery trials in calm water): 27.54 knots
Speed, service: 24.00 knots
Draught, off cushion full load (to the tip of the propellers): 2.45m
Draught, on cushion full load (to the tip of the propellers): 1.85m
Payload: 10.56 tonnes
Range, at service speed: 370km
Seakeeping capability
    This vessel can be operated safely on-cushion in Beaufort 7 gust winds and wave heights of 1.5m (3% highest observations).
Anti-capsizing capability
    It can meet the requirement of keeping afloat with one watertight compartment broken.
Power supply
    for propulsion: two MWM TBD V16
    for lift: one MWM TBD 234 VI6

MARIC 719 II

HULL

The main structure of this vessel is welded from steel type ZCA. The superstructure is riveted from aluminium type LY12CZ. A mixed framework system is adopted in hull construction, i.e., the framework in the bottom, front and stern part of the deck and the front parts of the sidewalls is formed by transverse panels; the framework in both sides of the hull, in sidewalls and the platform part of the bottom is formed by longitudinal panels. The frame distance is 0.5m.

The framework of the superstructure is formed by longitudinal panels.

MOORING DEVICES

A 100 kg anchor is adopted in this ship and is located on the bow structure by 15mm hawser with crosspieces, which goes through a hawsehole. An electric capstan is fitted on the bow deck for casting and weighing the anchor. The speed of weighing the anchor is 10.86m/min. The capstan, which provides a maximum pulling force of 1500 kg, can also be driven by hand.

RUDDERS

Two rudders with aerofoil section profiles are fitted at the stern behind the propellers. They are inter-connected and move synchronously by hydraulic actuation. A stand-by hydraulic system is provided. A hand oil pump is also provided for emergency use.

LIFE-SAVING AND FIRE-FIGHTING EQUIPMENT

To meet the life-saving requirements, six life buoys, 257 life jackets, 25 child life jackets and 7 working life jackets for crew are provided under passenger seats and in the store rooms.

As for fire-fighting, there are 8 fire-fighting extinguishers, type 1211 (MY6) installed in the ship. There are also some fire-fighting equipment provided, such as semicircle fire tub, fire axe, sand boxes etc.

SKIRTS

The bow seal is a bag and finger skirt, and the stern seal a two-lobe bag.

ACCOMMODATION

Cabins of this ship are on two decks: the upper cabin is on the wheelhouse deck and the lower cabin is on the main deck.

The upper deck carries the wheelhouse, first-class passenger cabin (48 seats), two high-class cabins (with 6 seats each) and two store rooms. On the lower deck there is a front passenger cabin (second class, 154 seats), aft passenger cabin (second class, 43 seats), an engine room, a crew cabin and a kitchen. There is a toilet near the aft passenger cabin and in the centre of the main deck there is a small shop and a toilet.

WHEELHOUSE

The wheelhouse is at the front part of the wheelhouse deck (between frame No. 54 to No. 62). In the wheelhouse there is a bridge, a rudder operating handle, a magnetic compass, a radar displayer, remote control device of the engine, engine ordering system and some chairs and sofa.

FIRST-CLASS PASSENGER CABIN

In the first-class passenger cabin there are 6 rows of 48 high-back sofa chairs with the pitch of 1m. There is a 0.6m aisle in the middle. Both sides of the cabin are panelled with 8 brown-tinted glass windows.

The MARIC 719 II steel-hull SES

Wheelhouse of MARIC 719 II

HIGH-CLASS PASSENGER CABINS

There are two high-class passenger cabins. In each compartment there are two three-seat sofas, one tea table, one unit of hanging air conditioning.

SECOND-CLASS FRONT PASSENGER CABIN

The second-class front passenger cabin has 154 high-back soft chairs arranged in 14 rows with a seat pitch of 0.85m.

ENGINE ROOM (FAN ROOM INCLUDED)

The control of engines is by remote control systems produced by HDW-Elektronik of West Germany with manual back-up. The lift engine is directly connected to three double-intake centrifugal lift fans via a clutch system and there is no speed reduction device between them. The propulsion engines drive the propellers through a West German speed reduction device type WVS 642. The engine room also contains an auxiliary engine and an electric generator.

The lift fan room is located between the frame No. 32 to No. 42. There are two double intake centrifugal fans in the fan room, arranged along the centre line of the ship.

SECOND-CLASS STERN PASSENGER CABIN, CREW CABIN, KITCHEN AND STERN TOILET

The second class stern passenger cabin contains 43 high-back soft chairs arranged into 4 rows with a pitch of 0.85m. There are two aisles 0.6m wide in this cabin.

TYPE 716 III DESIGN

News of this design was given at the International High-Performance Vehicle Conference given in Shanghai, 2–5 November 1988.

LIFT AND PROPULSION: Three Deutz BF 12L 413 C air-cooled diesel engines.

DIMENSIONS

Length, overall; hard structure: 20.50m

Beam, overall; hard structure: 8.00m

Height, overall; hard structure: 4.90m

WEIGHTS

Weight, max: 26 tonnes

Payload: 6 tonnes or 70 passengers

PERFORMANCE

Speed, sea state 0 to 1: 40 knots

Endurance: 4h

REFERENCE: *Design features of the model 716 II air cushion vehicle* by Zheng Rentao and Jiang Xianping, International High-Performance Vehicle Conference, CSNAME, Shanghai, 2–5 November, 1988.

JING-SAH RIVER TEST CRAFT

Please see *Jane's Surface Skimmers 1985* for details of this craft.

SHIPBUILDING AND MARINE ENGINEERING ESTABLISHMENT

Shanghai

2.8-TONNE UTILITY HOVERCRAFT

A fully amphibious utility hovercraft was completed in 1980 by the Shipbuilding and Marine Engineering Establishment, Shanghai. Although intended primarily for seismic prospecting in offshore areas and marshes, it is suitable for a variety of other utility roles. Sturdily built in riveted aluminium alloy, it carries a driver and up to seven passengers at a speed of 23–33km/h.

Two craft of this type are reported to be in service with the Chinese onshore oil industry. See 1987 edition for photograph.

LIFT AND PROPULSION: Lift is provided by an 85hp BJ492Q-1 four-stroke automobile petrol engine driving, via a universal coupling and gearbox, a centrifugal aluminium fan. Thrust is supplied by a second engine of identical type driving, via a transmission shaft, elastic coupling, transmission gear and thrust bearing, a 1.4m, four-bladed, variable-pitch aircraft propeller built

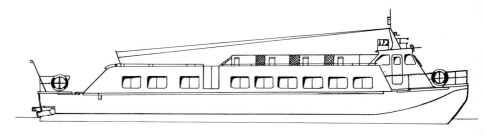

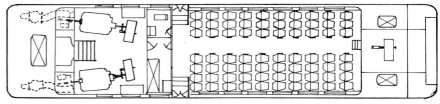

General arrangement of MARIC 717 II

Jing-Sah river test craft

in grp. Range of pitch variation is from +15 to −15 degrees. When the vehicle is operating with the propeller at constant pitch, the rotational speed is charged through the adjustment of the engine throttle. Cushion pressure is 94.5kg/m^2 (18lb/ft^2).

CONTROLS: Craft direction is controlled by twin aerodynamic rudders at the rear of the propeller duct.

HULL: Built in 919 medium strength seawater resistant aluminium alloy. Riveted construction.

SKIRT: Segmented bag-type fabricated in rubberised fabric. Height of fingers, 250mm, representing 50 per cent of the total skirt height. Tensile strength is 500 to 450kg/5cm width.

DIMENSIONS

Length: 9.19m

Width: 4.76m

Height: 3.32m

Deck area: 9m^2

Cabin, internal height: 1.47m

Average draught: 0.22m

WEIGHTS

Fully loaded: 2769kg

Useful load (8 personnel at 75kg each = 600kg, fuel and water, 118kg): 718kg

PERFORMANCE

Max speed during tests, still water: 42km/h

Speed at wind scale 3: 23–33km/h

Vertical obstacle clearance: 0.5m

CHAOHU SHIPYARD

Au-hui Province

and

SHANGHAI SHIP AND SHIPPING RESEARCH INSTITUTE (SSSRI)

Ministry of Communications

Head Office: 200 Minsheng Road, Shanghai, People's Republic of China

Telephone: Shanghai 840438

Telex: 33107SSSRI CN

Cable: Shanghai 5970

WR 901

The WR 901 is a waterjet-propelled, 40-seat, rigid sidewall hovercraft, designed for water-bus use on shallow rivers with a guaranteed depth of 0.8m.

The craft has been developed from a 5-ton experimental test craft designed by Shanghai Ship and Shipping Research Institute (SSSRI) built in Au-hui Province in 1975. The pre-production prototype was completed in December 1980. The design was jointly undertaken by the SSSRI and Communication Bureau of Au-hui Province and the craft was completed in the Chaohu Shipyard.

Official trials were completed in May 1981 on the river with depth of 0.8 to 1.2m. During a speed test over a measured mile with a full complement of passengers aboard, 38.5km/h (23.9mph) was attained.

Four of the first model of the WR 901 ACV were built.

LIFT AND PROPULSION: Integrated system powered by a main 12V 150Z diesel rated at 300hp continuous mounted aft and a second 485Q diesel engine rated at 30hp continuous, mounted forward.

The main engine (210hp at 1400rpm) drives a 365mm diameter two-stage waterjet unit for propulsion and supplies 20hp to drive two 300mm diameter centrifugal fans for lift.

The second engine drives two 500mm diameter centrifugal fans for lift.

The air cushion is retained between rigid longitudinal sidewalls, and flexible bow and rigid stern seals. Cushion pressure is 240kg/m^2.

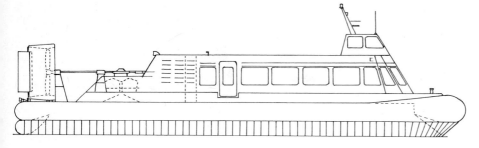
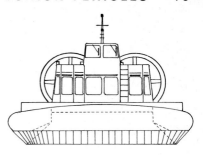

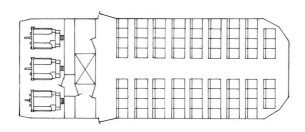

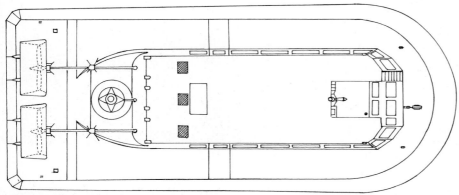

General arrangement of Type 716 III design

CONTROLS: Helm operated surfaces located in the waterjet stream provide directional control. Thrust reversal is achieved by the use of waterflow deflectors.

HULL: Single shell glass-reinforced plastic moulding with sub-moulding, frames, bulkhead and cabin and base panels bonded together.

Materials used include expanded pvc foam, glass fibre, polyester resins and wood. The hull bottom, deck and superstructure top have longitudinal frames and the sidewall transverse frames.

Thickness of plating on the side hull bottom is 4.5mm (6mm in the bow section) and on the sidewall 5mm (up to 6mm in the bow section). Deck plates are 4mm thick and the top of the superstructure is in 2.5mm plating.

ACCOMMODATION: Seats are provided for a crew of two in a raised wheelhouse and for 40 passengers. Access to the passenger saloon is through single doors at the bow and stern.

The craft runs bow-on to flat sloping banks to embark and disembark passengers.

SYSTEMS, ELECTRICAL: One 1.2kW 24V dc engine-driven generator and batteries.

COMMUNICATION: Car radio in wheelhouse and speakers in passenger saloon.

DIMENSIONS
Length overall: 19.30m
Beam overall: 3.95m
Hull beam: 3.75m
Height of hull top wheelhouse: 3.90m
Height of sidewalls: 0.50m
Draught load: 0.65m
Draught cushionborne at bow: 0.1m
　　at stern: 0.45m

WEIGHT
Max weight, with 40 passengers: 16 tons

40-passenger SES

Waterjet-propelled SES on Lake Tai

PERFORMANCE
Service speed, normal: 33km/h

JING-SAH RIVER PASSENGER FERRY

This craft is diesel powered and propelled by waterscrews. It was built during 1969 and began trials in 1970. Please see *Jane's Surface Skimmers 1985* for details.

TAI HU PASSENGER FERRY

A 42-seat waterjet-propelled passenger ferry, this craft has been built for operation across Lake Tai. It was delivered during early 1983. Unconfirmed reports credit the craft with a speed of 40km/h and a range of 450km.

ZHONG HUA SHIPYARD

Shanghai, Peoples Republic of China

Jing-Sah river passenger ferry

Builder of MARIC 719 II SES *Hong Xiang* operating between the Shanghai Municipality and Chong Ming Island

---

FINLAND

Finn-Leiju FL 600 (photo: *Markku Heikurimen*)

FINN-LEIJU OY CO LTD

Rattipolku 7, 45360 Valkeala, Finland

Telephone: (51)2 33321
Telex: 52004 KVOLA SF
Telefax: (51) 233241

Jyrki Hakanen, *Managing Director*

Builder of the successful Leiju 387 light hovercraft, this company has now developed new larger craft, diesel-powered, for over-ice use. The first craft was completed in 1988 for Board of Navigation, Finland.

FL 1010

LIFT AND PROPULSION: Two VM turbodiesel engines, 144hp each at 3200rpm.
PROPELLERS: two Hoffman 3-blade composite material, ground-adjustable blades, 1.4m diameter.
HULL: Diwinylcell sandwich, spray-coated with polyurethane.
ACCOMMODATION: Seats for 15 to 20 passengers plus 2 crew.
DIMENSIONS
Length (hard structure) overall: 10.80m
Beam: 4.60m
WEIGHTS
Empty weight: 1800kg
Payload: 1500kg

Finn-Leiju FL 1010

PERFORMANCE
Speed, max: 35–45 knots
Fuel consumption: 40 litres/h
Weather restrictions:
    Max, wind: 20 knots
    Max, wave height: 0.8m

FL-600

LIFT AND PROPULSION: Single VM turbo diesel, 144hp at 3200rpm, liquid cooled (or Rover V-8 direct fuel injection, 185hp at 4600rpm)

driving single centrifugal fan and two 4-blade Colechki New Aviation ground-adjustable duraluminium propellers, diameter 0.95m, ducted. An alternative arrangement incorporates a single 1.40m diameter propeller with three composite material blades.
CONTROLS: Aerodynamic rudders mounted in propeller slipstream and trimming elevators, similarly mounted, electrically operated. Fuel ballast system.
HULL: Composite sandwich construction, Diab-

Controls and instruments of Finn-Leiju FL 600

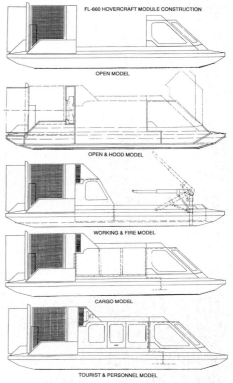

Alternative layouts possible with the Finn-Leiju FL 600 modular construction

Barracuda PVC foam panels, glass fibre covered. Modular construction permitting various layouts to be easily provided.
SKIRT: Polyurethane-coated nylon, loop and segment type.
SYSTEMS: 12 volt, heating, starting, radio, searchlight etc.
DIMENSIONS
Length: 6.60m
Beam: 2.80m hard structure
3.40m skirt inflated
Height, off cushion: 1.95m

WEIGHTS
Empty: 1320kg
1280kg with Rover engine
Disposable load: 800kg
ACCOMMODATION: Driver plus 6 passengers. Open layout: separate wheelhouse for driver and navigator. Workboat layout: rear wheelhouse, space for driver plus 3 passengers.
PERFORMANCE
Speed, max: 40 to 43 knots (75 to 80km/h)
Speed, cruising: 35 knots (65km/h)
Fuel consumption: 22-l/h

Endurance: 6h max
Rise height: 0.40m

WÄRTSILÄ MARINE INDUSTRIES INC.

Helsinki Shipyard, PO Box 132, SF-00151 Helsinki 15, Finland

Telephone: NAT.(90) 1941
(358) (0) 1941
Telex: 126008 WMARI SF
Telefax: (358) (0) 604 338

I.Ingvesgard, *President & C.E.O.*
K.Airaksinen, *Executive Vice President*
M.Saarikangas, *Executive Vice President*
H-P.Ihatsu, *Administration*
A.Pankakoski, *Legal Affairs*
J.Waris, *Business Development, Corporate Planning*

This company is no longer involved in the design and production of air cushion vehicles. Please see 1989 edition of this book for craft of this type that have been produced by the Wärtsilä company. Naval mono-hull patrol vessels produced by Wärtsilä appear in the High-speed Mono-hull Section of this current edition.

FRANCE

SOCIÉTÉ AEROPLAST sarl
Creux Redon de Cantadou, 34400 Lunel, France

Telephone: (67) 71 65 97
Telefax: 67719224

Guy Akerman, *Technical Director*

Aeroplast has developed over the past few years a range of light air cushion vehicles for sport and pleasure use which have led to a larger type, the ADOC 12, a 1.25-tonne payload utility craft supported in part by IFREMER.

ADOC 12
The ADOC 12 concept originally employed four very lightweight propulsion systems previously developed for much lighter craft. The same basic components are in use for Aeroplast one-, two-, three- and fourteen-seat craft allowing con-

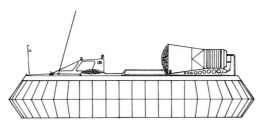
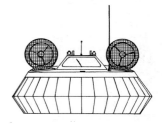
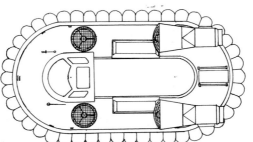

General arrangement of ADOC 12

ADOC 12 powered by four Peugeot diesel engines

siderable flexibility in manufacture and reduced stocks of spare parts.

Two lift fans supply the air cushion, of the same Multiwing type as the four air propellers.

The frame of the craft is constructed in grp, Bureau Veritas controlled.

ENGINES
Propulsion: two 52hp two-stroke or four-stroke
Lift: two 52hp two-stroke or four-stroke
ACCOMMODATION
Crew: 1 or 2
Passengers: 12
FUEL TANK
Capacity: 300 litres
DIMENSIONS
Length overall, rigid structure: 8.4m
　　on cushion: 9.4m
Width overall, rigid structure: 4.4m
　　on cushion: 5.4m
Height overall, rigid structure: 2.3m
　　on cushion: 2.9m

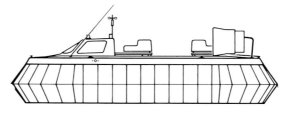

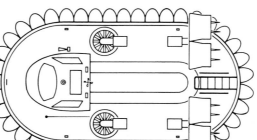

ADOC 12D

Propellers, dia: 800mm
Fans, dia: 800mm
WEIGHTS
Weight, max: 3000kg
Payload: 1250kg to 1500kg
PERFORMANCE
Speed, max, calm water: 40 knots

Speed, cruising, calm water: 30 knots
Range at cruising speed: 210n miles
Obstacle clearance capability: 0.5m
Fuel consumption: 40 litres/h
WEATHER LIMITATIONS
Wind, max: 20 knots
Wave height, max: 1.0m

ADOC 12D

A diesel powered version of the ADOC 12, powered by four Peugeot diesel engines, driving two ducted propellers with integrated reverse thrust systems.

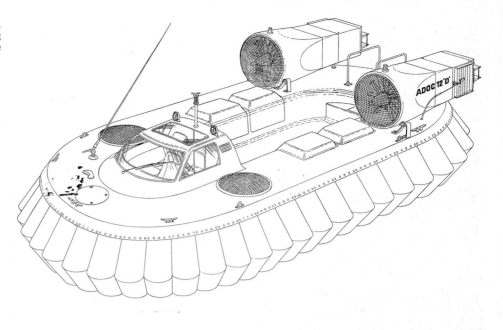

DIRECTION DES RECHERCHES, ETUDES ET TECHNIQUES (DRET)

26 Boulevard Victor, 75996 Paris Armees, France

Telephone: (1) 45 52 49 24
Telex: 204 648 F

and

DIRECTION DES CON-STRUCTIONS NAVALES (DCN)

2 rue Royale, BP No 1, 75008 Paris, France

Telephone: (1) 40 59 1606
Telex: 202 184 F

The Délégation Générale pour l'Armement (DGA) is currently engaged in a research and development programme on surface effect ships. So as to be able to fulfil perceived naval requirements for 1995, DCN is studying an SES project of approximately 1200 tonnes for anti-submarine warfare (ASW) on the high seas. These studies are being conducted by the Service Technique des Constructions et Armes Navales (STCAN) under the aegis of a technical-operational working group, within the framework of a project named EOLES (light oceanic surface effect escort craft). The task lays down a requirement for an off-cushion speed of 18 knots but with speeds in the order of 50 knots on cushion. Apart from its ASW armaments, the craft will be equipped with self-defence systems against air attack and surface ships.

Several stages of technology have to be passed through before this craft reaches the production phase. The experimental model, code-named MOLENES, has now finished its trials. In addition, DCN is involved in an inter-ministry programme aimed at developing the 200-tonne craft designed by STCAN. The NES (Navire à Effet de Surface) 200 SES, code-named AGNES 200, experience will guide the operational and technological options arising from the EOLES project.

MOLENES (Modèle Libre Expérimental de Navire à Effet de Surface)

In 1980, DCN built under contract from DRET (Direction des Recherches Etudes et Techniques) a 5-tonne craft, which had its trials in 1981 in the Toulon area. MOLENES is a dynamic manned model capable of proving the NES concept of a high length/beam ratio, and confirmed results obtained in the experimental tank and has pro-

MOLENES dynamic manned model of NES SES project *(STCAN-DOC)*

vided data on sea-worthiness, performance and manoeuvrability, as well as acceleration levels and their effects on the structure, equipment and fittings.

LIFT AND PROPULSION: Propulsion is provided by two 55hp waterjet units. The air cushion is effected by two centrifugal fans on vertical axes, giving a pressure of 1800Pa ($37.6lb/ft^2$) and a flow of $4m^3/s$ ($141ft^3/s$).

HULL: The timber side keels are joined together by a tubular pyramid structure of light aluminium alloy 7020.

DIMENSIONS
Length overall: 12.10m
Width overall: 3.43m
WEIGHT
Displacement: 5.5 tonnes

EOLES (Escorteur Océanique Léger à Effet de Surface) (DESIGN)
(Light oceanic surface-effect escort craft)

This project is being designed by STCAN under the control of a Technical Operational Group, commissioned with evaluating the capacity of EOLES to carry out the task of anti-submarine warfare. An operational research study has made it possible to compare EOLES with other solutions thought possible for future ASW.

The main advantage of this design is the combination of data available from the very low frequency sonar equipment with the availability of two on-board medium-weight helicopters, carried on an SES capable of high speed even in rough seas.

LIFT AND PROPULSION: Propulsion is provided by two waterjets driven by two TAG General Electric LM 2500 engines, each of 27 000hp.

Lift is provided by two centrifugal fans on vertical axes, driven by 5000hp diesel engines, which also provide propulsive power when operating off cushion.

ARMAMENT AND EQUIPMENT: Two medium helicopters, four missile launched tor-pedoes, 16 torpedoes launched from helicopters, four MM40 missiles, 16 SAAM missiles, 2 SATCP 'Sadral', ELW system.

DETECTION: ASW detection is effected by a towed linear antenna, EBTF, capable of being activated, and a dipping sonar (for use when stationary, with coverage being achieved by means of high-speed bounds). Air/surface detection is provided by SAAM radar, V15, DECCA and RODEO systems.

DIMENSIONS
Length overall: 89m
Width overall: 21.10m
Draught, off cushion: 3.60m
   on cushion: 1.60m
WEIGHT
Displacement, mean: 1200 tonnes
PERFORMANCE
Speed, off cushion: 18 knots
   on cushion: 50 knots
Range, off cushion: 4400n mi
   on cushion: 1900n mi

DIRECTION DES RECHERCHES, ETUDES ET TECHNIQUES (DRET)
26 Boulevard Victor, 75996 Paris Armees, France

Telephone: (1) 45 52 49 24
Telex: 204 648 F

and

DIRECTION DES CON-STRUCTIONS NAVALES (DCN)
2 rue Royale, 75200 Paris Naval, France

and

SOCIETE NOUVELLE DES ATELIERS ET CHANTIERS DU HAVRE (ACH)
BP 1390, 76066 Le Havre Cedex, France

Telephone: 35268177
Telefax: 35250970

and

CONSTRUCTION MÉCANIQUES DE NORMANDIE (CMN)
26 rue de Montevideo, 75116 Paris, France

Telephone: 45040877
Telex: 610097F

AGNES 200 [ex NES 200 (DESIGN)]

The AGNES 200 is being developed within the framework of an inter-ministry programme, in which the following are participating: The Ministry of Defence, The Ministry of Research and the Ministry of Industry. Delivery 1990.

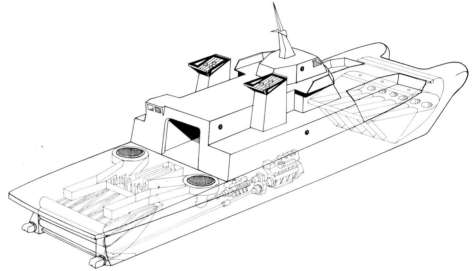

Arrangement of lift and propulsion systems in NES 200 SES design

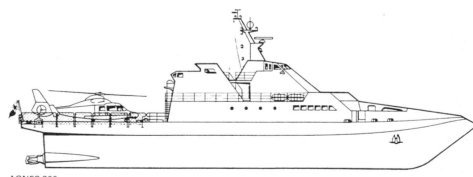

AGNES 200

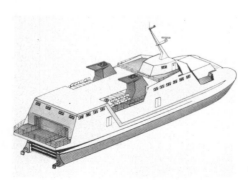

Isometric drawing of NES 200L passenger/car ferry

Involved in conducting the programme is, La Direction des Recherches, Etudes et Techniques (DRET).

Industrial concerns involved are DCN, in respect of the project design, and ACH and CMN shipyards, in respect of the construction.

The project which is envisaged to produce a craft in the region of 200 tonnes, is being designed in the form of a basic air cushion platform for both civil and military versions.

The major components (propulsion system, lift fans etc) are all existing technology, and therefore require only a limited degree of development. An evaluation prototype, named Agnes 200, is currently being built at Constructions Mécaniques de Normandie (CMN).

General specifications common to all the versions:

LIFT AND PROPULSION
Main propulsion: Two 2983kW (MTU 16V 538 TB 93 or SACM UD 33 M7) diesels driving two KaMeWa waterjet units
Lift: Two 746kW (MTU 8V 396 TB 83) diesels driving two NEU centrifugal fans, 180 000m³/h at 600kg/m². Off cushion, power transferable to the two KaMeWa waterjet units

DIMENSIONS
Length overall: 51.00m
   waterline: 44.8m
Width overall: 13.00m
Draught, off cushion: 2.30m
   on cushion: 1.00m

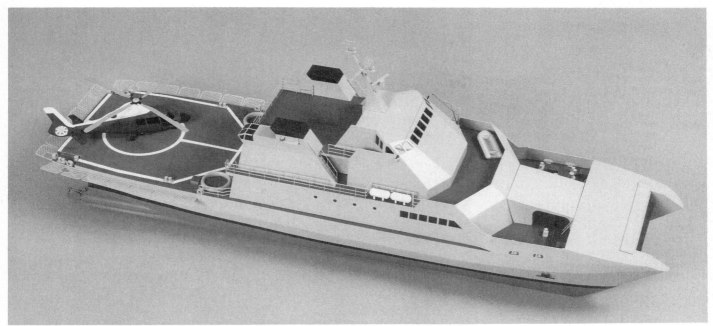

Model of AGNES 200 platform

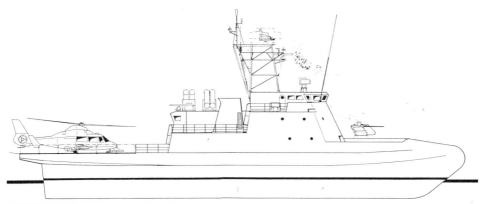

AGNES 200 platform in military configuration

WEIGHT
Displacement, loaded: 250 tonnes
PERFORMANCE
Speed, off cushion: 15 knots
  on cushion: over 40 knots
Range, off cushion: 1200n mi (14 knots)
  On cushion: 750n mi (25 knots)
COMPLEMENT
22 officers and crew plus 46 passengers

Anti-Surface Combat Version
Range, off cushion: 3200n miles at 12 knots
  1000n miles at 35 knots
Crew: 35
Weapon systems: one twin-barrel 30mm cannon
or one Sadral
  two Exocet MM 40 missiles
  one Dauphin helicopter + radar
  two AS 15 heli-borne missiles
  two Protean decoy missiles

one Triton S radar system
one Totem optronic guidance system
one DR 2000 Dalia
  This design permits a combination of great
mobility and over-the-horizon target definition by
the helicopter on board the craft, giving full effect
to the long-range MM 40 missiles.
  In addition, its range when powered off cushion
and the weapon capacity of the craft enable it to
carry out interdiction tasks within sea-approach-
es.

Coast Guard Version/Commando Transport
Range off cushion: 3200n miles at 12 knots
  1000n miles at 35 knots
Crew: 26 + 12 passengers
Weapons: one single-barrel 40mm Bofors cannon
  two 12.7mm machine-guns
  one navigation radar

Fast Patrol Version
Range: 3200n miles at 12 knots
  1000n miles at 35 knots
Crew: 29
Weapon systems: one 57mm Bofors cannon
  one twin-barrel 30mm cannon
  two 4 MM 40 missiles
  one Sadral
  one Triton S radar
  one Castor II B radar
  two Protean decoy launchers
  one DA 2000 Dalia

Passenger/Car Ferry
Displacement, full load, approx: 260 tonnes
Disposable load, approx: 63 tonnes
Passengers: 250
Cars: 27

(IFREMER)
INSTITUT FRANÇAIS
DE RECHERCHE POUR
L'EXPLOITATION DE LA MER
[DESIGN, RESEARCH AND
DEVELOPMENT ORGANISATION]
Centre de Brest, BP 70, 29273 Plouzané, France

Telephone: (98) 22 40 40
Telex: 940627OCEAN F

                    and

INGENIERIE MARITIME
ET COMMERCIALISATION
(IMC)/EFAIR
Bassin n° 3, BP 234, 17304 Rochefort Cedex

Telephone: (33) 46 99 05 97
Telex: 790073 F

NES 24
  The design of a 24-metre surface effect ship to
be used as a fast ferry has been completed in

collaboration with French shipyards. Its main
characteristics have to cope with commercial criteria, which were defined through a world wide
market survey. The prototype had entered its final
design and construction phase by the end of 1988.
It will be built by the group INGENIERIE
MARITIME ET COMMERCIALISATION
(IMC), SBERN (Naval Architect), CDK Composites (Structure) and BARILLEC S.A. (Electricity). A subsidiary company of IMC: EFAIR
will be in charge of the first commercial application of the prototype and of the sale of the series

of ships to be built by the group on the basis of
the prototype design. Delivery of the prototype is
scheduled by mid 1990. After a 6 months testing
period it should enter commercial application in
1991.

HULL: To be built in GRP sandwich.

LIFT AND PROPULSION: Propulsion can be
provided by two waterjets or by two surface piercing propellers. Air cushion pressure is provided
by two centrifugal fans (6500 Pa).

ENGINES

Propulsion: Two MAN D 2842 LYE (730kW) or
    DEUTZ-MWM TBD V12 (715kW).

Lift: Two DEUTZ-MWM-BF6L 913 C (130kW).

SKIRT

At the front, biconical system of 2x4 skirts which
has been used on the SEDAM hovercraft N500
and the ADOC 12 of Société AEROPLAST (see
above). A bag skirt system is fitted at the rear.

EQUIPMENT

Two 2.9kW + two 1.8kW electrical generators
24VDC driven by the lift and propulsion engines.
In harbour conditions, electricity can be provided
as well as via a shore connection box. Control and
stiring facilities are provided through a manual
system and a computerised automatic one.

ACCOMMODATION

The NES 24 will be operated by a crew of 4: 2 in
the upper deck wheelhouse, 2 in the passenger
saloons. Seats with a pitch of 80cm and a breadth
of 47cm are provided for 152 passengers in the
front and rear saloons separated by a bar/crew
accommodation area. Luggage stowage is provided over the propulsion engines and in overhead
compartments. Two toilet/wash basin units are
fitted at the rear of the ship. Main access doors
are at the stern; emergency exits are located at the
front of the passenger compartment. 220V AC
fluorescent tubes are lighting the passenger
saloons.

POWER

Lift: Approx 350hp

Propulsion: Approx 2000hp

ACCOMMODATION

Passengers: 150 to 160

DIMENSIONS

Length: Approx 24m

Beam: Approx 6.75m

Draught, on cushion: Approx 0.1m bow, 0.75m
    stern

Draught, on hulls: Approx 1.5m

WEIGHTS

Weight, max: Approx 45 tonnes

Weight, empty: Approx 28 tonnes

PERFORMANCE

Speed, max, calm water: Above 40 knots

Speed, cruising: Above 30 knots

Range: Approx 240n miles (8 hours operation)

Passengers 152 at 75kg: 11 400kg

Baggage 152 at 10kg: 1520kg

Crew 4 at 75kg: 300kg

Fuel 3100 kg

Model of NES 24, external design by B Pettier and P Rivoalem-Emsad(*R Gernot*)

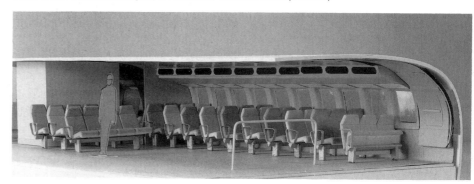

Model of NES 24 interior, design by B Pettier and P Rivoalem-Emsad(*R Gernot*)

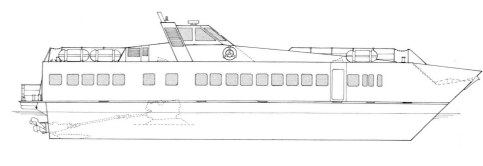

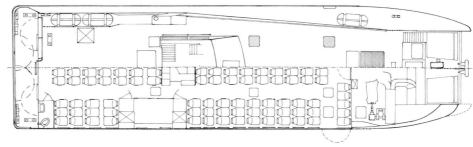

Internal arrangements of the NES 24, a 40 knot, 152
passenger SES developed by IFREMER in collaboration
with French shipyards

GERMANY, FEDERAL REPUBLIC OF

BLOHM + VOSS AG

857/8, Hermann-Blohm Str, 2000 Hamburg 11,
Federal Republic of Germany

Telephone: 040 31190
Telefax: 040 3191135

In early 1989 Blohm + Voss announced the
existence of their Corsair SES project. The vessel
is built in glass-fibre sandwich construction and
was designed to explore civil and military potential for this type of craft. An unusual feature of
the design is the provision of flow control flaps
situated upstream of each propeller. Corsair was
launched in April 1989.

PRINCIPAL PARTICULARS
Length, overall: 36.00m
Beam: 13.00m
Depth: 4.10m
Engines, propulsion: two MTU 16V 396 TB 94,
2560kW each
    Lift: two
Gearboxes: Maag
Propulsion: two Escher-Wyss surface-piercing c.p.
propellers, 7 blade
Displacement, standard: 160 tonnes
Speed: 52 knots

Corsair SES

MTG MARINETECHNIK GmbH

DEFENCE PLANNING AND DESIGNING
ORGANISATION
Wandsbeker Königstrasse 62, PO Box 70 12 49, D-
2000 Hamburg 70, Federal Republic of Germany
Telephone: (040) 65830
Telex: 215200
Telefax: (040) 6583392

Franz-Josef Görgen, *Managing Director*
Werner Kurz, *Commercial Director*

MTG Marinetechnik GmbH was founded in
1966 at the instigation of the Federal German
MoD as a central planning and design office for
naval systems, especially naval surface craft, and
general naval technology. Since 1984 MTG has
been working on the development of SES technology. Taking advantage of a data exchange
between the USA(NAVESA) and the Federal
Republic of Germany(Mod) a design study of the
fast test craft SES 700 was worked out by MTG.
Extensive model tests were carried out at the
David Taylor Research Center facilities.

MTG design for fast test craft SES 700

SES 700 (DESIGN)

LIFT AND PROPULSION: Air for the cushion
and the bow skirts is provided by four fans driven
by two diesel engines of 2000 kW each. Three of
the fans provide air directly for the cushion and
one provides air for the bow skirt. Air for the aft
skirt is provided by one electrically driven fan of
360 kW. The design incorporates a Ride Control
System (RCS) to improve seakeeping characteristics. Propulsive power is provided by four gas
turbines of 5500kW each with attached planetary
gears. Two units are arranged in each hull and
drive a KaMeWa waterjet type 125 562/6 via a
spur gear with integrated clutch couplings. Electric propulsion for silent hullborne operation provides an output of 300 kW per shaft.
CONTROLS: Craft heading is controlled by the
steerable nozzles of the water jet units and their
reverse thrust system.
HULL: Main structure is designed in steel and the
superstructure is designed in marine aluminium
alloy.

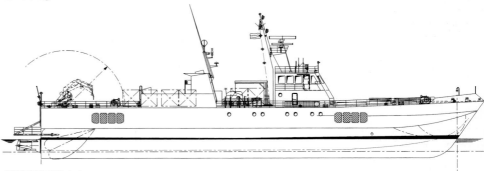

MTG SES 700 design

SKIRT: The skirt material is elastic neoprene-
coated nylon fabric. The bow skirt is designed as
a bag-&-finger system and the stern skirt as a 3-
lobe bag system.
ACCOMMODATION: Accommodation is provided for a crew of 12 and a team of 6 scientists.
DIMENSIONS
Length overall:67.00m

Beam overall:16.10m
Draught, hullborne:2.85m
Draught, cushionborne:0.95m
WEIGHTS
Operational displacement:720t
PERFORMANCE
Max.speed:50 knots plus
Endurance:5 days

HONG KONG

CHEOY LEE SHIPYARDS LTD

863–865 Lai Chi Kok Road, Kowloon, Hong Kong
P.O. Box 80040 Cheung Sha Wan, Kowloon, Hong Kong

Telephone: (3)743 7710
Telex: 56361 CLS HX
Telefax: (3)745 5312

Ken Lo, *Director*
C H Elliot Brown, *Technical Manager*

AIR RIDE 87

Licensed for the building of Air Ride Craft vessels, Cheoy Lee Shipyards is engaged in building the first Air Ride 87 yacht. This SES motor yacht is being built in Airex-cored fibreglass and the hull was nearing completion in December 1989 and has been sold.

The topside of the Air Ride 87 has been designed by Tom Fexas Naval Architects. Unlike conventional motor yachts and sports boats, this vessel has a relatively wide beam at 8.54 metres. The interior design is by Susan Puleo Design and Dave Jackson of REX.

PRINCIPAL PARTICULARS
Certification: ABS
Type: Motor yacht
Hull: Airex-cored fibreglass
Top side design: Tom Fexas
Length: 25.61m
Beam: 8.54m
Draught, on-cushion: 0.76m
Displacement: 61.2 tonnes
Speed: 52 knots
Engines,
    propulsion: Two DDC 16V 92TA each 716 kW (960 shp)
    lift: One DDC 8V 92TA (350shp)
Thrust device: Arneson ASD 14 surface propeller drive units
Ride control: Optional

AIR RIDE 84

The 25.6 metre SES passenger ferry is due to be built by Cheoy Lee in 1990 and is expected to be in operation in late 1990.
PRINCIPAL PARTICULARS
Certification: ABS
Type: Ferry

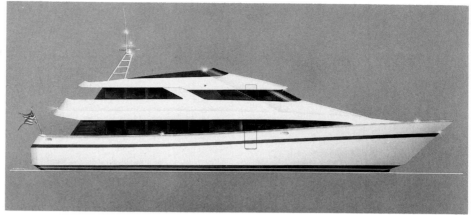
Air Ride 87 SES motor yacht

Air Ride 84 SES passenger ferry

Hull: Airex-cored fibreglass
Top side design: Cheoy Lee Shipyards Ltd
Length: 25.61m
Beam: 8.54m
Draught, on-cushion: 0.76m
Displacement, half load: 76.2 tonnes
Speed: 40 knots
Fuel consumption, cruise: 397 l/h
Passengers: 220–250
Fuel capacity: 5678 l
Water capacity: 757 l

Engines,
    propulsion: Two DDC 16V 92TA each 737 kW (988 shp)
    lift: One DDC 8V 92TA 261 kW
Thrust device: Arneson ASD 14 surface propeller drive units
Ride control: Optional
Lift fans: Gardon City Fan Co. model 34.125 AF6525 SWS-1 driven via a Capital HY-400 gear box (clutch and ahead gear only) and Cotta model RA1951 1.33:1 ratio right angle drive unit.

ITALY

FINCANTIERI-CANTIERI NAVALI ITALIANI SpA

(Cantieri Navali Riuniti SpA was incorporated in Fincantieri in July 1984)
Head Office: Via Genova 1, I-34121 Trieste, Italy
Naval Shipbuilding Division: Via Cipro 11, 16129 Genoa, Italy

Telephone: 00391059951
Telex: 270168 FINCGE I

Mario de Negri, *Naval Shipbuilding Division General Manager*
Franco Baracchini, *Technical Director*
Michele Diaz Satta, *Marketing & Sales Director*

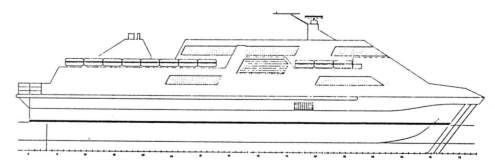

This company is involved in studies for an SES project.

JAPAN

MITSUBISHI HEAVY INDUSTRIES

5–1, Marunouchi 2-chome, Chiyoda-ku, Tokyo, Japan

Telephone: (212) 3111
Telex: 22443 J

SURFACE EFFECT SHIP

In August 1989 Mitsubishi completed the construction of an 18.5m SES for the Japanese Navy.

In mid April 1989 a joint research and development programme was announced by the Japan Defence Agency and Mitsubishi Heavy Industries for a 50 knot SES designed to operate safely in rough coastal waters. The interest of the Defence Agency is in applying the technology to mine sweepers, torpedo boats and patrol ships and stems from work started in 1983. A budget of YEN 800 million has been made available to Mitsubishi for the current year. An experimental craft of some 20 to 30 tonnes is to be completed by the end of 1990.

MITSUI ENGINEERING & SHIPBUILDING CO LTD

6–4, Tsukiji 5-chome, Chuo-ku, Tokyo 104, Japan

Telephone: 544–3462
Telex: 22821J, 22924 J

Kazuo Maeda, *Chairman*
Yasunosuke Ishii, *President*
Jiro Hoshino, *Executive Managing Director*
Mikihisa Komoto, *Deputy Director & General Manager, Marine Division*
Yutaka Ikeda, *General Manager, Advanced Craft Sales Dept.*

Mitsui's Hovercraft Department was formed in May 1964, following the signing of a licensing agreement in 1963 with Hovercraft Development Ltd and Vickers Ltd, whose ACV interests were later merged with those of British Hovercraft Corporation.

The company has been developing Mitsui hovercraft independently after terminating the licensing agreement in March 1986. The Mitsui Jet Hover and MV-PP10 represent such developments. The company has built nineteen MV-PP5s, four MV-PP15s and two MV-PP05s.

MV-PP1

The MV-PP1 is a small peripheral jet ACV built for river and coastal services and fitted with a flexible skirt. It seats a pilot and ten passengers and cruises at 40 knots.

The prototype, which was completed in July 1964 was designated RH-4, the first production model the PP1–01. The latter was sold to the Thai Customs Department for service in the estuary of the Menam Chao Phya and adjacent waters and has been named *Customs Hovercraft 1*. It has been in service with the Thai Customs Department since September 1967.

Details of construction, weights, performance, etc can be found in *Jane's Surface Skimmers 1970–71* and earlier editions.

MV-PP5

Mitsui's first large hovercraft, the 50-seat MV-PP5, is a gas-turbine powered craft intended primarily for fast ferry services on Japanese coastal and inland waters.

LIFT AND PROPULSION: All machinery is aft to minimise noise in the passenger cabin. A single IHI IM-100 gas turbine (licence-built General Electric LM100) with a maximum continuous rating of 1050hp at 19 500rpm drives the integrated lift/propulsion system. Its output shaft passes first to the main gearbox from which shafts extend sideways and upwards to two three-bladed Hamilton/Sumitomo variable-pitch propulsion propellers of 2.59m (8ft 6in) diameter. A further shaft runs forward to the fan gearbox from which a drive shaft runs vertically downwards to a 2.27m (7ft 7in) 13-bladed lift fan mounted beneath the air intake immediately aft of the passenger saloon roof. The fan is constructed in aluminium alloy and the disc plate is a 40mm (1.5in) thick honeycomb structure.

To prevent erosion from water spray the propeller blades are nickel plated.

MV-PP5

Craft built	Seats	Launched	Operator
Hakuchyo No 3	75*	June 1970	Oita Hoverferry Co Ltd
Hobby No 1	75*	May 1971	Oita Hoverferry Co Ltd
Hobby No 3	75*	September 1971	Oita Hoverferry Co Ltd
Hobby No 6	75*	October 1974	Oita Hoverferry Co Ltd
Angel No 2	51	June 1972	Oita Hoverferry Co Ltd
Angel No 5	75*	April 1975	Oita Hoverferry Co Ltd
Akatombo 52	51	-	Oita Hoverferry Co Ltd
Kamone (Sea Gull)	52	November 1971	
plus 11 others			

*Converted to Mk II configuration.

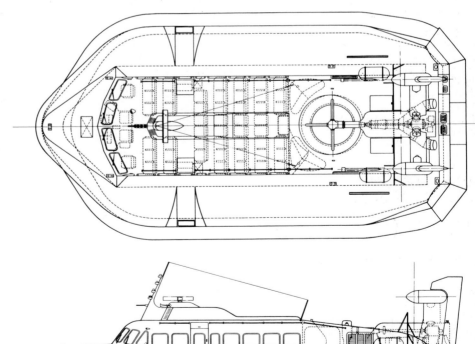

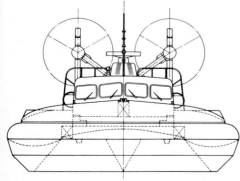

MV-PP5

Fuel is carried in two metal tanks, with a total capacity of 1900 litres (416 gallons), located immediately ahead of the lift fan assembly.

CONTROLS: Twin aerodynamic rudders in the propeller slipstream and differential thrust from the propellers provide directional control. The rudders are controlled hydraulically from the commander's position.

A thrust-port air bleed system provides lateral control at slow speeds. The thrust ports are actuated by air extracted from the engine compressor and are located beneath the passenger doors, port and starboard.

HULL: Construction is primarily of high strength A5052 aluminium alloy suitably protected against the corrosive effects of sea water. The basic structure is the main buoyancy chamber which is divided into eight watertight sub-divisions for safety, and includes fore and aft trimming tanks. Two further side body tanks, each divided into three watertight compartments, are attached to the sides of the main buoyancy chamber. To facilitate shipment the side body tanks can be removed, reducing the width to 3.75m (12ft 4in).

The outer shell of the main buoyancy chamber, the machinery deck space, the forward deck and the passage decks around the cabin exterior are all constructed in honeycomb panels with aluminium cores.

The lift fan air intake, radar cover, part of the air conditioning duct, and inside window frames are grp.

SKIRT: The flexible skirt was designed by Mitsui following research conducted with the aid of the RH-4 (MV-PP1 prototype). It is made of 0.8mm ($\frac{1}{32}$ in) thick chloroprene-coated nylon sheet. A fringe of finger type nozzles is attached to the skirt base at the bow and on both sides. At the stern a D-section bag skirt is used to avoid scooping up water.

Two transverse and one longitudinal stability bags are fitted.

ACCOMMODATION: The passenger cabin is sited above the forward end of the main buoyancy chamber. Seats for the two crew members are on a raised platform at the front of the cabin. All controls, navigation and radio equipment are concentrated around the seats. The windows ahead are of reinforced tempered glass and have electric wipers.

The two cabin entrance doors are divided horizontally, the lower part opening sideways, the top part upwards. The standard seating arrangement is for 42 passengers but ten additional seats can be placed in the centre aisle.

In accordance with Japanese Ministry of Transport regulations a full range of safety equipment is carried, including two inflatable life rafts, 54 life jackets, one automatic manually activated fire extinguisher for the engine casing and two portable fire extinguishers in the cabin. Other standard equipment includes ship's navigation lights, marine horn, searchlight and mooring equipment, including an anchor. The 12 side windows can be used as emergency exits and are made of acrylic resin.

SYSTEMS, ELECTRICAL: Two 2kW, 28.5V ac/dc generators driven by belts from the main gearbox. One 24V, 100Ah battery for engine starting.

PNEUMATIC SYSTEMS: A 4.7–7kg/cm² (56.8–99.5lb/in²) pneumatic system for thrust port operation.

COMMUNICATIONS AND NAVIGATION: Equipment includes a radio and radar.

EXTERNAL DIMENSIONS
Length overall: 16m (52ft 6in)
Beam overall: 8.6m (28ft 2in)
Height overall on landing pad: 4.81m (15ft 9in)
Skirt depth: 1.2m (3ft 11in)
Draught afloat: 0.2m (8in)
Cushion area: 88m² (741ft²)

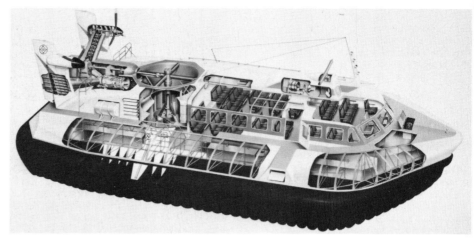
MV-PP5 showing integrated lift/propulsion system

MV-PP5 02 *Hakuchyo No 3*

MV-PP5 Mk II

INTERNAL DIMENSIONS
Cabin
Length: 7.1m
Max width: 3.8m
Max height: 1.9m
Floor area: 26m²
Doors: Two 0.65 × 1.4m one each side of cabin
Baggage-hold volume: 0.6m³ (21.2ft³)
WEIGHTS
Normal max: 16.3 tons
Normal payload: 4.3 tons
PERFORMANCE
Max speed, calm water: 102km/h (55 knots)
Cruising speed, calm water: 83km/h (45 knots)
Still air range and endurance at cruising speed: About 160n miles, 4 hours approx
Vertical obstacle clearance: 0.6m (2ft) approx

MV-PP5 Mk II

This is a stretched version of the MV-PP5 fast passenger ferry. Lift and propulsion systems and power arrangements are identical to those of the standard MV-PP5, but the hull has been lengthened by 2.18m (7ft 2in) raising the maximum passenger seating capacity from 52 to 76. Maximum speed in calm water is 52 knots. Endurance and cruising speeds are unaffected by the size increase.

Five PP5s have been converted to Mk II configuration and the original Mk II is in service with Japanese National Railways.

DIMENSIONS
Length overall: 18.18m
Beam overall: 8.6m
Height overall on landing pad to top of mast: 4.81m

Craft built (MV-PP5 Mk II)	Seats	Launched	Operator
Tobiuo (Flying Fish)	66	March 1980	—

Skirt depth: 1.2m
Draught afloat: 0.2m
Cushion area: 104m²
WEIGHTS
Normal max: 19.3 tons
Normal payload: 7.2 tons
PERFORMANCE
Max speed, calm water: approx 52 knots
Cruising speed, calm water: approx 45 knots
Endurance at cruising speed: approx 4 hours
Passenger capacity, max: 76

MV-PP15

(Four built)

Developed from the earlier PP5, the Mitsui MV-PP15 is designed for high-speed passenger ferry services on coastal and inland waterways. Accommodation is provided for 155 passengers and a crew of five.

Details of MV-PP15 can be found in Jane's High-Speed Marine Craft and Air Cushion Vehicles 1989 and earlier editions.

MV-PP05A

(Two built)

The first MV-PP05A amphibious utility craft were delivered to the Japanese National Institute of Polar Research expedition in Antarctica early in 1981. The expansion of expeditions in Antarctica has led to a greater need for a safe and rapid means of surface transport, for personnel and supplies, over floating ice and crevassed areas. One consideration was that ACVs would be less expensive to operate than helicopters and also less affected by adverse weather conditions. A unique feature of the MV-PP05A is the provision of an auxiliary propulsion system thought to be used for climbing slopes and attaining high speeds.

The two prototypes are considered as research craft only, but they are expected to lead to the design of a larger machine which will combine the duties of cargo and personnel carrier.

LIFT AND PROPULSION: Integrated system powered by a single 1990cc Nissan GA 135 petrol engine rated at 90kW at 5000rpm. Power is transmitted to two transverse shafts at the opposite ends of which are two 13-blade centrifugal lift fans. Air is fed downwards into the cushion and backwards through airjet ducts for propulsion. Auxiliary propulsion is supplied by two pylon-mounted, fixed-pitch free-air propellers at the rear of the fan volutes. These are powered by two 1584cc Volkswagen VW 126A automotive engines, each rated at 33kW at 3600rpm.

CONTROLS: Craft heading is controlled by interconnected rudder vanes set in the airjet ducts aft. The airflow is deflected forwards for braking and reversing by reversible vanes.

SKIRT: Peripheral loop segment type, 0.6m (2ft) deep. Cushion pressure is about 130kg/m² (26.6lb/ft²).

DIMENSIONS
Length overall, hard structure: 7.1m (23ft 3½in)
  overall, skirt inflated: 8.1m (26ft 7in)
Beam: 4.8m (15ft 9in)
Beam overall, hard structure: 3.8m (12ft 5½in)
Height, on cushion: 3.5m (11ft 6in)
WEIGHT
Max, with payload: 2.8 tonnes
Payload: 0.6 tonne
PERFORMANCE
Max speed, across ice: 55km/h (34mph)

ACVAS (ACV with Aft Skegs)

A new form of hovercraft has been developed by the Mitsui company, trials with the 10-metre prototype *Eaglet* having started in early 1986. The craft employs waterjet propulsion and is not therefore amphibious. The inlets for the two waterjet units are positioned in the underside of the two skegs which extend in either side of the craft for a length of approximately one-third of overall craft length. Over this length immersed

MV-PP15 showing raised control cabin, pylon-mounted propellers, lift fan air intakes and thrust ports beneath passenger doors, port and starboard

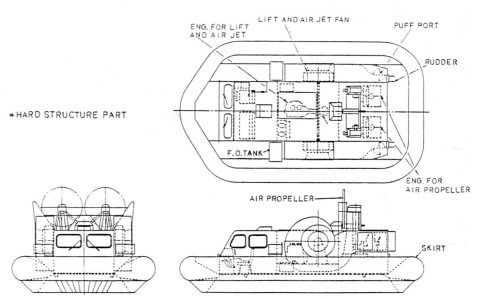

MV-PP05A General arrangement

areas of the skegs seal the air cushion; for the remainder of the cushion periphery a conventional loop and segment type skirt is employed. Unlike the sidewall hovercraft or surface-effect ships the craft is almost totally supported by its air cushion at cruising speed. The concept thus has the potential advantage of the fully skirted amphibious hovercraft for the attainment of high cruising speed with minimum hydrodynamic resistance

(and, at speed, minimum wave generation), but in addition it also secures full directional control and the very minimum of noise and vibration, by the use of skeg-mounted Hamilton 771 waterjet propulsion units.

The craft is provided with a Mitsui motion control system exerting control over cushion air pressure variation and is fitted with fin stabilisers. The skirt/skeg combination is also found to give good ride comfort over waves through its soft response.

The Mitsui ACVAS concept is aimed principally towards applications in shallow rivers, lakes and other smooth waters and for ultra-fast ferries for operation in coastal and inland sea routes.

EAGLET
ENGINE
Propulsion: Two 98hp (at 5000rpm) Nissan HA 120 marine petrol engines
Lift: Two Robin 22hp petrol engines
WATERJET UNITS: Two Hamilton 771 units.
AIR-CUSHION FANS: Two centrifugal.
HULL: Glass-reinforced plastic.
DIMENSIONS
Length overall: 10.90 m
Breadth overall: 5.10 m
Depth: 0.89 m
PERFORMANCE
Speed, max: Approx 27 knots

MV-PP05A polar terrain test craft

Mitsui's ACVAS experimental craft *Eaglet* fitted with Hamilton Jet waterjet units

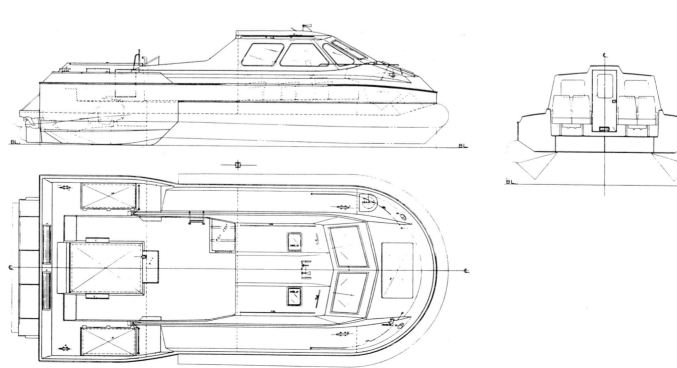

General arrangement of Mitsui ACVAS

ACVAS (ACV with Aft Skegs)

SUMIDAGAWA In August 1988, Mitsui received an order from the Tokyo Metropolitan Government Bureau of Construction for a river observation craft that can be used for observation and inspection of rivers in the Metropolis. The craft is fitted out in a manner suitable for international conferences to held on board. The vessel named *SUMIDAGAWA* was delivered in March 1989.

LIFT AND PROPULSION: Two 267kW high speed diesel engines are used for propulsion. The power is transmitted to two units through reduction gears. One 276kW high speed diesel engine drives two lift fans, DC generator, and cooler compressors through clutch and flexible joint.

HULL: The vessel structure is made of anti-corrosive aluminium alloy. The hull is a longitudinally stiffened structure with spaced frames. Extruded sections are used extensively. The upper structure is of plate construction consisting of welded and riveted anti-flexure material.

SKIRT: A flexible skirt made of rubberised nylon cloth is provided around the vessel excepting the skegs at the aft. The front part of the skirt system consists of a bag and fingers and the rear part has lobe seal construction. Air is supplied to the lobe seal from the bag at the front through a duct. The forward skirt is designed to minimise water spray for ease of navigation in rivers.

ACCOMMODATION: The layout of the passenger room can be changed by setting 80 seats for observation of rivers, 58 seats for observation of rivers and meetings, and 52 seats for conferences.

DIMENSIONS
Length overall: 19.95m
Beam moulded: 7.90m
Depth: 3.70m
Draught off cushion: abt. 1.5m
Draught on cushion: abt. 0.5m
PERFORMANCE
Max. speed: 30.4 knots
Cruising speed: 28.5 knots

MV-PP10

A new Mitsui hovercraft, the first two were ordered in 1989.

LIFT AND PROPULSION: The MV-PP10 is powered by four Deutz BF12L513CP air-cooled turbo-charged diesels, each rated at 441 kW (600 hp) at 2300 rpm maximum and 383 kW (520 hp) continuous. On each side of the craft, one engine drives two double-entry centrifugal fans for lift, and two engines aft drive two ducted variable-pitch propellers.

CONTROLS: Twin aerodynamic rudders

The Mitsui *Sumidagawa* in operation with the Tokyo Metropolitan Government Bureau of Construction

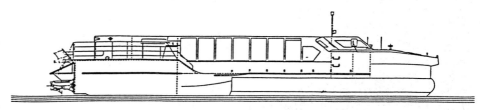

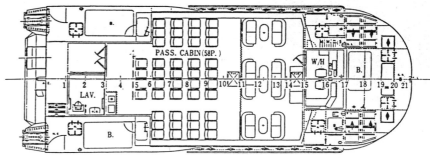

Upper Deck

Layout of *Sumidagawa*

The Mitsui ACVAS *Sumidagawa* river observation craft

mounted on the rear of the propeller ducts and differential thrust of the propellers provide directional control. Air bleed thruster parts are installed (one at the forward end, and two at the aft end of the craft). Each thruster has an opening and shutting vane.

HULL: The main hull of the craft is built in meldable anti-corrrosive aluminium alloy, and the superstructure is of rivetted construction.

ACCOMMODATION: Three seats for the crew are arranged at the front of the passenger cabin.

84 seats for passengers are in rows, 22 folding seats can be placed in the aisles. Two entrance doors, one port and one starboard, are at the aft end of the passenger cabin, and one door for the crew is at the port side of the forward passenger cabin. A cooling and heating system is provided.

SKIRT: The skirt is of bag and finger type and cushion depth is about 1.2 m. The lower side parts of fingers, particularly susceptible to wear, are replaceable in sections.

DIMENSIONS
Length, overall: 22 m
Beam, overall: 11 m
Height, on cushion: 6.5 m
PERFORMANCE
Max speed: about 53 knots
Cruising speed: about 45 knots
Endurance: 4 hours
WEIGHT
Max disposable load: 10 tons
Weight, max: abt. 38.5 tons

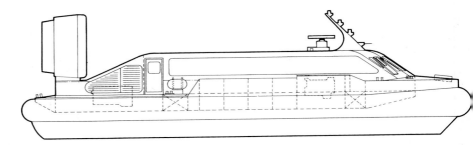

General arrangement of MV-PP10

KOREA, SOUTH

KOREA TACOMA MARINE INDUSTRIES LIMITED

Main office and shipyard: PO Box 339, 974–15 Yang duk-dong, Masan 630–728, South Korea

Telephone: Masan (0551) 55–1181/8, 93–2181
Telex: 53662KOTAMAN K
Telefax: (0551) 94–9449

Jong-Nak Kim, *Chairman*
Jung-Tae Kim, *President*
Sung-Jin Lee, *Executive Managing Director*
Mu-Ryong Bae, *Executive Managing Director*

Seoul office: CPO Box 4296, Seoul, South Korea

Telephone: (02) 777–0901/5
Telex: 27351 KOTAMI
Telefax: (02) 757 0884

Ever since its founding in 1971, Korea Tacoma Marine Industries Ltd (KTMI) has built a variety of fast patrol boats and high-speed passenger boats, and has concentrated its efforts on the development of high-speed SES and amphibious hovercraft for civil and paramilitary applications.

In 1977 KTMI began an ACV development programme, and the company designed and constructed a test surface effect ship in 1978. KTMI named its first surface effect ship Turt

II. This had a length of 8.2m, weight of 3.7 tons, and capacity for 7 passengers. To date KTMI has developed and constructed five 18m SESs (90-passenger), one 11m SES (56-passenger), one 17m SES (72 passenger), two 26m SESs (158-passenger), one 28m SES (200-passenger, modified 26m SES), a manned test amphibious hovercraft, a 12m diesel-powered prototype hovercraft and a 14m diesel-powered sea ambulance hovercraft.

TURT III

This fully-amphibious five-seater has an overall length of 7.65 metres and a maximum speed of 50 knots.

LIFT AND PROPULSION: Motive power for the lift system is a single 140hp engine. Thrust is supplied by a single 175hp engine driving a 1.35m diameter free-air propeller.

CONTROLS: Craft direction is controlled by twin aerodynamic rudders operating in the propeller slipstream.

HULL: Welded marine-grade aluminium.

SKIRT: Bag and segment type.

ACCOMMODATION: Enclosed cabin with seats for driver and four passengers.

DIMENSIONS
Length overall: 7.65m
Beam: 4m

KTMI test hovercraft Turt III

Height to tip of thrust propeller: 1.3m
　to top of cabin: 2.87m
WEIGHT
Loaded: 2.27 tonnes
PERFORMANCE
Max speed: 50 knots

8-METRE SES

This was the first of a projected series of multi-purpose surface effect craft.
LIFT AND PROPULSION: Motive power for the lift system is provided by a single 80hp automotive engine. Thrust is supplied by two water propellers powered by twin outboards or diesel outdrive units of 80, 100 or 150hp.
CONTROLS: Craft direction is controlled by twin water rudders aft or rotation of the engine/propeller units.
HULL: Primary structure in welded marine aluminium alloy.
SKIRT: Segmented skirt at the bow and stern.
ACCOMMODATION: Choice of seating arrangements for five, ten or fifteen passengers.
DIMENSIONS
Length overall: 8.2m
Beam overall: 4.4m
Draught, hullborne: 0.6m
　on cushion: 0.1m
WEIGHT
Normal max (according to power arrangements
　and passenger load): 3.5–4.5 tons
PERFORMANCE
Max speed, twin 80hp engines: 30 knots
　　twin 100hp engines: 40 knots
　　twin 150hp engines: 45 knots
Range: 120n miles

KTMI 8m SES

Height: 2.72m
WEIGHTS
Displacement, max: 11.5 tons

Payload: 5.5 tons
PERFORMANCE
Speed, max: 26.9 knots

Craft built (12m SES)	Seats	Owner	Route
Que-Ryoung	56	Dong-Bu Co Ltd	So-Yang river – (Yang gu) to In Jae

KTMI 12m SES waterbus *Que-Ryoung*

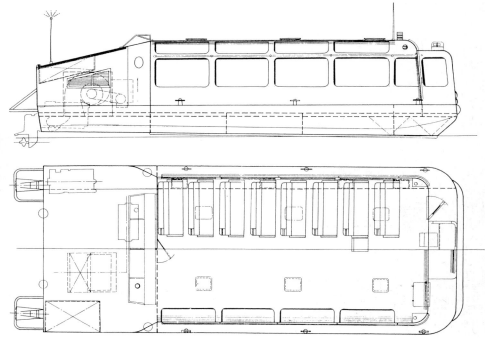

KTMI 12m SES

12-METRE SES

KTMI's 12m craft *Que-Ryoung* is a high-speed waterbus delivered and launched on the Soyang man-made lake near Seoul in 1982. The craft is designed to run bow-on to flat sloping beaches and river banks for the embarkation and off-loading of passengers and freight.
LIFT AND PROPULSION: Power for the lift fan is supplied by a single 72hp Volvo Penta MD 40A marine diesel. Propulsion engines are two 155hp Volvo Penta AQAD 40/280Bs, each incorporating stern-drive units.
CONTROLS: Both propeller units at the stern rotate for steering. Additional control is provided by the differential use of the water propellers.
HULL: The hull is built in welded marine aluminium alloy and the deckhouse is constructed in riveted marine aluminium alloy.
SKIRT: Flexible segmented skirt at the bow and stern.
ACCOMMODATION: Air-conditioned accommodation for 4 crew members and 56 passengers.
DIMENSIONS
Length overall: 12.0m
Width: 4.6m

18-METRE SES

The 18m (59ft) design has buoyant catamaran-type sidewalls almost identical in shape to those of the smaller craft.
LIFT AND PROPULSION: Power for the lift system is provided by a single marine diesel in the 400 to 500hp range. Power for the propulsion system is provided by twin diesels of 650, 800 or 1300hp, each driving a water propeller via a reversing gearbox and an inclined shaft.
CONTROLS: Twin water rudders aft, one on

each sidehull. Differential propeller thrust for slow-speed manoeuvring.
HULL: Main structure built in welded marine aluminium alloy.
SKIRT: Segmented skirt at the bow and stern.
ACCOMMODATION: Seating arrangements for 60, 80 and 90 passengers according to route requirements.
DIMENSIONS
Length overall: 18.1m

KTMI 18m SES

Beam overall: 9m
Draught, hullborne: 1.74m
  on cushion: 1.08m
WEIGHT
Normal max weight: 36 tons
PERFORMANCE
Max speed, twin 650hp diesels: 35 knots
    twin 800hp diesels: 40 knots
    twin 1300hp diesels: 50 knots

26-METRE SES

LIFT AND PROPULSION: The lift system is powered by a single General Motors Detroit Diesel Allison 12V-71TI rated at 510hp at 2100rpm. This engine directly drives a dual 1.075m diameter lift fan, to provide cushion air to the plenum chamber and, via toothed belts and hydraulic system, two secondary 0.61m diameter fans for stern skirt inflation. Propulsive power is supplied by two MTU 8V 396 TB 83 diesels, each rated at 1010hp at 1940rpm, each driving a water propeller via a reversing gearbox and an inclined shaft.

One GM 2–71 diesel generator, rated at 30kW 60Hz, 220V, is provided.
CONTROLS: Craft heading is controlled by twin balanced stainless steel rudders operated hydraulically by a steering wheel. Additional control is provided by differential use of the water propellers.
HULL: Main structure is built in welded marine aluminium alloy and the superstructure is constructed in riveted marine aluminium alloy.
SKIRT: The bow skirt consists of single bag and multi segments which are attached to the bag and connected to the underside of the hull by straps. The stern skirt is a multi-bag type consisting of three bag sections and is inflated to a pressure slightly above that of the cushion by two 0.61m fans on the deckhouse of the engine rooms.
ACCOMMODATION: Air-conditioning, audio system and airliner-type seating is provided for 10 crew members and 158 passengers. The bridge accommodates the commander, navigator and engineer.
DIMENSIONS
Length overall: 25.7m
Breadth: 10.2m
Depth: 2.7m
Draught, floating: 2.45m
  on cushion: 1.45m
WEIGHT
Displacement, max: 65 tons
Payload: 16.5 tons
PERFORMANCE
Speed, max: 35 knots
Range, full load: 250n miles

TURT IV

Builder of the first amphibious hovercraft in Korea, the Turt III type, a manned test craft launched in February 1981, KTMI followed it in December 1984 by the development of an amphibious utility hovercraft Turt IV type, the first diesel-powered amphibious hovercraft in Asia.
LIFT AND PROPULSION: The lift system comprises two single 1.075m fans driven by a Deutz air-cooled diesel engine rated at 320hp at 2300rpm. Thrust is supplied by a 422hp Deutz air-cooled diesel engine at 2300rpm driving a 2.75m ducted propeller.
CONTROLS: One rudder and one elevator positioned in the ducted propeller slipstream provide directional control and trim control respectively. Additional control in low speed is provided by two puff ports which are designed specially for turning and reversing and are supplied by cushion air.
HULL: The main hull is built in welded aluminium alloy 5086-H116 (plate) and 6061-T6 (extrusion), and the deck house is riveted.
SKIRT: The skirt is an open loop and segment

Craft built (18m SES)	Owner	Route
Air Ferry	Seo-Kyung Ferry Co.	Pusan to Gejae Island
Cosmos	Geo-Je Ferry Co.	Pusan to Gejae Island
Phinex	Geo-Je Development Co.	Pusan to Gejae Island
Sun Star	Kumsan Hungup	Yeosu to Near Island
Tacoma II	Hue Yang Ao Tougang Industrial Ltd	Hong Kong to Chinchun

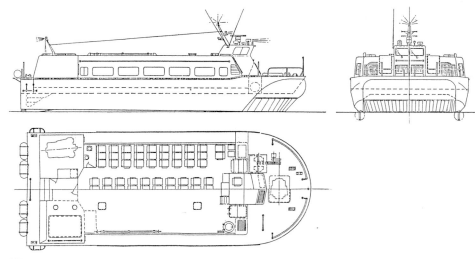

KTMI 18m SES

Craft built (26m SES)	Seats	Owner	Route
Young-Kwang I	158	Semo Co.	Pusan to Gejae Island
*Young-Kwang II**	200	Semo Co.	Pusan to Gejae Island
Tacoma III	158	Shin Young Shipbuilding and Engineering Co	Yeosu to Gemun Island

*Modified to 28m

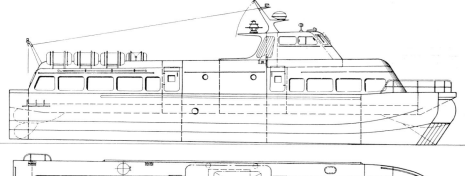

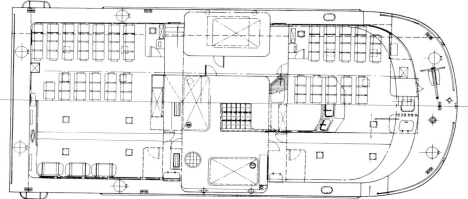

KTMI 26m SES

type and anti-bouncing ties are built into the loop.

Outstanding ride quality and stability have been demonstrated during sea trials and the craft was safely operated in seas up to 2m maximum wave height.

DIMENSIONS
Length overall: 12.65m
Beam overall: 7.04m
Height, on cushion: 4.70m
  off cushion: 4.20m

Cushion height: 0.80m
WEIGHTS
Light weight: 8.10 tons
Payload: 1.50 tons
PERFORMANCE
Speed, max: 55 knots
Speed, cruising: 40 knots
Range: 200n miles

TURT IV Mk 1

As a sea ambulance version, Turt IV Mk 1 is intended for quick transportation of patients from islands to land. The distinctive features of the craft compared with Turt IV are the twin propulsion units for increased manoeuvrability and the reduced lift power due to the developed skirt. Turt IV Mk 1 was under construction in 1987 and was delivered in April 1988.

LIFT AND PROPULSION: The lift system consists of two single 1.07m diameter fans driven by a Deutz air-cooled diesel engine rated at 272hp at 2300rpm. Thrust is supplied by two 272hp Deutz air-cooled diesel engines at 2300rpm driving two 2.0m diameter ducted propellers.

CONTROLS: Two rudders and two elevators positioned in each of the ducted propeller slipstreams provide directional control and trim control respectively. Additional control is provided by the differential thrust of the propellers. Directional control in low speed is provided by two puff ports which are designed specially for reversing and turning and are supplied by cushion air.

HULL: The main hull is built in welded aluminium alloy 5086-H116 (plate) and 6061-T6 (extrusion), and the deck house is riveted.

SKIRT: The skirt is an open loop and segment type and anti-bouncing ties are built into the loop.

DIMENSIONS
Length overall: 13.35m
Beam overall: 7.44m
Height, on cushion: 4.90m
        off cushion: 4.30m
Cushion height: 0.8m
WEIGHTS
Light weight: 11.0 tons
Payload: 2.0 tons
PERFORMANCE
Speed, max: 50 knots
Speed, cruising: 40 knots
Range: 150n miles
Weather restrictions: Operation in seas up to 2.0m
    max wave height

TURT IV Mk 2

This craft, of which two are built, is a stretched version of the TURT IV Mk 1. Lift and propulsion systems are identical to those of the TURT IV Mk 1, but the hull has been lengthened by 1.75m and propulsion engines are upgraded from 203kW (Deutz) to 254kW to improve the performance in rough seas.

CONTROLS: Three rudders positioned in each of the propeller ducts provide directional control at high speed, and directional control at low speed is provided by four puff ports which are designed specially for reversing and turning.

DIMENSIONS
Length overall: 15.30m
Beam overall: 7.64m
Height, on cushion: 5.30m
Height, off cushion: 4.75m
Rise height: 0.90m
WEIGHTS
Light weight: 15.0 tonnes
Payload: 1.3 tonnes
PERFORMANCE
Speed, max: 40 knots
Speed, cruising: 35 knots
Range: 150 n miles
Weather restrictions: Operation in seas up to 2.0m max wave height is permissible.

KTMI 26m SES

KTMI Turt IV type hovercraft *Eagle II*

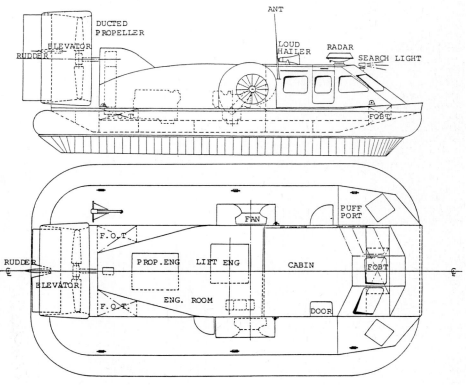

Layout of Turt IV

Craft built (TURT IV Mk 1)	Seats	Owner	Route
Jun-Nam 540	9	The Ministry of Health and Social Affairs	Coastal service

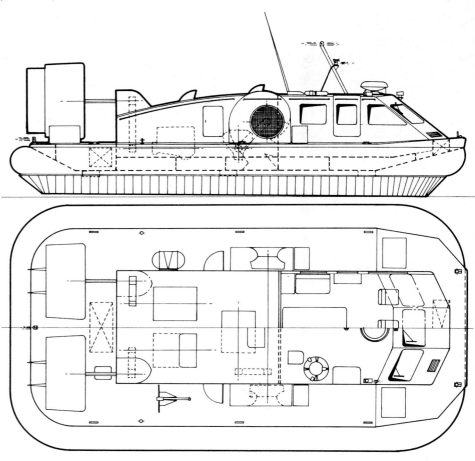

Layout of Turt IV Mk 1

Turt IV Mk 1

KTMI 17m SES *Que-Ryoung II*

17-METRE SES

The first 17m craft *Que-Ryoung II* is a high speed waterbus which was delivered and entered service on So-Yang man-made lake near Seoul in September 1988. The 17m SES is designed as a very reliable, cost-effective, high speed waterbus with good transportation efficiency for operating on inland waters such as lake, river and inland water ways. Good ride quietness and comfortable passenger space enhance this craft.

LIFT AND PROPULSION: Power for lift fan is supplied by a single 170hp VOLVO PENTA TAMD 41A marine diesel. Propulsion engines are two 292hp VOLVO PENTA TAMD 71A marine diesel.

CONTROLS: Twin rudders, one on each sidehull provide directional control. Additional control is provided by the differential thrust of the propellers.

HULL: The hull is built in welded marine grade aluminium alloy and the deckhouse is constructed in riveted marine grade aluminium alloy.

SKIRT: The bow and stern skirt consists of single bag and multi segments which are attached to the bag and connected to the underside of the hull by straps.

ACCOMMODATION: Audio system and airliner type seating is provided for 72 passengers and 3 crew members.

DIMENSIONS
Length, overall: 17.3m
Width: 5.0m
Depth: 1.2m
WEIGHTS: Normal max weight 21.5 tons
PERFORMANCE: Speed, max. 30.0 knots

Craft built (17m SES)	Seats	Owner	Route
Que-Ryoung II	72	Dong-Bu Co Ltd	So-Yang river to In-Jae

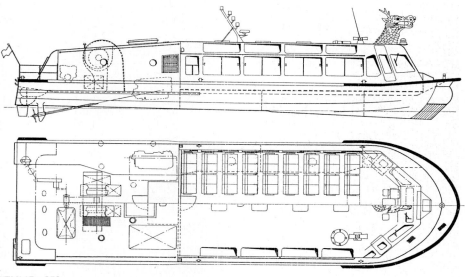

KTMI 17m SES

THE NETHERLANDS

HOVERTRANS BV

Remmerden 9, 3911 TZ Rhenen, The Netherlands

Telephone: (08376)16662/19004
Telex: 45695 NIWIN NL
Telefax: 0837612129

Drs Ing P C Helder, *Managing Director*

Also, Noordeinde 164, 2514 GR, The Hague, The Netherlands

Telephone: (070) 658471

PH11

The PH11 features a number of innovations in its design for which a patent application is pending. Among the features incorporated are extended sideboards reaching well over the skirt bag helping to reduce spray generation; provision for fitting lift fans of different diameter thus enhancing maximum flexibility of lift and thrust combinations; a layout permitting not only alternative lift fans to be fitted but also alternative engine installations; and a novel bow shape designed to enhance performance under adverse sea conditions. In addition, the thrust and lift systems have been designed to provide normal cruise performance at only 80% of maximum power. The PH11 incorporates requirements of a number of potential operations, including the Dutch Civil Water Authorities.

The Maritime Research Insititue of the Netherlands at Wageningen (MARIN) have performed both theoretical computations and measurements on board the craft to establish buoyancy requirements for maximum safety and stability on and off-cushion, according to the rules and regulations of the International Maritime Organization (IMO).

HULL: The hull of the hovercraft, constructed in glass reinforced polyester, incorporates floors to support the hull shell. An uninterrupted floor area over the full width of the hull has been realised to allow for the installation of seats or benches, or both. Removal of seats will transfer the craft into a cargo carrier. Cargo can then be loaded via the inverted U-shaped door, which opens up a full section of the cabin area.

An acceptable level of sound emission according to current environmental standards has been reached by the installation of an exhaust silencer and a low-tip-speed propeller. At a distance of 100 metres the maximum sound level is 80dBA. Moreover, specific construction materials are used to minimise internal noise levels.

Special attention has been given to the engine bay layout and ventilation to provide optimum conditions for the air-cooled diesel engine.

The cockpit (with 360° all-round view) situated above deck level at the far front of the craft has been fitted with electrical propeller pitch-and elevator rudder controls plus hydraulic steering to operate the craft without any physical effort required of the captain. Elevator rudders provide rapid pitch trim while diesel fuel is used for major trim adjustments. In case of emergency trim fuel can be used to increase operating hours.

CERTIFICATION: The Hovertrans BV production programme incorporates the standards of:

Lloyd's Register of Shipping
Civil Aviation Authority (CAA)
International Maritime Organization (I.M.O.)

The hovercraft is supplied with the following certificate:

'Maltese Cross' A1 Air Cushion Vehicle Group 2 LMC.

DIMENSIONS
Length overall, on cushion: 10.50m

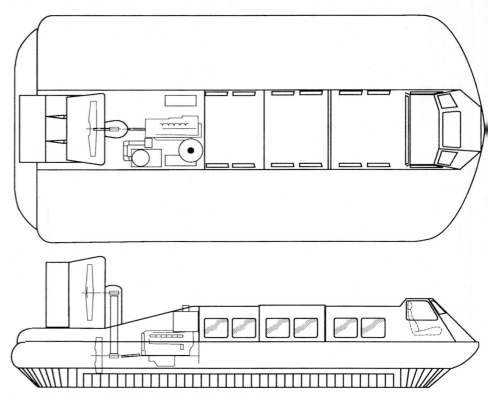

Layout of the Hovertrans PH11 showing the axial flow fan installation

Hovertrans PH11

Length overall, off cushion: 10.50m
Beam overall, on cushion: 5.70m
Beam overall, off cushion, sideboards retracted to vertical position: 2.20m
Width of sideboard: 1.75m
Length of sideboard: 10.00m
Total height on landing pads, including elevated cockpit: 3.15m
Cockpit height above deck: 1.30m
Width of passenger cabin: 2.00m
Length of passenger cabin: 5.25m
Height of passenger cabin: 1.60m
Height in cockpit area, max: 1.90m
ACCOMMODATION AND LOADS
Maximum number of passengers: 18

Crew: 1 or 2
Maximum disposable load (fuel, passengers @75 kg each,and cargo)
Normal maximum fuel capacity 200 litres: 170 kg
The maximum disposable load of 1500 kg can consist of any combination of passengers, cargo and fuel.
PERFORMANCE
Speed, maximum calm water: 40 knots
Speed, cruising: 30 knots
Maximum allowable windforce for operation: Beaufort 3
Maximum allowable wave-height for operation: 1.0m
Fuel consumption, at max. speed (40 knots): 32

litre/hour
Fuel consumption, at cruising speed (32 knots): 25 litre/hour
Range: 450 km
Endurance: about 8 hours
ENGINE: Deutz air cooled diesel, BF 6 L 913 C with intercooler with diesel/water separator and exhaust plus silencer; 190 hp at 2500 rpm.
PROPULSION: Hoffmann controllable pitch propeller, 1.50m diameter.
LIFT: Eight-blade axial flow fan, optional diameters of 0.90m or 1.00m.
TRANSMISSIONS: Toothed belt.
ELECTRICAL SYSTEM: 24 V, 2 batteries 180 Ah each.
OPERATION: The PH11 has been operating along the Rhine Delta between Rotterdam and the German border and is currently in service with the ecological department of the Dutch Water Authorities. The craft has also been fitted out for fire fighting to show the operational ease with which assistance can be provided.

The excellent manoeuvring capabilities of the PH11 have been demonstrated over water and land, in circumnavigating freighters, passing through locks and crossing extensive grass lands and sand banks.

The rudder and elevator control surfaces in the slipstream of the controllable-pitch Hoffmann propeller enable the craft to turn within its own length and thus provide the manoeuvrability required for a wide variety of tasks.

A large inverted U-shaped sliding door permits easy access for passengers and the vertical loading of freight.

The side decks can either be used to carry bulky loads, used as operating stations or fitted with containers for stowing equipment. Furthermore, the side decks are constructed in such a way as to provide a fender to enable coming alongside jetties, superstructures and vessels to be performed with good protection.
MAINTENANCE: The craft can be lifted by means of four marine bollards situated on the front and rear decks. The thrust and lift system can easily be removed.

Due to the construction method used, maintenance of the hull will only require basic grp techniques. Emphasis has been placed in the design and selection of parts to provide craft which are simple to operate and maintain.

35-SEAT PROJECT (DESIGN)

The application of twin power units based on the current design plus an increase in hull size, has allowed an increased carrying capacity of 35 people. Moreover, the Dutch rivers and canals dictate the need for course stability which can be enhanced with a twin-propeller installation. Developments are currently under way to reduce both drift and yaw angle, a common phenomena of hovercraft, by applying innovative techniques in co-operation with MARIN.

Hovertrans PH11 on trials with the Dutch Water Authorities

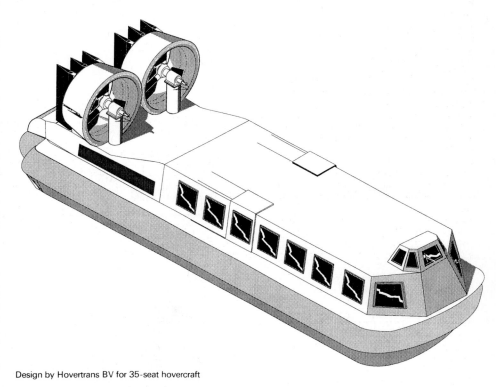

Design by Hovertrans BV for 35-seat hovercraft

LE COMTE-HOLLAND BV

Stuartweg 4, 4131 NJ Vianen, The Netherlands
Postbus 24, 4130 EA Vianen, The Netherlands

Telephone: (03473) 7 19 04
Telex: 40475LECOM NL

A le Comte, *General Manager*

Le Comte-Holland BV Shipyard has developed a sidewall hovercraft design with a new seal system (patents were granted in 1982) based on an array of floating, hydrodynamically-shaped planing elements hinged on the wet deck of the craft. Each element operates independently and has restricted vertical movement. Tank tests at Wageningen have successfully demonstrated the hydrodynamic drag and sealing characteristics of this system, even in higher sea states.

The initial cost of the system is higher than that of a flexible skirt, but its long life expectancy will reduce maintenance costs. Front skirt element changes can be made without docking.

The segments are made from polyaramide reinforced polyester, which combines high impact strength with low weight. Low friction polyethylene plates the segments' sides, and assists vertical movement.

It is said that the immersion depth of the vessel does not affect the system, which rotates around the hinges until the lift forces are balanced by the internal restraining forces. The system is claimed to give a more accurate following of irregular incoming wave patterns and to be resistant to damage by floating objects. If the front seal elements are damaged, replacement can be under-

taken without dry-docking the craft. A ride control system is also being developed.

The project, which is backed by the Netherlands government, has undergone extensive model tests. Designs have been prepared for passenger ferries and patrol craft of 27.1, 29.6, 32.1, 34.6 and 37.1 metres length. Construction of the first 27.1m SES started in late 1986.

27.1-METRE SES

LIFT AND PROPULSION: For propulsion two MTU 12V 396 TB83 high-speed diesels are installed giving a continuous power of 1150kW (1542bhp) each. Two Arneson surface-piercing, super cavitating propeller systems are fitted. For lift two Mercedes-Benz OM 423 diesels are installed giving 261kW (350bhp) each. These engines power a hydraulic transmission system driving two cushion lift fans, one for supplying the stern cushion seal.

CONTROLS: NACA profiled rudders control craft direction at high speed. Differential propeller thrust controls heading at low speed. An automatic roll stabilisation system is fitted.

HULL: Built in grp. Deck/wheelhouse is built in grp sandwich, including the bulkheads, for weight reduction and insulation against temperature differences. The deck is constructed of extruded aluminium alloy planking.

SYSTEMS, ELECTRICAL: Auxiliary generating units and electrical systems available for 24V dc, 110V ac and/or 220V ac. One Mercedes-Benz OM 314, rated at 42hp at 1500rpm (50 cycles) or 51hp at 1800rpm (60 cycles).

ACCOMMODATION: Up to 200 passengers.

DIMENSIONS
Length: Approx 27.1m
Beam: Approx 7.8m
Depth: Approx 3.1m
Cushion height: Approx 2.5m
Draught, on cushion: approx 1.5m
Draught, off cushion: approx 2.2m
Deck area for patrol boat version: Approx 75m^2

WEIGHTS/CAPACITIES
Max: 72 tonnes
Light ship: 54 tonnes
Fuel tank, patrol boat version: 6000 litres
Fuel tank, passenger boat version: 2000 litres

PERFORMANCE
Speed, cruise, on cushion, Sea State 0: 40 knots,
    Sea State 3: 36 knots
Speed, cruise, off cushion, Sea State 0: 16 knots,
    Sea State 3: 13 knots

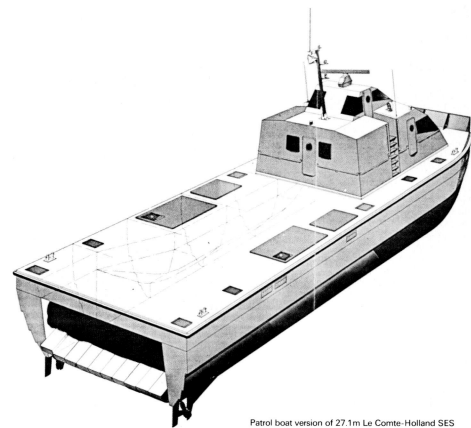

Patrol boat version of 27.1m Le Comte-Holland SES

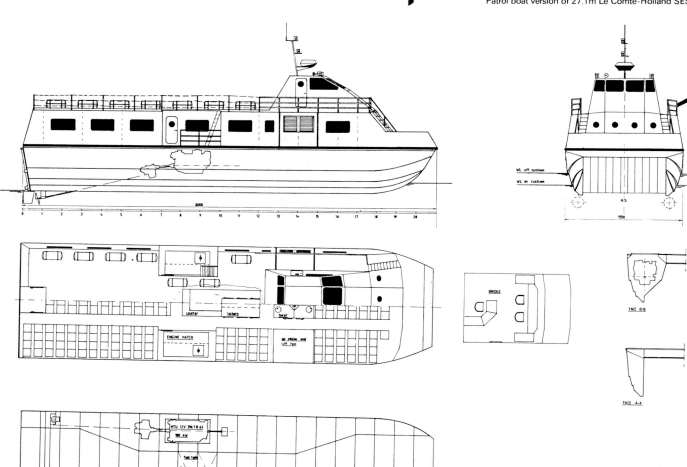

General arrangement of 27.1m Le Comte-Holland passenger ferry SES

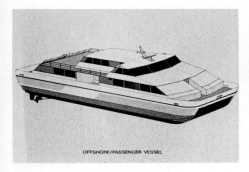

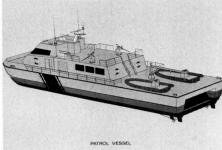

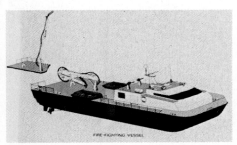

Various applications of the Le Comte SES designs

ROYAL SCHELDE
BV KONINKLIJKE MAATSCHAPPIJ
DE SCHELDE

PO Box 16, 165 Glacisstraat, 4380 AA Vlissingen,
The Netherlands

Telephone: (1184) 83911
Telex: 37815KMS NL
Telefax: (1184) 85010

A B A de Smit, *Chairman of the Managing Board*
C Hartog, *Vice Chairman of the Managing Board*
T C Bouwman, *Technical Director*
A van der Knaap, *Marketing and Sales*

In 1986 Royal Schelde started development of civil and military designs of a Surface Effect Ship project This development covered design, training and operational stages aspects. Since then the project has matured to a stage that after extensive testing of hull and skirt designs on a manned test craft of 8 metres length, the decision was taken to build a 23 metre full-scale vessel for passenger ferry application. This vessel was due to be completed in May 1990.

Different versions of the SES are proposed, a civil passenger craft, Seaswift 32, a multi-purpose military version, Seashark 32, a coastguard version, Seaguard 32, an offshore crew-utility vessel, a 23 metre passenger ferry for 146 persons, and a 60 metre vessel for 436 passengers, and 62 cars. Other applications in the design stage are luxury motor yachts, hydrographic research vessels, pilot vessels, etc.

As the market also demanded larger vessels capable of carrying cars as well as passengers, Royal Schelde responded with a design for a 70 metre catamaran, as well as the 60 metre SES mentioned above which can optionally carry cars and passengers or cooled perishable cargo, or a combination of both.

Looking toward the future, Royal Schelde is further considering the development of SWATH vessels.

SEASWIFT 23

The development of this project follows extensive testing of an 8 metre manned craft. The preliminary outline specification of the vessel gives the following details.
CLASSIFICATION
DnV + 1A1 R45 Light Craft, EO.
HULL: Welded marine grade aluminium alloy;

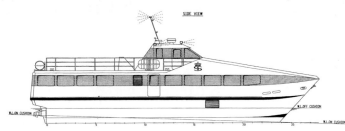

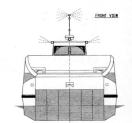

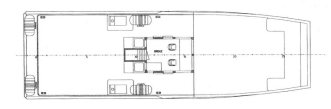

General arrangement of Royal Schelde Seaswift 23 SES passenger ferry

scantling dimensions assume a maximum midship vertical acceleration of 1g.
LIFT AND PROPULSION: Three centrifugal liftfans, resiliently mounted, the forward two being driven directly by the lift-system diesel engine and the aft one being driven hydraulically by the same engine. Propulsion is provided by two MWM TBD 234 12V diesels, 520kW each at 2200rpm MCR, driving KaMeWa 40S water-jet units.
ACCOMMODATION: 146 passenger seats on main deck. Passenger cabin and wheelhouse ven-

tilated by two-speed ventilation system which incorporates heating elements.
EQUIPMENT: Fire prevention, detection and extinguishing equipment, including Halon 1301 flooding systems for the engine rooms. Normal fuel, seawater cooling hydraulic oil and bilge systems.
DIMENSIONS
Length, overall: approx 24.25m
Length, waterline: approx 20.00m
Beam, moulded: approx 7.70m
Beam, overall: approx 7.94m

Depth, midship (base line to main deck): 2.15m
Draught, on-cushion, full-load: 0.35m
Draught, off-cushion, full-load: 1.30m
CAPACITIES
Fuel oil: approx 3.60m³
Fresh water: approx 0.50m³
Sewage: approx 0.10³

Weights,	at 65% payload	at 100% payload
Fuel (kg):	1500	3000
Fresh water (kg):	250	500
Sewage (kg):	50	50
Stores (kg):	50	50
Passengers,		
100 at 75kg:	7500	146 at 75kg: 10950
Luggage,		
100 at 5kg:	500	146 at 5kg: 730
Crew,		
two at 80kg:	160	160
Disposable load (kg):	10010	15440

PERFORMANCE
FUEL CONSUMPTION
"TRIAL" CONDITION, CALM SEA,

LIGHT WIND:		Kg/n mile
Speed, max at 100% MCR: 37 knots		7.7
Speed, service, at 85% MCR: 32 knots		7.6
MAXIMUM LOAD CONDITION,		
CALM SEA, LIGHT WIND:		
Speed, max, at 100% MCR: 34 knots		8.4
Speed, service, at 85% MCR: 27 knots		9.0

Construction of Seaswift 23 sidewall looking aft

SEAGUARD 32 (DESIGN)

(see 1989 edition of this book for General
Arrangement of this craft)

This vessel design is intended for coastguard
operation within 200 miles of an established
harbour or place of refuge. A quarter-scale
manned model has been used for establishing performance predictions under all operational conditions. The vessel would be built in welded
marine-grade aluminium alloy.
CLASSIFICATION
DnV + 1A1 R200 Light Craft, SF-LC, F-LC, EO.
HULL: Welded marine-grade aluminium alloy,
each side hull being divided into six water tight
compartments.
LIFT AND PROPULSION: Four hydraulically
driven lift fans. Propulsion is provided by two
MTU 16V 396 TB 84 engines, 2040kW each, at
1940rpm (MCR) or similar engines, driving waterjet units.
ACCOMMODATION: Wheelhouse accom-
modation for a crew of five, see General Arrangements for cabin accommodation for a standard
total crew of up to eight, suitable for operations
of up to one week's duration. An office, messroom,
galley, sanitary units, stores room and fan room
are provided.
EQUIPMENT: One 5.7m rigid inflatable ser-
vice/rescue boat, 48kW, 64hp, deployed by heave-
compensated hydraulic crane. Two 16-person
inflatable liferafts. Two manually-controlled
search lights.
DIMENSIONS
Length, overall, moulded: approx 33.75m
Length, waterline: approx 28.60m
Beam, moulded: approx 11.10m
Depth midship (base line to main deck): approx
3.50m
Draught, on-cushion (full load) approx 0.65m
Draught, off-cushion (full load) approx 1.75m
CAPACITIES
Fuel oil: approx 22.7m³
Fresh water: approx 1.2m³
Trim tanks, aft: approx 7.2m³
Trim tanks, fwd: approx 33.6m³
Lubricating oil: approx 0.8m³
Collecting tank: approx 3.6m³
Sewage: approx 0.8m³
Hydraulic oil: approx 1.6m³

Construction of Seaswift 23 sidewall looking forward

WEIGHTS

	"Trial" condition	Full load condition
Fuel (kg):	7000	13000
Lubricating oil (kg):	400	400
Fresh water (kg):	1000	1000
Stores (kg):	2900	2900
Victualling (kg):	840	840
Crew (6) (kg):	480	480
Luggage (kg):	300	300
Super numerary (kg):	—	640 (8 persons)
Luggage (kg):	—	240
Disposable load (kg):	12920	19800

PERFORMANCE
"TRIAL" CONDITION, CALM SEA, LIGHT
WIND:
Speed, max. continuous (MCR) on cushion: 48
knots, 700n miles on 13 tonnes fuel
Speed, service, (85% MCR) on cushion: 42 knots,
730n miles on 13 tonnes fuel
Speed, surveillance (off cushion): 10 knots, 930n
miles on 13 tonnes fuel
FULL LOAD CONDITION
Speed, max. continuous (MCR) on cushion: 46
knots, 680n miles on 13 tonnes fuel
Speed, service (85% MCR) on cushion: 39 knots,
680n miles on 13 tonnes fuel

Speed, surveillance (off cushion): 10 knots, 870n miles on 13 tonnes fuel

SEASWIFT 60 (DESIGN)

A new design announced in December 1989 for a 59 meter SES passenger/car ferry. The vessel is designed to carry 436 passengers and 62 cars. Preliminary details are given below but alternative engines and propulsion systems may be employed.

CLASSIFICATION:DnV + 1A1 R45 Light Craft, ECO

HULL: Welded marine grade aluminium alloy, scantlings assume a maximum midship vertical acceleration of 1g.

LIFT AND PROPULSION: Propulsion is provided by two MTU 20V 1163 TB83 diesel engines, 5420 kW each, at 1160 rpm, MCR. Each engine drives a KaMeWa 100 SII water-jet unit through a single stage reduction gear box. The lift system is powered by two Deutz MWM TB 604B V16 diesels, 1280 kW each, at 1200 rpm, directly driving four double-sided centrifugal fans, two in each hull. Ducting between the wet trimmed deck and the car deck delivers the air to the cushion and to the aft seal.

ACCOMMODATION: Seating is provided for 436 passengers at a seat pitch of 85 cm. The main passenger lounge is fitted with 354 seats and the first class passenger lounge has 82 seats.

CAR DECK: Doors at the forward and aft end of the car compartment avoid the necessity of vehicles turning when on board. Six straight car lanes are provided with a width of 2.4 meters. The two centre lanes are designed to take a maximum axle load of 1850 kg and the four side lanes, 850 kg.

TANK CAPACITIES

Fuel oil, two of each: 11.4m³ approx
Fresh water, two of each: 11.1m³ approx
Collecting, two of each: 2.6m³ approx
Sewage, two of each: 5.0m³ approx
Lubricating oil, two of each: 1.0m³ approx
Used oil, two of each: 1.0m³ approx

EXAMPLE LOADING CONDITION (TRIAL CONDITION)

Fuel oil: 25500 kg
Fresh water: 3150 kg
Lubrication oil: 1200 kg
Sewage: 1350 kg
Stores: 1750 kg
Cars, 43 at 1200 kg: 51600 kg
Passengers, 305 at 75 kg: 22875 kg
Luggage, 305 units at 5 kg: 1525 kg
Crew, 9 at 80 kg: 720 kg

Total useful load in this example: 109670 kg

MAXIMUM LOADING CONDITION

Fuel oil: 36500 kg
Fresh water: 4500 kg
Lubrication oil: 1200 kg
Stores: 2500 kg
Cars, 62 at 1200 kg: 74700 kg
Passengers, 436 at 75 kg: 32700 kg
Luggage, 436 at 75 kg: 32700 kg
Crew, 9 at 80 kg: 720 kg

Total useful load: 155000 kg

PERFORMANCE: The vessel is designed to attain a trial speed of at least 42 knots at 85% MCR in winds not exceeding Beaufort 2, calm water, clean hull. In the following figure, the ranges are based on a fuel load of 36500 kg.

Artists impression of Seaswift 23

Artists impression of Seaguard 32

In trial condition:
100% MCR, max speed: 46 knots, range 588n miles, fuel consumption 62 kg/n miles
85% MCR, service speed: 42 knots, range 632n miles, fuel consumption 58kg/n miles

In maximum loading condition:
100% MCR, max speed: 45 knots, range 575n miles, fuel consumption 63 kg/n miles
85% MCR, service speed: 41 knots, range 617n miles, fuel consumption 69 kg/n miles

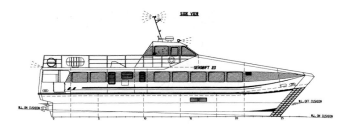

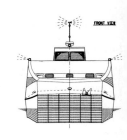

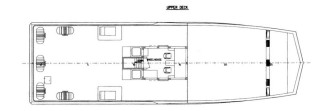

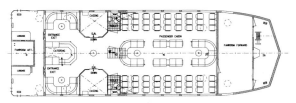

Low-density seating arrangement for Seaswift 23

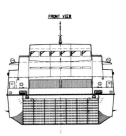

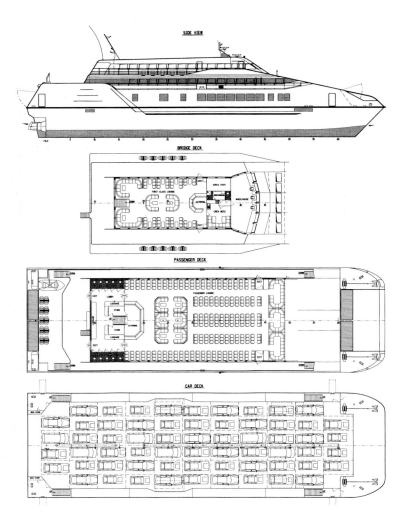

General arrangement of Seaswift 60 design

NEW ZEALAND

HOVERTREK LTD
27, Brisbane Street, Queenstown, South Island,
New Zealand
Telephone: (0294) 28 303

Mike Bird, *Principal*

In mid 1989 this company was in the process of completing the design for a 46–50 seat hovercraft for operation in the Southern Lakes tourism area of New Zealand.

NORWAY

BÅTSERVICE VERFT A/S
BÅTSERVICE MARINE
N-4500 Mandal, Norway

Telephone: (43) 61 011
Telex: 21862 YARD N
Telefax: (43) 64 580

K. R. Johnsen *Managing Director*

This company, now part of the Kvaerner group was awarded in November 1989 the contract for the building of 'Nine plus one' mine counter measures surface effect ships, for the Norwegian Navy. These vessels of 55m length will be of fibre reinforced sandwich construction. There will be four minehunters and five minesweepers. Displacements will be about 375 tonnes.

See also Addenda.

ULSTEIN INTERNATIONAL A/S
N-6065 Ulsteinvik, Norway

Telephone: (070)10050
Telex: 42342 UT N
Telefax: (070)12043

Gro Braekken, *Managing Director*

The Ulstein group have acquired major holdings in both Brødrene Aa Båtbyggeri A/S and Eikefjord Marine A/S in which yards building is undertaken of high-speed monohulls, catamarans and surface effect ships. Marketing and sales of these vessels is undertaken by Ulstein International A/S.

BRØDRENE AA
BÅTBYGGERI A/S
N-6780 Hyen, Norway

Telephone: (057) 69800
Telex: 42162BRAA N
Telefax: (057) 69914

EIKEFJORD MARINE A/S
N-6940 Eikefjord, Norway.

Telephone: (057) 49100
Telefax: (057) 49168

CIRRUS A/S,
(CONSULTING, CONTRACTING, ENGINEERING AND TRADING COMPANY)
Våkleiva 133, Box 130, N-5062 Bønes, Norway.

Telephone: (05)124550
Telex: 40422CIRR N
Telefax: (05)124565

CIRR AirCushion Catamarans (SES) are designed by CIRRUS A/S, Norway. The vessels are exclusively built by Brødrene Aa A/S and Eikefjord Marine A/S, now part of the Ulstein group, in their specialised yards for FRP construction in Hyen and Eikefjord, Norway. The co-operation between Brødrene Aa A/S and CIRRUS started in 1982 and has led to a strong expansion of both companies. In 1988 Ulstein A/S became a 50% owner of Brødrene Aa Båtbyggeri A/S.

The AirCushion Catamarans built by these companies comprise vessels from 18m to 60m with maximum speeds in excess of 50 knots. All the vessels are built in advanced FRP/sandwich materials.

The CIRR 200 high-speed passenger/car ferry project of 60m overall length is being developed by Cirrus A/S, and the first order has been placed with Eikefjord Marine A/S by a Norwegian operator. Other applications on routes up to 100n miles are anticipated for which it will be possible to undertake 6 crossings each day thereby offering considerable flexibility. Vehicle deck headroom will be 2.9m; the vessel will not be designed to take heavy transport vehicles. Aft loading for vehicles will be provided, with the vehicle deck having a 13m diameter U-turning area. Apart from this large SES offering improved comfort and speed, Cirrus have also achieved with their CIRR 60P type a very high-speed (52 knots) SES capability. Launched in November 1988 this vessel named *Harpoon* is being employed now for various tests and trials. This work will cover applications as well, since though the vessel is designed as a passenger craft the basic concept can have military and customs use.

Large structure FRP/sandwich construction technology has been developed by Cirrus enabling light-weight vessel structures to be considered for the heavy load conditions that will be encountered with these larger craft.

Cirrus also design, and Brødrene A/S and Eikefjord Marine A/S build, conventional high-speed monohull and catamaran craft and these are shown in the respective sections of this book.

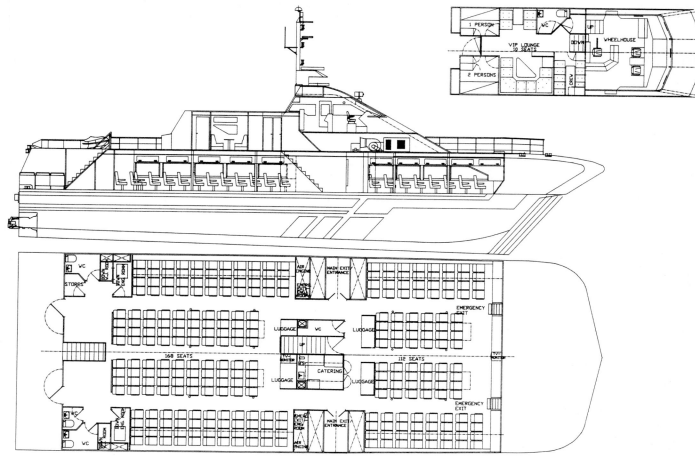

General arrangement inboard of CIRR 115 (*Ekwata*)

Craft built (SES)

Type	Name	Builder & Yard No.	No. of seats	No. of vehicle spaces	Original delivery date	Owner/operator and country of operation
CIRR 105P	*Fjordkongen* (ex *Norcat*)	Brødrene Aa A/S 169	264	0	June 1984	Troms Fylkes Dampskibsselskap, Norway
CIRR 115P	*Ekwata*	Brødrene Aa A/S 184	290	0	1986	K/S A/S Gabinor, Gabon
CIRR 120P	*Virgin Butterfly* (ex *Ekwata II*)	Brødrene Aa A/S 190	330	0	1987	Gabon Ferry Services, Gabon, and in 1989, Zademarine Ltd, Tanzania
CIRR 60	*Harpoon*	Brødrene Aa A/S 198	85	0	Nov. 1988	Norway
CIRR 120P	*Santa Maria*	Brødrene Aa A/S 199	330	0	Aug. 1988	Virtu Rapid Ferries Ltd, Malta
CIRR 120P	*San Pawl*	Eikefjord Marine A/S 200	330	0	Jan. 1989	Virtu Rapid Ferries Ltd, Malta
CIRR 120P	*Sant' Agata*	Brødrene Aa A/S 201	330	0	March 1989	Fekete & Co. A/S, Canary Is.
CIRR 120P	*San Pietro*	Eikefjord Marine A/S 8/202	330	0	May 1989	Virtu Rapid Ferries Ltd, Malta Rapid Ferries Italia, Italy Aliscafi SNAV, Italy
CIRR 120P	*San Francesca*	Eikefjord Marine A/S 204	330	0	7 Dec. 1989	—
CIRR 120P	—	205	—	0		
CIRR 120P	—	206	320	0	Sept. 1990	Yasuda Ocean Line, Japan
CIRR 200	—	214	364	56	1991	Norway
CIRR 200	—	215	—	—	1991	

General arrangement inboard of CIRR 120P (as for *Virgin Butterfly*)

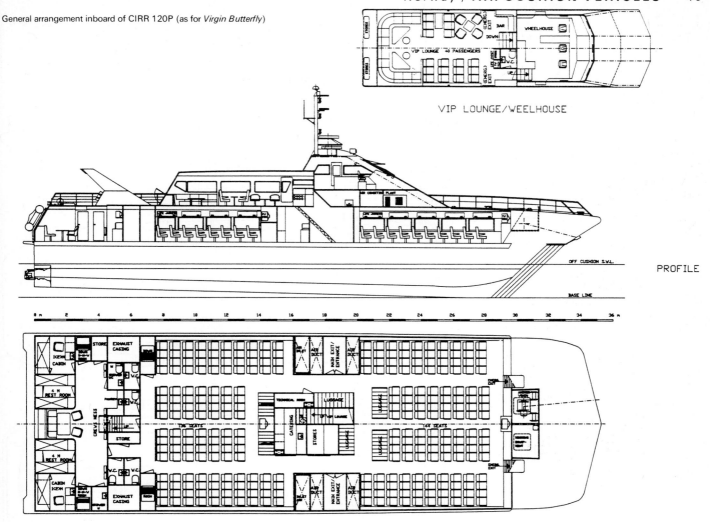

VIP LOUNGE/WEELHOUSE

PROFILE

MAIN DECK

CIRR 120P

By late 1989, seven vessels of this type had been built in addition to the two vessels (CIRR 105 and CIRR 115) which preceded the CIRR 120 design.

These vessels are built in accordance with the Norwegian Maritime Directorates' regulations for passenger vessels for service up to 90 nautical miles from harbour and comply with SOLAS 74. The CIRR 120P vessels are classified by DnV: +1A1-R90-LC,EO F-LC
HULLS: Semi-symmetrical, built in FRP/sandwich; fibre-reinforced polyester composites are laminated on both sides of PVC closed-cell core materials. Superstructure the same.
PROPULSION ENGINES: Two MWM TBD 604B V16, 1704kW at 1800rpm MCR, turbocharged, intercooled.
PROPULSION: Two KaMeWa 56/562 water-jet

units driven via ZF BW755D reduction gear boxes.
LIFT SYSTEM: Two MWM 234 8V turbocharged, 261kW at 2100rpm MCR, driving two dual inlet, centrifugal fans (made in stainless steel and FRP) via a hydraulically operated clutch. Power consumption: 186 to 209kW.
WEIGHTS
Payload (330 passengers): 24.75 tonnes
Crew including equipment: 0.75 tonnes
Fresh water (500 l): 0.50 tonnes
Fuel (600 l): 5.00 tonnes
Stores: 1.00 tonnes
Deadweight (full fuel): 32.00 tonnes
ACCOMMODATION: 330 passengers and crew.
DIMENSIONS
Length, overall: 35.25m

Beam, moulded: 11.50m
Depth, moulded: 3.50m
Draught, stationary, off cushion: 2.10m
Draught, stationary, on cushion: 0.70m
PERFORMANCE
Speed, max: 50 knots
Fuel consumption, at 45 knots, 50% payload:
   800 l/h, 17.7 l/n mile.
NAVIGATION & COMMUNICATIONS
Two radars, compass, log, satelite nav, two VHF telephones, intercom, TV/video for passengers, closed circuit TV.
RIDE CONTROL SYSTEM
Maritime Dynamics Inc ride control system operating two hydraulically-operated louvres.
AUXILIARY POWER: Two hydraulically driven generators: each 25 kVA/220V/50Hz.

Brødrene Aa CIRR 120 *Santa Maria*

CIRR 60P
HARPOON

This vessel is designed to explore appreciably higher speeds than at present obtainable with current types of SESs. At a designed service speed of 45 knots and maximum speed of 52 knots the craft operates at Froude Numbers up to 2.15.

The vessel is built according to the Norwegian Maritime Directorates[1] regulations for passenger vessels for service up to 25 nautical miles from harbour. *Harpoon* is classified by DnV: +1A2 Light Craft R25F EO/LC.

HULLS: Asymetric, built in FRP/sandwich; fibre-reinforced polyester composites are lamented on both sides of PVC core materials.

MAIN ENGINES: Two MWM TBD 234 V16, 895kW each, at 2200rpm MCR.

PROPULSION: Two Levi surface piercing propellers with steering nozzles, driven via gearbox.

LIFT SYSTEM: Single CIRR dual-inlet centrifugal fan, hydraulically driven from main engines.

WEIGHTS
Payload (86 passengers): 6.45 tonnes
Crew (2): 0.15 tonnes
Fresh water (300 l): 0.30 tonnes
Fuel (3000 l): 2.80 tonnes
Deadweight (full fuel): 9.70 tonnes

ACCOMMODATION: 86 passengers, 2 crew.

DIMENSIONS
Length, overall: 18.0m
Beam, moulded: 7.2m
Depth, moulded: 2.0m
Draught, stationary, off-cushion: 1.3m
Draught, stationary, on-cushion: 0.5m

PERFORMANCE
Maximum speed in Sea State 1, at MCR: 52 knots.
Fuel consumption: approx 500 l/h at max speed.

NAVIGATION AND COMMUNICATIONS
Radar, compass, log, trim indicator, roll indicator, standard instruments, VHF telephone, SSB radio, intercom.

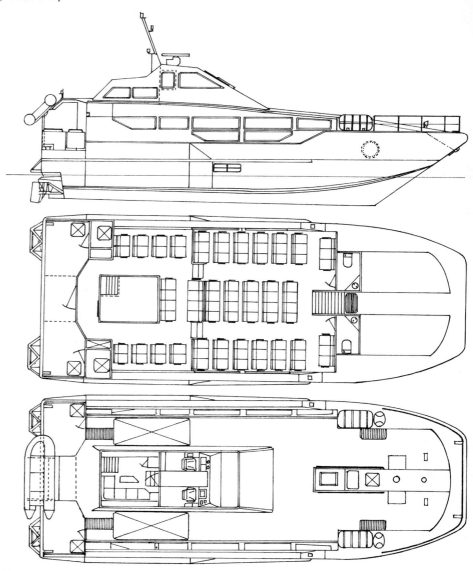

General arrangement of Cirrus type CIRR 60P *Harpoon*

The SES *Harpoon*

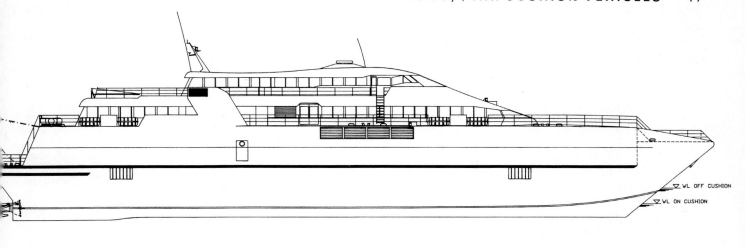

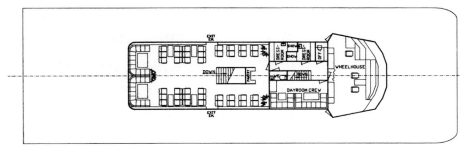

UPPER DECK

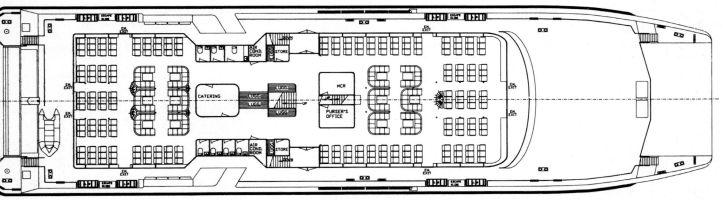

PASSENGER DECK

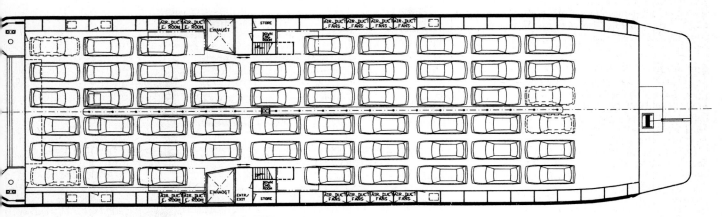

CAR DECK

General arrangement (Spring 1989) of CIRR 200 60.50m passenger/car ferry

CIRR 200

This Cirrus-designed passenger/car Air Cushion Catamaran (SES) is designed to the standards of the Norwegian Maritime Directorate and the IMO Code for Dynamically Supported vessels, resolution A373 X. The Cirr 200 will be classified DnV + 1A1 R90 light vessel SF-F-EO/LC.

HULL: Fibre-reinforced plastics (FRP)/sandwich construction.

PRINCIPAL PARTICULARS
Total installed power: 10440kW (two gas turbines, 4474kW each, two diesel engines, 746kW each)
Propulsion: Two waterjet units

Length, overall: 60.50m
Beam, max: 16.80m
Depth to main deck: 4.60m
Height, max., excluding mast: 13.30m
Draught, max., off cushion: 2.70m Draught, max.,
on cushion: 1.15m
Passenger capacity: 364

Car capacity: 56 'passenger car units'
Deadweight, typical: 125 tonnes
Displacement, max: 473 tonnes
Payload: 92.2 tonnes
Car parking area: 710m²
Car parking headroom: 2.90m
Passenger deck area: 500m²

Service speed: Sea state 0, 50% deadweight, 90%
MCR: 47 knots
  Sea state 3, 50% deadweight, 90% MCR: 42
knots
Fuel consumption: diesel fuel, max. speed, 100%
deadweight: 3300 l/h: 73 l/n miles.

Vehicle loading arrangement for Cirrus CIRR 200 SES ferry

WESTAMARIN A/S

PO Box 143, N-4501 Mandal, Norway

Telephone: (043)62222
Telex: 21514 WRIN N
Telefax: (043)62302

Westamarin A/S entered SES work in 1986
when the company concluded a licence agreement
with Karlskronavarvet AB of Sweden for the
fitting out of two grp hull SES 3400 Jet Rider
vessels designed by Karlskronavarvet under which
entry details of these craft are given. Following
this development,Westamarin embarked on the
design of a larger SES, originally designated SES
3800 but subsequently re-designated SES 4000,
and to be built in aluminium. These craft employ
air cushion systems licensed from Karlskronavarvet AB.

Two Westamarin SES 4000 vessels have been
built and at the time of going to press are owned
by JKL Shipping of Norway. One of the two,
Super Swede, entered service between Copenhagen
and Gothenburg June 16th 1989 but the service
was discontinued July 20th 1989 due to engine
problems. The second vessel, *Super Dane*, was not
delivered.

SES 4000
CLASSIFICATION: DnV + 1A1 R45 EO, Light
Craft Passenger Vessel
ACCOMMODATION: 309 passengers
ENGINES
Propulsion: Two SACM M7 UD 33 V16, each
2720kW at 1600 rpm
Lift: Four GM V6–92 TA, each 270kW
Auxiliary: Two GM V6–71T, each 201kW
PROPULSION: Two Liaaen Speed – Z type CPZ
60/42–125 MkII propeller units
TANKS
Fuel oil, two 7600 l and two 3800 l
Fresh water, 1500 l
NAVIGATION: Two radars, one gyro com-
pass/magnetic compass, log, navigator echo
sounder
COMMUNICATION: Two VHFs, radio tele-
phones, mobile telephone, intercommunication,
TV, radio and PA facility
DIMENSIONS
Length, overall: 40.00 m

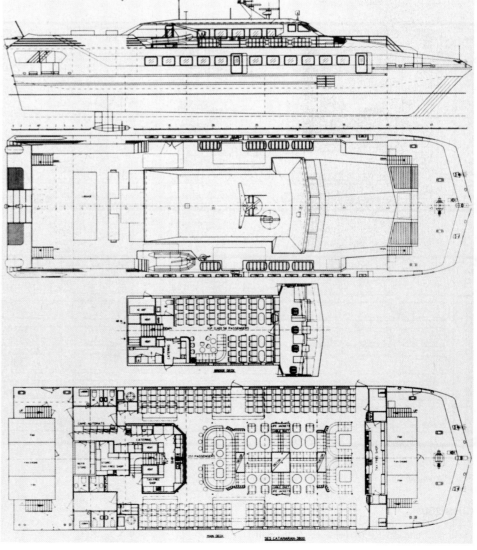

General arrangement of Westamarin SES 4000

Beam: 12.60 m
Draught, loaded: 2.21 m
GRT: 551
PERFORMANCE
Speed, service: 46 knots
Speed, max: 52 knots
Fuel consumption at service speed: 23 l/n miles
Range, at service speed: 780 n miles

SES Craft built, SES 4000 (ex SES 3800)

Yard No	Name	Seats	Owners	In Service	Routes operated
97	*Super Swede*	309	JKL Shipping	16 June 1989 to 20 June 1989	Copenhagen-Gothenburg
96	*Super Dane*	309	JKL Shipping	—	—

Westamarin SES 4000 *Super Dane*

SINGAPORE

SINGAPORE SHIPBUILDING AND ENGINEERING LTD

7 Benoi Road, Singapore 2262
PO Box 138, Jurong Town Post Office, Singapore
9161

Wong Kin Hoong, *Senior Manager, Marketing &
Business Development*

Telephone: 8612244, 8616844
Telex: 21206SINGA RS
Telefax: 8613028/8611601

TIGER 40

This Air Vehicles Tiger 40 was built for a leasing
company in Singapore, SAL Leasing, which owns
the craft. In 1987 this craft was leased to the
Singapore Navy. Details of the Tiger 40 are given
in the entry for Air Vehicles Ltd. Tiger 40 craft
are marketed in the Far East by Singapore Shipbuilding and Engineering Ltd.

Air Vehicles Tiger 40 built by Singapore Shipbuilding and Engineering Ltd

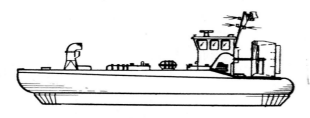

PROFILE

FRONT VIEW

PLAN VIEW

Tiger 40

SPAIN

BAZAN EMPRESA NACIONAL

Castellana 55, 28046 Madrid, Spain:
(Apartado postal 90)

Telephone: (91)4415100/4416100
Telex: 27480/46450 E
Telefax: (91)4415090

With funding from the Spanish Ministry of
Defence, Bazan and CHACONSA have developed
an SES programme

The first joint project was the BES-16 research
craft launched in 1988. In 1989 a new project was
announced, the BES-50, a 55 metre missile patrol
boat, designed to meet Spanish Navy requirements. Details of both craft are given under the
CHACONSA entry; construction of BES-50 is
expected to start in 1990.

CHACONSA SA

COMPAÑIA HISPANO AMERICANA DE CONSTRUCCIONES CONSERVERAS SA
Mayor, 17–30006 Puente Tocinos, Apartado 419/30080, Murcia, Spain

Telephone: 68–230200; 238512; 230604
Telex: 67248ABRO E

Carlos Ruiz Valero, *ACV Programme Manager*

VCA-2

CHACONSA launched its air cushion vehicle research programme in 1973. In 1976 it received a contract for the development of the VCA-36 from the Spanish Ministry of Defence. Design of the lift and propulsion system was aided by experiments with laboratory models. Two manned research models, the 750kg VCA-2 and the 5-tonne VCA-3, were later built to evaluate and refine the system.

In addition to its military programme, CHACONSA plans to build commercial hovercraft and is also examining industrial and agricultural applications of air cushion technology.

VCA-2

The first manned air cushion vehicle to be designed and built by CHACONSA, the VCA-2 has a maximum weight of 750kg. Like the VCA-3, described and illustrated below, it was employed as a test craft during the development of the lift system for the VCA-36 amphibious assault craft.

VCA-3

VCA-3

A 2.5 scale model of the VCA-36, the VCA-3, was built in 1978. Powered by two Porsche engines, it seats seven and has a maximum speed of 50 knots. At least one variant is likely to enter production.

LIFT AND PROPULSION: Integrated system powered by two 300hp Porsche 928–5 automotive engines. Each engine drives a centrifugal lift fan and a 2m diameter variable-pitch, two-bladed propeller for thrust.

CHACONSA VCA-36 propeller installation

CONTROLS: Craft heading is controlled by twin aerodynamic rudders operating in the propeller slipstream. At low speed direction control is by differential propeller pitch. A ballast system adjusts longitudinal and transverse trim.

HULL: Corrosion-resistant aluminium alloy. Buoyancy chamber includes compartments filled with plastic foam for reserve buoyancy. Six rubber landing pads are fitted to the hull base. Four lifting eyes are provided in the hull.

SKIRT: 0.53m deep, fingered-bag type of CHACONSA design, fabricated in nylon coated with synthetic rubber.

EXTERNAL DIMENSIONS
Length overall, on cushion: 10.36m
Beam overall, on cushion: 4.45m
Height, on cushion: 4m
Skirt depth: 0.53m

INTERNAL DIMENSIONS
Cabin, max dimensions
Length: 4.1m
Width: 3.2m

WEIGHTS
Max: 5000kg
Payload: 1000kg

PERFORMANCE
Max speed: 50 knots
Cruising speed: 40 knots
Max gradient, continuous: 12%
Endurance: 3 hours

CHACONSA VCA-36 during anti-submarine sea trials

VCA-36

Designed to improve the rapid-lift capability of the Spanish armed forces, the VCA-36 will carry a 14-tonne payload, equivalent to three Land-Rovers and 70 fully-armed marines or infantrymen, to a beach landing zone at a speed of 60 knots. It could also be used for lighter-over-the-shore applications. Its dimensions will allow it to operate from the docking wells of a number of LSDs, and from ro/ro vessels with sufficient headroom and suitable ramps. Lifting eyes in the hull will enable it to be hoisted on and off the decks of cargo ships. A removable roof above the cargo deck will permit the craft to be loaded alongside supply ships.

NAVY EVALUATION PROGRAMME: Last summer VCA-36 finished its navy evaluation programme in the Sierra del Retin (Cadiz) 300 miles away from its base at Murcia. Trials lasted one month and the craft negotiated high winds, different obstacles and types of terrain in the area where Spanish Marines carry out exercises. Some civil demonstrations have also been made in this area of Spain and the craft navigated about 1000

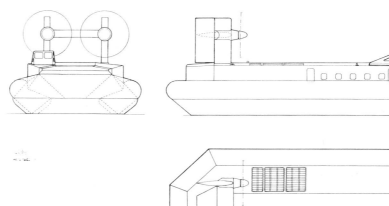

General arrangement of VCA-36

CHACONSA VCA-36

miles during the trials. In 1990 the craft will be transferred to the Navy and it is believed that it will have its base in the Mar Menor near Cartagena.

LIFT AND PROPULSION: Integrated system powered by two Textron Lycoming TF25 gas turbines, each with a maximum output of 2500hp. Each drives two centrifugal fans and a 4m diameter, five-bladed, variable-pitch propeller. Power is transmitted via two gearboxes with auxiliary outputs for lubrication, hydraulic pumps and generators. The combined epicyclic and bevel (splitter) gearbox (lower unit) transmits 1100hp from 14 500rpm to 1080rpm for the lift fans and 1900hp from 14 500rpm to 1988rpm for the pylon propulsion gearbox (upper unit). The pylon bevel gearbox reduces the speed from 1988rpm to the 1011rpm of the propulsion propeller.

CONTROLS: All controls are in a raised cabin, well forward on the starboard quarter and providing a 360-degree view. Directional control is by twin aerodynamic rudders and differential propeller pitch. A ballast system adjusts longitudinal and transverse trim.

HULL: Riveted aluminium structure based on a grid of longitudinal and transverse frames which form a number of watertight buoyancy compartments. Fuel, ballast tanks and bilge systems are contained within these compartments. Access to the cargo deck is via hydraulically-operated bow and stern ramps or the removable cargo deck roof. The central cargo deck is 18.65m long by 2.6m wide by 2.25m high. Two main longitudinal vertically stiffened bulkheads run the length of the hull. These separate the central vehicle/cargo deck from the sidestructures which contain the gas turbines, lift fans, transmissions, auxiliary power systems and cabins. Marines or assault troops are accommodated in two 35-seat cabins, 7.4m long by 2.35m wide, one in the forward section of each sidestructure. Four landing pads are fitted to the hull base. Four lifting eyes are provided for hoisting the craft.

SKIRT: 1.4m deep, fingered-bag type of CHACONSA design in nylon coated with synthetic rubber.

SYSTEMS, ELECTRICAL: Two 15kVA generators driven by the main engines provide three-phase 50Hz at 380V for ac and dc supplies.

DIMENSIONS
Length overall, on cushion: 25.5m
Beam overall, on cushion: 11.04m
Height on cushion: 9.5m
Skirt depth: 1.4m
WEIGHTS
Max: 36 tonnes
Payload: 14 tonnes
PERFORMANCE
Max speed: 60 knots
Cruising speed: 50 knots
Endurance: 3 hours

CHACONSA BES-16

BES (BUSQUE DE EFECTO SUPÉRFICE)

Early in 1987 it was announced that CHACONSA SA had teamed up with the Bazán yard (builder of naval fast craft) to develop a new surface effect ship, BES (Busque de Efecto Superfice). CHACONSA will work on the air cushion components at its El Carmeli factory while Bazán will be responsible for the hulls and engines, this work to be undertaken at its Cartagena yard. An initial investment of Ps160 million will be made by both companies.

BES-16

At the end of 1984 CHACONSA established a 50/50 joint programme with Empresa Nacional Bazán for the study, analysis and development of SES craft technology in order to design and build these craft in the range of 50 to 500 tonnes, full load displacement.

The first craft to be built is the BES-16 research craft, launched in the first half of 1988.

HULL: Welded Al-Mg 4, 5 alloy.

PROPULSION: Two Isotta Fraschini diesel

CHACONSA BES-16

engines, 450hp each, two Castoldi 06 waterjet units.
LIFT: Two VM-HRI 492 diesel engines, 110hp each, six centrifugal lift fans.
DIMENSIONS
Length overall: 16.78m
Beam overall: 5.40m
Depth: 1.90m
Draught, mean: 0.75m
WEIGHT
Displacement: 14 tonnes

BES-50 (DESIGN)
CONSTRUCTION: Main hull structure in welded light alloys, superstructure in riveted light alloy.

ENGINES, Propulsion: Two Allison 570 KF gas turbines
   Lift: Four MTU 6V 396 TB83, each 500 kW
PROPULSION: Two KaMeWa S62–90 water jet units
LIFT FANS: Four HEBA B
AUXILIARY SYSTEMS: Two 440V 60 Hz generators, l20 kVA each
DIMENSIONS
Length, overall: 55.00m
Beam: 14.50m
Depth: 6.90m
Cushion length: 44.00m
Cushion beam: 9.50m
Draft, on cushion, max: 1.20m
Displacement, full load: 350 tonnes

PERFORMANCE
Speed, max: 50 knots
Speed, cruising: 12 knots
Range, at max.speed: 800 miles
Range at cruising speed: 2000 miles
COMPLEMENT
   One Commanding Officer, five Officers, six Petty Officers and eighteen enlisted men
WEAPONS
   The following may be carried: two Bazan-Bofors 40/70 guns, two 4 Harpoon launchers, one ESM system, one chaff launcher, one light helicopter.
COMMUNICATION AND CONTROL
   One air and surface exploring radar, one navigating radar, two optronic directors, one log, one radio direction finder, one gyrocompass.

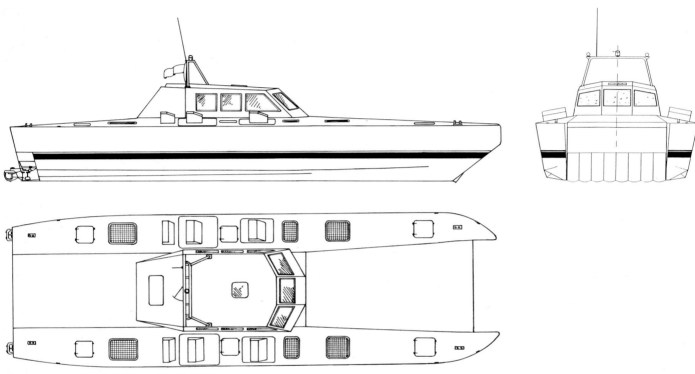

General arrangement of CHACONSA BES-16

Model of CHACONSA BES-50 design

FM-AERODESLIZADORES

URB. Neuvos Horizontes No.8, 28970, Grinon, Madrid, Spain

Julián Martin Sanz, *Project Manager, Mechanical Engineer*
Joaquin Heras, *Electrical Engineer*

Two craft preceded the FM-HC-004X. Details of these, the FM-HC-001X and FM-HC-002 are given in the 1989 edition of this book.

FM-HC-004X

FM-HC-004X

This multipurpose craft is designed to operate without modifications in ambient air temperatures from −20°C to +70°C. Trials began in July 1986.
LIFT AND PROPULSION: Two 70hp BMW engines are used to drive the mechanically integrated lift and propulsion units, each engine positioned between a six-blade 800mm centrifugal lift fan and a six-blade ducted propeller. A centrifugal clutch is incorporated in each power unit and power transmission is by toothed belt/pulley arrangements.
CONTROLS: Craft direction is controlled by twin rudders positioned at the rear of the propeller ducts and operated by foot pedals. Three elevators are similarly positioned to provide control in pitch and roll and are operated by a hand wheel.
HULL: The craft is built in glass reinforced plastic and Plasticell. Sealed compartments provide reserve buoyancy.
SKIRT: Open loop segmented type. The rear segments are of conical form in order to avoid water scooping. The skirt is constructed of neoprene-coated nylon fabric.
ACCOMMODATION: The enclosed cabin has seating for one pilot and five passengers or one pilot, and co-pilot and a 400kg payload. A stretcher may be accommodated beside the pilot.
EXTERNAL DIMENSIONS
Length, with inflated skirt: 6.11m
Width, with inflated skirt: 3.73m

Height, without inflated skirt: 1.975m
Cushion area: 14.63m^2
INTERNAL DIMENSIONS (cabin)
Length: 1.75m
Width: 1.5m
Height: 1.25m
WEIGHTS
Empty: 900kg
Max payload plus fuel: 600kg
PERFORMANCE
Max speed over water: 75km/h
Max speed on land: 85km/h
Cruising speed: 65km/h
Gradient climbing capability: 1 in 7
Endurance: 5 hours
Max vertical obstacle clearance: 0.4m

VARIANTS: The design is adaptable for coastguard and patrol work and for search and rescue duties.

FM-HC-005 HOVERBUS
FM-HC-002 AND FM-HC-003 (PROJECT DESIGNS)

Details of these designs for a gas-turbine powered two-seater and a 48-seat diesel powered 'Hoverbus' are given in the 1989 edition of this book.

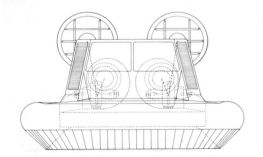
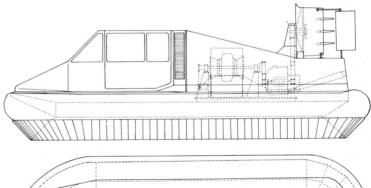
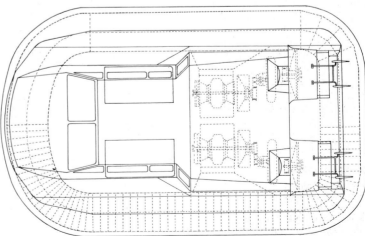

FM-HC-004X

NEUMAR SA

La Rinconada, B-6 28023 Madrid, Spain

Telephone: (91) 2071998/5636053
Telefax: (91) 5636113
J Peire, *General Manager*
M de la Cruz, *Technical Director*
J A Barbeta, *Manufacturing Manager*

Neumar SA was founded in 1983 as a consulting engineers and designers company for air cushion technology. The services it offers include research and development with an emphasis on lift systems; hovercraft design; project management, which can comprise construction subcontracting with collaborating shipyards; hovercraft skirt design and manufacturing; and technical and economic feasibility studies.

The company offers a range of hovercraft designs which are based on a new lift system that it has recently developed and patented. This has been called an Automatic Transversal Air Distribution (ATAD) lift system because of the main function it performs in providing very high stability with low power requirements and reduced manufacturing and maintenance costs. To prove the viability of this lift system, several two-dimensional models and two prototypes have been built and tested.

ATAD LIFT SYSTEM

The ATAD lift system has been developed with the aim of obtaining high stability values with low lift power requirements. It is a pressure-stability, fully-segmented system that is based on a longitudinal flexible keel which has the inherent ability to increase the pressure difference between the two chambers into which it divides the air cushion, while keeping the pressure ratio between the air distribution duct and the air cushion at a very low level.

The stability keel has the same effect as a valve which is open to both air cushion chambers while the craft is level and which, when the craft heels, closes to the risen side while opening the air passage still further to the fallen side. This results in a very sharp rise of the pressure ratio between both cushion chambers even for very low duct-to-cushion pressure ratios. A second effect is that the lift air flow requirement is reduced in comparison to conventional systems. The keel is made of independently replaceable segments.

The peripheral skirt used with this lift system has been made fully segmented, each segment consisting of three independently replaceable sectors. It offers low drag over waves and low manufacturing and maintenance costs, and it has low geometrical stability in order to make any ride control system more effective.

A by-product of this lift system is a hull design which further increases the hovercraft seakeeping qualities. The hull bottom cross-section has the form of a 'W', both 'Vs' ending in conical surfaces which at the bow are prolonged upwards and forward forming a planing surface to prevent adverse consequences of any plough-in phenomena. This hull form greatly reduces water impact loads and at the same time it has a high structural efficiency that in turn leads to a lower structure weight.

NEUMARAN NM-6

This three-/four-seat hovercraft has been designed for the pleasure boat market and for those other applications, for example coastal or inland water patrol and harbour policing, for which a high-speed small boat is required with the added advantage of its amphibious qualities. The design has sought a compromise between low cost and high performance, measuring the latter in terms of high speed, good manoeuvrability and very good seakeeping qualities for its size.

LIFT AND PROPULSION: The NM-6 features

Neumaran NM-6 prototype approaching land

Trials of the Neumaran NM-6 prototype over mud and reeds

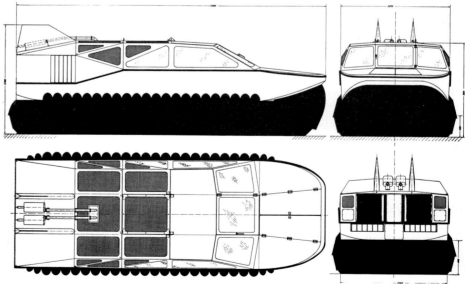
General arrangement of Neumaran NM-6

an integrated lift and propulsion system with a single engine driving twin 800mm diameter axial flow fans that provide the airflow required for both functions. The transmission consists of HTD toothed belts and pulleys. For the prototype a 120hp petrol engine has been chosen, but any engine from 100 to 150hp could be installed, depending on speed and payload requirements.

CONTROL: Yaw control is obtained by one aero-dynamic rudder situated in the air outlet duct of each of the two fans. Top rudder deflection closes the outlet duct, directing the airflow forward through louvre nozzles at each side of the craft, thus producing a braking effect. Since each rudder can be independently deflected, a very effective yaw control is obtained at all speeds. Roll control is performed by two venting valves located in the transom of the craft that discharge air from each of the two chambers into which the air cushion is divided.

HULL: The hull is made of moulded grp with extensive use of sandwich structures. The hull form is that described above for the ATAD lift system, which greatly reduces water impact loads while offering high structural efficiency.

SKIRT: The skirt design corresponds to the ATAD lift system described before. All skirt elements are made of neoprene-covered nylon fabric.

ACCOMMODATION: The prototype provides seating accommodation for three persons in a fully enclosed cabin, but different superstructure and cabin layouts are also possible and an open cockpit with seating accommodation for four persons is projected.

DIMENSIONS

Length, hard structure: 5.80m
Beam, hard structure: 2.05m
Height on cushion: 2.10m
Cushion depth, minimum: 0.40m
     mean: 0.52m

WEIGHTS

(With 120hp engine)
Displacement, light: 850kg
Useful load (including fuel): 350kg
Displacement, full load: 1200kg

PERFORMANCE

(With 120hp engine)
Speed, max, calm water: 42 knots
Speed, cruising: 30–35 knots
Gradient from standing start, max: 10%
Endurance at cruising power, max: 5 hours
Range, max: 150–175n miles

WEATHER LIMITATIONS

Waves: 1m
Wind: Beaufort 5

NEUMARAN NM-6/S

The NM-6/S is a sports variant of the NM-6. The hull and skirt are identical to those of the latter craft, but this design has an open cabin with seating capacity for five persons, and the machinery is different.

Details of this craft are as for the NM-6 with the following exceptions.

LIFT AND PROPULSION: This craft has independent lift and propulsion systems. Power for the lift system is provided by a ROTAX 462 two-stroke, water-cooled engine rated at 38hp, which drives an aluminium centrifugal fan through a toothed belt transmission. Thrust is obtained by means of a 1.60 meter diameter, three-bladed, fixed-pitch propeller which is driven through a reduction gearbox by a ROTAX 532, two-stroke, water-cooled engine with a power rating of 64hp. Both engines are provided with electric starting.

CONTROL: Yaw control is obtained by means of three aerodynamic rudders situated in the propeller slipstream. Pitch control and trim is obtained with a horizontal elevator situated over the vertical rudders. Roll control is performed by two venting valves located near the stern on both sides of the hull that discharge air from each of the two chambers into which the air cushion is divided. The location of these valves provides an added yawing force that enhances yaw control at all speeds.

ACCOMMODATION: This craft has accommodation for four or five persons in an open cabin, with two bucket seats for the pilot and one passenger fore and a bench seat for two or three passengers aft.

WEIGHTS

Light displacement: 700kg
Useful load (including fuel): 400kg
Full load displacement: 1100kg

PERFORMANCE

Calm water speed, max: 40 knots
Speed, cruising: 30–35 knots
Gradient from standing start, max: 12%
Operating conditions, max: 1m waves and Beaufort 5 wind

Neumaran NM-6/S

Endurance at cruising power, max: 4 hours
Range, max: 120 to 140n miles

NEUMARAN NM-15 (DESIGN)

This amphibious assault landing craft design followed a specific requirement, but other military and civil variants can be derived from the basic layout. Among the former, coastal patrol and counter-insurgency missions can be mentioned, while some of its possible civil applications would be passenger ferry, crewboat or as a luxury amphibious yacht. The design philosophy that has been applied, which is based on the ATAD lift system, leads to a cost-effective craft through the use of diesel engines and a grp structure, while craft performance can be adapted to each specific requirement through the installation of the adequate engine power.

LIFT AND PROPULSION: The basic design has twin lift and propulsion integrated systems, each consisting of a diesel engine that drives both a centrifugal lift fan and a ducted variable-pitch propeller. The proposed diesel engines are two Deutz air-cooled units of the type BF12L 513 FC, with a maximum rated power of 525hp each. Transmission from the engines to fans and propellers is through toothed belts and pulleys.

CONTROL: Yaw control at high speed is obtained through three aerodynamic rudders located in the slipstream of each propeller, and at low speed, differential propeller pitch may be used.

Pitch control is by means of horizontal elevators also situated in the propeller slipstreams. Pitch trim is obtained through a fuel ballast system. Roll control is performed by two venting valves installed in the transom of the craft as described for the NM-6.

HULL: The hull is made of moulded grp using sandwich structures with expanded PVC cores. For special applications requiring maximum weight-saving, Kevlar and carbon fibre reinforcements could be used at an increased cost. The hull form is as described above for the ATAD lift system.

SKIRT: The skirt design corresponds to the ATAD lift system described before. All skirt elements are made of neoprene-covered nylon fabric.

ACCOMMODATION: The basic design provides seating accommodation for 24 combat troops. This layout is based on the requirement to have an endurance of 8 hours, but if this figure is reduced to 3 hours, 36 troops could be easily seated in the main cabin. Access to this cabin takes place through a bow ramp 2.50m wide. There are also two emergency exits, one at each side of the craft. Three seats can be installed in the raised control cabin, which provides 360° visibility. Access to this cabin is provided by a ladder from the operations room below and there is also a door that leads from the control cabin to the aft deck. Two gunner wells have been allowed for in

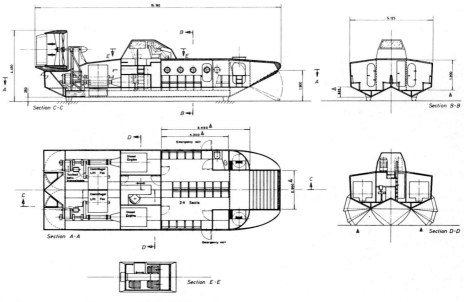

Interior arrangement of Neumaran NM-15 design

the foredeck, where two 12.7mm or smaller calibre machine guns could be installed. Direct access has been provided from the main cabin to the two gunner wells.

EXTERNAL DIMENSIONS
Length, hard structure: 15.19m
Beam, hard structure: 5.13m
Height on cushion: 5.20m
Cushion depth, minimum: 1.00m
Cushion depth, mean: 1.31m

INTERNAL DIMENSIONS
Main cabin floor area: 22m²
Main cabin length: 5.40m
Main cabin width: 4.80m
Bow ramp width: 2.50m

WEIGHTS
Displacement, light: 11 300kg
Useful load (including fuel): 3700kg
Design fuel load (8 hours endurance): 1200kg
Design military load: 2500kg
Displacement, full load: 15 000kg

PERFORMANCE
Speed, max, calm water: 55 knots
Speed, cruising in Sea State 2: 40 knots
Gradient from standing start, max: 10%
Endurance with internal tanks at cruising power, max: 16 hours
Range at cruising speed, equivalent max: 640n miles

WEATHER LIMITATIONS
Waves: 2.5m
Wind: Beaufort 7

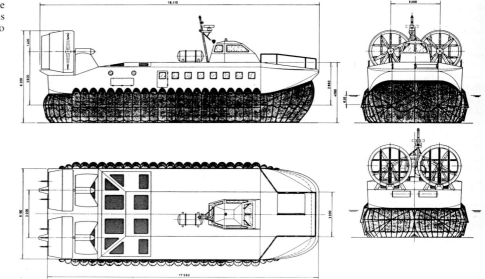

General arrangement of Neumaran NM-15 design

NEUMARAN NM-17 (DESIGN)
NEUMARAN NM-30 (DESIGN)
For details of these craft please see 1989 edition of this book

---

SWEDEN

KARLSKRONAVARVET AB
S-371 82 Karlskrona, Sweden

Telephone: 45519440
Telex: 8395018KKRV S
Telefax: 45517934

Hans G Frisk, *Managing Director*
Hans Hedman, *Marketing Manager*

Karlskonavarvet is a member of the Celsius Group and is a dockyard for the design, construction maintenance and modernisation activities mainly for the Royal Swedish Navy.

During the last six years extensive design and development work has been carried out to develop a surface effect ship for naval use as well as for passenger transportation.

SES 3400 JET RIDER
SEA PRINCE (ex SLEIPNER)
SEA PRINCESS (ex DRAUPNER)
These two surface effect ships were built as a result of a co-operative agreement between Karlskronavarvet AB of Sweden and Westamarin A/S of Norway for the supply of two SESs for the Stavanger to Bergen 'Flaggruten' service. This contract was cancelled when the craft failed to

meet the required performance, but they were subsequently bought (23 March 1988) by JKL Shipping for service between Copenhagen (Kastrup) and Helsingborg. The craft were then leased to Interscandic Line which operated them under the name Fast Ferries from June 1989 till 24 August 1989 when Interscandic went into liquidation. Karlskronavarvet obtained air cushion and skirt technology knowhow from Textron Marine Systems, USA in exchange for their fibre reinforced plastics knowhow. At the beginning of this arrangement the US Navy was sponsoring the design of a mine counter measures SES (not subsequently proceeded with) for which the

Karlskronavarvet SES 3400 *Jet Princess* (ex *Draupner*) sister vessel to *Jet Prince* (ex *Sleipner*)

knowhow exchanges were also employed. Design of the Karlskronavarvet surface effect ships was supported by extensive model testing at the SSPA in Gothenburg.
CLASSIFICATION: DnV + 1A1 R15 EO
HULL: Fibre reinforced plastics (FRP) construction. Divinicell PVC cellular plastic core, 40 to 60 mm thick, density 60 to 100 kg/m^3. Facing of sandwich construction: glass reinforced polyester resin, E grade glass, 800 g/m^2 woven roving and 100 or 300 g/m^2 chopped strand mat.
ACCOMMODATION: Initially 244 passengers and 6 crew (upper deck overnight cabins for crew), later modified to carry 292 passengers by removing overnight crew cabins, allowing a 48 seat 'Royal Class' saloon to be provided.
PROPULSION: Two KaMeWa 63562/6 water jet units driven through ZF BU 750 reduction gear boxes.
SKIRT SYSTEM: Rubber-coated nylon, bow skirt has eight open segments, rear skirt or seal has three lobes, bolted to each other; air is fed into the upper lobe and via feed holes into the lower lobes. Skirt design and manufacture by Karlskronavarvet AB.

Craft built SES 3400 Jet Rider, hull and superstructure*

Yard No.	Name	Seats	Owners	In service	Routes operated
427	*Jet Prince* (ex Sleipner)	292 (initially 244)	JKL Shipping	June 1988	Copenhagen-Helsingborg
428	*Jet Princess* (ex Draupner)	292 (initially 244)	JKL Shipping	19 June 1989 to 24 August 1989	Malmo-Kastrup

*fitted out by Westamarin A/S, Norway.

FANS: Four 0.76 m dia. double-inlet, centrifugal type, welded aluminium (designed and made by Karlskronavarvet AB), and driven via hydraulic transmission. Two fans in bow and two in stern.
RIDE CONTROL SYSTEM: Heavy damping, pressure monitoring system with electronic feedback.
GENERATORS: Two Stamford MSC 334A
TANKS: Fuel 10 m^3
PERFORMANCE
Speed, half load, MCR: 42 knots
Speed, full load, MCR: 39 knots
Range: 200n miles at 35 knots, 4 tonnes of fuel
DIMENSIONS
Length overall: 33.40m
Length waterline: 28.20m
Beam overall: 10.50m
Depth moulded to main deck: 3.25m
Draught, hullborne: 1.75m
Draught, on cushion: 0.25m

General arrangement of Karlskronavarvet SES 3400 Jet Rider, 292 seat layout

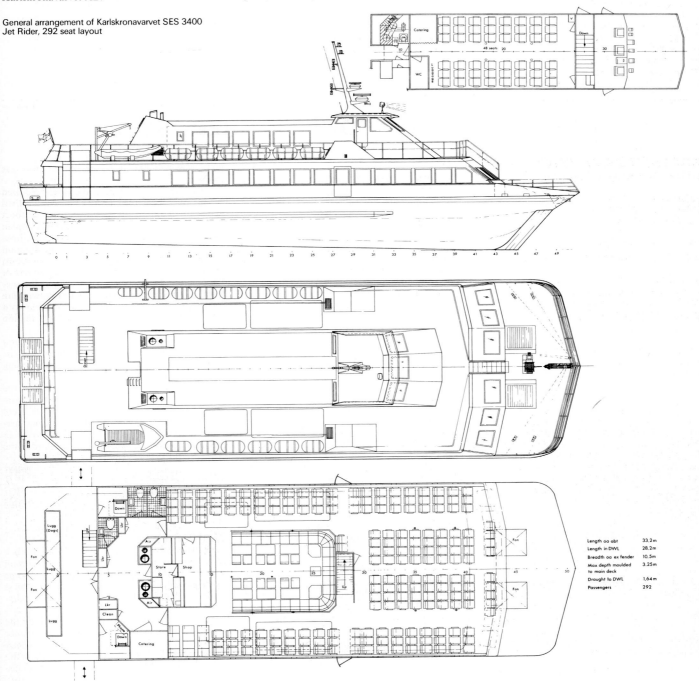

TAIWAN

CHIVALRY UNIVERSAL COMPANY

PO Box 36–48 Taipei, Taiwan

Telephone: 026212197/7692511
Telex: 11153HUOKZ-1 TP
Telefax: (02) 763 7101

C S Lee, *President*
H J Tsai, *Vice President, Research and Development*
T P Doo, *Vice President, Engineering*

Overseas Office: International Vehicle Research Inc, 14074 Nacogdoches Road, Suite No 322, San Antonio, Texas 78247, USA

Telephone: (512) 650 5188

Johnny Tseng-Pei Doo, *President*

Chivalry Universal produce both light sports and utility hovercraft. Details of the light models, CY-10 and CY-10 Mk II are to be found in the Light/Sports Air Cushion Vehicles section.

Chivalry is conducting the research and development, testing and design work in conjunction with the International Vehicle Research Inc, who also has the marketing responsibility for

the CY-series hovercraft in the North American area.

CY-6

CY-6 Mk III is a five-/six-seater utility amphibian hovercraft. The production version is very similar to the prototype design in external dimensions but the internal transmission system and supporting structure has been redesigned for simpler maintenance procedures and lighter structure weight.

CY-6 Mk IV is a stretched version of the CY-6 Mk III. The fuselage is stretched 1.0m in length and the side-panel widened 0.25m per side to provide additional payload capability, while the engine power is also increased to 145hp. The prototype was on trials in January 1988.

LIFT AND PROPULSION: CY-6 Mk III has a single 120hp L20E engine with integrated transmission system which drives the lift and propulsion fan via toothed belts. Cushion air is supplied by two 0.53m diameter centrifugal fans. Thrust is provided by a 1.07m diameter axial flow ducted propeller. CY-6 Mk IV has a larger 145hp engine but utilise the same transmission system.

HULL: Glassfibre-reinforced plastic with close-cell form sandwich structure.

CONTROLS: Four rudder vanes at aft end of thrust fan duct provides heading control. Elevator

is added on the CY-6 Mk IV to provide trim control.

SKIRT: Bag-finger type.

ACCOMMODATION: Enclosed cabin for the pilot and five passengers for the CY-6 Mk III; seven passengers and the pilot for the CY-6 Mk IV.

SYSTEMS, ELECTRICAL: 12V dc system.

DIMENSIONS

Length,
   off cushion: 5.80m (Mk III); 6.80m (Mk IV)
   on cushion: 6.15m (Mk III); 7.15m (Mk IV)
Beam, off cushion: 3.30m (Mk III); 3.80m (Mk IV)   on cushion: 3.75m (Mk III); 4.25m (Mk IV)
   side-panel folded: 2.05m (Mk III and Mk IV)
Height,
   off cushion: 1.36m (Mk III); 1.46m (Mk IV)
   on cushion: 1.70m (Mk III); 1.90m (Mk IV)
WEIGHTS
Normal empty: 900kg (Mk III); 1150kg (Mk IV)
Gross: 1350kg (Mk III); 1750kg (Mk IV)
Payload: 450kg (Mk III); 600kg (MK IV)
PERFORMANCE
Max speed: 40 knots
Cruising speed: 35 knots
Endurance: 3.5 hours

UNION OF SOVIET SOCIALIST REPUBLICS

KRASNOYE SORMOVO SHIPYARD AA ZHDANOV

Exporter: V/O Sudoexport, Chaikovsky St 11, Moscow, 123231, USSR
Telephone: 095 255 18 13
Telex: 411116 KURS SU

Head Office and Works: Gorki, USSR

M Yuriev, *Shipyard Director*
Ivan Yerlykin, *Chief Hydrofoil Designer*

Export Enquiries: Sudotransport (V/O Sudoimport), 10 Uspenski Per, Moscow 103006, USSR

Telephone: 2510505/299 58 77/299 02 14
Telex: 411272/411387/411443 SUDO SU

This shipyard began work in the ACV field by building a five-passenger air cushion river craft, known as the Raduga, in 1962. Since then it has built the Sormovich, a 30-ton peripheral jet ACV for 50 passengers, and the Gorkovchanin, a 48-seat prototype sidewall craft for shallow, winding rivers. It is believed that the Gorkovchanin, Zarnitsa, Orion, Chayka and Rassvet were all designed by the Gorki Institute of Water Transport Engineers.

The production version of the Gorkovchanin, the Zarnitsa, of which more than 100 have been built, is employed on almost all the river navigation lines of the Russian Federative Republic as well as on the rivers of the Ukrainian, Moldavian, Byelorussian and Kazakhstan Soviet Socialist Republics.

The design of an 80-seat rigid sidewall ferry, the Orion, was approved by the Soviet Ministry of Inland Waterways in 1970. Construction of the prototype began in 1972 and trials were successfully undertaken in 1975. The craft has been in series production.

A third sidewall vessel is the Rassvet, designed

to carry up to 80 passengers along local sea routes. Like Zarnitsa, the craft is able to run bow-on to flat sloping beaches and does not require piers or specially prepared moorings. Work is in hand aimed at evolving a substantially bigger sidewall ACV ferry which has been given the name, Turist. This craft has a design speed of 36 knots and is intended for shallow waterways unsuitable for hydrofoils. Two variants have been projected, a 300-seat passenger ferry and a mixed-traffic model for 15 cars and 100 to 120 passengers.

In 1969 prototypes of two fully-skirted hovercraft made their debut: the Briz, a light utility craft and the Skate, a 50-seat passenger ferry with an all-up weight of 27 tonnes and a cruising speed of 57mph. While there is no evidence of the Skate going into production, a military version, known in the West by the NATO code name Gus, is in service with the Soviet marine infantry and army. Gus was designed by a special Soviet Navy High-Speed Ship Design Bureau, in Leningrad, which was also responsible for the design of the Soviet Union's biggest skirted hovercraft, known in the West as Aist. More than 16 Aists are in service with the Soviet Navy as amphibious assault landing craft. Aist can cross water, beaches and marginal terrain to deliver tanks, armoured transporters, equipment and personnel well beyond the shore line. Aist is generally similar in shape, size and performance to the BHC SR.N4 Mk 2.

Among military air cushion vehicles to enter production for the Soviet armed forces are a 90-tonne amphibious assault landing craft known by the NATO code name Lebed, a craft similar in size and overall appearance to the BH.7 and a successor to Gus.

Soviet air cushion vehicle activity is widely varied. Part of this activity is devoted to meeting Soviet military needs, but in the main it is devoted to the production of sidewall ACVs and to the development and construction of amphibious carriers and snowgoing and marshgoing vehicles capable of providing reliable year-round transport in the Soviet north and north-eastern regions where a number of vital development projects are

under way including the Siberia-West Europe gas pipeline.

Only a small percentage of the freight required can be delivered to these areas by helicopter. Estimates of the Institute of Integrated Transport Problems, operating under the USSR Gosplan Institute, have indicated that the use of air cushion vehicles, apart from speeding up the construction of important facilities under difficult conditions, will enable haulage costs over difficult routes of the north and north-east to be reduced by one-third. As a result, savings in transport expenditure for the work volume forecast for the Eleventh Five-Year Plan will be 1200 to 1500 million roubles annually.

The use of amphibious ACVs in agricultural production enables operations including the application of fertilisers, herbicides and weeding to be conducted regardless of weather.

Large-load air-cushion platforms allow the movement of beet, potatoes and other crops from fields regardless of soil conditions. Expenditure for the chemical treatment of fields using self-propelled ACVs is half the cost of employing an AN-2 aircraft for this work and is one-third of the cost of an Mi-2 helicopter.

CIVIL CRAFT
GORKOVCHANIN

For details of this craft see 1989 edition of this book

ZARNITSA

Evolved from Gorkovchanin, the Zarnitsa is a 48 to 50-seat waterjet-propelled rigid sidewall ferry designed to operate on shallow rivers, some less than 0.7m (2ft 3in) deep. Series production is under way, and large numbers have been delivered.

The prototype was put into trial service on the Vyatka river, in the Kirov region, in the summer of 1972, and the first production models began operating on shallow, secondary rivers later in the year. During 1973–74, Zarnitsas entered service on tributaries of the Kama, Lena and Volga. More

Summary of principal civil air cushion vehicle types built

Civil	Payload	No built	Year built	Designed by	Builders
Neva amphibious ACV	38 passengers	one			
Briz (Breeze)	6 passengers		1968		
Skate	50 passengers		1969		
Raduga amphibious ACV	5 passengers	one	1962		Krasnoye Sormovo Shipyard, Gorki
Sormovich amphibious ACV	50 passengers	one	1965		Krasnoye Sormovo Shipyard, Gorki
Gorkovchanin sidewall ACV	48 passengers	one	1969–70	Gorki Institute of Water Transport Engineers, Gorki	Krasnoye Sormovo Shipyard, Gorki
Zarnitsa sidewall ACV (based on Gorkovchanin)	48 passengers	over 100	1972	Gorki Institute of Water Transport Engineers, Gorki	Krasnoye Sormovo Shipyard, Gorki
Orion sidewall ACV	80 passengers		1973* 1975†	Gorki Institute of Water Transport Engineers, Gorki	Leningrad Shipyard
Chayka sidewall ACV	80 passengers	one		Gorki Institute of Water Transport Engineers, Gorki	Sosnovka Shipyard
Rassvet sidewall ACV	80 passengers	one		Gorki Institute of Water Transport Engineers, Gorki	Sosnovka Shipyard
Plamya sidewall ACV (based on Orion hull)	fire-fighting craft	one?		Central Design Bureau, Gorki	
Raduga-2 amphibious ACV	0.65 tonnes	n/a		Krasnoye Sormovo Shipyard, Gorki	
SAVR-1M amphibious ACV		one	1978		
SAVR-1 (CABP-1) amphibious ACV	1.3 tonnes	production version of the 1M	1980	A M Gorki Memorial Marine Institute of Technology	
SAVR-2 (CABP-2) amphibious ACV	3 tonnes		1982	A M Gorki Memorial Marine Institute of Technology	
SAVR-3 (CABP-3) amphibious ACV	2 tonnes		1981	A M Gorki Memorial Marine Institute of Technology	
SAVR-5GD (CABP-5GD) amphibious ACV	5 tonnes		1981 onwards	A M Gorki Memorial Marine Institute of Technology	
SAVR-40 (CABP-40) amphibious ACV	50 tonnes		1987	A M Gorki Memorial Marine Institute of Technology	
MP-18 amphibious ACV	0.6 tonnes				
MPI-20 amphibious ACV	2- and 5-tonne versions				
Neptun AKVPR-001 amphibious ACV	research craft		1977	Neptun Central Design Bureau, Moscow	
Barrs-1 (Snow Leopard) amphibious ACV	0.65 tonnes or 7 passengers	30	1981	Neptun Central Design Bureau, Moscow	
Gepard (Cheetah)	5 passengers	40+, in production	1981 onwards	Neptun Central Design Bureau, Moscow	
Taifun amphibious ACV	20 passengers or 3 tonnes			UFA Aviation Institute, Tyumen	
Klest amphibious ACV	4 seats?		1981	Vostok Central Design Bureau, Leningrad	
Luch sidewall ACV	66 passengers	reported in series production	1983 onwards		Astrakhan Shipyard
Puma	16 passengers	two prototypes	1985	Neptun Central Design Bureau, Moscow	
-	32 passengers	one 1989	1988/89	Neptun Central Design Bureau, Moscow	
Barguzin	130 passengers		1989		

* trials
† series production began

MILITARY CRAFT Summary of principal military air cushion vehicle types built

Military	Capacity	No built	First launched	Designed by	Builders
NATO Code name: **Gus** amphibious ACV	25 troops	31	1969, production ended 1974		
NATO Code name: **Aist** amphibious ACV	up to 100 tonnes	Possibly 16 in service	1970		Dekabristov Shipyard, Leningrad
NATO Code name: **Lebed** amphibious ACV	35 tonnes		1975	Soviet Navy's High-Speed Ship Design Bureau, Leningrad	
NATO Code name: **Pomornik**	-	3	1986?	Design Bureau, Leningrad	Leningrad
Utenok Class	-	2	-	-	Feodosiya Shipyard
Tsaplya Class	40 tonnes	3	1982	-	Feodosiya Shipyard

than 100 are employed on almost all the river navigation lines of the Russian Federative Republic as well as on the rivers of the Ukrainian, Moldavian, Byelorussian and Kazakhstan Soviet Socialist Republics.

LIFT AND PROPULSION, CONTROLS, HULL: Arrangements almost identical to those of the Gorkovchanin.

ACCOMMODATION: Seats are provided for two crew members, who are accommodated in the raised wheelhouse forward, and 48–50 passengers. Access to the passenger saloon is via a single door at the bow in the centre of the wheelhouse. The craft runs bow-on to flat sloping banks to embark and disembark passengers.

DIMENSIONS
Length: 22.3m
Beam: 3.85m
Skeg depth: 0.45m
WEIGHTS
Light displacement: 9 tonnes

Zarnitsa

Zarnitsa

Passenger saloon in Zarnitsa looking aft

All-up weight, with 48 passengers, crew and fuel: 15 tonnes
PERFORMANCE
Service speed: 33–35km/h (20–22mph)

LENINGRAD SHIPYARD
ORION-01

Design of the Orion, a rigid sidewall ACV with seats for 80 passengers, was approved in Moscow in autumn 1970. The prototype, built in Leningrad, began trials in October 1973 and arrived at its port of registry, Kalinin, in late 1974, bearing the serial number 01.

The craft is intended for passenger ferry services along shallow rivers, tributaries and reservoirs and can land and take on passengers bow-on from any flat sloping bank. It is faster than the Zarnitsa and its comfort and performance are less affected by choppy conditions. Cruising speed of the vessel, which is propelled by waterjets, is 53km/h (32.3mph). It belongs to the 'R' class of the Soviet River Register.

Several variants are under consideration, including a 'stretched' model seating 100 passengers on shorter routes, a mixed passenger/freight model, an all-freight model and an 'executive' version for carrying government officials.

Experimental operation of the Orion-01 was organised by the Port of Kalinin, Moscow River Transport, the initial run being Kalinin-1 May Factory, a distance of 99km (61.5 miles), of which 45km (28 miles) is on the Volga, 42km (26 miles) on the Ivanov reservoir and 12km (7.5 miles) on the shallow waters of the Soz. The first weeks of operation showed that there was an insufficient flow of passengers on this particular route.

The vessel was then employed on public holidays only for carrying holiday makers and day trippers on such runs as Kalinin-Putlivo 31km (19 miles), Kalinin-Kokoshky 19km (12 miles) and Kalinin-Tarbasa 28km (17.3 miles), and subsequently on a regular schedule to Putlivo. Finally, Orion-01 was used on the Kalinin-Kimry run, a distance of 138km (85.7 miles), of which 70km (43.4 miles) passes through the Ivanov reservoir and 68km (42 miles) on the Volga.

Particular attention was paid to skirt reliability. The side sections of the lower part of the bow skirt were badly chafed and split due to contact with the skegs when coming onto the shore. Upper parts of the skirt were not damaged. Problems were also experienced with the aft skirt made from a balloon type fabric. Layers of rubber in the aft part of the segments peeled off; chafing was caused by securing washers and splitting was experienced in the vicinity of the fastenings.

In order to reduce the time spent on repairs, sections of the stern skirt were attached to removable frames. Later a new stern skirt was introduced, based on panels made from a 12mm (0.47in) thick conveyor belt. This enabled the stern draught, on cushion, to be reduced by 10cm (3.87in) and the speed to be increased by 1.5km/h (0.87mph). It also improved the reliability of the craft. During the 200 hours under way from the time the skirt was fitted until the end of the vessel's trials, there was no damage.

It was considered that, in the main, the Orion met the requirements of the Soviet operators for the rapid transport of passengers on 'R' class rivers and reservoirs. The elimination of the defects revealed during the experimental operation will improve the vessel's operational characteristics and increase its reliability.

Series production of this vessel is being undertaken at the Sosnovka Shipbuilding Yard in Kirovskaya Oblast.

LIFT AND PROPULSION: Integrated system powered by two 520hp 3D12N-520 diesels mounted in an engine room aft. Each engine drives a Type Ts 39–13 centrifugal fans for lift, and via a cardan shaft, a semi-submerged single-stage waterjet rotor for propulsion. Fan air is fed via ducts to the bow skirt, a transverse stability slot and to the fingered bag skirt aft. Casing of the waterjet system, which is removable, forms the stern section of the vessel. The waterjets are mounted on shock absorbers to reduce vibration.

HULL: Similar in overall appearance to Zarya and Zarnitsa types. All-welded structure in AlMg-61 aluminium-magnesium alloy. Lateral framing throughout hull with the exception of the bow and stern decks, where longitudinal frames have been fitted. Superstructure and wheelhouse are of welded and riveted duralumin construction on longitudinal framing.

ACCOMMODATION: Seats for operating crew of three, which is accommodated in a raised wheel-

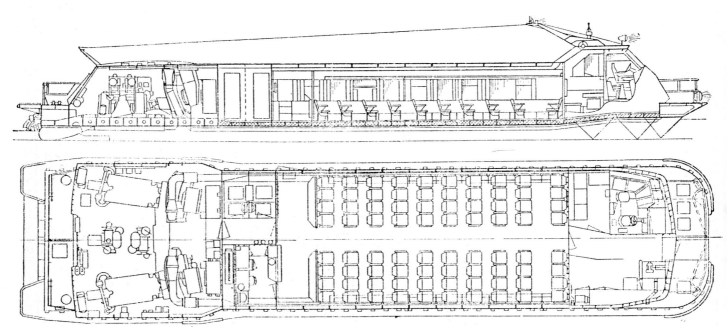

General arrangement of Orion

house, a barman, two seamen and 80 passengers. At the aft end of the passenger saloon are two toilet/washbasin units and a bar. An off-duty cabin for the crew. Access to the passenger saloon is via a single door at the bow, in the centre of the wheelhouse. A ram-air intake provides ventilation while the craft is under way. Stale air is drawn out by the lift fans aft.

CONTROLS: Rudders located aft of the waterjet inlets and two waterjet deflectors control craft direction. Rudder and flap movement is by cables.

SYSTEMS, ELECTRICAL: Two G-73Z engine-driven generators, linked with two sets of STK-18M batteries, provide 28V, 1200W. One battery set is employed for engine starting, the other for supplying current for the ship's systems.

COMMUNICATIONS: Standard equipment comprises an R-809MZ radio-telephone, a Kama-3 UHF radio and an Unja cabin announcement system.

DIMENSIONS

Length overall: 25.8m
Beam overall: 6.5m
Height overall to mast top: 5.27m
Height to top of wheelhouse: 3.97m
Draught, displacement condition, fully loaded: 0.84m
  empty: 0.76m
Draught, cushionborne, bow: 0.1m
  stern: 0.5m

WEIGHTS

Loaded displacement: 34.7 tonnes
Light displacement: 20.7 tonnes

PERFORMANCE

Max speed: 60km/h
Cruising speed, full load: 53km/h
Max wave height on scheduled runs: 1.2m
Range: 400km
Diameter of turn to port: 182m
Time to complete turn with rudders at 33 degrees: 187 seconds
Time taken from start of berthing procedure to completion: 1 minute approx
Time taken to attain cruising speed from leaving berth: 2 minutes approx

SOSNOVKA SHIPYARD
Kirovskaya Oblast
RASSVET (DAWN) AND CHAYKA (GULL)

A waterjet-propelled sidewall passenger ferry, Rassvet is designed for local sea routes of limited water depth. It is an offshore counterpart to the Orion sidewall ACV. Plans call for the Rassvet to serve resort routes in the Crimea, on the Caspian and Baltic Seas as well as on large lakes and reservoirs. Like the Orion and Zarnitsa, its two predecessors, it can run bow-on to flat, sloping beaches to embark and disembark passengers. Landing on a beach is facilitated by an articulated gangway with a hydraulic drive.

Rassvet's features include shallow draught, good manoeuvrability and relatively simple construction.

The waterjet reversing/steering system is specially protected to enable the craft to moor alongside existing berths built originally for small conventional displacement ferries.

The Rassvet prototype, named Chayka-1 (Gull-1), is undergoing trials. The Chayka-1 was the first of thirty of its type to be built at the Sosnovka Shipyard in Kirovskaya Oblast for the Black Sea Shipping Line. In January 1976 it was stated that the vessel was the first seagoing passenger ACV to be built in the Soviet Union. The extent of the remote control, automation and monitoring provided for the power plant and systems generally is sufficient to permit the craft to be operated by one person, with intermittent attendance to the machinery space.

Rassvet is designed to carry 80 passengers during daylight hours on coastal routes in conditions up to force 4. It complies with USSR

ORION-Stopping and starting characteristics	Shallow water	Deep water
Distance run by vessel from Full Ahead to Stop		
Metres	136	120
Time in seconds	67	40
Distance run by vessel from Full Ahead to Full Astern		
Metres	84	65
Time in seconds	23	20
Distance necessary for attainment of Full Speed from Stop		
Metres	250	330
Time in seconds	60	80

Registration classification KM*II Ⓘ Passenger ACV Class.

LIFT AND PROPULSION: Power for the waterjet system is provided by two 3D12N-520 lightweight (3.54kg/kW) irreversible, high-speed four-cycle V-type marine diesels each with a gas-turbine supercharger and a rated power of 383kW at 1500rpm. Each powers a two-stage waterjet impeller. Water inlet scoops are arranged in the sidewalls and the pump ports, each of which comprises two rotors and two straightening devices, are installed in the sidewalls behind the transoms. Cushion air is generated by a single 110kW PD6S-150A diesel driving an NTs6 centrifugal fan via a universal joint and a torque-limited coupling.

CONTROLS: Craft direction is controlled by twin balanced rudders operating in the water discharged by each of the two waterjets. Reversal is achieved by applying rotatable deflectors to reverse the waterflow.

SKIRT: Double-row segmented type at bow; two-tier bag type skirt aft. Repair or replacement of sections of the bow skirt can be undertaken with the bow run on to a flat, gently sloping beach. The stern skirt is secured to special hinged sections which permit inspection and maintenance while still afloat.

HULL: Hull and superstructure are built in aluminium-magnesium alloy. The hull is of all-welded construction in AlMg-61 and the decks, superstructure, pilot house and partitions are in AlMg-5 alloy. Hull, superstructure and pilot house have longitudinal frames. Single-piece pressed panels are employed for the lower sections of the sidewalls. Corrugated sheets are used for the hull bottom. Below the passenger deck the hull is subdivided by transverse bulkheads into seven watertight compartments, access to which is via hatches in the passenger deck. The craft will remain afloat in the event of any one compartment flooding.

Chayka-1

Chayka-1

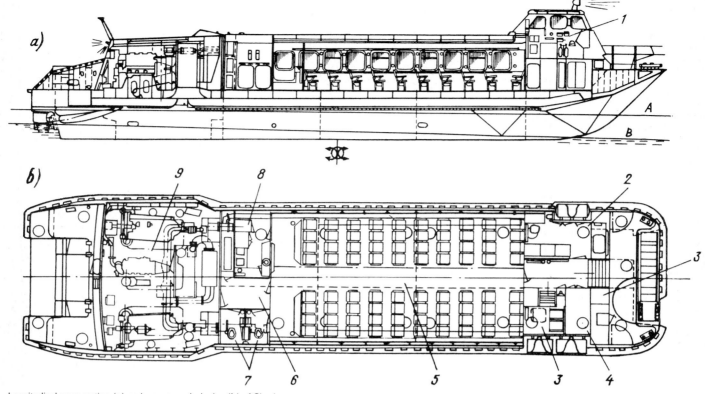

Longitudinal cross section (**a**) and passenger deck plan (**b**) of Chayka
(**A**) waterline in displacement condition; (**B**) waterline underway on air cushion; (**1**) pilot house; (**2**) crew's off-duty cabin; (**3**)storeroom; (**4**) baggage compartment; (**5**) passenger lounge; (**6**) companionway; (**7**) toilets; (**8**) buffet;(**9**) machinery space

ACCOMMODATION: Rassvet seats 80 passengers in a single fully ventilated and heated saloon amidships. Airliner-type seats are provided, beneath each of which a life-jacket is located. Decks in the passenger cabin, pilot house and crew's off-duty cabin are covered with carpet and the floors of the companionways with pvc linoleum. Pavinol aircraft-type leather substitute decorates the deckheads. Large windows give passengers a good view. At the aft end of the cabin are a small buffet and two toilets. At the forward end of the cabin are the wheelhouse, a duty crew restroom and a vestibule. The operating crew of six comprises captain, engineer, motorman, radio operator, seaman and one barman. Passenger embarkation at piers designed for the berthing of small ferries of the local services takes place across the section of open deck forward of the pilot house. Where conventional berthing facilities do not exist the craft runs bow-on to a flat sloping bank where landing facilities are provided by an articulated gangway with a hydraulic drive.

SYSTEMS, ELECTRICAL: Power supply requirements are met by a 28V, KG-2.9kW generator driven by a power take-off shaft from the main engine and three 28V, 1.2kW G-732 charging generators mounted on the main engine. Two banks of storage batteries are installed. One, comprising two Type 6STK-180M storage batteries, supplies dc power when the craft is operating. The second bank, comprising four batteries of the same type, is employed for engine starting and for powering the diesel engine control circuits and emergency alarm systems. An inverter is installed for navigation and other equipment requiring ac supplies. An auxiliary circuit can be connected to shore systems for a 220V single-phase 50Hz ac supply.

SAFETY EQUIPMENT: PSN-10M and PSN-6M inflatable life rafts are installed in containers along each side of the craft. The number of rafts is designed to meet the requirements of all passengers and crew. Life raft release is remotely controlled from the landing positions at the bow and stern. Individual lifesaving devices, lifebelts and lifejackets are also provided.

FIREFIGHTING, HYDRAULICS, BILGE, BALLASTING, WATER SUPPLY: Complete systems installed as standard.

COMMUNICATIONS: Lastochka radio telephone transceiver for ship-to-shore and ship-to-ship communications; Kater uhf transceiver and Plot-M portable emergency transceiver. Ryabin passenger announcement and broadcast relay system. Omega radar for navigating along shorelines, in narrow waterways and in poor visibility.

ANCHOR: Single 100kg (220lb) Matrosov anchor operated by a hydraulic winch.

DIMENSIONS
Length overall: 26.7m
Beam, max: 7.1m
    amidship: 6m
Height overall, hull: 2.2m
    sidewall only: 1.5m
Draught hullborne: 1.27m
    cushionborne at bow: 0.1m
    stern: 0.8m

WEIGHTS
Loaded displacement: 47.5 tonnes
Passenger capacity: 80 persons
PERFORMANCE
Cruising speed: 23 knots
Max speed: 29 knots
Range: 352km (190n miles)

PLAMYA (FLAME) ACV RIVER FIRETENDER

The Central Design Bureau at Gorki has developed a river-going firetender. The craft is based on the hull of the Orion sidewall-type passenger ferry, but the passenger cabin superstructure has been replaced by an open deck forward to accommodate a tracked or wheeled firefighting vehicle and its crew. Plamya is designed for the fast delivery of an off-the-road fire-fighting vehicle and its crew to points on lakes, reservoirs and major rivers near forest fires. The craft can be beached bow-on on the river bank and the fire-

Plamya

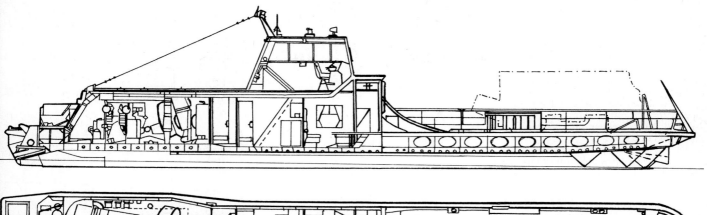

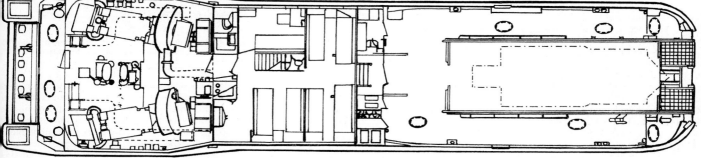

Inboard profile and deck plan of Plamya

fighting vehicle or bulldozer off-loaded across the bow ramp.

Plamya meets the requirements of the Register of Shipping of the USSR and is constructed to Class R in the RSFSR Inland Waterways Register. It is in service on the River Kama.
LIFT AND PROPULSION: Integrated system powered by two 520hp 3D12N-520 marine diesels. Each engine drives a Type Ts 39-13 centrifugal fan for lift and, via a cardan shaft, a semi-submerged single-stage waterjet rotor for propulsion.
CONTROLS: Rudders aft of the waterjet inlets and two waterjet deflectors control craft direction.
HULL: All-welded structure in AlMg-61 aluminium-magnesium alloy. Frames, plates, partitions and roof of superstructure in D16 alloy.
SKIRT: Bow, triple-row, fully segmented type; stern, fingered bag type.
ACCOMMODATION: As opposed to the 'Orion' class the Plamya's pilothouse is amidships, with a large cargo deck forward to facilitate the carriage of a firefighting vehicle or bulldozer and the crew. Alternative loads include an ATsL-3(66)-147 forest firefighting tracked vehicle, a VPL-149 firefighting cross-country vehicle, a truck with portable firefighting equipment and a crew of 18, or a bulldozer with a crew of three. Beneath the pilothouse superstructure are storerooms for portable firefighting equipment, a lounge for the firefighting squad, an off-duty cabin for the crew of three and a toilet. Engine room is aft.
SYSTEMS, ELECTRICAL: 24V dc, supplied by two 1.2kW engine-driven generators linked with two sets of storage batteries.
COMMUNICATIONS: Kama-S UHF radio and PZS-68 passenger announcement system. Granit-M and Groza-2 transceivers for communication with firefighting team.
DIMENSIONS
Length overall: 26.1m
Beam: 6.5m
Height overall, amidship: 5.5m
Draught displacement condition: 0.88m
Draught, on cushion, at stern: 0.7m
WEIGHTS
Fully loaded: 34.5 tonnes
Cargo capacity: 7.3 tonnes
PERFORMANCE
Max speed: 50km/h

RADUGA-2

Little is known about this amphibious ACV, which was first reported in the Soviet press in late spring 1981. Designed at the Krasnoye Sormovo ship and ACV building facility at Gorki, Raduga-2, in common with the Gepard and Klest, is powered by an automotive engine, the Chayka. The 1962 Raduga was described in *Jane's Surface Skimmers 1985* and earlier editions.

SIDEWALL PASSENGER FERRIES

Details of two Soviet surface effect ship (SES) passenger ferry projects were published in Leningrad in late 1979, one seating 120 passengers, the other 150. Preliminary specifications of each are given below.

23.5-METRE SES PASSENGER FERRY

LIFT AND PROPULSION: Integrated system, powered by two 1000hp diesels.
CONTROLS: Craft heading is controlled by water rudders.
HULL: Welded marine aluminium.
ACCOMMODATION: 120 passengers.
DIMENSIONS
Length overall: 23.5m
Max beam: 7m
Sidewalls, height: 1.5m
  breadth: 5m
Air cushion, length: 20m
  breadth: 5m
  area: 100m²
WEIGHTS
Empty: 15.3 tonnes
Max weight: 48.6 tonnes
Displacement tonnes/passenger: 0.406
PERFORMANCE
Max operating speed: 32 knots

25.6-METRE SES PASSENGER FERRY

LIFT AND PROPULSION: Integrated system, probably similar to that employed on Chayka and Turist, powered by two 1000hp marine diesels.
CONTROLS: Craft direction is controlled by water rudders.
HULL: Welded marine aluminium.
ACCOMMODATION: Seats are provided for 150 passengers.
DIMENSIONS
Length: 25.6m
Max beam: 7m

Air cushion, length: 22.5m
  breadth: 5m
  area: 110m²
WEIGHTS
Empty: 18 tonnes
Max weight: 52.8 tonnes
Displacement tonnes/passenger: 0.354
PERFORMANCE
Max operating speed: 31 knots

TURIST DESIGN

The Central Scientific Research Institute has completed the design of a new sidewall ACV ferry, the Turist. The vessel, which is based on extensive experience gained from the operation of the Zarnitsa, Orion and Rassvet, is virtually a scaled-up version of the latter. It has a design speed of 36 knots and is intended for use along shallow waterways unsuitable for hydrofoils. Propulsive thrust appears to be supplied by two gas-turbine driven waterjets, one in each sidewall. Two variants are projected, a 250- to 300-seat passenger ferry and a mixed traffic variant for 10 to 15 cars and 100 to 120 passengers. Turist is due to go into series production at the Nakhodka yard following the completion of shipbuilding facilities there.

Recent reports suggest that, as a result of detailed assessments undertaken in the Soviet Union over a period of years, a range of large sidewall hovercraft is being developed for the conveyance of freight.

ASTRAKHAN SHIPYARD
LUCH-1

A new sidewall ACV for river use was completed at the Astrakhan Shipyard and underwent State trials in September 1983. Designed to replace the twelve-year-old Zarnitsa, the craft, named Luch, Design No. 14351, carries two crew and up to 66 passengers, 15 standing. Of all-welded aluminium construction, it has a maximum operating weight of 22.6 tonnes and a top speed of 44km/h. The shallow on-cushion draught of just over 0.5m allows it to run bow-on to flat sloping river banks to embark and disembark passengers. A ladder is fitted at the bow.

New design features will permit operation on large rivers such as the Don, Kama, Oka and Volga, where high waves are encountered. However, the yard emphasises that it will be used primarily by oil and gas personnel and timber rafters who work on the banks of small rivers.

Among the basic design requirements were: that the Zarnitsa's general characteristics should be preserved; increased reliability; easier maintenance; increased service speed; widened operating potential and improved ride comfort.

Compared with the Zarnitsa, Luch has a more powerful diesel, the 380kW 81H12A, and uses a lighter form of construction. The overall dimensions of the craft permit rail transport to distant rivers and canals.

During trials before the commissioning of the first of the class it was demonstrated that its operating and technical performance is significantly superior to that of the Zarnitsa. The craft is built to the requirements of the 'R' class of the USSR's River Craft Registry. It is in series production and will be available for export in 1988.

LIFT AND PROPULSION: Power provided by single 81H12A marine diesel with normal service output of 346kW at 1500rpm. The engine is mounted aft and drives, via a transmission shaft, a centrifugal fan for lift and a waterjet rotor for propulsion. The waterjet rotor and its bearing can be replaced while the craft is in displacement condition without having to lift it out of the water.

CONTROLS: Twin rudder vanes in the waterjet stream control craft heading. Thrust reversal achieved by waterflow deflectors.

HULL: The buoyancy structure is built in welded AlMg-61 aluminium alloy. The superstructure is built in D16 alloy. Superstructure and bulkheads are riveted together. Pressed panels are employed throughout the hull to improve the external appearance and reduce the volume of assembly work necessary during construction.

SKIRT: Fingered type at bow, bag-type aft. Bow segments attached to an easily replaceable module.

ACCOMMODATION: Seats are provided for a crew of two, in a raised wheelhouse, and 51 passengers. On route sectors of 1 hour or less, the capacity can be increased to 66 by allowing 15 standing in the passenger cabin. The hull is divided into eight basic sections: a forward platform, the control cabin, service room, vestibule, passenger cabin, auxiliary rooms, engine room and stern platform. The bow platform has a gangway/ladder for embarkation and landing on unequipped stopping points, jetties and for mooring. The location of the control cabin at the bow simplifies handling on narrow waterways. A service room, aft of the control cabin, provides rest accommodation for the relief crew.

The lounge has 51 passenger seats, one seat for a guide and racks for small items of luggage. Large sliding windows ensure good visibility and ventilation. The lounge and crew rooms are air conditioned. The passenger cabin is separated' from the engine room by a store room on the port side and a toilet on the starboard side, an arrangement which reduces the noise level. Mooring, refuelling, taking-on oil and water, discharging sewage and oil-contaminated waters to container vessels or shore based containers are all performed from the aft platform. A hatch on the aft platform gives access to the waterjet rotor.

SYSTEMS, ELECTRICAL: One 1.2kW 24V dc engine-operated generator and batteries. During prolonged night stops power can be supplied by a shore based 220V, 50Hz electrical supply.

COMMUNICATIONS: VHF, Kama 'R', marine transceiver. PA and crew command systems.

ENGINE
Type 81H12A diesel, max power: 380kW (500bhp)
Normal operating power: 346kW (470bhp)
DIMENSIONS
Length overall: 22.81m
Length, bp: 21.80m
Beam overall: 3.85m
Height overall: 3.35m
   side: 1.2m
   skegs: 0.45m

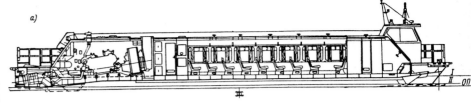
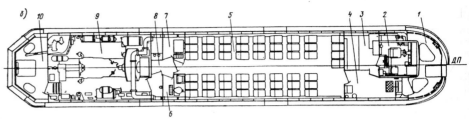

Inboard profile and plan of Luch: (a) longitudinal section (b) deck plan (I) waterline in displacement mode (II) waterline when cushionborne (1) fore deck (2) wheelhouse (3) duty compartment (4) vestibule (5) passenger saloon (6) toilet (7) storeroom (8) vestibule (9) engine room (10) aft deck

Depth: 1.25m
Guaranteed aft draught at water intake when travelling on air cushion at full displacement: 0.5m
Draught at full displacement, stationary: 0.65m
WEIGHTS
Max: 20.1 tonnes
Empty: 14.2 tonnes
Light displacement: 15.40 tonnes
Load displacement (cargo, 51 passengers and baggage): 21.2 tonnes
Extreme load displacement (cargo, 66 passengers and baggage): 22.6 tonnes
PERFORMANCE
Speed, max: 44km/h, 23.75 knots
Range, max fuel reserves: 300km
Endurance: 8 hours

MILITARY CRAFT
GUS (NATO Code Name)

A variant of the Skate, which was designed as a 50-seat amphibious passenger ferry, but which was not put into production, Gus is now employed extensively by the Soviet Naval Infantry for river patrol, small-unit troop insertion and amphibious assault. The Soviet Navy's amphibious landing ship, the *Ivan Rogov*, can carry three amphibious assault ACVs of the Gus type. Each of these craft can carry a fully-armed platoon onto a landing beach at speeds of up to 60 knots. The prototype was launched in 1969 and it is thought that 31 of these 27-tonne vehicles are in service. Production of this class is thought to have been completed in 1979. A derivative with twin ducted propellers is under development.

LIFT AND PROPULSION: Motive power is provided by three 780hp TVD-10 marine gas turbines mounted aft. Two drive 3m diameter three-bladed variable and reversible-pitch propellers for thrust and the third drives an axial lift fan. Cushion air is drawn through a raised intake aft of the cabin superstructure.

CONTROLS: Craft direction is controlled by

Gus

Gus

differential propeller pitch, twin aerodynamic rudders and forward and aft puff ports. Elevator provides pitch trim at cruising speed.

HULL: Hull and superstructure are in conventional corrosion-resistant marine light alloy. Basic structure comprises a central load-carrying platform which incorporates buoyancy tanks and outer sections to support the side ducts and skirt. The cabin, fuel tanks, lift fan bay engines and tail unit are mounted on the platform.

ACCOMMODATION: Air-conditioned cabin for up to 25 troops. Commander and navigator are seated in a raised wheelhouse. Battle crew of six, including two responsible for opening the two entry/exit doors forward and amidship, port and starboard.

DIMENSIONS

EXTERNAL

Length overall, power on: 21.33m
Beam overall, power on: 7.8m
Height to top of fin: 6.6m

WEIGHT

Normal operating: 27 tonnes

PERFORMANCE

Max speed: 60 knots
Cruising speed: 43 knots
Range: 230n miles

AIST (NATO Code Name)

The first large amphibious hovercraft to be built in the Soviet Union. Reports suggest that 16 have entered service to date. Built in Leningrad it is similar in appearance to the SR.N4 Mk 2 Mountbatten though giving the impression of being very much heavier than the British craft. It is likely that the bare weight, equipped but with no payload, crew or fuel, is as much as 170 tons. The prototype was launched in 1970 and production began in 1975.

Several variants have been built and differ externally in fin height, overall length, superstructure detail and defensive armament.

An Aist combat mission simulator has been introduced by the Soviet Navy to improve the ability of Aist commanders in operating the craft across sea and beach interfaces and Aist pro-

Gus craft during exercise in eastern Baltic Sea

Training variant of Gus with raised second cabin

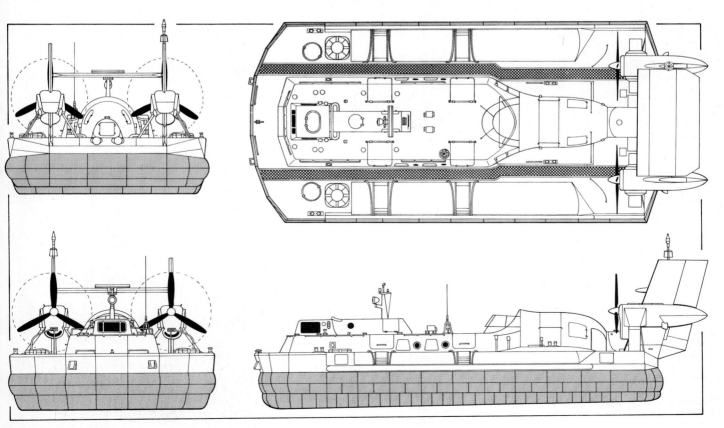
General arrangement of Gus

duction facilities at Dekabristov, Leningrad, have been doubled.

A modified main engine air intake has been installed on all Soviet Navy Aists which are in service with the Baltic and Black Sea fleets. The intakes are believed to incorporate new filters to reduce the ingestion of salt water, sand and dust particles into Aist's engines and machinery, limiting the effects of salt corrosion and erosion. Due to high cushion pressure, Aist develops exceptionally heavy cushion spray, especially at low speeds.

Since delivery to the Soviet Navy, craft of this type have been employed largely as an amphibious assault landing and logistic supply craft, delivering naval infantry, its vehicles and weapons, mechanised infantry, self-propelled weapons, and main battle tanks to simulated beach-heads. Alternative military uses for amphibious craft of the Aist type would be mine countermeasures and fast patrol.

LIFT AND PROPULSION: Integrated system with motive power supplied by two NK-12MV marinised gas turbines, each of which is likely to be rated at 2400shp. Each gas turbine drives two 3.65m diameter variable-pitch axial fans and two identical, pylon-mounted propellers, arranged in a facing pair, with the pusher propeller forward and the puller aft. The propellers, which are of the four-bladed variable- and reversible-pitch type are mounted so closely as to be virtually contraprops. Diameter of each propeller is thought to be about 6m.

Modified engine air intakes are being installed on all Soviet Navy Aists. Several types are being tested. One modification involves the replacement of the original single, curved spine-like trunk above the longitudinal centreline by a mushroom sectioned box forward and a ribbed, shortened arch duct aft. The T-piece running athwartships across the stern superstructure between the twin

fins has also been replaced by a ribbed arch duct. Alternative modifications include removing the athwartships T-piece and the shortened arch duct on the centreline leaving the mushroom sectioned box forward. Modified lift fans and new lift fan intakes are also being introduced.

Additional intakes appear to be sited in the sides of the superstructure towards the stern.

An auxiliary gas turbine is at the rear end of the combat information centre (CIC) at the back of the cabin superstructure.

CONTROLS: Deflection of twin aerodynamic rudders aft, differential propeller pitch and fore-and-aft thrust ports provide steering control. Rudders are controlled by a wheel and propeller pitch by levers. All controls are in a raised bridge well forward on the superstructure.

HULL: Built mainly in welded marine corrosion resistant aluminium alloys. Structure appears to follow standard practice for large amphibious

Aist

Forward port quarter of Aist showing long bridge super-structure. Emblem in centre indicates amphibious ship, second insignia is combat efficiency award for operational readiness, rating craft an 'outstanding ship of the Soviet Navy'

Aist in foreground has original main engine intake while second Aist has newsplit air intake

Three-quarter view of Aist

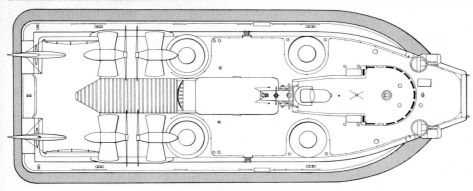

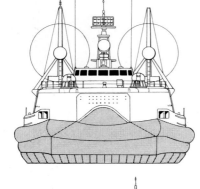

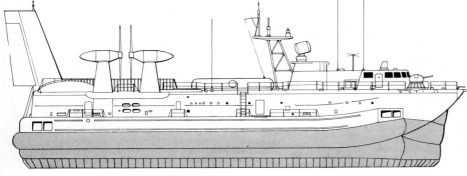

General arrangement of Aist with modified main engine air intake

ACVs. The main hull is formed by a buoyancy raft based on a grid of longitudinal and transverse frames which form a number of flotation compartments. Two main longitudinal vertically stiffened bulkheads run the length of the craft separating the central load deck from the outer or sidestructures, which contain the gas turbines and their associated exhausts, lift fans, transmissions, auxiliary power systems and seating for half a company of troops in cabins in the forward port and starboard quarters.

A full width ramp at the bow and a second at the stern, provide through loading facilities.

Typical vehicle loads include one or two T-62 or T-72 tanks or four PT-76 tanks; mobile radio trucks, armoured troop carriers, supply vehicles and ambulances.

ACCOMMODATION: Crew accommodation includes the control cabin or commander's cabin (Aist is described as being the sole warship type in the Soviet fleet in which the commander himself is responsible for steering), galley, radio room, sleeping and living quarters, engine mechanic's watch room and combat information centre (CIC). Naval infantrymen are seated in cabins on both sides of the central vehicle deck.

SKIRT: 2.5m deep double bag type in rubberised fabric with finger fringe beneath. Features include a high bow skirt line to protect the bow loading door against wave impact.

SYSTEMS, WEAPONS: Two twin 30mm fully-automatic dual-purpose mountings, controlled by Drum Tilt radar for close-in AA defence and by optical director and manual control for surface targets, including the suppression of LMG and rifle-fire during beach assaults.

DIMENSIONS (estimated)
Length overall, off cushion: 47.3m
Beam overall, off cushion: 17m
Height, control cabin: 1.98m
Length, control cabin: 10.5m
Width, bow ramp: 4.41m
  rear ramp: 4.87m
WEIGHTS (estimated)
Empty weight: 170 tons
Crew, fuel, AFVs or two main battle tanks and
  ½ company of naval infantry or troops: 90 tons
Max weight: 260–270 tons
PERFORMANCE (estimated)
Max speed: about 70 knots
Cruising speed: 50 knots
Endurance: about 5 hours
Range, cruising: 350n miles

LEBED (NATO Code Name)

Primary roles of this multi-duty hovercraft are as an amphibious initial assault landing craft and high-speed vehicle for LOTS (Logistics-over-the-shore) operations, providing Soviet naval infantry with a rapid lift capability to move personnel and equipment from the well decks of landing ships across water, beaches and marginal terrain to assembly points well above the shore line.

Smaller than both the US Navy's Jeff (A) and (B) and the Royal Navy's Vosper Thornycroft VT 2, Lebed has an overall length of about 24.4m, a gross weight of 86 tonnes and a maximum speed of 70 knots.

Two Lebeds or three Gus-type craft can be carried in the well deck of the Soviet Navy's LPD, the 13 100-ton *Ivan Rogov*, which also accommodates up to a battalion of naval infantry, 40 tanks and a range of supporting vehicles. Two Lebeds were demonstrated in South Yemen when the vessel called there on the way to the Soviet far east in 1979. The first of the 'Lebed' class was launched in 1973 and the craft entered production in 1976–77. If production rates have been similar to those of Gus (two to four units per year), it is likely that some 18 to 19 units are now operational. For use in the initial assault role, Lebeds would be pre-loaded before the *Ivan Rogov* sailed. Typical vehicle payloads include two PT-76 light amphibious tanks, two BMP-1 armoured personnel carriers, mobile radio trucks or supply vehicles up to a total weight of 35 tonnes. Design of Lebed is thought to have been undertaken by the Soviet Navy's High-Speed Ship Design Bureau in Leningrad.

LIFT AND PROPULSION: Integrated system powered by two marinised gas turbines mounted one each side of the cargo deck aft. Engines are two AI-20s, each rated at 4150shp continuous. Air for the two main engines appears to be drawn in through two rectangular, filtered intakes then fed aft through a curved spine-like trunk above the longitudinal centreline and terminating between the two fins. The intakes for the axial-flow lift fans are outboard of the two gas turbine air intakes. Each engine drives via a main gearbox and shaft a variable-pitch axial lift fan in light alloy. The fans deliver air to the cushion via a continuous peripheral loop skirt with segmented fringes. A second shaft from each main gearbox transmits power via bevel gears to a pylon-mounted four-bladed variable-pitch propulsion fan. The two propulsion fans are contained within aerodynamically shaped ducts which are partly submerged in the hull sidestructures. Apart from attenuating noise the ducts protect the fans from accidental damage. Exhaust covers are provided for both gas turbines aft at the rear of the port and starboard sidestructures.

CONTROLS: Control cabin is well forward above the port sidestructure and provides a 360-degree view. Directional control at normal operating speeds is by twin aerodynamic rudders aft of the thrust fan ducts and operating in the fan slipstreams. Differential pitch to the propulsion units augments the turning moment provided by rudder operation. Reverse thrust is applied for braking and reversing. Forward and aft thrust

Lebed   *(Danish Defence)*

Lebed unloading PT-76 tank

Lebed showing details of skirt at bow

Two Lebeds leave floodable well deck of Soviet Navy LPD,   *Ivan Rogov*

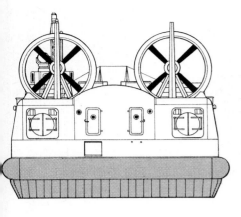

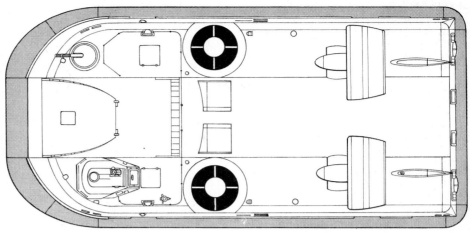

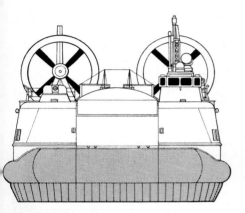

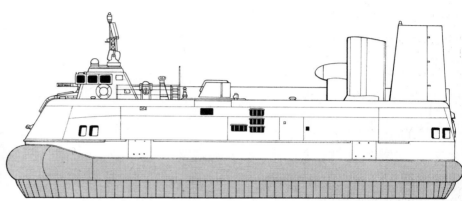

General arrangement of Lebed

ports, port and starboard, aid directional control at low speeds.

HULL: Riveted skin and stringer structure employing alloy sheet. Structure follows standard practice for large and medium size amphibious ACVs. The main hull is formed by a buoyancy raft based on a grid of longitudinal and transverse frames which form a number of flotation compartments. Two main longitudinal vertically stiffened bulkheads run the length of the craft separating the 4.8m central load deck from the outer sidestructures which contain the gas turbines and their associated exhausts, lift fans, transmissions and auxiliary power systems. The freight deck is reinforced for the carriage of tanks, armoured troop carriers, self-propelled guns, rocket launchers and heavy vehicles. Drive-on, drive-off loading facility is provided by a full-width hydraulically-operated bow door/loading ramp. This is hinged from the base and has an overlapping hatch cover. Personnel doors are provided aft. Photographs suggest that six landing pads are built into the craft's undersurface.

SKIRT: Loop and segment type with raised hinge line at bow.

ARMAMENT: One remotely-controlled six-barrel Gatling-action 30mm cannon in barbette on forward quarter of the starboard sidestructure. Employed in conjunction with fire-control radar for close-in anti-aircraft and anti-missile defence and with optical sighting and manual control for surface targets including suppressing LMG and rifle fire during beach assaults.

It is reported that a new gun is being installed on Soviet 'Lebed' class medium air cushion landing craft. It has a 54cm long tapered barrel, with a 50mm external muzzle diameter and a 100mm diameter base at the gunhouse. As with the previous arrangement, the gun is mounted on a circular barbette on the starboard bow. A periscopic sighting device is fitted for manual operation and the gun can be elevated from about 13 degrees negative to 90 degrees vertical. The gun house is 134cm in diameter and 63cm high.

Lebed

DIMENSIONS
Length overall: 24.4m
Beam overall: 10.8m
WEIGHTS
Max all-up weight: 86 tonnes
Max payload: 35 tonnes
PERFORMANCE
Max speed, calm conditions: 70 knots
Cruising speed, calm conditions: 50 knots

PORMORNIK (NATO Code Name)

A new 55 knot Soviet hovercraft which appeared in the Baltic in the first half of 1986.
ENGINES: Three NK-12 gas turbines for propulsion, two for lift fans.
DIMENSIONS
Length: 57.00m
Beam: 22.00m
Bow and stern ramps (stern on port side) at either end for roll-on, roll-off working

Propeller duct diameter: Approx 6.0m
WEIGHTS
Displacement: 350 tonnes, probably full operational condition
Disposable load: 100 tonnes estimated

UTENOK

A 70-tonne ACV powered by a single gas turbine. Two propellers give the craft a speed of 65 knots. Two Utenok-class ACVs have been built, 1982.
DIMENSIONS
Length: 26.30m
Beam: 13.00m

TSAPLYA

A 105-tonne ACV powered by two gas turbines with total power of 8000bhp, built 1982.
DIMENSIONS
Length: 26.00m
Beam: 13.00m

PELIKAN

An inshore minesweeping air cushion vehicle,
several commisioned in 1985/86. Displacement
100 tonnes, length 85.3m, beam 42.7m.

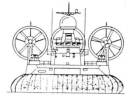
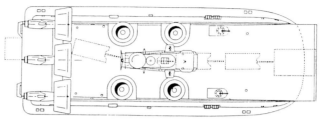
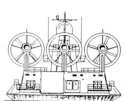

General arrangement of Pormornik

Pormornik

(West German Defence Ministry)

Pormornik

(Federal German Navy)

FURTHER CIVIL CRAFT

BARGUZIN

This hovercraft design announced in 1989 is provided with skegs and is intended for use in inland waters. (See page 80 for illustration)

PRINCIPAL PARTICULARS
Length: 32.40m
Beam: 6.40m
Depth: 2.30m
Skeg vertical dimension: 1.50m
Height, overall, main deck to rudder house roof: 6.85m
Draught, at stern, off-cushion, light: 1.46m
Draught, at stern, off-cushion, full load: 1.47m
Draught, at stern, on-cushion, full load: 0.80m
Displacement, full load: 69.44 tonnes
Displacement, light-ship: 53.18 tonnes
Engines, propulsion: two 820 kW diesels, M-401 A-1/1
Engines, lift: one 224 kW diesel
Speed: 27 knots
Range: 325n miles
Accommodation: 130 passengers

MARIJSKI POLYTECHNICAL INSTITUTE

3 Lenin Square, Yoshkar-Ola, Mari, USSR

S F Kirkin, *Scientific Head*

The student design group at the Marijski Institute of Technology has been involved in ACV development since 1971. It specialises in designing amphibious hovercraft for operation in the less accessible areas of the Soviet Union and has successfully built and tested craft commissioned by the Soviet Union's oil, gas and fisheries authorities. It has also adapted hovercraft for forestry and agricultural roles and for use in establishing communication networks.

Further studies include an investigation into soil damage caused by agricultural machines crossing farmland. The findings are likely to result in the wide scale use of hovercraft for Soviet agriculture. The Institute claims that conventional agricultural machinery is too heavy, and compacts the soil when crossing fields, whether on wheels or tracks. The subsequent disintegration of the soil structure results in a reduction in fertility and a loss of yield. It has been recommended that the size of these vehicles should be greatly reduced and, in some cases, they may be taken out of service.

Extensive use of hovercraft is seen as the answer, since their low pressure on the soil prevents any damage to its structure.

SAV SERIES
SAVR-1M

In 1977 the Institute was awarded a contract by the Soviet Gas Industry for a small snow-mobile/hovercraft to carry a driver and two passengers, plus 500kg of cargo, over snow, ice and water. It also was required to travel over mud to ensure year-round operation on rivers. The first stage of the programme was the design and construction of an experimental model, designated SAVR-1.
LIFT AND PROPULSION: Separate lift and propulsion systems enable the craft to be operated at its maximum clearance height and speed depending on the surface and weather conditions. Two engines are fitted, the propulsion engine, which develops 72kW and the lift engine, developing 30kW. The propulsion engine drives a two-bladed airscrew and the lift engine an axial fan ahead of the cockpit.

SAVR-1M (CABP-1M)

WEIGHTS
Total weight: 1.8 tonnes
Load capacity: 0.8 tonnes
PERFORMANCE
Max speed, across snow: 70km/h
across water: 40km/h

SAVR-1 (CABP-1)

Built in 1980, this production version of the SAVR-1M is intended for high-speed ferrying of personnel and urgent cargoes of up to 1.3 tonnes over roadless areas all year round.
LIFT AND PROPULSION: Cushion air is supplied by a 98hp car engine driving two standard centrifugal fans. A clutch between the engine and fans allows the fans to be disconnected during engine startup and idling. Thrust is supplied by a 118kW (158hp) engine, aft, which drives a 2m diameter propeller. Distribution of power between cushion and thrust is varied according to terrain conditions.

CONTROLS: Directional control is by two air rudders operating in the slipstream.
HULL: Built in duralumin sheet. Buoyancy chamber of honeycomb construction.
DIMENSIONS
Length: 7.5m
Beam: 3.8m
Height, with propeller vertical: 3.3m
WEIGHTS
Max weight: 2.9 tonnes
Max useful load: 1.3 tonnes
PERFORMANCE
Cruising speed, across snow: 65km/h
across water: 60km/h

SAVR-2 (CABP-2)

SAVR-2 made its appearance in 1982. It was designed and built to a specification prepared by the Soviet Ministry of Fisheries for a craft to serve the inaccessible water regions of North and West Siberia.

SAVR-2 (CABP-2)

LIFT AND PROPULSION: Lift is provided by a single petrol engine aft of the crew cabin driving, via a split transverse shaft, two centrifugal fans. Thrust is supplied by a single 294kW (394hp) Ivchenko AI-14ChR air-cooled radial piston engine driving an AV-14 3-blade variable-pitch propeller. Fuel is carried in two 400-litre tanks, one for each engine. Fuel employed is standard automotive petrol. Engine compartment separated from the cabin by thermo-insulating and soundproofing partitions.

CONTROLS: Craft heading is controlled by twin vertical aerodynamic rudders aft operating in the propeller slipstream. Reverse propeller pitch is employed for braking and reversing. A horizontal stabiliser is mounted between the twin rudders to adjust pitch trim. By altering its incidence angle the centre of gravity can be moved along the longitudinal axis should an uneven load distribution cause it to move.

HULL: Believed to be a composite light alloy and glass fibre structure. Flotation compartments and basic raft structure filled with plastic foam make hull unsinkable.

ACCOMMODATION: Cabin seats driver with a passenger on each side. Interior lined with layer of polyurethane and pvc for thermal insulation. Passenger module seating 14 to 16 can be fitted on cargo platform aft of lift fan system.

SKIRT: Segmented skirts fore and aft. Bag-type skirts at sides. An experimental model of the SAVR-2 has two flexible side skids replacing the conventional skirt. The skids consist of a number of right-angled plates, hinged together, and fitted with removable stainless steel or polyethylene soles. The plates are fixed to the hull by lever suspension and spring shock absorbers. The area between skid and hull is covered with rubberised fabric. Flexible skids reduce to a minimum the air escaping from the cushion when travelling over rough ground, so reducing the power required from the lift system, as they follow the ground contours more accurately. When the craft is supported by the skids the pressure of the air cushion can be considerably reduced. Flexible skids provide lateral stability when the craft is stationary and when travelling over snow, ice and mud, and surfaces covered in a thin layer of water. The least cushion pressure is required over damp, muddy terrain or land covered with a thin layer

SAVR-1 (CABP-1)

of water. To cross open water the pressure must be increased from 1000 to 1200Pa (70 to 80 per cent maximum) and over dry soil and ploughland it has to be increased to the maximum, 1400Pa.

DIMENSIONS
Length: 9.8m
Beam: 4.5m
Height: 3.7m
WEIGHTS
Total: 5900kg
Payload: 2 tonnes
PERFORMANCE
Fully laden, max speed: 50km/h
Range: 200km

SAVR-3

In 1981 the Ministry of Oil and Gas approved a programme for the construction of trackless modes of transport, building machines and pipe-laying equipment for muddy soils. Within this programme, which spans the period 1981–1985, the Institute was constructing three new transport hovercraft with the following load capacities: SAVR-3, 2 tons; SAVR-5, 5 tons; SAVR-40, 40 tons.

The SAVR-3 has the following characteristics:
ENGINE: 380kW (510hp) nominal rating, 300kW (402hp) cruise.
WEIGHT
Disposable load capacity: 3000kg

PERFORMANCE
Speed, max, over snow: 75km/h
Speed, max, over water: 50km/h
Slope (gradient) capability, sustained: 10°
   short duration: 25°

At the end of 1986 a decision was taken to build a working batch of SAVR-3 craft. In the spring of 1985 and 1986 early top dressing of winter crops with granulated fertilisers and sowing of wheat and barley in damp soil were undertaken with the first SAVR-3.

SAVR-5

Developed by the Institute in 1983 for freight transport of year round construction of pipelines on swamps. Road tests began in the first half of 1987.

The SAVR-5 is propelled by caterpillar tracks from T54B tractors, driven by a series-produced diesel as is the fan for the air cushion system. Maximum vehicle weight is 10 tonnes.

SAVR-40

A 40-tonne load-capacity air cushion vehicle for similar duties to the SAVR-5. Building of an experimental SAVR-40 was due to start at the end of 1987.

Reference: Development and Test Results of Air Cushion Vehicles Designed by The A M Gorki Mari Polytechnical Institute by S F Kirkin. Canadian Air Cushion Technology Society Conference, Montreal, October 1987.

SAVR-3 (CABP-3)

NEPTUN CENTRAL DESIGN BUREAU
Moscow, USSR

G E Andreyev, *Chief Engineer*
Alexander Sergeyevich Kudriavtsev, *Chief Designer, AKVPR project*
Valeriy V Protsenko, *Designer*
Alexander V Rubinov, *Test Engineer*

Air cushion vehicles designed by the Neptune Central Design Bureau are supplied by Sudo-export:

AKVPR-001

V/O SUDOEXPORT
Chaikovosky St.11, Moscow, 123231, USSR
Telephone: (095) 2551813
Telex: 411116 KURS SU

The Neptun Central Design Bureau is concerned primarily with the design of small launches, yachts and runabouts for leisure and commercial applications on Soviet inland and coastal waters.

The AKVPR-001 airjet-propelled amphibious ACV, Neptun's first attempt at designing and building a hovercraft, is intended for research only. Several variants are under development including the Barrs-1 which is destined for service in Siberia and other underdeveloped areas of the Soviet Union. A 20-seat derivative has been suggested and the bureau has a four-seater, the Gepard, on the drawing board.

AKVPR-001

This multi-purpose amphibious five-seater was initially designed for use in geological expeditions, to provide communications in the Soviet far north and Siberia, in river rescue services and for emergency services when ice is forming and breaking up on inland waterways. The nomenclature AKVPR signifies 'Amphibious Air Cushion Craft, Airjet, Rivergoing'. A film of the craft taken during trials in the winter of 1977 and spring of 1978 showed the craft successfully operating across broken ice, negotiating ice hummocks at speed and crossing boggy terrain and marshes.

LIFT AND PROPULSION: Integrated lift/propulsion system. Power is supplied by a single automotive engine, aft of the cabin. Power is transmitted via a gearbox to two transverse shafts at the opposite ends of which are axial fans. Air is fed downwards into the cushion and through circular thrust outlets aft for propulsion.

CONTROLS: Craft heading is controlled by interconnected rudder vanes set in the airjet ducts aft and operated by a wheel. Airflow for braking and reversing is provided by deflecting thrust air upwards and through forward facing roof apertures.

HULL: Built mainly in corrosion resistant light alloy. Basic structure is the main hull which is divided into watertight sub-divisions for safety.

PERFORMANCE: Has achieved 50km/h across calm water over a measured mile.

BARRS (SNOW LEOPARD)

The prototype of this enlarged variant of the AKVPR-001 seats a driver and seven passengers. A cargo version carries a load of 650kg (1433lb).

A feature of the design is the use of a Kamov Ka-26 helicopter piston engine to power the integrated lift/propulsion system. The engine, the M-14V-26, has a rigidly-prescribed operational life and its use in Barrs is the outcome of a search to find a terrestrial application for it once it had reached the end of its airborne career.

Barrs-1 is designed for year-round operation and can be used as a light passenger ferry, light freighter or as a service crews' launch on routes in remote and scarcely-developed regions of western and eastern Siberia, the far north and the far east,

Barrs-1, an AKVPR-001 variant, some 30 have been built as rescue and mail boats

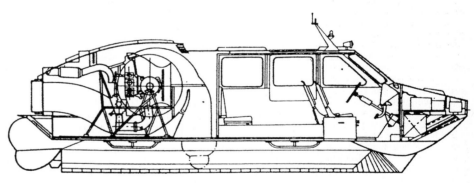

Barrs (Snow Leopard)

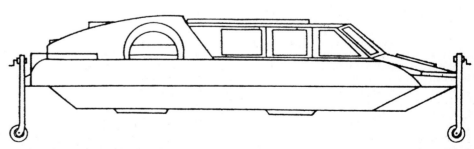

Barrs prepared for transport

which have a thinly developed network for year-round transport of domestic goods.

Trials have shown that Barrs can operate safely in wave heights of up to 0.6m and can clear obstacles of up to 0.5m in height. It is said to 'ride superbly over sand and snow-covered ice'. During long runs it normally operates with a six-degree bow-up trim. It meets the requirements of Class 'L' in the Inland Waterway Register of the Russian Soviet Federated Socialist Republic

(RSFSR).

LIFT AND PROPULSION
Engine: Vedeneyev M-14V-26 helicopter engine, radial air-cooled 175kW nominal output (Ed. note: this engine in helicopter application has a take-off rating of 242kW at 2800rpm, 205kW max continuous at 2450rpm and a lower max continuous rating of 142kW at 2350rpm). The engine drives a low-tip-speed centrifugal fan with forward-facing blades supplying air both for the

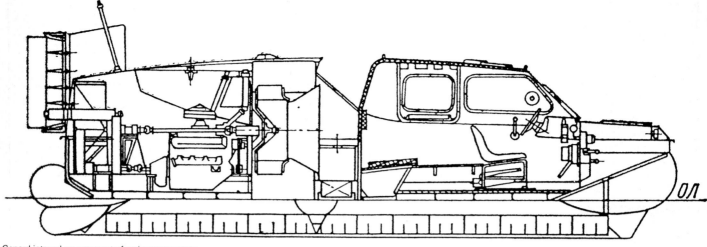

Gepard internal arrangement of main components

air cushion and for the propulsive nozzles. These nozzles are fitted with reverse thrust devices.
CONTROLS: Craft heading is controlled by interconnected rudder vanes set in the airjet ducts aft and operated by a wheel. Airflow for braking and reversing is provided by deflecting thrust air upwards and through forward-facing roof apertures.
HULL: Light metal alloy structure. Main hull divided into watertight sub-divisions for safety. Designed for mass production.
PRINCIPAL PARTICULARS
Class: R standards of the River Register of the Russian Soviet Federal Republic
Length: 7.00 m
Width, when operating: 3.35 m
Width, for transport: 2.50 m
Height, less mast: 1.84 m
Displacement, normal payload: 2.50 tonnes
Displacement, maximum: 2.65 tonnes
Accommodation: 7 to 9 people
Speed, flat calm conditions: 70 km/h, 38 knots
Speed, 5 m/s headwind, 0.25 m waves: 45 km/h, 24 knots
Rise height: 0.45 m
Limiting conditions: winds of 15 m/s, wave heights of 0.75 m, temperatures: −40°C, +40°C, waves when floating: 1.2 m
Buoyancy when damaged: remains afloat if any one compartment is flooded; flooding of two adjacent compartments excluded if hull tears are less than 10% of hull length
Fuel tank capacity: 470 l normal 470 l when external tanks added
OPERATIONS
Extensive trials have been undertaken by Barrs type hovercraft, described in the following account.
    The craft is fitted with lifting/transport attachments enabling it to be rolled aboard a helicopter or an aircraft, as well as for transit within airfield boundaries. It is intended to transport the Barrs attached externally under the Mi-8 helicopter.
    Experimental Barrs craft have undergone comprehensive trials under the most varied climatic and terrain conditions. During trials in the Arkhangelsk region over a period of one year the Barrs was tested along two routes of 200 and 170 km in length. The craft was used daily, serving one of these routes every day and carried mail to 16 postal distributing posts situated along the banks of the Pinega river. During the winter-spring and autumn-winter periods the Barrs was also used along different tracks: it could 'jump' over highways, overcome hummocks and piled-up ice of 0.5–1.0 m in height, and it could move over loose and freshly-fallen snow, frozen snow crust, smooth and broken ice, as well as over drifting ice; tests also took place at night. In the summer period the craft could move across a floating

breakwater without reducing speed, over sand banks and sandy spits. During these trials lasting from April 1983 to May 1984 the Barrs travelled 36 800 km, was in use for 218 days, working for 900 hrs and travelling for 800 hrs at an average speed of 45.7 km/h. Its (average) specific fuel consumption amounted to 1.08 kg/km (47.5 kg/hr), and its operational availability was 79%.
    Trials with the Barrs in the central and southern districts of the USSR gave the following results. Moving over water, the fully-loaded craft operated against winds of up to 10 m/sec and waves up to 0.5 m in height. Without reducing speed, it could cross dry sections overgrown with rush (reeds) up to 1.8 m in height and from a running start would float over 50 m sections (strips) of compact old rushes (reeds) up to 2.5 m in height. The manoeuvring qualities of Barrs allowed it to move along rivers not wider than 12 m at speeds of about 30 km/h, and to tackle bends up to 180° every 50–100 m of the track. The highest speed recorded over flat waters at full load was 83 km/h.
    Moving across dry land the craft could effortlessly cross glutinous clayey shallows, marsh-ridden spaces, fields and meadows covered with growth up to 80 cm in height and furrows 10 cm wide and high. From a running start the craft would overcome hillocks up to 4–5 m in height and steepness of about 15°, and it passed across burrows of up to 1.5 m in width and took smoothed-down obstacles of up to 0.8 m in height.

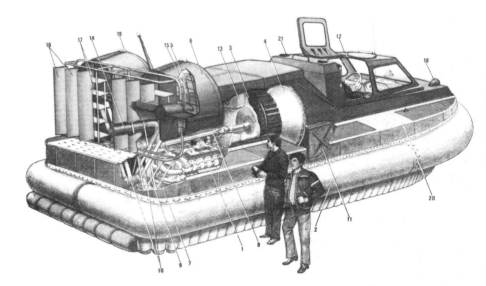

Cutaway of Gepard: (**1**) ZMZ-53 power plant (**2**) bag skirt (**3**) fan (**4**) fan air scoop (**5**) thrust fan (**6**) duct (**7**) main (cardan) shaft (**8**) fan drive (cardan) shaft (**9**) fan transmission belts (**10**) airscrew transmission belts (**11**) fuel tank (**12**) deck cabin (**13**) water and oil radiators (**14**) exhaust pipe (manifold) (**15**) fan duct (**16**) vertical rudders (**17**) elevators (**18**) headlights (**19**) navigation and landing lights (**20**) drainage plate (**21**) ventilator heads

GEPARD (CHEETAH)

    A multi-role five-seater introduced in 1981, Gepard has been designed to provide convenient, reliable and inexpensive transport in remoter areas of the Soviet Union. Specialist professions in those areas were questioned about their transport needs before finalising the design. Early in 1983 a Gepard successfully underwent trials at Andreyevskoye Lake, near the centre of the Tyumen Oblast. Forty Gepards had entered service by November 1988.
    The craft is designed to operate in an ambient air temperature range from −40°C to +40°C.
    The following service life trials have been carried out:
Moscow to Lake Seleger and back: about 1000km
Along small rivers to the city of Vyshnii Volochek and back: about 1000km
Moscow by the Volga-Baltic route to Leningrad: about 2000km
Moscow to Volgograd on the lower Volga River: about 3500km
LIFT AND PROPULSION: Integrated system, powered by a 120hp ZMZ-53 lorry engine (a widely used engine), aft of the cabin. Output is transmitted to a centrifugal lift fan (0.97m diameter with grp blades) and a duct-mounted, multi-bladed 0.95m diameter glass-fibre propeller for thrust, the blade leading edges being protected with stainless steel sheaths. Power transmission is by toothed-belt drives, and a clutch is provided between the engine and propeller and fan drives.

The five-seat, 42-knot Gepard powered by a single 120hp ZMZ-53 petrol engine

CONTROLS: Directional control by interconnected rudder vanes hinged to the rear of the thrust fan ducts and operated by a wheel. Horizontal vane surfaces are also provided.

HULL: Corrosion-resistant light alloy hull. Moulded pigmented glass-fibre cabin superstructure.

DIMENSIONS
Length overall: 6.88m
Width overall: 3.80m
Height overall: 2.75m
Cabin width: 1.50m
Cabin height: 1.40m

WEIGHT
Loaded weight: 1.86 tons

PERFORMANCE
Max speed, fully loaded, calm water: 60km/h, on ice 70km/h, cruising 50km/h
Endurance: 5 hours
Rise height: 0.40m
OPERATIONS: Multi-purpose; one is in use with a hydrological expedition on the Yamal Peninsula in the Arctic

PUMA

Design and building of this craft was completed in less than a year. The first three variants were undergoing comprehensive trials in 1988. As an ambulance the Puma is equipped with an operating table and related medical apparatus including oxygen bottles, making it possible to provide urgent medical aid on board, including simple operations. The passenger variant is fitted with 16 aircraft type seats, while the passenger/cargo variant has ten folding seats.

LIFT AND PROPULSION
Two ZMZ-53 90 kW petrol engines driving two centrifugal fans and two reversible-pitch propellers with toothed-belt drives.

PRINCIPLE PARTICULARS
Class: R standard of the River Register of the Russian Soviet Federal Republic
Length, on cushion: 12.20 m
Length, between perpendiculars: 11.10 m
Width, on cushion: 5.20 m
Width, off cushion: rigid hull: 2.50 m
Displacement, empty: 4.04 tonnes
Displacement, fully loaded: 5.70 tonnes
Disposable load: 1.66 tonnes

Puma twin petrol-engine hovercraft designed by the Neptun Control Design Bureau, Moscow

Speed, max: 60 km/h, 32 knots
Speed, service: 40 km/h, 22 knots
Endurance, nominal: 5 h
    with additional fuel: 15 h
Rise height: 0.6 m
Gradient capability, continuous 5°
    from max speed: 12° for short distance
Obstacle clearance: 0.3 m
    smooth projections: 0.8 m

OPERATIONS

The first Puma, built as an ambulance, underwent trials in 1985 in the Tomsk region (Tomsk to Kolpashevo). In winter the craft had to overcome 400 km of icy hummocks with blocks of ice up to 0.6 m in height, the rise height of the air cushion. The second Puma, a passenger version has been engaged in trials near Moscow and in September 1987, over shallow water areas of the Caspian Sea, reached by travelling down the Volga from Volgograd. An interesting result reported is that in water Puma craft are using 20 to 30% less engine power than in summer and with an average service speed some 5 to 10 km/h higher.

1988 saw the first all-year-round passenger service in the Soviet Union between Tomsk and Krasny Yar. Several Pumas are in operation along this 100 km route. It is anticipated that these 16-seat Pumas will be superceded by 32-seat air cushion vehicles. The 1988 fare for the route was 4 roubles, 20 kopeks; the 32-seat craft will allow the fare to be reduced to 3 roubles.

16 METRE ACV

A 32-passenger craft under construction at the end of 1988.
Hull: riveted aluminium with gap superstructure
Length: 16.00 m
Width: 6.10 m
Weight, light: 6.5 tonnes
Rise height: 0.7 m
Speed, service: 40 km/h, 22 knots
Engines: two Deutz diesel 190 hp each
Lift and propulsion: two centrifugal fans and two ducted propellers, toothed belt transmission

18.7 m SEA-GOING CARGO ACV

Developed by the Neptun Bureau since 1984, a diesel-powered low-speed air-cushion platform with steel hull and aluminium superstructure. First of the craft was built in 1986, with a cargo capacity of 10 tonnes, designed for arctic ship-to-shore unloading.

Length: 18.7 m
Width: 9.1 m
Weight, light: 45 tonnes
Speed, service: 5.5 knots
Engines: three 400 hp diesel, one driving a centrifugal fan and two driving variable-pitch propellers

The special feature of this craft is a bow-mounted connection system, which makes it possible to push a non-propelled air-cushion platform with a cargo capacity of 20–25 tonnes. Two such platforms were built in 1986. They have matching connection elements and their hulls, deck devices and machinery are identical to those of the pusher. Unlike the pusher, the non-propelled air-cushion platforms have no propelling plant, permitting an increase in the platform deck size to 8×12 m and the installation of a portal crane with a lifting capacity of 5 tonnes.

A pusher with a non-propelled platform connected to it can travel at a speed of 5 knots in extreme shallow water, cross minor sand bars, floating and breaking ice and push out the platform up to a half-hull distance on the compact ice or the beach with a slope of up to 6°.

In late 1988 the system was being subjected to intensive trials in the Barents Sea.

Irbis

27 m GEOPHYSICAL & CARGO-CARRYING ACV

The Neptun Central Design Bureau is developing a sea-going hovercraft for geophysical explorations on a shallow sea shelf. This craft has a length of 27 m, width 13 m, light-ship weight 95 tonnes and speed up to 7 knots. The hovercraft will be equipped with geophysical instruments and winches for towing the seismographic equipment. A cargo version of the hovercraft will have a capacity of up to 40 tonnes. Two 1500 hp diesel engines will be installed on it, each of them driving a centrifugal fan and a rotable variable-pitch ducted propeller, the latter being installed in diagonally opposite corners of the hull to better the craft performance.

All hovercraft developed in the Neptun Bureau are tested on models in a trial basin. The designs and engineering developments of the Central Design Bureau are not confined to the above mentioned vessels, the Bureau envisaging further prospects in hovercraft development taking into consideration the various geographical conditions of the USSR.

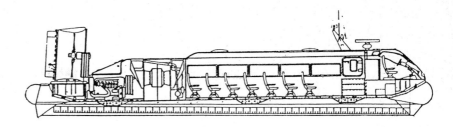

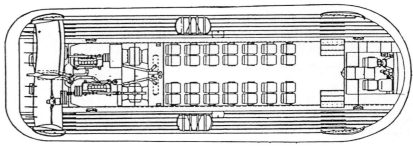

General arangement of Irbis

IRBIS

A new twin-engine amphibious hovercraft designed to carry up to 32 passengers. Intended applications for this type include the transport of geologists and oil industry workers and their associated equipment, cargo shipment up to 2.5 tonnes and support for geophisical exploration. The craft is designed to operate in a wide range of operating conditions in ambient temperatures from −40°C and maximum wind speeds up to 15m/s and up to 30 miles from base; in significant wave heights up to 0.7m when cushion borne, across deep or shallow water; across snow and compact ice and across broken and sludge ice. The craft has folding sidebodies for ease in transport.

DIMENSIONS
Length overall, on cushion: 17.50m
Length, bp: 26.00m
Width overall, on cushion: 6.20m
Width, rigid hull: 2.80m
Height overall, on cushion: 4.00m
Draught, light: 0.20m
Draught, full load: 0.27m
WEIGHTS
Lightweight, passenger version: 7.40 tonnes
Lightweight, freight version: 6.50 tonnes
Full load: 10.70 tonnes
Deadweight, passenger version: 3.30 tonnes
Deadweight, freight version: 4.00 tonnes
(Figures include 0.56 tonnes diesel fuel, 0.15 tonnes crew)
ENGINES
Two Deutz BF6L 913C air-cooled diesels, 141 kW (191hp) at 2500 rpm max rating.
PROPULSION
Two four-blade, variable-pitch (forward and reverse thrust) ducted propellers.
ACCOMMODATION
32 passengers plus crew.
PERFORMANCE
Speed, max, calm water: 32.4 knots (60km/h)
Speed, cruising: 24.3 knots (45km/h)
Speed, max, over ice: 37.8 knots (70km/h)
Speed, cruising, over ice: 29.7 knots (55km/h)
Weather limitations for safe operation: Sea State 3, winds up to 8 knots(15km/h)
Obstacle clearance: 0.4m high separate obstacles, short 4° slopes
Endurance: 12 hours, increasing to 18 or 24 hours if twin fuel tanks are used
Fuel consumption: 55 l/h

Taifun cargo carrying hovercraft

SYSTEMS
Trim (fuel transfer), hydraulic power provision, heating and special cold starting system (down to -40°C). Generator output: two 1.0 kW generators. Voltage: 24 dc.

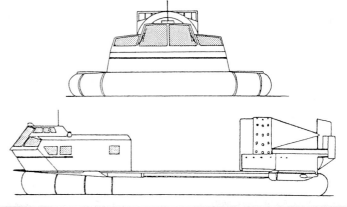

Approximate elevations of Taifun

Barguzin

UFA AVIATION INSTITUTE
Tyumen, USSR

F Nuriakhmetov, *Head of Propulsion Systems Group*
I Shalin, *Design Engineer*
S Komarov, *Candidate of Science (Technical)*

Designers at the UFA Aviation Institute have been active in ACV development since the mid-1960s when they exhibited an experimental craft, named Skat, with a circular platform at the USSR National Economy Achievements Exhibition in Moscow.

TAIFUN
A multi-duty amphibious vehicle designed for all-weather, 24-hour operation. Please see *Jane's High-Speed Marine Craft and Air Cushion Vehicles 1987* for details.

VOSTOK CENTRAL DESIGN BUREAU
Leningrad, USSR

V D Rubtsov, *Chief Designer*
B V Baymistruk
Ye A Meschchanov
S F Gorbachevskiy

KLEST
Development of this small utility hovercraft began at the Vostok Central Design Bureau in 1979. Trials of the prototype, named *Metan 1*, were undertaken in the Gulf of Finland and at Bolshaya Nevka, Leningrad in summer 1981. An integrated lift/propulsion system is employed, powered by a single Volga Automotive Plant (VAZ) automotive engine. Power is transmitted to two ducted propulsion fans and a single lift fan. The fans are scaled-down and modified versions of conventional industrial fans used in Soviet coalmines. Parts for the engine and servicing can be provided by any Zhiguli service station, a network of which now exists in the Soviet Union. Series production is proposed. Maximum speed is 80km/h (50mph).

Klest

UNITED KINGDOM

AIR VEHICLES LIMITED

Head Office and Factory: Unit 4, Three Gates Road, Cowes, Isle of Wight, England

Telephone: (0983) 293194
Telex: 86513HVWORK G
Telefax: (0983) 291987

C B Eden, *Director*

Air Vehicles Limited was founded in 1968 and has concentrated on the design and development of rugged fully amphibious hovercraft using welded marine aluminium hulls, simple systems and conventional piston engines. The company offers craft from 4 seats with designs of up to 200 seats and customers include the British, French and Canadian Ministries of Defence, the People's Republic of China, the Nigerian Police, the Bahrain Ministry of the Interior and the Republic of Singapore Navy.

Air Vehicles Limited is approved by the Civil Aviation Authority and undertakes modifications to larger craft. These have included flat-deck freight conversions of the BHC SR.N5 and SR.N6 hovercraft, power-assisted rudder packs for both types, and the conversion of an SR.N6 Mk 1S for high-speed hydrographic surveying.

Air Vehicles Limited worked with British Hovercraft Corporation and Hovertravel Limited to produce the diesel amphibious hovercraft, the AP1–88. Air Vehicles produced a conceptual feasibility study for a four-engined diesel-powered hovercraft to meet the requirements of Hovertravel Ltd. The eventual requirement of Hovertravel led to the design of the BHC AP1–88 for which Air Vehicles undertook much of the detail design work.

HYDROGRAPHIC SURVEY CRAFT

An SR.N6 Mk 1S has been modified for high-speed hydrographic surveying for Eurosense Belfotop N.V. of Belgium. The cabin is fitted with an air-conditioned computer room, and a control area for the survey crew. External modifications are flat side decks to ease crew movement; two 12.5kVA generators and two hydraulically operated 'fish', fitted with depth transducers, which are lowered into the water when taking depth measurements. The craft can operate at 25 knots while measuring depth and records its position by means of a Trisponder system.

A similar conversion has also been provided on a Tiger 12 craft. The cabin is converted to carry the recording instruments and is fully air-conditioned. A 2.5kW power supply is provided and the single transducer is mounted on a hydraulically deployed 'fish' at the front of the craft. Positioning is again by Trisponder and surveying is carried out at speeds up to 20 knots.

Operations from the shore in shallow areas are easily undertaken without requiring any prepared docking facilities.

TIGER 12

The standard production craft has 12 seats (including the driver's) and the non-structural cabin top can be removed to suit various requirements. Fully amphibious, the craft can operate over a variety of surfaces such as mud, ice, sand and shallow water.

LIFT AND PROPULSION: Motive power for the integrated lift/propulsion system is provided by a single AMC 5900cc petrol engine delivering 180hp at 3600rpm. The engine output is transferred to a 12-blade centrifugal lift fan and a 1.37m diameter, four-blade, ducted propeller through a toothed belt system. Normal fuel capacity is 213 litres.
CONTROLS: Multiple rudders hinged at the aft

Crash rescue Tiger 12 fitted with six 36-man life rafts

Tiger 12 with high-speed, hydrographic 'fish' deployed in the water

end of the propeller duct provide directional control. Elevators provide trim and, when raised fully, assist braking by reducing thrust. A water ballast system is used to adjust trim in pitch for varying load states.
HULL: Superstructure and all bulkheads are of marine grade aluminium sheet welded to form a strong rigid box structure. Side members are inflatable, giving additional buoyancy and protection for the craft when mooring. By deflating the side members the vehicle can be trailed behind any large car or small truck. Built-in jacking system provided for loading and maintenance.
ACCOMMODATION: Enclosed cabin for driver and up to 11 passengers. Access via sliding doors, one port, one starboard. Driver's seat forward right; navigator's forward left. Adequate space for radar, radios and navigation equipment ahead of these positions.
SKIRT: Pressurised bag type with separate segments. Inflatable sides and skirt attached to craft with quick-release piano hinges.
SYSTEMS, ELECTRICAL: 12V dc, negative earth, with engine driven 35A alternator and 60Ah battery.
DIMENSIONS
Length: 8.0m
Width, inflated: 3.85m
Transport width: 2.44m
Height, off cushion: 2.26m
Hoverheight: 50–55cm
Cabin, length: 3.9m
    width: 1.8m
WEIGHTS
Empty: 1910kg
Max: 2865kg
Disposable load: 910kg
PERFORMANCE
Max speed: 65km/h
Cruise speed: 46km/h
Fuel consumption, cruise: 27–45 litres/h
    max: 70 litres/h
WEATHER LIMITATIONS
Max conditions: 46km/h wind
    1.25m sea

TIGER 16

The Tiger 16 is a fully amphibious hovercraft capable of carrying 16 people over a variety of terrain including shallow water, sand, mud and ice. The first craft was completed at the end of 1985.

LIFT AND PROPULSION: Various engine options are available according to duty and include the Deutz BF6L 913C air-cooled diesel rated at 190hp at 2500rpm and the Deutz BF 8L 513 rated at 360hp at 2300rpm. The engine power is transmitted via a toothed belt drive system to a 12-blade centrifugal lift fan and a 1.5m diameter, Robert Trillo Ltd designed four-blade ducted propeller. The propeller duct is designed to give efficient air entry and the outlet is shaped to provide for larger control surfaces. The propeller is designed to give high thrust per horsepower with low noise and is fitted with full length stainless steel leading edge protection.

CONTROLS: Four large rudders fitted at the propeller duct outlet provide directional control. Five elevators control pitch trim and when fully raised shut off the thrust. A skirt shift system provides rapid control of trim in pitch and roll.

BALLAST AND FUEL SYSTEM: A fuel ballast system adjusts the craft trim in pitch, transferring fuel to the bow or stern of the craft. The main engine fuel tank is positioned amidships and is linked to the ballast system via a manually operated valve so that ballast fuel can be used to increase duration.

CAPACITIES
Engine fuel tank: 340 litres
Ballast system normal: 225 litres
Ballast system full: 450 litres
Max long range capacity: 790 litres

HULL AND ACCOMMODATION: The hull is a fully welded, light but robust, aluminium structure and offers a variety of options in the cabin layout. Seat mounting/load tie down rails allow easy conversion of the cabin for passenger or load carrying duties. The cabin options give any combination from fully trimmed and enclosed

Tiger 16 with forward cabin and open well-deck

to a simple open workboat.

Rigid side bodies provide a convenient work platform when surveying and a carrying area for long loads. For transportation the side decks are easily removed.

An inflatable ring around the periphery of the craft provides for coming alongside and a 'soft edge' when working off the side decks.

SKIRT SYSTEM: An open loop and segment skirt is fitted. The skirt assembly is attached to the craft using an aluminium piano hinge. Segments are individually and easily replaced. A skirt shift system is fitted.

ELECTRICAL SYSTEM: 24V dc negative earth with engine-driven 45A alternator and 90Ah batteries.

DIMENSIONS
Length: 11.27m
Width: 4.1m
Transport width: 2.3m
Height, static to top of mast: 3.2m
Hoverheight: 0.65m
Cabin, length: 5.00m
  width: 1.80m
WEIGHTS
Empty: 2500kg
Payload: 1500kg
PERFORMANCE
Max speed: 33 knots
Cruise speed: 25 knots
Fuel consumption, cruise: 45 litres/h
  max: 65 litres/h
WEATHER LIMITATIONS
Max weather conditions: 46km/h (25 knot) wind
  1.25m sea

TIGER 40

The Tiger 40 project is a development of the Tiger 12 and Tiger 16. It uses the same design approach and incorporates many of the features and components of the smaller craft.

The propulsion and lift machinery are fitted in the side bodies leaving the centre of the craft clear for a variety of layouts thus ensuring a well balanced craft at any load state. Different cabin modules fit the craft for a number of roles, ranging from workboat and patrol craft to cargo carrying and passenger transport.

LIFT SYSTEM: The lift system supplies pressurised air to lift the craft and power the bow thruster. Power is supplied by two air-cooled

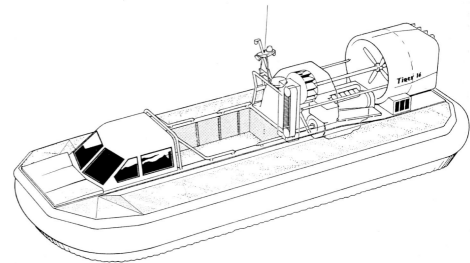

diesel engines mounted in the hull side-bodies each driving three co-axial, centrifugal fans via a toothed-belt transmission system. The front fan delivers air to the bow thruster only and the rear two supply the skirt system. The fans are 0.84m diameter and manufactured in aluminium alloy and are all similar except with regard to direction of rotation.

Two BF6L 913C air-cooled, turbocharged and intercooled diesel engines supply the lift system power. Each engine has a capacity of 6.9 litres and is rated at 141kW at 2500rpm. Both engines and the complete lift fan assembly are rubber mounted.

BOW THRUSTERS: Bow thrusters at the forward end of the craft augment the directional control system. The rotatable thruster ducts are situated one on each side of the craft and are supplied with air from the forward fans. Each fan is driven by, but is isolated from, its respective lift system. Each duct is operated by a dc servo motor controlled from the pilot's position by a simple rotary switch. The bow thrusters can be operated ahead or astern and are provided with isolation switches.

THRUST SYSTEM: The thrust system is powered by two air-cooled diesel engines each driving a Robert Trillo Ltd designed 1.83m diameter four-blade, fixed-pitch, ducted propeller via

a toothed-belt transmission system. The engines and transmission frames are mounted in the hull side-bodies and the ducted propeller assemblies are mounted on top of the athwartship beam at the rear of the craft.

Two BF8L 513C air-cooled, turbocharged diesel engines supply the thrust system power. Each engine has a capacity of 12.7 litres and is rated at 235kW continuously at 2300rpm. Both engines and the thrust system assemblies including the propeller ducts are rubber mounted. Four rudder blades at the rear of each propeller duct provide main directional control. Three elevator blades inside each propeller duct give rapid control of craft pitch trim.

CONTROLS: Multiple rudders hinged at the aft end of the twin propeller ducts provide directional control. Elevators provide rapid pitch trim and the bow thruster units provide reverse thrust, a righting moment when cornering or in a beam wind, and accurate control at slow speed. The bow thrusters also supplement the forward thrust at speed.

HULL: The hull is in three sections, two side bodies and a central deck, all constructed in welded marine grade aluminium alloy. The two side bodies form the main longitudinal beams and house the engines, transmission assemblies, lift fans and propulsion units. The central deck assembly comprises floor and buoyancy compartments, with box members at the bow and stern.

ACCOMMODATION: The Tiger 40 layout gives complete flexibility for any duty. The clear deck allows various configurations without major changes in the basic structure, from a simple open workboat to a full passenger cabin. Cabin modules can be isolated from the primary structure to reduce cabin noise levels.

SKIRT SYSTEM: A tapered, open loop, segmented skirt is fitted. The hoverheight at the bow is 1m and segment changes and skirt maintenance are all easily carried out without lifting the craft.

BALLAST AND FUEL SYSTEM: A four-tank, diagonally-linked ballast system adjusts the trim in pitch and roll for various loads or weather conditions. The system uses diesel fuel and is linked to the engine fuel tanks to give extended duration if required.

The engine fuel system consists of two tanks fitted amidships, one port and one starboard. Each tank supplies the lift and propulsion engine on the same side.

CAPACITIES

Engine fuel tanks: Two 450 litres each
Ballast system normal: 450 litres
Ballast system full: 900 litres
Max long range capacity: 1800 litres

DIMENSIONS

Length: 16.5m
Width: 6.0m
Height (off cushion) to top of mast: 5.24m
Hoverheight, average: 0.8m

WEIGHTS

Payload: 3000kg

PERFORMANCE

Max speed: 38–40 knots
Endurance: 5 hours at cruising speed

WEATHER LIMITATIONS

Max weather conditions: 46km/h (25 knot) wind
    1.5m sea

TIGER 200 (DESIGN)

Air Vehicles also have various craft designs between 40 and 200 seats using well proven design and manufacturing methods. These designs are offered for building under licence.

The Tiger 200 is a robust, fully amphibious vehicle design capable of carrying a 20–25 ton payload over a variety of terrain. The raft type hull structure gives a large open payload area, easily and quickly adapted to suit the task in

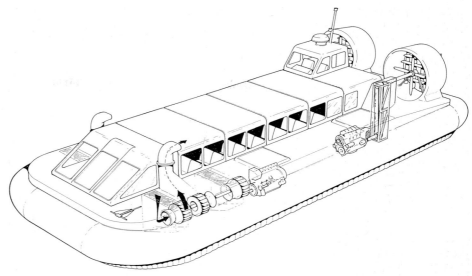

Tiger 40 passenger ferry design

hand. The engine modules, lift fan assemblies and propeller ducts are all deck-mounted for easy access and maintenance. Power is supplied by five, water-cooled, diesel engines rated at 1213kW continuously and up to 1335kW intermittently. Multiple rudders fitted to the outside propeller ducts and steerable bow thrusters ensure precise control, even with an engine stopped.

HULL: The hull is constructed from welded and rivetted marine aluminium alloy and is essentially an 'egg-box' raft structure. A series of transverse, fabricated 'I' beams and longitudinal intercostals form a strong cellular framework closed by stiffened top and bottom plating. At the bow, a 3m wide, lowering ramp can be fitted to provide vehicle access to the load bay. The deck can be designed to suit various axle loadings.

All the engines and running gear for the lift and thrust systems are surface mounted for easy access and maintenance. The load area is self-draining.

The series of watertight compartments formed by the hull give a large buoyancy reserve and meet the British Hovercraft Safety Requirements damage cases.

LIFT SYSTEM: The lift system supplies pressurised air to lift the craft and power the bow thrusters. Power is supplied by two diesel engines, surface mounted to the deck, each driving four

coaxial, centrifugal fans via a toothed belt transmission system. The front fan delivers air to the bow thruster only and the remaining three fans supply the skirt system through ducts in the hull structure. Bearings for the fan assembly are also surface mounted on the deck to allow easy access for maintenance. The fans are 1.5m in diameter and manufactured in aluminium alloy and are all similar except with regard to direction of rotation.

BOW THRUSTERS: Bow thrusters at the forward end of the craft augment the directional control system and provide additional forward thrust. The rotatable thruster ducts are situated one on each side of the craft and are supplied with air from the forward fans. Each fan is driven by, but is isolated from, its respective lift system. Each duct is operated by a DC servo motor controlled from the pilot's position by a simple rotary switch. The bow thrusters can be operated ahead or astern and are provided with isolation switches.

THRUST SYSTEM: The thrust system is powered by three diesel engines each driving a 3.65m diameter four-blade, fixed-pitch ducted propeller via a toothed belt transmission system. The engines, transmission system and duct assemblies are all surface mounted to the deck at the rear of the craft.

Four rudder blades mounted at the rear of each

Tiger 40 well-deck version as constructed by Singapore Shipbuilding and Engineering Ltd

of the two outside propeller duct assemblies provide main directional control.

POWER UNIT

All five engines used for the lift and thrust systems are the same.

Type: CRM BR-1/2000 diesel

Displacement: 57.25 litres

Power: Maximum intermittent rating: 1335kW at 2075rpm

      Continuous rating: 1213lW at 2075rpm at air temperature: 20°C.

Total fuel consumption (5 engines):

      At maximum intermittent rating: 1795 litres/hour

      At continuous rating: 1590 litres/hour.

Each engine has a self contained closed circuit water/air heat exchanger system with the airflow managed by an engine driven fan. Cooling and combustion air is cleaned by inertial vane filters.

All engines are housed in similar individual compartments with ample access provided for general servicing. The compartment cowl is hinged to allow easy engine removal. Each engine bay has stainless steel firewalling throughout and lightweight armour can be fitted.

FUEL SYSTEM: A comprehensive fuel system provides fuel for the five engines and a fuel ballast system to compensate for variations in roll and pitch caused by load state and/or weather conditions. The fuel is contained in tanks fitted within the hull structure.

SKIRT: The skirt is a tapered, open loop and segment type and varies in height from 2.5m at the bow to 2.0m at the stern. The skirt comprises the outer loop and a series of discrete segments. The segments are easily and quickly replaced without lifting the craft. The material used is nylon fabric coated with a neoprene outer layer.

CONFIGURATION: The open deck design allows complete flexibility with regard to craft configuration, cabin modules or other equipment being quickly mounted using the deck tie-down system. Various sized cabins up to 200 passenger capacity, gun and missile mounts, mine laying and

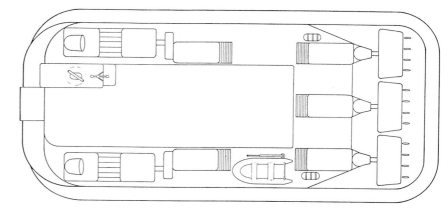

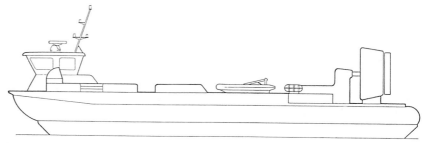

Tiger 200 well-deck craft design

hunting equipment and self loading containers for logistics work are some of the possible options.

PERFORMANCE

Maximum speed: 45 knots

Weather restrictions:

maximum wave height: 2m significant

maximum wind speed: Beaufort 7

DIMENSIONS

Length, hard structure: 36.5m

Beam, hard structure: 18.3m

Height off cushion approx: 6.6m

Load space, length: 22.0m

Load space, beam: 7.5m

WEIGHTS

Basic weight: 69.54 tonnes

Disposable load (Crew, payload and fuel): 30.46 tonnes

Maximum weight: 100 tonnes

BRITISH HOVERCRAFT CORPORATION (BHC)

(Division of Westland Aerospace) East Cowes, Isle of Wight, England PO32 6RH

Telephone: (0983) 294101
Telex: 86761WAD G
Telefax: (0983) 291006

C C Gustar, *Managing Director, Westland Aerospace*
P Starke, *General Manager*

The roots of the Corporation extend back to the world's first hovercraft, the SR.N1, which was built by Saunders Roe Limited in 1959, just prior to its being taken over by Westland.

BHC was formed in 1966, uniting the hovercraft interests of Westland and Vickers and also involving NRDC.

The corporation deals with a wide variety of applications of the air cushion principle, the emphasis being on the development and production of amphibious hovercraft.

The world's first full-scale hovercraft production line was established at East Cowes in 1964. Since then BHC has produced 10- to 17-ton SR.N6 craft, 50-ton BH.7 craft and 200- to 300-ton SR.N4 craft. The 39-ton AP1–88 is the current production craft.

Six SR.N4 class craft wre built. Five are in service, as passenger/car ferries on the Dover to Boulogne/Calais routes, with Hoverspeed, the cross-Channel operator, formed as the result of the merger between Hoverlloyd Limited and Seaspeed in October 1981. The sixth craft was broken up in 1988.

Three of the craft are to Mk 2 standard and two have been converted from Mk 1 to Mk 3 (Super 4) standard. By the end of 1987 the SR.N4's had carried 30 million passengers.

One BH.7 has been in service with the Royal Navy and six with the Iranian Navy. Four of the Iranian BH.7s have been refurbished by BHC at Cowes.

Military and general duty variants of the SR.N6 hovercraft are now in service with the Egyptian Navy, Iraqi Navy, Iranian Navy, and the Canadian and Saudi Arabian Coast Guard.

SR.N6's have been operated in Africa, Canada, Denmark, Finland, India, South America and the Middle and Far East, logging well over 250 000 operating hours.

Commercial variants of the SR.N6 are in service with the Department of Transport, Canada, and Hoverwork Limited. The SR.N6 is also used for general-purpose roles including hydrographic and seismic survey, freighting and search and rescue duties.

The latest addition to the BHC range is the

AP1–88 diesel-powered, general-purpose hovercraft. Built in welded aluminium alloy employing shipbuilding techniques, it combines a 10-ton payload with a performance equal to that of the SR.N6. AP1–88's are in passenger ferry service in Australia, between Denmark and Sweden, in Norway and in the UK. Two craft are in service with the US navy as trainers under the L.C.A.C. programme, and a half-well deck variant is operated by the Canadian Coastguard.

SR.N4 Mk 2

The SR.N4 is the world's largest commercial hovercraft and is designed for passenger/vehicle ferry operations on stage lengths of up to 185km (100n miles) on coastal water routes.

LIFT AND PROPULSION: Power is supplied by four 3400shp Rolls-Royce Marine Proteus free-turbine, turboshaft engines located in pairs at the rear of the craft on either side of the vehicle deck. Each has a maximum rating of 4250shp but usually operates at 3400shp when cruising. Each engine is connected to one of four identical pro-

Craft built	Yard No	Operator	Route
BHC SR.N4 Mk 1 *Swift* (GH 2004) in service 1969 modified to Mk 2 in 1973	002	Hoverspeed Ltd	Dover to Calais and Boulogne
BHC SR.N4 Mk 1 *Sure* (GH 2005)* in service 1969 modified to Mk 2 in 1974	003	-	-
BHC SR.N4 Mk 1 *Sir Christopher* (GH 2008) in service 1972 modified to Mk 2 in 1974	005	Hoverspeed Ltd	Dover to Calais and Boulogne
BHC SR.N4 Mk 2 *The Prince of Wales* (GH 2054) in service 1977	006	Hoverspeed Ltd	Dover to Calais and Boulogne

* broken up in 1988

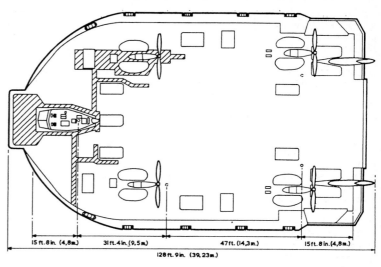

15 ft. 5 in. (4,8 m.)   31 ft. 4 in. (9,5 m.)   47 ft. (14,3 m.)   15 ft. 8 in. (4,8 m.)

128 ft. 9 in. (39,23 m.)

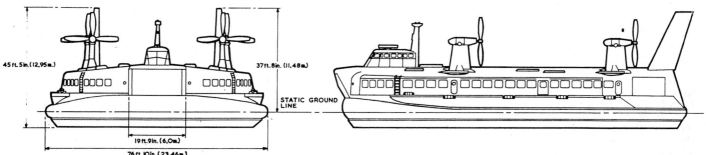

45 ft.5 in.(12,95 m.)   37 ft.8 in. (11,48 m.)

STATIC GROUND LINE

19 ft. 9 in. (6,0 m.)

76 ft. 10 in. (23,46 m.)

General arrangement of the BHC SR.N4 Mk 2

peller/fan units, two forward and two aft. The propulsion propellers, made by Hawker Siddeley Dynamics (now part of British Aerospace), are of the four-bladed, variable and reversible pitch type, 5.79m in diameter. The lift fans, made by BHC, are of the 12-bladed centrifugal type, 3.5m in diameter.

Since the gear ratios between the engine, fan and propeller are fixed, the power distribution can be altered by varying the propeller pitch and hence changing the speed of the system, which accordingly alters the power absorbed by the fixed pitch fan. The power absorbed by the fan can be varied from almost zero shp (ie boating with minimum power) to 2100shp, within the propeller and engine speed limitations. A typical division on maximum cruise power would be 2000shp to the propeller and 1150shp to the fan; the remaining 250shp can be accounted for by engine power fall-off due to the turbine rpm drop, transmission losses and auxiliary drives.

The drive shafts from the engine consist of flanged light-alloy tubes approximately 2.28m long supported by steady bearings and connected by self-aligning couplings. Shafting to the rear propeller/fan units is comparatively short, but to the forward units is approximately 18.27m.

The main gearbox of each unit comprises a spiral bevel reduction gear, with outputs at the top and bottom of the box to the vertical propeller and fan drive shafts respectively. The design of the vertical shafts and couplings is similar to the main transmission shafts, except that the shafts above the main gearbox are of steel instead of light alloy to transmit the much greater torque loads to the propeller. This gearbox is equipped with a power take-off for an auxiliary gearbox with drives for pressure and scavenge lubricating oil pumps, and also a hydraulic pump for the pylon and fin steering control.

The upper gearbox, mounted on top of the pylon, turns the propeller drive through 90 degrees and has a gear ratio of 1.16:1. This gearbox has its own self-contained lubricating system.

SR.N4 Mk 2 *Swift*, a conversion of the Mk 1

SR.N4 Mk 2 *The Prince of Wales*

Engines and auxiliaries are readily accessible for maintenance from inside the craft, while engine, propellers, pylons and all gearboxes can be removed for overhaul without disturbing the main structure.

The fan rotates on a pintle which is attached to the main structure. The assembly may be detached and removed inboard onto the car deck without disturbing the major structure.

CONTROLS: The craft control system enables the thrust lines and pitch angles of the propellers to be varied either collectively or differentially. The fins and rudders move in step with the aft pylons. The pylons, fins and rudders move through ±35 degrees, ±30 degrees and ±40 degrees respectively.

Demand signals for pylon and fin angles are transmitted electrically from the commander's controls. These are compared with the pylon or fin feed-back signals and the differences are then amplified to actuate the hydraulic jacks mounted at the base of the pylon or fin structure. Similar electro-hydraulic signalling and feed-back systems are used to control propeller pitches.

The commander's controls include a rudder bar which steers the craft by pivoting the propeller pylons differentially.

For example, if the right foot is moved forward, the forward pylons move clockwise, viewed from above, and the aft pylons and fins move anti-clockwise, thus producing a turning movement to starboard. The foregoing applies with positive thrust on the propellers, but if negative thrust is applied, as in the case of using the propellers for braking, the pylons and fins are automatically turned to opposing angles, thus maintaining the turn. A wheel mounted on a control column enables the commander to move the pylons and fins in unison to produce a drift to port or starboard as required. The control of the distribution of power between each propeller and fan is by propeller pitch lever. The pitch of all four propellers can be adjusted collectively over a limited range by a fore-and-aft movement of the control wheel.

HULL: Construction is primarily of high strength, aluminium-clad, aluminium alloy, suitably protected against the corrosive effects of sea water.

The basic structure is the buoyancy chamber, built around a grid of longitudinal and transverse frames, which form 24 watertight sub-divisions for safety. The design ensures that even a rip from end-to-end would not cause the craft to sink or overturn. The reserve buoyancy is 175%, the total available buoyancy amounting to more than 550 tons.

Top and bottom surfaces of the buoyancy chamber are formed by sandwich construction panels bolted onto the frames, the top surface being the vehicle deck. Panels covering the central 4.9m section of the deck are reinforced to carry unladen coaches, or commercial vehicles up to 9 tons gross weight (maximum axle load 5900kg), while the remainder are designed solely to carry cars and light vehicles (maximum axle load 2040kg). An articulated loading ramp 5.5m wide, which can be lowered to ground level, is built into the bows, while doors extending the full width of the centre deck are provided at the aft end.

Similar grid construction is used on the elevated passenger-carrying decks and the roof, where the panels are supported by deep transverse and longitudinal frames. The buoyancy chamber is joined to the roof by longitudinal walls to form a stiff fore-and-aft structure. Lateral bending is taken mainly by the buoyancy tanks. All horizontal surfaces are of pre-fabricated sandwich panels with the exception of the roof, which is of skin and stringer panels.

Double curvature has been avoided other than in the region of the air intakes and bow. Each fan air intake is bifurcated and has an athwartships bulkhead at both front and rear, supporting a beam carrying the transmission main gearbox and the propeller pylon. The all-moving fins and rudders behind the aft pylons pivot on pintles just ahead of the rear bulkhead.

The fans deliver air to the cushion via a peripheral fingered bag skirt.

The material used for both bags and fingers is nylon, coated with neoprene and/or natural rubber, the fingers and cones being made from a heavier weight material than the trunks.

ACCOMMODATION: The basic manning requirement is for a commander, an engineer/radio operator and a radar operator/navigator. A seat is provided for a fourth crew member or a crew member in training. The remainder of the crew, ie those concerned with passenger service or car handling, are accommodated in the main cabins. The arrangement may be modified to suit individual operator's requirements.

The control cabin, which provides nearly 360-degree vision, is entered by one of two ways. The normal method, when the cars are arranged in four lanes, is by a hatch in the cabin floor, reached by a ladder from the car deck. When heavy vehicles are carried on the centre section, or if for some other reason the ladder has to be retracted, a door in the side of the port forward passenger cabin gives access to a ladder leading onto the main cabin roof. From the roof a door gives access into the control cabin.

The craft currently in service carry 282 passengers and 37 cars.

The car deck occupies the large central area of the craft, with large stern doors and a bow ramp providing a drive-on/drive-off facility.

Separate side doors give access to the passenger cabins which flank the car deck. The outer cabins have large windows which extend over the full length of the craft. The control cabin is sited centrally and forward on top of the superstructure to give maximum view.

EXTERNAL DIMENSIONS
Overall length: 39.68m
Overall beam: 23.77m
Overall height on landing pads: 11.48m
Skirt depth: 2.44m

INTERNAL DIMENSIONS
Passenger/vehicle floor area: 539m^2
Vehicle deck headroom-centre line: 3.43m
Bow ramp door aperture size (height × width): 3.51 × 5.48m
Stern door aperture size (height × width): 3.51 × 9.45m

WEIGHT/CAPACITY
Normal gross: 200 tons
Fuel capacity: 20 456 litres

PERFORMANCE (at normal gross weight at 15°C)
Max water speed over calm water, zero wind (cont power rating): 70 knots
Average service water speed: 40–60 knots
Normal stopping distance from 50 knots: 480m
Endurance at max cont power on 2800 Imperial gallons: 2.5 hours
Negotiable gradient from standing start: 1 : 11

SR.N4 Mk 3 (SUPER 4)

The Super 4 differs from earlier Marks of the SR.N4 primarily in that it is 16.76m longer, increasing the overall length to 56.38m with a beam of 28.04m.

Modification of an SR.N4 Mk 1 to Super 4 standard necessitates adding a new 16.76m section amidships, widening the existing superstructure and strengthening the original bow and stern halves to accept the increased stresses resulting from the 40 per cent increase in length. The propeller pylons are raised to allow 6.4m diameter propellers to be fitted, the transmission systems are realigned and four uprated 3800shp Rolls-Royce Marine Proteus gas turbines are installed.

A more efficient low-pressure-ratio skirt system with larger fingers is fitted, giving a mean air cushion depth of 2.7m. Passenger cabin trim and seating have been completely revised and sound-proofing increased.

Compared with the SR.N4 Mk 1, the Super 4 has a 70 per cent greater revenue earning capability, but costs only about 15 per cent more to operate. The increased length and advanced skirt system give both a higher performance in

Craft built	Yard No	Operator	Route
BHC SR.N4 Mk 1 *The Princess Margaret* (GH 2006) in service 1968, modified to Mk 3 in 1979	001	Hoverspeed Ltd	Dover to Calais and Boulogne
BHC SR.N4 Mk 1 *The Princess Anne* (GH 2007) in service 1969, modified to Mk 3 in 1978.	004	Hoverspeed Ltd	Dover to Calais and Boulogne

SR.N4 Mk II forward passenger cabin, starboard side

(*Hoverspeed Ltd*)

Control cabin of Super 4

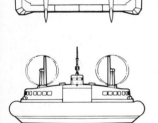
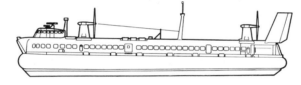

General arrangement of SR.N4 Mk 3 (Super 4)

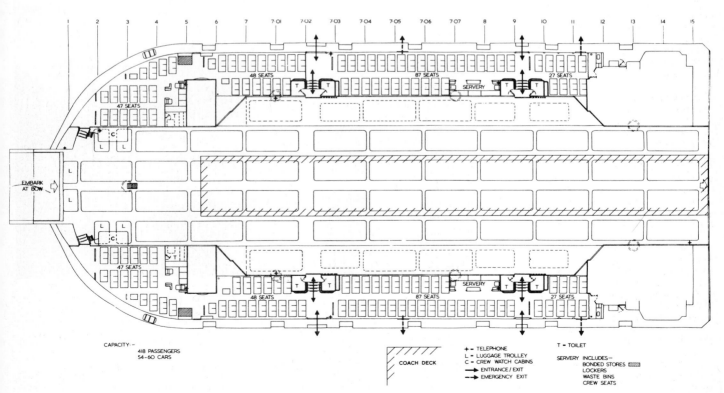

CAPACITY:—
418 PASSENGERS
54–60 CARS

COACH DECK

+ — TELEPHONE
L — LUGGAGE TROLLEY
C — CREW WATCH CABINS
→ ENTRANCE / EXIT
⇢ EMERGENCY EXIT

T — TOILET

SERVERY INCLUDES:—
BONDED STORES
LOCKERS
WASTE BINS
CREW SEATS

Layout of vehicle deck and passenger cabins on SR.N4 Mk 3 (Super 4)

adverse weather and greatly improved ride comfort for the passengers.

Craft handling and skirt behaviour have proved completely satisfactory over the entire weight range from 212 to 300 tons in sea conditions up to Force 8 to 9. Measurements taken in the passenger cabins of acceleration forces show a three-fold improvement in ride comfort over the SR.N4 Mk 2. The uprated Rolls-Royce Proteus gas turbines have been trouble-free and the new propellers have substantially reduced external noise when operating into and out of hovercraft terminals.

Super 4 has a payload of 418 passengers and 60 vehicles, a laden weight of 300 tons and a top speed in excess of 65 knots.

LIFT AND PROPULSION: Motive power is supplied by four Rolls-Royce Marine Proteus Type 15M/529 free-turbine turboshaft engines, located in pairs at the rear of the craft on either side of the vehicle deck. Each engine is rated at 3800shp continuous under ISA conditions and is connected to one of four identical propeller/fan units, two forward and two aft. The propellers, made by British Aerospace Dynamics, are of four-bladed, controllable-pitch type D258/485A/2. The lift fans, made by BHC, are of 12-bladed centrifugal type, 3.5m in diameter. Maximum fuel tankage, 28.45 tonnes; normal fuel allowing for ballast transfer, 18.29 tonnes.

AUXILIARY POWER: Two Lucas turboshaft engines driving 55kVA 200V, 400Hz Lucas alternators.

DIMENSIONS
Length overall: 56.38
Beam, hardstructure: 23.16m
Height overall, on landing pads: 11.43m
Bow ramp door aperture size,
    Height: 3.5m
    Width: 5.48m
Stern door aperture size,
    Height: 3.51m
    Width: 9.45m
Car deck area: 631m^2

WEIGHTS
Max laden: 300 tons
Max disposable load: 112 tons
Typical fuel load: 20 tons
Payload: 54–60 cars, 418 passengers

PERFORMANCE
Typical cruise water speeds:
Calm (2ft waves, 5 knots wind): 60–65 knots
Moderate (5ft waves, 20 knots wind): 50–55 knots
Rough (8ft waves, 27 knots wind): 35–45 knots
Endurance per ton of fuel: 0.23 hour

SR.N6

Craft built	
SR.N6 Mk's 1 to 5	42
SR.N6 Mk 6	7
SR.N6 Mk 8	8

Designed primarily as a fast ferry for operation in sheltered waters, the SR.N6 Mk 1 can accommodate either 38 passengers or 3 tons of freight.

Fully amphibious, it can operate from relatively unsophisticated bases above the high water mark, irrespective of tidal state.

Directional control is achieved by twin rudders and and skirt lift, with a thrust port system to assist in low speed manoeuvring. Two manually actuated elevators provide pitch trim at cruising speed.

SR.N6's have been in regular civil operations since 1965. Operators include Hoverwork Limited and the Canadian Coast Guard.

Military variants are in service with the Egyp-

SR.N4 Mk 3 (Super 4), *The Princess Anne*

SR.N4 Mk 3 (Super 4), *The Princess Anne*

Vehicle deck, SR.N4 Mk 3 (Super 4)

tian Navy, Iraqi Navy (type Mk 6C), Iranian Navy and the Saudi Arabian Frontier Force.

LIFT AND PROPULSION: Power for the integrated lift/propulsion system is provided by a Rolls-Royce Marine Gnome gas turbine with a maximum continuous rating at 15°C of 900shp. This drives a BHC 12-blade centrifugal 2.13m diameter lift fan, and a Dowty Rotol four-blade

variable pitch 2.74m diameter propeller for propulsion.

EXTERNAL DIMENSIONS
Overall length: 14.8m
Overall beam, skirt inflated: 7.7m
Overall height on landing pads: 3.8m
Overall height, hovering: 5m
Skirt depth: 1.22m

INTERNAL DIMENSIONS
Cabin size (length × width): 6.62 × 2.34m
Cabin headroom-centre line: 1.83m
Door aperture size (height × width): 1.75 × 0.99m
WEIGHT
Max: 10 tons
PERFORMANCE (at normal gross weight at 15°C)
Max water speed over calm water, zero wind, (continuous power rating): 96km/h (52 knots)
Average service water speed in sheltered coastal waters: 55–65km/h (30–35 knots)
Endurance at max continuous power rating on 265 Imperial gallons of fuel: 3.6 hours

SR.N6 Mk 1S

In 1972 a 'stretched' version of the SR.N6 passenger craft known as SR.N6 Mark 1S was introduced, increasing the seating capacity from 38 to 58.

The Mark 1S is 3 metres longer than the Mark 1 and has additional baggage panniers on the rear sidedecks. To maintain performance the rating of the Rolls-Royce Gnome gas turbine is increased by 100 to 1000shp.

Three Mark 1S craft have been built.

SR.N6 Mk 6 GENERAL PURPOSE

The SR.N6 Mk 6 is the most recent development in the successful SR.N6 series and represents significant steps forward in terms of all-weather performance and increased manoeuvrability, especially in high winds and at low speeds. There is also a significant reduction in the external noise level.

These advances have been achieved by the introduction of twin propellers, a more powerful engine and a redesigned skirt. The tapered skirt, which is deeper at the bow than the stern, cushions the effect of operating over larger waves and surface obstacles and enables the craft to operate in winds of up to Beaufort Scale 8 and waves of up to 3.04m.

The cabin is the same size as on the SR.N6 Mk 1S.

LIFT AND PROPULSION: Originally motive power was supplied by a single 1125hp Rolls-Royce Marine Gnome GN 1301 but the craft has been modified for hydrographic survey work and is now fitted with a Gnome GN 1051/1. Two 3.05m diameter Dowty Rotol variable-pitch propellers are fitted.
DIMENSIONS
Length overall: 18.80m
Beam overall: 7.92m
Height overall, on landing pads: 4.00m
on cushion: 5.5m
WEIGHT
Max operating: 17 010kg
PERFORMANCE
Max speed over calm water: 60 knots

SR.N6 Mk 6C

This is a military twin-propeller SR.N6, of similar layout to the SR.N6 Mk 6. However, the construction of its side decks is different.
LIFT AND PROPULSION: Integrated system powered by a single Rolls-Royce GN 1452 rated at 1310 shp at 15°C. Auxiliary power is supplied by a lucas SS923 gas turbine driving a three-phase alternator.
DIMENSIONS
Length overall: 18.31m
Beam overall: 9.08m
Height overall, on cushion: 6.78m
TANKS: A single bag tank of 1205 litres capacity is installed behind the cabin below the main engine support structure. Four long range fuel tanks, each of 454 litres are fitted, two each side, within the side structure. A ballast system, of normal content 908 litres is fitted, its tanks within the plenum chamber, close to the four corners of the craft. The fuel it contains can be transferred to

SR.N6 Mk 6 general purpose hovercraft showing twin-propeller arrangement and tapered skirt

SR.N6 operated by Canadian Coast Guard hovercraft units

the main fuel tank for extended range and, for furtherendurance, the ballast system can be filled to its maximum capacity of 1816 litres.
CONTROLS: The craft is controlled by means of two rudders and the elevator assembly in conjunction with collective and differential propeller pitch control, roll control and yaw control doors.

The roll control system consists of two hydraulically actuated doors, normally open, fitted across the air feed to the rear trunks. They are controlled by means of solenoid valves selected by a switch at the commander's position. On selection of a roll control door, pressure in the port or starboard rear trunk is reduced, causing the craft to bank.

The propeller pitch change mechanism is actuated collectively by means of a lever adjacent to the elevator lever. Engine power is controlled by a twist grip on the propeller collective pitch lever, thus enabling the hover height and speed of the craft to be controlled with one hand. Differential pitch control is by means of a knob at the subpanel below the main instrument panel. Movement of the commander's pitch controls is converted into movement of the hydraulic pitch actuators by means of an electronic processing unit and electric actuators. The commander's throttle control is connected to the engine mounted throttle actuator.

ACCOMMODATION: The forward part of the cabin is occupied by the crew. Within the crew area, the commander's position is forward on the starboard side, with the radar station immediately behind. Forward on the port side is a platform for the observer and behind that the radio operator's position. A semi partition, carrying a weapon rack, is fitted at the rear of the crew area.

Behind the partial partition, the crew area is equipped with longitudinal bench seating for eighteen persons. The seating is readily convertible to provide bunks for eight and seating for two. Two doors each side give access from the personnel area onto the sidedecks.

At the back of the personnel area, a full partition with a door is fitted, behind which is the radio and electrics compartment which houses the radio racks and the electrical distribution panels.

Windscreens are of toughened glass and are fitted with wipers and washers. The cabin side windows are of Perspex.

SR.N6 Mk 8

The latest military variant of the single propeller SR.N6, the Mk 8 has the same overall measurements as the SR.N6 Mk 6C twin-propeller model.

In the logistic support role the Mk 8 can carry up to 55 fully-equipped troops or loads of up to 6 tons. Access to the cabin, which measures 9.5 × 2.3m, is via a bow door. The floor is fitted with tie-down points for stores and equipment. Loads up to ½ ton which are too long for the cabin may be carried externally on the side-decks.

In the coastal patrol role, the operational flexibility of the SR.N6 is greatly improved by its ability to work from beaches and other unprepared sites and to navigate freely in shallow water. At the same time the craft is seaworthy and can operate in most weather conditions by day or night.

LIFT AND PROPULSION: Single Rolls-Royce GN 1451 marine gas turbine rated at 1080shp at 15°C. Auxiliary power by a Lucas SS923 gas turbine driving a three-phase alternator. Main fuel tank capacity is 1204 litres. Long-range tanks are incorporated, giving an additional capacity of 1818 litres.

ARMAMENT: Either a ring-mounted machine gun (0.5in or 7.62mm) or short range wire-guided surface-to-surface missiles mounted on the side-decks.

DIMENSIONS
Length overall: 17.78m
Beam overall: 7.97m
Height overall on cushion: 6.32m
PERFORMANCE
Max speed, calm water: 50 knots
Endurance, on main tanks: 2.4 hours
    on long-range tanks: 6 hours
A further 1.8 hours endurance can be obtained by using the fuel carried in the craft's trim system giving a maximum endurance of 7.8 hours.

BH.7

BH.7 is a 55-ton hovercraft which was designed specifically for naval and military roles. The prototype, designated BH.7 Mk 2, has been in service with the Royal Navy since 1970 where it has been evaluated in a number of roles including fishery protection, ASW and MCM work.

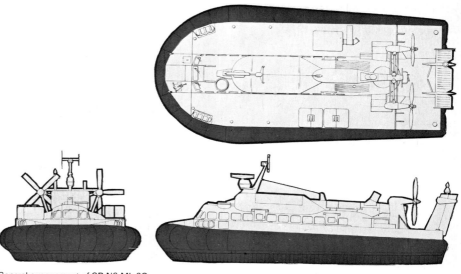

General arrangement of SR.N6 Mk 6C

SR.N6 Mk 8 craft

In 1982/83 the RN craft was equipped with an operational mine hunting fit comprising: Plessey 193M and 2048 Speedscan sonar equipment and a Racal Decca NAV/AIO system. Using this equipment the craft completed a very successful series of trials, operating from the Royal Navy Air Station at Portland.

The second and third craft, designated Mk 4, and a further four Mk 5As, are in service with the Iranian Navy.

LIFT AND PROPULSION: Power for the integrated lift propulsion system on the Mk 2 and Mk 4 is provided by a Rolls-Royce Marine Proteus 15M/541 gas turbine with a maximum rating at 23°C of 4250shp. On the Mk 5A, a 15M/549 is installed with a maximum rating of 4250shp. In both types the engine drives, via a light alloy driveshaft and bevel drive gearbox, a BHC 12-blade, centrifugal 3.5m diameter lift fan and a British Aerospace Dynamics four-blade, variable-pitch pylon-mounted propeller. Propeller diameter on the Mk 4 is 5.79m and 6.4m on the Mk 2 and Mk 5A. Normal fuel capacity is up to 13 635 litres.

CONTROLS: Craft direction is controlled by swivelling the propeller pylon angle by a foot-pedal. Thrust ports are fitted at each quarter to assist directional control at low speed, and a hydraulically-operated skirt-lift system helps to bank the craft into turns, thereby reducing drift.

Fuel is transferred between forward and aft tanks via a ring main to adjust fore and aft trim.

HULL: Construction is mainly of corrosion resistant light alloy. Extensive use is made of components which were designed for the N4. The bow structure is a Plasticell base covered with glass fibre.

SKIRT: The fan delivers air to the cushion via a continuous peripheral fingered bag skirt made in neoprene-coated nylon fabric. The skirt provides an air cushion depth of 1.68m. The cushion is divided into four compartments by a full length longitudinal keel and by two transverse keels located slightly forward of amidships.

ACCOMMODATION: The raised control cabin, located slightly forward of amidships on the hull centre line, accommodates a crew of three, with the driver and navigator/radar operator in front and the third crew member behind. The driver sits on the right, with the throttle and propeller pitch control lever on his right, and the pylon angle pedal and skirt-lift column in front.

The navigator, on the left, has a Decca radar display (Type 914 on the Mk 5) and compass in front and Decometers in an overhead panel.

The large main cabin area permits a variety of operational layouts. In a typical arrangement, the operations room is placed directly beneath the control cabin and contains communication, navigation, search and strike equipment and associated displays.

The craft has an endurance of up to 11 hours under cruise conditions but this can be extended considerably as it can stay 'on watch' without using the main engine.

Provision can be made for the crew to live aboard for several days.

SYSTEMS, ELECTRICAL: Two Rover IS/90

APUs provide, via two 55kVA generators, three-phase 400Hz ac at 200V for ac and dc supplies.
EXTERNAL DIMENSIONS
Length overall: 23.9m
Beam overall: 13.8m
Overall height on landing pads: 10.36m
Cushion depth: 1.76m
INTERNAL DIMENSIONS (Main Cabin)
Cabin length: 13.2m
Cabin width: 4.17m
Headroom (on centre line): 2.38m
WEIGHTS
Max: 56 tonnes
Disposable load, incl role equipment: 18.3 tonnes
PERFORMANCE (at max operating weight at 15°C)
Max continuous calm water speed: 58 knots

BH.7 Mk 2

Craft built

One for the British Royal Navy, P235

BH.7 Mk 4 LOGISTIC SUPPORT VERSION

Craft built

Two BH.7 Mk 4s for the Iranian Navy

ACCOMMODATION: In this role, the main hold floor area of 56m² (600ft²) of the Mk 4 provides an unobstructed space suitable for loading wheeled vehicles, guns and military stores.

Two side cabins, filled with paratroop-type seats, can accommodate up to 60 troops and their equipment.

Access at the bow is through a 'clamshell' door.

Machine guns can be fitted in gun rings on the roof on either side of the cabin and provision can be made for armour plating to protect personnel, the engine and vital electrical components.
TYPICAL MILITARY LOADS: 170 fully equipped troops or three field cars and trailers plus 60 troops or two armoured scout cars or up to 20 NATO pallets.

BH.7 Mk 5A COMBAT/LOGISTICS VERSION

Craft built

Four BH.7 Mk 5As for the Iranian Navy

Designed for coastal defence operations, the BH.7 Mk 5A carries medium-range surface-to-surface missiles, such as Exocet, on its sidedecks. Secondary armament consists of two roof-mounted 20mm guns.

The main central cabin, employed on the BH.7 Mk 4 for load-carrying, is equipped as an operations and fire-control room. The bow door is retained providing a dual missile/logistic capability. Since it is fully amphibious, the BH.7 can be operated from relatively unprepared bases on beaches and can head directly towards its target on interception missions regardless of the tidal state and marginal terrain. Also, since none of its solid structure is immersed, it is invulnerable to underwater defences such as acoustic, magnetic and pressure mines and to attack by torpedoes.

A full range of electronic navigational aids permits the craft to operate by day or night.

AP1–88

Major advances in hovercraft technology in recent years enabled British Hovercraft Corporation to offer a 7-tonne payload craft with a performance equal to that of the well-proven SR.N6. Built in welded aluminium alloy AP1–88 is powered by air-cooled marine diesels. Not only is it substantially cheaper in first and operating costs than the SR.N6 but it is considerably more

BH.7 Mk 5A as supplied to Iranian Navy

Royal Navy BH.7 Mk 2 equipped for minehunting with Plessey 193M sonar immersed

BH.7 Mk 2 with retracted Plessey 193M sonar tube

AP1–88 (half well-deck) search and rescue craft building for the Canadian Coast Guard, autumn 1986

One of BHC AP1–88s on the DSØ Malmö to Copenhagen route

robust than many earlier generation craft of this size. Most of its components are commercially available. AP1–88 has low crew and maintenance requirements, footprint pressure and noise levels.

The craft can be employed in a wide variety of commercial, military and para-military roles including:

Passenger Ferrying
Search and Rescue
Hydrographic Surveying
Ice breaking
Anti-smuggling
Firefighting
Logistic Support
Counter Insurgency
Mine Countermeasures
Anti-submarine Warfare
Minelaying

In its civil passenger configuration it can seat up to 101 passengers and as a troop carrier up to 90 fully-kitted troops. In a logistics role the AP1–88 will carry two Land-Rovers, a BV202 tracked vehicle and trailer unit or about 10 000 kg of stores.

The first two AP1–88s *Tenacity* and *Resolution* began operating with Hovertravel between Ryde and Southsea in 1983. In 1985 *Resolution* was chartered to the US Navy as an LCAC trainer and a third 80-seater *Perseverance* was built to replace it on the Ryde-Southsea route. These three craft are built to the 2.4m shorter/80 configuration with Deutz 278kW BF10L 413F lift engines and Deutz 367kW BF12L 413FC propulsion engines.

During 1984 two of the production standard craft entered service with A/S Dămpskibsselskabet sresund (DSØ) of Denmark on a route linking Copenhagen's Kastrup airport and Malmö.

AP1–88s have been built under license in Australia by NQEA Australia (see entry) at Cairns and operate ferry services in Australia, Spain and Taiwan.

A half-well deck variant is in service with the Canadian Coast Guard undertaking search and rescue, navaid maintenance and icebreaking tasks on the St Lawrence River and its tributaries. The new hovercraft replaces the Voyageur ACV of the Coast Guard.

The craft is of a half well-deck configuration with accommodation for up to 12 crew members or technicians and up to 12 tons of cargo. This AP1–88 is equipped with a hydraulic crane,

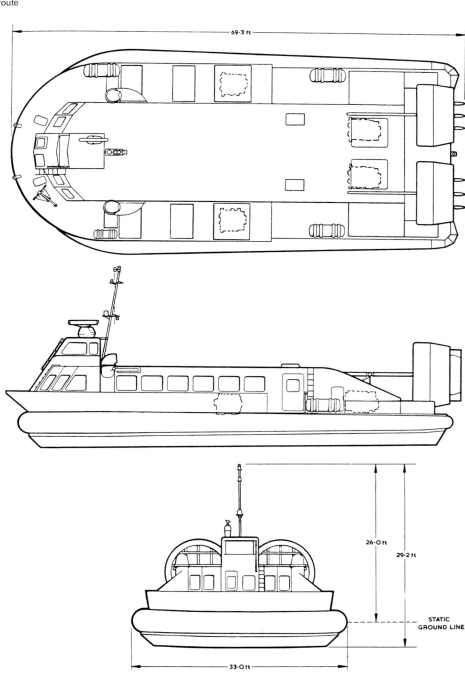

General arrangement of AP1–88/80 hovercraft

capstan and winch to facilitate the conduct of a variety of specialised coast guard tasks.

The design and construction of the AP1-88 comply with the BHSR, IMO and DnV standards and the craft is cleared to operate in winds up to 30 knots mean, 40 knots gust and in wave heights up to 2.4m (1.5m significant).

ENGINES: The AP1-88/100 craft is powered by four Deutz BF12 513FC 12-cylinder air-cooled diesels each rated at 386kW maximum (2300rpm) and 336kW continuous (2200rpm).

LIFT AND PROPULSION: Two of the engines, housed in the side box structures, power the lift and bow thruster systems. On each side of the craft one engine drives three 0.84m diameter double-entry centrifugal fans, two of which supply air to the cushion via the skirt system and the third supplies air to the rotatable bow thruster. The well-deck version for the Canadian Coast Guard has four 0.885m diameter fans for the lift system with two 0.84m fans for the bow thrusters.

Propulsion is by two 2.74m diameter 4-blade Hoffman ducted propellers each driven by one of the diesels via a toothed belt. On craft 001, 103, 003, 004 and 005 the propellers are of fixed-pitch type, but ground adjustable through ± 5°. Craft 002 and 006 have variable-pitch propellers, type HO-V-254P2DFR/D275. The belt-drive reduction ratio is 1:0.6.

FUEL/BALLAST SYSTEM: Fuel is carried in four tanks, one at each bow corner and two on the centre line at the stern. Fuel can be transferred between tanks for trimming purposes.
Total tank capacity: 4500 litres
Normal usable fuel capacity: 1800 litres

CONTROLS: Directional control is provided by two sets of triple aerodynamic rudder vanes mounted on the rear of the propeller ducts, differential propeller thrust and by swivelling bow thrusters. In the straight-aft position, the bow thrusters contribute to forward thrust. Trim is controlled by fuel ballast transfer.

STRUCTURE: Basic hull is formed by a buoyancy tank made almost entirely of very wide aluminium alloy extrusions, one extrusion being used for the I-beams forming the transverse frames and a second for the integrally stiffened planking used for the bottom and deck. The remainder of the rigid structure is built from smaller welded extrusions and plating, with the exception of the roof, made from riveted light gauge corrugated panels. The propeller ducts are a composite structure of light alloy and Kevlar reinforced plastic. Marine alloys are used, including N8 plate and HE30 extrusions. In general, plate thicknesses are 2 or 3mm except for the light gauge roof plating. The structure is welded throughout to eliminate mechanical fastenings which can be sources of corrosion. Detachable panels give easy access for engine and fan removal and facilitate the inspection of ventilation ducting and tail control cable runs. Lifting, for the inspection of the craft underside and skirts, is achieved by three jacks which are fitted and operated from inside the craft. However, for general maintenance, the craft is put down on fly-over blocks.

SKIRT: Low-pressure ratio tapered skirt based on that of the Super 4. Mean cushion depth 1.37m.

ACCOMMODATION: The superstructure is divided into four main components: a large central accommodation area forward of a propulsion machinery bay and two side bodies containing the lift system machinery. A control cabin is mounted on top of the main cabin. In addition to the full-cabin and half well-deck versions, full well-deck variants are also available. The commercial full-cabin version seats a maximum of 101 passengers with the seats arranged in rows of seven across the cabin. The rows are divided by two gangways 600mm wide which separate the seats into a 2-3-2 configuration. Two doors, one port and one starboard, are at the aft end of the cabin. Doorways are 1.75 by 0.9 metres. An emergency door

Craft built (in UK)	Reg No	Serial No	No of seats	Name	Launched	Operator
AP1–88/80	GH 2087*	001	80	*Tenacity*	1983	Hovertravel Ltd
AP1–88/80	GH 2088*	002	80	*Resolution***	1983	US Navy
AP1–88/80	GH 2100*	103	80	*Perseverance***	1985	US Navy
AP1–88/100	GH 9029†	003	81	*Idun Viking*, (ex *Expo Spirit*)	1984	A/S Dämpskibsselskabet Øsresund**
API-88/100	GH 9030±	004	81	*Freja Viking*	1984	A/S DSØ
AP1–88/100	GH 9031	005	81	*Liv Viking*	1984	A/S DSØ
AP1–88/200 half well-deck	CH-C-CG	006	12	*Waban-Aki*	1987	Canadian Coast Guard
AP1–88	GH 2107	007	95	*Double-O-Seven*	May 1989	Hovertravel Ltd

* hulls built at Fairey Allday Marine and fitted out by Hovertravel Ltd at Bembridge, Isle of Wight
† leased by BHC for five months (May to September) in 1986 to Hoverwest Ferry Services Inc, Canada and named *Expo Spirit*. The craft operated a service from Victoria, Vancouver Island to Canada Place at the Expo '86 site, Vancouver, BC
‡ hull built by Fairey Allday Marine and fitted out by BHC
** this craft now owned by DSØ was leased to Hovertransport A/S in 1987
*** sold to Textron Marine Systems, then leased to US Navy

AP1–88/100

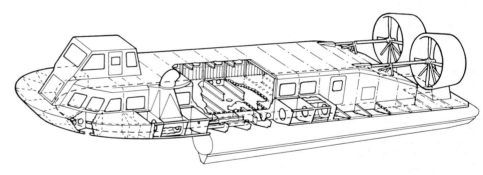

1.06 by 0.9 metres is at the forward end of the passenger cabin. Craft built to standard include a cabin heating and ventilation system adequate for operation in temperate climates, more elaborate systems are available as options. There are two sets of four luggage panniers on the sidedecks aft of the cabin doors. Total volume of the eight panniers is approximately 6.6 cubic metres.

COMMUNICATIONS: A Sailor RT 145 VHF international marine band radio or similar equipment.

RADAR: Racal-Decca 914C. Antenna turning unit and transceiver on control cabin roof. Display unit mounted in control cabin on port side. Display is north-up stabilised by gyrocompass. NAVIGATION: Remote reading gyrocompass; a Lambda T.12 spherical compass. Optional range of automatic and semi-automatic navigational aids.

EXTERNAL DIMENSIONS
Length overall: 24.4m
Beam overall: 11.0m
Height on cushion: 9.5m
Mean cushion depth: 1.37m

INTERNAL DIMENSIONS
Cabin, length: 14.4m (47.3ft)
Beam: 4.8m
Headroom: 1.95m
WEIGHTS
Basic equipped craft: 29 480kg
Max disposable load (crew, fuel, provisions, fresh water, freight, passengers): 11 340kg
Max weight: 40 820kg
PERFORMANCE
Max calm water speed: 50 knots (93km/h)
Total fuel consumption at continuous power (full throttle): 368 litres/h

P AP1–88/200
WABAN-AKI
This craft entered service with the Canadian Coast Guard in 1987
LIFT AND PROPULSION: Four Deutz BF12L 513CP air-cooled turbocharged diesels, 441kW each, at 2300rpm. Two Hoffman 2.75m diameter variable-pitch propeller type HO-V-254P2DFR/D275, ducted. Four centrifugal lift

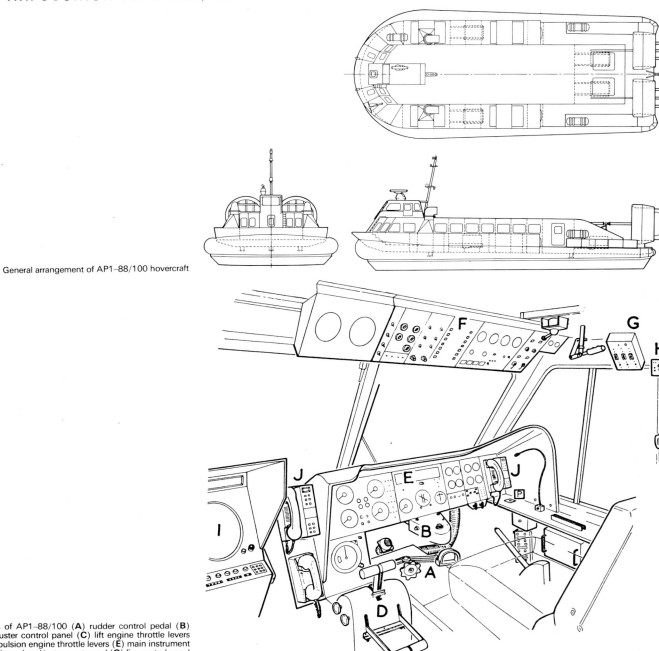

General arrangement of AP1–88/100 hovercraft

Controls of AP1–88/100 (**A**) rudder control pedal (**B**) bow thruster control panel (**C**) lift engine throttle levers (**D**) propulsion engine throttle levers (**E**) main instrument panel (**F**) overhead instrument panel (**G**) fire control panel (**H**) electrical bay smoke detector warning panel (**I**) Kelvin Huges 1600 radar display (**J**) VHF radio (2 sets)

BHC AP1–88/200 prior to delivery to the Canadian Coast Guard, 1987

fans 0.885m diameter. Two bow thrusters, centrifugal fans 0.840m diameter.

The following details are specifically applicable to *Waban-Aki*.

COMMUNICATIONS: VHF radio FM Wulfsberg RT 7200, VHF radio AM King KY 196 Silver Crown, HF King KHF 990.

NAVIGATION

Radar: Decca RM 914C, VHF (FM/AM) ADF: OAR Type ADFS-347EH, HF ADF Sitex 511 AADF

Navigator

Plotter: Loran 'C' with RS 200 Shipmate colour track plotter. Gyromagnetic compass: AIM system

ELECTRICAL SYSTEM: Main system 28V dc; auxiliary system 240/120V ac 60Hz single phase. Dc supply: four Bosch Type T1, 28V, 120A-17 generation. Ac supply: diesel engine auxiliary power unit, 12kW output. Batteries: start/service S1 two 12V, 143Ah; start/service S2 two 12V, 143Ah; essential service two 12V; 143Ah.

FUEL SYSTEM: Engine fuel and ballast transfer for adjustment of craft trim; fuel type: marine gas oil LS to SD 2869 1970 A1 (Canadian Grade CAN 2-3.6-M83); max tank capacities: four 1138-litre, two 680-litre, total 5900-litre.

HYDRAULIC SYSTEMS: Power assistance to rudders; control of variable-pitch propellers; auxiliary hydraulic components.

DIMENSIONS

Length overall: 24.50m

Beam, rigid structure: 4.40m
  on-cushion: 11.20m

Height at rest on ground, to top of radar scanner: 5.90m
  on cushion, to top of mast: 10.00m

WEIGHTS

Max weight: 47 150kg

Max disposable load: 12 450kg

PERFORMANCE

Speed, max: 50 knots

Endurance, normal max: 10 hours approx

General arrangement of P AP1–88/200 as delivered to the Canadian Coast Guard, 1987

GRIFFON HOVERCRAFT LIMITED

Head Office: Carlton House, Ringwood Road, Woodlands, Southampton SO4 2HT, England

Telephone: (0703) 813461
Telex: 47423GIFTEK G
Telefax: (0703) 813462

D R Robertson, *Director*
E W H Gifford, *Director*
J H Gifford, *Director*

Founded in 1976, Griffon Hovercraft has concentrated on the design and development of small amphibious hovercraft.

The company's first design, Griffon, used a four-blade ducted propeller for propulsion with a centrifugal fan for lift, both driven by a Jaguar automobile engine. This craft was subsequently put into production as the Skima 12, built by Pindair Limited under licence from Griffon Hovercraft Ltd. Many of this type of craft have been in service throughout the world in a variety of roles.

The initial choice of a petrol engine was due to its superior power-to-weight ratio, although the advantages of the diesel engine were recognised. The development of the turbocharged air-cooled diesel led to the company's decision, early in 1982,

that a small commercial diesel-powered hovercraft would be feasible and would carry a useful payload.

Construction of the Griffon 1000 TD prototype began in June 1982. Performance trials began in May 1983 and exceeded expectations. The prototype is now with the company's US licensees, Frank W Hake Inc of Eddystone, Pennsylvania. Operating hours are in excess of 1500. Three craft of this type have been supplied to Geophysical Surveys Inc of Dallas, USA, for use in an oilfield survey on the Yellow River, China. Due to the intensive nature of these operations, thousands of operating hours have been accumulated with minimal maintenance, proving the inherently rugged nature of the design. In 1987, a 1000 TD was supplied to the Water and Power Development Authority of Pakistan for survey work. Various features were added to the craft to meet the customer's particular requirements.

The success of the 1000 TD has led to a range of craft being developed with 1- to 4-tonne payloads, using similar machinery units and control systems. The company intends to concentrate on the requirements for a low-cost easily maintained craft for use in workboat, patrol and ferry applications.

All Griffon hovercraft are designed to comply with the IMO, the British CAA and the Canadian Coast Guard Regulations. The 1000 TD and 1500

TD have CAA Type approval, the 2500 TD is approved by the US and the Canadian Coast Guard. The company's design and manufacturing philosophy is such that the customer's individual requirements, both as modifications to the company's standard range or complete special design projects, can be met on a cost-effective basis.

The success of the 1000 TD has led to a range of craft being developed with 0.5 to 7.0 tonne payloads, using similar machinery units and control systems.

In January 1989 an improved and modified range of Griffon hovercraft was introduced. A six-seat hovercraft, the Mini 500, powered by a VW/Audi automotive engine, and constructed in composite sandwich with Kevlar, has been designed for a specific customer. Of the larger craft, the Griffon 1000 TD continues to attract survey and paramilitary users and the new Griffon 2000 TD and 2000 TDX are replacing the 1500 TD and 1500 TDX respectively (the numerals in the name/title of the Griffons reflect their payload in kilograms). The 2500 TD and 2500 TDX are now being replaced by the 37-seat 3000 TD and whereas the 4000 TD remains the same, a new 5000 TD with a separate lift engine has been introduced. All craft in the Griffon range have commonality of design, systems and spare parts, and are designed to comply with IMO, the British CAA and the Canadian Coastguard Regulations.

Sales and marketing for the company's products on a worldwide basis are being carried out by Hovercraft Sales and Marketing, PO Box 7, Sarisbury Green, Southampton, Hants SO3 6YS, UK. Tel: (042 121) 3547; Telex: 477164 HOVSAM G.

Craft built
By licensed builder: 16
By Griffon Hovercraft Ltd: 15

1000 TD

The smallest craft in the TD range, the 1000 TD carries a payload of 1000kg or 10 passengers. The craft is powered by a single diesel engine and is available with a variety of superstructures. Folding sidedecks enable it to be loaded onto its purpose-built trailer and towed behind a small truck. It can also be fitted into a 20-foot container, after removal of bow and stern sections.

Craft built 1000TD

001	Hover Systems Inc.
002	Geophysical Surveys Inc, USA for Yellow River, China, 1984
003	Geophysical Surveys Inc, USA for Yellow River, China, 1984
004	Geophysical Surveys Inc, USA for Yellow River, China, 1984
008	Water and Power Development Authority, (WAPDA), Pakistan (GH 8456)

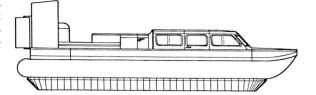
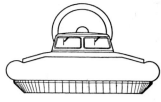
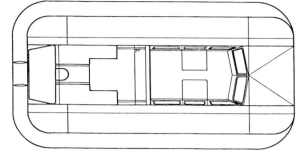
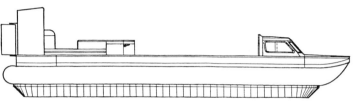

Above: 1000 TD with hard top cabin; below: 1500 TD with open deck

LIFT AND PROPULSION: Integrated lift/propulsion system powered by a single Deutz BF6L 913C air-cooled six-cylinder, in-line, turbocharged and intercooled diesel rated at 190hp (140kW) at 2500rpm. A 760mm diameter centrifugal lift fan is driven from the front of the crankshaft, via an HTD toothed belt. Power for the 1.37m diameter, four-blade Robert Trillo propeller is transmitted from the back of the engine via an automotive clutch to another HTD toothed belt transmission. Enclosed within a pylon, the belt drive is protected from the weather. The engine, transmission, duct and pylon are mounted on a welded aluminium alloy subframe attached to the hull via resilient mounts. On the latest craft, a simple system allows vertical movement of both pylon and duct, enabling very quick and accurate transmission belt adjustment to be made.

Cooling air for the engine passes through a Knitmesh filter to remove spray and is drawn into the front of the engine bay by the engine cooling fan before passing over the cylinders and being drawn out from the rear of the engine bay by the propeller.

CONTROLS: Triple rudders in the grp duct provide directional control. Elevators within the duct provide a degree of fore and aft trim, augmented by a fuel ballast system. The craft is fitted with an HDL-type skirt shift system, operated by a small electric winch, which provides responsive control on roll trim, offsets cross-wind effects and banks the craft into turns.

HULL: Main hull and side structures are of welded, riveted and bonded marine grade aluminium. Side bodies fold upward for transport and they are locked into the running position by five struts on each side. Removable bow and stern sections reduce the length of the 1000 TD to 5.6m for shipment.

ACCOMMODATION: Seats forward for driver and passenger/navigator. A four-person inward-facing bench-type seat is positioned on each side.

Griffon 1000 TD as supplied to the Pakistan Water and Power Development Authority

Front seats and controls are behind a grp cabin with the front left-hand seat for driver. Radar can be fitted in front of right-hand seat. Options for remaining accommodation space are: grp cabin top, pvc cover over aluminium frame, open area, without cover.

SKIRT: HDL open loop/segment type, with similar segments at bow and sides. Cones are fitted at the stern. Segments are fitted to the loop with stainless-steel bolts and the inner ends are attached to the hull using plastic shackles. All skirt maintenance can be done without lifting the craft.

SYSTEMS: Electrical system is 24V as standard with a 12V option, 35A alternator, two 75 Ah, 12V batteries.

DIMENSIONS (hard structure)
Length: 8.40m
Width: 3.82m
Height: 2.68m
Hoverheight: 46.0cm
Cabin,
Length: 3.20m
Width: 1.80m
Height: 1.42m
WEIGHTS
Empty: 2000kg
Payload: 1000kg
PERFORMANCE
Max speed: 35 knots
Cruise speed: 28 knots
Max operating conditions: wind, 25 knots; waves, 1m
Fuel consumption, max: 31.8 litres/h
    cruise: 22 litres/h

1500 TD

This variant is 1.8 metres longer than the 1000 TD, but with identical machinery. Capacity is increased to 1.5 tonnes or 16 persons. Bow and stern sections are not removable but folding side-decks allow transportation within a 40ft container.

Craft built	1500 TD
001	Griffon 1500 TD, Clements, Solomon Islands (GH-9452), 1987
002	Chiniqui Hovercraft, Panama, November 1985 to 1987
003	Griffon Hovercraft demonstrator(GH 2102)

These craft have been sold for tourism, survey work and pilot duties.

Details of this craft are as for the 1000 TD with the following exceptions:
DIMENSIONS
Overall length: 10.15m
Cabin length: 5.00m
WEIGHTS
Empty: 2300kg
Payload: 1500kg
PERFORMANCE
Max speed: 33 knots
Cruising speed: 27 knots
Fuel consumption, max: 31.8 litres/h
    cruise: 26 litres/h

2000 TD

The Griffon 2000 TD is now replacing the 1500 TD. Whereas the basic design, the engine and the systems remain the same, the 2000 TD has a larger propeller, larger fan, and an improved design of skirt. These modifications enable the 2000 TD to carry a 33% larger payload but still retain exactly the same performance as its predecessor. The cabin has also been slightly enlarged enabling the 2000 TD to carry a total of 20–24 persons.

LIFT AND PROPULSION: Integrated lift/propulsion system powered by a single Deutz BF6L 913C air cooled six cylinder, in line, turbo charged and intercooled diesel rated at 190hp (140kW) at

Road transport of the 16-seat Griffon 1500 TD

1500 TD with modified cabin for film contract in Italy

Griffon 1500 TD deploying Vikoma anti-oil pollution equipment in shallow water

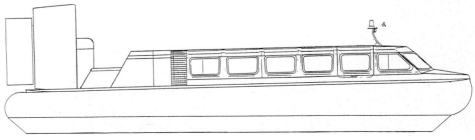
Griffon 2000 TD

2500rpm. A 0.91m diameter centrifugal lift fan is driven from the front of the crankshaft via an HTD toothed belt. Power for the 1.8m diameter four-blade Robert Trillo designed ducted propeller is transmitted from the back of the engine via an automotive clutch to another HTD toothed belt transmission running inside the propeller support pylon.

The engine, transmission, duct and pylon are mounted on a welded aluminium alloy subframe attached to the hull via resilient mounts.

Cooling air for the engine passes through a Knitmesh filter to remove spray and is drawn into the front of the engine by the engine colling fan before passing over the cylinders and being drawn out from the rear of the engine bay by the propeller.

CONTROLS: Triple rudders in the GRP duct provide directional control. Elevators within the duct provide a degree of fore and aft trim augmented by a fuel ballast system. The craft is fitted with a skirt shift system operated by a small electric winch which provides responsive control on roll trim, offsets cross wind effects and banks the craft into the stern.

HULL: Main hull is of welded rivetted and bonded marine grade aluminium.

Side bodies made from composite materials fold upward for transport and are locked into the running position by use of struts either side. Forward and aft ballast tanks are fabricated from aluminium.

ACCOMMODATION: Two or three persons (including the driver) can be carried in the wheelhouse and a further 18–22 passengers can be carried in inward facing bench-type seats in the cabin.

SKIRT: Tapered HDL open loop type with similar segments at bow and sides. Cones are fitted at the stern. Segments are fitted to the loop with stainless steel bolts and inner ends are attached

Griffon 2000 TD (GH2110)

using plastic shackles. All skirt maintenance can be done without lifting the craft.

SYSTEMS: Electrical system as 24 volt standard with 12 volt option. 35 amp alternator, two 75 A/hr 12 volt batteries fitted.

DIMENSIONS
Length: 10.6m
Width: 4.5m
Height: 2.8m
Hover height: 0.5m
Cabin: Length: 5.9m Width: 1.95m Height: 1.42m

WEIGHTS
Empty: 2600kg
Payload: 2000kg

PERFORMANCE
Maximum speed full load: 31kts
Cruise speed full load: 27kts

2000 TDX

This craft is virtually the same as the 2000 TD but is powered by the more powerful (239kW) V8 Deutz BF8L 513 engine. This gives it a top speed

Griffon 2000 TD in the foreground with a 2000 TDX (GH9457)

of over 45 knots and a superior into-wave and into-wind performance. All details are the same as the 2000 TD except for the engine and the following:
PERFORMANCE
Speed, max, full load: 45 knots
Speed, cruise, full load: 38 knots

2500 TD

This craft uses two identical machinery units from the smaller craft and carries 24–28 passengers. Seating can be provided with either forward-facing aircraft type seats or sideways-facing bench seats.

The workboat version can be either supplied open with only the two-person cab, or with a portion of the deck covered.

A bow-loading ramp is also available to enable a vehicle (such as a long wheel-base Land-Rover) to be carried.

Two 2500 TD craft have been built for ferry/tourist operations. The first one was launched in November 1985 and having completed its trials and with Canadian Coast Guard Certification, started passenger carrying at Expo '86 in Vancouver. The craft ran a 10-hour day, seven-day week shuttle service for the duration of Expo '86 operating off a floating pontoon in Canada Place along a 7-mile route to alongside a pier in the Expo '86 site.

LIFT AND PROPULSION: Two separate lift and propulsion systems, mechanically integrated, each identical to that of the single engine craft.
CONTROLS: Similar systems to the single engine craft are employed with duplication in some areas. Triple rudders in each duct operated by a steering yoke via stainless steel cables provide directional control. Fore and aft trim is achieved by a liquid ballast system whilst lateral trim is provided by an electrically operated skirt shift system. Twin engine throttles are mounted near to the driver's left hand whilst two clutch pedals (operated by the driver's feet) are provided for the propellers. By using only one propeller at low speed together with the rudder and skirt shift, the craft is highly manoeuvrable. Control systems are powerful enough to allow the craft to be operated and controlled by only one engine, although at a much reduced speed.
HULL: The main hull is of welded marine grade aluminium alloy providing a very cost effective light and durable structure, consisting of four longitudinal box sections linked fore and aft by two transverse box sections. Side bodies, also in

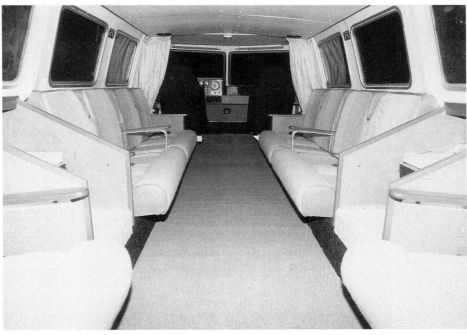

Interior of Griffon 2000 TD

Craft built 2500TD	Name	In service	Owner
001 Griffon Hovercraft 2500 TD	*Rain Dance*	November 1985	Hover Systems Inc, USA, (1986 Canadian registration CH-FHI)

2500 TD standard cabin version

Griffon 2500 TD *Rain Dancer* at the Canada Pavilion base, Expo '86, Vancouver, October 1986

light alloy, can fold upward reducing width for road and sea transportation.
ACCOMMODATION: Superstructure can be to the customer's specification. The standard passenger cabin is constructed in light alloy with grp mouldings at the front and back. A great emphasis has been placed on passengers having good visibility and big windows and narrow pillars are featured. Also a portion of the roof is transparent. Forward-facing aircraft seats are provided as standard with four seats to a row with an aisle either side. In this configuration, up to 28 seats can be fitted. Air conditioning and heating systems can be provided and toilet/galley facilities can also be fitted if seating capacity is reduced.
CREW CABIN: A raised crew cabin is provided

offering 360° visibility for two crew, although for most operations only one operator is required. Radio and radar can also be fitted.
SKIRT: HDL open loop/segment type with similar segments at bow and sides. Cones fitted at stern. Segments attached to outer loop with stainless steel bolts. All skirt maintenance can be carried out without lifting the craft.
DIMENSIONS
Length: 14.40m
Width: 5.78m
Height: 2.87m
Cabin length: 8.05m
Cabin width: 3.30m
PERFORMANCE
Max speed: 31 knots

Cruise speed: 26 knots
Hoverheight: 600cm
Max disposable load, crewboat version: 38 tonnes
Fuel consumption, max: 63 litres/h
   cruise: 45 litres/h
Fuel capacity (standard): 568 litres
Max operating conditions: 25 knots wind
   1.25m wave height

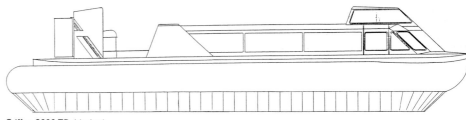

Griffon 3000 TD (design)

2500 TDX (DESIGN)

During 1986 a new version of the 2500 TD has been added to the range. This version is identical to the previous model except that the engines have been changed to Deutz BF8L 513, together with a corresponding increase in size of lift fans, propellers and transmission.

The specification is as for the 2500 TD except for:
DIMENSIONS
Craft length: 15.10m
PERFORMANCE
Max speed: 40 knots
Cruise speed: 38 knots
Max disposable load, crewboat version: 4.9 tonnes
Max operating conditions: 30 knots wind

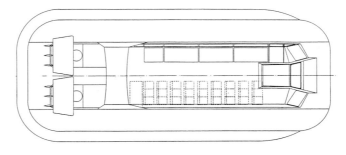

3000 TD (DESIGN)

The Griffon 3000 TD design supercedes the 2500 TD and the 2500 TDX. Seating up to 37 passengers, the 3000 TD uses two Deutz BF8L513 engines and incorporates the very latest in skirt design and technology. The hoverheight is also increased over its predecessors and with its larger propellers and fans it now has a significantly improved rough weather capability.
LIFT AND PROPULSION: The 3000 TD uses two identical machinery units from the 2000 TDX fitted next to each other.
CONTROLS: Similar controls are fitted as the single engine craft except no elevators are used.

Three rudders mounted in each duct are operated by a steering yoke via stainless steel cables to provide directional control. Fore and aft trim is achieved by an electrically operated skirt shift system. Twin engine throttles are mounted near to the driver's left hand whilst clutch pedals (operated by the driver's feet) are provided for the propellers. By using only one propeller at low speed, together with the rudder and skirt shift, the craft can turn in its own length. Control systems are powerful enough to allow the craft to be operated and controlled on only one engine, although at a much reduced speed.
HULL: The main hull is of welded marine grade aluminium alloy providing a very cost effective light and durable structure. It consists of a number of fore and aft spars linked by the cabin floors and the craft bottom. This provides an immensely stiff structure.

Side bodies, made of composite materials, fold upwards reducing width for road and sea transportation.
ACCOMMODATION: The superstructure can be designed to suit the customer's specification. The standard passenger cabin is constructed in light alloy with GRP mouldings at the front and back. Great emphasis has been placed on giving the passengers clear uninterrupted views through the large windows, and narrow pillars are featured. A portion of the roof can be transparent if required and air-conditioning and heating systems can be installed. Aircraft-type seating is arranged in up to six rows of six seats, three either side of a central aisle. Luggage racks, toilets and a galley may also be provided to suit customers' specific requirements.
CREW CABIN: (As before).
SKIRT: A tapered HDL open loop type skirt is fitted.
SYSTEM: The electrical system is 24 volts. Main and emergency supplies are provided. Each engine has a 35 amp alternator.

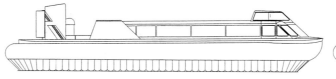

Griffon 4000 TD (design)

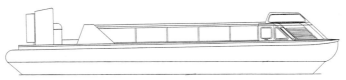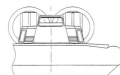

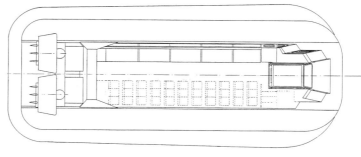

Griffon 5000 TD (design)

DIMENSIONS
Length: 16.0m
Width: 7.0m
Height: 3.3m
Cabin: Length: 7m Width: 3.90m Height: 1.98m
WEIGHTS
Empty: 8200lg
Payload: 3000kg
PERFORMANCE
Maximum speed full load: 40kts
Cruise speed full load: 36kts

4000 TD (DESIGN)

The 4000 TD is basically a stretched version of the 3000 TD (and the proven 2500 TD). It can carry up to 54 passengers at a cruising speed of 36 knots. Previously the vanguard of the Griffon fleet, the 4000 TD is the largest Griffon hovercraft with only two engines.
LIFT AND PROPULSION: The same twin engine system as the 3000 TD but 400hp Deutz engines are fitted together with 1.98m diameter Robert Trillo ducted propellers.

Transmission details are similar to the smaller craft.

CONTROLS: As for the 3000 TD.
HULL: Exactly the same cross section and construction method as the 3000 TD but 2.2m longer.
ACCOMMODATION: The accommodation is normally arranged in up to nine rows of six seats, similar to those of the Griffon 3000 TD. Customers can specify their freight/passenger requirements and versions of this craft, like the 3000 TD, can include roll-on roll-off facilities, with a bow ramp.
SKIRT: A tapered HDL open loop type skirt is fitted.
SYSTEMS: As the 3000 TD.
DIMENSIONS
Length: 18.2m
Width: 7.0m
Height: 3.6m
Cabin: Length: 8.0m Width: 3.9m Height: 1.98m
PERFORMANCE
Maximum speed full load: 40kts
Cruise speed full load: 36kts

5000 TD (DESIGN)

The 5000 TD is the only design in the Griffon range to utilise three engines: two for propulsion and one for lift. Speeds of up to 47 knots are possible with this craft and it has the best rough weather performance of any craft in the Griffon range. The 5000 TD seats up to 72 passengers.

LIFT AND PROPULSION: A single Deutz diesel engine mounted in the bow of the craft drives four lift fans. Two 400hp Deutz 513 engines each drive a 1.98m diameter thrust propeller mounted in ducts at the stern of the craft. All transmission is by HTD belts.

CONTROLS: Triple rudders in each duct operated by a steering yoke via stainless steel cables provide directional control. Fore and aft trim is achieved by a liquid ballast system whilst lateral trim is provided by an electrically operated skirt shift system. Three engine throttles are mounted near to the driver's left hand.

HULL: Similar to the 3000 TD and 4000 TD except longer.

ACCOMMODATION: Very similar to the 4000 TD, the 5000 TD can seat up to twelve rows of six seats, three seats either side of a central aisle. Like the 4000 TD, many configurations of the cabin/deck can be specified to suit particular customer requirements.

SKIRT: A tapered HDL open loop type skirt is fitted.

DIMENSIONS
Length: 19.0m
Width: 7.0m
Height: 3.6m
Cabin: Length: 10.0m Width: 3.9m Height: 1.98m
PERFORMANCE
Maximum speed full load: 47kts
Cruise speed full load: 36kts

MINI 500

The Mini 500 is the smallest craft in the Griffon range and is the only Griffon craft to be equipped with an automotive water-cooled engine. The Mini 500 is constructed in composite sandwich with Kevlar and is powered by 96hp VW/Audi diesel engine. The resin used in the composite material construction of the craft is of a type that will not become brittle in temperatures down to −25°C. The Mini 500 is designed for slightly lighter duties than the rest of the Griffon "workhorse" range (this is reflected in its very competitive price) but it incorporates all the same well-proven Griffon systems. The first Mini 500 was sold to a community in Norway at Larvik for taking school children from a small island to the mainland, regardless of ice conditions in the winter.

LIFT AND PROPULSION: A VW 6 cylinder 2.4 litre engine producing 98hp at 4000rpm drives two fan shafts. Each fan has one centrifugal fan at the forward end and an 820mm ducted multi-wing fan at the other. Transmission to the fan shafts is by HTD belt.

CONTROLS: Steering is achieved by use of swivelling buckets behind the duct. The buckets can be closed individually by separate controls to reduce thrust differentially. Engine speed is controlled by a hand throttle.

The craft can also be fitted with an optional ballast system and a skirt shift system depending on the operational requirements.

HULL: The hull is constructed from composite material.

DIMENSIONS
Length: 7.1m
Width: 3.6m
PERFORMANCE
Maximum speed: 30kts
Cruise speed: 25kts
ACCOMMODATION: There are two rows of 3 abreast bench seating, which includes the driver in the front left hand seat.

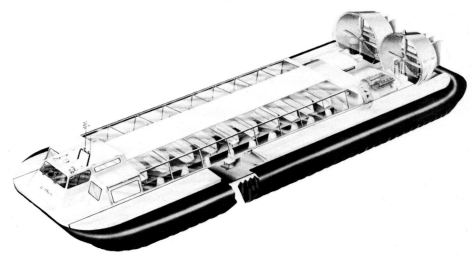

Isometric drawing of 4000 TD (design)

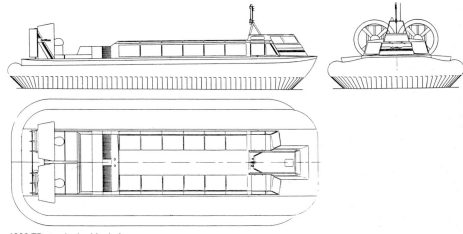

4000 TD standard cabin design

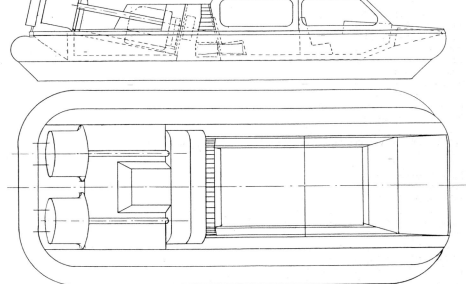

Griffon Mini 500

Griffon Mini 500

HOVERCRAFT DEVELOPMENT LIMITED (HDL)

[PATENT HOLDING AND LICENSING ORGANISATION]
101 Newington Causeway, London SE1 6BU, England

Telephone: 071–403 6666
Telex: 894397G

M L Martin, *Chairman*
D J Veasey, *Director*
J Williams, *Secretary*

Hovercraft Development Limited (HDL) was formed in January 1959 by the National Research Development Corporation (NRDC) which is now part of the British Technology Group. The company uses its portfolio of patents as the basis of licensing agreements with hovercraft manufacturers in the UK and overseas. HDL or British Technology Group, may, in certain cases, provide financial backing to assist project development.

HDL's principal patents concern craft with segmented skirts. These skirt systems are now used by all major manufacturers of hovercraft. The skirt is a series of pockets arranged around the craft which when inflated seal against each other. The skirt is flexible and conforms to the contours of the surface over which it passes, and has a low drag characteristic both in calm water and waves. Should an individual segment be lost, the performance is not substantially affected.

Also included in the patent portfolio is the HDL skirt shift system.

Licences are available to all companies in the industry.

HOVERMARINE INTERNATIONAL LTD

Spitfire Quay, Hazel Road, Woolston, Southampton, Hampshire SO2 7GB, England

Telephone: (0703) 443122
Telex: 47141G
Telefax: (0703) 444429

P J Hill, *Director and General Manager*
E G Tattersall, *Director*

Hovermarine since its formation in 1966 has sold 106 surface effect ships (SES) to 33 countries and is one of the most experienced designers and builders of these craft. Hovermarine has its yard at Woolston, Southampton with an undercover area of more than 2300m².

Production designs are the 200 and 500 series craft. The 200 series comprises the HM 218 (18m, 84- to 103-seat) passenger ferries, 28 of which have been delivered to the Hongkong and Yaumati Ferry Company; the HM 218 multi-role harbour craft, four of which have been delivered to the Port of Rotterdam Authority; the HM 218 crewboat for the oil industry; the HM 221 (21m) fireboat; the HM 221 (21m) 112- to 135-seat passenger ferry and the HM 221 (21m) crewboat. Other variants of the 200 series craft are offered for hydrographic survey, coastguard and patrol duties. The HM 500 series includes the Series 2 (27m, 256-seat) and the Series 3 (27m, 300 seat) passenger ferry design. The new HM 424 design is larger than the HM 200 series but smaller than the HM 500 series. Incorporating all the well proven systems (the results of 25 years experience in design, manufacture and operation of SES) the HM 424 can be specified with GM or MWM engines, giving cruising speeds of 35 knots and 45 knots respectively, with full payloads. Other designs are available for the following roles: naval fast strike and patrol craft, crewboat, hydrographic survey and coastguard patrol. All craft are type-approved in the UK by the Civil Aviation Authority and for operating permits issued by the Department of Transport. The craft have also been certified by Lloyds' Register of Shipping, Bureau Veritas, USCG etc.

HM 216 FERRY

About ten of this early 16m HM2 type are still with operators. Full details of these craft are given in the 1978 edition of Janes Surface Skimmers.

HM 218 FERRY

The HM 218 ferry represents a 40 per cent improvement in payload over the earlier HM 216 ferry for only a 15 per cent increase in operating costs. It can carry 84 to 103 passengers at cruising speeds of up to 35 knots. An extended bow skirt permits passenger operations in up to 1.5m (5ft) waves. A computerised roll stabilisation system can be fitted to customer order.

The first HM 218 ferry went into service in 1976. A major operator of the type is the Hongkong and Yaumati Ferry Company, which has 24 in commuter service within Hong Kong and on an 100n mile international route to Guangzhou (Canton) in the People's Republic of China. Other HM 218 ferries operate in Brazil, the People's Republic of China, Indonesia, Japan, Kuwait, Malaysia, Singapore and Venezuela.

LIFT AND PROPULSION: Two General Motors Detroit Diesel Allison 8V-92TI V, eight-cylinder marine diesels, each developing 465bhp at 2300rpm, provide propulsive power. A single Caterpillar 3208 90-degree V, eight-cylinder marine diesel rated at 206bhp at 2800rpm drives the 0.6m diameter centrifugal lift fans.

The lift engine drives two pairs of forward fans through toothed belts and one aft fan through a hydraulic system. Air for the forward fans is drawn through inlets at each forward cabin quarter and in the base of the wheelhouse structure. Air for the aft fan is drawn through an inlet in the rear companionway.

The two propulsion engines each drive a 0.45m diameter aluminium bronze three-bladed propeller through a reversing gearbox and 1:1 ratio vee box. Fuel is carried in stainless steel tanks, two beneath the aft companionway and one under the main lift fans. Electrical power for instruments, radio, radar, lighting and air conditioning is supplied by ac/dc alternators driven by the lift and propulsion engines.

CONTROLS: Craft direction is by twin balanced stainless steel rudders operated hydraulically by a steering wheel. Additional control is by differential use of the water propellers.

HM 218 *Calypso* for service with Gozo Channel Line, Malta

Craft built (list not complete) HM 216 (16m SES)

Type	Name	No. of seats	Yard No.	Original delivery date	Owner/Operator	Country of origin
HM 216	(ex HYF 101)	60	326	1974	Associated Marine Sdn. Bhd	Malaysia
HM 216	Sea Express 101	—	—	1976	Bataam Manilla Ferry Services	The Philippines (laid up)
HM 216	Sea Express 102	—	—	1976	Bataan Manilla Ferry Services	The Philippines (laid up)
HM 216	Sea Express 103	—	—	1976	Bataan Manilla Ferry Services	The Philippines (laid up)
HM 216	Gavea	65	321	1976	TRANSTUR	Brazil (one operating)
HM 216	Gragoata	65	322	1976	TRANSTUR	Brazil (one operating)
HM 216	Suratiba	65	323	1976	TRANSTUR	Brazil (one operating)
HM 216	HYF 103	74	328	1975	The Hong Kong and Yaumati Ferry Co	Hong Kong (laid up)
HM 216	HYF 104	60	329	1975	The Hong Kong and Yaumati Ferry Co	Hong Kong (laid up)
HM 216 (USA built)	American Skimmer	62	—	1974	American Skimmer Co	USA

HULL: Built in grp mouldings and various types of sandwich panels. The mouldings consist of the main deck, deck and superstructure centre section, forward intakes and wheelhouse, inner side-linings, aft companionway and engine bay cowlings. The first three are joined by a system of transverse frames. The floor panels are bonded to the frames and to the longitudinal intercostal members.

The outer shell of the hull, including the bottom between the sidewalls and under the bow, is moulded in one piece, gunwale to gunwale. The hull moulding incorporates local thickening of the laminate to meet the design load requirements and to facilitate the incorporation of fittings and apertures. Frames and bulkheads are manufactured from sandwich panels of expanded pvc foam covered with grp. All frames and bulkheads are laminated into the hull.

ACCOMMODATION: The HM 218 ferry can be operated by a crew of two. Controls are in an elevated wheelhouse, with a 360-degree view, at the forward end of the passenger saloon. The saloon can be fitted out with up to 84 aircraft-type seats or 92 to 103 utility seats. These are normally arranged three abreast in banks of three. Toilet and baggage compartments are located aft. Up to six luggage containers, able to hold a total of 1500kg, may be carried on the saloon roof.

Passenger access to the saloon is via a double width door aft. Crew and emergency access is forward via two hatch doors, one on each side of the wheelhouse. Knock-out emergency windows are fitted in the passenger saloon. Safety equipment includes life rafts, life jackets under the seats, fire detectors and extinguishers.

SKIRTS: The extended bow skirt consists of a single loop extending from the bow chine to a line just below the base of the main hull. 32 segments are attached to the main loop and connected to the underside of the hull by terylene ropes. An inner loop overlaps the fan volute outlet and causes the bow skirt to inflate.

The rear seal consists of a membrane and loop which is suspended front and rear by transverse continuous sheets of material. It is inflated to a pressure slightly above that of the cushion by the rear fan in the starboard propulsion engine room.

DIMENSIONS
Length overall: 18.29m
Beam overall: 6.1m
Height overall: 4.88m
Draught floating, loaded: 1.72m
  on cushion, loaded: 1.07m
Saloon length: 9.75m
  beam: 4.88m
  height: 1.93m
WEIGHTS
Max: 27 900kg
Normal disposable payload: 7154kg
Normal fuel capacity: 1455 litres
PERFORMANCE
Cruising speed (full payload): 34 knots
Acceleration 0–30 knots: 45 seconds
Standard range at cruising speed: 200n miles
Standard endurance at cruising speed: 4 hours

Craft built HM 218 (18m SES)

Type	Name	No. of seats	Yard No.	Original delivery date	Owner/Operator	Country of operation
HN 218	Calypso	84		May 1988	Gozo Line	Malta
HM 218	Klassis	82		1989	Naviga Line	Turkey
HM 218	Hover Express	84				Norway
HM 218	Bukom Deras	90		1983	Shell Eastern	Singapore
HM 218	Bukom Pantas	90		1983	Petroleum	Singapore
HM 218	Bukom Lekas	90		1983	Petroleum	Singapore
HM 218	Bukom Maju	90		1983	Petroleum	Singapore
HM 218	Bukom Jaya	90		1983	Petroleum	Singapore
HM 218	HYF 105	100	435	1976	Hong Kong Yaumati Ferry Co.	Hong Kong
HM 218	HYF 106	100	443	1976	Hong Kong Yaumati Ferry Co.	Hong Kong
HM 218	HYF 107	100	445	1976	Hong Kong Yaumati ferry Co.	Hong Kong
HM 218	HYF 111	100	457	1979	Hong Kong Yaumati Ferry Co.	Hong Kong
HM 218	HYF 112	100	458	1979	Hong Kong Yaumati Ferry Co.	Hong Kong
HM 218	HYF 113	100	459	1980	Hong Kong Yaumati Ferry Co.	Hong Kong
HM 218	HYF 114	74	462	1980	Hong Kong Yaumati Ferry Co.	Hong Kong
HM 218	HYF 115	100	463	1980	Hong Kong Yaumati Ferry Co.	Hong Kong
HM 218	HYF 116	84	464	1980	Hong Kong Yaumati Ferry Co.	Hong Kong
HM 218	HYF 117	100	469	1980	Hong Kong Yaumati Ferry Co.	Hong Kong
HM 218	HYF 118	74	470	1980	Hong Kong Yaumati Ferry Co.	Hong Kong
HM 218	HYF 119	74	473	1980	Hong Kong Yaumati Ferry Co.	Hong Kong
HM 218	HYF 120	100	474	1980	Hong Kong Yaumati Ferry Co.	Hong Kong

Craft built HM 218 (18m SES)

Type	Name	No. of seats	Yard No.	Original delivery date	Owner/Operator	Country of operation
HM 218	*HYF 121*	74	475	1980	Hong Kong Yaumati Ferry Co.	Hong Kong
HM 218	*HYF 122*	100	476	1980	Hong Kong Yaumati Ferry Co.	Hong Kong
HM 218	*HYF 123*	74	477	1980	Hong Kong Yaumati Ferry Co.	Hong Kong
HM 218	*HYF 124*	74	478	1980	Hong Kong Yaumati Ferry Co.	Hong Kong
HM 218	*HYF 125*	100	479	1980	Hong Kong Yaumati Ferry Co.	Hong Kong
HM 218	*HYF 126*	100	480	1980	Hong Kong Yaumati Ferry Co.	Hong Kong
HM 218	*HYF 127*	100	481	1980	Hong Kong Yaumati Ferry Co.	Hong Kong
HM 218	*HYF 130*	74	484	1980	Hong Kong Yaumati Ferry Co.	Hong Kong
HM 218	(ex *RTS 101*)	—	466	1986	Discovery Bay Transportation Services	Hong Kong
HM 218	(ex *RTS 102*)	—	468	1987	Discovery Bay Transportation Services	Hong Kong
HM 218	(ex *RTS 103*)	—	471	1986	Discovery Bay Transportation Services	Hong Kong
HN 218	(ex *HYF 108*)	92	446	1976	Discovery Bay Transportation Services	Hong Kong
HM 218	(ex *HYF 109*)	92	447	1979	Discovery Bay Transportation Services	Hong Kong
HM 218	(ex *HYF 110*)	92	448	1979	Discovery Bay Transportation Services	Hong Kong
HM 218	(ex *HYF 129*)	—	—	1983	Changjiang Shipping Admin. Bureau	China, P.R.
HM 218	(ex *HYF 130*)	74	484	1982	Changjiang Shipping Admin. Bureau	China, P.R.
HM 218	*Kijang Mas*	—	—	Feb. 1984	Kedah & Perlis Ferry Service Sdn. Bhd.	Malaysia
HM 218	*Rey del Titikaka*	—	—		Hovermarine Titikaka Transport	Bolivia (not in service)
HM 218	*Reina del Titikaka*	—	—		Hovermarine Titikaka Transport	Bolivia (not in use)
HM 218	—	—	—		Shenzou Transport Co.	China, P.R.
HM 218	*Semandera Satu*	78	—	1986	PT Hover Maritim Semandera	Indonesia
HM 218	*Semandera Desu*	78	—	1986	PT Hover Maritim Semandera	Indonesia
HM 218	*Pomas No. 1*	95	—	April 1986	Pomas Sdn. Bhd.	Malaysia
HM 218	*Havendienst 7*	N/A	—	1979	Port of Rotterdam Authority	The Netherlands (laid up)
HM 218	*Havendienst 10*	N/A	452	1979	Port of Rotterdam Authority	The Netherlands (laid up)
HM 218	*Havendienst 9*	N/A	451	1980	Port of Rotterdam Authority	The Netherlands (laid up)
HM 218	*Havendienst 8*	N/A	—	1980	Port of Rotterdam Authority	The Netherlands (laid up)
HM 218	*Innovator I*	—	—	1977	Federal Ministry of Transport, Nigeria	Nigeria (laid up)
HM 218	*Innovator II*	—	440	1977	Federal Ministry of Transport, Nigeria	Nigeria (laid up)
HM 218	*Innovator III*	—	439	1977	Federal Ministry of Transport, Nigeria	Nigeria (laid up)
HM 218	*Auto Batam 1*	78	472	1982	Yang Passenger Ferry Service	Singapore
HM 218	*Auto Batam 2*	—	—	—	Yang Passenger Ferry Service	Singapore
HM 218	*Zumbador*	70	454	1979	Maraven SA	Venezuela
HM 218	*Zumaya*	70	455	1980	Maraven SA	Venezuela
HM 218	*Barroso*	70	471	1980	Maraven SA	Venezuela
HM 218	*Auhah*	82	—	Feb. 1983	Kuwait Public Transport Co.	Kuwait
HM 218	*Umn Al Maradam*	82	—	1983	Kuwait Public Transport Co.	Kuwait
HM 218	*J/Kubbar*	82	—	1984	Kuwait Public Transport Co.	Kuwait
HM 218	*Yin Bin 1*	—	—	1986	China Merchants	China, P.R.

HM 218 CREWBOAT

Since 1979 three HM 218 crewboats have been operating in Venezuela, transporting crew to-and-from oil rigs on Lake Maracaibo. Five more have been delivered to Shell (Eastern) in Singapore. The crewboat is based on the HM 218 passenger ferry but has a substantially reinforced hull to withstand the buffeting which the craft receives alongside offshore installations.

A bow-loading technique has been developed; rollers are fitted to the bow allowing the craft to approach installations and transfer crew over the bow. This is safer than the conventional stern transfer system as the captain can view the whole operation.

Luggage containers (grp) may be fitted above the superstructure for extra baggage. An alternative version of the HM 218 crewboat accommodates 25 passengers, with a well deck for 3 tonnes of cargo.

LIFT AND PROPULSION: Two General Motors 8V-92TI marine diesels driving fixed pitch propellers through Capitol reversing gearboxes and BPM V-drive gearboxes. Lift is by one Cummins V-555-M marine diesel driving two pairs of forward fans through toothed belts and one aft fan through a hydraulic system.

HULL: Shell mouldings, sub-mouldings, frames, bulkheads and major attachments in grp, using polyester resins and pvc foam. Construction is to Lloyds' survey requirements.

ACCOMMODATION: Air-conditioned accommodation for up to 99 passengers in airline-type seats. Toilet compartment in stern.

DIMENSIONS
Length overall: 18.29m
Beam overall: 6.1m
Height (underside of propeller to top of mast light): 7.4m
Draught, off cushion: 1.72m
 on cushion: 1.07m

PERFORMANCE
Max speed (fully loaded, calm water): 34 knots
Endurance (max continuous power, half load): 200n miles

HM 218 MULTI-ROLE HARBOUR CRAFT

Four HM 218 multi-role harbour craft were delivered to the Port of Rotterdam Authority in 1979–80. The design retains the standard HM 218 passenger ferry hull fitted with two superstructure modules to house port-monitoring and emergency-service equipment.

Details are given in the 1988 edition, p. 84.

HM 221 FIREFIGHTING CRAFT

Two HM 221 firefighting craft were ordered by the city of Tacoma, Washington, USA in 1978. The first of these was delivered in May 1982 and the second late in 1982. They are fitted with a comprehensive range of firefighting, rescue, navigation and communications equipment.

LIFT AND PROPULSION: Two General Motors 8V-92TI marine diesels drive fixed pitch propellers via direct-drive reversing gearboxes and V-drive gearboxes. Lift power is from one General Motors 6V-92TI marine diesel which is also used as a pump engine. A second pump engine is provided by a General Motors 6V-92TI marine diesel. Propulsion, lift and pumping machinery is controlled from the wheelhouse. All engines electrically started.

ACCOMMODATION: Utility-standard crew accommodation comprises six-berth cabin with cooker, sink and toilet compartment.

EQUIPMENT: Two remotely-controlled bow-mounted monitors each of 9400 litres/minute water flow rate; one wheelhouse-mounted monitor of 20 800 litres/minute water flow rate; two under-wharf monitors of 9400 litres/minute water flow rate and one remotely-controlled 5600 litres/minute foam/water monitor fitted to the telescopic end of a high-level (10.5m) ladder which doubles as a crane. The monitors are remotely controlled for rotation and elevation from a console in the wheelhouse. The ladder is controlled from its base. All fire monitors, except the wheelhouse monitor, can be controlled from a straight stream to 90-degree fog.

FENDERING: Hardwood fendering fitted to the gunwale.

DIMENSIONS
Length overall: 20.9m
Beam overall: 6.1m
Height above water, off cushion: 6.3m
Draught, off cushion: 1.55m
 on cushion: 1.1m

LOGISTICS
Fresh water storage: 90 litres
Fuel storage: 2950 litres

HM 218 *Klassis* now operating on the sea of Marmara in Turkey

An HM 218 operating near Oslo in 1989

Craft built	Delivered	Status
HM 218 *Havendienst 7*	1979	Laid up
HM 218 *Havendienst 10*	1979	Laid up
HM 218 *Havendienst 9*	1980	Laid up
HM 218 *Havendienst 8*	1980	Special operations

HM 221 crewboat

Craft built HM 221	In service	Operator
HM 221 *Defiance* (Fireboat No 5)	December 1982	City of Tacoma Fire Department
HM 221 *Commencement* (Fireboat No 15)	February 1983	City of Tacoma Fire Department

Allowance for miscellaneous firefighting equipment: 500kg
Firefighting AFFF foam: 1136 litres
PERFORMANCE
FULLY LOADED, CALM SEA
Max speed: 30 knots
Endurance, max speed: 120n miles, including 5½ hours continuous pumping at rated capacity, plus a fuel allowance of 426 litres for station-keeping

HM 221 PASSENGER FERRY

Based on the HM 221 (21-metre) hull, this variant seats 112 to 135 passengers depending on route requirements and has a continuous speed in excess of 31 knots in calm conditions and a range of 140n miles. The structure is designed to Lloyds Register Classification +Class ACV, Group 2, +LMC, CCS.
LIFT AND PROPULSION: Power for the lift system is provided by a single Cummins VT-555-M-BC marine diesel with a continuous rating of 270bhp at 2800rpm. Propulsive power is supplied by two General Motors 8V-92TI marine diesels, each rated at 490bhp at 2300rpm continuous. Power outputs correspond to ambient air temperature of 29°C and sea water temperature of 27°C. Lift and propulsion systems are mechanically controlled from the wheelhouse. Fuel capacity is 1450 litres when 95 per cent full.
HULL: Single shell grp mouldings, with sub-mouldings, frames, bulkheads and other attachments bonded together.
ACCOMMODATION: Within the saloon of the 112-seat variant there are two toilet compartments, each with a WC and washbasin. Seats have a depth of 420mm, breadth of 430mm and a seat pitch of 460mm. Aisle width is a minimum of 470mm. Saloon and wheelhouse are air-conditioned. The air-conditioning plant is belt driven off the lift engine. Design conditions, internal 29.4°C dry bulb not greater than 65% relative humidity with ambient temperature of 34.4°C dry bulb 65% relative humidity.
CONTROLS: Power assisted manual/hydraulic system operating twin rudders with a hard over angle of 30°-0–30° when set with a zero rudder divergence. Hydraulic pump mechanically operated from the lift engines.
SYSTEMS
Electrical voltage: 24V dc nominal negative earth
Generation/charging equipment: Two propulsion engine driven ac/dc alternators rated at 27.5V, 100A. One lift engine driven ac/dc alternator rated at 27.5V, 100A
Batteries: Two 24V lead acid batteries, each with

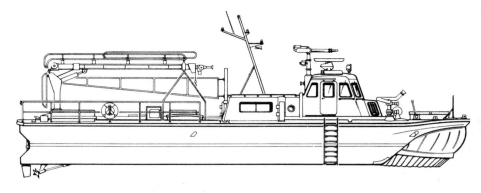

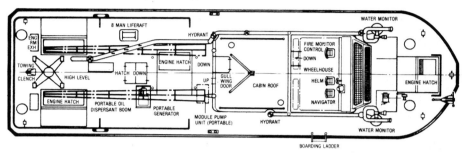

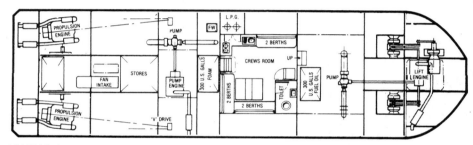

HM 221 firefighting craft

HM 221 CREWBOAT

Craft built	In service	Operator
HM 221 *Grayspear*	1982–1985	-

Details are given in the 1988 edition, p 85.

Craft built	Seats	Built	Operator
HM 221	112	1985	Donau-Dampfschiffahrts-Gesellschaft (DDSG)

HM 221 in operation with Donau-Dampfschiffahrts-Gesellschaft

sufficient capacity to provide six starts for each engine

Lighting: Normal: 18-watt fluorescent tubes supplied from 24V dc system via invertors; Emergency: 24V incandescent fittings sited throughout craft

Communications: PA system between wheelhouse and passenger saloon; External: one VHF(FM) Sailor RT146/C401 radio telephone, frequency range 155.4 to 162.6MHz. Output 25/1W

Navigation: One Marinex Meteor transmitting magnetic compass. One emergency magnetic compass, Smith's type E2B. One Firebell Blipper radar reflector on mast. One Furono relative motion radar. One Vistar 301 night vision unit, comprising camera, main control and slave display

Containers: Four grp luggage containers

Heating: Recirculating warm air heating system employing propulsion engine hot coolant

Bow loading: Flush foredeck, guardrails and bow polyethylene fenders arranged for bow loading of passengers

DIMENSIONS
Length overall: 21.19m
Beam overall: 5.91m
Height (underside of propeller to top of mast anchor light): 7.47m
Draught, off cushion: 1.76m
on cushion, aft, loaded: 1.21m

WEIGHTS
Passengers, 112 at 66kg: 7392kg
Baggage, 112 at 9kg: 1008kg
Crew, 3 at 66kg: 201kg
Oil fuel: 1100kg
Payload: 8400kg

PERFORMANCE
Cruising speed, calm conditions, full payload, half fuel: 33 knots
Endurance: 140n miles

HM 527

The first HM 527 was launched in January 1982 capable of carrying up to 200 passengers at a cruising speed of 36 knots and has been designed to operate on coastal and inland waters in wave heights of up to 3m with a payload of 21 000kg. Normal range is 200n miles. A computerised roll stabilisation system is fitted as standard. The first four craft, ordered by Sealink Ferries Limited, were delivered before the end of 1983. Other designs based on the HM 527 hull include a hydrographic survey vessel and all-passenger crewboats and mixed payload supply boats for the offshore oil industry.

LIFT AND PROPULSION: The marine diesels are in two amidships engine rooms, both accommodating one propulsion engine and one auxiliary power unit. The lift engine is an MTU 6V 396 TB83 rated at 550kW at 2300rpm which drives lift fans. via a gearbox, to provide cushion air and drives, via a hydraulic pump and hydraulic motors, two secondary fans for skirt inflation. The propulsion engines are MTU 12V 396 TB83 diesels rated at 1050kW at 1800rpm. Each incorporates a ZF BW 455 reverse-reduction gearbox and drives a single three-bladed propeller via transmission shafting inclined at 13 degrees. The outward rotating propellers operate at up to 900rpm. Two Perkins 4.236M marine diesels rated at 27.2kW, 50Hz, 220V drive the ac alternators and compressors for the air-conditioning system.

Fuel is carried in two tanks in the transom bay, in-line athwartships. Fuel capacity is 4.2 tonnes. Separate salt-water ballast tanks are provided with a capacity of 5 tonnes.

CONTROLS: Vessel heading is controlled by power-operated twin water rudders. Additional control is provided by differential use of the propellers. An automatic roll-stabilisation system operates through inclined independent rudders.

HULL: Single shell grp moulding with sub-moulding, frames, bulkheads and cabin sole

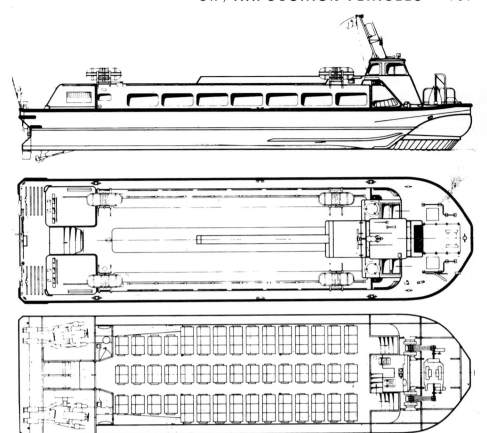

HM 221 ferry

Craft built HM 527	No of seats	In service	Operator
HM 527 *Tejo*	200	1983	Sealink Ferries Ltd, Hong Kong
HM 527 *Douro*	200	1984	Sealink Ferries Ltd, Hong Kong
HM 527 *Sado*	200	1984	Sealink Ferries Ltd, Hong Kong
HM 527 *Mondego*	200	1984	Sealink Ferries Ltd, Hong Kong

Shipment of first HM 527, *Tejo*, to Hong Kong

panels bonded together. Materials used include expanded pvc foam, glass fibre, polyester resins, wood and aluminium alloy.

ACCOMMODATION: The bridge normally accommodates the commander, navigator and engineer. Passenger access is via doors port and starboard in the forward saloon and rearward double door for aft saloon. Emergency exits are located in both saloons. Four toilet/washbasin units are provided plus luggage space. Eight luggage containers can be mounted on the roof of the craft. Safety equipment includes life rafts, inflatable life jackets, lifebuoys and line-throwing apparatus.

SKIRTS: Main plenum chamber receives air from two lift fans via ducts located amidships port and starboard. Bow and stern skirts receive air from port and starboard fans, driven hydraulically by lift engine gearbox pumps, via ducts forming part of the superstructure.

Bow skirt is made up of two tailored neoprene/nylon loops suspended in 180-degree arcs sidewall to sidewall and joined at their lower edges to form an irregularly shaped inflatable compartment. When inflated, the loops support 20 single fabric segments, attached at the loop joint line, and absorb wave impact shock to a degree. Four additional corner segments are attached on each side by ropes and shackles.

Three similar tailored loops are suspended under the stern. These are joined to form a single inflatable compartment.

DIMENSIONS
Length overall: 27.2m
Beam overall: 10.2m
Height overall: 4.9m
Draught floating, loaded: 2.55m
  on cushion, loaded: 1.7m
Standard passenger capacity, forward saloon: 135
  aft saloon: 121
WEIGHT
Max gross: 87 000kg

HM 527 SERIES 3 (DESIGN)

The refinements incorporated into this variant of the HM 527 result from experience gained with the Series 1 and 2 craft. With only a single diesel 332kW lift engine and carrying 44 more seats than the HM 527 Series 2 the Series 3 offers greater economy with the same performance levels.

LIFT AND PROPULSION: Power is supplied by three marine diesels amidship in separate engine rooms in-line athwartships. The two outer engine rooms each accommodate one propulsion engine and one auxiliary power unit, the central engine room housing the lift engine. Lift is provided by a 550kW MTU 6V 396 TB53 driving, via a flexible coupling and Cardan shaft, two 1.22m diameter HEBA B centrifugal fans and, via a hydrostatic system, a secondary fan for aft skirt inflation. The propulsion engines are MTU 12V 396 TB83 diesels rated at 1150kW at 1800rpm continuous. Each incorporates a ZF BW 455 reverse-reduction gearbox and drives a single three-bladed propeller via transmission shafting inclined at 13 degrees. The outward rotating propellers operate at up to 900rpm. Fuel is carried in two tanks in the transom bay and fuel capacity is 4.2 tonnes. Machinery is monitored by a programmable controller and visual display.

CONTROLS: Lift and propulsion machinery controls in the wheelhouse meet Lloyds' requirements for unmanned machinery spaces. All diesel engines are electrically started. A plug-in portable unit provides bridge wing control of the propulsion gearbox clutches. Craft heading is by power-operated twin water rudders with a hard-over angle of 26°-0–26° when set with a zero rudder divergence. Additional control is by differential use of the propellers. Provision is made for emergency control from the aft deck. A Marconi Avionics automatic roll-stabilisation system operates through inclined independent rudders.

HULL: Grp structure comprising shell mouldings, sub-mouldings, frames, bulkheads and major attachments built from glass fibre weaves and mats using polyester resin matrix. Frame and bulkhead cores are end grain balsa or polyvinyl chloride foam.

ACCOMMODATION: Seats for 300 passengers in two saloons, forward and aft. Passenger access via doors, port and starboard, aft of forward saloon and double door at rear of aft saloon. Two emergency exits in both saloons. Bridge normally accommodates commander and navigator/

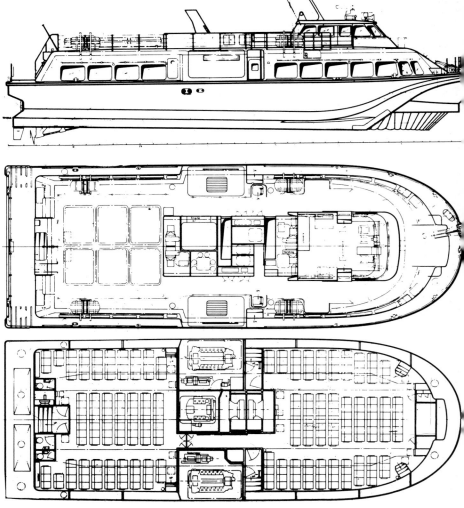

HM 527 Series 2 passenger ferry

engineer. Each passenger saloon has three hinging seats with safety belts for stewards/stewardesses. Safety equipment includes life rafts, inflatable life jackets, lifebuoys and line-throwing apparatus.

VENTILATION: Fresh air ventilation for passenger saloons, wheelhouse and toilet.

HEATING: Warm air heating.

FIRE SAFETY: Engine rooms: fire detection and extinguishing systems. Wheelhouse: two CO_2 portable fire extinguishers. Passenger areas: four AFFF portable fire extinguishers.

SYSTEMS, ELECTRICAL: Ship's service electrical plant comprises two diesel-driven, brushless, air-cooled ac generators rated at 45kVA, 36kW at 0.8 power factor lagging. Each machine can supply the normal running load. Medium voltage supply is 220V, 3-phase, 50Hz, 3 wire. Supply for engine starting, essential services and exit point illumination is provided by 24V batteries.

COMMUNICATIONS

INTERNAL: Two-way amplified speech between wheelhouse, navigation positions, machinery compartments and steward's positions. Public address system.

EXTERNAL: One VHF (FM) radio telephone Type 145. Frequency range 155 to 163.2 MHz. Power output 25/1 watt. One Marconi Marine Survivor 3 emergency portable radio.

NAVIGATION

RADAR: Racal Decca RM 1216 relative motion radar with combined antenna/transceiver unit and one 12-inch master and one 9-inch slave displays.

COMPASS: Marinex transmitting magnetic compass with tape repeater and input to navigation radar displays. Smiths Type E2B emergency compass.

LOG: Chernikeeff Aquacatch EM Log with transducer and master unit.

DIMENSIONS
Length overall: 27.2m
Beam overall: 10.2m
Height (wheelhouse top): 4.9m
Draught, off cushion: 2.7m
  on cushion: 1.7m
WEIGHTS
Oil fuel: 3500kg
Passengers and baggage, 256 at 75kg: 19 200kg
Crew, 7 at 75kg: 525kg
Fresh water: 180kg
Total payload: 23 405kg
PERFORMANCE
Max speed (fully loaded, zero wave height, zero wind speed): 36 knots
Speed, 85% continuous power: 28.5 knots
Endurance (at 85% continuous power and one generator running at 70% rated load): 300n miles

HM 424 (DESIGN)

The most important new design from Hovermarine is the 165–200 seat HM 424. This craft has a top speed of 39 or 50 knots, depending on the engines specified. Passenger accommodation consists of a single through-cabin, insulated from the engines, gearboxes and transmission, thus reducing vibration and noise to the minimum.

LIFT AND PROPULSION: Power for the lift system is supplied by either a Deutz BF12L513C marine diesel engine developing 440hp at 2300rpm, or by a GM 8V92TA marine diesel engine developing 490hp at 2100rpm. The propulsion engines can be specified as either two MWM type TBD 604 B V12 marine diesels each developing 1657hp at 1800rpm, or two GM 16V 92TA marine diesels each developing 960hp at 2100rpm. Oil fuel storage capacity is either 4650 litres or 3500 litres giving an approximate range of 300n miles for either type of engine.

HULL: Designed and built to Lloyds Register of Shipping requirements, the structure consists of shell, frames, bulkheads and major attachments of glass reinforced plastics or aluminium alloy, according to customer preference.

ACCOMMODATION: Depending upon customer requirements, the HM 424 can be equipped with 165–200 seats, two toilets with wash basins and air-conditioning/heating. Two exits each side of the craft ensure rapid embarkation and disembarkation of passengers. Provision for wheelchairs is also provided.

CONTROLS: Lift and propulsion machinery is controlled from the wheelhouse. Mechanical control of lift and propulsion engine governors are provided. Diesel engines are electrically started.

FIRE SAFETY: Fire detection and fixed BTM gas extinguishing systems are fitted in the engine rooms. Portable AFFF fire extinguishers are also supplied in the engine rooms and the passenger saloon with a portable carbon dioxide fire extinguisher carried in the wheelhouse.

ELECTRICAL SYSTEMS: A 220V 50Hz single phase supply is provided, together with 24V 2 wire dc, insulated from earth. ac generation is by 27.5 KVA generators, with dc coming from three engine-driven 24V dc alternators, each rated at 100 amps.

COMMUNICATION: A two way amplified speech facility is provided between wheelhouse and weather decks. The passenger saloon uses a public address system which also has a cassette facility. RF communication is provided by one RT 'Compact' 2047 VHF radio telephone, with a frequency range of 155–162.6 MHz.

NAVIGATION: One Furuno 8100 daylight reading radar is supplied, together with a Marinex transmitting magnetic compass and emergency E2B compass. A Seafarer Microlog EM log with transducer and master unit is also supplied, with a Seafarer Seascribe Echo Sounder for use off-cushion.

DIMENSIONS
Length overall: 24.90m
Beam overall: 10.10m
Draught, on cushion: 0.80m

PROJECT DESIGNS
In 1987 a design of the HM 221 fitted with waterjets was announced, length overall 21.90m, beam overall 6.60m, draught off-cushion 1.21m.

Hovermarine International Ltd has drawn up many craft designs for particular applications based on the basic HM 218, HM 221 and HM 527 hulls. These include designs for patrol craft, strike craft, crewboats etc.

A completely new design of SES was completed during 1988 designated the Hy-Jet HM 934 which will carry 400 passengers at speeds of 47–54 knots in seas of up to 4 metres. In addition, designs for larger capacity craft, the HM 760 and HM 780 have now been model tested. These craft will carry up to 80 cars plus 600 passengers at speeds of 50–54 knots in waves of up to 6 metres.

SLINGSBY AVIATION LIMITED
Head Office: Kirkbymoorside, Yorkshire YO6 6EZ, England

Telephone: (0751) 32474
Telex: 57597SLINAV G

Hovercraft Division Office: Guild House, 151 Albert Road South, Southampton SO1 1FR, England

Telephone: (0703) 37412
Telex: 477795KRACON G
Telefax: (0703) 32572

P G Pollock, *Chairman*
J S Tucker, *Chief Executive and Managing Director*
R Dobson, *Financial Director*
S A Cooper, *Contract Director*
M R Mobbs
Dr R Stanton Jones
Sir Peter Wykeham
A F White, *General Manager, Hovercraft*

Formed in the 1930s as Slingsby Sailplanes, the company has grown over the years to its present size with around 200 employees, working on a site with covered factory space of 13 935m².

In the last 15 years the company has specialised in the fabrication of composite material structures and products for both marine and aviation markets. Work has been undertaken for the Royal Navy, Royal Air Force, Royal Marines, British Army, Airship Industries (UK) Ltd and oil companies. In addition a training aircraft, the Firefly, is produced, which is fully certificated by the CAA.

The company has full CAA approval and is also approved under MoD defence standard 05–21. Work is undertaken to meet Lloyds' and other marine regulatory authorities' standards.

The Hovercraft division was formed in 1984, to design and manufacture a 1500kg payload amphibious hovercraft in composite materials in order to complement Slingsby's existing product range.

In 1985 Slingsby Hovercraft operated a charter contract for an oil exploration company and has operated and maintained two hovercraft in the Middle East carrying out port maintenance and pollution duties from August 1985. The commercial department can arrange lease, charter or outright purchase to meet customer requirements and the product support department will offer

Slingsby 2200 logistic support version

Slingsby 2200 passenger version

substantial after sales service for customers worldwide.

In 1987 Slingsby Aviation became a member of the ML Holdings plc group of companies.

SAH 2200 (formerly SAH 1500)
In May 1986 the first SAH 1500, UK Registration No GH 9651, was delivered to the trials site in Southampton. Extensive trials and evaluation were carried out up to November 1986 when the craft was shipped overseas. Performance evaluation trials proved the craft exceeded all design criteria with a 14% increase in speed, 47% increase in payload and 2% decrease in weight. As a result the craft has been re-designated the SAH 2200 and the specification altered accordingly.

Since November 1986 when the first craft was shipped overseas, craft have been delivered and are operating in Europe, the Far East, the United States, the Caribbean, the Middle East and the UK. A sale of note was the craft purchased by the Department of Natural Resources (DNR) Police, Maryland. The craft's duties include search and rescue, medical evacuation, icebreaking and coastguard liaison. DNR Police have been leasing a hovercraft for over 18 months prior to purchasing the SAH 2200.

The SAH 2200 is an amphibious hovercraft capable of carrying 23 passengers or 2200kg of disposable load. The design is such that rapid changes between cargo and passenger versions can be made. Diesel power has been chosen to reduce operating costs and maintenance time to a minimum. The composite plastics structure offers high strength, good fatigue characteristics and avoidance of corrosion for long life and low maintenance.

LIFT AND PROPULSION: Integrated system. A single Deutz BF6L 913C air-cooled diesel, rated at 190bhp at 2500rpm, drives a centrifugal lift fan and a Hoffman variable-pitch ducted propeller. The engine is mounted on resilient attachments and all machinery components are easily accessible for maintenance.

CONTROLS: Aerodynamic rudders mounted in the propeller slipstream provide directional control; similarly mounted elevators provide fore and aft trim. A fuel ballast system and roll control system is incorporated to counteract adverse loading and to improve craft performance in high wind and sea states. A controllable-pitch propeller allows variable thrust both in forward and reverse giving enhanced control particularly over land and in difficult downwind sea conditions.

HULL: Heavy duty composite plastics structure strengthened with Kevlar in high load areas. Heavy duty marine landing skids are provided. Four marine bollards on the deck form lifting rig attachments and guides for the integral jacking system. Sidedecks are rigid and enable large, bulky items to be carried outside the main load space. The side decks fold to allow transport of the craft by road vehicles or shipping within a 40ft flat rack container.

SKIRT: Loop and segment type.

SYSTEMS: 24V electrical supply is standard. Provision is made for optional extras such as radar, air conditioning, heating and searchlights.

ACCOMMODATION: Seats forward for commander and passenger/navigator are in a self-

A Slingsby SAH 2200 as supplied to the Department of Natural Resources (DNR) Police, Maryland, USA

Craft built	Name	Seats	Operator	
SAH 2200 001				
SAH 2200 002			1987	Swedish military evaluation
SAH 2200 003	*Challenger No 1*	22	1987	Hover Travel Sdn Bhd
SAH 2200 004			1987	Maryland Natural Resources Police

contained wheelhouse. The load space is flexible in layout and two quick-release composite canopies allow conversion to three versions:

PASSENGER VERSION: Bench seating running fore and aft providing a total of 23 passenger seats. Access is port and starboard through sliding doors mounted in canopies.

SUPPLY BOAT VERSION: Covered accommodation for eight passengers with open load space with capacity for up to 1400kg of cargo.

LOGISTIC SUPPORT VERSION: With canopies and seats removed, integral cargo lashing rails are provided to enable a disposable load of up to 2200kg to be carried.

In addition to the above, purpose designed pods to fit the load space can be manufactured to carry specialist equipment.

ACCOMMODATION
Disposable load: 2200kg
Seats: 24

SHIPPING INFORMATION
Can be airlifted, trailed or shipped within a 40ft

flat rack. Packed dimensions with duct removed.
Length: 12.0m
Height: 2.0m
Beam: 2.4m
Weight: 3 tonnes
DIMENSIONS
Length: 10.60m
Beam: 4.20m
Height (off cushion): 2.60m
PERFORMANCE
Speed, max: 74km/h (40 knots)
Fuel consumption, average: 23 litres/h
Range, max: 930km (500n miles)
Obstacle clearance: 0.50m

SAH 4000 (DESIGN)
A new project started in 1987.

UNITED STATES OF AMERICA

AIR RIDE CRAFT INC
[PATENT HOLDERS, DESIGNERS AND DEVELOPERS]
15840 SW 84th Avenue, Miami, Florida 33157, USA

Telephone: (305) 233 4306
Telex: 6974096 LARAMIE
Telefax: (305) 233 1339

Don Burg, *President*

The Air Ride concept, designed and patented by Don Burg is now classified as a surface effect ship (SES) but is of a unique tri-hull form having only a bow skirt to contain the air cushion, the stern configuration being such as to make a stern seal or skirt unnecessary, appreciably simplifying the flexible structure reequirements and their maintenance.

Air Ride craft are under construction by two yards, Avondale Boat Division of Avondale Industries, New Orleans and Cheoy Lee Shipyards Ltd of Hong Kong.

Don Burg started thinking of ways to improve, and simplify the generic SES concept in the mid-seventies and this led to the building of a 7.32 metre Air Ride test craft in 1978, a 12.80 metre demonstration hull in 1980, and a 19.82 metre crew/supply boat in 1983. All of these Air Ride SES's were successful and the crew/supply boat was converted to a 150 passenger ferry that remains in day-to-day operation in the U.S. Virgin Islands today. These early Air Ride SES designs had a very simple pressurised air cavity in their underside and had no flexible seals. As such they offered ride qualities similar to a conventional monohull in a seaway.

Don Burg sought ways to improve the design further as far as ride qualities were concerned. The resulting and newest Air Ride designs retain the proven bow-shaped air chamber stern seal that is part of the hull structure or the earlier designs

while incorporating a simple flexible seal at the bow that is easily changed with the boat waterborne i.e. off-cushion. The flexible bow seal reduces wave impacts since it allows for the passage of waves into the air chamber. The pressure in the air chamber reduces the height of the waves and they are then directed out past inverted-V shapes in the aft air chamber seal at the stern. Further, the air chamber includes a deep-V hull shape on the centerline that is clear of water contact during calm sea operation while improving rough sea operation by slicing and reducing air chamber waves. It also helps off-cushion performance as good low speed handling characteristics are experienced with the cushion fan off.

Other improvements include a more pointed yacht shaped bow, efficient and low-noise-level airfoil shaped fan impeller blades coupled with tuned venturi silencers on fan inlets, extensive vibration isolation mounting of all diesel engines, and advanced high strength lightweight hull designs in either cored fiberglass or marine aluminium. Preferred propulsion units are either waterjets or surface piercing propellers for minimum draught and maximum efficiency at high speeds.

These design improvement efforts resulted in the current Air Ride SES designs and worldwide patents.

Air Ride 109 400 passenger ferry

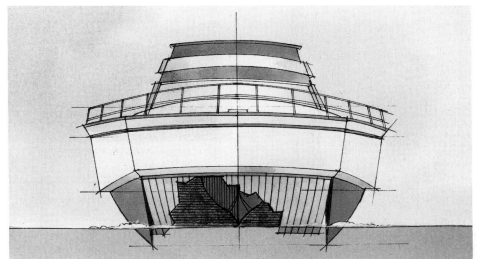

Future Air Ride design showing centre-line hull form within air cushion

Air Ride 109 for New York service

AVONDALE BOAT DIVISION, Avondale Industries Inc

4132 Peters Road, Harvey, Louisiana 70059

Telephone: (504) 366 7217
Telefax: (504) 368 6740

AIR RIDE 109

In late 1988 Avondale Boat Division announced the building under license from Air Ride Craft Inc of Air Ride Craft 109 (400 passenger) surface effect ships for Tri-State Marine Transport Inc to operate between John F. Kennedy Airport and lower Manhattan, the first of these craft (to be followed by four more) to enter service in the spring of 1990. The Air Ride Craft concept developed by Tom Burg represents a unique form of surface effect ship in that a flexible seal or skirt is only used at the bow to contain the air cushion. The Avondale craft are built in marine grade aluminium alloy and form part of the diversified range of ship and boat building, conversion, repair, foundry and propeller work undertaken by the company.

PRINCIPAL PARTICULARS:
Certification: USCG + ABS
Type: Ferry
Hull: Aluminium
Top side design: Avondale Boat Division
Length: 33.23m
Beam: 10.37m
Draught, on-cushion: 0.91m
Displacement, half load: 140 tonnes
Speed: 44 knots
Fuel consumption, at cruise: 851 l/h
Passengers: 360 to 400

Fuel capacity: 9463 l
Water capacity: 1514 l
Engines,
    Propulsion: Two Deutz MWM TBD 604B V16 each 1603 kW (shp 2150)

Lift: One Deutz MWM TBD 234 V12, 336 kW (450 shp)
Thrust device: KaMeWa water-jet units
Ride control system: Standard
Operation: Metro Marine Express, Inc

Launch of *Metro Manhattan* Air Ride 109 ferry

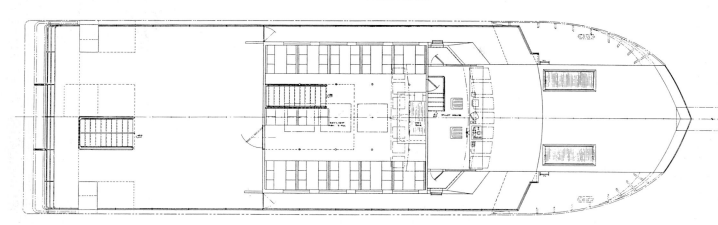

UPPER DECK ARRANGEMENT
68 PASSENGER SEATS

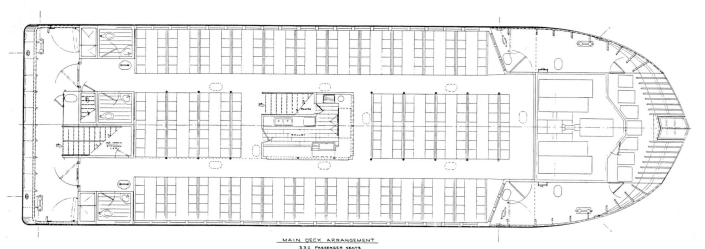

MAIN DECK ARRANGEMENT
332 PASSENGER SEATS

Air Ride 109 passenger ferry

BERTELSEN INC

Head Office and Plant: 113 Commercial Street, Neponset, Illinois 61345, USA

Telephone: (309) 594 2041

William R Bertelsen, *Chairman of the Board, Vice President and Director of Research*
William C Stein, *President and Treasurer*
Charles A Brady, *Secretary*

Dr William R Bertelsen, a general practitioner and talented engineer, was one of the first to build and drive an air cushion vehicle.

Dr Bertelsen designed his first Aeromobile air cushion vehicle in 1950, and has since built and tested 16 full-scale vehicles, ranging from simple plenum craft to ram-wings. The 5.4m long Aeromobile 200–2 was a star exhibit at the US Government's Trade Fairs in Tokyo, Turin, Zagreb and New Delhi in 1961. Descriptions of the Aeromobile 14 and 15 can be found in *Jane's Surface Skimmers 1980* and earlier editions.

Dr Bertelsen's two earliest vehicles, the Aeromobile 35 and the Aeromobile 72, were acquired by the Smithsonian Institution's National Air and Space Museum in January 1981.

During 1984 the company concentrated on improving the operating efficiency of the Mercury V6 150hp outboard engines in a 40in diameter duct driving a new computer-designed 12-blade axial lift/propulsion fan. The lift fan has been designed by the Turbo Machinery Engineering Faculty at the University of Illinois to produce 581lb thrust at 2900rpm or at a 2:1 reduction from engine rpm of 5800 at 150hp.

The company is developing an ACV crawler tractor which overcomes the problems of hill climbing, steering and obstacle clearance. It is designed to carry substantial loads at very low ground pressures.

AEROMOBILE 16

Interest in this 7.82m long utility vehicle, the largest to be constructed by Bertelsen, is being shown by potential customers throughout the USA and Canada. It employs a lift, propulsion and control system similar to that of the earlier Aeromobile 15. The craft is being retrofitted with 1.01m diameter spun aluminium ducted fans powered by two 150hp Mercury outboard engines for increased thrust and efficiency. The ice-breaking capabilities of the A-16 were demonstrated during the winter of 1978–79. The craft can operate on cushion with one engine only, the other being employed for full propulsion and steering. It is one of the few air cushion vehicles capable of sidehill operation.

LIFT AND PROPULSION: Power is supplied by two duct-mounted, 150hp, 122in^3 displacement Mercury V-6 outboard engines, each driving a 1.01m diameter axial fan fabricated in spun aluminium. Each duct is spherical and gimbal-mounted at its centre so that it can be tilted and rotated in any direction. When the fan shaft is vertical the total airflow is discharged into the cushion. By tilting the gimbal the operator allows air from the fan to escape across the stern to provide propulsive thrust.

The thrust force is instantly available throughout 360 degrees and, metered finely by degree of tilt, provides propulsion, braking or yaw torque. The maximum available force is equal to 100 per cent of the propulsion force.

Under test is a variant with new HTD belt drive. Fan tip speed will be only 121.9m/second. Thrust is expected to be 1162lb per unit, nearly double that of the earlier system. About 30 per cent of this is employed for lift at 90 degrees tilt.

Fuel is carried in two 90-litre tanks, one behind the forward engine and one forward of the aft engine. Type of fuel recommended is regular automobile petrol. Fuelling points are on deck above tanks.

HULL: Basic structure built in mild steel tubing. Designed to carry 907kg payload. Total buoyancy 6803kg.

ACCOMMODATION: Enclosed cabin with driver's seat forward and midship and rear bench seats behind, each seating three to four passengers. Access is via two doors, one each side. Seats are removable should the craft be required to undertake light utility roles. Cabin may be heated or air conditioned.

SYSTEMS, ELECTRICAL: Two 12V alternators and two 12V storage batteries.

EXTERNAL DIMENSIONS
Length overall, power off: 7.44m
  skirt inflated: 7.82m
Beam overall, power off: 4.31m
  skirt inflated: 5.48m
Structure width, power off, folded: 2.28m
Height overall, on landing pads: 1.82m
  skirt inflated: 2.23m
Cushion area: 24.15m^2
Cushion height (hardstructure clearance): 406mm
INTERNAL DIMENSIONS
Cargo bay
Length: 3.35m
Max width: 1.82m
Max depth: 0.68m
Deck area total: 27.78m^2
WEIGHTS
Normal empty: 1587kg
Normal max weight: 2268kg
Normal payload: 680kg

Aeromobile 16 lift/propulsion unit under test

Aeromobile 16

Aeromobile 16

PERFORMANCE
Max speed, calm water, max power: 97km/h
Cruising speed, calm water: 80km/h

Turning circle diameter at 30 knots: 152m estimated
Max wave capability: 1.2m
Max survival sea state: 1.8m waves

Still air endurance at cruising speed: 8 hours
Max gradient, static conditions: 10 degrees
Vertical obstacle clearance: 406mm

EQUITABLE SHIPYARDS INC
(A Trinity Industries Company)

P O Drawer E, Highway 21, Madisonville, Louisiana 70447, USA
Telephone: :(504)845 3556
Cliff Anglin, *General Manager*

A 22.87m experimental SES ferry was completed in June 1989. The craft is fitted with Arnesen surface drive propeller systems.

HOVER SYSTEMS INC

1500 Chester Pike, Eddystone, Pennsylvania 19013, USA

Telephone: (215) 876 8241
Telex: 6291456(Easylink)
Telefax: (215) 876 5902

James D Hake, *President*
Joseph J Nestel, *Executive Vice President*
Harvey C Cook *Director, Hovercraft Training and Operations*

Hover Systems Inc has design, manufacturing and test facilities located at Eddystone, Pennsylvania to supply and support hovercraft and other air cushion handling equipment.

In 1980 the company designed and built D-PAAC, a 50-ton payload, diesel-powered air cushion amphibious barge. Details of this vehicle are given in the Low-Speed Air Cushion Platforms section of this book.

Husky G-1500 TD operating on the Antarctic ice shelf with the Erebus Volcano in the background

HUSKY G-1000, G-1500 AND G-2500 TD

In 1984 Hover Systems Inc concluded an agreement with Griffon Hovercraft Ltd of Southampton, UK as the exclusive US licensee for the construction and marketing of the Griffon G-1000 TD, G-1500 TD and G-2500 TD. The first of these craft, re-named Husky 1000 was delivered to the State of Maryland Natural Resources Police in May 1984. The craft has been successfully operated in many roles including search and rescue, emergency medical and icebreaking operations.

All US-built Husky TD Models are built to comply with rigid US Coast Guard Regulations and will carry US Coast Guard certification.

A Griffon 2500 TD hovercraft obtained Canadian Coast Guard certification and was in regular scheduled service at Expo '86 in Vancouver, British Columbia. The craft operated from a floating pontoon adjacent to the Canada Harbour Place section of the exposition along a seven-mile route to the main Expo '86 site. This craft operated 7 days a week and 10 hours a day throughout the Expo '86 period.

A second G-2500 TD was manufactured at the Hover Systems Inc facility in Eddystone, Pennsylvania and thus meets the requirements of the Jones Act for commercial transportation service in the US. This craft has completed US Coast Guard trials in the Delaware River and Atlantic Coast areas and has made numerous trips through the Chesapeake Bay and in the Atlantic Ocean between Cape May, New Jersey and New York City. This craft is US Coast Guard certified.

The G-2500 TD hovercraft is fabricated from riveted and welded marine-grade aluminium. The primary structure consists of four longitudinal members enclosing multiple welded watertight

The first Hover Systems-built Husky G-2500TD *Bravo*, operating on the Delaware River

compartments forming the main hull. Separate bow and stern sections are also fabricated from welded aluminium and bolted to the main hull. Secondary structural side bodies are attached to the hull with struts permitting the side bodies to be hinged upwards for transportation. The flexible neoprene-coated nylon loop and segment skirt is attached to the two side bodies and also to a skirt shift linkage to provide a lateral trim capability. All skirt maintenance can be performed without lifting the craft. Thrust is provided by two ducted propellers powered by two 190hp Deutz air-cooled turbocharged diesel engines. Commercial

vehicle type clutches are fitted at the aft end of each engine which allow the propeller drive to be disconnected for hovering and independent control of each propeller. The clutch output shafts are fitted with sprockets to transmit power via toothed belts to the fixed-pitch four-bladed propellers mounted in aerodynamically shaped ducts. Lift fans are driven via toothed belts and pulleys from the forward end of each engine. In addition to the lateral trim control, longitudinal trim is provided by a fuel transfer system.

The control station includes seating for two crew members and is raised to provide good all-round visibility. Only one crew member is required to operate the craft, rudders in each duct are controlled by a steering yoke, the propeller clutches are operated with foot pedals. A full instrumentation layout and switches for craft control and engine monitoring are provided and circuits are protected by circuit breakers. The 24V dc electrical system is supplied by two engine-driven alternators. The passenger cabin provides good visibility and accommodation and includes four abreast aircraft type seating for up to 32 passengers. The passenger cabin is ventilated by an offtake of cushion air distributed from an overhead duct and warm air is provided by a heater installed behind the rear bulkhead of the passenger compartment. A workboat version of this craft can be provided with an open or closed deck area and with a bow loading ramp.

HUSKY 2500 TDX (DESIGN)

A modified version of the G-2500 TD craft was designed. This craft is identical to the G-2500 TD except that the engines have been replaced with Deutz BF8L 513 engines capable of developing 320hp each at 2300rpm. In addition, the craft has larger ducts and propellers than the G-2500 TD and the hull length has been increased, resulting in predicted increased speed and operating capability of a maximum speed of 40 knots and a cruise speed of 38 knots.

HUSKY G-1500 TD

In 1988 a Husky G-1500 TD was purchased by the National Science Foundation for service in the Antarctic by ITT Antarctic Services Inc. Special design features were incorporated in the craft, along with careful selection of equipment and materials, in order to meet the low temperature and hostile environment of Antarctic operations. The craft was delivered in early February 1988 after completing acceptance tests on the Delaware River and over-ice trials have been completed in the McMurdo Sound area of the Antarctic. In 1990 the craft is to be fitted with a variable-pitch propeller.

The craft operates over sea ice as a support vehicle for scientists, also complements helicopter operations and relieves shuttle services to William Field during periods of soft ice surface conditions.

The Husky G-1500 TD can be loaded into a single C-130 aircraft and further over-ice applications are being evaluated.

HUSKY 400

In 1988 the Husky 400, a rugged multi-role hovercraft was completed and certified by the National Marine Manufacturer's Association (NMMA). The craft's hull is fabricated in fibreglass providing maximum strength and rigidity. The unique skirt system of the Husky 400 incorporates an inflatable collar which provides added buoyancy along with improved stability.

Power is provided by a water-cooled petrol engine, which drives a six-bladed ducted propeller. The craft incorporates a centrifugal fan at the bow supplying air to the cushion and skirt system. The propeller and lift fan are powered by separate hydraulic motors from two hydraulic pumps driven in tandem by the petrol engine. The

Craft built	Name	Date completed
Husky G-2500 TD, Reg No PA 2994X	*Bravo*	1986
Husky G-2500 TD	—	1987

Hover Systems Husky 400

	G-1000 TD	G-1500 TD	G-2500 TD
Payload	978kg	1497kg	2494kg
Weight, empty	1995kg	2300kg	6757kg
Speed, max (no wind)	35 knots	33 knots	31 knots
Speed, cruise	28 knots	27 knots	26 knots
Standard seating	10 persons	16 persons	24–32 persons
Crew	1	1	2
Obstacle clearance	38cm	38cm	38cm
Weather limitations:			
Max wind	25 knots	25 knots	25 knots
Max wave height	1.0m	1.0m	1.0m
Engine	One BF6L 913C	One BF6L 913C	Two BF6L 913C
	190hp at 2500rpm	190hp at 2500rpm	190hp at 2500rpm
Length, overall	8.41m	10.15m	13.99m
Beam, hard structure	3.81m	3.81m	5.78m
Beam, side bodies removed	2.26m	2.26m	4.24m
Height, off cushion	2.68m	2.68m	2.87m
Cabin length	3.20m	5.00m	8.05m
Cabin width	1.80m	1.80m	3.29m

hydraulic drive allows independent control of the lift fan and the propeller which also enables the propeller to be run in reverse.

Directional control of the Husky 400 is provided by two rudders in the rear of the duct, the controls necessary to operate the craft include a conventional steering wheel, an engine throttle control, a switch to engage the lift fan and a mode switch to select forward or reverse thrust.

The craft is fitted with a flexible neoprene coated nylon loop and segment skirt system that can be maintained without lifting the craft.

The Husky 400 can be operated over land, on ice and in areas of white water rapids, marsh land,

shallow water, river estuary or light sea conditions. It can be used for search and rescue, light cargo and leisure purposes and as a work boat or military assault craft.

PRINCIPAL PARTICULARS
Length, overall (hard structure): 5.79 m
Beam (hard structure): 2.29 m
Weight, max: 1542 kg
Pay load, max: 454 kg
Accommodation: 6 people
Engine: 150 hp
Fuel capacity: 60 l
Speed, max: 30.5 knots
Speed, cruise: 24.5 knots

 **Marine Systems**
Division of Textron Inc.

(TMS)
Division of Textron Inc
6800 Plaza Drive, New Orleans, Louisiana 70127-2596, USA

Telephone: (504) 245 6600
Telex: 6711199TMSNOLA
Telefax: (504) 245 6634

John J Kelly, *President*
Joseph J Halisky, *Vice President, Operations*
L W Frank, *Vice President, Manufacturing*
Frank P Higgins, *Vice President, Product Reliability and Support*
D F Bobeck, *Program Director, LCAC*
William M Rickett, *Program Director, Motor Lifeboat*
J D O'Bryan, *Program Director, Lighterage ACVs*
James W Kratzer, *Vice President, Finance and Administration*
Larry N Hairston, *Executive Director of Marketing*

Bell Aerospace Textron began its air cushion vehicle development programme in 1958. In 1969, the New Orleans Operations was established to develop air cushion vehicles and surface effect ships for military and commercial markets. On 1 July 1986, Bell New Orleans Operations was renamed Textron Marine Systems (TMS). TMS operates as a separate company independent of the other Bell Aerospace Divisions.

Bell Halter Inc was formed in 1980 as a joint venture of Bell Aerospace Textron and Halter Marine Inc for the purpose of constructing surface effect ships and air cushion vehicles. In early 1988,

The fourteenth Landing Craft, Air Cushion (LCAC) built by Textron Marine Systems and delivered 4 November 1988, operating in Lake Borgne,Louisiana, during trials

Textron Inc. purchased Bell Halter Inc. from Halter Marine Inc., a wholly owned subsidiary of Trinity Industries Inc. Renamed Textron Marine Systems Shipyard Operations, it continues to be managed by Textron Marine Systems Division of Textron Inc. Textron Marine Systems delivered LCAC-14 at the end of 1988. The first six were delivered by TMS in 1986. The current TMS building programme is for a total of 36, the US Navy planning additional procurement for a total of 90, including Avondale-built craft.

The company has rights to manufacture and sell in the USA machines employing the hovercraft principle through a licensing arrangement with the British Hovercraft Corporation and Hovercraft Development Ltd.

Craft which have been built by the company range in size from the SES-100B to the LCAC (Landing Craft, Air Cushion) currently in production for the US Navy. Textron Marine Systems delivered a total of 14 LCAC's to the US Navy by the end of 1989 and 31 further craft are in production.

On 6 June 1986, LCAC-3, the third craft in the series, travelled over open water from New Orleans, Louisiana, to Panama City, Florida, at an average speed in excess of 40 knots. The voyage, which coincided with the 42nd anniversary of the World War II invasion of Normandy, marked the longest single trip ever made by a US air cushion assault landing craft. During 1987, the LCACs successfully completed a series of amphibious exercises with the US Fleet, and LCAC-4 participated in operations in Okinawa, Japan, marking the first entry of the craft on foreign soil. Since then, LCAC's have

Principal craft built—Textron Marine Systems

SESs

SES-100B	surface effect ship test craft (see *Jane's Surface Skimmers 1984* and earlier editions)	on trials February 1972
Model 210A (110 Mk I)	demonstration SES, became USCG *Dorado* (WSES-1)	launched 1978 June 1981
Model 730A	became Model 730A, US Navy SES-200, with 15.24m extension, USS *Jaeger*	
Model 720A	*Rodolf*—hydrographic survey boat for US Army Corps of Engineers	delivered 1980
Model 212A (110 Mk II)	crewboats: *Speed Command* *Swift Command*	delivered February 1981 delivered July 1981
Model 522A (110 Mk II)	'Seabird' class: *Sea Hawk* (WSES-2) } US Coast Guard, *Shearwater* (WSES-3) } Key West, Florida *Petrel* (WSES-4)	October 1982 June 1983
Model 212B	Model 212A *Speed Command* and *Swift Command* converted to become Model 212B crewboats: *Margaret Jill* (chartered by Tidewater Inc.) *Speed Tide* (chartered by Tidewater Inc)	1984 1985

AMPHIBIOUS AIR CUSHION VEHICLES

AALC JEFF(B)	amphibious assault landing craft	completed March 1977
LACV-30	lighter, air cushion vehicle. 24 completed by 1986 for US Army Troop Support Command	first ones delivered 1981
LCAC	Landing Craft, Air Cushion	fourteen delivered by end of 1989 31 more on order as of 8 January 1990
UACV	Utility air cushion vehicle demonstrator	1988
UACV 1200	Delivered to Shell Offshore Inc.	June 1989

been successfully deployed in operations around the world.

Earlier work on air cushion vehicles which has led to current TMS developments may be summarised as follows:

In January 1969 the US Surface Effect Ships Project Office awarded TMS a contract for the detailed design of a 100-ton surface effect ship test craft. Construction began in September 1969 and a test and evaluation programme began in February 1972.

In March 1971 the company was awarded a Phase II contract by the US Navy to start work on a programme covering the detail design, construction and test of an experimental 160-ton AALC (amphibious assault landing craft), designated JEFF(B). Built at the NASA Michoud Assembly Facility, New Orleans, the craft was later transferred to the Naval Coastal Systems Center, Panama City, Florida. After preliminary testing the craft was delivered to the US Navy's Experimental Trials Unit at Panama City for crew training and operational trials.

Full details of the JEFF(B) are given on pp 93–94 of *Jane's High-Speed Marine Craft and Air Cushion Vehicles, 1987.*

In January 1974 the company announced the successful completion of tests by the SES-100B, which confirmed the suitability of the design technology required for a 2000-ton ocean-going surface ship.

In July 1974 the Naval Materiel Command awarded TMS a US $36 million 18-month contract to conduct an advanced development programme for a 2000-ton, high-speed, ocean-going operational warship-the 2KSES. The company continues to support surface effect ship development through studies in advanced systems in lift and propulsion.

In autumn 1979 Bell Aerospace Textron signed a US $21 million contract with the US Army Mobility Equipment R & D Command (MERADCOM) for the first four of twelve LACV-30s (lighter, air cushion vehicles, 30 short ton payload) with the first deliveries made in 1981. In January 1981 an additional four craft were ordered and in autumn 1982 a further 12. A total of 26 production craft have been delivered, and the programme has been transferred from Bell Aerospace Niagara Frontier Operations to Textron Marine Systems.

In 1985, TMS entered into a joint venture with Avon Industrial Polymers Ltd, a British rubber company, to form Bell Avon. Bell Avon, located in Picayune, Mississippi, manufactures skirts for TMS air cushion craft as well as other products.

The Textron Marine shipyard is located on a 10.1-hectare (25-acre) site in eastern New Orleans, Louisiana, and has direct access to the Intercoastal Waterway, the Mississippi River, and the Gulf of Mexico. Vessels built at the shipyard are in service with the US Army, the US Army Corps of Engineers, the US Navy, the US Coast Guard, and the commercial sector, and have accumulated many thousands of hours of service.

LCAC (24 delivered by March 1990) (LANDING CRAFT, AIR CUSHION)

Craft built	Delivered to US Navy
LCAC-1	December 1984
LCAC-2	February 1986
LCAC-3	June 1986
LCAC-4	August 1986
LCAC-5	November 1986
LCAC-6	December 1986
LCAC-7	March 1987
LCAC-8	June 1987
LCAC-9	June 1987
LCAC-10	September 1987
LCAC-11	December 1987
LCAC-12	December 1987
LCAC-13	September 1988
LCAC-14	November 1988

On 5 June 1981 TMS signed a US $40 million contract with the US Navy for the detail design and long-lead materials for an amphibious assault landing craft designated by the Navy as the LCAC (Landing Craft, Air Cushion). The LCAC is the production version of the JEFF craft. The contract contained two options for the later construction of six craft. In February 1982 the US Navy exercised the first option for the production of three lead craft and in October 1982 it ordered a further three craft.

In March 1984 TMS was awarded a contract to build six more LCACs. By December 1986 TMS had been awarded a contract to build two more LCACs bringing the total to fourteen craft. The LCACs are being assembled at the Textron Marine Systems shipyard in eastern New Orleans, Louisiana.

On 1 July 1987, the US Navy awarded a US $187 million contract to TMS to construct another 10 LCACs. This contract marked the start of full production for the LCAC programme.

On 15 December 1988 a second full production contract for 12 LCAC's was awarded to TMS, along with central procurement activities for long-lead-time materials. This contract is valued at US $228 million. The LCAC is a high-speed, ship-to-shore, and over-the-beach amphibious landing craft, capable of carrying a 60-ton payload. It can transport equipment, personnel, and weapons

Textron Marine Systems LCAC in well-deck of landing ship

One of the bow thrusters on the LCAC which provide up to 10% of total thrust

systems (including the main battle tank) from ships located at increased stand-off distances, through the surf zone, and across the beach to hard landing points beyond the waterline. The craft is supported on a pressurised cushion of air and travels at much higher speeds than are presently possible with current conventional landing craft. Over-the-horizon launches are made possible by the high transit speeds of the LCAC.

The LCAC is capable of travelling over land and water. Compared to conventional landing craft, the percentage of the world's shorelines suitable for landing is increased from 17 to 70 per cent. The LCACs will operate from well-deck-equipped amphibious ships.

MACHINERY

Propulsion System

Engines: Four Avco Lycoming TF40B gas turbines, 3955shp each, max continuous

Fuel: Diesel marine (MIL-F-16884) or JP-5 (MIL-T-5624)

Propellers: Two Dowty Rotol 3.582m diameter four-blade variable, reversible pitch, ducted

Lift fans: Four double-entry centrifugal type, diameter 1.60m

DIMENSIONS

Length overall, on cushion: 26.82m

Beam, on cushion: 14.33m

Height, on cushion: 7.22m

Draught, off cushion:

Hard structure: 0.71m

Landing rails: 0.91m

Draught, on cushion:

Cargo space: 20.43 × 8.23m

Cargo deck area: 168 m²

WEIGHTS

Light-ship displacement: 92.5 tonnes

Design combat displacement: 103.1 tonnes

Payload:

design: 54.3 tonnes

overload: 67.9 tonnes

PERFORMANCE (Combat weight)

Speed, max calm water: 50 knots

Speed, in Sea State 2: over 40 knots

Speed, in Sea State 3: over 30 knots

LACV-30 (LIGHTER, AIR CUSHION VEHICLE, 30 SHORT TONS PAYLOAD) MODEL 7467

This stretched version of the Voyageur was designed to meet the US Army's requirements for a high-speed amphibious vehicle for logistics-over-the-shore operations.

In 1975 Bell Aerospace Textron built two prototypes as a joint development between the company's Niagara Frontier Operations near Niagara Falls, New York and Bell Aerospace Canada Textron at Grand Bend, Ontario. The prototypes, owned by the US Army, have been upgraded to production craft configuration by Bell. Delivery of the 26 production craft was completed in 1986. The programme has since been transferred to Textron Marine Systems.

The chief modifications are a 3.35m lengthening of the deck ahead of the raised control cabin to facilitate the carriage of additional ISO containers and wheeled and tracked vehicles.

The LACV-30 is employed by the US Army as an amphibious lighter for efficient cargo removal from ship to shore and inland when no port facilities exist. Capable of travelling up to 99km/h, it can operate over water, land, snow, ice, marshes, swamps and low brush, through 2.5m surf and over 1.2m obstacles. The craft can carry a variety of containerised cargo, wheeled and tracked vehicles, engineer equipment, pallets and barrels.

The craft can be used on 70 per cent of the world's beaches compared to the 17 per cent accessible to conventional lighterage craft, permitting dry landings of cargo. As for many air cushion vehicles, its air cushion makes it an effect-

LCAC-1 crossing coastal scrub land

Stern of LCAC

Bow ramp of LCAC

ive icebreaker. The LACV-30 can operate in harsh environments, from arctic to tropical conditions, including sand beaches and salt water and has achieved the best productivity per craft of all the US Army lighterage systems. In the last five years, these craft have participated in many major US Department of Defense training exercises on both the Atlantic and Pacific Coasts and in the Gulf of Mexico.

The LACV-30 can be carried, fully assembled, on containerships and break-bulk cargo ships, and all other US flag cargo ships. Not requiring dock or berthing facilities, it can be launched by its crew and readied for service within an hour.

Endurance at cruising speed depends on the configuration role in which the craft is used. The craft can carry payloads of 27.22 tonnes (30 short tons) with an endurance from 5 to 10 hours.

The craft is also suitable for a number of roles such as coastal, harbour and inland waterway patrol, search and rescue, medical evacuation, water and fuel supply, vehicle, personnel and troop transport, augmentation of fixed ports, pollution and fire control.

LIFT AND PROPULSION: Integrated system, powered by two Pratt and Whitney ST6T Twin-Pac gas turbines mounted aft, one at each side of the raised control cabin. Each engine is rated at 1800shp maximum and 1400shp at normal output. The output of each is absorbed by a three-bladed Hamilton Standard 43D50–367 reversible-pitch 2.74m propeller and a 2.13m diameter, twelve-blade, fixed-pitch light aluminium alloy, centrifugal lift fan.

FUEL: Recommended fuel is standard aviation kerosene-Jet A-1, JP4, JP5, JP8 or light diesel fuel oil. Main usable fuel capacity is 8600 litres. Fuel ballast/emergency fuel capacity 5795 litres.

SYSTEMS, ELECTRICAL: Starter generators: four gearbox-driven, brushless, 28V dc, 200A each. One ac generator, gearbox driven, 400Hz, 115V. Batteries: two nickel cadmium, 28V dc, 40Ah each.

DIMENSIONS
Length overall, on cushion: 23.3m
Beam overall, on cushion: 11.2m
Height overall, on cushion: 7.52m
    off cushion: 6.56m
Skirt height, nominal: 1.21m
Height, cargo deck, off cushion: 1.16m
Cargo deck: 15.69 × 9.9m

LACV-30

LACV-30

LACV-30–10

Craft built	Owner
LACV-30–1	US Army
LACV-30–2	US Army
LACV-30–3	US Army
LACV-30–4	US Army
LACV-30–5	US Army
LACV-30–6	US Army
LACV-30–7	US Army
LACV-30–8	US Army
LACV-30–9	US Army
LACV-30–10	US Army
LACV-30–11	US Army
LACV-30–12	US Army
LACV-30–13	US Army
LACV-30–14	US Army
LACV-30–15	US Army
LACV-30–16	US Army
LACV-30–17	US Army
LACV-30–18	US Army
LACV-30–19	US Army
LACV-30–20	US Army
LACV-30–21	US Army
LACV-30–22	US Army
LACV-30–23	US Army
LACV-30–24	US Army
LACV-30–25	US Army
LACV-30–26	US Army

WEIGHTS
Light condition: 25 397kg
Design max: 52 154kg
Operating max: 53 515kg
Max: 56 689kg
Payload, max: 22.7 to 27.2 tonnes

PERFORMANCE (estimated)
Standard day, zero wind, calm water, at gross
    weight of 52 154kg:
    Normal rating: 74km/h, 40 knots
    Max rating: 99km/h, 54 knots
Estimated fuel consumption during lighterage
    missions: 984 litres/h

General arrangement of the TMS Model 7467 LACV-30

MODEL 720A HYDROGRAPHIC SURVEY BOAT (RODOLF)

Rodolf was built in 1979 and delivered to the US Army Corps of Engineers (Portland District) in early 1980.

The vessel operates as a displacement catamaran at low speeds and as an air-cushion-assisted planing catamaran at high speeds. With the lift system shut down, speeds in excess of 24km/h are possible, with the sidehulls supporting 100 per cent of the weight through a combination of buoyancy and planing forces. The lift system can be employed at any speed to support part of the weight of the boat. At high speeds, up to 85 per cent of the weight can be supported by the air cushion, with a resulting increase of lift-to-drag ratio from 5 to approximately 11. The maximum speed is thereby increased to 56.32km/h. Over the complete speed range, from 24 to 56km/h approximately, total power requirements, and hence fuel consumption, can be reduced by selecting the appropriate lift fan rpm settings.

LIFT AND PROPULSION: The lift system is powered by a single Detroit Diesel 4-53N rated at 105shp at 2600rpm. Propulsive thrust is supplied by twin Detroit Diesel Allison 8V-92N marine diesels rated at 360hp at 2100rpm, each driving a propeller via a standard Allison M reduction gear with a ratio of 1.52:1. Fuel is carried in four tanks, each with a capacity of 1325 litres.

CONTROLS: Directional control is provided by twin water rudders aft, one on each sidehull, in addition to the differential use of propeller thrust for slow speed manoeuvring.

HULL: Primary structure is built of welded marine aluminium alloy 5086. The structure is of catamaran configuration and consists of two sidehulls, separated by decks and the cabin structure. The sidehull shell plating varies between ⅛ and ¼in thick, depending on local pressures, and is stiffened by T-section longitudinals. Sidehull shape is maintained by frames and bulkheads, spaced generally at 0.91 to 1.52m, that support the hull longitudinals.

Three watertight bulkheads are used in each sidehull and across the centre section between the

hulls. Two are at the forward and aft ends of the cabin and one is forward of the helmsman's platform. The latter also forms a collision bulkhead. The bulkheads provide transverse bending and torsional continuity to the hull structure. There are also longitudinal watertight bulkheads running the full length of the craft aft of the collision bulkhead.

SKIRT: Flexible skirts at bow and stern. The bow seal consists of six fingers, each approximately 3.96m long, 0.6m wide and 1.95m high. All fingers are identical.

The stern seal has a constant cross-section and consists of two inflated lobes of coated-fabric material, with a horizontal diaphragm to sustain pressure loads. End caps, which bear partly on the sidehulls, contain the air at the ends of the seal. Principal dimensions of the stern seal are length 2.13m and height 1.21m. Each lobe has a radius of approximately 304mm.

ACCOMMODATION: Deckhouse structure contains pilothouse, cabin and lift system housing. Pilothouse is in forward portion with pilothouse deck slightly higher than weather deck elevation. Main cabin deck is recessed below weather deck between sidehulls. Main cabin profile is lower than pilothouse to allow visibility directly aft through rear-facing pilothouse windows. Two interior stairways lead from main cabin deck level; one to pilothouse level and one to the aft section of

weather deck. Provision is made for complement of seven crew and/or observers.

EXTERNAL DIMENSIONS
Length overall: 14.63m
Beam overall: 7.31m
Height overall: 4.72m
Draught, max static: 1.6m
Skirt depth, bow: 1.82m
          stern: 1.21m
Cushion area: 62.92m²

INTERNAL DIMENSIONS
Length: 7.01m
Max width: 3.65m
Max height: 2.13m
Floor area: 25.64m²

WEIGHTS
Normal empty: 18.6 long tons
Survey equipment: 1.2 long tons
Fuel capacity: 4.4 long tons
Normal gross: 24.2 long tons

SURVEY ELECTRONICS: Decca Survey Systems, Inc, Integrated Electronic Surveying System; Del Norte Trisponder electronic positioning; Ross Laboratories Digitising Fathometer; Houston Instruments X-Y Plotter; Digital Equipment computer and terminal; Digital Equipment magnetic and punch tapes; Decca Survey Interfaces, software, and left/right indicators.

Hydrographic survey boat, *Rodolf*

PERFORMANCE

Max speed over calm water, max continuous
power: 33 knots (29°C)
Cruising speed, calm water: 23 knots
Water speed in 1.22m waves and 15 knot headwind: 24 knots
Still air range and endurance at cruising speed:
1090n miles and 50 hours

MODEL 210A (110 Mk I) DEMONSTRATION SES

Launched in late 1978, the Model 110 demonstration boat has undergone extensive successful testing by both commercial operators and
the US Coast Guard. The basic hull and machinery layout permits modification of the deckhouse
and arrangement of the deck space for a number
of alternative applications, from crew boat and
275seat passenger ferry to fast patrol boat.

In September 1980 the US Navy purchased the
Demonstration SES (110 Mk I) to be used in a
joint US Navy/US Coast Guard programme. The
US Coast Guard, designating the boat the USCG
Dorado (WSES-1), conducted an operational
evaluation of the craft for the first six months of
the programme. The craft was modified to
conform to US Coast Guard requirements for
an operational evaluation vessel. The US Coast
Guard has completed its evaluation and a 15.24m
hull extension was added to the boat for the US
Navy to assess the performance of a higher length-
to-beam vessel. The craft has been designated the
SES-200 by the US Navy (see later subentry for
model 730A).

MODEL 522A US COAST GUARD SES

In June 1981 the US Coast Guard awarded a
contract for the purchase of three Model 522A
(110 Mk II) high-speed cutters, the first two of
which were delivered in October 1982.

The craft, known as the 'Seabird' class, are
designated *Sea Hawk* (WSES-2), *Shearwater*
(WSES-3) and *Petrel* (WSES-4). *Petrel* was delivered in June 1983. These vessels are based at Key
West, Florida, at a new Coast Guard facility, and
are being used to intercept drug runners operating
in the Gulf of Mexico and in the Caribbean Sea.

LIFT AND PROPULSION: Cushion lift is provided by two Detroit Diesel Allison 8V-92N 350hp
marine diesels each driving a double-inlet centrifugal fan. Motive power for the propulsion
system is furnished by two DDA 16V-149TIB
marine diesels each rated at 1800hp at 1900rpm.
Each drives a 1.06m diameter, 1.17m pitch three-
bladed, fixed-pitch Nibral propeller Gawn-Burrill
Series type. Maximum fuel load is 34 050 litres.

CONTROLS: Craft direction is controlled by
twin rudders, one aft on each sidehull. Differential
propeller thrust is employed for slow-speed manoeuvring. The steering system is electro-hydraulic
and can be operated from any of the control
stations in the pilothouse and the wing bridges.

HULL: Primary structure is built in welded
marine aluminium alloy 5086. The structure is
of catamaran configuration and consists of two
sidehulls separated by decks and transverse bulkheads. The sidehull shell plating varies between
¼ and ½in depending on local pressures, and is
stiffened by T-section longitudinals. The spacing
of the longitudinals is 457mm on the bottom
plating and 381mm on the side plating. Sidehull
shape is maintained by bulkheads spaced generally at 2.44m which support the hull longitudinals. Bulkheads have ¼in webs with T-section
and flat bar stiffening and flat bar caps sized
appropriately for each bulkhead.

Six of the bulkheads in each sidehull and also
across the centre section between the hulls are
watertight. Two are in the accommodation area,
and one is forward of the deckhouse. The latter
also forms a collision bulkhead. The bulkheads
provide the transverse bending and torsional continuity to the hull structure.

Model 110 Mk I demonstration SES

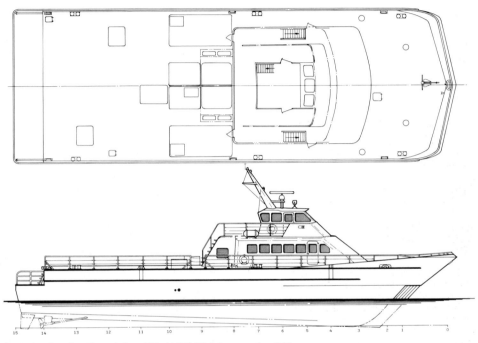
Original outboard profile and plan of Model 110 Mk I demonstration SES

USCG *Dorado* (WSES-1), formerly Model 110 Mk I demonstrator before conversion by lengthening to become the SES 200

US Coast Guard cutter *Petrel*

The cabin superstructure consists of T-section frames fabricated from flat bars and spaced as the frames on the hull. T-stiffened plate is welded to the framing.

SKIRT: The bow seal consists of eight equally spaced fingers, each of which is attached to the underside of the centre hull. The stern seal, which has a constant cross section, consists of two inflated horizontal lobes of coated-fabric material.

ACCOMMODATION: Deckhouse super-structure contains pilothouse at 01 level with communications and navigation equipment. Auxiliary control stations are provided plus additional controls on each wing bridge. Main deckhouse contains ship's office, armory, captain's stateroom, quarters for three officers and three men. Second deck accommodation includes galley and additional quarters for 12 crew.

ARMAMENT: Two 50-calibre machine guns on the foredeck.

EXTERNAL DIMENSIONS
Length overall: 33.52m
Beam overall: 11.88m
Height, on cushion: 12m
  off cushion: 10.26m
Draught, on cushion: 1.67m
  off cushion: 2.51m
Skirt depth, bow: 2.28m
  stern: 1.52m
INTERNAL DIMENSIONS
Control cabin
Length: 4.57m
Max width: 3.35m
Max height: 2.13m
Main cabin
Length: 8.53m
Max width: 9.14m
Max height: 2.13m
Floor area: 78.04m^2
WEIGHTS
Max displacement: 150 long tons
Normal displacement: 134 long tons
Light ship displacement: 105 long tons
PERFORMANCE

Speed,	Sea State 0	Sea State 3
on cushion:	30 knots	28 knots
hullborne:	19 knots	16 knots

RANGE
Sea State 0: 1550n miles
Sea State 3: 1250n miles

MODEL 212B (110 Mk II)

The Model 212B is a conversion of the model 212A. The two craft converted are the *Margaret Jill* (ex *Speed Command*) and *Speed Tide* (ex *Swift Command*).

Sea Hawk and *Shearwater*, the first two Model 522A cutters to be delivered to US Coast Guard

Model 212B, *Margaret Jill*

US Navy SES-200, USS *Jaeger* (lengthened conversion of the 110 Mk I) showing spray discharging from the ride-control vent on the deck aft of the wheelhouse

HULL MATERIALS: 5086 Aluminium.
MACHINERY
Main engines: Two Detroit Diesel Allison 16V-149TIB engines, diesel, turbocharged, inter-cooled, heat exchanger cooled, air start-1650bhp at 1900rpm
Gears: Two ZF BW 455 reduction gears. Input shafts-identical rotation, output shafts-opposite rotation (2:1 ratio)
Lift engines: Two GM 8V-92 engines, diesel, heat exchanger cooled, air start-350shp at 2100rpm
Lift fans: Two TMS 42-inch welded aluminium centrifugal fans
Generators: Two GM 3–71 65 kVA heat exchanger cooled, one air start, one hydraulic start
UNDERWATER GEAR
Propeller shafts: 4-inch diameter 17–4 PH stainless steel
Bearings: 4-inch BJ Byplex rubber bearings
Propellers: 3-blade stainless
Rudders: Stainless steel built-up blades with 5-inch diameter stainless rudder stocks
Bearings: 5-inch BJ Byplex rubber bearings
ACCOMMODATION
Passenger accommodation: 119 4-inch thick cushioned bench seats on two deck levels. Two passenger heads provided.
Crew accommodation: Six in two single and two two-person cabins with hanging lockers. Two crew heads with showers provided. Mess area for six adjoins galley.
DIMENSIONS
Length, moulded: 33.25m
Breadth, moulded: 11.89m
Depth, moulded: 4.62m
Max draught:
    Normal hullborne: 2.52m
    Loaded hullborne: 2.82m
    Normal cushionborne: 1.68m
CAPACITIES
Fuel capacity: 20 212 litres
Freshwater capacity: 3081 litres
Deck cargo: Up to 26 light tons
PERFORMANCE
Cruise speed: 31 knots in calm water

MODEL 730A (USN SES-200)
HIGH LENGTH-TO-BEAM RATIO TEST CRAFT

The original 33.53m SES demonstration boat is now owned by the US Navy. The boat was modified by adding a 15.24m hull extension. The hull was cut amidships; the lift fans and engines remaining in the bow and the main engines remaining in the stern. Bow and stern sections were then moved apart and a 15.24m plug section inserted between them. All major systems remained the same as they were in the original vessel, including the GM 16V-149TI engines.

In this configuration, the vessel has a 60 per cent greater disposable load than the demonstration boat, while its maximum speed is only reduced by 3 to 4 knots. At intermediate speeds, the power requirements are lower than for the shorter vessel, despite the greater displacement.

The engine rooms of the SES-200 can accommodate larger diesels, or CODOG/CODAG arrangements of diesels and gas turbines, to extend the speed capability up to the 50-knot range. Simple modifications can be made to reinforce the aft deck for helicopter operations. In this configuration, the beam of the vessel and the forward location of the superstructure results in a flight deck as large as those normally found on multi-thousand-ton naval combatants.

In 1986, the SES-200 successfully completed an eight-month series of joint technical and operational trials. The trials, which were conducted in Britain, Spain, France, Germany, Sweden, Norway and Canada, provided each host nation opportunities for direct evaluation of the high length-to-beam SES in their own waters.

ENGINES
Propulsion: Two GM 16V-149TI, 1600bhp each (driving 1.016m dia fixed-pitch propellers)
Lift: Four GM 8V-92TI, 435bhp each (driving 1.067m dia Bell centrifugal fans)
ELECTRICAL SYSTEM: GM diesel generator, 85kW plus 55kW back-up driven off one lift engine.
DIMENSIONS
Length overall: 48.7m
Beam overall: 11.88m
Height, on cushion: 12m
Depth, moulded: 4.63m
Draught, off cushion: 2.83m
Draught, on cushion: 1.67m
Wet deck height: 2.29m
Cushion length: 40.62m
Cushion beam: 9.63m
Cushion length/beam ratio: 4.25:1
WEIGHTS
Displacement, light ship: 127 tonnes
Fuel capacity: 80 128 litres
Displacement, full load: 207 tonnes
PERFORMANCE
Speed, max: 28 knots
    in 2.5m Significant Wave Height: 18–22 knots (max safe)
Time to accelerate to max speed: 60 seconds
Range, Sea State 0: 2950n miles at 30 knots
    3850n miles at 20 knots
Range, Sea State 3: 2400n miles at 25 knots
    2900n miles at 20 knots
Reference: *The United Kingdom Trials of the SES-200* by B J W Pingree, B J Russell and J B Wilcox. Paper given at the Fourth International Hovercraft Conference, 6–7 May 1987

ALL-TERRAIN CRASH RESCUE VEHICLE (ATCRV) (DESIGN)

News of this combined air cushion and wheel-supported project was first announced on 18 March 1986. A 15-month design contract for US $290 000 was placed with Bell Aerospace Textron, the design engineers working with the US Air Force Engineering and Services Center (AFESC) at Tyndall AFB, Florida, and with the Air Force Flight Dynamics Laboratory at Wright-Patterson AFB, Dayton, Ohio. A feasibility analysis and preliminary design has been undertaken by the Flight Dynamics Laboratory, funded by HQ AFESC/RDCF, Fire Research, Tyndall AFB, Florida. A 272kg scale model has been constructed by Textron Marine Systems for stability evaluation with the Flight Dynamics Laboratory whirling arm facility. The total development programme is expected to extend to four or five years. In late 1989, TMS was awarded a US $100,000 contract to refine the skirt system for the vehicle and update the scale model for further testing. Full scale development is expected to begin in the latter part of 1990.

A paper describing the preliminary design of the vehicle is listed in the bibliography section of this edition of *High-Speed Marine Craft and Air Cushion Vehicles*.

The approach adopted was to develop a multi-surface crash rescue vehicle incorporating a retractable air cushion system and with a performance comparable to the US Air Force Crash/Fire/Rescue (CFR) vehicle, the latest Class I Major Fire Fighting Vehicle, the P-19. Under most conditions, the air cushion skirt system would be retracted but over soft surfaces or rough terrain, the air cushion system would be deployed. In addition to propelling the vehicle while operating on a hard surface, the tyres will be used to stabilise and propel it while operating on air cushion over adverse terrain and water (waves not exceeding 0.3m in height), where a co-axial 'paddle track' gives additional propulsion.
PRINCIPAL PARTICULARS (PRELIMINARY DESIGN)
MATERIALS
Craft body structural material: aluminium honeycomb sandwich

MODEL 730A PERFORMANCE WITH ALTERNATIVE ENGINES

PERFORMANCE	3200 hp diesels	CODOG (GE LM500 or Allison 570-KF)
Speed,		
calm:	39 knots	54 knots
Sea State 3:	32 knots	45 knots
Sea State 5:	27 knots	38 knots
RANGE		
High speed:	1140n miles	860n miles
Low speed:	1420n miles	1500n miles

Artist's impression of the US Air Force air cushion all-terrain crash rescue vehicle

MACHINERY

Engine: Detroit Diesel 8V-92TA

Gearbox: HT-7500R 5-speed

Air cushion system: Skirt with open 50.8cm wide
  segments (knuckle shaped), 43° outer angle to
  ground, air cushion length: 8.74m
  air cushion width: 4.57m

Cushion pressure: $0.035kg/cm^2$

Fans: Two 61mm dia, $25.5m^3/s$ at 3400rpm

Air gap: 23mm

DIMENSIONS

Not to exceed (for C-130 aircraft loading):

Length: 10.67m

Width: 2.82m

Height: 2.67m

Weight: 13 605kg

Firefighting water and/or foaming agent: 3785
  litres

Rescue boom, extended length: 13.56m

Boom platform, max height: 15.55m at 9.375m
  from front of cab

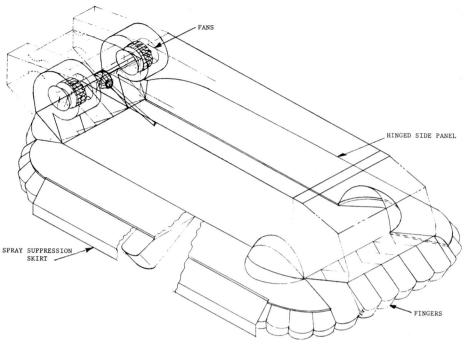

Components of the air cushion of the all-terrain crash rescue vehicle (ATCRV)

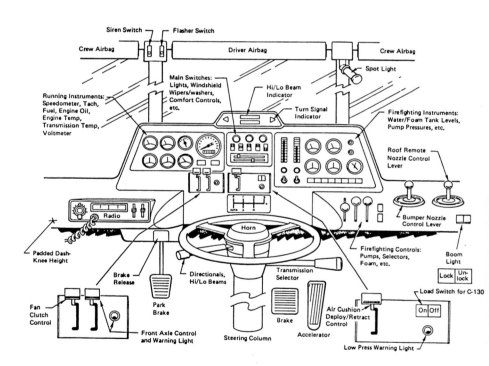

Proposed driver's controls and instruments for ATCRV

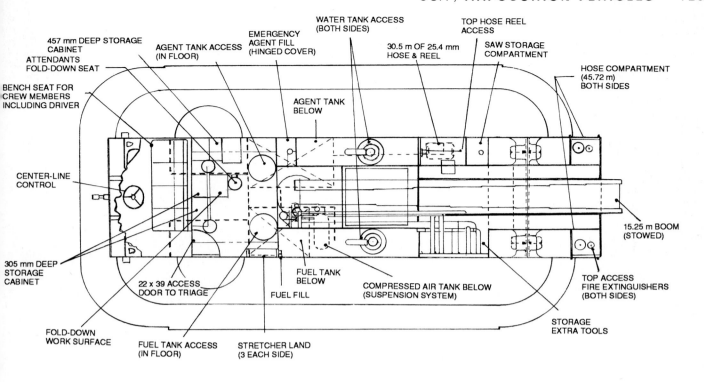

457 mm DEEP STORAGE CABINET ATTENDANTS FOLD-DOWN SEAT

AGENT TANK ACCESS (IN FLOOR)

EMERGENCY AGENT FILL (HINGED COVER)

WATER TANK ACCESS (BOTH SIDES)

TOP HOSE REEL ACCESS

30.5 m OF 25.4 mm HOSE & REEL

SAW STORAGE COMPARTMENT

HOSE COMPARTMENT (45.72 m) BOTH SIDES

BENCH SEAT FOR CREW MEMBERS INCLUDING DRIVER

AGENT TANK BELOW

CENTER-LINE CONTROL

305 mm DEEP STORAGE CABINET

15.25 m BOOM (STOWED)

22 x 39 ACCESS DOOR TO TRIAGE

FUEL TANK BELOW

FUEL FILL

COMPRESSED AIR TANK BELOW (SUSPENSION SYSTEM)

TOP ACCESS FIRE EXTINGUISHERS (BOTH SIDES)

STORAGE EXTRA TOOLS

FOLD-DOWN WORK SURFACE

FUEL TANK ACCESS (IN FLOOR)

STRETCHER LAND (3 EACH SIDE)

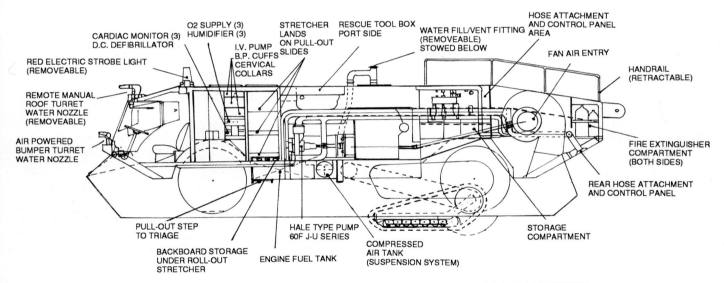

CARDIAC MONITOR (3) D.C. DEFIBRILLATOR

O2 SUPPLY (3) HUMIDIFIER (3)

STRETCHER LANDS ON PULL-OUT SLIDES

RESCUE TOOL BOX PORT SIDE

WATER FILL/VENT FITTING (REMOVEABLE) STOWED BELOW

HOSE ATTACHMENT AND CONTROL PANEL AREA

RED ELECTRIC STROBE LIGHT (REMOVEABLE)

I.V. PUMP B.P. CUFFS CERVICAL COLLARS

FAN AIR ENTRY

HANDRAIL (RETRACTABLE)

REMOTE MANUAL ROOF TURRET WATER NOZZLE (REMOVEABLE)

AIR POWERED BUMPER TURRET WATER NOZZLE

FIRE EXTINGUISHER COMPARTMENT (BOTH SIDES)

REAR HOSE ATTACHMENT AND CONTROL PANEL

PULL-OUT STEP TO TRIAGE

HALE TYPE PUMP 60F J-U SERIES

COMPRESSED AIR TANK (SUSPENSION SYSTEM)

STORAGE COMPARTMENT

BACKBOARD STORAGE UNDER ROLL-OUT STRETCHER

ENGINE FUEL TANK

LAMP-H (DESIGN)

The movement of large quantities of military supplies from ship to shore has historically proven to be a difficult task when piers are not available. Until recently, this logistics-over-the-shore (LOTS) mission has used either shallow draught landing craft that get as close to the beach as possible before discharging cargo, or amphibious craft that combine a crude boat hull with either wheels or tracks for overland operation. Both types of lighterage craft are severely limited in the sea conditions, beach profile, and littoral terrain that can be accommodated.

The successful introduction of the LACV-30 into full Army service has demonstrated the potential of air cushion systems to improve the operational efficiency of the LOTS mission. Accordingly, the US Army initiated a programme to develop a heavier lift air cushion lighter, known as the LAMP-H (Lighter, Amphibious-Heavy).

In 1987, Textron Marine Systems conducted a conceptual design study for the LAMP-H. The results of this study, plus other studies by the US Army, have established the basis for the LAMP-H. In 1990, the US Army will begin development of the craft.

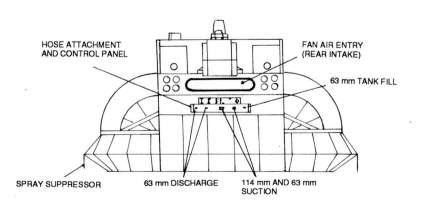

HOSE ATTACHMENT AND CONTROL PANEL

FAN AIR ENTRY (REAR INTAKE)

63 mm TANK FILL

SPRAY SUPPRESSOR

63 mm DISCHARGE

114 mm AND 63 mm SUCTION

General arrangement of ATCRV

UTILITY AIR CUSHION VEHICLE (UACV) DESIGNS

The Utility Air Cushion Vehicle designs provide an efficient and economical method of transporting personnel and cargo over inaccessible terrain such as remote coastal wetlands, rivers and streams, swamps, tundra, snow, and ice.

The UACV can be built in either a cargo or passenger configuration and outfitted to suit individual requirements for seating, interior, and electronics. The hull and superstructure are constructed of glass-reinforced plastic to provide economy of manufacturing, strength, increased safety, and improved maintenance characteristics.

On 21 June 1989, TMS delivered a UACV to Shell Offshore Inc. for use in oil and gas fields located in remote waters and marshes near the mouth of the Mississippi River. Named *Hover 1*,

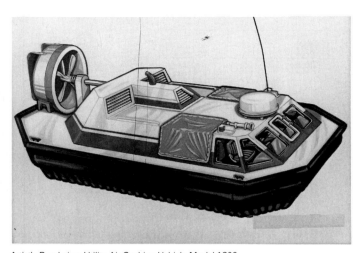
Artist's Rendering-Utility Air Cushion Vehicle Model 1200

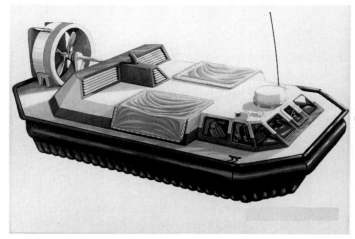
Artist's Rendering-Utility Air Cushion Vehicle Model 2000

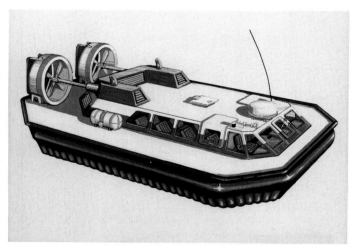
Artist's Rendering-Utility Air Cushion Vehicle Model 3000

Artist's Rendering-Utility Air Cushion Vehicle Model 4000

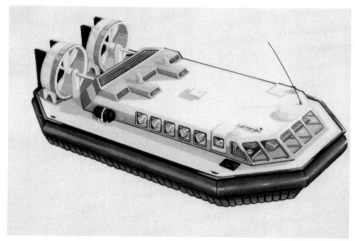
Artist's Rendering-Utility Air Cushion Vehicle Model 5000

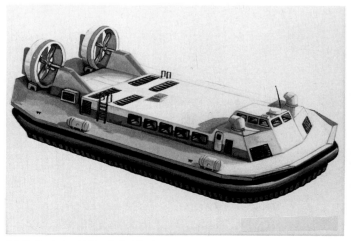
Artist's Rendering-Utility Air Cushion Vehicle Model 15K (82-Passenger Ferry)

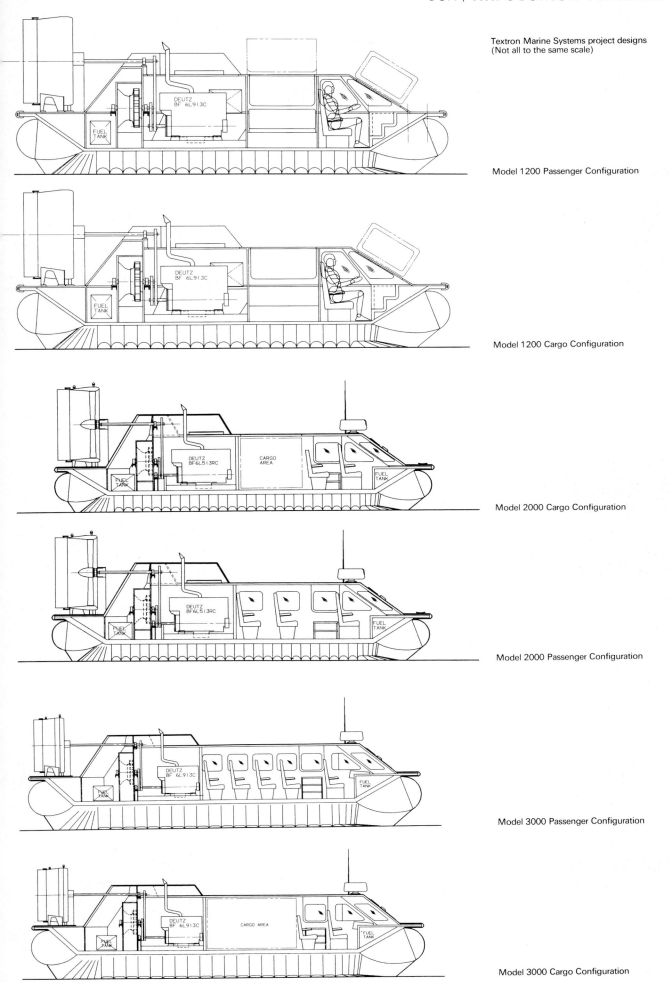

Textron Marine Systems project designs
(Not all to the same scale)

Model 1200 Passenger Configuration

Model 1200 Cargo Configuration

Model 2000 Cargo Configuration

Model 2000 Passenger Configuration

Model 3000 Passenger Configuration

Model 3000 Cargo Configuration

Textron Marine Systems project designs
(Not all to the same scale)

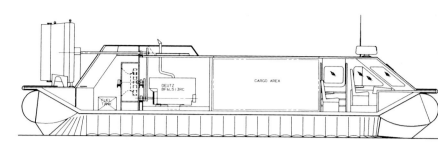

Model 4000 Cargo Configuration

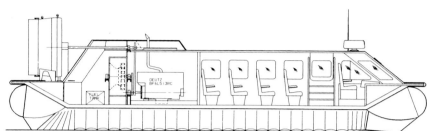

Model 4000 Passenger Configuration

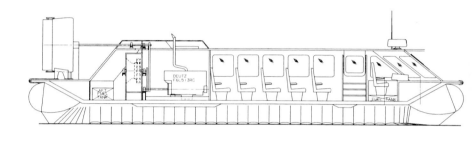

Model 5000 Passenger Configuration

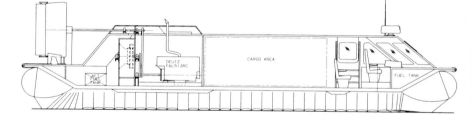

Model 5000 Cargo Configuration

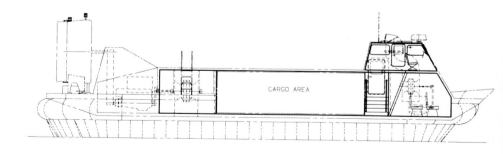

Model 15K Cargo Configuration

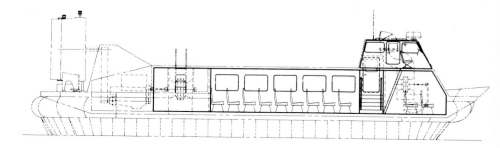

Model 15K Passenger Configuration

it is 7.31m long with a 3.66m beam and carries a 544kg payload over shallow water and mud flats that were previously almost impossible to access by conventional craft.

There are six models available including an 82-passenger ferry configuration. The UACV models range from 7.3 to 20.7m in length and can carry payloads from 550 to 6800kg.

PRINCIPAL PARTICULARS			UACV MODEL			82-PASSENGER FERRY
DIMENSIONS	1200	2000	3000	4000	5000	
Length, hard structure less fender (m)	7.92	9.75	11.90	13.72	15.54	20.73
Beam, hard structure less fender (m)	4.26	5.18	6.40	7.01	7.92	10.97
Depth to main deck (m)	0.76	0.76	0.91	0.92	0.92	1.07
Cushion depth (m)	0.46	0.46	0.76	0.76	0.76	1.07
WEIGHTS						
Empty (kg)	2495	3175	5171	6124	7711	24948
Payload (kg)	544	907	1360	1814	2268	6803
Fuel (kg)	136	227	272	454	454	2268
Maximum (kg)	3402	4309	6804	8392	10433	34020
MECHANICAL						
Installed power (bhp)	190	268	two 190	two 268	two 268	two 600 two 160
Fuel capacity (l)	170	265	340	530	530	2650
LOAD DETAILS-CARGO MODEL						
Number of passengers	1	4	4	4	4	4
Number of crew	1	1	1	1	1	1
LOAD DETAILS-PASSENGER MODEL						
Number of passengers	4	8	14	20	30	82
Number of crew	1	2	2	2	2	2
Maximum speed, calm water (knots)	33+	33+	33+	33+	30+	30+

UACV Model 1200, *Hover 1*, in use as oilfield utility boat

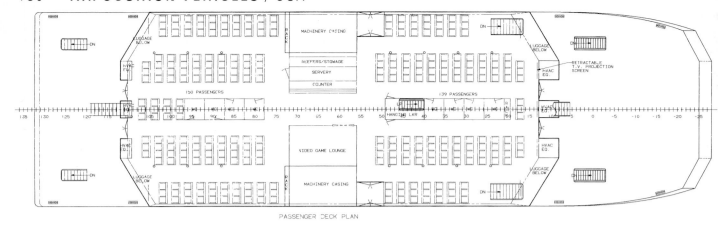

PASSENGER DECK PLAN

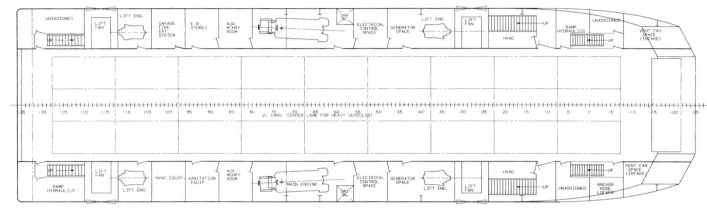

MAIN DECK PLAN

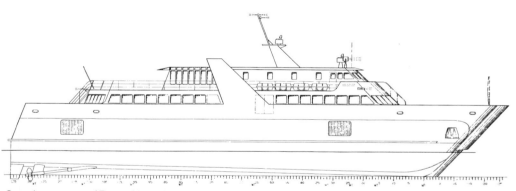

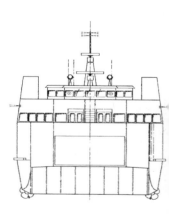

General arrangement of Textron Marine Systems Model 350B Passenger/Car Ferry Design

MODEL 350B PASSENGER/CAR FERRY (DESIGN)

This design applies SES technology to a configuration able to transport both people and cars. The Model 350B is a 49.39m all-welded-aluminium ferry designed to carry 289 passengers, 27 cars, and a crew of 10. All passenger lounges are located above the vehicle spaces for maximum all-around visibility.

The standard ferry is powered by two MTU 16V1163TB83 diesel engines for a cruising speed of up to 40 knots. As with other TMS designs, the power plant can be adapted to suit customer requirements.

PRINCIPAL MATERIALS OF CONSTRUCTION: 5456 Marine Aluminium

CERTIFICATION: Conforms to applicable US Coast Guard requirements and IMO Code of Safety for dynamically supported craft

DIMENSIONS
Length: 49.39m
Beam: 14.63m
Height (on cushion): 11.59m
Height (off cushion): 9.91m
Draft (on cushion): 2.59m
Draft (off cushion): 3.35m

DISPLACEMENT
Maximum: 295 tonnes
Light ship: 213 tonnes
CAPACITY
Crew: 10
Passengers: 289
Cars: 27
Baggage 3400kg
Freshwater: 37851
Fuel: 367151
PERFORMANCE (at maximum load)
Maximum speed (on cushion) 43 knots
Cruise speed (on cushion) 40 knots, calm; 31 knots, sea state 3
Range: 600 nautical miles
VESSEL STRUCTURE: Welded 5456 aluminium plate and 5456 extrusion and flat bar. Longitudinal framing with transverse bulkheads
MACHINERY
Main engines: Two MTU 16V1163TB83 diesel engines, turbo-charged, intercooled, heat-exchanger cooled, air start, 5,810bhp (US) at 1,160rpm
Gears: Two ZF BW 3500 reduction gears. Input shafts, identical rotation; output shafts, opposite rotation

Propellers: Two 1473mm-diameter, four-bladed, controllable reversible pitch, nickel-aluminium bronze
Lift engines: Four Detroit Diesel 8V92N diesel engines, heat-exchanger cooled, air start, 350bhp (US) at 2100rpm
Lift fans: Four Textron Marine 1067mm-diameter, welded-aluminium centrifugal fans
Generators: Two 200kW, 480V, 3-phase, 60-Hz diesel-driven generators, heat-exchanger cooled, air start
ELECTRICAL SYSTEM
AC: 480/240/120V, 60-Hz, 3-phase system with shore-power connection
DC: 12 and 24V battery-powered systems for main engine electronics, communication and navigation electronics, navigation lights, alarm and emergency lighting
Lighting: Fluorescent
COMMUNICATIONS/NAVIGATION
Radios: Based on customer requirements
Navigation: Based on customer requirements
Fathometer: One Morrow fathometer
Speedometer: One Kenyon knotmeter
Compass: Based on customer requirements

Public address system: Based on customer requirements

AUXILIARIES

Bilge/Ballast/Firemain: Two interconnected electrically driven pumps:one for bilge and ballast, one for bilge and firemain service

Potable water: Pressurised system. Integral aluminium tank, ultraviolet purifier, and water heater

Sanitary system: Low flush water closets, holding tanks, and discharge pumps

Fire extinguishing: Equipment in accordance with applicable USCG regulations

Air conditioning/heating: Individual air conditioning and heating units for temperature control in passenger spaces, crew spaces, and pilothouse

Compressed air: Two compressors and two USCG-approved air receivers

Engine controls: Main engine throttles, propeller pitch selection, and lift engine throttle controls at pilothouse station. Main engine throttle and propeller pitch controls at backing station. Pneumatic system

Steering: Electrohydraulic, multistation steering system controlling twin rudders

OUTFITTING AND FURNISHING

Passenger spaces/seats: 289 aircraft-style passenger seats with integral approved life jackets

Public water closets: Four, each with one water closet and lavatory

Lifesaving: Equipment in accordance with applicable USCG requirements

Insulation: Foil-backed 7.6cm-thick fibreglass insulation in pilothouse and deckhouse. Sprayed mineral fibre insulation on boundaries of fire hazard areas in accordance with USCG requirements

Panelling/overheads: Based on customer requirements

Deck covering: Based on customer requirements

Hull protection: Anodes installed as required to ward off electrolytic action

Crew accommodation: Berthing, galley, and mess facilities for ten crew

Crew water closets: Two, each with water closet having integral holding tank, lavatory, and shower

Finish: Exterior sandsweep. Coating selection and colour based on customer requirements

Car deck: Finished in a nonskid surface. Deck to be strengthened for wheel loads from vehicles. Tiedown fittings will be provided to secure against movement in rough seas

---

TRINITY MARINE GROUP
TRINITY INDUSTRIES INC

P O Box 29266, 6600 Plaza Drive, New Orleans, Louisiana 70189, USA

Telephone: (504) 245 4509
Telex: 6821246
Telefax: (504) 245 7869

Jim Rivers, *Vice President, International Sales*

See entry under group company, Equitable Shipyards Inc.

LIGHT/SPORTS AIR CUSHION VEHICLES

AUSTRALIA

TURBO HOVERCRAFT PTY LIMITED

91 Pitt Street, Eltham, Victoria 3095, Australia

Telephone: (03) 439 9727

Paul Moody, *Director*
Owen Ellis, *Director*

Turbo Hovercraft Pty Limited was formed in 1983 by two engineers with extensive experience in hovercraft design and construction in Australia. The aim of the company is to develop a series of practical, 'state-of-the-art' craft to suit harsh Australian conditions. The first craft, the 225 Wedge, was released for sale in May 1984 and an uprated version, the 235 Superwedge first sold in kit form in June 1986. The company supplies kits, components and commercial craft on a 'one-off' basis. The design has been certified for commercial use by the Marine Authorities in certain states.

TURBO 225 WEDGE

This craft was designed as a plan set for the home builder. Approximately 60 of these craft have been built but this model has now been substantially superseded by the 235 Superwedge model. Details of the 225 Wedge are given in the 1986 edition.

TURBO 235 SUPERWEDGE

This model was developed after extensive experience of the variety of conditions met by the 225 Wedge. A more powerful and reliable engine and a larger fan allow the craft to tackle almost any conditions.

LIFT AND PROPULSION: A Yamaha 485cc, 51bhp, twin-cylinder, two-stroke petrol engine drives, via a toothed belt, a 12-bladed, ducted Multiwing fan for both lift and propulsion, an aerodynamically integrated system. The engine, transmission, fan and duct are flexibly mounted to the hull, isolating the hull from vibration and the fan from shocks. Very fine tip clearances are maintained, giving good fan efficiency. The engine is in a fully enclosed engine bay, designed to reduce contamination of the engine air supply.

CONTROLS: Directional control is by five aerodynamic rudders in the fan slipstream, controlled by handlebars forward of the seat. Engine control is via a twist grip throttle on the handlebars.

HULL: The hull is a plywood monocoque construction, using 'stitch and glue' and sandwich panel techniques. A unique method of folding plywood allows sophisticated shapes to be made easily. An enclosed buoyancy tank around the hull periphery provides positive buoyancy and excellent floating stability in most sea states. There are storage compartments under the longitudinal seat and in the engine bay. A 23-litre marine fuel tank is located under the seat at the centre of mass of the craft.

SKIRT: The neoprene-coated nylon skirt uses an individually fed extended segment system. A skirt development programme is under way to improve the dynamic stability, increase the life and reduce the first cost of the skirt.

DIMENSIONS
Length: 3.52m
Width: 1.98m
Height: 1.22m
Hard structure clearance: 245mm
Prop/fan dia: 840mm

Turbo Hovercraft Nos 12, 18, 19, 20 and 25

Yamaha engine installation in Turbo 235 Superwedge

Turbo Hovercraft 235 Superwedge

WEIGHTS
Empty: 180kg
Payload: 235kg (3 adults)
PERFORMANCE
Speed, max (ideal conditions): 100km/h
Speed, cruise (50–70% max engine rpm): 50km/h
Lift off: 45% engine speed
Climbing ability, static: 1 in 6 gradient
    dynamic: 1 in 3 gradient
Fuel consumption: 7 litres/h
FUTURE DEVELOPMENT
A programme is currently under way to develop a new craft incorporating modular design using high module composite technology and employing a new, unique construction technique.

This craft will be based on the Turbo Superwedge, utilising its proven technology and significantly up-grading it with a high strength, lightweight plastic hull. The hull will be constructed from vacuum-formed epoxy/fibreglass pvc foam sandwich with additional Kevlar and carbonfibre reinforcement. Use of a modular design concept will ultimately allow the craft to be supplied in various configurations, suiting a range of applications. For convenience and reduced freight costs, it is anticipated that the craft will be supplied in 'knock-down' form, allowing rapid assembly by individual customers or local dealers.

W A LIGHT HOVERCRAFT COMPANY
281 Main Street, Balcatta 6021, Western Australia, Australia

Telephone: (09) 3446093

M Dixon, *Proprietor*
T Dixon, *Proprietor*

The proprietors of this company have been building hovercraft for almost ten years and in 1985 the partnership was formed to offer plans and components for small hovercraft. Services include repair work and sales of Yamaha motors and plans for Simple Cyclone hovercraft.

AQUATERRA
In 1986 the partnership went into production of the Aquaterra, a two-seat fibreglass craft for the pleasure and sport market with agricultural uses as well. Aquaterra is available as a bare hull, in assembly-kit form, or completed craft. The craft features quiet operation, low spray and good performance. Several craft have been sold to customers in the far north of Western Australia and have operated in some very diverse and harsh conditions, from waterless desert in 45°C heat to plains flooded by monsoonal rains. This craft has also operated in the huge tidal areas of King Sound, where the tide ranges up to 10m, and has made a trip down the Fitzroy River.

HULL: Gel-coated chopped strand mat, hand laid-up in a monocoque construction with buoyancy foam an integral part of the construction. The seat is a motorcycle type with the tank built-in and engine bearers moulded into cockpit floor.
ENGINE: Yamaha PE 485 twin-cylinder two-stroke developing 51bhp at 6500rpm, driving a 740mm diameter fan through timing belt reduction and tapered roller bearing fan hub.

SKIRT: Sixty-five separate segments of pvc-coated nylon.
STEERING: Handle-bar type with twist-grip throttle control.
DIMENSIONS
Length: 3.4m
Width: 1.94m
Ground clearance: 230mm
WEIGHTS/CAPACITIES
Fuel capacity: 20 litres
Total weight: 158kg
Payload: 200kg
PERFORMANCE
Speed, max: 100km/h (calm conditions)
Gradient, max (standing start): 25° (driver only)
Fuel consumption, approx: 4 to 8 litres/h
PRICES (Nov 1988) including tax
Bare hull: A$1200
Assembly kit: A$6750
Completed craft: A$9750

Aquaterra

Aquaterra

BRAZIL

DECORFIBRA INDUSTRIAL LIMITADA
Rua Guaianésia, 410-Chácaras Reunidas, Caixa Postal 381, São José dos Campos-SP, Brazil

Telephone: (0123) 31–2103

W Baere, *President*
Mª EmIlia F M Lima, *Sales and Marketing Director*
R Baere, *Production Director*
F J X Carvalho, *Engineering and Consultancy Director*

Decorfibra Industrial Ltda is a company engaged in the development of high technology composite materials and their applications and for the past 20 years has supplied these materials for all aircraft produced by EMBRAER, Empresa Brasileira de Aeronautica.

GLM-S
The development of this two-seat craft started in 1984. A 12-blade propeller, 0.79m diameter, supplies both thrust and air for the lift system, air being ducted to the air cushion via six ducts.
ENGINE: 24hp, 2-cylinder, 2-stroke.
HULL: Fibreglass/Kevlar.
DIMENSIONS
Length: 3.50m
Width: 2.00m
PERFORMANCE
Speed, max: 43 knots, 80km/h
Rise height: 0.18m

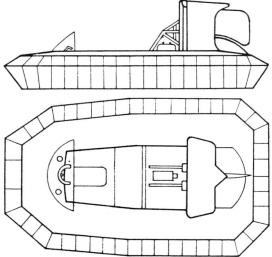

General arrangement of Decorfibra GLM-S

Decorfibra GLM-S

CANADA

HALTON HOVERCRAFT LTD
Burlington, Ontario, Canada

HOVERGUARD
A hovercraft designed for rescue work. Hull in grp, two mouldings, closed cell polyurethane foam reinforcement.

PRINCIPAL PARTICULARS
Length: 3.81m
Width: 1.98m
Height, on cushion: 1.73m
Rise height: 20 cm
Weight, including full fuel: 295 kg
Payload: 272 kg

Propulsion and lift: ducted propeller, 0.91m dia
Engine: Yamaha 485cc two-cylinder, two-stroke, 37–3kW (50 hp)

ULH HOVERCRAFT CANADA INC

PO Box 478, Carleton Place, Ottawa, Ontario K7C 3P, Canada

Telephone: (613) 257 5219/224 5875

Ron Fishlock, *President*
David Harwood, *Vice President*

Formed in 1984, as Ultralight Hovercraft the company has to date concentrated its efforts in the design, development and testing of its Canair series of fully amphibious two-seat ACVs. An information package and a comprehensive set of plans are available to home builders. The company is working towards being able to supply less readily available items such as fans, timing belts, pulleys, glassfibre fan ducts, skirt material and studs.

ULH is presently developing a kit version of the Canair series, which will include every part necessary to assemble the craft. Other developments currently being worked on are a stretched version of the Canair 500, increasing its overwater payload to over 332kg as either a two-seater plus cargo or a four-seater craft. Another development is the addition of a central wheel that can be deployed when operating over roadways to reduce side slip.

Canair's special features include high manoeuvrability with variable lift air flow and a controllable reverse system, all of which are operated through one central control joystick; comfortable side-by-side seating on a movable seat used for pitch trim control; buoyant folding sides that can carry a useful payload and only take 5 minutes to fold up or deploy; and if fitted with an HDL/Fishlock loop segmented skirt offers low drag, smooth ride, low spray levels, low vulnerability to wear and tear, plus snap-on standard segments.

A single engine and Multiwing fan installation is used and when fitted with a current production snowmobile silencer system will result in an ACV with low noise emission.

CANAIR 340/440/500
TRANSMISSION: 50.8mm wide toothed belt.
CONTROLS: Single joystick, operates forward turning, reverse, throttle and variable lift flow.
STARTER: Hand pull.
FUEL: Petrol (82 Octane mix).
OIL: 2-cycle mix.
NOISE: Modern snowmobile level.

	Type 340	440	500
Engine, Snowmobile, 2-cycle:	340cc	440cc	503cc
2-cylinder, air-cooled:	28hp	36hp	45hp
Fan: Single axial, 800mm diameter:	10 blades	20 blades	20 blades
Empty weight:	158kg	172kg	181kg
Payload, normal:*	154kg	193kg	231kg
Payload, max:**	181kg	226kg	272kg
Speed, max over water, calm, no wind:*	25mph	32mph	40mph
max over flat smooth ice:**	36mph	45mph	50mph
Endurance, on 19 litres of petrol:	3 hours	2.5 hours	1.5 hours

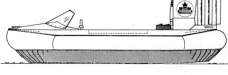
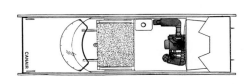
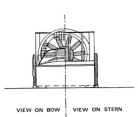
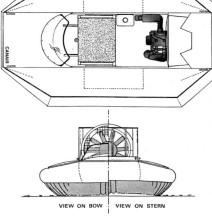

VIEW ON BOW | VIEW ON STERN   VIEW ON BOW | VIEW ON STERN

Canair craft with sides retracted for easy transport   General arrangement of Canair Type 340

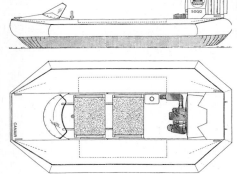

Layout of Canair 500/2

ULH Canair 500   (Bill Sargeant)

DIMENSIONS
Length: 3.84m
Width, on hover: 2.18m
Width, side folded: 1.22m
Hoverheight: 25cm

CANAIR 500/2
Trials of the stretched Canair started in August 1987. This craft is one of the original two-seater prototypes, having been cut in half and a 1.14m mid-section added. The original 503cc engine has remained for the first phase of the trials.
WEIGHTS
Normal payload: 295kg
Max payload: 332kg
PERFORMANCE
Speed over water (max) calm sea, no wind, normal payload: 26 knots (30 mph)
The second trial phase will evaluate the craft fitted with a 60hp to 70hp rated engine.

KIT CANAIR

The hull is in fibreglass using aircraft composite structural techniques, a structure which also provides positive flotation.

The Kit Canair design accommodates a wide variety of vehicle layouts. From the basic two-seat runabout, a fast sports machine, a utility pick-up through to a fully enclosed, winterised custom-equipped four-seater. All these vehicles are built around common interchangeable parts. For example, the Kit Canair can start out as a high performance two-seater then later on additional parts can be purchased so it can be stretched to a four-seater if desired.

The Kit Canair's special sectional design, will permit direct shipping from ULH in a small container, thereby significantly reducing shipping costs and the purchase price.

The Kit Canair is delivered with the lift/propulsion unit pre-assembled and all other parts ready to put together, including all necessary tools.

The high length-to-beam ratio Canair 500/2 showing the reverse-thrust foil system

WIND RIDERS INC

For Details of craft built please see 1989 edition of this book

FINLAND

FINN-LEIJU OY CO LTD

Rattipolku 7, 45360 Valkeala, Finland

Telephone: (951) 233321
Telex: 52004KVOLA SF
Telefax: (951) 233241

Jyrki Hakanen, *Managing Director*

FL 387

Produced to order.
LIFT AND PROPULSION: Cushion air is supplied by a 9.5hp Solo engine, driving a 0.56m diameter 5-blade Multiwing 2H or 32C fan. Thrust is supplied by a Rotax 503, or 427 (liquid-cooled) engine driving, via a toothed belt, one 0.75m diameter Multiwing 5 ZL fan, ducted.
CONTROLS: Rudders set in propeller slipstream for directional control.
HULL: Built in moulded glassfibre with expanded polyurethane with some parts in sandwich construction.
SKIRT: Loop plus 72 segments in 227g/m² polyurethane-coated nylon.
ACCOMMODATION: Two seats in tandem; if enclosed 45kg extra weight.
DIMENSIONS
Length: 3.80m
Beam: 2.02m
Hoverheight: 0.25m
WEIGHTS
Empty weight: 310kg
Payload: 290kg (over water)
PERFORMANCE
Speed, max over water: 75 to 80km/h, 40 to 43 knots
    over ice and snow: 15% higher
Fuel consumption: 8 to 14 litres/h

FL 400 AB

A new model developed in 1988.
LIFT AND PROPULSION: Integrated system, powered by a Hirth 2703 ROE 39kW (52 hp) at 6500 rpm petrol engine, electric start, centrifugal clutch and 2.5:1.0 reduction belt drive. A two-carburettor version of the engine is also available giving 41kW (55 hp). Power is transmitted to a multiple-blade axial-flow fan (Multi Wing 5ZL) which is ducted, diameter 950mm. Flow is directed to provide thrust and the air cushion. Fuel capacity is 22 litres, two stroke mixture.
CONTROLS: Two rudder-mounted on the duct are operated by handlebars to provide directional control.
Engine speed is controlled by handlebar-mounted twistgrip.

Finn-Leiju FL 387 at speed over snow

Finn-Leiju FL 400 AB

HULL: Full inflatable-boat type, airfilled, five separate pontoons, full floating type. Pontoon tube diameter 470mm.

SKIRT: Loop segment, material; softened PVC cool resist −28°C, or polyurethane −52°C.

DIMENSIONS
Length: 4.10m
Beam: 1.90m
Rise height: 25cm

WEIGHTS
Unladen: 178kg (including 22 litres fuel)
Payload, max: 300kg (three persons)

PERFORMANCE
Speed, cruising over land and water: 60km/h
Speed, max over land and water: 85–90km/h
Fuel consumption: average 12.5 litres/h
Craft is on serial production.

FL FORMULA

A new single-seat racing craft from Finn-Leiju, completed in late September, 1989; has won Finnish Champion competition.

PRINCIPAL PARTICULARS
Hull: Divinycell sandwich construction bottom, glass fibre/Kevlar topside
Length: 3.02m
Width: 1.83m
Weight, zero fuel: 182 kg
Thrust engine: Hirth 2703, 39/41kW, reduction belt-drive and centrifugal clutch to propeller. More powerful engines may be fitted e.g. Hirth

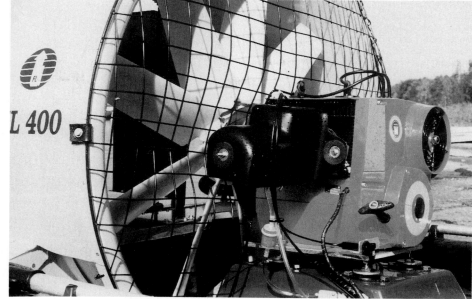

Hirth engine installation on Finn-Leiju FL 400 AB

F30, 4-cylinder Boxer 95, or 97 kW.
Thrust with Hirth 2703, 41kW: 143 kgf
Lift engine: Solo 8.95kW

Fan: 0.56m dia, 9 blades Multi-Wing 32L
Propeller: 1.10m dia, 9 blades Multi-Wing 52L, rpm: 2460

FL Formula racing hovercraft in action

FL Formula racing hovercraft in action

FRANCE

Lestes 03

JACQUES M THILLOY

22, rue d'Erstein, 67150 Osthouse, France

Telephone: 88988137

Since 1979 this company has offered a range of three light amphibious hovercraft in kit form for home building or ready to use. Other businesses may manufacture the Rov' Air range under licence. The two-seat Lestes 03 is designed for cruising on inland waterways, the single-seat Rov' Air for use in junior competitive events and Rov' Air Mk 2 for European Formula 3 racing, or other leisure applications.

With Rov' Air, the company introduces a new concept in hovercraft construction: micro-hovercraft or microcraft. The company now plans to build hovercraft which can be employed either on light utility applications (surveying, expedition, rescue) or as recreational craft (exploration, cruising, leisure). Initial tests of the prototype, Rambler, began during summer 1988. Good stability and handling qualities were observed.

LESTES 03

This was the first craft from the company, completed in July 1979. The front fan delivers lift air to the cushion via a peripheral fingered bag skirt, which insures a better trim over rough surfaces and allows high speed over water. The single-seat Lestes 03 is ideal for cruising or exploration.

LIFT AND PROPULSION: A single JLO 198cc engine, rated at 7.3bhp at 4500rpm, drives a 600mm diameter, five-bladed Multiwing axial lift fan. Blades have 30-degree pitch. A single Hirth twin-cylinder 438cc engine rated at 32bhp at 5600rpm is employed for propulsion and drives, via a toothed belt, a 1.1m diameter two-bladed ducted propeller. Cushion pressure of the loaded craft is 45kg/m². The craft can carry 30 litres of fuel for cruising.

CONTROLS: A throttle lever controls the lift engine and a twist-grip throttle controls the propulsion engine. Twin aerodynamic rudders, operated by handlebar, provide directional control. Electric starter is available on propulsion engine.

HULL: All-wooden hull built in 4mm marine plywood with wooden stringers. The fuel tank and battery are under the seat. Closed compartments along each side of the hull, packed with polyurethane foam, provide 150% buoyancy.

SKIRT: Bag and segments system. Skirt fabric is neoprene-coated nylon.

ACCOMMODATION: Although designed as a single-seater, the craft is capable of carrying two persons in tandem. In single-seater form, there is room enough for equipment such as extra fuel tanks, tent and food containers.

DIMENSIONS
Length overall: 3.6m
Width overall: 1.9m
Height overall, hovering: 1.75m
    at rest: 1.5m
WEIGHTS
Empty: 160kg
Max weight, one person: 245kg
Total disposable load: 140kg
PERFORMANCE
Max speed: 43 knots (80km/h)
Cruising speed: 21.5 knots (40km/h)
Endurance: 2 hours
Cruising range: 160km
Obstacle clearance: 0.25m

ROV' AIR

A new concept aimed at achieving a small-sized amphibious hovercraft, easy to carry, and able to travel at speed, this new micro-hovercraft is suitable for river cruising and runabout trips, fishing or exploring marginal terrain. This 2.4-metre single-seater is a low-cost craft of simple design, easy to operate and to maintain. Rov' Air is available in kit form for home building and can also be supplied as a partially- or fully-assembled structure. A wide range of completed components is offered from the engine mounting to the skirt system.

The Rov' Air micro craft is the smallest air cushion vehicle built up to now, with good performance on land and water.

LIFT AND PROPULSION: Integrated system. An 8hp Rowena Solo two-stroke engine, rated at 4200rpm drives directly a 600mm diameter ducted axial fan. Air from this unit is used for lift and thrust. The engine frame is rubber-mounted to reduce vibration and entry to the fan duct is covered by a heavy mesh safety guard.

CONTROLS: For simplicity only two controls are provided: a lever control for the engine throttle is mounted on the control column, which operates a single aerodynamic rudder.

HULL: Marine grade 4mm plywood construction. Hull has full hydrodynamic surfaces. Polystyrene foam within the hull floor and side bodies provides buoyancy. Highly stressed areas are strengthened with glassfibre.

SKIRT: Either a simple bag skirt made from polyurethane nylon fabric or a pressure-fed segmented skirt in neoprene-coated nylon can be fitted. Each option gives about 0.17m obstacle clearance.

ACCOMMODATION: Open cockpit with single seat for driver. A removable 10-litre fuel tank, and dead-man switch are standard.

DIMENSIONS
Length overall: 2.4m
Width: 1.4m
Height on landing pads: 0.75m
WEIGHTS
Empty: 60kg
Payload: 75kg
PERFORMANCE
Max speed over calm water: 17.5 knots (32km/h)
Hard structure clearance: 0.17m
Endurance: 1 hour

ROV' AIR MK 2

Rov' Air Mk 2 is a single-seat microcraft designed for racing, following British and European Club Formula 3 regulations (engine capacity under 250cc). It can also be used for cruising in sheltered waters for various leisure applications. Microcraft Rov' Air Mk 2 is available as a kit or as a fully-assembled structure.

LIFT AND PROPULSION: Integrated system powered by a single 249cc Robin two-stroke

Rov' Air single-seater

Rov' Air Mk 2

Prototype of Rambler

engine running at 5500rpm. Power is transmitted via a toothed-belt to a 600mm diameter axial fan. Engine frame is rubber-mounted to reduce vibration and to ease dismantling. This microcraft can be fitted with any suitable light powerful two-stroke engine.

CONTROLS: A handlebar, incorporating the engine throttle, operates a large single aerodynamic rudder.

HULL: Built in 3mm marine grade plywood. Base of the hull and stressed areas are reinforced with grp. Polystyrene foam within hull floor provides buoyancy.

SKIRT: Pressure-fed segmented type in neoprene-coated nylon material, with separate air-feed to every segment.

ACCOMMODATION: Open cockpit with a single seat for driver. 10-litre removable fuel tank

beneath driver's seat, dead-man switch and a set of tools are standard.

DIMENSIONS
Length overall: 2.6m
Beam overall: 1.6m
Height, off cushion: 0.7m
WEIGHTS
Empty: 65kg
Payload: 85kg
PERFORMANCE
Speed over calm water: 35–40km/h
Clearance: 0.2m
Endurance: 1 hour

RAMBLER

The prototype of this two-seat utility or recreational craft was completed in 1988. The craft can be towed on a trailer behind most cars.

LIFT AND PROPULSION: A single 8bhp lift engine provides power to an axial lift fan of 558mm diameter, fitted with Multi-Wing blades. Thrust is provided by a two-cylinder two-stroke Rotax 50bhp engine, driving a 1.21m diameter three-bladed propeller at 2200rpm. Power transmission is via a large toothed-belt pulley arrangement. The power module, engine and transmission, is mounted on a rubber-seated frame. Access to the engine and rear compartment is possible through a large door on each side. A wide choice of alternative power plants is available ranging from 45bhp to 60bhp. Fuel capacity is 60 litres.
CONTROLS: Craft heading is controlled by three rudders in inverted 'Y' configuration, operating in the slipstream of the propeller, and activated by foot pedals. Conventional throttle controls are fitted and an electric starter for both engines. Full instrumentation is provided.
HULL: Wooden construction in 4mm Marine Grade Plywood; the hull and stressed areas, are reinforced with fibreglass (landing pads, towing point, engine mountings). A sealed polyurethane block is used at the base of the craft for buoyancy. The engine bay is lined with aluminium alloy sheet and storage compartments are provided for tools and spares.
SKIRT: Finger skirt fabricated in polyurethane-coated nylon fabric. An open-loop segment type skirt is under development.
ACCOMMODATION: Access to the fully enclosed cabin is provided by two wide butterfly doors. Large windscreen and lateral windows give good visibility and passenger comfort.
DIMENSIONS
Length: 3.80m
Beam: 1.90m
WEIGHT
Unladen: 190kg
Normal payload: 100kg
Max payload: 150kg
PERFORMANCE
Max speed: 48.5 knots (90km/h)
Cruising speed: 32.5 knots (60km/h)
Endurance: 4 hours
Ground clearance: 0.30m

SOCIÉTÉ AEROPLAST sarl
Creux Redon de Cantadou, 34400 Lunel, France

Telephone: 67 71 65 97

Guy Ackerman, *Technical Director*

Aeroplast have developed over the past few years a range of light air cushion vehicles for sport and pleasure use and have also entered the utility vehicle market with their 1250kg payload ADOC 12 design in association with IFREMER. The ADOC 12 is described in the ACV Builders section of this book.

ADOC SPORT
This craft is offered in kit form by Aeroplast, a kit which takes about 30 to 40 hours to assemble. The hull is constructed in reinforced polyester.
ENGINE: 20 or 50hp
DIMENSIONS
Length: 3.05m
Width: 1.85m
Height: 1.10m
WEIGHTS
Empty: 95kg
Payload: 90kg

MINI ADOC
A compact, high-performance, single-seat craft, the hull being of monocoque glass-reinforced polyester moulded construction with a polyurethane foam-sandwich bottom.
CONTROLS: Twist grips on handlebar for rudders and throttle.
SKIRT: French made bi-conical segment type.
ENGINE: Rotax two-cylinder two-stroke 25hp.
WEATHER LIMITATIONS
Wind, max: Beaufort 3 to 4
Wave height, max: 0.4m
FUEL TANK: 20 litres.
DIMENSIONS
Length: 3.0m
Width: 1.8m
Height: 1.15m
Prop/fan dia: 800mm
WEIGHTS
Weight, empty: 130kg
Payload: 120kg
PERFORMANCE
Speed, max: 70km/h
Speed, cruising: 40km/h
Gradient capability, from static: 5°
Gradient capability, at speed: 45°
Obstacle clearance: 0.20m
Fuel consumption: 8–10 litres/h

ADOC 3S TRIPLACE
A three-seat craft for touring, exploration and surveying. Built-in buoyancy 150%. Aerodynamically integrated lift and thrust.
ENGINE: Rotax 50hp.
DIMENSIONS
Length: 3.6m
Width: 1.8m

ADOC Sport   (Aeroplast)

Mini ADOC   (Aeroplast)

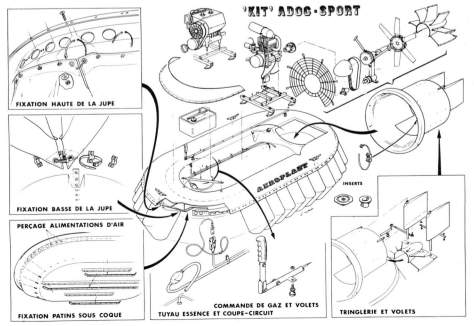
ADOC Sport kit of parts

Height: 1.2m
Prop/fan dia: 800mm
WEIGHTS
Weight, empty: 150kg
Payload: 240kg
PERFORMANCE
Speed, max: 80km/h
Speed, cruising: 40km/h
Gradient capability, from static: 5°
Gradient capability, at speed: 45°
Obstacle clearance: 0.20m
Fuel consumption: 8–10 litres/h

ADOC 6 (DESIGN)

This design of a diesel-powered amphibious hovercraft is to be produced in 1990.
POWER
Lift: 22hp
Propulsion: 43hp
DIMENSIONS
Length: 5.60m
Width: 2.80m
Height, on cushion: 1.93m
Rise height: 0.35m
Cushion area: 14.0m²
WEIGHTS
Weight, max: 900kg
Weight, empty: 400kg
Disposable load: 500kg
PERFORMANCE
Thrust, static forward: 104kg
Thrust, static reverse: 42kg

ADOC 3S Triplace   *(Aeroplast)*

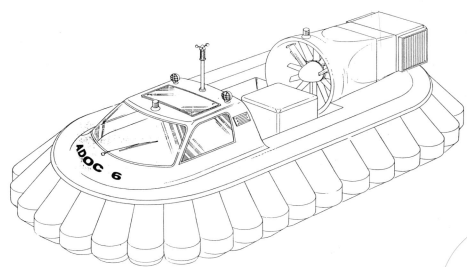

Design for ADOC 6 prototype

GERMANY, FEDERAL REPUBLIC

BUDERUS SELL GmbH

The manufacture of Buderus Sell hovercraft has been taken over by König Maschinebau GmbH. Details of early Buderus Sell hovercraft are given in the 1989 edition of this book.

KÖNIG MASCHINEBAU GmbH

Sophienstrasse 52–54, D 6330, Federal Republic of Germany

Harry König, *Director*
Gerald Pohatschka, *Director*
Ulrich Gorschlüter, *Sales Manager*

König Hooverkraft Corporation

(Sales company for USA)
793 N.E. Dixie Highway, Jensen Beach, Florida 34957–6176, USA

Telephone: (407) 334 4697
Telefax: (407) 334 4698

Harry König, *Principal*
Todd Resnick, *President*
Ulrich Gorschlüter, *Vice President*

The hovercraft division of König Machine Manufacturing Company produces and sells the Air Rider range of hovercraft. The manufacturing programme of the company includes special metal working machines, combinations and connections, 8 types of oxygen generators (0.5 to 50m³) and special gas heated furnaces, infrared-heat.

Prototype of Air Rider Wild Cat

AIR RIDER BOOSTER

A modern single seat sports craft, powered by a 41 kW (55hp) engine, with a maximum speed of approximately 70 km/h.
Length: 3.70m
Weight: 190kg

AIR RIDER WILD CAT

A luxury four-seater craft equipped with a 127kW (170hp) BMW engine. The approximate maximum speed is quoted at 110km/h.
Length: 5.80m
Weight: 850kg

NORWAY

AERO CONSULT A/S
PATENT HOLDER, DESIGNER AND DEVELOPER
Postboks 73, 2007 Kjeller, Norway

Telephone: (06) 812457

Paul Kjølseth, *Managing Director*

AEROMARAN 640

Paul Kjølseth has designed a number of marine research craft aimed at exploring a variety of methods for improving efficiency, ride and other important characteristics for high speed craft operating over ice and water. Designer of two advanced helicopters built for the Norwegian Air Force, his latest project is the Aeromaran 640 air boat.

In 1985 the twin prop-fan Aeromaran air-cushion catamaran was built, a 25 knot craft (in water) of length 4.5 m and beam 2.0 m. This was followed in 1987 by a second design and in 1989 a further 6.25 m, 4-seat project, Aeroman 640 was launched combining features and experience gained with earlier test craft.

Aeromaran 640

SPAIN

ALBERTO GIMENEZ DE LOS GALANES
Reyes 7, Madrid 8, Spain

Telephone: (1) 231 5289

Jorge Gomez Gomez, *Director*
Eduardo Sanchiz Garrote, *Director*

After several years of studying the theoretical aspects of hovercraft at the Escuela Tecnica Superior de Ingenieros Aeronauticos in Madrid, a group of aeronautical engineers decided in September 1979 to verify their technical predictions by constructing a small craft. The craft, named Furtivo I, is being used to provide confirmation of earlier theoretical studies, but a design is being developed which is likely to incorporate certain improvements such as the HDL Skirt Shift system. Furtivo I performed its first flight in February 1980.

FURTIVO I
LIFT AND PROPULSION: Lift is provided by a single Kyoritsu KEC 225cc two-stroke driving a 550mm diameter Multiwing axial fan. Cushion pressure is 10lb/ft^2. Thrust is provided by a single 38.5hp Rotax 640 two-stroke, air-cooled engine driving a 710mm diameter ducted axial fan filled with Multiwing blades. The fan provides forward or reverse thrust.
CONTROLS: Craft heading is controlled by a centrally-located column which operates a single aerodynamic rudder. The throttle control for the thrust engine is mounted on the stick. Another small column in the cockpit operates the thrust reversal mechanism.
HULL: Plywood structure with grp skin.
SKIRT: Fully-segmented type in neoprene-coated nylon.
ACCOMMODATION: Side-by-side seating for two in an open cockpit.
DIMENSIONS
Length overall, power off: 4m
Beam overall, power off: 2m
Height overall, skirt inflated: 1.58m
Draught afloat: 8.5cm
Cushion area: 7.78m^2
Skirt depth: 0.3m

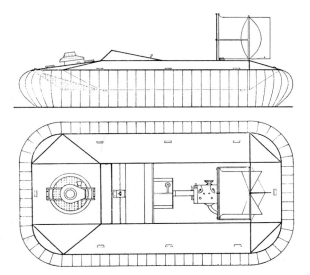

General arrangement of Furtivo I

Furtivo I

WEIGHTS
Normal empty: 203kg
Normal payload: 183kg
Max payload: 197kg

PERFORMANCE
CALM CONDITIONS
Max speed: 78km/h
Gradient capability: 1 : 7
Vertical obstacle clearance: 0.3m

FM-AERODESLIZADORES

Urb. Nuevos Horizontes, No. 8, Grinon, Madrid, Spain

Julián Martin Sanz, *Mechanical Engineer*
Joaquin Heras, *Electrical Engineer*

FM-HC-002

The construction of this two-seat hovercraft began in May 1989.
LIFT AND PROPULSION: Aerodynamically integrated; two Multiwing prop/fans, type 560/9/4Z.
ENGINE: One Rotax, type 503, 52hp, 497cc, two carburettors.
HULL: Grp/sandwich construction.
SKIRT: Segmented with 75 segments.
ACCOMMODATION
Open cockpit with seat for two/three passengers.
DIMENSIONS
Length: 4.00m
Width: 2.00m
Height: 0.72m
WEIGHT
Max: 300kg
Payload: 170kg
PERFORMANCE
Speed, max: 70km/h
Obstacle clearance: 0.25m
Fuel consumption, average: 15 l/h

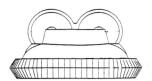
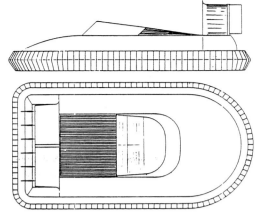

FM-Aerodeslizadores FM-HC-002

TAIWAN

CHIVALRY UNIVERSAL COMPANY LIMITED

PO Box 36–48 Taipei, Taiwan

Telephone: (02) 6212197/7692511
Telex: 11153HOUKZ-1 TP
Telefax: (02) 7637101

C S Lee, *President*
H J Tsai, *Vice President, Research and Development*
T P Doo, *Vice President, Engineering*

Overseas Office: International Vehicle Research Inc, 14074 Nacogdoches Road, Suite 322, San Antonio, Texas 78247, USA

J T Doo, *President*

With the success of the CY-6 Mk III utility hovercraft, the development work of CY-6 Mk IV, a stretched version of CY-6 Mk III, was launched in early 1987 and testing started in early 1988. CY-6 Mk IV is 1.0m longer in comparison with the previous version CY-6 Mk III and carries 8 passengers or 600kg of payload.

The schedule for the CY-12 project has been extended due to funding delays, although the design work is still in progress. The payload capability of the CY-12 has been increased and the design for the stretched version, CY-12B, has also been initiated.

The design work of a 4.5-ton utility amphibian hovercraft CY-14 was initiated in January 1987, and the prototype construction is scheduled to start mid-1988. The prototype will also serve as an experimental test bed to verify some of the CY-12 design variables.

Chivalry Universal Co is conducting the research and development, testing and design work in conjunction with the International Vehicle Research Inc in the United States, which also has the marketing responsibility for the CY-series hovercraft in the North American area.

Siren CY-10

SIREN CY-10

A highly manoeuvrable light ACV, the CY-10 is intended for recreational use. The design combines an frp hull with an integrated lift/propulsion system and a fully segmented skirt.
LIFT AND PROPULSION: Integrated system powered by a single 40hp Hirth 276R 3E two-stroke. This drives, via a toothed belt, a 12-blade ducted fan which provides air for lift and propulsion.
CONTROLS: Twin rudders at rear of thrust duct, in conjunction with cg movement, control craft heading.
HULL: Fibreglass reinforced plastic structure filled with polyurethane and pvc foam.
SKIRT: Nylon (coated) segmented skirt.
ACCOMMODATION: Open tandem seat for driver and passenger.
SYSTEMS, ELECTRICAL: 12V dc with engine-driven 123W magneto generator and 40Ah battery for engine starting and navigation lights.

DIMENSIONS
Length overall: 3.7m
Beam: 1.9m
Height: 1.3m
WEIGHTS
Empty: 190kg
Payload: 150kg
PERFORMANCE
Speed, max: 35 knots

CY-10 MK II

The latest version of the CY-10 series recreational hovercraft. A new cushion air distribution system improves the cushion stability and efficiency and also helps to prevent the plough-in phenomenon. In addition, a more aerodynamically efficient propeller duct with four rudders improves the acceleration and directional control.
LIFT AND PROPULSION: Aerodynamically integrated system powered by a single Rotax 503,

43hp, two-stroke engine which drives, via a toothed belt, a 12-blade ducted fan which provides air for propulsion and lift.
CONTROLS: Four rudders at rear of thrust duct, in conjunction with cg movement, control craft heading.
HULL: Fibreglass reinforced plastic structure filled with polyurethane and pvc foam.
SKIRT: Nylon (coated) segmented skirt.
ACCOMMODATION: Open tandem seat for driver and passenger.
SYSTEMS, ELECTRICAL: 12V dc with engine-driven 123W magneto generator and 40Ah battery for engine starting and navigation lights.
DIMENSIONS
Length overall: 3.7m
Beam: 1.9m
Height: 1.3m
WEIGHTS
Empty: 190kg
Payload: 150kg
PERFORMANCE
Speed, max: 35 knots

Chivalry CY-10 Mk II

UNITED KINGDOM

ABILITY INDUSTRIES
Unit 12, Maritime Business Estate, Maritime Close, Medway City Estate, Rochester, Kent, ME2 4DJ, UK

Telephone: (0634) 717760

Robert L Fowler, *Proprietor*

Ability Industries is a newly formed business manufacturing the new AIRSPREE range of hovercraft. Designed and developed for rough water use with very high stability, the sport, cruiser and fun craft are all based around a single body hull design employing the unique triple cushion skirt. This skirt design allows offset and uneven loads to be accommodated without affecting craft trim or handling and together with the wave-rider nose virtually eliminates plough-in.

AIRSPREE SPORT
The Sport is the top of the range and is supplied with the most powerful choice of engines. The design of this craft combines very high performance with excellent handling and is designed to be used in coastal waters even in rough conditions.
LIFT AND PROPULSION: Integrated system powered by a choice of Hirth 521 (55bhp) or Rotax 503 36.5 kW (49bhp) 2-cycle engines. Depending on engine choice, power is transmitted via either belts and pulleys or a gearbox to a single 0–81 diameter multi-bladed ducted fan. A variable splitter plate is used to duct between 0 and 40% of the air into the skirt system while the rest is used for thrust. At zero lift and 100% thrust manoeuvring accurately and quietly at slow speeds on water is made much easier.
CONTROLS: Four aerodynamic rudders operated by a 'V' grip steering column control craft direction. Splitter plate movement controls the lift to thrust ratio for optimum performance and is operated by a dashboard mounted lever. A foot pedal operates the engine throttle.
HULL: Monocoque construction, fibre

Airspree hull mouldings

reinforced plastic with foam sandwich and permanent foam flotation incorporating the unique wave-rider nose for excellent rough water performance.
ACCOMMODATION: Two adjustable tandem bucket seats in open cockpit with storage compartments in hull side bodies. A double width bench seat can be supplied as an option in place of the rear bucket seat for 1 + 2 seating.
SKIRT: Unique advanced triple cushion closed-loop segmented type. Hoverheight 0.25m plus. Material is neoprene coated nylon.
DIMENSIONS
Length: 4.20m
Shipping length (nose removed): 3.55m
Width: 2.00m
Height: 1.20m
WEIGHTS
Empty: 180 kg
Payload: 170 kg

PERFORMANCE
Speed: up to 100 km/h
Obstacle Clearance: over 0.25m

AIRSPREE CRUISER
The Cruiser is ideal for cruises on coastal and inland waters and for general day tripping. It is equipped as for the Sport except as follows:
LIFT AND PROPULSION: Choice of Hirth 493 32kW (43 bhp) or Rotax 447 29.8kW (40 bhp) 2-cycle engines.
CONTROLS: Splitter plate control available as optional extra only.
WEIGHTS
Empty: 170 kg
Payload: 190 kg
PERFORMANCE
Speed: to 43 knots, 80 km/h

AIRSPREE FUN

The bottom of the range AIRSPREE is designed for general hovering around mainly in calm conditions on inland waters. It is equipped as for the Cruiser except as follows:

LIFT AND PROPULSION: Choice of Hirth 383 28 bhp or Rotax 277 19.4kW (26 bhp) 2-cycle engines. Fixed splitter plate.

ACCOMMODATION: Bench seat option not available.

WEIGHTS
Empty: 150 kg
Payload: 150 kg

PERFORMANCE
Speed: to 30 knots, 55 km/h

AIRSPREE EXTRAS

A full list of options and extras is available including trailer, In-Shore, On-Shore and Off-Shore packages.

Airspree 2 seater

AIR VEHICLES LIMITED

Head Office and Factory: Unit 4, Three Gates Road, Cowes, Isle of Wight, England

Telephone: (0983) 293194
Telex: 86513HVWORK G
Telefax: (0983) 291987

C B Eden, *Director*

TIGER 4

The Tiger 4 is a lightweight four-seat hovercraft which can operate at speeds of up to 30 knots over a wide variety of surfaces. Costing about the same as a four-seat all-wheel-drive vehicle or shallow water powerboat, it can often take the place of both, and operates economically in areas where neither can go.

The Tiger 4 was first introduced in 1973, and the concept has proven itself worldwide in a variety of military and private uses. The latest design has a unique inflatable hull, patented skirt, high power engine with electric start, high thrust ducted fan, low noise level, spacious and comfortable cockpit and many detailed refinements.

LIFT AND PROPULSION: The integrated lift and propulsion system has a single axial fan operating in a glass-fibre duct and driven by a high torque, toothed belt transmission. The 497cc twin cylinder, air-cooled 2-stroke engine has a high power-to-weight ratio and an excellent reputation for reliability.

CONTROLS: The simple, centrally-mounted controls can be operated by either front seat occupant.

HULL: The four-compartment inflatable hull is made from Hypalon/nylon material. As well as providing massive peripheral buoyancy which gives a stable working platform, it also acts as an impact absorbing fender.

COCKPIT: The spacious cockpit has comfortable seats which can be laid flat for sleeping or removed for carrying goods. The wrap-around windscreen gives good protection and is made of unbreakable polycarbonate.

SKIRT: The latest type of loop/segment skirt gives good stability, long life and excellent sealing with minimum drag on all types of surface. There are 100 separate segments which are easily attached and quickly replaced in the event of wear

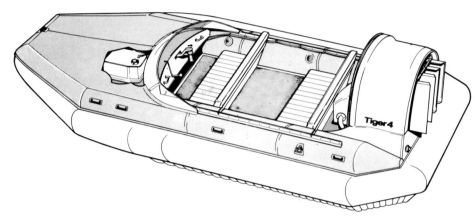

Tiger 4 hovercraft

Air Vehicles Tiger 4 being loaded onto its trailer

or damage. The possibility of damage is reduced by the weak link attachments. The neoprene/nylon material is suitable for all climatic conditions and has excellent wear and tear characteristics.

DIMENSIONS
Length: 5.10m
Width: 2.38m
Transport width: 2.36m
Height: 1.27m

WEIGHTS
Empty: 225kg
Max: 550kg
Disposable load: 325kg

PERFORMANCE
Max speed, over water: 30 knots
over land: 28 knots
Fuel consumption, average: 11 litres/h

BILL BAKER VEHICLES LIMITED (BBV)

Quarry Road, Hornton, Near Banbury, Oxon OX15 6DF, England

Telephone: (0295) 87465

W R L Baker, *Managing Director*
R V H Baker, *Director*

Bill Baker Vehicles Limited designs and manufactures multi-purpose hovercraft and also supplies components. The latter include tapered roller-bearing fan hubs, nylon pulleys and other items for racing and two-seat integrated cruising craft. Hirth, Rotax and Solo motors, Multiwing and Truflo fans are also available.

Since 1979 a range of craft has been developed for manufacture by the company or to be made under licence by suitable UK or foreign manufacturers. This has enabled the company to develop products such as a cab and cab heater for use in sub-zero conditions, tests being undertaken in Finland, Norway, Sweden and the USA on various winter surfaces to monitor performance.

The company supports the Hoverclub of Great Britain and international race meetings. Development of racing hovercraft is felt to be important for overall improvement of products from small-engined, integrated pleasure craft to larger four-seater craft.

BBV-1 (THE GNAT)

The smallest craft in the range is a low-price single-seater with a bag skirt and an 18hp Robin engine. BBV-1 can also be fitted with the larger 48hp Rotax engine making it highly competitive in European Formula 'S' racing events (single engine, any size, single duct of 800mm maximum) and can be carried on a roof rack.
DIMENSIONS
Length: 3.0m
Beam: 1.8m
WEIGHTS
20hp motor: 85kg
40–50hp motor: 110kg

BBV-1-S

This racing craft, derived from the BBV-1, features a pressure-fed, segmented skirt and a full 800mm duct. Engines of between 20 and 80hp can be installed.
PRICE (dependent on engine type): complete craft, £2800-£3450 (1989)

BBV-2

This two- to three-seat craft has been designed for easy construction by the inexperienced kit builder. The main hull consists of a top and bottom moulding with a captive foam block set in the floor. The top and bottom outer edge is first bonded together and then riveted through an aluminium angle which gives considerable strength to the edge of the craft as well as providing a uniform attachment for the skirt.

The bottom moulding is constructed shiny side outwards, allowing all skirt location points to be moulded in for easy drilling. Four aluminium channel sections fit over moulded-in ribs, giving the craft a rigid, hard wearing bottom.

The craft uses an 8-bladed 915mm diameter fan supplying air for both lift and thrust which is highly efficient, giving more than adequate thrust from engines of over 40hp. The drive system has been designed so that should it be necessary the fan blades or drive belt can be easily changed. The bottom pulley hub uses sealed high-speed bearings and is driven through a flexible coupling. This design permits small automobile engines to be used, in addition to the standard range of 40 to 80hp two-cycle engines, without changing the thrust system.

BBV-2

BBV-2+2

BBV-4

The craft is fitted with spray dodger and windscreen, which coupled with optional side-by-side or pillion seating ensures a degree of comfort not normally found on a small craft. The segmented skirt design has evolved from BBV craft racing experience, giving a good stable performance even in adverse conditions. The ease of maintenance is a standard feature on all craft in the BBV range.
ENGINE
40hp 440cc two-stroke Hirth or
48hp 496cc two-stroke Rotax (petrol/oil mixture)
DIMENSIONS
Length: 3.83m
Beam: 2.0m
Hoverheight: 20cm
WEIGHTS/CAPACITIES
Empty weight: 145kg
Payload: 180kg
Fuel tank: 22.75 litres
PERFORMANCE
Speed: 45–50km/h
Fuel consumption: 10–16 litres/h
PRICE: complete craft, £4750-£4925 (1989)

BBV CRUISING CRAFT

More efficient hulls and the better matching of fans to installed power has improved the performance of BBV designs over the last few years.

Two- to three-seat hulls are available which take a variety of engines with outputs of between 40 to 100hp. These cruising hovercraft can be bought with or without engines.

BBV-2+2

This is a lengthened version of the BBV-2, and

is fitted with electric start and four seats, plus further refinements as standard. Finished craft, from £5840 (1989). Details as for BBV-2 except length: 4.57m; beam: 2.0m; payload: 300kg.

BBV-4

This is a new craft embodying a great deal of both racing and cruising experience. The craft is available with two- or four-stroke engines of 80 to 100hp. Air from both 838mm diameter fans is used for lift and thrust. A full cabin is available giving good visibility and passenger comfort. With this craft a considerable reduction in noise has been achieved, whilst substantially improving the performance. A number of options are available, including a longer version if required. The hull and cab are made of self-coloured grp. Prices from £10 000 (1989).
ENGINES
Subaru 80hp four-cycle
Fuji-Robin (Polaris) 85hp two-cycle
Rotax 530 80hp two-cycle
SKIRT: Fully segmented neoprene/nylon.
DIMENSIONS
Length: 5.11m
Beam: 2.34m
Hoverheight: 28cm

BBV-1-F1 RACING HOVERCRAFT

Winner of the 1984 European Formula One Championship, this craft uses the same hull shape and skirt design as the BBV-1-S, and BBV has also drawn on the experience gained during the development of its earlier Formula One racing craft, the BBV-11. The 9hp Solo lift engine drives a 558mm, 5-blade fan, and the Rotax 48–60hp engine drives two 645mm thrust fans, giving 110 to 140kg of thrust.

CONTROLS: Craft heading is controlled by twin rudders, one hinged to the rear of each thrust duct. Handlebars control rudder movement.

HULL: Two-part grp construction with foam buoyancy and a motorcycle-type seat moulded-in. Hull has full hydrodynamic surfaces and internal-skirt feed ducts.

SKIRT: Pressure-fed segmented system in neo-prene-coated nylon.

DIMENSIONS
Length: 2.95m
Beam: 1.82m
WEIGHT
Unladen: 145kg
PERFORMANCE
Max speed, calm conditions: 88.51km/h
PRICE (approx): £3200 (1985)

BBV-1-F1

DRAGONFLY LEISURE LTD

Lodge Farm, Hankelow, Crewe, Cheshire CW3 0JE.

Telephone: (0270) 811671
Telefax: (0270) 812157

DRAGONFLY

Introduced in 1988 the Dragonfly may be fitted with a 34 kW or 39.5kW two-stroke petrol engine. The air cushion has a rise height of 20cm and the craft is capable of a speed up to 35 knots. This craft is priced between 4000 and 7000 depending on specification.

Dragonfly

GP VEHICLES LTD

Unit 7, Worton Hall, Worton Road, Isleworth, Middlesex TW7 6ER, England

Telephone: (01) 568 4711/4664
Telex: 477019GP G
Telefax: (01) 5682426

John Jobber, *Managing Director*
Gary Bradley, *General Manager*

HOVER HAWK

This four-seat utility ACV is intended for survey and patrol duties as well as the leisure industry. Orders have been placed by countries throughout the world including North and South America, Europe, Scandinavia, South Africa, Australia, the Middle and the Far East. The price of the Hover Hawk in 1989 was £6700, and a car trailer for carrying the craft was £320.

LIFT AND PROPULSION: Integrated system. A single 1835cc Volkswagen VW4 air-cooled engine drives, via a belt, a ducted fan aft. Propulsion air is expelled rearwards and lift air is ducted into the plenum below. Fuel capacity is 28 litres. Fuel recommended 93 octane.

CONTROLS: Single control column operates a single rudder hinged to the rear of the fan duct. Column incorporates a twist-grip throttle for the engine.

HULL: Moulded glassfibre reinforced plastics structure.

SKIRT: Fully-segmented type in neoprene-coated nylon, with 68 air bag segments.

ACCOMMODATION: Open cockpit with seating for driver and up to three passengers.

DIMENSIONS
Length overall: 4.12m
Width: 2.5m
Height, on cushion: 1.27m

Hover Hawk

Hover Hawk

WEIGHTS
Empty: 200kg
Payload: 249kg
PERFORMANCE
Max speed: Over 40 knots

Gradient capability: 1:7 from static hover
Obstacle clearance: 0.3m
Endurance, max: 3 hours
Fuel consumption, average: 7.8km/litre

HOVERSERVICES SCARAB HOVERCRAFT

24 Hazel Grove, Wallingford, Oxon OX10 0AT, England

Telephone: (0491) 37455
Telex: 859224 FLEXON G

Graham Nutt, *Proprietor*

Hoverservices was formed in 1972 to market Scarab hovercraft plans and components. The company now offers a range of light hovercraft plans for the single-seat Scarab I and two-seat Scarab II, in addition to plans for other racing craft such as the Snoopy II and Eccles. All of these plans are marketed world-wide.

The company has a wide range of fans, grp ducts, skirt material and other components in stock and provides a complete engineering service.

SCARAB II (Plans)

Scarab II is a two-seater light hovercraft designed for cruising in calm coastal or sheltered estuarial waters. With its larger size it will accept a variety of engines for lift and propulsion.

LIFT AND PROPULSION: A typical lift engine for this craft would be a 5bhp Briggs & Stratton, driving a 558mm diameter axial lift fan fitted with Multiwing blades. For propulsion the craft could use various powerplants up to 42bhp driving either 609mm or 762mm diameter ducted Multi-wing fans.

CONTROLS: Employs a single rudder positioned in the thrust duct which is activated by a joystick in the open cockpit. A twist grip throttle is used for the thrust engine and a quadrant type lever for lift.

HULL: This is made from triangular plywood boxes upon a framework of pine with grp tape for additional strength for joints etc. A full flow loop skirt is fitted.

ACCOMMODATION: Side-by-side seating for driver and one passenger in open cockpit.

DIMENSIONS
Length: 3.5m
Width: 1.83m
Hoverheight: 228mm
WEIGHTS
Empty: 113kg
Normal payload: 181kg (two people)
Max weight: 295kg
PERFORMANCE
Over land and water Scarab II craft, with propulsion units of 35–42bhp, can achieve speeds of 48–56km/h

SCARAB 16 (Plans)

A development of the Scarab 14 (see 1986 edition) and built to comply with British and European Formula 3 racing regulations for craft with engines up to 250cc. Building plan sets are available.

LIFT AND PROPULSION: Aerodynamically integrated lift and propulsion system powered by a Robin EC25, Rotax 248 or Yamaha RD 250 engine.

HULL: Extremely lightweight hull built in tri-angulated box sections formed in epoxy-saturated 4mm ply, bonded with epoxy foam and grp tape.
SKIRT: Pressure fed segmented.
DIMENSIONS
Length: 3.04m
Width: 1.82m
Rise height: 0.23m
WEIGHTS
Weight, empty: 79kg
Payload: 79kg

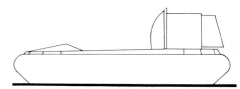

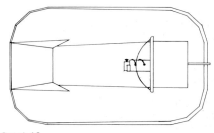

Scarab 16

INGLES HOVERCRAFT ASSOCIATES LIMITED/ MISSION AVIATION FELLOWSHIP

Ingles Manor, Castle Hill Avenue, Folkestone, Kent CT20 2TN, England

Telephone: (0303) 41356

S Sendall-King, *General Director*
D G Staveley, *UK Director*
T J R Longley, *Design Consultant*

Ingles Hovercraft Associates Limited administers the design and patent rights relating to the hovercraft developed by the Mission Aviation Fellowship (MAF).

MAF's first craft was the Missionaire, a general purpose amphibious five-seater. This was succeeded by the six-seat River Rover. Following evaluation trials by the Naval Hovercraft Trials Unit, the River Rover was chosen by the 1978–79 British Joint Services Expedition to Nepal. For a period of four months, two Mk 2 craft were successfully used over a 60-mile stretch of the turbulent Kali Gandaki river in support of a medical aid programme.

One of these craft is now in regular use by a mission in Irian Jaya, Indonesia, on the Baliem river and its tributaries, three are in service on the upper reaches of the Amazon in Peru; one with the Taiwanese Police and one with the Australian Army on tidal flats in South Australia.

RIVER ROVER

Designed as a water-borne counterpart to the Land Rover utility vehicle, River Rover is a sturdily constructed, six-seat cabin hovercraft which has proved its usefulness and reliability in many parts of the world where navigation by conventional boats is difficult or impossible.

The four main requirements for such a craft are:
Low cost, both of manufacture and of operation;
Positive control characteristics, enabling the

River Rover Mk 3

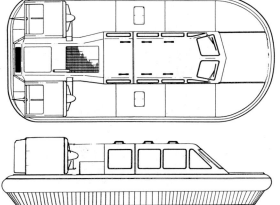

General arrangement of River Rover Mk 3

craft to follow safely the course of a narrow, winding river with the minimum of sideways skidding;
Simple bolt-together unit construction, facilitating transport and simplifying maintenance and repair;
An efficient and reliable skirt system, combining good wear resistance with ease of repair.
The following information refers to the River Rover Mk 3.

LIFT AND PROPULSION: Motive power is provided by a single 100bhp Renault R-20TS automotive engine. This drives a 630mm diameter lift fan, and two 710mm thrust fans mounted on either side of the lift fan. Power is transmitted via three Uniroyal HTD toothed belts and pulleys enclosed in streamlined fairings. All three fans are housed in grp ducts. Air from the lift fan is channelled through 90 degrees down beneath the craft via the skirt bag. Fuel consumption at cruising speed is 20.3 litres/h. Standard capacity 82 litres.

CONTROLS: The primary means of control are two horizontally-pivoted elevons, one in each of the two square-sectioned ducts immediately aft of the thrust fans. Movement of foot pedals rotates the elevons jointly or differentially. Employed together, craft longitudinal trim is adjusted and, when rotated fully, braking is achieved. Used differentially, small deflections of the elevons enable the craft to be banked into a turn, thereby reducing sideways skidding. Greater pedal movement progressively closes the duct on the 'inside' of the turn, the outside duct remaining open. Thus differential thrust is added to the bank initially applied to the craft. Conventional vertically-pivoted aerodynamic rudders, controlled by a steering yoke, are fitted immediately aft of the elevons. These are used during operation in crosswinds, in conjunction with the elevons.

HULL: Aluminium alloy angle frame covered with 6mm marine grade plywood panels. Engine bay bulkheads and sides are in aluminium alloy sheet. Structure is bolted together for ease of repair and simplicity of breakdown and reassembly. The entire hull is surrounded by an inflatable

One of three River Rovers employed by 1982 British Joint Services Expedition to Peru

collar at deck level, providing all-round fendering and additional reserve buoyancy. The sliding cabin canopy is of moulded grp.

ACCOMMODATION: Three bench-type seats. These can be folded flat to provide sleeping accommodation for two persons, or, with cushions removed, for the carriage of freight. Alternatively, a stretcher can be carried aft on the port side of the cabin.

SKIRT: HDL-type loop and segment skirt in neoprene-coated nylon.

DIMENSIONS
Length: 6.19m
Width: 2.62m
Height, off cushion: 1.45m
WEIGHTS
Empty: 780kg
Total weight: 1230kg
PERFORMANCE
Max speed: 55km/h
Cruising speed: 40km/h

OSPREY HOVERCRAFT LIMITED

No 1 Work Base, The Historic Dockyard, Chatham, Kent, ME4 4TZ England

Telephone: (0444) 645791
Telefax: 0634831635

P V McCollum, *Managing Director*
P D McCollum, *Technical Director*
D McCollum, *Director & Secretary*

This company has been established over 14 years and has been responsible for the design of over 6000 light hovercraft produced on the commercial, international market.

Osprey Hovercraft have now moved to their new premises at The Chatham Historic Dockyard where they produce a range of leisure craft.

P V (Kip) McCollum has been producing light hovercraft since 1970 and is now recognised as one of the leading authorities in this field. His son, Paul, has designed and built his own Pintail Racing Hovercraft and is currently the UK champion for two years running, 1988 and 1989.

PINTAIL 2

This craft is an extremely powerful craft designed exclusively for racing. It is highly manoeuvrable both on land and water.

LIFT AND PROPULSION: A twin cylinder Rotax 532, 521.2 cc two stroke engine developing 47.7 kw at 6500 rpm drives, a flexible coupling and via an HTD belt drive, a twin-ducted 0.74m diameter glass-filled-nylon blade fan.

Lift is provided by a 342cc Weslake engine developing 18.6 kw at 5200 rpm driving a 0.55m nylon-blade fan.

CONTROLS: Craft is controlled by twin aerodynamic rudders hinged to the rear of the thrust duct and operated by a handlebar.

HULL: Monocoque construction in self-coloured glassfibre incorporating a preformed sealed polyurethane block for buoyancy.

SKIRT: Segmented type in neoprene-coated nylon fabric.

Length: 3.05m
Beam: 1.89m
Height: 1.16m
Weight: 172 kg
PERFORMANCE: In excess of 61 knots, 113 km/h across land and water.
RISE HEIGHT: 18 cm

Pintail 2

Osprey 3

OSPREY 3

The Osprey 3 has been specifically designed by the Osprey Team, Kip McCollum and Paul McCollum for leisure activities. It carries 3 adults, or 2 adults and 2 children with maximum safety

and reliability at speed up to 30 knots, 56 km/h.

REVERSE THRUST CONTROL SYSTEM: This feature is unique in this size of craft. It allows the Osprey 3 to hover whilst remaining stationary, and provides effective braking and control in emergencies without losing hover height. The wide body design gives extra stability and 500 kg of positive built-in buoyancy makes it almost unsinkable.

The four-stroke four-cylinder water-cooled car engine with key start makes it one of the quietest craft of its size now produced.

PRINCIPAL PARTICULARS
Payload: 227 kg
Unladen weight: 272 kg
Length: 3.96m
Width: 2.13m
Height: 1.52m
Cruising speed: 40 km/h
Maximum speed: 56 kmm/h
Fuel consumption: 8 km per litre, at cruising speed in calm weather conditions
Range: 8 hours at cruising speed in calm conditions
Obstacle clearance: 0.23m
Engine: 850 cc, 40 hp, 4 cylinder, 4 stroke gasolene/petrol, liquid cooled, with key start and charging
Fuel tank: 36.4 litres
Fan: 8 blades, 014 mm diameter
Body: Self-coloured reinforced glass fibre. Available in red, blue, yellow and white as standard, other colours on request.

OSPREY 5

This craft was developed from the Osprey 3 because of increasing demand from both private and commercial users for a larger craft providing a greater payload and higher cruising speed. It will carry up to 5 adults. Commercial applications are as follows: movement of light goods and personnel by oil, construction and survey companies etc.; use by Military, Police, Customs, Coastguard and Rescue Authorities; and transport or ferrywork over difficult terrains such as frozen lakes, tidal mud flats, weed-filled tropical rivers etc.

The Osprey 5 is fitted with the Reverse Thrust Control System and has a more powerful 63.4 kW Citroen four-stroke engine.

Osprey 5

PRINCIPAL PARTICULARS
Payload: 378 kg
Unladen weight: 350 kg
Length: 4.87m
Width: 2.13m
Height: 1.52m
Cruising speed: 56 km/h
Maximum speed: 80 km/h
Fuel consumption: 4.93 km per litre, at cruising speed in calm weather conditions
Range: Over 3 hours at cruising speed in calm conditions
Obstacle clearance: 0.23m
Engine: 1360 cc, 85 hp, 4 cylinder, 4 stroke, Citröen gasolene/petrol, liquid cooled, with key start and charging

Fuel tank: 36.4 litres
Fan: 9 blades, 014 mm diameter
Body: Self-coloured reinforced glass fibre. Available in red, blue, yellow and white as standard, other colours on request.

CORMORANT
FALCON
KESTREL GT
KESTREL
GOSHAWK

These earlier craft are described in the 1989 edition of this book.

UNITED STATES OF AMERICA

DOBSON PRODUCTS CO

32901 Morrison Place, Lake Elsinore, California 92330, USA

Telephone: (714) 546 3646/678 4534

Franklin A Dobson, *Director*

Dobson Products Co was formed by Franklin A Dobson in 1963 to develop and market small ACVs either in complete, factory built form, or as kits for private use. His first model, the Dobson Air Dart, won the first ACV race in Canberra in 1964.

The first Dobson craft designed for quantity production was the Model H. Since good results have been obtained with the Dobson six-bladed variable-pitch propeller and more positive control is desirable at low and negative speeds, Model K has been developed using two side-by-side ducted thrust units. This gives powerful yaw control at all speeds in addition to a very considerable increase in positive as well as negative thrust together with low noise level.

Jane's Surface Skimmers 1985 contains full details of various Air Car models.

AIR CARS, MODELS A to F
(1963 to 1970)

These are similar designs using an integrated system with a large slow-turning fan and vents for thrust and control. The central body acts as a splitter, giving good roll stability. The craft have

Dobson Air Car Model H

Air Car Model K (modified)

coverings of fabric or lightweight plastic, supported by curved side members, and flexible skirts made up of combined hinged and flexible members. They have been sold in large numbers as plans and kits.

One was used by Boston Museum for demonstration and display; another won the first ACV race at Canberra. The company's Model F two-seater was described and illustrated in *Jane's Surface Skimmers 1973–74* and earlier editions.

Length: 3.66m
Width: 2.1m
Power: 7–12hp
Empty weight: 43–59kg
Max weight: 136–181kg
Performance: 25–30mph

AIR CAR, MODEL D (1969)

Two-place integrated design, generally similar to Models A/F.
Length: 4.27m
Width: 2.1m
Power: 15hp
Empty weight: 91kg
Max weight: 226kg
Performance: 30mph
Ten of these have been sold in kit form.

AIR CAR, MODEL H (1972)

This is a single-engined design using a variable-pitch ducted fan for thrust and braking, with a separate lift fan driven through a long shaft and right-angle gearbox. There are several variants, one using a fixed-pitch thrust fan with thrust reverser. The flexible skirt is supported by hinged floats.
Length: 3.35m
Width: 2.89m
Power: 18hp
Empty weight: 104kg
Gross weight: 272kg
Performance: 40mph

AIR CAR, MODEL K (1980)

A single-engined design, using two variable-pitch ducted fans for thrust, control and braking, with a lift fan driven through shaft and gearbox. The segmented skirt is supported by removable floats. The engine is controlled by a governor. The craft has excellent control in forward or backward flight and a very low noise level.
Length: 3.69m
Width: 2.89m
Power: 18hp Briggs and Stratton 2 cylinder 4-stroke engine
Empty weight: 127kg
Gross weight: 272kg
Performance: 35mph

AIR CAR, MODEL K (modified)

This is similar in general design to the Model K but is lighter and more streamlined. There is an additional lift fan at the rear, pulling air past the engine for cooling, thus allowing use of a totally-enclosed engine. It has a conical segment skirt, supported on removable floats.
Power: 22hp Chaparral engine
Empty weight: 118kg
Otherwise similar to Model K.

HERMES

A new lightweight, single-engine two-place folding model combining the unusual feature of being able to operate at reduced clearance without a skirt if necessary. The lift fan is driven through a constant velocity universal joint which is quieter and lighter than gearboxes used in former designs.

A new control system is incorporated in this model. The 0.813m diameter Multiwing thrust propeller operates in a duct of roughly elliptical cross-section. Around the duct and extending aft from it are two curved streamlined covers hinged on a vertical axis near the rear and held against the duct by springs. There are two rudders which

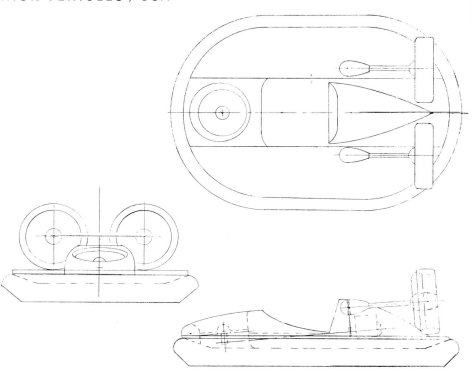

Air Car Model K

Dobson Hermes prototype

Dobson Hermes prototype

normally operate together when the control stick is moved sideways. If the control stick is pulled back the rudders turn outward, forcing the air against the covers which then open, exposing turning vanes which direct the thrust air forward for reverse thrust and control.

The Hermes uses a forward-facing 0.61m diameter Multiwing lift fan and a splitter body as on some earlier Dobson craft. A new type of skirt is employed made up of four interchangeable sections with Velcro attachment. The fan and skirt combination give reduced momentum drag, resulting in improved performance. Cushion pressure is 46.4kg/m².
ENGINE: Chaparral G25A, 22hp at 7000rpm.
DIMENSIONS
Length: 3.96m
Width: 2.44m
Width, folded: 1.22m
Cushion area: 5.1m²
Obstacle clearance: 203mm
WEIGHTS
Weight, empty: 102kg
Weight, max: 238kg
Payload: 136kg

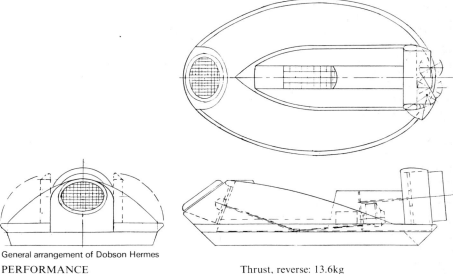

General arrangement of Dobson Hermes
PERFORMANCE
Thrust, forward: 34.0kg

Thrust, reverse: 13.6kg
Drag, at hump: 12.1kg

HOVERCRAFT INDUSTRIES INC
11352 Space Boulevard, Orlando, Florida 32821, USA

Telephone: (305) 857 4343

SUNRIDER I
ENGINE: Rotax Model 277, two-stroke 27hp, petrol/oil 40:1 mix, hand start.
SKIRT: Neoprene-coated nylon, segmented.
DIMENSIONS
Length: 3.2m
Beam: 1.83m

Height, max: 1.22m
Prop/fan dia: 0.737m
WEIGHT
Empty: 141kg
PERFORMANCE
Rise height: 203mm
Tank capacity: 30.3 litres
Speed, max: 48km/h

SUNRIDER II
ENGINE
Lift: 12hp, single-cylinder, 2-cycle
Thrust: 50hp, two-cylinder in line, 2-cycle, electronic start

CONTROLS: Two rudders, control column operated; thrust engine throttle, foot operated; lift engine throttle, hand operated.
DIMENSIONS
Length: 4.06m
Beam: 1.98m
Height: 1.12m
WEIGHTS
Empty: 299kg
Payload: 200kg
PERFORMANCE
Obstacle clearance height: 229mm
Tank capacity: 37.9 litres
Gradient capability from static hover: 1:8

NEOTERIC HOVERCRAFT INC
1649 Tippecanoe Street, Terre Haute, Indiana 47807, USA

Telephone: (812) 234 1120
Telefax: (812) 234 3217

J Christopher Fitzgerald, *President*
Tracy Wilkerson, *Secretary*

Neoteric Hovercraft Incorporated was formed in 1975 by three of the founders of Neoteric Engineering Affiliates Pty Ltd, Melbourne, Australia. The Neova range of two-seat ACVs, which is now being manufactured and marketed by Neoteric USA, was first introduced by the Australian associate. The fully amphibious Neova is available in kit or ready-built form. Other businesses may manufacture the Neoteric range under licence.

In 1986 Neoteric introduced its largest craft in the range, the six-seat, 5.95m Neova 6 and also the Neova 4 a slightly smaller four-seat craft.

NEOVA 2
A highly-manoeuvrable light ACV, the Neova is an amphibious two-seater intended primarily for recreational use. Neova 2 is supplied in kit form in two versions, Standard and Super. The Standard model comprises four basic modules: the fibreglass base, machinery, ducts and controls and skirt system. The Super model includes two additional modules: fibreglass-moulded upper hull and hatch and a trailer. Individual components are also supplied, enabling the homebuilder to assemble any part of the complete vehicle.

The overall dimensions of the machine—2.13 × 4.27m—allow it to be transported by road on a flat trailer.

Neova II two-seater

LIFT AND PROPULSION: Integrated system powered by a 1600cc, 46hp, 124A or 126A Volkswagen engine. The company has developed a new timing belt drive transmission. The new drive features a centrifugal clutch and an all-aluminium pod structure. Maintenance is reduced substantially and the life of the drive is increased. In addition assembly time is further reduced. Assembly time of the complete kit is 350 hours. Airflow is ducted into the plenum for lift and two outlets aft for thrust. The power module, comprising engine, transmission and axial-flow fans, is mounted on a rubber-seated frame, secured to the main hull by three bolts and is totally enclosed for safety. A large hatch provides ready access to the engine and all components. Fuel consumption, full throttle is 13.6 litres/h.
SKIRT: Multi-cell jupe type.
CONTROLS: Back and forward movement of a dual stick control column operates two thrust buckets which vary the power and the direction of the thrust. The column is pulled back for reverse

thrust and moved ahead for forward thrust. Differential use of the two columns, with one stick forward and the other back, is used for changing craft direction. The aerodynamic rudders at the rear of the propulsion ducts are normally used only for small corrections in heading at cruising speeds.
HULL: Fibreglass structure with solid foam buoyancy. Safety skids beneath. An integral siphon system prevents the collection of excessive water within the hull. Buoyancy is 150%. The skirt module is removable as two single units.
ACCOMMODATION: Side-by-side seating for two.
DIMENSIONS
Length overall: 4.27m
Beam overall: 2.13m
Height overall, skirt inflated: 1.4m
WEIGHTS
Empty weight: 341kg
Payload, max: 196kg

PERFORMANCE
Speeds: 48–96km/h
Hard, beach: 56km/h
Water: 51km/h
Land: 48km/h
Ice: 72km/h
Firm snow: 65km/h
Max gradient from standing start: 1 : 10
Vertical obstacle clearance: 0.2m
Fuel consumption: 13.6 litres/h
Endurance on full power: 3 hours with 34-litre tank
Range with 34-litre tank: 128km

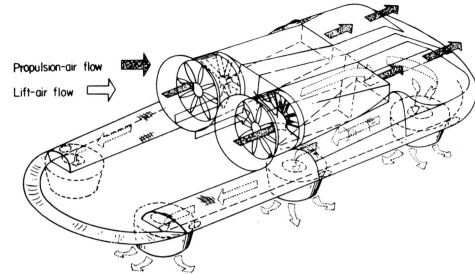
Propulsion-air flow
Lift-air flow
Air flow system of Neova 2

EXPLORER

The Explorer, previously known as the Lémere, is an all-terrain, two-seater built in glassfibre and pvc foam. Maximum speed is about 64km/h. The craft can be towed behind a standard car on a single axle.
LIFT AND PROPULSION: Lift is provided by a single 8hp Briggs & Stratton type 319cc Series 190702 four-cycle petrol engine driving an axial flow four-blade wooden fan. Thrust is supplied by a single 55hp Fuji Robin EC34PL or 50hp EC44PM liquid-cooled two-cycle engine driving a ducted fan type 0.609m diameter Multiwing 42 PAG, reduction ratio: 1.9:1.0.
HULL: Composite structure in glassfibre and pvc foam.
SKIRT: Bag type in neoprene/nylon material, riveted construction, 16oz/yd^2.
ACCOMMODATION: Side-by-side seating for two.
DIMENSIONS
Length, hardstructure: 3.5m
Width, hardstructure: 2.03m
Height, on landing pads: 0.91m
WEIGHTS
Empty: 188kg
Payload: 227kg
PERFORMANCE
Range: 64km
Obstacle clearance height: 0.15m
PRICE: US $9195 (1988) including all options.

RACER

Introduced in late 1984 for hoverclub racing and cruising events, the Racer is a glassfibre hulled two-seater powered by a 50hp Fuji engine and capable of 80km/h. It is available in kit or ready-built form.
LIFT AND PROPULSION: Integrated system powered by 39.5kW Fuji 44 2PM air-cooled, two-cycle engine. Alternative engines of similar output are acceptable on craft built from kits. Fuel capacity is 25.7 litres. Recommended fuel is two-cycle mix, 40:1. Fan: 609mm diameter Multiwing 4Z PAG, 9 blades, reduction ratio: 1.9:1.0.
CONTROLS: Handlebar operates rudders at rear of propulsion duct. Throttle on handlebar. Foot-operated thrust reverse buckets.
HULL: Composite structure in glassfibre and pvc foam.
SKIRT: Bag type in neoprene-coated nylon material, glued construction or 20cm deep segment type, in any colour.
ACCOMMODATION: Seating for three in tandem.
DIMENSIONS
Length: 3.50m
Width: 2.03m
Height, off cushion: 0.94m
WEIGHTS
Empty: 159kg
Payload: 270kg
PERFORMANCE
Speed: 80km/h
Hoverheight: 20cm
Range: 64km good weather
PRICE: 1988, US $4954

Neova 2's propulsion transmission arrangement

Explorer 2- to 3-seater

NEOVA IV

A four-seat variant of the Neova 2, the latter having been marketed successfully for the past 12 years. Neova 4 was released to the market in July 1986.
ENGINE: 90hp Fuji EC60 PL-01 or two 55hp Fuji EC44PM or Subaru 4-cycle.
SKIRT: Segmented with inner jupes if additional stability required.
DIMENSIONS
Length: 4.27m
Width: 2.13m
WEIGHTS
Empty: 272kg
Payload: 365kg
PERFORMANCE
Speed, max: 80km/h
Fuel consumption: 22.7 litres/h
Tank capacity: 64.3 litres
Operating temperature range: −30°C to +32°C
Obstacle clearance height: 25cm
PRICE: 1988, US$19500

NEOVA 6

The largest craft of the Neoteric range, the first one being built in 1986 and engaged in October 1986 on trials for the US Army Corps of Engineers. The Neova 6 is a four-seater built in pvc foam, 4lb/ft^2 density, and polyurethane foam 2lb/ft^3 density with 10oz/yd^2 fibreglass cloth and polyester resin. Eight fibreglass-coated wooden skid pads are provided on the hull underside. The craft is fitted with a Hadees Model 356 heater.
LIFT AND PROPULSION: The powerplant is a Chrysler LH 318 (87–312) 4-cycle petrol engine fitted with two California Turbo 40120 mufflers. Fans for lift and propulsion are Multiwing, 91.44cm dia, 16 blades, type 16–4Z-45 deg. Power transmission is by toothed HTD belts, type 8M-2000–85, 48-tooth drive shaft pulley, 75-tooth fan shaft pulley, drive ratio 1.563:1.
CONTROLS: Reverse thrust bucket, rudders and throttle all operated by Morse Red Jacket cables.
SKIRT: The skirt is constructed of 16oz/yd^2 'nylon-reinforced neoprene rubber'. There are eight jupes surrounded by 62 segments.
DIMENSIONS
Length overall: 5.95m off cushion
　　6.17m on cushion
Width: 2.59m off cushion
　　2.97m on cushion
Height: 1.76m off cushion
　　2.07m on cushion
WEIGHTS
Weight, empty: 862kg ±45kg
Payload: 363kg normal
　　455kg max
PERFORMANCE
Speed, max: 72km/h
Speed, cruising, 2500rpm: 48km/h
Range: 201km
Tank capacity: 94.6 litres
Obstacle clearance: 30.5cm
Operational temperature range: −34.4°C to 43.3°C
Weather restrictions: Wave height, max, 0.6m wind speed, 48km/h
PRICE: US $40 000 (1986)

NEOVA WORK-HORSE

A new model produced in 1988.
LIFT AND PROPULSION: Lift engine: 8hp (3600rpm) Briggs and Stratton, 319cc air-cooled, 4-cycle. Thrust engine: 50hp (3600rpm) Fuji, 44 PM air-cooled, 2-cycle, electric start.
REVERSE THRUST: Bucket system operated by Land levers.
HULL: Composite fibreglass and urethane foam, 105% of laden weight in urethane foam floatation plus additional 200% displacement buoyancy.
SKIRT: Segmented 400 denier nylon.
ACCOMMODATION: Bench seating for two.

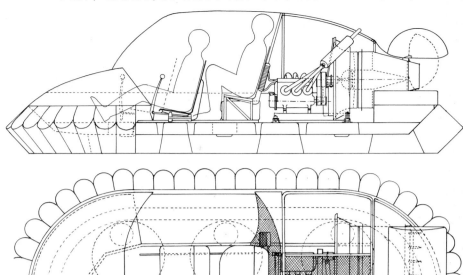

Layout of Neoteric Neova 4

80km/h Neoteric Racer

Neova 4

DIMENSIONS
Length: 4.88m
Width: 2.44m
Work area: 2.17m x 1.60m
WEIGHTS
Empty: 308kg
Max laden: 649kg
PERFORMANCE
Speed, max: 30.5 knots
Static thrust: 84.5kg
Rise height: 20cm
PRICE: 1988, US$18000

Neoteric Neova 6

Neova Work-horse

SCAT HOVERCRAFT INC

10621 N Kendall Drive, Suite 210, Miami, Florida
33176, USA

Telephone: (305) 274 7228/for USA only 4879
Telex: 293894 SCAT
Telefax: (305) 598 2033

Ron Molina, *President and Chief Executive*
William Flett, *Vice President*
Kevin Bedsworth, *Chief Engineer*

SCAT 11

Designed by Scat Hovercraft Inc, the Scat two-
seat hovercraft has been in production since June
1985. In February 1986 the Scat company completed a US $3.5 million public offering of shares
and warrants, enabling it to expand significantly
its marketing and production capabilities. The
craft is built in a 4645m² plant in Miami and is
sold through over 400 dealer outlets.
LIFT AND PROPULSION: A 35hp (6200rpm)
Cuyuma 428cc two-stroke engine drives through
a 2:1 gear reduction systema 6-blade axial-flow
fan 0.8 in diameter, two-thirds of the air going to
thrust and one-third to the cushion. A 22.7-litre
fuel tank is fitted.
CONTROLS: Throttle and handlebar steered
single rudder.
HULL: Glassfibre upper surfaces available in six
colours, injection foam-filled deck, high impact
ABS bottom.
SKIRT: Neoprene-coated nylon fabric, 64 seg-
ments.
DIMENSIONS
Length: 2.90m

Scat 11 HP

Width: 1.83m
Height: 1.27m
WEIGHTS
Empty: 159kg
Payload, max: 136kg
PERFORMANCE
Speed, max: 30.5 knots (35mph)

Rise height: 20cm
Sea state capability: 0.6m
Stopping distance: 18m from 30.5 knots
Fuel consumption: 5.68 litres/h
Sound level, full throttle at 15.25m: 80dBA
PRICE
November 1987: Under US $5000

SCAT HP

Of similar form to Scat 11, the Scat HP is a higher performance model and differs in the following respects:

LIFT AND PROPULSION: A 42hp Cuyana 2-cylinder, 2-stroke engine. If requested a 52 hp, 500cc Rotax engine can be fitted.
CONTROLS: Four rudders
WEIGHTS
Empty: 180kg
Payload, max: 180kg (over land)
PERFORMANCE
Speed, max: 39 knots (72km/h)
Fuel consumption: 7.57 litres/h
INSTRUMENTS
Tachometer, voltmeter, hourmeter, cylinder head temperature.

SCAT HP 12

LIFT AND PROPULSION: A 52hp Rotax engine, electric starting. Six-blade fan.
CONTROLS: Four rudders
HULL: Injection, foam-filled, one piece ABS plastic.
SKIRT: Neoprene-coated nylon fabric
DIMENSIONS
Length: 3.67m
Width: 1.83m
Height: 1.27m
WEIGHTS
Empty: 230kg
Payload, max: 340kg (over land)
PERFORMANCE
Speed, max: 39 knots (45mph)
Rise height: 15 to 20cm
Sea state capability: 0.6m chop
Fuel consumption: 11.4 litres/h
INSTRUMENTS
Tachometer, voltmeter, hourmeter, cylinder head temperature

NX14 STREAK

A new Scat Hovercraft design for a multi-purpose 5-seat hovercraft.
PRINCIPAL PARTICULARS
Hull: all composite fiberglass construction
Colour: white
Length: 4.27m
Width: 2.44m
Weight: 998 kg (craft only)
Maximum speed: 39 knots (72 km/h)
Maximum payload (person): 5
Maximum payload weight: 544 kg
Lighting: bow & stern
Starter: electric
Instruments: tachometer, voltmeter, hourmeter, cylinder head temperature
Handrails: polished stainless steel
Electrical system: magneto and battery
Thrust engine: 532 liquid cooled Rotax, 2 cycle, 2 cylinder

Scat 11 HP jumping wave crests

Scat HP 12

Maximum power: 47.7kW (64 hp) at 6500 rpm thrust variable-pitch fan, 30kW (40 hp) lift fan
Fuel capacity: 114 l
Fuel consumption: 15.1 l/h per hour
Skirts: individual neoprene-coated nylon
Hover height: 30.5 cm
Wave capabilities: 1m chop maximum

Available in 2 standard configurations, a working platform with standard tie downs for cargo applications and with an enclosed canopy and passenger compartment with optional heating and air conditioning.

Full rescue outfitting available upon request, factory 4-day training required.

SEVTEC INC

PO Box 846, Monroe, Washington 98272, USA

Telephone: (206) 794 7505

Barry Palmer, *Owner*

Sevtec Inc was formed to research and market hovercraft technology. Emphasis has been placed on low operating costs and low noise levels for these craft. Consulting services are available and a home construction programme for hovercraft ranging from a 7hp one-seat craft, a four-seat 40hp craft through to an 80hp eight-seat craft.

The 18hp, two-seat prototype for the home builders' programme is a distillation of design efforts over the past 15 years in which prototypes from a 4hp vehicle capable of going over still deep water, still air hump drag conditions with 72.5kg aboard to a 56hp craft are capable of successfully carrying 8 adults.

The prototype homebuilder's programme specifications are:
Length: 4.24m
Width: 1.83m
Power: Briggs and Stratton 18hp at 3600rpm (13.23kW)
Empty weight: 175kg
Normal payload: 168kg
Max payload over hump: 227kg
Top speed, smooth water: 48km/h
Fuel consumption, 39km/h cruise: 5.3 litres/h
All specifications are for still deep water, still air.

A direct-drive 0.66m diameter, six-blade lift fan is located directly under the engine, and a Vee-belt drive turned through a right angle is used to drive, via a pair of idlers, an aluminium 0.122m diameter two-blade propeller.

The ducted propeller version of the craft has been abandoned in favour of the wire-guarded, open propeller version for improvement in both handling and straight line performance.

The hull of the four-seat craft is a 61cm stretch of the basic hull and craft empty weight is about the same as the prototype due to the replacement of the 18hp industrial engine with a lightweight snowmobile engine. Maximum planeout payload weight is expected to be over 364kg and top speed well over 64km/h. Essential parts kits consisting of rotors, drive components and skirt material are available from Sevtec Inc.

Hull construction is of wood with foam positive flotation. Glassfibre covers both sides of the wood in areas where moisture absorption or rot can cause damage and the deck is covered with aircraft fabric, providing a structure that can be stored outdoors.

The skirt is of 745g/m² vinyl, formulated for cold weather use and bonded together with vinyl contact cement. Skirt configuration is similar to the bag type except that two curtain type skirts cross the craft at the bow and about 30% behind the bow, compartmenting the 6.7m² base area into 1.67m² and 5.0m² fore and aft cushions. Forward cushion pressure can be controlled from the operator's position to aid in stopping and turning the craft. Foam flotation is placed on the skirt so that, together with a good drain system, skirt water purge problems normally associated with bag type skirts have been eliminated.

Propellers and fans can be built of wood by the homebuilder or purchased in aluminium from Sevtec Inc. A 61cm lift fan and 122cm 2-blade propeller (ducted) are used on machines of 7 to 18hp and 76cm lift fan and 152cm 2-blade propeller are used on the machines above 18hp.

A larger version of the basic 18hp craft has been built as a home construction project entirely from Sevtec plans. Performance was as predicted despite the fact that no prototype was built. The craft is a 4/3 scaled-up version of the basic 18hp craft hull, with automotive engine mounted above the deck. The hull is of composite foam and polyester resin-fibreglass construction. Vee-belt drives are used to drive the rotors. A single 0.96m dia-

New twin-propeller Sevtec craft

meter twelve-blade aluminium axial-flow fan, which is located aft, directly under the engine, provides cushion air, while a pair of 1.52m diameter two-blade aluminium propellers provide thrust.

PRINCIPAL PARTICULARS
Length: 5.65m
Width: 2.44m

Engine: Datsun 1600cc, 66hp (84.3kW) at 3900rpm max, geared to rotors
Empty weight: 495kg
Normal, max payload: 518kg (6 persons)
Top speed, smooth water: 39 knots (72km/h)
Fuel consumption at 56km/h, 3300rpm, normal cruise: 12.2 litres/h

---

UNIVERSAL HOVERCRAFT

1204 3rd Street South, Box 281, Cordova, Illinois 61242, USA

Telephone: (309) 654 2588

R J Windt, *Director*

Formed in 1969, this company has designed and built over 80 different sports and utility ACV prototypes, ranging from an ultra-light single-seater to the 12-seat UH-26S powered by a 225hp automotive engine. Plans for some of these designs are available to homebuilders. The company has developed three new single-engined amphibious craft: a 3.65m two-seater, a 3.96m (13ft) four-seater and a 5.48m six-seater.

Work has also been undertaken on air cushion vehicles propelled by waterjets, outboard motors and sails.

Descriptions of the UH-10C, UH-11S and UH-11T will be found in *Jane's Surface Skimmers 1980* and earlier editions.

Numerous craft have been built by this company and details of craft types UH-10T through to UH-18T can be found in the 1989 and earlier editions of this book.

UH-19P

This new design is similar to the UH-15P but is larger. It has slightly less stability in roll than a craft with a rectangular hull, but has greater pitch stability and lower drag, giving it higher speeds. Seating is three in the front and two in the aft of the open cockpit. With an enclosed cabin the craft can attain 90mph across ice and snow. Construction time is approximately 200 to 350 hours. Cost is between US $1000 to $2000 (1984).

The craft has been employed in attempts to establish a new water craft speed record between New Orleans and St Louis, a distance of 1027 miles along the Mississippi.

Two attempts had been made up to November 1984 on the present record of 23 hours 9 minutes. One was foiled by a storm which damaged the craft, the second was completed in 25 hours. Difficulties encountered on the journey are rough water created by up to 150 barges encountered, each creating several miles of rough water; bad weather and the avoidance of obstacles at night.

UH-19P

Further attempts were to be made during the summer of 1985.

LIFT AND PROPULSION: Motive power for the lift system is provided by an 18hp Briggs & Stratton vertical shaft mower engine driving an

axial fan. Thrust is supplied by almost any automobile engine of up to 1600cc, weighing less than 300lb. The craft would still be very fast with the smaller 1100cc Datsun and Toyota engines.

DIMENSIONS
Length: 5.91m
Width: 2.28m
WEIGHTS
Empty: 424kg
Payload: 454kg
PERFORMANCE
Max speed, ice and snow, with closed cabin: 144km/h
Max speed, calm water: 128km/h
Max gradient capability: 30°-45°
Clearance height: 0.2m

UH-19S

This is a single-engine version of the UH-19P. The fan axis is set at 45 degrees to the horizontal and is driven by a variable automatic lift system similar to that used in the UH-18S. The engine is a Chevrolet Citation type of about 115hp. Estimated maximum speed is 144km/h cruise 112km/h.

In 1985 this craft was used to set a speed record on the Mississippi from New Orleans to St Louis in 21 hours 47 minutes, beating the old record by 1 hour 22 minutes.

UH-26S

This 12- to 16-seat ACV is the largest homebuilt craft available. Ribs and stringers are in fir and pine and covered with a 6.3mm plywood skin. The

UH-19P

driver's seat is placed high and forward for good visibility. The passenger compartment can seat 16 or eight plus 544kg of cargo. The craft may also be equipped for touring with sleeping space for four to seven persons. In the hands of its designer, Bob Windt, the UH-26S completed a 4409km trip from Cordova, Illinois to New Orleans, Louisiana and back in three weeks.

LIFT AND PROPULSION: Integrated system. Power supplied by a standard V-8 283–400in³ automobile engine driving a 1.06m diameter, four-bladed fan for lift and a 2.43m diameter two-bladed propeller for thrust. Maximum recommended installed power is 225hp.

The lift fan is driven off the pulley end of the engine, employing a double Auto-lift system, drive shaft and right-angle drive gearbox. The two-bladed propeller is belt-driven from the flywheel end of the engine.

DIMENSIONS
Length: 7.92m
Width: 3.65m
Hoverheight: 0.35m
WEIGHTS
Empty: 1134kg
Payload: 1134kg
Max weight capacity: 1359kg
PERFORMANCE
Max speed, over land: 105km/h
    over water: 89km/h
Max gradient: 25%

Bob Windt and Mike Kiester at speed in the UH-19S, a modified UH-19P

UH-26S

LOW-SPEED
AIR CUSHION PLATFORMS
CANADA

VITRI ROBOTS AND VEHICLES INC (VRV)

238 De Brullon Street, Boucherville, Quebec J4B 2J8, Canada

Telephone: (514) 641 3914
Telex: (Via USA) 750 846
Telefax: (514) 397 9496

Pierre F Alepin, *President*

Please see ACV Builders section for background on company and VRV air cushion vehicles and trailers.

AEROBAC TRAILER (DESIGN)

Muskeg type tracked vehicles have light footprint pressure allowing them to move over marshes and other waterlogged terrains typical of the northern regions of Canada. An air cushion trailer will permit an increase in cargo load without an increase in tractor footprint pressure thus reducing surface damage. The trailer is equipped with wheels, able to carry the full load of the trailer, and is attached to the tractor with a fifth-wheel pin, as on conventional road equipment.

AT-20 TRAILER (DESIGN)

Length: 15m (17.5m to pin)
Width: 6m (reduced to 3m on-road)
Payload: 20 tonnes
Weight: 35 tonnes
Engine: Detroit 8V-92TA
Power: 310kW
Cushion pressure, max: 5kPa
Fans: Two VIM HCHB-050
Total flow: 36m³/s (at 6kPa)

AT-10 TRAILER (DESIGN)

Length: 12m (14.5m to pin)
Width: 4.6m (reduced to 2.6m on-road)
Payload: 10 tonnes
Weight: 20 tonnes
Engine: Detroit 6V-92TA
Power: 230kW
Cushion pressure, max: 5kPa
Fans: Two VIM HCHB-040
Total flow: 25m³/s (at 6kPa)

AT-5 TRAILER (DESIGN)

Length: 9m (11.5m to pin)

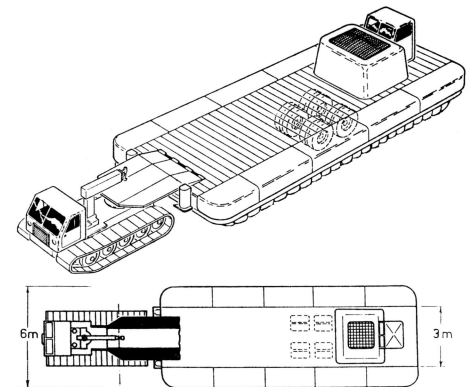

Aerobac AT-20 hybrid trailer design for 20-tonne payload

Width: 3.5m (reduced to 2.6m on-road)
Payload: 5 tonnes
Weight: 11 tonnes
Engine: Deutz (KHD) BF6L 413F
Power: 160kW
Cushion pressure, max: 5kPa
Fans: Two VIM HCHB-031
Total flow: 18m³/s (at 6kPa)

CHINA, PEOPLE'S REPUBLIC

HEILONGJIANG RESEARCH INSTITUTE OF WATER TRANSPORT SCIENCE

12 Dong Dazhi, Harbin, People's Republic of China

Telephone: Harbin 38151/38081

Zhang Li, *President*

Two air cushion barges, converted from 300-ton deck barges, have been supplied to the Ministry of Communications. Between May 1981 and June 1982, they carried 6000 tonnes of cargo, travelled

A Heilongjiang air cushion barge on the Songhua River.

24 000km and during trials recorded fuel savings, compared with conventional barges, of 20 to 30 per cent.

CHARACTERISTICS

The Heilongjiang air cushion barge employs an air cushion in order to reduce skin friction resistance. The air cushion takes the form of a layer of air, supplied by a blower and maintained beneath the hull by longitudinal side walls extending below the under surface of the barge and similarly, by lateral boundary walls beneath the bow and stern. The layer of air is trapped and once supplied by the blower only requires additional air supply in the event of wave disturbances causing a loss of air to occur. The wetted area of the air cushion barge is about 30 to 35% of a conventional barge.

The reduction in resistance is of the order of 27 to 38% at normal service speed. Other advantages include easier re-floating of the vessel after standing in silted channels (over supply of air enabling silt to be blown away) and a reduction in the amount of marine fouling that may occur.

Chinese Patent No. CN 87 202204 has been granted for the invention. Two 200–300 tonne and two 600 tonne air cushion barges are now in use on the Songhua River. It has been found that the lower the Froude Number, the higher is the reduction in resistance.

Reference: The Developed Heilongjiang Air Cushion Barges by Applying the Principle of Air Cushion for Reducing Resistance. by Fan Hongji, Heilongjiang Research Institute of Water-transport Science, International High-Performance Vehicle Conference, 2–5 November 1988, Shanghai, China.

MARINE DESIGN AND RESEARCH INSTITUTE OF CHINA (MARIC)

346 Sichuanzhong Road, Central, PO Box 002–053, Shanghai, People's Republic of China

Telephone: Shanghai 3215044
Telex: 33029MARIC CN
Cable: 5456 Shanghai

Prof Su Ba-Ying, *Director*
Prof Yun Liang, *Deputy Chief Naval Architect*

DONGFENG SHIPYARD
Hangzhou

Jiuxi, Hangzhou, Zhejiang, People's Republic of China

Telephone: Hangzhou 62904
Cable: Hangzhou 0009

TYPE 7301

Designed by MARIC, the air cushion platform Type 7301 was completed in Dongfeng Shipyard in May 1987. The craft will undergo oil field trials and evaluation, operating in both offshore and onshore areas for transporting workers and equipment.

MARIC Type 7301 platform

A Deutz F4L912 air-cooled diesel engine provides auxiliary power, driving a 24kW generator. Four 2m³ ballast tanks are positioned at the corners of the hull for trimming the platform.

HULL: Main hull is built in welded marine steel construction, the superstructure is of aluminium alloy construction.

LIFT AND PROPULSION: Two Henun Diesel Type 12V180 four-stroke, water-cooled, turbocharged marine diesel engines rated at 590kW at 1500rpm, driving two twin-air-inlet 1.4m diameter type G4–73–11 centrifugal fans (steel) and two ducted 3m diameter air propellers.

The blades are constructed in grp with foam plastic core. Stainless steel sheaths protect the leading edges. Maximum static thrust 2499kg.

CONTROLS: Directional control is by two sets of twin vertical aerodynamic rudders mounted on the rear of the propeller ducts.

DIMENSIONS
Length overall, on cushion: 19.20m
Beam overall, on cushion: 12.20m
Height overall, on cushion: 6.90m
Length, rigid structure: 17.2m
Beam, rigid structure: 10.2
Depth, moulded: 1.1m
Length, cushion: 17.0m

MARIC-designed Type 7301 air cushion platform built at the Dongfeng yard. An anti-spray skirt is fitted

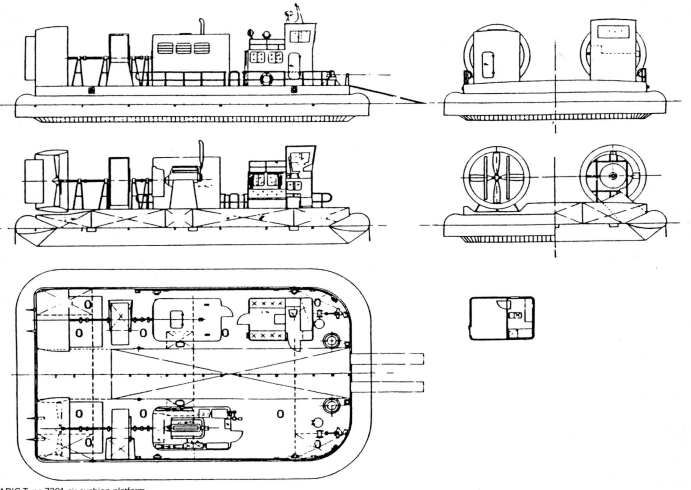

MARIC Type 7301 air cushion platform

Beam, cushion: 10.0m
Draught, average, on cushion: 0.50m
    off cushion: 0.61m
WEIGHTS
Max weight: 80 tons

Max Payload: 35 tonnes
CUSHION PRESSURE
5000 Pa (104.4lb/ft²)
PERFORMANCE
Max calm water speed: 10km/h, 6 knots

Max ground speed: 10–20km/h
Endurance: 6 hours
Obstacle clearance: 0.8m at 10 knots
Ditch crossing, water filled: 15m wide, 0.7m deep
Wind and wave limits: 8.6m/s, 1.0m

FINLAND

OY WÄRTSILÄ AB
(Please see entry under Air Cushion Vehicles
Section)

This company is no longer engaged in low speed
air cushion platform developments.

UNION OF SOVIET SOCIALIST REPUBLICS

ALL-UNION OIL MACHINERY RESEARCH INSTITUTE, WEST SIBERIA

This organisation was responsible for some of the
earlier developments of air cushion platforms in
the USSR. Details of these can be found in the
1989 edition of book.

LENINGRAD CENTRAL DESIGN & PROJECT BUREAU (LCPKB) MINISTRY OF MERCHANT MARINE OF THE USSR

Krasnoy Konnitsy Str 6, 193015, Leningrad,
USSR

V J Peresypkin, *Director*

Telex: 121558 CPKB SU

In a paper given to the Canadian Air Cushion
Technology Society in Montreal, September 1987
written by S V Yakonovsky, Chief Designer of
the Leningrad Central Design and Project Bureau,
details were given of a number of ACV lightering
barges. In the late 1970s and early 1980s the Ministry of Merchant Marine ordered 18 hoverbarges,
four built in the USSR to the designs of the
LCPKB and 14 designed and built by Wärtsilä in
Finland which purchased a licence for the design
and construction of hoverbarges using LCPKB

documentation. The various designs are similar,
fan location being the main difference.

PROJECT 10352
The following description is an extract from the
above mentioned paper:

    The hoverbarge is a towed pontoon with a skirt
attached along its perimeter, the powerplant and
control station being arranged aft. The midship
and fore parts of the deck remain free and are
used for the carriage of cargo. Cargo to be trans-

ported on the marine hoverbarge can be up to 12m long, 8.1m wide and up to 35 tonnes, as well as vehicles, containers and bulk cargo.

The service area is restricted to area of navigation III (according to the Rules of the USSR Register of Shipping). The barge may proceed not more than 10 miles from the shore or the ship at Sea State up to 4. Stability meets the requirements of the USSR Register Rules.

The marine hoverbarge remains afloat with any one compartment flooded.

The skirt may be of two types: bag or segmented. Attached to the external surface of the skirt is an apron. The skirt material is a rubberised fabric which is frost-resistant down to −40°C. The barge has an all-welded hull with longitudinal framing, the thickness of sides and bottom is 3mm, of deck 4mm, with local thicknesses increased to 6mm.

Anchor arrangements consist of one high-holding-power anchor of 100kg weight and a special mooring capstan with electrical and manual drives.

Mooring and towing arrangements include four mooring bollards installed in the bulwark in the hull corners, two mooring capstans in the forward part and two towing eyebolts welded into the deck. A ramp is constructed as four separate girders each 320 × 3700mm in size and of 132kg weight with a permissible concentrated load of 40kN.

Life-saving appliances include 6-man liferaft in a container with a launching device and individual life-saving appliances.

The powerplant consists of a 220kW, four-cycle, non-reversible V-engine driving through a jaw clutch a centrifugal lift-air supply fan having a capacity of 33m³/s at a pressure of 0.0054MPa, and an AC diesel-generator with a power output of 20kW.

Provision is made for a ballast (heeling) system and a water fire-main system serviced by an electrically driven pump having a capacity of 10m³/h at a head of 40mwg.

The barge is non-self-propelled. Special towing means are used for its water and land surface movement.

The craft is to be carried on board and thus be compatible with the existing ships. Therefore due to the limitations of the barge dimensions and mass, the development of a self-propelled ACV would result in a reduction of payload and hence impair economic indices.

Operation of hoverbarges under real conditions of the Arctic began in 1980. Initially non-amphibious towing vehicles had been employed, namely 70kW tug boats for towing in water and land tractors of the same power for overground movement. In so doing, two or more tractors have been required to overcome slopes of more than 4–5°. Such operational schemes, however, do not permit the full realisation of all the advantages of the hoverbarge as an amphibious craft. The transfer of the towing rope from the tug boat to the tractor and vice versa involves delays and it is inconvenient to operate with two or more tractors simultaneously.

In this connection, a need appeared to create a special amphibious towing vehicle to tow a hoverbarge from the ship to the storehouse. Using running gear of one of the tracked vehicles as a basis, a design was developed and three amphibious towing vehicles were constructed in 1981–82.

The main requirements for a new amphibious towing vehicle are: pressure on the ground not in excess of 0.4kg/cm²; slope to be overcome with a towed hoverbarge of about 80 tonnes at a speed of 1.5–2.0km/h, up to 15°; maximum speed of hoverbarge towing in water, 5.0 knots; fuel endurance, about 24 hours; restricted area of navigation with a distance from the shore or a ship equal to 10 miles; operation is to be ensured in ambient air temperatures from −25°C to 35°C, and of water from −1°C to 20°C; winter stay at temperatures

Main particulars of marine hoverbarges built in the USSR

	Project 10351	Project 10352
Length overall		
in displacement mode	19.85m	18.29m
on air cushion, with bag skirt	19.95m	18.41m
Breadth, extreme		
in displacement mode	9.20m	9.10m
on air cushion, with bag skirt	9.20m	9.91m
on air cushion, with segmented skirt	—	9.91m
Depth	1.00m	1.10m
Draught, design	0.64m	0.66m
Displacement, full-loaded	71.80 tonnes	74.70 tonnes
Displacement, light	40.50 tonnes	38.00 tonnes
		Cargo areas
length	8.80m	12.00m
breadth	8.10m	8.10m
Clearance height	0.70m	0.55m
Air cushion pressure	4860Pa	4860Pa
	(495kg/m²)	(495kg/m²)
Air cushion area	146m²	151m²
Air cushion pattern	one-chamber	two-chamber
Payload	28.4 tonnes	35.00 tonnes
Crew	2	2
Gross tonnage	47.20	36.00

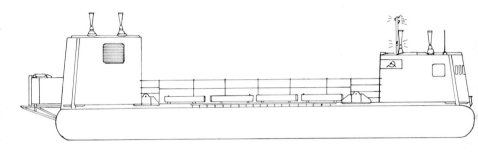

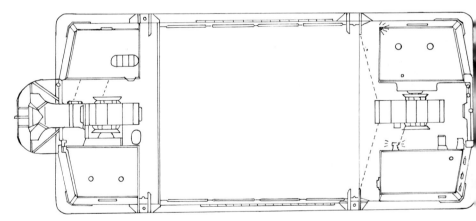

Project 10351 marine hoverbarge

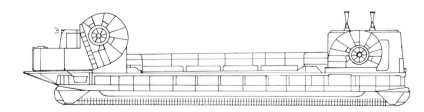

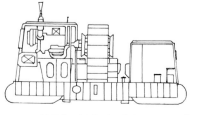

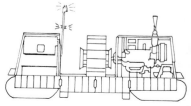

Project 10351 longitudinal and transverse sections

down to −50°C; provision is to be made for a towing winch with a pull of about 350kN (35 tonnes) and a drum having a capacity of about 100m of wire rope.

Main particulars of amphibious towing vehicle
Length, design11.80m Breadth: 3.90m
Depth: 2.14m
Draught: 1.10m
Displacement, full-load: 27.40 tonnes
Displacement, light: 25.00 tonnes
Main engine: Diesel engine
Engine output: 280kW (380hp)
Number of propellers: 2
Number of gears: 3
Speed
    in water: About 5 knots
    over land: About 30.0km/h
Bollard pull: 24.5kN (25 tonnes)
Pull when moved over land surface using first gear
    (at a speed about 5km/h: 122.2kN (12.5 tonnes)

LAISKI SHIPYARD
MPVP-40

During 1977–80, the Leningrad Central Design Bureau, in conjunction with the Northern Shipping Line, undertook a research and development programme for the construction of a 40-tonne capacity seagoing hoverbarge to be employed as a lighter at landing points along the Northern Sea Route between Murmansk and Uelen.

Designated MPVP-40, the craft is intended to operate in conditions up to Sea State 4. Under normal conditions the craft is towed by tugs over water and by tractors over land. Provision has been made, however, for the craft to be propelled independently by air expelled through thrust nozzles which can be fitted aft of the fan casings. These provide a speed of 2.5 knots over calm water and ice and permit the craft to operate over stretches of shallow water.

The craft were to be produced at several Soviet shipyards and were intended primarily for operation from SA-15 type 20 000dwt, arctic multipurpose icebreaking cargo vessels, 28 of which are under construction for Soviet shipping operators at yards in Finland and the Soviet Union. Each is designed to carry two MPVP-40s or its Finnish-built counterpart, the TAV 40.

LIFT: Cushion air is supplied by a single 600hp (441kW) V2–800TK-S3 marine diesel driving, via a reduction gear, two VTsD-II fans, each of 1800m³/minute capacity. The engine compartment contains the essential accessories and pumps as well as a dc generator. Also included in the power pack are a PZhD-600 preheater and VTI-4 air filters. Engine cooling is of closed type, with radiator. Rotor of the VTsD-II fan, which is 1.1m in diameter and develops 5KPa static pressure, is built in welded stainless steel. Blades are in hollow stainless steel filled with foam plastic.

Fan transmission comprises a flexible coupling, friction clutch, reduction gear, neck bush and three jointed shafts.

CONTROLS: Rotating thrust ports control craft direction when operating independently of tugs and tractors. Twin metal wheels keep the platform on course during towing at sea or over ground.

HULL: Ribbed, carbon steel structure. Cargo deck and side plates, 4mm thick; deck and bottom, 3mm thick. Hull divided into three watertight compartments. The craft will remain afloat in the event of any one compartment flooding.

The engineer's cabin is on the port side in line with the engine. On the starboard side are the battery box and a heater used to preheat the lubricant and the liquid coolant during cold weather. A demountable signal mast is installed above the engineer's cabin. A deflection system protects the fan housing against spray. Both sides of the platform are enclosed by rope railings. At the bow are anchor and ramp equipment, bollards, cable chocks, and mallets and pulleys for moving the

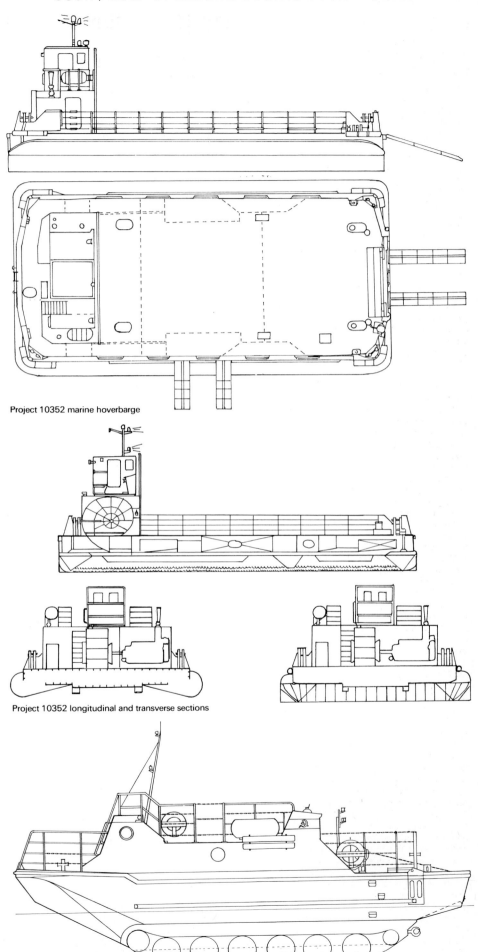

Project 10352 marine hoverbarge

Project 10352 longitudinal and transverse sections

Amphibious towing vehicle for marine hoverbarges

load on the deck. The platform is equipped with a 50kg Matrosov anchor, two hand windlasses for weighing the anchor, lifting and lowering the ramps, and for mooring. Four separate ramps are fitted for cargo transhipment as well as the loading and offloading of wheeled and tracked vehicles.

SKIRT: Fingered bag type with transverse stability trunk and longitudinal stability keel in rear section. Cushion area, 14m².

DIMENSIONS
Length: 20.2m
Deck width: 8.5m
Structure height: 1m
Designed draught: 0.64m

WEIGHTS
Empty: 29 tonnes
Loaded: 69 tonnes

PERFORMANCE
Cruising endurance: 24 hours
Max permissible Sea State: 4
Max speed, independent air-jet propulsion: 2.5 knots

MPVP-40 hover platform under tow

MPVP-40

MARIJSKI POLYTECHNIC

3, Lenin Square, Yoshkar Ola, Mari, USSR
S. F. Kirkin, *Scientific Head.*

SWAMP ROVER

A 14 tonne payload self-propelled hover platform designed by Yuri Okhotin of the Marijski Polytechnic for steel pipe transport in the oil and gas fields of West Siberia.

The MARI Polytechnic Swamp Rover

NEPTUN CENTRAL DESIGN BUREAU

Moscow, USSR

BIZON 10 TONNE CAPACITY (SELF-PROPELLED)

A self-propelled air-cushion platform designed for ship-to-shore work and for push-towing of non self-propelled air-cushion platforms. The hull is built in steel; a two level forward cabin is built in aluminium. Propulsion is by two ducted air propellers.

The craft is built to the USSR Register of Shipping class.

Operating area is restricted to a distance of 10 miles from base or supply ship.

The craft may be operated in temperatures down to −40°C, in significant wave height up to 1 metre and in the event of flooding of one compartment is designed to float safely in conditions up to Sea State 4 and Beaufort wind 6.

DIMENSIONS
Length, overall: 19.70m
Length, Hull, rigid structure: 18.00m
Width, overall: 9.10m
Platform height: 0.90m
Rise height: 0.60m
Cargo deck area: 5m × 8m

WEIGHTS
Displacement, full load: 55 tonnes
Displacement, light: 42 tonnes
Disposable load: 10 tonnes

ENGINES
Two 294 kW diesels, (1600 rpm) four-stroke, high-speed, liquid cooled.
Service output: 220 kW at 1500 rpm.
Fuel consumption: 227 g/kWh.

PROPULSION
Two variable-pitch, 3m diameter, ducted propellers, driven via flexible pneumatic coupling, belt transmission (3 flat belts) and cardan shafts.

CONTROLS
Three rudders mounted on the propeller ducts plus air thruster unit at bowusing cushion air for low-speed manoeuvring.

PERFORMANCE
Speed, cruising: 5.5 knots (10.2 km/h)

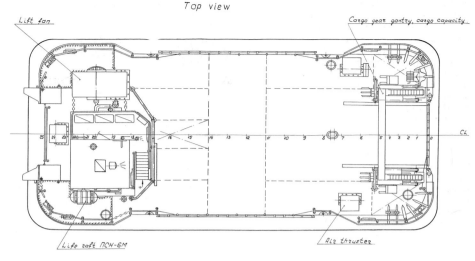

Top view

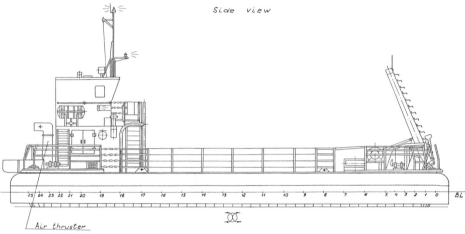

Side view

General arrangement of 20 tonne capacity non-self-propelled Bizon air-cushion platform

Speed, cruising, in a train with Bizon air cushion platform: 5 knots (9.3 km/h)
Endurance (at continuous rating): 10h

The Bizon 20 tonne capacity non-self-propelled air-cushion platform

BIZON 20 TONNE CAPACITY (NON-SELF PROPELLED)

A fully equipped non self-propelled air-cushion platform designed for ship to shore operation. The hull is built in steel; a two level aft cabin is built in aluminium.

The platform is built to the USSR Register of Shipping class.

Operating conditions are as for the 10 tonne capacity Bizon.

DIMENSIONS
Length, overall on cushion: 20.40m
Length, rigid hull: 18.00m
Width, overall, on cushion: 9.10m
Width, rigid hull: 8.00m
Platform height: 0.90m
Rise height: 0.60m
Cargo deck area: 12m × 8m

WEIGHTS
Displacement, full load: 57 tonnes
Displacement, light load: 34 tonnes
Carrying capacity: 20 to 25 tonnes

ENGINE
Lift fan is driven by a four-stroke high-speed diesel, liquid-cooled V-engine, 294 kW at 1600 rpm. Service output: 220 kW at 1500 rpm. Fuel consumption: 227 g/kWh.

CONTROLS
Two bow air-thrusters (cushion air discharge parts just above deck level).

The Bizon 10 tonne capacity self-propelled air-cushion platform

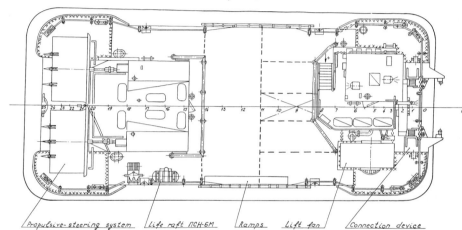

Top view

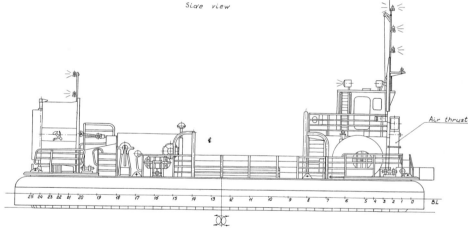

Side view

General arrangement of 10 tonne capacity self-propelled Bizon air-cushion platform

A Bizon 10 tonne capacity self-propelled air-cushion platform pushing a Bizon 20 tonne capacity platform in a ship-to-shore operation

UNITED STATES OF AMERICA

HOVER SYSTEMS INC

1500 Chester Pike, Eddystone, Pennsylvania 19013, USA

Telephone: (215) 876 8241
Easylink Telex: 62914561
Telefax: (215) 876 5902

James D Hake, *President*
Joseph J Nestel, *Executive Vice President*

D-PAAC AMPHIBIOUS BARGE

In 1980 the company designed and built D-PAAC, a 50-tonne payload, diesel-powered, air cushion amphibious barge. Propulsion is provided by a unique hydraulic drive unit operating a set of eight fully articulated wheels outboard of the air cushion. The wheel loading is controllable so that traction can be maintained over almost any terrain. Deep treads are provided on the wheels for traction over land and paddle wheels cantilevered laterally from the wheel hubs provide propulsion over water. This craft successfully completed a one-year test for the State of Alaska, Department of Transportation operating on the Kuskokwim River and adjacent areas.

During summer 1984 D-PAAC operated as successfully over open water as it had during winter conditions. The craft delivered fuel oil to Eskimo villages (12 000 gallons from internal tanks, pumped and metered to village storage tanks), together with lumber and construction material loaded on to the deck.

The average distance of a summer (or winter) voyage was over 200 miles, servicing four villages on three separate routes every three weeks. The average continuous hover time each trip was 28 hours, with no shutdowns or overnight stops.

The paddle wheels provide a speed equivalent to that of shallow-draught Alaskan river tug-barges. Two grounded barges and one tug were pulled to safety during the annual low river water period in August. The craft was subsequently sold to the US Army and is in service at Fort Belvoir, Virginia.

FF-3

A 46-tonne capacity air cushion platform, non-self-propelled.
POWERPLANT
Detroit Diesel 16V-71N
Fuel (5 hours): 1360kg
Fans: Alldays Peacock BA 1200 515W centrifugal
SKIRT
Depth: 1.22m
Cushion pressure: 10.29kN/m² (215lb/ft²)
DIMENSIONS
Length overall: 16.77m
Beam overall: 13.72m
Length, cushion: 13.41m
Beam, cushion: 10.37m
Cushion area: 131.83m²
Clear deck area: 127.7m²
WEIGHTS
Weight, empty: 93.35 tonnes
Payload, normal: 46 tonnes
Weight, max: 140 tonnes

D-PAAC underway on paddle wheels on Kuskokwim river, Alaska

D-PAAC operating in Alaska

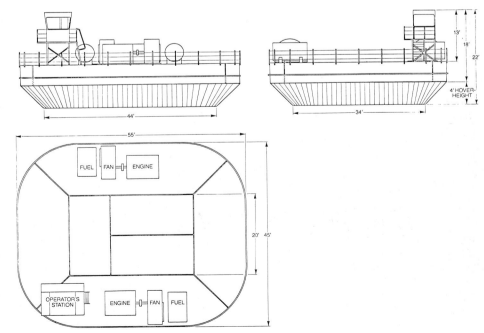
FF-3 46-tonne capacity air cushion platform

NEOTERIC HOVERCRAFT INC

1649 Tippecanoe Street, Terre Haute, Indiana, USA 47807

Telephone: (812) 234 1120
Telex: (812) 234 3217

HOVERLIFTER

Developed in 1988 the Neoteric Hoverlifter is an air cushion platform designed for carrying heavy loads over difficult surfaces where the avoidance of concentrated point loads is particularly important. Neoteric's first Hoverlifter was supplied to the Aluminium Company of America (ALCOA) for the specific purpose of carrying rooftop ventilation fans over roof top surfaces. Priced at US $35000 at the end of 1988, the Hoverlifter is capable of carrying a payload of 1000kg, with the cushion air supply being provided by a single centrifugal fan driven by a 24hp Onan T260G petrol engine. The platform is built in grp with polyurethane foam. There are eight lifting points. The underside is protected by a 1.9cm thick foam rubber coating.

Neoteric Hoverlifter during acceptance trials, 22 Nov 1988

Neoteric Hoverlifter showing load platform

A 1 tonne winch is provided on the platform, 12V electric, side winching of 1 tonne load can be accomplished over a 1 in 10 smooth ramp.

PRINCIPAL PARTICULARS

Length, hard structure: 5.55m
Width, hard structure: 3.00m
Height, off cushion: 1.47m
Load deck height, off cushion: 0.495m
Load deck, width and length: 1.63m × 2.44m
Engine: Onan T260G, 24hp, 17.9kW petrol
Fan: DWD1 0.622m diameter aluminium centrifugal fan, 9 blades
Fuel tank capacity: 22.7l (2h duration)
Weight, empty: 682kg
Payload capacity: 1545kg
Cushion pressure, with 1000kg payload: 112.3kg/m^2
Skirt: extended segment type, neoprene coated nylon, 0.39kg/m^2 (16oz/yd^2), 80 segments
Rise height: 23cm

HYDROFOILS

AUSTRALIA

CARRINGTON SLIPWAYS PTY LIMITED

Old Punt Road, Tomago, New South Wales 2322, Australia

Telephone: (049) 648071
Telex: 28185AA
Telefax: (049) 648316

D Laverick, *Managing Director*

RODRIQUEZ RHS 160F

An RHS 160F was to have been built by Carrington Slipways Pty Ltd under licence from Rodriquez Cantieri Navali SpA for service with the Urban Transit Authority of New South Wales. Two sister vessels, the *Manly* and the *Sydney* were delivered by the Italian yard in 1984 and 1985 respectively, total outfitting of *Manly* having been carried out by Carrington Slipways. These vessels seat 238 passengers. Please see the Rodriquez entry for details of the RHS 160F.

The 238-seat RHS-160F *Manly* (fitted out by Carrington Slipways Pty Ltd) passing the Sydney waterfront

BOLIVIA

HELMUT KOCK

44125 West Point Loma Blvd, Apartment 209, San Diego, California 92110, USA

Telephone: (619) 224 6657

Helmut Kock, designer of the Honald Albatross hydrofoil, which operated New York's first commercial hydrofoil service, and former chief engineer of International Hydrolines Inc, designed and built a 15.27m hydrofoil ferry for Crillon Tours of La Paz, Bolivia. The craft, the *Bolivia Arrow*, was built during 1976 at Huatajata, on the shore of Lake Titicaca (3700m) and entered service in February 1977.

All materials, equipment, engines, tools and machinery were imported from the USA. The entire craft is of welded aluminium and was built by Helmut Kock with the aid of a few Bolivian Indians who, in order to undertake the work, were taught how to use modern hand and electric tools and automatic welding techniques.

He has been responsible for modifying the three Sea World hydrofoils to improve their load capacity and performance.

ALBATROSS

Crillon Tours Ltd, La Paz, Bolivia, operates six of Helmut Kock's 20-seat Albatross craft on tourist routes across Lake Titicaca. The need to cope with increasing tourist traffic and to provide a craft capable of crossing the full length of the lake led to a decision by Darius Morgan, Crillon's chief executive, to build a craft tailored to the company's requirements on the shore of the lake. Construction of the first craft in Bolivia, *Bolivia Arrow*, began in December 1975 and it was launched in September 1976. The craft entered service in February 1977. It is designed for medium range fast ferry services on rivers, bays, lakes and sounds.
FOILS: Surface-piercing trapeze foil system with 'W' configuration pitch stability subfoil. Welded aluminium construction designed by Helmut Kock, US patent no 3, 651, 775.
POWERPLANT: Twin Cummins VT-8-370 diesels, each developing 350shp at sea level and oversize to compensate for loss of power due to altitude. Each engine drives its own propeller via

Bolivia Arrow showing foil system

Helmut Kock Albatross hydrofoil *Flecha Guarani* operating on Lake Itaipai, Paraguay   (Darius Morgan)

an inclined shaft. Engine room is amidships, after the third row of seats.
ACCOMMODATION: Crew comprises a captain, deckhand and a tourist guide. The captain is accommodated forward in a raised

wheelhouse. His seat is on the hull centreline with the wheel, engine controls and main instrumentation in front. Passengers are accommodated in a single saloon with seats for 40. Seats are arranged in ten rows of two abreast, separated by a central aisle. A washbasin/WC unit is provided and also a luggage compartment. All void spaces are filled with polyurethane foam.

DIMENSIONS
Length overall: 15.24m

Hull beam: 3.55m
Width across foils: 5.79m
Draught, hullborne: 2.28m
WEIGHT
Displacement fully loaded: 14 tons

PERFORMANCE
Cruising speed: 32 knots

INDIA

VENKATAPATHY ENGINEERING (PTE) LIMITED
151 Khadar Nawazkhan Road, PO Box No 4533, Madras 60006, India

Telephone: 471412
Telex: 418198COIN IN

Supramar Hydrofoils AG announced at the beginning of 1986 that Venkatapathy Engineering (Pte) Ltd had become a licensee for Supramar hydrofoil craft.

INDONESIA

PT PABRIK KAPAL INDONESIA (PERSERO) PT PAL INDONESIA

Head office: BPP Teknologi Building, 12th Floor, JL M H Thamrin No 8, Jakarta, Indonesia

Telephone: (21) 323774
Telefax: 31 22516
Telex: 61331ATP JKT

Works: Ujung Surabaya, PO Box 134, Indonesia

Telephone: 24139, 291403
Telex: 31223PAL SB

Prof Dr Ing B J Habibie, *President Director*
Suleman Wiriadidjaja, *Director of Technology*
Sukono, *Director of General Affairs*
Hariadi Soemarsono, *Director of Production*
Karsono, *Director of Maintenance*

M S M Harahap, *Assistant to President Director for Computers*
Pramono S, *Assistant to President Director for Programme*
Suparto S, *Assistant to President Director for Material*
Sunu Notodihardjo, *Assistant to President Director for Marketing*
Sion H S, *Assistant to President Director for Finance*
Parlin Napitupulu, *Assistant to President Director for Inspectorate*

With origins as a repair and maintenance facility for the navy in 1892, PT PAL now employs 6000 people, occupies an area of 150 hectares and has capacity for designing and building vessels from 60 tonnes to 30 000 tonnes.

Apart from the first Jetfoil 929–115 (*Bima Samudera I*) to be fitted out, two Jetfoil 929–119 were to be fitted out and later, two 929–120 models.

Bima Samudera I fitted out by PT Pabrik Kapal Indonesia

ISRAEL

ISRAEL SHIPYARDS LIMITED
This company is no longer actively engaged in the building of hydrofoil vessels; please see 1989 edition of this book for details of the two Grumman Flagstaff hydrofoil patrol craft built in 1982 and 1985.

ITALY

FINCANTIERI-CANTIERI NAVALI ITALIANI SpA
(Cantieri Navali Riuniti SpA was incorporated in Fincantieri in July 1984)
Head Office: Via Genova 1, I-34121 Trieste, Italy
Naval Shipbuilding Division: Via Cipro 11, 16129 Genoa, Italy

Telephone: (010)59951
Telex: 270168FINCGE I

Mario de Negri, *Naval Shipbuilding Division General Manager*
Franco Baracchini, *Technical Director*
Michele Diaz Satta, *Marketing & Sales Director*

The original Cantieri Navali Riuniti SpA took over the interests of Alinavi which was formed in

Three Sparviero hydrofoil missile craft at Fincantieri yard at Muggiano

1964 to develop, manufacture and market advanced military marine systems.

Under the terms of a licensing agreement, Fincantieri has access to Boeing technology in the field of military fully-submerged foil hydrofoil craft.

In October 1970, the company was awarded a contract by the Italian Navy for the design and construction of the P420 Sparviero hydrofoil missile craft. This is an improved version of the Boeing PGH-2 Tucumcari. The vessel, given the design name Sparviero, was delivered to the Italian Navy in July 1974. An order for a further six of this type was placed by the Italian Navy in February 1976.

Craft built	Commissioned
P420 Sparviero (class type)	1974
P421 *Nibbio*	1981
P422 *Falcone*	1982
P423 *Astore*	1982
P424 *Grifone*	1982
P425 *Gheppio*	1983
P426 *Condor*	1983

SPARVIERO

The Sparviero missile-launching hydrofoil gunboat displaces 60.5 tonnes and is designed for both offensive and defensive missions. Its combination of speed, firepower, and all-weather capability is unique in a ship of this class.

The vessel has fully-submerged foils arranged in canard configuration and an automatic control system. A gas-turbine powered waterjet system provides foilborne propulsion and a diesel-driven propeller outdrive provides hullborne propulsion. A typical crew comprises two officers and eight enlisted men.

Sparviero's advanced automatic control system considerably reduces the vertical and transverse acceleration normally experienced in rough seas. In Sea State 4 the maximum vertical acceleration likely to be found is in the order of 0.25g (rms), while the maximum roll angle is not likely to be greater than ±2 degrees.

In the lower Sea States Sparviero class hydrofoils have a maximum continuous speed of 44 knots, decreasing to 40 knots in Sea State 4.

P420 Sparviero

Turning radius of Sparviero hydrofoils at 40 knots is under 125m

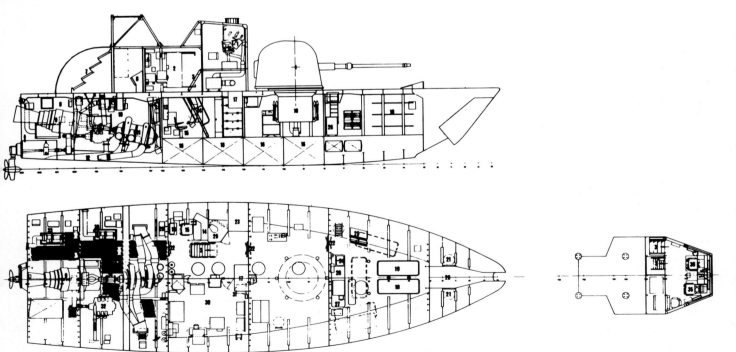

Inboard profile and deck plan of Sparverio: **(1)** helm/main control console **(2)** combat operations centre (COC) door **(3)** companionway ladders **(4)** COC electric power distribution panel **(5)** COC **(6)** air intake forward machinery room **(7)** filtering panels for combustion air **(8)** aft machinery room **(9)** gas turbine engine: foilborne propulsion **(10)** forward machinery room **(11)** waterjet pump **(12)** waterjet nozzle (P/S) **(13)** main electrical power distribution panel **(14)** engineer's console **(15)** engineer's station **(16)** fuel oil tanks **(17)** automatic control system **(18)** cannon revolving feeding machine **(19)** crew berths **(20)** forward hydrofoil retraction well **(21)** rope locker (P/S) **(22)** watertight doors **(23)** galley stores locker **(24)** lavatory **(25)** crew lockers **(26)** refrigerator **(27)** folding mess table with benches **(28)** main electrical switchboard **(29)** water closet **(30)** electronic equipment bay **(31)** gyrocompass **(32)** diesel engine: hullborne (unmanned) propulsion **(33)** turbine generator set **(34)** pump drive coupling **(35)** conning station **(36)** helm station

FOILS: Fully-submerged canard arrangement, with approximately one-third of the dynamic lift provided by the bow foil and two-thirds by the two aft foils. The aft foils retract sideways and the bow foil retracts forwards into a recess in the bow. Bow doors preserve the hull lines when the forward hydrofoil is either fully extended or retracted. Foils and struts are built in high resistance stainless steel.

Anhedral is incorporated in the aft foils to enhance the directional stability of the craft at shallow foil depths. In addition, the anhedral assures positive roll control by eliminating tip broaching during rough water manoeuvres.

CONTROLS: Automatic system incorporating two aircraft-type gyros, one to sense pitch and roll and the other to sense yaw, plus three accelerometers to sense vertical movements (heave) of the craft. Ultrasonic height sensors detect and maintain flying height above the water surface. Information from the sensors is sent to a hermetically-sealed solid-state computer, which calculates movement of the control surfaces necessary to maintain boat stability and/or preselected flying height, and sends appropriate commands to the servo-mechanisms that control trailing edge flaps on bow and stern foils.

FOILBORNE STEERING: Helm-commanded automatic control system controls hydraulic servo-actuated hydrofoil flaps and steerable forward hydrofoil strut to produce co-ordinated (banked) turns in design sea conditions. Forward foil strut is steerable through 10 degrees, port and starboard.

HULLBORNE STEERING: Helm-commanded steerable retractable outdrive unit driven by 160hp Isotta Fraschini diesel via toothed belt transmission. Outdrive unit can be steered through 360 degrees for maximum manoeuvrability when

P421 *Nibbio*

hullborne. Manual emergency hullborne steering is provided on the aft deck.

HULL: Hull and superstructure are built in corrosion-resistant aluminium, the hull being welded and the superstructure riveted and welded.

ACCOMMODATION: Ten berths are provided in the forward crew space. One toilet and one sink. A folding table with benches in the forward crew space.

POWERPLANT, FOILBORNE: Power for the waterjet is supplied by one 4500shp Rolls-Royce Proteus 15M/553 gas turbine.

Engine output is transferred to a single double-volute, double-suction, two impeller centrifugal pump. Water is taken in through inlets on the nose of each aft foil at the foil/strut intersection and passes up through the hollow interiors of the

struts to the hull, where it is ducted to the pump. From the pump, the water is discharged through twin, fixed-area nozzles located beneath the hull under the pump.

POWERPLANT, HULLBORNE: An Isotta Fraschini ID 38 6VN marine diesel drives via a toothed belt a steerable propeller outdrive unit, which is mounted on the centreline of the transom. The unit is retractable and rotates through 360 degrees. Propeller is fixed-pitch. Continuous speed, hullborne, is 8 knots.

APUs: Two, each comprising a 150hp Solar T-62-T-32 gas turbine driving one 208V 400Hz three-phase 75kVA alternator, one 30V dc 200A starter generator and one hydraulic pump for ships services.

Craft may be refuelled through main deck con-

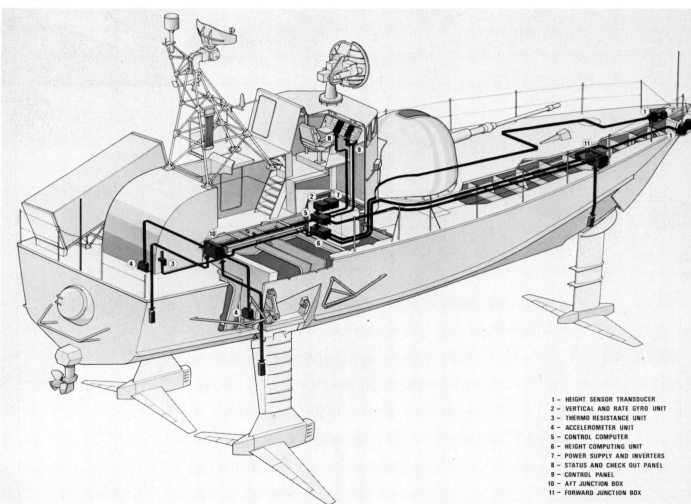

1 – HEIGHT SENSOR TRANSDUCER
2 – VERTICAL AND RATE GYRO UNIT
3 – THERMO RESISTANCE UNIT
4 – ACCELEROMETER UNIT
5 – CONTROL COMPUTER
6 – HEIGHT COMPUTING UNIT
7 – POWER SUPPLY AND INVERTERS
8 – STATUS AND CHECK OUT PANEL
9 – CONTROL PANEL
10 – AFT JUNCTION BOX
11 – FORWARD JUNCTION BOX

EPA (Società de Elettronica per l'Automazione SpA) Automatic Attitude Control System (SEPA AN 700) as fitted to Sparviero class hydrofoil craft

nection at dock or at sea. The fuel tanks are equipped with fuel level indicators and vents.
ARMAMENT: A typical military payload consists of:
   one dual purpose 76mm/62-calibre automatic OTO Melara gun and 110 rounds of ammunition
   two fixed missile launchers and two ship-to-ship missiles, eg Sea Killers, Otomat or Exocet
   one Elsag NA 10 mod, 3 fire-control system
   one Orion 10X tracking radar
   one SMA MM SPQ 701 search and navigation radar
   A variety of other payloads may be carried according to customer needs.
FIRE CONTROL SYSTEM: SPG 73 tracking radar, SXG 75 low light level tv and 2AC50C console. Console includes tv monitor and 12in PPI screen for search radar video presentation.
DIMENSIONS
Length overall: 22.95m
   foils retracted: 24.6m
Width across foils: 10.8m
Deck beam, max: 7m
WEIGHT
Max displacement: 60.5 tonnes
PERFORMANCE
   Exact craft performance characteristics depend on the customer's choice of foilborne gas turbine and operating conditions which can affect the quantity of fuel carried. Performance figures shown below, therefore, are representative.
Foilborne intermittent speed in calm water: 50 knots

P422 *Falcone*

continuous speed in calm water: 44 knots
continuous speed in Sea State 4: 38/40 knots
Hullborne continuous speed, foils down: 8 knots
Foilborne range at max continuous speed: Up to 400n miles

Hullborne range: Up to 1000n miles
Turning radius at 45 knots: Less than 150m
Rate of turn at max continuous speed, foilborne: 10 degrees/s

RODRIQUEZ CANTIERI NAVALI SpA

Via S Raineri, 22–98122 Messina, Italy

Telephone: (090) 77651
Telex: 980030RODRIK I
Telefax: (090) 675294

Cav del Lavoro Carlo Rodriquez, *President*
Dott Ing Giovanni Morace, *General Manager*
Dott Salvatore Mancuso, *Vice President*
Dott Ing Claudio Buccini, *Technical Manager*

Rodriquez Cantieri Navali SpA, formerly known as Cantiere Navaltecnica SpA and as Leopoldo Rodriquez Shipyard, was the first company to produce hydrofoils in series, and is now the biggest hydrofoil builder outside the Soviet Union. On the initiative of the company's president, Carlo Rodriquez, the Aliscafi Shipping Company was established in Sicily to operate the world's first scheduled seagoing hydrofoil service in August 1956 between Sicily and the Italian mainland.

The service was operated by the first Rodriquez-built Supramar PT 20, *Freccia del Sole*. Cutting down the port-to-port time from Messina to Reggio di Calabria to one-quarter of that of conventional ferry boats, and completing 22 daily crossings, the craft soon proved its commercial viability. With a seating capacity of 72 passengers the PT 20 carried between 800 and 900 passengers a day and conveyed a record number of some 31 000 in a single month.

Details of the Supramar PT 20 and PT 50 craft are given in the Supramar Hydrofoils Ltd entry.

Eight main types of hydrofoil have now been produced: the Supramar PT 20 and PT 50, the RHS 70, RHS 110, RHS 140, RHS 150, RHS 160 and RHS 200. Many of the early craft built are still operating and the following table lists these craft built under Supramar licence.

In the summer of 1989 the company had one RHS 160F one RHS 150FL and two RHS 150F's under construction and the hull of one more RHS 160F was to be laid down. In the autumn of 1985 an order was placed by the Italian Ministero dei Trasporti for a new series of hydrofoils for oper-

Rodriquez Supramar PT 20 hydrofoil craft at the Messina works of Rodriquez Cantieri Navali SpA

Rodriquez Supramar PT 50 *Freccia di Sorrento* built in 1959 and now in use by the Ministero dei Mercantile Marine for anti-pollution work

ation on Lake Como, Lake Garda and Lake Maggiore. A possible growth area for hydrofoils is in the offshore oil industry.

The RHS series are now fitted with a Rodriquez electronic Seakeeping Augmentation Controller.

RHS 70

This is a 32-ton coastal passenger ferry with seats for 71 passengers. Power is supplied by a single 1430hp MTU diesel and the cruising speed is 32.4 knots.

FOILS: Surface-piercing type in partly hollow welded steel. During operation the angle of the bow foil can be adjusted within narrow limits from the steering position by means of a hydraulic ram operating on a foil support across the hull.

HULL: V-bottom hull of riveted light metal alloy construction. Watertight compartments are below the passenger decks and in other parts of the hull.

POWERPLANT: A single MTU 12V 331 TC 82 diesel, developing 1430hp at 2340rpm, drives a three-bladed bronze aluminium propeller through a Zahnradfabrik W 800 H 20 gearbox.

ACCOMMODATION: 44 passengers are accommodated in the forward cabin, 19 in the rear compartment and 8 aft of the pilot's position, above the engine room, in the elevated wheelhouse. A wc/washbasin unit is provided in the aft passenger compartments. Emergency exits are provided in each passenger compartment. Cabin noise level is approx 76dBA.

SYSTEMS, ELECTRICAL: 24V generator driven by the main engine; batteries with a capacity of 350Ah.

Forward foil arrangement of Rodriguez Supramar PT 50 *Freccia del Mediterraneo*

HYDRAULICS: 120kg/cm³ pressure hydraulic system for rudder and bow foil incidence control.

DIMENSIONS
Length overall: 22m
Width across foils: 7.4m
Draught hullborne: 2.7m
 foilborne: 1.15m

WEIGHTS
Displacement fully loaded: 31.5 tons
Useful load: 6 tons
PERFORMANCE
Cruising speed, half loaded: 32.4 knots
Max speed, half loaded: 36.5 knots at 1400rpm

Craft built (SUPRAMAR PT 3, PT 20) 1956 to 1971 (many of the craft names in this table have now been changed)

Type	Name	Yard No	No of seats	Operated in	Date	Owner/Operator (1987/88)
Supramar PT 3	Hitachi PT 3	055	12	Japan	1957	—
Supramar PT 3	Supramar PT 3	056	12	Switzerland	1957	—
Supramar PT 20	*Freccia del Sole* (laid up 1986)	051	72	Italy	1956	Aliscafi SNAV SpA
Supramar PT 20	*Flying Fish*	052	72	USA	1957	—
Supramar PT 20	*Freccia delle Eolie*	053	72	Italy	1957	Aliscafi SNAV SpA
Supramar PT 20	*Freccia del Tirreno*	057	72	Italy	1957	Aliscafi SNAV SpA
Supramar PT 20	*Freccia del Garda*	058	80	Italy	1958	Navigazione Sul Lago di Garda
Supramar PT 20	*Flecha Mara*	060	72	Venezuela	1958	—
Supramar PT 20	*Flecha del Lago*	061	72	Venezuela	1958	—
Supramar PT 20	*Flecha del Zulia*	067	72	Venezuela	1959	—
Supramar PT 20	*Freccia delle Egadi*	068	72	Italy	1959	—
Supramar PT 20	*Alilauro III*	069	72	Italy	1960	—
Supramar PT 20	*Freccia dello Stretto*	070	72	Italy	1960	Aliscafi SNAV SpA
Supramar PT 20	*Alivit* (ex *Alinapoli*, 1984; ex *Ekspressen*, 1969)	071	72	Norway	1961	Alivit Due
Supramar PT 20	Hitachi PT 20	072	72	Japan	1960	—
Supramar PT 20	*Freccia del Peloro*	073	72	Italy	1961	Aliscafi SNAV SpA
Supramar PT 20	*Freccia di Reggio*	074	72	Italy	1961	Aliscafi SNAV SpA
Supramar PT 20	*Isola del Giglio* (ex *Fleche d'Or IV Le Corsaire*)	075	72	Italy	1962	—
Supramar PT 20	*Nefertiti*	082	72	Egypt	1962	—
Supramar PT 20	*Cleopatra*	083	72	Egypt	1963	—
Supramar PT 20	*Aligrado*	084	72	Italy	1962	Rodriguez C.N. SpA
Supramar PT 20	*Flecha Fluminense*	085	72	Brazil	1962	—
Supramar PT 20	*Freccia dell'Arcipelago*	086	72	Italy	1966	—
Supramar PT 20	*Freccia di Ustica*	087	72	Italy	1965	—
Supramar PT 20	*Hatshepsut*	094	72	Egypt	1964	—
Supramar PT 20	*Flecha de Cabinas*	095	72	Venezuela	1963	—
Supramar PT 20	*Flying Fish*	096	72	Philippines	1963	—
Supramar PT 20	*Enrique*	097	72	Philippines	1963	—
Supramar PT 20	*Manu-Wai*	098	72	New Zealand	1964	Ossie James, NZ
Supramar PT 20	*Coloane*	099	72	Hong Kong	1964	—
Supramar PT 20	*Flecha de Icarai* (ex *Flying Phoenix*)	100	85	Hong Kong	1964	TRANSTUR
Supramar PT 20	*Flecha de Ribeira* (ex *Flying Kingfisher*)	101	85	Hong Kong	1964	TRANSTUR
Supramar PT 20	*Flying Swift* (scrapped)	102	68	Hong Kong	1964	—
Supramar PT 20	*Freccia del Verbano*	103	72	Italy	1964	Navigazione Lago Maggiore
Supramar PT 20	*Freccia del Lario*	104	72	Italy	1964	Navigazione Lago di Como
Supramar PT 20	*Albatros*	105	72	Switzerland	1964	—

Craft built (SUPRAMAR PT 3, PT 20) 1956 to 1971 (many of the craft names in this table have now been changed)

Type	Name	Yard No	No of seats	Operated in	Date	Owner/Operator (1987/88)
Supramar PT 20	Flecha da Ribeira (ex Flying Heron)	107	85	Brazil	1964	TRANSTUR
Supramar PAT 20	Camiguin (patrol duties) (laid up)	108	—	Philippines	1965	—
Supramar PAT 20	Siquijor (patrol duties) (laid up)	109	—	Philippines	1965	—
Supramar PT 20	Freccia degli Ulivi	110	72	Italy	1965	Navigazione Sul Lago di Garda
Supramar PT 20	Flecha das Ilhas	112	83	Brazil	1966	TRANSTUR
Supramar PT 20	Sunda Karya I	113	72	Indonesia	1965	—
Supramar PT 20	Freccia del Vesuvio	114	72	Italy	1966	Aliscafi SNAV SpA
Supramar PT 20	Flecha de Rio	115	83	Brazil	1969	TRANSTUR
Supramar PT 20	Flecha de Niteroi	116	83	Brazil	1970	TRANSTUR
Supramar PT 20	Pinturicchio	117	70	Italy	1968	SIREMAR
Supramar PT 20	Freccia del Ticino	127	72	Italy	1968	Navigazione Lago Maggiore
Supramar PT 20	Porto Corsini	130	32	Italy	1969	Aliscafi SNAV SpA
Supramar PT 20	Angel	149	71	South Korea	1971	Hanryeo Development Co Ltd
Supramar PT 20	Freccia delle Azalee	126	72	Italy	1969	Navigazione Lago di Como

Craft built (SUPRAMAR PT 50) 1959 to 1970

Type	Name	Yard No	No of seats	Operated in	Date	Owner/Operator
Supramar PT 50	Freccia di Messina*	059	125	Italy	1959	—
Supramar PT 50	Freccia di Sorrento	062	125	Italy	1959	Ministero dei Mercantile Marine
Supramar PT 50	Freccia d'Oro	063	130	Italy	1959	Aliscafi SNAV SpA
Supramar PT 50	Freccia Atlantica	064	125	Italy	1960	Aliscafi SNAV SpA
Supramar PT 50	Freccia del Sud	065	50 + 7t cargo	Italy	1960	Aliscafi SNAV SpA
Supramar PT 50	Pisanello	066	130	Italy	1961	SIREMAR
Supramar PT 50	Queenfoil (ex Sleipner)	076	125	—	1961	Transtour SA
Supramar PT 50	Freccia di Lipari	077	125	Italy	1961	Aliscafi SNAV SpA
Supramar PT 50	Flecha de Buenos Aires	078	125	Argentina	1962	Alimar SA
Supramar PT 50	Flecha de Colonia (ex Flecha de Montevideo)	079	125	Argentina	1962	Alimar SA
Supramar PT 50	Flecha del Litoral**	080	125	Argentina	1963	—
Supramar PT 50	Freccia del Mediterraneo	081	125	Italy	1963	Aliscafi SNAV SpA
Supramar PT 50	Freccia di Sicilia	088	125	Italy	1964	Aliscafi SNAV SpA
Supramar PT 50	Nibbio	089	125	Italy	1964	Adriatica di Navigazione SpA
Supramar PT 50	Flying Albatross	090	125	Hong Kong	1964	Hongkong Macao Hydrofoil Co Ltd
Supramar PT 50	Flying Skimmer	091	125	Hong Kong	1965	Hongkong Macao Hydrofoil Co Ltd
Supramar PT 50	Svalan†	092	125	—	1965	ex Tarnan Line, Limassol, Cyprus
Supramar PT 50	Flying Condor	093	125	Hong Kong	1966	Hongkong Macao Hydrofoil Co Ltd
Supramar PT 50	Freccia delle Isole	111	125	Italy	1966	Aliscafi SNAV SpA
Supramar PT 50	Tarnan	118	120	—	1966	ex Tarnan Line, Limassol, Cyprus
Supramar PT 50	Freccia Adriatica	119	125	Italy	1969	Aliscafi SNAV SpA
Supramar PT 50	Fairlight (scrapped 1988)	120	140	Australia	1966	—
Supramar PT 50	Flying Flamingo (scrapped)	121	125	—	1967	ex Hongkong Macao Hydrofoil Co Ltd
Supramar PT 50	Star Capricorn (ex Springeren)	122	117	Italy	1967	COVEMAR Eolie
Supramar PT 50	Stilprins (ex Teisten)	123	125	Norway	1970	Simon Møkster (ex Hardanger Sunnhordlandske-Steamship Co)
Supramar PT 50	Long Reef (laid up)	124	140	Australia	1969	NSW State Transit Authority
Supramar PT 50	Sun Arrow	125	125	Italy	1968	Aliscafi SNAV SpA
Supramar PT 50	Dee Why (scrapped 1988)	132	140	Australia	1970	—

* destroyed by fire 12 June 1986, en route to Lipari
** destroyed by fire 1986
† blown up by Israeli agents in Messina harbour 30 January 1986

RHS 110

A 54-ton hydrofoil ferry, the RHS 110 was originally designed to carry a maximum of 110 passengers at a cruising speed of 37 knots.

FOILS: Surface-piercing type, in partly hollow welded steel. Hydraulically operated flaps, attached to the trailing edges of the bow and rear foils, are adjusted automatically by a Hamilton Standard stability augmentation system for the damping of heave, pitch and roll motions. The rear foil is rigidly attached to the transom, its incidence angle being determined during tests.

HULL: V-bottom of high-tensile riveted light metal alloy construction, using Peraluman plates and Anticorrodal profiles. The upper deck plates are in 3.5mm thick Peraluman. Removable deck sections permit the lifting out and replacement of the main engines. The superstructure, which has a removable roof, is in 2mm thick Peraluman plates, with L and C profile sections. Watertight compartments are below the passenger decks and other parts of the hull.

POWERPLANT: Power is supplied by two 12-cylinder supercharged MTU MB 12V 493 Ty 71 diesels, each with a maximum output of 1350hp at 1500rpm. Engine output is transferred to two three-bladed bronze-aluminium propellers through Zahnradfabrik W 800 H20 gearboxes. Each propeller shaft is 90mm in diameter and supported at three points by sea water-lubricated rubber bearings. Steel fuel tanks with a total capacity of 3600 litres are aft of the engine room.

ACCOMMODATION: The wheelhouse/observation deck saloon seats 58 and the lower aft saloon seats 39. Additional passengers are accommodated in the lower forward saloon, which contains a bar.

In the wheelhouse, the pilot's position is on the port side, together with the radar screen. A second seat is provided for the chief engineer. Passenger seats are of lightweight aircraft type, floors are covered with woollen carpets and the walls and ceilings are clad in vinyl. Two toilets are provided, one in each of the lower saloons.

SYSTEMS, ELECTRICAL: Engine driven generators supply 220V, 50Hz, three-phase ac. Two groups of batteries for 24V dc circuit.

HYDRAULICS: Steering, variation of the foil flaps and the anchor windlass operation are all accomplished hydraulically from the wheelhouse. Plant comprises two Bosch pumps installed on the main engines which convey oil from a 60-litre (13-gallon) tank under pressure to the control cylinders of the rudder, foil flaps and anchor windlass.

FIREFIGHTING: Fixed CO_2 plant for the main engine room, portable CO_2 and foam fire extinguishers of 3kg and 10-litre capacity in the saloons, and one water firefighting plant.

DIMENSIONS

EXTERNAL
Length overall: 25.6m
Width across foils: 9.2m
Deck beam, max: 5.95m
Draught hullborne: 3.3m
  foilborne: 1.25m
WEIGHT
Displacement, fully loaded: 54 tons
PERFORMANCE
Max speed: 40 knots
Cruising speed: 37 knots
Range: 486km

RHS 140

This 65-ton hydrofoil passenger ferry seats up to 150 passengers and has a cruising speed of 32.5 knots.

FOILS: Surface-piercing V foils of hollow welded steel construction. Lift of the bow foil can be modified by hydraulically-operated trailing-edge flaps.

RHS 70 *Shearwater 3*, sister vessel to three other RHS 70s delivered to Red Funnel Ferries

Craft built (RHS 70) 1972 to 1982

Type	Name	Yard No	No of seats	Operated in	Date	Owner/Operator
RHS 70	*Shearwater 3*	150	67	England	1972	Red Funnel Ferries
RHS 70	*Shearwater 4*	156	67	England	1973	Red Funnel Ferries
RHS 70	*Freccia delle Betulle*	185	71	Italy	1974	Navigazione Lago di Como
RHS 70	*Freccia delle Camelie*	186	71	Italy	1974	Navigazione Lago Maggiore
RHS 70	*Freccia del Benaco*	187	71	Italy	1974	Navigazione Sul Lago di Garda
RHS 70	*Freccia delle Magnolie*	188	71	Italy	1975	Navigazione Lago Maggiore
RHS 70	*Freccia delle Gardenie*	189	71	Italy	1976	Navigazione Lago di Como
RHS 70	*Freccia dei Gerani*	196	71	Italy	1977	Navigazione Sul Lago di Garda
RHS 70	*Shearwater 5*	197	67	England	1980	Red Funnel Ferries
RHS 70	*Shearwater 6*	221	67	England	1982	Red Funnel Ferries

Craft built (RHS 110) 1971 to 1973

Type	Name	Yard No	No of seats	Operated in	Date	Owner/Operator
RHS 110	*Cacilhas*	147	110	Hong Kong	1971	—
RHS 110	*Flecha de Angra* (ex *Flying Phoenix*)	148	140	Brazil	1970	Laid up
RHS 110	*Barca*	157	122	Hong Kong	1972	—
RHS 110	*Praia*	158	111	Hong Kong	1973	—
RHS 110	*Cerco*	159	111	Hong Kong	1973	—

Craft built (RHS 140) 1971 to 1977

Type	Name	Yard No	No of seats	Operated in	Date	Owner/Operator
RHS 140	*Colonia del Sacramento* (ex *Condor*)	133	140	Uruguay	1971	Belt SA
RHS 140	*Flying Dragon*	134	140	Hong Kong	1971	Hongkong Macao Hydrofoil Co Ltd
RHS 140	*Flying Egret*	152	125	Hong Kong	1972	Hongkong Macao Hydrofoil Co Ltd
RHS 140	*Santa Maria del Buenos Aires* (ex *Tyrving*)	153	116	Uruguay	1972	Belt SA
RHS 140	*Farallón* (ex *Løberen*)	154	111	Uruguay	1972	Belt SA
RHS 140	*Curl-Curl*	155	140	Australia	1972	NSW Transit Authority
RHS 140	*Rapido de Ibiza* (ex *Viggen*)	161	120	Spain	1973	Flebasa Lines
RHS 140	*Flying Sandpiper*	180	125	Hong Kong	1972	Hongkong Macao Hydrofoil Co Ltd
RHS 140	*Flying Swift* (ex *Flying Goldfinch*)	180	125	Hong Kong	1973	Hongkong Macao Hydrofoil Co Ltd
RHS 140	*Flying Ibis*	182	125	Hong Kong	1975	Hongkong Macao Hydrofoil Co Ltd
RHS 140	*Condor 4*	184	136	UK	1974	Condor Ltd
RHS 140	*Duccio* (ex *Fabricia*)	193	140	Italy	1977	TOREMAR SpA
RHS 140	*Albireo*	194	150	Italy	1977	CAREMAR SpA

HULL: Riveted light metal alloy design framed on longitudinal and transverse formers.
ACCOMMODATION: Up to 150 passengers seated in three saloons. The belvedere saloon, on the main deck above the engine room, can be equipped with a bar. Wc washbasin units can be installed in the forward and aft saloons.
POWERPLANT: Power is provided by two MTU 12V 493 Ty 71 12-cylinder supercharged engines, each developing 1350hp at 1500 rpm. Engine output is transmitted to two, three-bladed 700mm diameter bronze propellers through Zahnradfabrik gearboxes.
SYSTEMS, ELECTRICAL: Two engine-driven generators supply 24V dc. Two battery sets each with 350Ah capacity.
HYDRAULICS: Steering and variation of foil flap incidence is accomplished hydraulically from the wheelhouse. Plant comprises two Bosch pumps installed on the main engines and conveying oil from a 70-litre tank under pressure to the control cylinders of the rudder and foil flaps.
FIREFIGHTING: Fixed CO_2 plant for the engine room; portable CO_2 and foam fire extinguishers in the saloons. Water intake connected to bilge pump for fire hose connection in emergency.
DIMENSIONS
Length overall: 28.7m
Width across foils: 10.72m
Draught hullborne: 3.5m
    foilborne: 1.5m
WEIGHTS
Displacement, fully loaded: 65 tons
Carrying capacity, including 3 tons bunker, and 5 tons fresh water, lubricating oil and hydraulic system oil: 12.5 tons
PERFORMANCE
Max speed, half load: 36 knots
Cruising speed: 32.5 knots
Range at cruising speed: 550km

RHS 150

Combining features of both the RHS 140 and the RHS 160, the RHS 150 hydrofoil passenger ferry is powered by two 1430hp MTU supercharged 4-stroke diesels which give the craft a cruising speed of 32.5 knots and a cruising range of 130n miles.
FOILS: Surface-piercing W foils of hollow welded steel construction. Lift of the bow foil can be modified by hydraulically-operated trailing edge flaps.

Craft built (RHS 150) 1980

Type	Name	Yard No	No of seats	Operated in	Date	Owner/Operator
RHS 150	*Xel-Ha* (laid up)	203	151	Mexico	1980	Secretaria de Turismo, Mexico

HULL: Riveted light metal alloy design framed on longitudinal and transverse formers.
ACCOMMODATION: The standard model seats 150 in three saloons. High density model design originally for services on the Italian lakes seats 180: 63 in the aft saloon, 45 in the forward saloon and 72 in the belvedere. The forward and stern saloons each have a toilet/wc unit.
POWERPLANT: Motive power is furnished by two supercharged MTU MB 12V 331 TC 82 four-stroke diesels each developing 1430hp at 2140rpm continuous. Engine output is transmitted to two bronze propellers via two Zahnradfabrik BW 255L gearboxes.
SYSTEMS, ELECTRICAL: Two 1300W engine-driven generators supply 24V dc.
DIMENSIONS
Length overall: 28.7m
Width across foils: 11m
Draught hullborne: 3.1m
    foilborne: 1.4m
WEIGHT
Displacement, fully loaded: 65.5 tons
PERFORMANCE
Cruising speed, fully loaded: 32.5 knots
Cruising range: 240km (130n miles)

RHS 150 SL

This variant has been designed for inland navigation, particularly on the Great Lakes in Northern Italy. Because of the less severe conditions on such waters it has been possible to re-design the hull structure to allow for larger windows in the lower saloons and the superstructure, greatly increasing visibility for sightseeing. In addition, because the safety rules are less demanding than for open-water routes, there is a saving in weight in the design allowing an increase in passenger

Craft built (RHS 150 SL and FL) 1979 to 1989

Type	Name	Yard No	No of seats	Operated in	Date	Owner/Operator
RHS 150 SL	*Freccia del Giardini*	204	190	Italy	1980	Navigazione Lago Maggiore
RHS 150 SL	*Freccia delle Valli*	199	190	Italy	1979	Navigazione Lago di Como
RHS 150 SL	*Freccia dei Gerani*	196	190	Italy	1980	Navigazione Lago Maggiore
RHS 150 SL	*Freccia delle Riviere*	206	190	Italy	1981	Navigazione Sul Lago di Garda
RHS 150 SL	*Galileo Galilei*	208	190	Italy	1982	Navigazione Sul Lago di Garda
RHS 150 SL	*Enrico Fermi*	220	190	Italy	1984	Navigazione Lago Maggiore
RHS 150 SL	*Guglielmo Marconi*	207	190	Italy	1983	Navigazione Lago di Como
RHS 150FL	*Goethe*	232	200	Italy	1988	Navigazione Lago di Gardo
RHS 150FL	*Voloire*	237	200	Italy	1989	Navigazione Sul Lago di Como
RHS 150FL	*Byron*	238	200	Italy	1990	Navigazione sul Lago Maggiore

RHS 150FL *Voloire* delivered 1989 for service on Lake Como, Italy

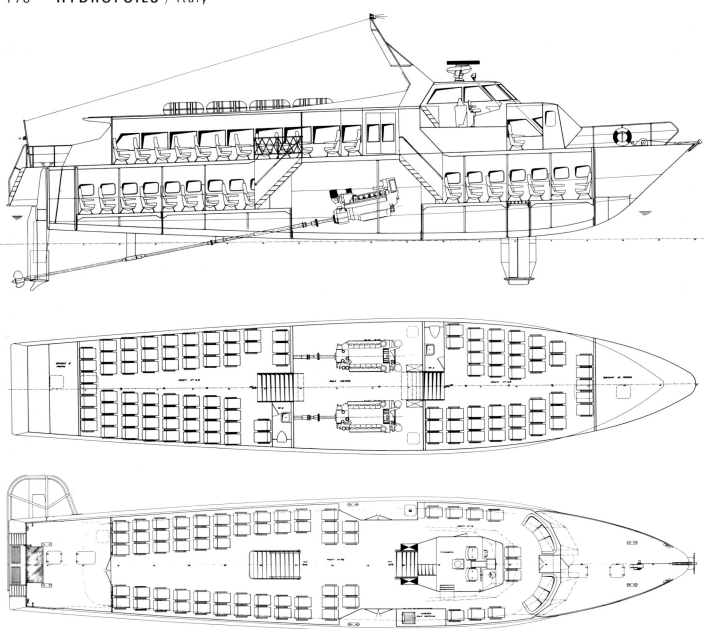

RHS 150

RHS 150 F *Dynasty* operated by Aliscafi SNAV SpA

numbers, so that 200 may be carried, with light-weight seats fitted.

RHS 150 F

This variant has a wider deck and the super-structure volume has been increased to give a more aesthetic shape as well as greater volume for passengers, giving greater comfort. Improvements have also been incorporated in this variant increasing performance and reducing maintenance costs.

RHS 160

A 95-tonne passenger ferry with seats for up to 180 passengers and a cruising speed of 32 knots.

In March and May 1986 two RHS 160s were used for oil spill clean-up trials.

Reference: Hydrofoil: High Speed Control and Clean up of Large Oil Spills by RADM Marcello Vacca-Torelli, Alberto L Geraci and Antonio Risitano. Dept of Civil Protection, Rome and University of Catania, Sicily, Italy, 1986.

FOILS: Surface-piercing W foils of hollow welded steel construction. Craft in this series feature a bow rudder for improved manoeuvrability in congested waters. The bow rudder works simultaneously with the aft rudders. Hydraulically-operated flaps, attached to the trailing edges of the bow and rear foils, are adjusted automatically by a Hamilton Standard electronic stability augmentation system, for the damping of heave, pitch and roll motions in heavy seas.

HULL: Riveted light metal alloy longitudinal structure, welded in parts using inert gas. The hull shape of the RHS 160 is similar to the RHS 140 series. In the manufacture of the hull, plates of aluminium and magnesium alloy of 4.4 per cent are used while angle bars are of a high-resistant aluminium, magnesium and silicon alloy.

ACCOMMODATION: 180 to 200 passengers seated in three saloons. 57 passengers are accommodated in the forward cabin, 63 in the rear compartment and 60 in the belvedere. Forward and aft saloons and belvedere have a toilet, each provided with wc, washbasin units and the usual toilet accessories.

Craft built (RHS 150 F) 1984

Type	Name	Yard No	No of seats	Operated in	Date	Owner/Operator
RHS 150 F	*Dynasty*	210	161	Italy	1984	Aliscafi SNAV SpA
RHS 150 F	—	233	161	Italy	1990	Aliscafi SNAV SpA
RHS 150 F	—	234	161	Italy	1990	Aliscafi SNAV SpA

RHS 160 *Princess Zoe* engaged in anti-oil pollution trials

POWERPLANT: Power is provided by two supercharged MTU MB 12V 652 TB 71 four-stroke diesel engines each with a maximum output of 1950hp at 1460rpm under normal operating conditions. Engine starting is accomplished by compressed air starters. Engine output is transmitted to two, three-bladed bronze propellers through two Zahnradfabrik 900 HS 15 gearboxes.

SYSTEMS, ELECTRICAL: Two 35kVA generating sets, 220V, 60Hz, three-phase. Three insulated cables for ventilation, air-conditioning and power. Two insulated cables for lighting, sockets and other appliances, 24V dc for emergency lighting, auxiliary engine starting and servocontrol. A battery for radio telephone supply is installed on the upper deck. Provision for battery recharge from ac line foreseen.

HYDRAULICS: Hydraulic steering from the wheelhouse. Plant comprises a Bosch pump installed on the main engines and conveying oil from a 45-litre (10-gallon) tank under pressure to the control cylinders of the rudder and anchor windlass, whilst a second hydraulic pump, which is also installed on the main engines, conveys oil

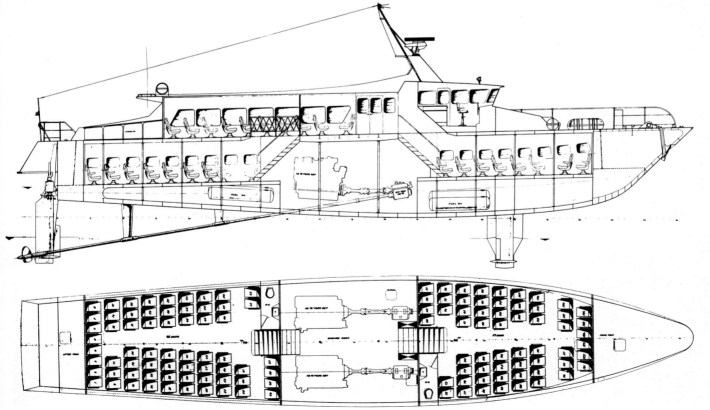

Inboard profile and lower deck plan of RHS 160

under pressure to the flap control cylinders.
FIREFIGHTING: Fixed CO_2 plant of four CO_2 bottles of about 20kg each for the engine room and fuel tank space; portable extinguishers in various parts of the craft. Water intake is connected to fire pump for fire connection in emergency.

DIMENSIONS
Length overall: 30.95m
Width across foils: 12.6m
Beam, moulded: 6.20m
Draught hullborne: 3.7m
        foilborne: 1.35m

WEIGHTS
Displacement, fully loaded: 95 tonnes
Payload, passengers and baggage: 13.5 tons

PERFORMANCE
Max speed: 36 knots
Cruising speed: 32 knots
Cruising range: 483km
Fuel consumption: 0.5 tonnes/h
Seakeeping capability in Sea State 4: Roll, less than 2° with electronic control; less than 3° without electronic control

RHS 160F

A further addition to the Rodriquez range is the RHS 160F, a 91.5-ton passenger ferry with seats for up to 238 passengers and a cruising speed of 34.5 knots.
FOILS: Surface-piercing W foils of hollow welded steel construction. Craft in this series feature a bow rudder for improved manoeuvrability in congested waters. The bow rudder works sim-

Craft built (RHS 160) 1974 to 1986

Type	Name	Yard No	No of seats	Operated in	Date	Owner/Operator
RHS 160	Princess Zoe (ex Alijumbo Ustica, ex Lilau)	181	160	Italy	1974	Aliscafi SNAV SpA
RHS 160	Diomedea	190	160	Italy	1975	Adriatica di Navigazione SpA
RHS 160	Condor 5	191	180	UK	1976	Condor Ltd
RHS 160	Algol	195	180	Italy	1978	CAREMAR
RHS 160	May W Craig (ex Alijumbo)	198	180	Italy	1979	Aliscafi SNAV SpA
RHS 160	Alioth	200	180	Italy	1979	CAREMAR
RHS 160	Botticelli	201	180	Italy	1980	SIREMAR
RHS 160	Donatello	202	180	Italy	1980	SIREMAR
RHS 160	Nicte-Ha	205	160	Mexico	1982	Secretaria de Turismo, Mexico

ultaneously with the aft rudders. Hydraulically-operated flaps, attached to the trailing edges of the bow and rear foils, are adjusted automatically by a Hamilton Standard electronic stability augmentation system, for the damping of heave, pitch and roll motions in heavy seas.
HULL: Riveted light metal alloy longitudinal structure, welded in parts using inert gas. The hull shape of the RHS 160F is similar to the RHS 140 series. In the manufacture of the hull, plates of aluminium and magnesium alloy of 4.4 per cent are used while angle bars are of a high-resistant aluminium, magnesium and silicon alloy.
ACCOMMODATION: 210 passengers seated in

three saloons. 58 passengers are accommodated in the forward cabin, 63 in the rear compartment and 89 in the belvedere. Forward and aft saloons and belvedere each have a toilet with wc, wash-basin units and toilet accessories.
POWERPLANT: Power is provided by two supercharged MTU 16V 396 TB 83 four-stroke diesel engines each with a maximum output of 1400kW at 2000rpm under normal operating conditions. Engine starting is accomplished by compressed air starters. Engine output is transmitted to two, three-bladed bronze propellers through two Zahnradfabrik BW 7505 gearboxes, or, alternatively, through two Reintjes WVS 1032U gear-

RHS 160F *Condor 7*

RHS 160F *Barracuda* (photo: *Dr Saro Armone*)

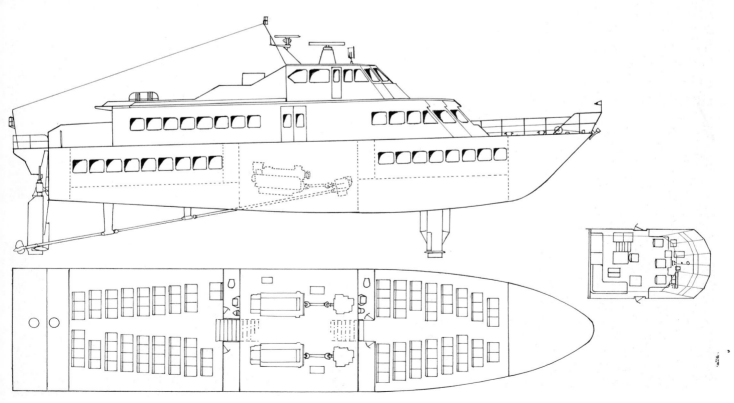

RHS 160F inboard profile and lower deck arrangement

boxes as fitted to the RHS 160F craft supplied to the NSW State Transit Authority, Australia.

SYSTEMS, ELECTRICAL: Two 35kVA generating sets, 220V, 60Hz, three-phase. Three insulated cables for ventilation, air-conditioning and power. Two insulated cables for lighting, sockets and other appliances, 24V dc for emergency lighting, auxiliary engine starting and servocontrol. A battery for radio telephone supply is installed on the upper deck. Provision for battery recharge from ac line is foreseen.

HYDRAULICS: Hydraulic steering from the wheelhouse. Plant comprises a Bosch pump installed on the main engines and conveying oil from a 45-litre (10-gallon) tank under pressure to the control cylinders of the rudder and anchor windlass, whilst a second hydraulic pump, which is also installed on the main engines, conveys oil under pressure to the flap control cylinders.

FIREFIGHTING: Fixed CO_2 plant of four CO_2 bottles of about 20kg each for the engine room and fuel tank space; portable extinguishers in various parts of the craft. Water intake connected to fire pump for connection in emergency.

DIMENSIONS
Length overall: 31.2m
Length, waterline: 26.25m
Beam (hull), moulded: 6.70m
Depth (hull), moulded: 3.69m
Width across foils: 12.6m
Draught hullborne: 3.76m
    foilborne: 1.7m

WEIGHTS
Displacement, fully loaded: 91.5 tons
Payload, passengers and luggage: 17.8 tons

PERFORMANCE
Max speed: 38 knots
Cruising speed: 34.5 knots
Cruising range: 100n miles

Craft built/being built (RHS 160F) 1984 to 1989

Type	Name	Yard No	No of seats	Operated in	Date	Owner/Operator
RHS 160F	Manly	211	238	Australia	1984	NSW State Transit Authority
RHS 160F	Sydney	216	238	Australia	1985	NSW State Transit Authority
RHS 160F	Condor 7	217	200	UK	1985	Condor Ltd
RHS 160F	Pez Volador (ex Alijumbo Eolie)	218	220	Spain	1986	Compañia Naviera Mallorquina
RHS 160F	Alnilan	227	210	Italy	1986	CAREMAR
RHS 160F	Fabricia	228	210	Italy	1987	TOREMAR
RHS 160F	Aldebaran	229	210	Italy	1987	CAREMAR
RHS 160F	Masaccio	230	210	Italy	1988	SIREMAR
RHS 160F	Mantegna	231	210	Italy	1989	SIREMAR
RHS 160F	-	236	210	Italy	1990	Alisafi SNAV SpA
RHS 160F	Giorgione	239	210	Italy	1989	SIREMAR
RHS 160F	Monte Gargano	240	210	Italy	1989	Adriatica SpA di Navigazione
RHS 160 F	Barracuda	002/160	204	Spain	1989	Trasmediterranea SA
RHS 160 F	Marrajo	003/160	204	Spain	1989	Trasmediterranea SA
RHS 160F	-	243				

RHS 200

Powered by two supercharged MTU MB 16V 652 TB 71 four-stroke diesel engines, the 254-seat RHS 200 has a cruising speed of 35 knots.

FOILS: Surface-piercing W foils of hollow welded steel construction. Craft in this series feature a bow rudder for improved manoeuvrability in congested waters. The bow rudder operates simultaneously with the aft rudders. An advantage of the W configuration bow foil is its relatively shallow draught requirement in relation to the vessel's overall size. Hydraulically-operated flaps are fitted to the trailing edge of the bow foil to balance out longitudinal load shifting, assist take-off and adjust the flying height. The craft can also be equipped with the Hamilton Standard electronic stability augmentation system, which employs sensors and servomechanisms to position flaps automatically on the bow and stern foils for

RHS 160F Marrajo

the damping of heave, pitch and roll motions in heavy seas.

HULL: V-bottom hull of high tensile riveted light metal alloy construction, employing Peraluman plates and Anticorrodal frames. The rake of the stem is in galvanised steel.

ACCOMMODATION: Seats for up to 400 passengers, according to the route served. In typical configuration there are three main passenger saloons and a bar. The standard seating arrangement allows for 116 in the main deck saloon, 58 in the aft lower saloon and 66 in the bow passenger saloon. Seating is normally four abreast in two lines with a central aisle. The bar, at the forward end of the wheelhouse belvedere superstructure, has either an eight-seat sofa or 19 seats.

The wheelhouse, which is raised to provide a 360-degree view, is reached from the main deck belvedere saloon by a short companionway. Controls and instrumentation are attached to a panel on the forward bulkhead which extends the width of the wheelhouse. In the centre is the steering control and gyrocompass, on the starboard side are controls for the two engines, gearboxes and controllable-pitch propellers, and on the port side is the radar. Seats are provided for the captain, chief engineer and first mate. In the wheelhouse are a radio telephone and a chart table.

POWER PLANT: Motive power is supplied by two supercharged MTU MB 16V 652 TB 71 4-stroke diesel engines, each with a maximum output of 2600hp at 1460rpm under normal operating conditions. Engine output is transferred to two supercavitating, controllable-pitch propellers.

SYSTEMS, ELECTRICAL: Two generating sets: one 220V, three-phase ac, for all consumer services, the second for charging 24V battery sets and operating firefighting and hydraulic pumps. Power distribution panel in wheelhouse for navigation light circuits, cabin lighting, radar, RDF, gyrocompass and emergency circuits.

FIREFIGHTING: Fixed CO_2 self-contained automatic systems for powerplant and fuel tank spaces, plus portable extinguishers for cabins and holds.

DIMENSIONS
Length overall: 35.8m
Width across foils: 14.5m
Draught hullborne: 4.55m
  foilborne: 2.05m
WEIGHT
Displacement fully loaded: 130 tonnes
PERFORMANCE
Cruising speed: 35 knots
Max speed: 37 knots
Cruising range: 200n miles
Fuel consumption: 785kg/h

RHS ALIYACHT

A luxury hydrofoil yacht of light alloy construction, the RHS Aliyacht is derived from the RHS 110 passenger ferry. For detailed information please see *Jane's Surface Skimmers 1985* and earlier editions.

RHS 70 HYDROIL *PORTO CORSINI*

This name was given to an offshore crew/supply version of the RHS 70 which was delivered to the ENI Oil Corporation for use in the Adriatic. Full details are given in *Jane's Surface Skimmers 1985* and earlier editions.

PROJECT DESIGNS

Details of the following project designs are given in *Jane's Surface Skimmers 1985* and earlier editions: RHS 140 & 160 Hydroils, M-RHS 150 Search and Rescue, M-RHS 150 Patrol, M100, M150, M200 Patrol, M300 & 600 Fast Strike Craft.

MEC 2–200 (MAXIMUM EFFICIENCY CRAFT) (DESIGN)

A new hydrofoil design developed in a joint

Craft built (RHS 200) 1981 to 1984

Type	Name	Yard No	No of seats	Operated in	Date	Owner/Operator
RHS 200	*Superjumbo*	192	254	Italy	1981	Aliscafi SNAV SpA
RHS 200	*San Cristobal* (ex *Stretto di Messina*)	209	254	Italy	1984	Aliscafi SNAV SpA
RHS 200	—	235	—	—	—	
		(under construction 1987)				

Belvedere cabin of RHS 200

Wheelhouse of RHS 200

RHS 200 *Superjumbo*

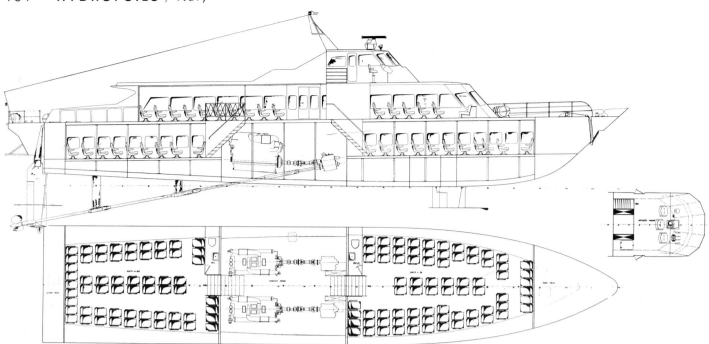

Inboard profil and lower deck arrangement of RHS 200

effort with CETENA (the Italian Ship Research Institute) and incorporating Rexroth hydrostatic power transmission. The design embodies a new Rodriguez surface-piercing foil system and hull form (fully automatic welding construction), with the rear foil unit carrying the maximum possible weight. It has been shown to be desirable to have a very stiff (in response to waves) front foil with low damping and a very soft rear foil with high damping and it is then convenient to carry the maximum possible weight on the rear foil, the Canard lift distribution allowing a finer hull bow form to be used.

The hull form has been derived from the well known 65 Series.

In comparison with comparable hydrofoils, a passenger capacity increase of about 25% is anticipated, a speed increase of 9%, while displacement increases by less than 5%. For equal passenger capacity, the installed power would be reduced by some 18% with a consequent reduction in fuel

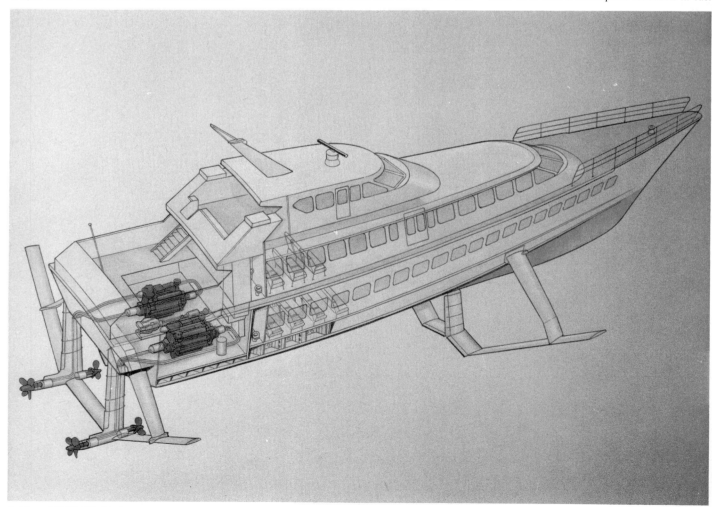

Rodriguez MEC 2–200 (Maximum Efficiency Craft) design

consumption. Due to the aft location of the power plant a passenger cabin noise reduction of 3 to 5dBA is expected.

PRINCIPAL PARTICULARS
Length, overall: 31.90m
Length, waterline: 26.70m
Foil spacing: 22.35m
Beam, max: 7.20m
Draught, hull only: 1.32m
Engines: Two MTU 12V 396 TB83, 1250kW each
Passenger capacity: 200
Speed, cruising: 36 knots
Range: 200n miles
HYDROSTATIC POWER TRANSMISSION
  Please see page in Transmission Section Rexroth entry for discussion of the basic concept and for details of system as applied to an early Rodriguez Supramar PT20 hydrofoil craft, *Aligrado*.

Rexroth hydrostatic power transmission with tandem propellers as applied to an early Rodriguez Supramer PT20, *Aligrado*.

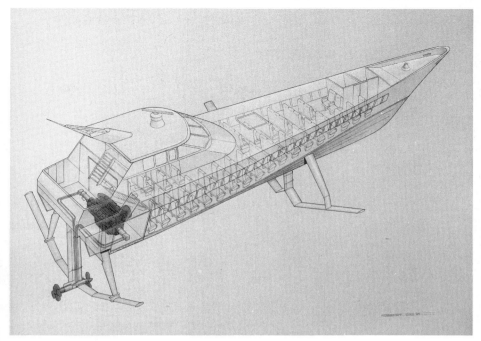

Rodriguez 100 seat MEC 1 design

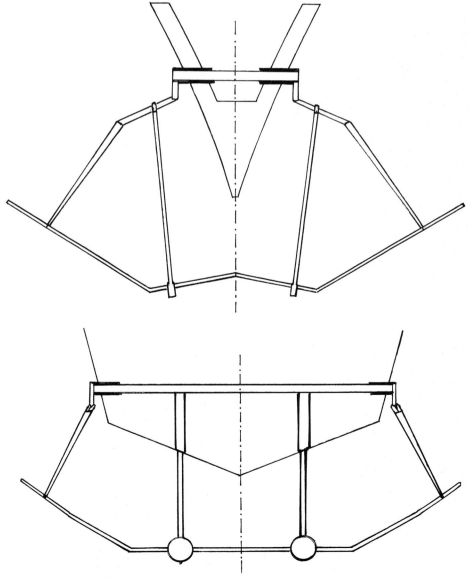

One possible arrangement for front and rear foil systems on Rodriguez MEC 2–200

JAPAN

HITACHI ZOSEN CORPORATION

Head Office: 6–14 Edobori 1-chome, Nishi-ku, Osaka, Japan

Telephone: (06) 443 8051
Telex: J 63376

Works: 4–1 Mizue-cho, Kawasaki-ku, Kawasaki, Kanagawa Pref, Japan

Telephone: (044) 288 1111
Telex: 3842524
Telefax: (044) 276 0022

Toshio Murayama, *President*
Shojiro Okada, *Executive Vice President*
Motohiro Yamaoka, *General Manager, Kanagawa Works*
T Shinoda, *Manager of Naval Ship Design, Kanagawa Works*

Hitachi Zosen, the Supramar licensee in Japan, has been building Supramar PT 20, PT 32 and PT 50 hydrofoils since 1961. By 1970 some 32 hydrofoils had been built and another ten by 1981. The majority of these have been built for fast passenger-ferry services across the Japanese Inland Sea, cutting across deep bays which road vehicles might take two to three hours to drive round, and out to offshore islands. Other PT 20s and 50s have been exported to Hong Kong, Australia and South Korea for ferry services.

Specifications of the PT 32 (*Jane's Surface Skimmers 1967–68*), PT 20 and PT 50 will be found under Supramar (Switzerland) *(Jane's Surface Skimmers 1985)*. The Hitachi Zosen craft are identical apart from minor items.

In 1974 the company completed the first PT 50 Mk II to be built at its Kawasaki yard. The vessel, *Hikari No 2,* is powered by two licence-built MTU MB 820Db diesels, carries 123 passengers plus a crew of seven and cruises at 33 knots. It was delivered to Setonaikai Kisen KK of Hiroshima in March 1975. Hitachi Zosen has constructed 25 PT 50s and 17 PT 20s.

In conjunction with Supramar, Hitachi Zosen has developed a new roll stabilisation system for the PT 50. The first PT 50 to be equipped with this new system was completed in January 1983 and is now in service.

PT 20 *Ryusei* operated by Ishizaki Kisen KK

PTS 50 Mk II *Housho*

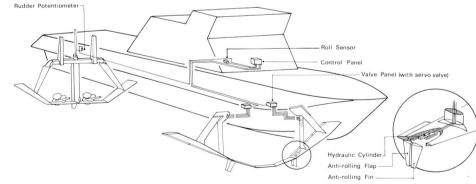

Rudder Potentiometer
Roll Sensor
Control Panel
Valve Panel (with servo valve)
Hydraulic Cylinder
Anti-rolling Flap
Anti-rolling Fin

PTS 50 Mk II roll-stabilising system as fitted to *Housho*

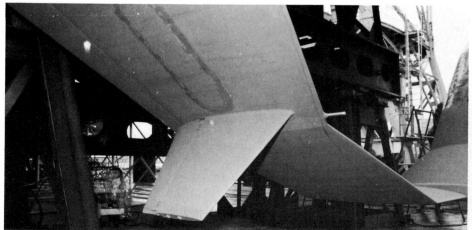

Flapped roll-stabilisation fin on *Housho*

ROLL-STABILISED SUPRAMAR PTS 50 Mk II

Housho, the first PTS 50 Mk II to be equipped with this new system, was delivered to Hankyu Kisen KK on 19 January 1983 and is operating on the Kobe-Naruto route. The system, which was developed by Hitachi Zosen in conjunction with Supramar, reduces the PTS 50's rolling motion by between one-half and one-third.

The underside of the bow foil is fitted with two flapped fins to improve riding comfort. Operated by automatic sensors, the fins augment stability and provide side forces to dampen rolling and transverse motions.

Housho is powered by two MTU 12V 331 TB82 marine diesels, each rated at 1380hp at 2150rpm. It seats 123 passengers and has a maximum speed of about 38 knots.

DIMENSIONS
Length overall: 27.55m
Beam, hull: 5.84m
Width across foils: 10.8m
Draught hullborne: 3.5m
   foilborne: 1.4m
GRT: 128
WEIGHT
Displacement, loaded: 62 tonnes
PERFORMANCE
Max speed: About 38 knots

Hitachi hydrofoils believed to be currently in operation

Type	Name	Seats	Launched	Operator
Hitachi Supramar PT 20	*Hayate No 1*		April 1962	Showa Kaiun Co Ltd
Hitachi Supramar PT 20	*Kansei*		July 1962	Ishizaki Kisen KK
Hitachi Supramar PT 20	*Hibiki*		November 1966	Setonaikai Kisen KK
Hitachi Supramar PT 20	*Hibiki No 3*	66	March 1968	Setonaikai Kisen KK
Hitachi Supramar PT 20	*Shibuki No 2*		June 1969	Boyo Kisen Co Ltd
Hitachi Supramar PT 20	*Myojo*		June 1970	Ishizaki Kisen KK
Hitachi Supramar PT 20	*Kinsei*		July 1972	Ishizaki Kisen KK
Hitachi Supramar PT 20	*Ryusei*		March 1981	Ishizaki Kisen KK
Hitachi Supramar PT 50	*Ohtori*	113	January 1968	—
Hitachi Supramar PT 50	*Kosei*		February 1969	Ishizaki Kisen KK
Hitachi Supramar PT 50	*Ohtori No 2*	113	February 1970	Setonaikai Kisen KK
Hitachi Supramar PT 50	*Zuihoh*		December 1971	Hankyu Kisen KK
Hitachi Supramar PT 50	*Hoh'oh*		February 1972	Hankyu Kisen KK
Hitachi Supramar PT 50	*Condor*	121	June 1972	Setonaikai Kisen KK
Hitachi Supramar PT 50	*Ohtori No 3*		October 1972	Setonaikai Kisen KK
Hitachi Supramar PT 50	*Ohtori No 5*		May 1973	Setonaikai Kisen KK
Hitachi Supramar PT 50	*Shibuki No 3*		October 1973	Boyo Kisen Co Ltd
Hitachi Supramar PT 50	*Saisei*		March 1974	Ishizaki Kisen KK
Hitachi Supramar PT 50	*Condor No 2*	121	April 1974	Setonaikai Kisen KK
Hitachi Supramar PT 50	*Condor No 3*	100	August 1974	Setonaikai Kisen KK
Hitachi Supramar PT 50 Mk II	*Hikari No 2*	123	March 1975	Setonaikai Kisen KK
Hitachi Supramar PT 50 Mk II	*Shunsei* (ex *Kariyush I*)		June 1975	Ishizaki Kisen KK
Hitachi Supramar PTS 50 Mk II	*Housho*	123	January 1983	Hankyu Kisen KK

KAWASAKI HEAVY INDUSTRIES LTD
Ship Group

Tokyo Head Office: World Trade Center Bldg., 4–1 Hamamatsu-cho 2-chome, Minato-ku, Tokyo 105, Japan

Telephone: (03) 435 2111
Telex: 242–4371 KAWAJU J
Telefax: (03) 436 3038 G3/G2

Kobe Works: 1–1 Higashi Kawasaki-cho 3-chome, Chuo-ku, Kobe 650–91, Japan

Telephone: (078) 682 5150
Telex: 5623–931 KHIKOB J
Telefax: (078) 682 5515

Yoshiro Manabe, *Managing Director and Senior General Manager of Ship Group*

The second Kawasaki Jetfoil to be built, the 264-seat *Toppy*

BOEING JETFOIL 929–117

In January 1987, Kawasaki Heavy Industries Ltd acquired a licence for the design, manufacture, marketing, maintenance and repair of Boeing Jetfoil 929–117 hydrofoil craft.

POWERPLANT: Two Allison 501-KF gas turbines, each rated at 2834kW (3 800 hp) at 13 120 rpm at 15°C (59°F). Each is connected to a Kawasaki Powerjet 20 axial-flow pump through a gearbox drive train.

DIMENSIONS

Length overall, foils extended: 27.4m
    foils retracted: 30.4m

Beam overall: 9.1m

Draught hullborne,
    designed draught moulded: 1.5m
    foils retracted, max: 2.2m
    foils extended, max: 5.4m

WEIGHT

Fully loaded displacement: 118.9 tonnes

PERFORMANCE

Speed, foilborne, max: 45 knots

Speed, service: 43 knots

For details of the Jetfoil 929 series please see entry under Boeing Aerospace.

Craft built (Kawasaki Jetfoil 929–117 type)

Yard No	Name	Seats	Delivery	Operator
KJ01	*Tsubasa*	266	March 1989	Sado Kisen Kaisha
KJ02	*Toppy*	264	June 1989	Kagoshima Shosen Co., Ltd
KJ03	*Nagasaki*	180	Sept 1989	Japan Ocean Cruise Line
KJ04	*Pegasus*	269	March 1990	Kyūshū Shōsen Co., Ltd
KJ05	*Beetle*	234	April 1990	Kyushu Railway Company
KJ06	—	286	July 1990	Compania Trasmediterranea, S A
KJ07	—	233	October 1990	Higashi-Nihon Ferry Co Ltd
KJ08	—	190	January 1991	Kyushu Railway Company
KJ09	—	263	March 1991	Kyūshū Yūsen Co Ltd
KJ10	—	266	April 1991	Sado kisen kaisha

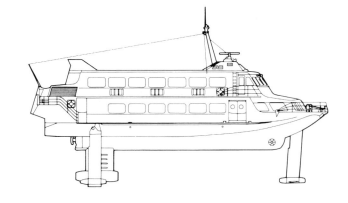
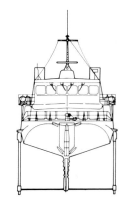
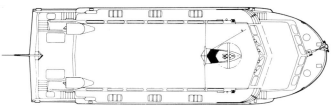

General arrangement of Kawasaki Jetfoil 929–117

Kawasaki Jetfoil *Tsubasa*

Kawasaki Jetfoil *Nagasaki*

KOREA, SOUTH

HYUNDAI HEAVY INDUSTRIES COMPANY LIMITED
Special and Naval Shipbuilding Division
1, Cheonha-Dong, Dong-Gu, Ulsan, Kyung-Nam, South Korea

Telephone: (0522) 32 1101/1307/1308
Telex: 52220HYARD K
Telefax: (0522) 32 4007

K H Jun, *Senior Manager of Marketing and Business Department*

RHS 70
Builder of a RHS 70 hydrofoil, *Angel IX*, which entered service with Hanryeo Development Co Ltd, Seoul, in January 1985.
ACCOMMODATION: 71 passengers.
ENGINE: One MTU 12V 493, 1350bhp at 1500rpm.
DIMENSIONS
Length overall: 21.87m
Beam over deck: 4.80m
Width across foils: 7.78m
Draught, hullborne: 2.70m
Draught, on foils, cruising: 1.15m
WEIGHT
Displacement, fully loaded: 32.0 tonnes

Hyundai RHS 70 hydrofoil *Angel IX*

(Hyundai)

MALTA

SEASPEED Ltd
Malta

Subsidiary company of Rodriquez SpA, Messina,
Italy

Craft building
RHS 160F Alijumbo Stromboli 001/160 Italy,
Aliscafi SNAV SpA
RHS 160F 004/160

ROMANIA

HYDROFOIL PATROL VESSELS
Pleases see 1989 edition of this book for details
of the Chinese-designed Hu Chwan class hydrofoil
torpedo boats built for the Romanian Navy.

SWITZERLAND

SUPRAMAR HYDROFOILS LIMITED
(PATENT HOLDERS AND DESIGNERS)
Ausserfeld 5, CH-6362 Stansstad, Switzerland

Telephone: (041) 613194
Telex: 78228SUPR CH
Telefax: 8142441

Dipl Ing Volker Jost, *President*
Dipl Ing Harry Trevisani, *General Manager*
Dipl Ing Eugen Schatté, *Research and Development*
Dr Ing Herrmann de Witt, *Hydrodynamics*
Dipl Ing Otto Münch, *Stabilisation and Control*
Jürg Bally, *Board Member*

Supramar Hydrofoils Ltd and its predecessor
Supramar Ltd (formed in 1952) developed on a
commercial basis the hydrofoil system introduced
by the Schertel-Sachsenberg Hydrofoil syndicate
and its licensee, the Gebrüder Sachsenberg Shipyard. The development started in the 1930s and
led to the realisation of a number of military
hydrofoils of up to 80 tonnes displacement and 41
knots in speed.

The inherently stable, rigid surface-piercing
V-foil system which is typical for the Supramar
type craft was developed by the late Baron Hanns
von Schertel.

In May 1953 the world's first passenger hydrofoil service started on Lake Maggiore in Italy with
a Supramar type PT 10 craft *Freccia d'Oro*. She
was later transferred to Lake Lucerne. A larger
craft, the PT 20 was first built by Lürssen Shipyard

in 1953 and named *Bremen Pioneer*. Since then
many Supramar type hydrofoils have been built
under licence from Supramar, mainly by
Rodriquez, Hitachi and Westermoen and in 1986
Venkatapathy Engineering (PTE) Ltd, India, also
became a licensee. Full details of all Supramar
designs are given in *Jane's Surface Skimmers 1985*
and earlier editions. A considerable number of
Supramar PT 20 and PT 50 hydrofoil vessels are
still in service.

Supramar Hydrofoils Ltd is also engaged in
new designs of high-speed craft such as fast monohulls and catamarans as well as general engineering services. The company has recently completed the re-engining of Kometa type hydrofoils,
which involved the substitution of the original
Russian engines by MTU diesel engines.

UNION OF SOVIET SOCIALIST REPUBLICS

KRASNOYE SORMOVO
A A ZHDANOV
SHIPYARD
Head Office and Works: Gorki, USSR

M Yuriev, *Shipyard Director*
Ivan Yerlykin, *Chief Hydrofoil Designer*

Export Enquiries: V/O Sudoexport USSR,
Moscow 123231, Chaikovsky St. 11, USSR

Telephone: (095) 255 18 13
Telex: 411116, KURS SU

Krasnoye Sormovo is one of the oldest established shipyards in the Soviet Union. In addition
to building displacement craft of many kinds for
the Soviet River Fleet, the yard constructs the
world's widest range of passenger hydrofoils,
many of which are equipped with the Alexeyev
shallow draught submerged foil system. The late
Dr Alexeyev started work at the end of 1945 on
the design of his foil system which had to be
suitable for operation on smooth, but open and
shallow rivers and canals. He succeeded in making
use of the immersion depth effect, or surface effect,
for stabilising the foil immersion in calm waters
by the use of small lift coefficients.

The system comprises two main horizontal
lifting surfaces, one forward and one aft, with
little or no dihedral, each carrying approximately
half the weight of the vessel. A submerged foil
loses lift gradually as it approaches the surface
from a submergence of about one chord. This

effect prevents the submerged foils from rising
completely to the surface. Means therefore had to
be provided to assist take-off and prevent the
vessel from sinking back to the displacement condition. The answer lay in the provision of planing
sub-foils of small aspect ratio in the vicinity of the
forward struts arranged so that when they are
touching the water surface the main foils are submerged approximately to a depth of one chord.

The approach embodies characteristics of the
Grunberg principle of inherent angle of attack
variation, comprising a 'wing' and a stabiliser
system. When the Alexeyev foils drop below the
shallow draught zone, the craft converts momentarily to the Grunberg mode of operation,
duplicating its configuration. The otherwise inactive sub-foils, coming into contact with the water
surface, become the Grunberg stabilisers and
cause the foils to climb up into the shallow draught
zone where they resume normal operation in the
Alexeyev mode.

The foils have good riding characteristics on
inland waters and in sheltered waters.

The system was first tested on a small launch
powered by a 77bhp converted car engine. Three
more small craft were built to prove the idea, then
work began on the yard's first multi-seat passenger
craft, the Raketa, the first of which was launched
in June 1957 and has completed more than 25
years of service.

The yard also co-operates with the Leningrad
Water Transport Institute in the development of
seagoing craft with fully submerged V-type and
trapeze-type surface-piercing foils, similar in configuration to those of the Schertel-Sachsenberg

system. Craft employing V or trapeze foils are
generally described as being of the Strela-type,
Strela being the first operational Soviet design to
use trapeze foils. Seating 82 to 94 passengers, the
vessel is powered by two M-50 diesels and in
appearance is a cross between the PT 20 and the
PT 50, though smaller than the latter. A military
derivative, the Pchela (Bee), is employed by the
Soviet frontier police for coastal patrol in the
Baltic and Black Seas.

The first hydrofoil vessels to enter service with
the Soviet Navy were the 75-ton 'P8' class,
wooden-hulled torpedo boats which were
equipped with bow foils and gas-turbine boost.
These have now been retired. No new military
hydrofoils have appeared since the Babochka in
1978.

Included in this entry are illustrations of the
260-tonne Matka (pre 1977), which was designed
to replace the 25-year-old Osa missilecraft. Like
the Turya (pre 1973) fast-attack torpedo craft,
also based on an Osa hull, Matka has a bow foil
only. Powered by three 5000hp radial-type diesels
it has a top speed of 40 to 45 knots under calm
conditions. Other military hydrofoil craft are a
330-tonne fast strike craft, known to NATO by
the code name Sarancha, and the 400-tonne fast
patrol boat known as Babochka. The Sarancha,
armed with four SS-N-9 missiles is capable of
speeds in excess of 50 knots. With an overall
length of 50m and a maximum weight of 400
tonnes, Babochka is the biggest military hydrofoil
in operational service in the world.

Soviet passenger hydrofoils in production or
being prepared for series production at yards on

the Baltic and Black Seas are the Zenit, designed to replace Meteor and the Albatros and Kolkhida, Kometa replacements with seats for 120, stability augmentation and speeds of 36 knots. Smaller hydrofoils are also under development including the 50-seat Polesye at the river-craft shipyard at Gomel and Lastochka, which has been designed to supercede Voskhod.

Substantial numbers of Soviet hydrofoils have been exported, especially Kometas, Meteors, Raketas, Voskhods, Volgas and recently three Kolkhidas, which have been sold to a Greek operator. Countries in which they are being or have been operated include Austria, Bulgaria, Czechoslovakia, Finland, Yugoslavia, Italy, Iran, France, Cyprus, Greece, East Germany, Morocco, Spain, West Germany, the Philippines, Poland, Romania, the United Kingdom and the USA.

CIVIL CRAFT

RAKETA

The prototype Raketa was launched in 1957 and was the first multi-seat passenger hydrofoil to employ the Alexeyev shallow draught submerged foil system. Several hundred are now in service on all the major rivers of the Soviet Union.

In August 1982 it was announced that the prototype was still in service and has carried more than two million passengers. The distance travelled by the craft during the period was stated to be equal to '52 voyages around the equator'.

More than 300 Raketas are being operated on rivers and lakes in the Soviet Union, including 66 in service with the Volga United River Shipping Agency.

Variants include the standard non-tropicalised Raketa M, seating 64 passengers; the 58-seat Raketa T, which is both tropicalised and air-conditioned, and the Raketa TA, which was modified in London by Airavia Ltd and licensed by the UK Department of Trade to carry up to 100 passengers (58 seated) on high-density commuter and tourist routes on sheltered waters such as Westminster-Greenwich. On short-range commuter services additional passengers are seated around the promenade deck aft and others can stand.

A substantial number of Raketas have been exported. Examples are in service in Austria, Bulgaria, Czechoslovakia, the Federal Republic of Germany, Hungary, Poland, Romania and Yugoslavia.

Production of the Raketa has now stopped and yards previously involved in their construction are building Voskhod and other designs.

The description that follows applies to the Raketa T, the standard export variant, powered by an M-401A diesel and with a cruising speed of about 58km/h (32 knots).

The vessel is designed for high-speed passenger ferry services during daylight hours on rivers reservoirs and sheltered waters in tropical climates. It meets the requirements of the Soviet River Register Class 'O' with operation restricted to 0.8m waves when foilborne and up to 1.5m when hullborne.

The passenger saloon is provided with natural and induced ventilation and seats 58. The crew comprises a captain, engineer, deckhand and barman.

FOILS: The foil system comprises one bow foil, one aft foil and two dart-like planing sub-foils, the tips of which are attached to the trailing edges of the outer bow foil struts. Foils, sub-foils and struts are in welded stainless steel. The bow foil, which incorporates sweepback, and the straight aft foil, are both supported by three vertical struts.

The base of the centre strut aft provides the end bearing for the propeller which is beneath the foil.

HULL: The hull is framed on longitudinal and transverse formers and all the main elements-plating, deck, partitions, bulkheads, platforms

Principal Civil hydrofoil craft built in the USSR

Type	Yard	No of seats	First launched
Raketa (produced in quantity and exported)		58	1957
Meteor (produced in quantity and exported)	Gorki	116	1960
Kometa (produced in quantity and exported)	Poti & Feodosiya	100	
Sputnik	Gorki	300	1961
Mir		92	1961
Strela (two built)		94	1962
Vikhr (seagoing verison of Sputnik)		268	1962
Burevestnik (one built)		130–150	1964
Chaika	Gomel		1965
Byelorus			1965
Kometa-ME		116–120	1968
Typhoon (one built)	Leningrad	98–105	1969
Voskhod (produced in quantity and exported)	Gorki	71	1969
Delphin (Strela derivative)			pre 1968
Nevka (in production 1969–70)	Leningrad		1969
Volga		6	1972
Voskhod-2			1974
Kolkhida (exported to Greece, Italy and Yugoslavia) & Albatros (replacement for Kometas)	Poti	120	1980
Tsiklon (Cyclone)	Poti	270	1987
Polesye	Gomel	53	1985
Lastochka (replacement for Voskhod)		64	1986
Cyclone		250	1986

Military

Type	Number built	Weight	In service
P8-Class (wooden hull)		-	retired
Pchela	2	75 tonnes	1968 or earlier
Turya	30	250 tonnes	1973 or earlier
Matka	16	260 tonnes	1977 or earlier
Sarancha (NATO code name)	1	320 tonnes	1977 or earlier
Babochka	1	400 tonnes	1978 or earlier
Muravey	1 +	230 tonnes	1983

Raketa operating as fire tender in Leningrad

Bow foil and planing stabiliser foils of Raketa

and wheelhouse-are in riveted duralumin. The stem is fabricated in interwelded steel strips. Below the freeboard deck the hull is divided into six watertight compartments employing web framing.

ACCOMMODATION: The passenger saloon seats 58 in aircraft-type, adjustable seats. At the aft end of the saloon is a bar. The saloon has one exit on each side leading to the promenade deck and one forward, leading to the forecastle. Aft of the saloon is the engine room, promenade deck with additional seats, two toilets, a storeroom and a companionway leading up to the wheelhouse.

The craft carries a full range of life-saving and firefighting equipment. There are 62 life jackets stowed in the passenger saloon and four for the crew in the wheelhouse and under the embarkation companionway. Two lifebelts are provided on the embarkation platform and two on the promenade deck. Firefighting equipment includes four foam and four CO_2 fire extinguishers, two fire axes, two fire buckets and two felt cloths.

POWER PLANT: Power is supplied by a single M-401A water-cooled, supercharged 12-cylinder V-type diesel, with a normal service output of 900hp. The engine drives, via a reverse gear and inclined stainless steel propeller shaft, a three-bladed cast bronze propeller. The fuel system comprises two fuel tanks with a total capacity of 1400kg, a fuel priming unit, and a hand fuel booster pump. A compressed air system, comprising a propeller shaft-driven air compressor and two 40-litre compressed air bottles, is provided for main engine starting, emergency stopping, operating the foghorn and scavenging the water intake.

The diesel generator unit comprises a Perkins P3.152 diesel engine employed in conjunction with a Stamford C20 alternator.

CONTROLS: The wheelhouse is equipped with a hydraulic remote control system for the engine, reverse gear and fuel supply. The balanced rudder, made in aluminium-magnesium alloy, is controlled hydraulically by turning the wheel. A hand tiller is employed in an emergency. Employment of gas exhaust as a side-thruster to assist mooring is permitted at 850rpm.

SYSTEMS, ELECTRICAL: A 3kW generator, rated at 27.5V and coupled to the main engine, is the main source of power while the vessel is under way. A 50Hz, 230V, 1500rpm three-phase alternator supplies ac power. Four 12V acid storage batteries, each with a 132Ah capacity and connected in series to give 24V, supply power during short stops.

HYDRAULICS: The hydraulic system for controlling the main engine, reverse gear and fuel supply, consists of control levers located in the wheelhouse and on the main engine, power cylinders located on the engine, a filler tank, pipelines and fittings.

HEATING AND VENTILATION: Passenger saloon and wheelhouse are provided with natural ventilation, using ram inflow when the boat is in

Raketa M

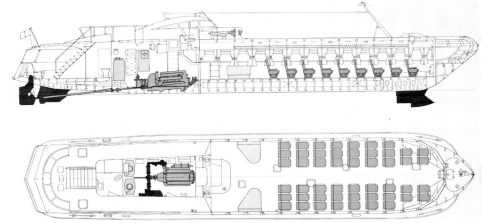

Inboard profile and plan view of standard 50-seat Raketa

motion. Norris Warming air-conditioning is fitted for use in hot weather. One conditioner is installed in the wheelhouse and eight are installed in the passenger saloon and bar. The cooled air is distributed throughout the saloon by electric fans installed on the ceiling. One is provided in the wheelhouse. A radio-telephone with a range of about 30km (19 miles) is installed for ship-to-shore and ship-to-ship communication. The vessel also has a public address system and intercom speakers linking the engine room, wheelhouse and forecastle.

DIMENSIONS
Length overall: 26.96m
Beam amidships: 5m
Freeboard: 0.8m
Height overall (excluding mast): 4.46m
Draught, hullborne: 1.8m
  foilborne: 1.1m
WEIGHTS
Displacement, fully loaded: 27.09 tonnes
  light: 20.31 tonnes

PERFORMANCE
Service speed: about 58km/h
Max wave height, foilborne: 0.8m
  hullborne: 1.5m
Turning diameter, hullborne: 3–4 boat lengths
  foilborne: 15–16 boat lengths

METEOR

Dr Alexeyev's Meteor made its maiden voyage from Gorki to Moscow in 1960, bringing high performance and unprecedented comfort to river boat fleets, and setting the pattern for a family of later designs.

The craft is intended for use in daylight hours on local and medium-range routes of up to 600km in length. It meets the requirements of Class O, experimental type, on the Register of River Shipping in the USSR.

Accommodation is provided for a crew of five and 116 passengers. Cruising speed at the full load displacement of 54.3 tonnes across calm water

Meteor

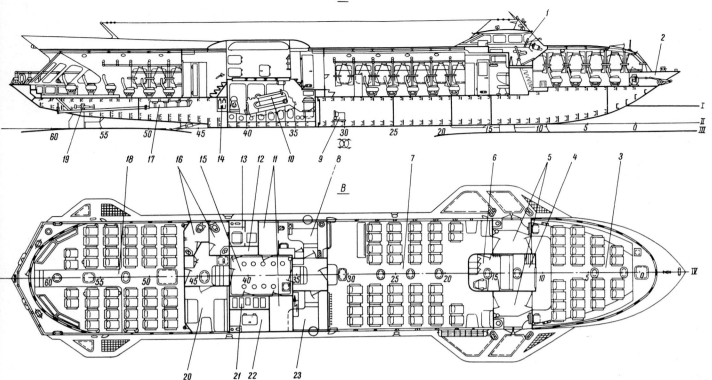

Meteor:
(**A**) inboard profile (**B**) main deck plan (**I**) waterline hullborne (**II**) hull base line (**III**) waterline foilborne (**IV**) longitudinal centreline (**1**) wheelhouse (**2**) anchor compartment (**3**) forward passenger saloon, 26 seats (**4**) luggage rack (**5**) embarkation companionway (**6**) crew duty room (**7**) midship passenger saloon, 42 seats (**8**) bar (**9**) refrigeration unit (**10**) engine room (**11**) pantry (**12**) boatswain's store (**13**) calorifier (**14**) fire fighting equipment (**15**) promenade deck (**16**) wcs (**17**) tank (**18**) aft passenger saloon, 44 seats (**19**) tiller gear (**20**) four-seat passenger cabin (**21**) storage batteries (**22**) hydraulic units (**23**) main switchboard

and in winds of up to Beaufort Force 3 is about 65km/h.

Outside the Soviet Union Meteors are operated in Bulgaria, Hungary, Poland and Yugoslavia.

FOILS: The foil arrangement comprises a bow foil and a stern foil, with the struts of the bow system carrying two additional planing sub-foils. The foils are attached to the struts, which are of split type, by flanges and bolts. The foils are in stainless steel, and the sub-foils in aluminium magnesium alloy. The foil incidence can be adjusted when necessary by the insertion of wedges between the flanges and the foils when the vessel is in dock.

HULL: With the exception of the small exposed areas fore and aft, the Meteor's hull and superstructure are built as an integral unit. The hull is framed on longitudinal and transverse formers and both hull and superstructure are of riveted duralumin construction with welded steel members. Below the main deck the hull is subdivided longitudinally into eight compartments by seven bulkheads. Access to the compartments is via hatches in the main deck. The craft will remain afloat in the event of any two adjacent compartments forward of amidship flooding or any one compartment aft of midship. Frame spacing in the hull is about 500mm while that in the superstructure is 1000mm.

POWER PLANT: Power is supplied by two M-401A 12-cylinder, four-stroke, supercharged, water-cooled diesels with reversing clutches. Each engine has a normal service output of 1000hp at 1700rpm and a maximum output of 1100hp at 1800rpm. Specific consumption at rated output g/bhp/h is not more than 193, and oil, not more than 6. Guaranteed overhaul life is 1000 hours. Each engine drives its own inclined propeller shaft through a reverse clutch. Propeller shafts are in steel and the propellers, which are five-bladed, are in brass. The drives are contra-rotating.

Refuelling is via filler necks on each side of the hull. Fuel is carried in six tanks located in the engine room. Total fuel capacity is 3200kg.

Meteor operating in Leningrad   (J K Pemberton)

Lubricating oil, total capacity 370 litres, is carried in two service tanks and a storage tank located on the forward bulkhead in the engine room. Fuel and lubricating oil are sufficient for a cruising range, foilborne, of not less than 600km.

AUXILIARY UNIT: 12hp diesel for generating electrical power when the craft is at its moorings, warming the main engines in cold weather and operating drainage pump.

CONTROLS: Control of the engines, reverse gear and fuel supply is effected remotely from the wheelhouse with the aid of a hydraulic system comprising transmitter cylinders in the wheelhouse, and actuators on the engine. The engines can also be controlled from the engine room.

Craft heading is controlled by two balanced rudders, the blades of which are in solid aluminium magnesium alloy. The rudders are operated hydraulically from the wheelhouse, the rudder angle being checked by an electric indicator in the wheelhouse. In an emergency, with the craft in hullborne conditions, the rudder is put

over with the aid of a detachable hand tiller fitted to the rudder stock.

At low speed the craft can turn in its own length by pinwheeling—employing both engines with equal power in opposite directions—one ahead, the other astern.

Minimum diameter of the turning circle is approximately 250m with the engines running at low speed (700–750rpm) and with the rudder put through an angle of 35 degrees. Turning circle diameter when operating foilborne with the rudder at an angle of 10 degrees is approximately 750m.

The vessel takes off for foilborne flight in 120 to 140 seconds, ie within a distance of 25 to 28 lengths of its hull.

Landing run, with engines reversed, ranges from 1.5 to 2 hull lengths, while the braking distance without reversing the engines is within 3 to 4 lengths of the hull.

ACCOMMODATION: Passengers are accommodated in three compartments, a forward saloon seating 26, and central and aft saloons seating 46 and 44 passengers respectively. The central saloon has three exits, two forward leading to the embarkation platforms and one aft leading to the promenade deck above the engine room. On the port side of the central saloon, aft, is a small buffet/bar. Beneath the wheelhouse is a duty crew room and a luggage compartment which opens into the forward saloon.

The aft saloon has two exits, one leading to the promenade deck above the engine room and one to the weather deck aft. Forward and aft on both sides of the craft are sponsons to protect the foil systems during mooring. The forward pair are used as embarkation and disembarkation platforms.

SYSTEMS, ELECTRICAL: 24 to 28.5V dc from the vessel's power supply or 220V ac, 50Hz, from shore-to-ship supply sources.

RADIO: Ship-to-shore radio telephone operating on any of ten pre-selected fixed frequencies. Also passenger announcement system and crew intercom.

NAVIGATION: Magnetic compass.

COMPRESSED AIR: System comprises two 40-litre air storage bottles for starting the main engines, operating emergency stop mechanism, closing feed cocks of the fuel tanks, recharging the hydraulic system accumulator and the ship's siren.

FIREFIGHTING: Remote system for fighting outbreak in engine room, with automatic light and sound indicator operating in wheelhouse. Hand-operated foam and CO_2 extinguishers provided in passenger saloons and wheelhouse.

DIMENSIONS
Length overall: 34.6m
Beam overall: 9.5m
Height foilborne above water surface: 6.8m
Draught hullborne: 2.35m
     foilborne: 1.2m
WEIGHTS
Light displacement: 36.4 tonnes
Fully loaded: 53.4 tonnes
PERFORMANCE
Cruising speed, calm water: 65km/h
Endurance: 600km
Limiting Sea States, foilborne: Beaufort Force 3
     hullborne: Beaufort Force 4

SERGO ORDZHONIKIDZE SHIPYARD

KOMETA

Derived from the earlier Meteor, the Kometa was the first seagoing hydrofoil to be built in the Soviet Union. The prototype, seating 100 passengers, made its maiden voyage on the Black Sea in 1961, after which it was employed on various passenger routes on an experimental basis. Operating experience accumulated on these services led to the introduction of various modifications before the craft was put into series production.

Kometas are built mainly at the S. Ordzhonikidze Shipbuilding and Repair Yard at Poti on the Black Sea and the Feodosiya Yard.

Kometa operators outside the Soviet Union include Kompas Line, Yugoslavia; Empresa Nacional de Cabotage, Cuba; Alilauro SpA, Naples, Italy; and Transportes Touristiques Intercontinentaux, Morocco. Other vessels of this type have been supplied to Bulgaria, German Democratic Republic, Greece, Iran, Poland, Romania and Turkey. More than 60 have been exported.

Export orders have mainly been for the Kometa-ME, designed for service in countries with a moderate climate, which was introduced in 1968. Two distinguishing features of this model are the employment of new diesel engines, with increased operating hours between overhauls, and a completely revised surface-piercing foil system, with a trapeze bow foil instead of the former Alexeyev shallow draught submerged type.

Kometa craft built

Type	Name	Yard	Built	Operator/area in USSR
	10	—	1967	Sochi
	12	—	1967	Sochi
	13	Poti	1968	Odessa
	16	Poti	1969	Odessa
	17	Poti	1970	Yalta
Kometa	19	Poti	1973	Azov Shipping Co, Zhdanov
	20	Poti	1973	—
	21	Poti	1982	—
	21	Poti	1974	Caspian Shipping Co, Astrakan
	22	Poti	1974	Azov Shipping Co, Zhdanov
	23	Poti	1974	Yalta
	24	Poti	1975	Sochi
	25	Poti	1975	Murmansk
	27	Poti	1975	Black Sea Shipping Co
	28	Poti	1975	Caspian Shipping Co
	29	Poti	1976	—
	30	Poti	1976	Murmansk Shipping Co
	31	Poti	1977	—
	32	Poti	1977	Black Sea Shipping Co
	33	Poti	1976	Sochi
	34	Poti	1977	Soviet Danube Shipping Co, Izmail
Kometa	35	Poti	1978	Soviet Danube Shipping Co, Izmail
Kometa	36	Poti	1978	Soviet Danube Shipping Co, Izmail
	38	—	1978	USSR
	40	—	1979	Black Sea Shipping Co, Yalta
	41	—	1979	Black Sea Shipping Co, Odessa
	43	—	1980	—
	46	—	1980	—
	47	—	1980	—
	48	—	1981	—
	49	—	1981	—
	51	—	1981	—
	53	—	1982	—
	54	—	1982	—
	55	—	1982	—
	57	—	1983	—

Some of the above Kometas may have been exported. The following list shows Kometas operated outside the USSR:

Kometa craft built

Type	Name	Yard	Built	Operator/area
Kometa	1	—	1962	Navigation Maritime Bulgare (1977), Varna, Bulgaria
Kometa	2	Poti	1979	Navigation Maritime Bulgare
Kometa	2	Poti	1965	Navigation Maritime Bulgare
Kometa	3	—	1979	Navigation Maritime Bulgare
Kometa	Daria (ex 4)	Poti	1967	Zegluga Szczecinska, Poland (ex Navigation Maritime Bulgare)
Kometa	5	Poti	1970	Navigation Maritime Bulgare
Kometa	6	—	1972	Navigation Maritime Bulgare
Kometa	7	Poti	1974	Navigation Maritime Bulgare
Kometa	8	Poti	1974	Navigation Maritime Bulgare
Kometa	9	—	1974	Navigation Maritime Bulgare
Kometa	10	—	1975	Navigation Maritime Bulgare
Kometa	11	—	1975	Navigation Maritime Bulgare
Kometa	12	—	1976	Navigation Maritime Bulgare
Kometa-MT	18	Poti	1973	Empresa Nacional de Cabotage, Cuba
Kometa-MT	Scheherazade (ex 37)	Feodosiya	197?	(ex Transtour SA, Morocco, ex Black Sea Shipping Co, Odessa)
Kometa-MT	Sindibad	—	1968	Transtour SA, Morocco
Kometa-MT	Aladin	—	1971	Transtour SA, Morocco
Kometa	Aliapollo 1984 (ex Alitunisi, ex Alispan Secondo, 1980, ex Atalanta, 1971)	Feodosiya	1970	Alilauro SpA
Kometa	Alieros (ex Aliconamar, 1984, ex Alibastea, 1982)	Poti	1973	Alilauro SpA
Kometa	Alivenere (ex Aligiglio)	Poti	1972	Alilauro SpA
Kometa	Alisaturno (ex Alielba)	Poti	1972	Alivit Due
Kometa	Alisorrento	—	—	Alilauro SpA
Kometa	Alivesuvio	—	—	Alilauro SpA
Kometa	Alivulcano 1977 (ex Alipan Primo, 1977, ex Lepa Vida, 1970)	Poti	1970	Alilauro SpA

A fully tropicalised and air-conditioned version is now in production and designated Kometa-MT.

The present standard production Kometa-ME seats 116 to 120. Because of the additional weight of the Kometa-MT's air-conditioning system and other refinements, the seating capacity is reduced in the interest of passenger comfort to 102.

Official designation of the Kometa in the USSR is Hydrofoil Type 342. The craft meets the requirements of the Rules of the Register of Shipping of the USSR and is constructed to Hydrofoil Class KM ★ 2 11 Passenger Class under the Register's technical supervision. IMCO recommendations on fire safety are taken into account and non-flammable basalt fibres are employed for sound and heat insulation and the engine room is clad with titanium plating. The craft is designed to operate during daylight hours on coastal routes up to 81km from ports of refuge under moderate climatic conditions.

The standard craft has proved to be exceptionally robust and has a good, all-round performance. On one charter, a Kometa-ME covered 5310km by sea and river in 127 hours. It can operate foilborne in waves up to 1.7m and travel hullborne in waves up to 3.6m.

One of the features of the more recent models is the relocation of the engine room aft to reduce the noise in the passenger saloons and the employment of a V-drive instead of the existing inclined shaft. The arrangement is expected to be similar to that on the Voskhod-2. The revised deck configuration allows more seats to be fitted. These modifications are also incorporated in the recently announced Kometa derivative, the Kolkhida, which will be fitted with two 1500hp engines.

FOILS: Employment of a surface-piercing trapeze-type bow foil provides the Kometa-ME with improved seakeeping capability in waves. The foil system comprises a bow foil, aft foil, and two auxiliaries, one (termed 'stabiliser') located above the bow foil for pitch stability, the other sited amidship near the longitudinal centre of gravity to assist take-off. The foils are connected to the hull by struts and brackets. Middle and side struts of the bow foil are of the split type. The lower and upper components of each strut are connected by flanges and bolts. The upper sections are connected to the hull by the same means.

The bow and stern foils are of hollow welded stainless steel construction. The midship and pitch stability foils and the upper components of the foil struts are in aluminium-magnesium alloy.

HULL: Similar in shape to that of the earlier Meteor, the hull has a wedge-shaped bow, raked stem and a spoon-shaped stern. Hull and superstructure are built in AlMg-61 and AlMg-6 alloys. Hull and superstructure are of all-welded construction using contact and argon arc welding. The hull is framed on longitudinal and transverse

Kometa craft built

Type	Name	Yard	Built	Operator/area
Kometa	*Freccia Pontina* (ex *Wera*)	Poti	1978	Societa di Navigazione Basso Lazio srl, Gaeta, Italy
Kometa	*Poseidon*	—	1970	Intreprinderea de Exploatare a Floti Maritime NAVROM, Galatz, Romania
Kometa-M	*Flying Dolphin I*	Poti	1975	Ceres Flying Hydroways Ltd, Piraeus, Greece
Kometa-M	*Flying Dolphin II*	Poti	1975	Ceres Flying Hydroways Ltd, Piraeus, Greece
Kometa-M	*Flying Dolphin III*	Poti	1976	Ceres Flying Hydroways Ltd, Piraeus, Greece
Kometa-M	*Flying Dolphin IV*	Poti	1977	Ceres Flying Hydroways Ltd, Piraeus, Greece
Kometa-M	*Flying Dolphin V*	Poti	1976	Ceres Flying Hydroways Ltd, Piraeus, Greece
Kometa-M	*Flying Dolphin VI*	Poti	1976	Ceres Flying Hydroways Ltd, Piraeus, Greece
Kometa-M	*Flying Dolphin VII*	Poti	1976	Ceres Flying Hydroways Ltd, Piraeus, Greece
Kometa-M	*Flying Dolphin VIII*	Poti	1977	Ceres Flying Hydroways Ltd, Piraeus, Greece
Kometa-M	*Flying Dolphin IX*	Poti		
Kometa-M	*Flying Dolphin X*	Poti	1978	Ceres Flying Hydroways Ltd, Piraeus, Greece
Kometa-M	*Flying Dolphin XI*	Poti	1979	Ceres Flying Hydroways Ltd, Piraeus, Greece
Kometa-M	*Flying Dolphin XII*	Poti	1979	Ceres Flying Hydroways Ltd, Piraeus, Greece
Kometa-M	*Flying Dolphin XIV*	Poti	1981	Ceres Flying Hydroways Ltd, Piraeus, Greece
Kometa-M	*Flying Dolphin XV*	Poti	1981	Ceres Flying Hydroways Ltd, Piraeus, Greece
Kometa-M	*Flying Dolphin XVI*	Poti	1981	Ceres Flying Hydroways Ltd, Piraeus, Greece

formers, the spacing throughout the length of the hull is 500mm and in the superstructure 1000mm.

Below the freeboard deck, the hull is divided by watertight bulkheads into thirteen compartments, which include the engine room, fuel compartments, and those containing the firefighting system, tiller gear and fuel transfer pump.

ACCOMMODATION: The Kometa-MT seats 102 passengers. It carries an operating crew of six, comprising captain, engineer, motorman, radio-operator, seaman, and one barman. Embarkation platforms immediately below the wheelhouse provide passenger and crew access.

The captain and engineer are accommodated in a raised wheelhouse located between the forward and main saloons, and equipped with two seats, a folding stool, chart table, sun shield and a locker for signal flags. The wheelhouse also contains a radar display and radio communications equipment.

Main engine controls are installed in both the wheelhouse and engine room.

Passengers are accommodated in three compartments, a forward saloon seating 22, and central and aft saloons seating 54 and 26 respectively. The central saloon has three exits, two forward, leading to the embarkation platforms, and one aft, leading to the promenade deck. This is located in the space above the engine room and is partially covered with a removable metallic awning.

In the current production model of the Kometa-ME, the forward saloon seats 24, the central saloon 56 and the aft saloon 36.

To the starboard side is a crew's off-duty cabin, hydraulic system pump room, bar store and bar,

A Kometa of Kompas Line, Yugoslavia, arriving at Venice, June 1986

and to the port are two toilets, boiler room, battery room and fire extinguishing equipment.

The aft saloon has two exits, one forward leading to the promenade deck, the other aft, leading to the weather deck, which is used for embarking and disembarking when the vessel is moored by the stern.

Floors of the passenger saloons, crew's cabins, bar and wheelhouse are covered in linoleum and the deckhead in the passenger saloons, as well as bulkheads and the sides above the lower edge of the windows, are finished in light coloured Pavinol. Panels of the saloons beneath the windows are covered with plastic.

Passenger saloons are fitted with upholstered chairs, racks for small hand luggage and pegs for clothing. The middle and aft saloons have niches for hand luggage and the former is fitted with cradles for babies. The bar is fully equipped with glass washers, an ice safe, an automatic Freon compressor, electric stove, etc.

SAFETY EQUIPMENT: A full range of life-saving equipment is carried including five inflatable life rafts, each for 25 persons, 135 life jackets, and four circular life belts with life lines and self-igniting buoyant lights. There are two life rafts on the forward sponsons and two on the aft sponsons. When thrown into the water the life rafts inflate automatically. Life jackets are stowed under the seats in all saloons, and the circular life belts are stowed on the embarkation and promenade platforms. Kometas for export are provided with life jackets on the basis of 25 persons per raft.

FIREFIGHTING EQUIPMENT: An independent fluid firefighting system is provided for the engine room and fuel bay. An automatic light and sound system signals a fire outbreak. The firefighting system is put into operation manually from the control deck above the engine room door. Boat spaces are equipped with hand-operated foam and CO_2 fire extinguishers, felt cloths and fire axes.

POWERPLANT: Power is supplied by two M-401A water-cooled, supercharged 12-cylinder V-type diesels, each with a normal service output of 1000hp at 1550rpm and a maximum output of 1100hp at 1600rpm. Guaranteed service life of each engine before first overhaul is 2500 hours. Each engine drives via a reverse gear its own inclined shaft and the twin propellers are contra-rotating. The shafts are of steel and are parallel to the craft.

The propellers are of three-bladed design and made of brass.

Main engine controls and gauges are installed in both the wheelhouse and the engine room. A diesel-generator compressor-pump unit is provided for charging starter air bottles; supplying electric power when at rest; warming the main engines in cold weather and pumping warm air beneath the deck to dry the bilges.

Diesel oil tanks with a total capacity of 3000kg for the main engines and the auxiliary unit are located in the afterpeak. Two lubricating oil service tanks and one storage tank located at the fore bulkhead of the engine room have a total capacity of 250kg. Diesel and lubricating oil capacity ensures a range of 370km.

CONTROLS: The wheelhouse is equipped with an electro-hydraulic remote control system for the engine reverse gear and fuel supply, fuel monitoring equipment, including electric speed counters, pressure gauges, lubricating and fuel oil gauges. The boat has a single, solid aluminium magnesium alloy balanced rudder, which is controlled through a hydraulic steering system or a hand-operated hydraulic drive. In an emergency, the rudder may be operated by a hand tiller. Maximum rudder angle is 35 degrees in hullborne conditions and 5.6 degrees foilborne. In the event of the steering gear failing the craft can be manoeuvred by differential use of the main engines, the rudder being locked on the centre

Craft built

Type	Name	Yard	Built	Operator/area
Kometa	*Marilena*	—	1981	Nearchos Shipping Co, Greece
Kometa	*Gina*	—	1981	Nearchos Shipping Co, Greece
Kometa	*Poszum*	Poti	1973	Zegluga Gdanska, Gdansk, Poland
	Poweiw	Feodosiya	1973	Zegluga Gdanska, Gdansk, Poland
	Poryw	Poti	1976	Zegluga Gdanska, Gdansk, Poland
	Poswist	Poti	1975	Zegluga Gdanska, Gdansk, Poland
	Pogwizd	Poti	1977	Zegluga Gdanska, Gdansk, Poland
	Polot	Poti	1977	Zegluga Gdanska, Gdansk, Poland
Kometa	*Flying Dolphin*, 1983 (ex *Podmuch*, 1973)	—	—	Motion Shipping Co Ltd, Limassol, Cyprus
Kometa	*Stoertebeker I*	—	1974	Fahrgastechiffahrt Staisund, GDR
	Stoertebeker II	—	1974	Fahrgastechiffahrt Staisund, GDR
Kometa	*Stoertebeker III*	—	1974	Fahrgastechiffahrt Staisund, GDR
Kometa	*Patmos* (ex *Alkyonis I*)	Poti	1978	Dodecanese Hydrofoils, Greece
Kometa	*Rodos* (ex *Alkyonis II*)	Poti	1978	Dodecanese Hydrofoils, Greece
Kometa	-	—	1966	—
Kometa	*Lida*	—	1971	Zegluga Szczecinska, Poland
Kometa	*Kalina*	—	1973	Zegluga Szczecinska, Poland
Kometa	—	—	1975	—
Kometa	*Liwia*	—	1978	Zegluga Szczecinska, Poland
Kometa	—	—	1970	Vedettes Armoricaines, Brest, France
Kometa	*Iran Resalat*, 1980 (ex *Arya Ram*)	Feodosiya	1971	Islamic Republic of Iran Shipping Lines, Khorramshahr, Iran
Kometa	*Iran Taveeghat*, 1980 (ex *Arya Baz*, ex *Kometa S-26*)	Feodosiya	1969	Islamic Republic of Iran Shipping Lines, Khorramshahr, Iran
Kometa	*Krila Kornata*	Poti	1980	Kompas-Jugoslavija, Koper, Yugoslavia
Kometa	*Krila Kvarnera*	Poti	1970	Kompas-Jugoslavija, Koper, Yugoslavia
Kometa	*Krila Pirana*	Poti	1979	Kompas-Jugoslavija, Koper, Yugoslavia
Kometa	*Krila Primorske*	Poti	1980	Kompas-Jugoslavija, Koper, Yugoslavia
Kometa	*Krila Slovenije*	Poti	1977	Kompas-Jugoslavija, Koper, Yugoslavia
Kometa	*Alischia*		1977	Alilauro SpA, Italy
Kometa	*Alicapri*		1983	Alilauro SpA, Italy

line. The vessel can be pinwheeled in hullborne condition by setting one engine slow ahead, the other slow astern and turning the rudder hard over.

SYSTEMS, ELECTRICAL: Power supply is 24V dc. A 1kW dc generator is attached to each of the two engines and these supply power during operation. A 5.6kW generator is included in the auxiliary unit and supplies power when the craft is at rest. It can also be used when under way for supplying the heating plant or when the 1kW generators are inoperative. Four 12V acid storage batteries, each of 180Ah capacity and connected in series to provide 24V, supply power during short stops.

HYDRAULICS: The hydraulic system for controlling the main engines and reverse gear consists of control cylinders located in the wheelhouse, power cylinders located on the engines, a filler tank, pipe lines and fittings.

ANCHORS: The craft is equipped with two Matrosov anchors: a main anchor weighing 75kg and a spare anchor weighing 50kg. The main anchor is raised by an electric winch located in the forepeak. The cable of the spare anchor can be heaved in manually and is wound over a drum fitted with a hand brake.

COMMUNICATIONS: A radio transmitter/ receiver with r/t and w/t facilities is installed in the wheelhouse for ship-to-shore and intership communications on SW and MW bands. A portable emergency radio and automatic distress signal transmitter are also installed in the wheelhouse. A broadcast system is fitted in the passenger saloons and a two-way crew communications system is installed in the wheelhouse,

Kometa-ME

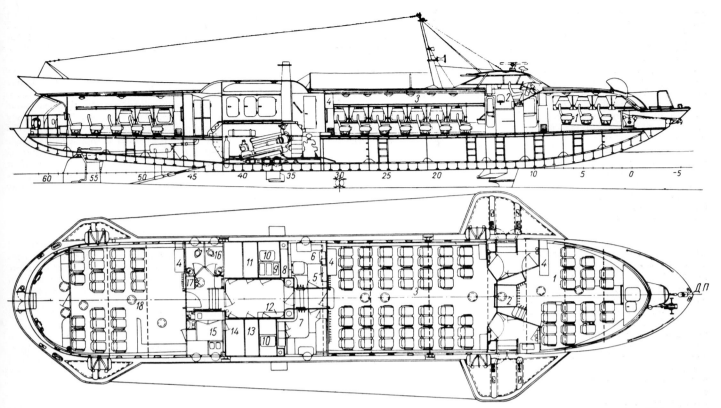

Internal arrangement of Kometa-MT, designed for tropical operation: (1) 22-seat forward passenger saloon (2) wheelhouse (3) 54-seat main passenger saloon (4) luggage rack (5) engine room door (6) control position (7) duty cabin (8) liquid fire extinguisher bay (9) battery room (10) engine room (11) boiler room (12) installation point for portable radio (13) store (14) provision store (15) bar (16) wc washbasin units (17) boatswain's store (18) 26-seat aft passenger saloon

engine room, anchor gear compartment and mooring stations.

NAVIGATION: The following navigation aids are standard: a gyrocompass, magnetic compass (reserve) and log.

KOMETA-ME
DIMENSIONS
Length overall: 35.1m
Beam overall: 11m
Height, foilborne from waterline to tip of mast: 9.2m
Draught, hullborne: 3.6m
  foilborne: 1.7m
WEIGHTS
Light displacement: 44.5 tonnes
Fully loaded displacement: 60 tonnes
PERFORMANCE
Max speed, intermittent: 66.8km/h
Cruising speed: 58km/h
Fuel consumption: 172g/hp/h

Oil consumption: 4.5g/hp/h
Max Sea State: Speed of the Kometa-M at full load displacement in Sea States 0–2 and wind conditions up to Force 3 is 32 knots. Under the worst permissible conditions under which the craft is able to navigate (Sea State 5, Wind Force 6) it will operate hullborne at 10 to 12 knots. Sea States up to 4 and wind conditions up to Force 5 are considered normal for Kometa operation.

KOMETA-MT
DIMENSIONS
Length overall: 35.1m
Beam: 11m
Height, foilborne, waterline to tip of mast: 9.2m
Draught, hullborne: 3.6m
  foilborne: 1.7m
WEIGHTS
Light displacement: 45 tonnes
Fully loaded displacement: 58.9 tonnes

PERFORMANCE
Max speed: 61km/h
Service speed: 58km/h
Fuel consumption: 180g/hp/h
Oil consumption: 5g/hp/h
Range: 240km

Development of the Kometa is continuing. Current research is aimed at the introduction of a stability augmentation system employing either control flaps on the bow foil or air stabilisation on the stern foil and struts; the reduction of labour involved in construction; the introduction of design improvements through the use of grp and sandwich construction; noise reduction in the saloons and the extension of the cruising range.

VOSKHOD-2
Designers of the Voskhod, which has been gradually replacing craft of the Raketa series, drew on engineering experience gained with the Raketa and also the more sophisticated Meteor

Voskhod-2

and Kometa. Voskhod, in turn, was due to be succeeded by the new 50-seat Lastochka.

Among the basic requirements were that the Raketa's general characteristics should be preserved; foilborne operation should be possible in 1m high waves, with a 3 per cent safety factor; accommodation should be acceptable from health and safety viewpoints; noise levels should be significantly reduced, and the maximum use should be made of standard mechanical, electrical and other components and fittings proven on the Raketa.

In fact, the end product bears little resemblance to its predecessor. Visually the Voskhod is more akin to a scaled-down Kometa with its engine room aft, replacing the rear passenger saloon.

In June 1974 Voskhod 2–01 began service on the Gorki-Kineshma route, across the vast Gorki reservoir which cannot be navigated by the Raketa because of its limited seaworthiness. It continued in service until the end of the 1974 navigation season. During this time it was demonstrated that its operating and technical performance was significantly superior to that of the Raketa.

Experience accumulated during this experimental service indicated the need for minor modifications which have been incorporated in the first series of production craft.

Voskhod 14 was launched in June 1980 and delivered to the Amur Line for summer services along the Amur river.

At the time of its inception, it was announced that the Voskhod would be available in a number of versions to suit local navigation and traffic requirements. Voskhod 3 will be powered by a gas turbine.

The vessel is designed for high-speed passenger ferry services during daylight hours on rivers, reservoirs, lakes and sheltered waters. It meets the requirements of Soviet River Register Class 'O' with the following wave restrictions (3% safety margin): foilborne, 1.3m; hullborne, 2m.

The passenger saloons are heated and provided with natural and induced ventilation. Full air-conditioning can be installed in craft required for service in tropical conditions. The crew comprises a captain, engineer, motorman and barman.

FOILS: Fixed foil system, comprising one bow foil with a pitch stability sub-foil immediately behind, one aft foil, plus an amidship foil to facilitate take-off. Bow and amidship foils appear to be of shallow V configuration and each has four vertical struts. The fully submerged stern foil has two side struts and is supported in the centre by the end bracket of the propeller shaft. The surface and lower parts of the foil struts and stabiliser are in Cr18Ni9Ti stainless steel, while the upper parts of the struts and stabiliser and also the amidship foil are in AlMg-61 plate alloy.

HULL: Similar in shape to the Kometa and earlier models of the Sormovo hydrofoil series, with a wedge-shaped bow, raked stem and spoon-shaped stern. A single step is provided to facilitate take-off. In fabricating the basic structure, which is largely in AlMg-61 aluminium magnesium alloy, extensive use has been made of arc and spot welding. The hull is framed on longitudinal and transverse formers. Below the deck it is divided into eight watertight compartments by transverse bulkheads. It will remain afloat with any one compartment or the machinery space flooded. Access to the forepeak, which houses the anchor capstan,

is via the forward passenger saloon and then through a rectangular hatch on the forecastle. Aft of the main passenger saloon is an area split into three compartments by two longitudinal bulkheads. The lower central space contains the reduction gear and V-drive, the starboard compartment contains the sanitary tank and the port compartment forms part of the double-bottom. Entrance to the engine compartment is via a door on the port side of the main deck. An emergency exit is provided starboard aft.

POWERPLANT: Power is supplied by a single M-401A four-stroke water-cooled, supercharged 12-cylinder V-type diesel, delivering 809.6kW at 1600rpm maximum and 736kW at 1550rpm cruising. The engine, which has a variable-speed governor and a reversing clutch, is sited aft with its shaft inclined at 9 degrees. Output is transferred via a flexible coupling to a single six-bladed variable-pitch propeller via an R-21 V-drive gearbox. Guaranteed service life of the engine before the first overhaul is 3000 hours. Specific fuel consumption, including attached units, is not more than 6g/ehp/h. Specific oil consumption is not more than 6g/ehp/h. The engine room is insulated with fire-retardant, heat and sound-insulating materials. Perforated aluminium alloy sheet is laid over the insulating materials.

CONTROLS: Single semi-balanced rudder in AlMg plate provides directional control. Operation of the engine, rudder, reverse gear and fuel supply is effected hydraulically from the wheelhouse.

ACCOMMODATION: Voskhod-2 carries an operating crew of three, comprising captain, engineer and motorman, plus a barman. Embar-

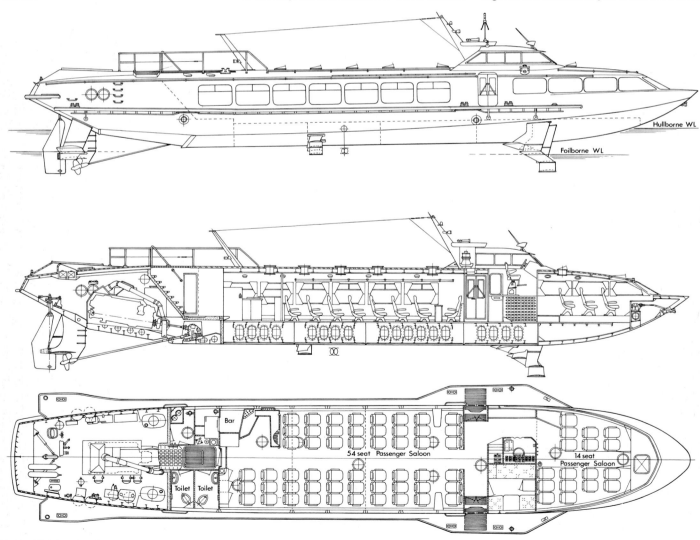

Voskhod-2, inboard profile and deck plan

kation platforms immediately below the wheel-house provide passenger and crew access. Passengers can embark from both sides and from the stern.

The captain and engineer are accommodated in a raised wheelhouse located between the forward and main saloon. Main engine controls are in both the wheelhouse and the engine room.

Passengers are accommodated in two saloons, a forward compartment seating 17 and a main saloon seating 54. The main saloon has three exits, two forward, leading to the embarkation plat-forms, and one aft, leading to the stern embark-ation area. Between the two saloons, on the starboard side, is a crew rest cabin. The saloons are fitted with upholstered seats, racks for small hand-luggage and coat pegs. Spacing between seats is 900mm and the central aisle is 800mm wide.

At the rear of the main saloon is a small buffet and bar and aft of the main saloon, at the foot of the rear embarkation steps, are two wc/washbasin units.

SYSTEMS, ELECTRICAL: Power supply is 24–27V dc. A 3kW generator is attached to the engine and supplies 27.5V while the craft is operating. Four 12V storage batteries, each of 180Ah capacity and connected in series-parallel to form a single bank, supply power during short stops. An auxiliary circuit can be connected to shore systems for 220V, single-phase, 50Hz ac supply.

FIREFIGHTING: Four carbon dioxide and four foam fire extinguishers for the passenger saloons and wheelhouse. Remote-controlled system employing '3.5' compound in the engine room.

HEATING AND VENTILATION: Heating in the saloons is provided by pipes circulating water from the internal cooling circuit of the engine. Ventilation is natural, using the dynamic pressure of the approaching air flow, and induced, by means of electric fans.

During the spring and autumn, the temperature of the ventilating air can be heated to 21°C.

DRINKING WATER: Hot and cold water sup-plies. An electric boiler supplies hot water for washbasins and the small kitchen behind the snackbar. Drinking water tank has a capacity of 138 litres.

BILGE WATER: System designed for bilge water removal by shore-based facilities or service vessels.

ANCHOR: Matrosov system, weighing 35kg, attached to an anchor cable 8.4mm in diameter and 80m long, and operated by hand winch in the forepeak.

DIMENSIONS
EXTERNAL
Length overall: 27.6m
Hull length: 26.3m
Beam overall: 6.2m
Height above mean water level, foilborne, includ-ing mast: 5.7m
Draught hullborne: 2m
    foilborne: 1.1m
INTERNAL
Deck area: 105m²
    per passenger: 1.48m²
WEIGHTS
Displacement, fully loaded: 28 tonnes
Light displacement: 20 tonnes
Passengers per displacement tonne: 2.55
Payload, passengers and buffet/bar equipment: 5.9 tonnes
Payload/displacement: 21.2%

PERFORMANCE
Max speed, calm water, wind not in excess of Force 3,
    at 1550rpm: 70km/h
    at 1450rpm: 60km/h
Turning circle diameter
    hullborne: 106m
    foilborne: 380m
Range, based on normal fuel supply of 1400kg: 500km
Max wave height, with 3% safety margin
    hullborne: 2m
    foilborne: 1.3m

LASTOCHKA

Successor to the 71-seat Voskhod, the first Lastochka was launched in 1986. The vessel is designed specifically for use over major rivers and reservoirs whose wave heights are unlikely to exceed 1.5 metres in height. The design is approved by certificate number 18202 and by four inventors certificates. A high level of power plant auto-mating is provided, an ACK C AC 30–12 emerg-ency warning signal and protection system, an automatic engine starting system and a remote control system controlling power plant con-ditions.

Loading conditions are optimised by means of a flap control on the bow foil arrangement.

PRINCIPAL PARTICULARS
Length, overall: 29.00m
Beam, overall: 7.20m
Hull width: 4.40m
Draught, foilborne, max: 2.5m
Displacement, full load: 37.3 tonnes

Model of Lastochka showing foil configuration

Displacement, full load: 37.3 tonnes
Displacement, light ship: 28.0 tonnes
Engines, propulsion: two 994 kW (846 kW service)
Speed: 90 km/h
Range: 500 km

Lastochka

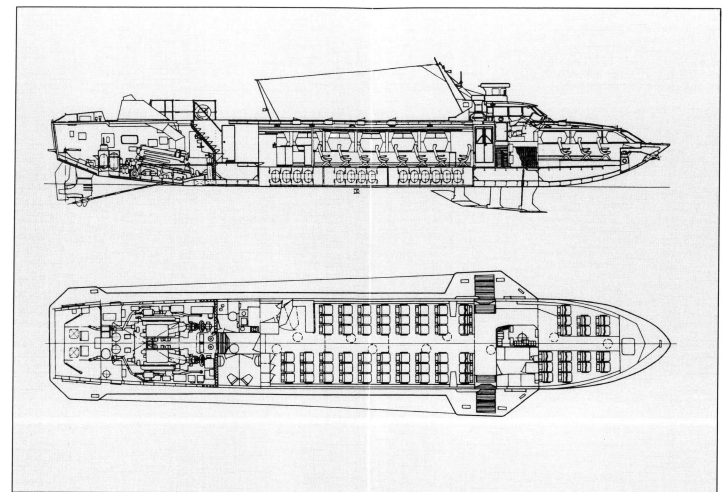

Layout of Lastochka

ZENIT

Described as 'a second-generation fast passenger ferry', Zenit was reported in 1982 as being
developed to replace Meteor. Design speed of the
new craft is 90km/h compared with the 65km/h
cruising speed of Meteor.

GOMEL YARD
Belorussiya, USSR

BYELORUS

This craft was developed from the Raketa, via the Chaika, for fast passenger services on shallow winding rivers less than 1m deep and too shallow for conventional vessels.

It was put into series production at the river shipyard at Gomel, Byelorussiya in 1965. Byelorus was expected to be succeeded in service by the 53-seat Polesye.

FOILS: The shallow draught submerged foil system consists of one bow foil and one rear foil.
HULL: Hull and superstructure are built in aluminium magnesium alloy. The hull is of all-welded construction and the superstructure is riveted and welded.
ACCOMMODATION: Aircraft type seats for 40 passengers. The prototype seated only 30.
POWERPLANT: Power is supplied by an M-50 F-3 or M-400 diesel rated at 950hp maximum and with a normal service output of 600hp. The wheelhouse is fitted with an electro-hydraulic remote control system for the engine and fuel supply.
DIMENSIONS
Length overall: 18.55m
Hull beam: 4.64m
Height overall: 4.23m
Draught foilborne: 0.3m
 hullborne: 0.9m
WEIGHTS
Light displacement: 9.6 tons
Take-off displacement: 14.5 tons
PERFORMANCE
Cruising speed: 60km/h (34 knots)

POLESYE

This shallow-draught hydrofoil craft (27 built by early 1989) is intended for the high-speed transportation of passengers and tourists during daylight hours in the upper reaches of major rivers, river tributaries and freshwater reservoirs in regions with temperate climate. The craft is classified ★R on the RSFSR Register of River Shipping and is suitable for use in conditions with a wave height of 0.5m when running on the hydrofoils, and with a wave height of up to 1.2m in the displacement mode.

The craft has capacity for 53 passengers. The passengers are accommodated in a single lounge area in the midsection of the vessel. In calm waters

Byelorus on Karakum Canal, Turkmenia

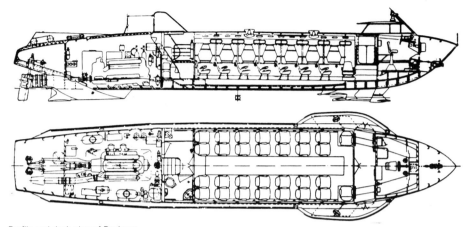

Profile and deck plan of Byelorus

with wind conditions up to Force 3, the vessel is capable of a speed of 65km/h. The vessel is capable of running on the hydrofoils on river channels with a radius of turn of up to 100–150m.

The time to accelerate from the stationary condition to becoming fully foilborne does not exceed 1.5 minutes. The distance from service speed to stop, with the propeller in reverse, is five to six boat lengths.

The hull is divided into five compartments by means of watertight bulkheads. The foils and side fenders are removable to facilitate overland transport. The vessel incorporates facilities for the prevention of environmental pollution and for the reduction of noise and vibration levels. The upholstered seats and wide windows in the lounge ensure that the passengers travel in comfort. The

heating system for the vessel consists of water heating appliances and piping. The water is supplied from the internal circuit of the main engine. In the autumn and spring sailing periods, the air in the forced ventilation system is heated with a water heating appliance.

The vessel is powered by a 12-cylinder 'V' diesel engine with a maximum capacity of 810kW at 1600rpm. The engine is installed at an angle of 12°30 to the horizontal and transmits power to the propeller via a direct-coupled reversing-gear unit.

Ship-to-shore communications are provided by an on-board fixed-frequency radio station, and for public address and broadcasting purposes the vessel has a standard public-address and transmission broadcasting package. The vessel is sup-

Polesye

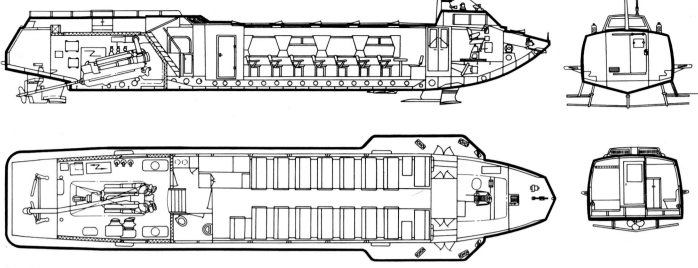

General arrangement of Polesye

plied complete with supplies and spare parts in accordance with RSFSR River Register rules and with the boatbuilder's practice.

DIMENSIONS
Length, overall: 21.25m
Hull length, overall: 21.00m
Beam, overall: 5.0m
Hull width, overall: 3.60m

Hull height, midsection: 2.60m
Hull height, with deckhouse: 3.20m
Draught, extreme load (in displacement mode): 0.95m
Draught, extreme draught on hydrofoils: 0.40m
WEIGHTS
Displacement, light: 13.7 tonnes
Displacement, full load: 20.0 tonnes

PERFORMANCE
Range, full tanks: 400km
Endurance, full tanks: 8 hours
Speed, calm water, Beaufort Force 3: 35 knots (65km/h)
Sea State limits: Foilborne in waves up to 0.5m
Hullborne in waves up to 1.2m

Ś ORDZHONIKIDZE SHIP-BUILDING AND REPAIR YARD
Head Office and Yard: Poti, Georgia, USSR

Z N Archaidze, *Yard Director*
I Ye Malechanov, *Chief Designer*
Yu Golubkin, *Deputy Chief Designer*
B Pavlyuk, *Chief Engineer*
G A Terentyeb, *Manager, Sea Trials*

KOMETA
A large number of Kometas have been built at the Poti yard. Please see earlier entry in this section.

CYCLONE
Detailed information on this large hydrofoil passenger vessel became available in 1989. The design is approved by certificate No. 19931, 20 June 1985 and by the inventor's certificate dating from 1969 to 1984. Acceptance and pre-commissioning trials took place in 1986 and experimental operation of the vessel was first undertaken in 1987. This vessel is designed to Hydrofoil Passenger Class KM*2A2 of the Register of Shipping of the USSR. Cyclone is a gas-turbine-powered hydrofoil designed for coastal routes and operations up to 100 miles of a port of refuge. She may operate foilborne in waves up to 3.5 metres in height. Details of an earlier Cyclone project are given on pages 212 and 213 of the 1989 edition of this book.

DIMENSIONS
Length, overall: 44.20m
Beam, overall: 12.60m
Hull width: 7.30m
Draught, max, foilborne: 2.40m
Draught, max, hullborne: 4.30m
WEIGHTS
Displacement, full load: 143 tonnes
Displacement, light-ship: 106 tonnes
Deadweight: 37 tonnes
ENGINES:
One 5150 kW gas turbine
One 735 kW diesel (for slow running)

The gas-turbine-powered 250 seat Cyclone at sea

PERFORMANCE
Speed, foilborne: 43 knots
Speed, hullborne (slow running): 7 knots
Range: 300 n miles
ACCOMMODATION
Passengers: 250
Crew: 9

KOLKHIDA
Designed to replace the 20-year-old Kometa fast passenger ferry, Kolkhida is available in two versions: the Albatros, which will operate on domestic services within the Soviet Union, and the Kolkhida, intended for export. Keel for the prototype was laid at a ceremony attended by the First

Secretary of the Central Committee of the Georgian Communist party in May 1980. The occasion also marked the entry of the craft into series production.

Kolkhida is faster than Kometa, seats more passengers, uses less fuel and can operate foilborne in higher Sea States. Among the various design innovations are a new foil system with automatic lift control, the use of new materials in the hull structure and a more rational cabin layout, permitting a substantial increase in seating capacity. The engine room is aft, as on the Voskhod, to reduce the noise level. Overall dimensions are almost identical to those of Kometa-M.

Trials of the Kolkhida prototype took place in

Model of Cyclone

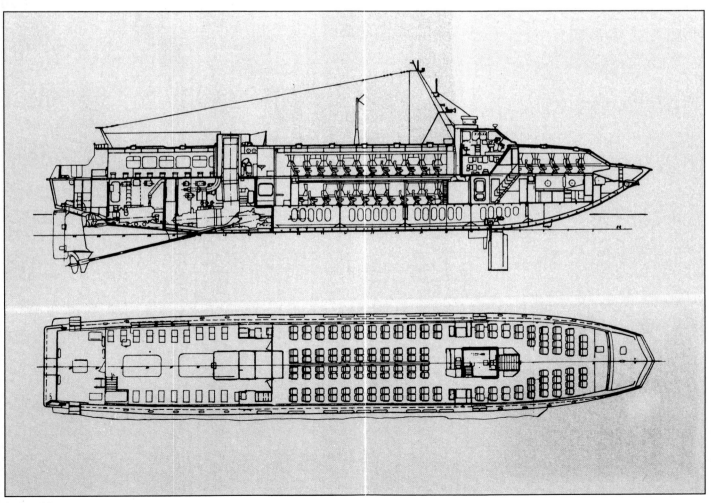

Layout of Cyclone

the Baltic between March and June 1981 and the vessel has been in production since with sales being achieved in Greece, Italy and Yugoslavia. The craft meets the requirements of the Register of Shipping of the USSR and is constructed to Hydrofoil Class KM★ 2 A2 Passenger Class SPK under the Register's technical supervision. It complies fully with the IMO Code of Safety for Dynamically Supported Craft.

Kolkhida is designed to operate under tropical and moderate climates up to 50 miles from a port of refuge in open seas and up to 100 miles from a port of refuge in inland seas and large lakes, with a permissible distance between two ports of refuge of not more than 200 miles.

Foilborne, the craft can operate in waves up to 2m and winds up to Force 5; hullborne it can operate in waves up to 3m and winds up to Force 6. FOILS: The foil system, which is similar to that of Kometa, comprises a trapeze-type bow foil, an aft and an amidship foil, close to the longitudinal centre of gravity to assist take-off. The foils are connected to the hull by struts and brackets. A sonic/electronic autopilot controls lift by operating trailing edge flaps on the centre section of the bow foil and on the inner sections of the aft foil. The foil flaps are adjusted hydraulically to dampen heave, pitch, roll and yaw motions in heavy seas and provide co-ordinated turns. Bow and stern foil surfaces and the lower ends of the bow and stern foil struts are in steel alloy. The amidship foil, struts, upper sections of the bow and stern foil struts are in aluminium-magnesium alloy. A cast, balanced rudder in 40mm thick aluminium-magnesium alloy is fitted. Total blade area is 2.75m^2. Rudder movement is controlled hydraulically by any one of three systems: push-button, manual or via the autopilot.
HULL: Double-chine, V-bottom type, with raked stern and streamlined superstructure. Hull and superstructure are built in aluminium-magnesium alloys. Framing is based on T and T-angle webframes. Frame spacing is 600mm. Longitudinal framing of the sides, decks and hull bottom is based on stiffening ribs, keelson, stringers and deck girders. Below the main deck the hull is subdivided by watertight bulkheads into nine compartments. The craft will remain afloat with any two adjacent compartments flooded.
POWERPLANT: Power is supplied by two MTU 12V 396 TC 82 water-cooled, supercharged 12-cylinder V-type four-stroke marine diesels, each with a normal service output of 960kW, 174.5rpm and 1050kW, 1800rpm maximum. Guaranteed service life of each engine before first major overhaul 9000 hours; maximum service life is 12 years. Output is transferred to twin 740mm diameter contra-rotating fixed-pitch propellers through reversible gearboxes which are remotely controlled from the wheelhouse. The propeller shafts are inclined at 14 degrees and supported by rubber and metal bearings.
ACCOMMODATION: Standard passenger-ferry version is designed to carry an operating crew of six and 120 passengers. A tourist sight-

Kolkhida

Kolkhida

Kolkhida forward starboard foils and struts

Craft built

Type	Name	Built	Operator
Kolkhida		1983	Black Sea Shipping Co, Odessa, USSR
Kolkhida	2	1984	Black Sea Shipping Co, Odessa, USSR
Kolkhida	3	1984	Black Sea Shipping Co, Odessa, USSR
Kolkhida	4	1984	Black Sea Shipping Co, Odessa, USSR
Kolkhida	5	1984	Black Sea Shipping Co, Odessa, USSR
Kolkhida	6	1985	Black Sea Shipping Co, Odessa, USSR
Kolkhida	Magnolija	1986	Kvarner Express, Yugoslavia
Kolkhida	Kamelija	1986	Kvarner Express, Yugoslavia
Kolkhida	Mirta	1986	Kvarner Express, Yugoslavia
Kolkhida	Mimosa	1986	Kvarner Express, Yugoslavia
Kolkhida	Aliatlante	June 1986	Alilauro SpA, Italy
Kolkhida	Alieolo	July 1986	Alilauro SpA, Italy
Kolkhida	Flying Dolphin XVII	1986	Ceres Flying Hydroways Ltd, Piraeus, Greece
Kolkhida	Flying Dolphin XVIII	1986	Ceres Flying Hydroways Ltd, Piraeus, Greece
Kolkhida	Flying Dolphin XIX	1986	Ceres Flying Hydroways Ltd, Piraeus, Greece
Kolkhida	Aligea	1986	Alilauro SpA, Italy
Kolkhida	Tiburon	1988	Compania Naviera Mallorquina, Spain
Kolkhida	Alikenia	1986	Alilauro SpA, Italy
Kolkhida	Aliflorida	1988	Alilauro SpA, Italy

Kolkhida

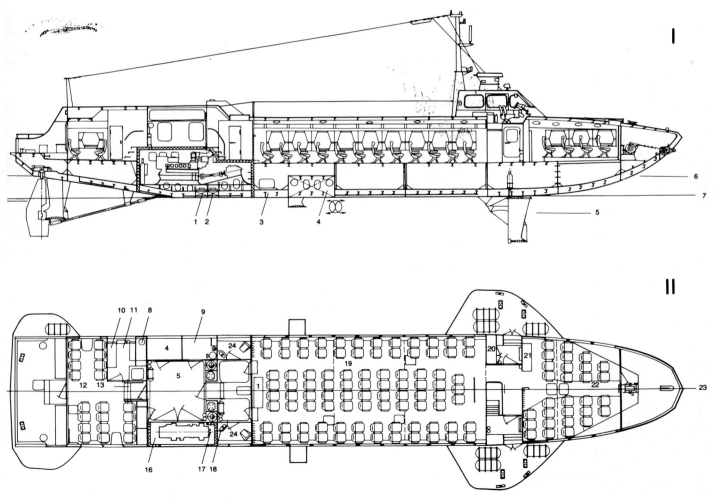

Kolkhida (area shown occupied by seats rows 12 and 13 is now a bar)
Longitudinal section: (1) waste oil collection tank (2) oil-containing water tank (3) sewage water tank (4) fuel tank (5) waterline when foilborne (6) waterline when hullborne (7) base line
Main deck plan: (8) hydraulic station (9) fuel and oil filling, waste water scavenging, fire-fighting station (10) conditioner (11) control post (12) 20-seat passenger saloon (13) VP (14) luggage room (15) promenade platform (16) auxiliary unit room (17) gas exhaust trunk (18) air intake trunk (19) 91-seat passenger saloon (20) Aggregate room (21) conditioner (22) 29-seat passenger saloon (23) central line (24) toilet

Kolkhida aft foil arrangement

seeing version seats 150. Crew comprises a captain/engineer, two motormen, one seaman, one seaman/radio operator and a barman. On the tourist version, no barman is carried. Embarkation platforms immediately below the wheelhouse provide access for passengers and crew. Captain and engineer are accommodated in a raised wheelhouse between the forward and main saloon.

The wheelhouse contains a radar display and radio-communications equipment. Main engine controls are installed in both the wheelhouse and engine room. Passengers are accommodated in three air-conditioned compartments, a forward saloon seating 29, a middle saloon seating 91 and an aft saloon with 20 seats. Facilities include two promenade decks, one immediately aft of the main

Controls and instruments in Kolkhida wheelhouse

Port double entrance doors on Kolkhida

saloon above the engine room, the other on the weather deck at the stern, toilets and a buffet/bar. Passenger saloons are equipped with airliner-type, reclining-back seats arranged four, three or two abreast. Extensive use is made of heat, sound and vibration absorbing and insulating materials. Decks in saloons and serving places are carpeted.
APU: Combined unit comprises a four-cylinder diesel engine rated at 33kW, a six-cylinder freon compressor, a 4.5kW 27.5 dc generator, a self-priming pump and a starting air compressor. Unit supplies electric power to shipboard consumers, operates air-conditioning system and replenishes starting bottles with compressed air.
SYSTEMS, ELECTRICAL: Engine-driven generators supply power while the craft is operating. The 4.5kW generator included in the auxiliary unit supplies power when the craft is at rest. Acid

storage batteries connected in series supply power during short stops.
ANCHOR: Single Matrosov 75kg main anchor and LGY 20 M1 hydraulic windlass. Also appropriate mooring, towing and anchoring equipment.
COMMUNICATIONS: Radio transmitter/receiver with r/t and w/t facilities is installed in the wheelhouse for the ship-to-shore and intership communications on SW and MW bands. Unified communications and relay equipment provides simplex command communication between wheelhouse, engine room, stern, control post, forward embarkation platforms and anchor winch compartment as well as relaying broadcasts and information announcements to the passenger saloons.
NAVIGATION: Gyrocompass, magnetic compass and log are standard.

AIR-CONDITIONING: Anton Kaiser-type module, comprising 33kW four-cylinder diesel, six-cylinder Freon compressor, a 27.5V, 4.5kW dc generator, self-priming circulating pump and starting compressor, all mounted on a single frame.

HYDRAULICS: System for operating rudder, foil flaps and windlass.

SAFETY EQUIPMENT: Six 25-seat inflatable life rafts in addition to life jackets, life belts, life lines and self-igniting buoyant lights. Chemical- and foam-type fire-extinguishing system installed throughout vessel.

DIMENSIONS
Length overall: 34.5m
Beam overall: 10.3m
    hull: 5.8m
Height overall from water level, hullborne: 8.9m
    foilborne: 10.8m
Draught, hullborne: 3.5m
    foilborne: 1.9m
GRT: 143

WEIGHTS
Light displacement: 56.0 tonnes
Fully-loaded displacement: 72 tonnes

PERFORMANCE
Cruising speed, fully loaded: 34 knots
Take-off time: 20–40 seconds
Hullborne speed: 12 knots
Range, on foils: Over 150n miles
Specific fuel consumption: 215g/kW/h

Interior of Kolkhida cabin

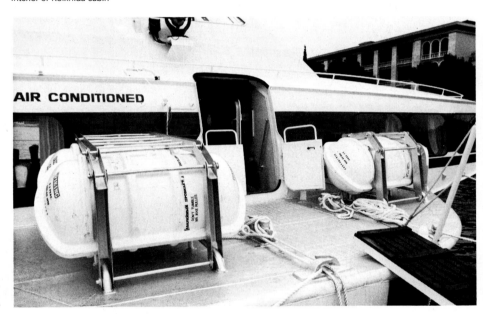

Liferaft installation on Kolkhida

MILITARY CRAFT
PCHELA (BEE)

This military derivative of the Strela is in service with the KGB for frontier patrol duties in the Baltic and Black Seas. 25 were built between 1968 and 1972, but it is believed that only four remain in service.

POWERPLANT: One 4000bhp M-503 diesel.

ARMAMENT: Two twin 23mm AA mounts with remote optical director and two-to-four depth charges.

RADAR: Surface search and navigation, Pot Drum. IFF, High Pole B.

SONAR: Dipping type.

DIMENSIONS
Length overall: 27m
Hull beam: 6m
Width across foils: 8m
Draught, hull: 1m
    foils: 2.6m

WEIGHTS
Fully loaded: 75 tonnes
Standard: 60 tonnes

PERFORMANCE
Max speed: 42 knots

Pchela

Turya

TURYA

Based on the well-proven Osa missile-firing FPB hull, Turya is equipped with a fixed, surface-piercing V or trapeze foil set back approximately one-third of the hull length from the bow. At 25 knots, in relatively calm conditions, the foil system generates sufficient lift to raise the forward hull clear of the water, providing a 'sprint' speed of 40 to 45 knots.

In addition to improving the maximum speed, the foils reduce the vessel's wave impact response, thus enhancing its performance as a weapon platform.

The installation of a dipping sonar on the transom suggests that the primary duty of Turya is anti-submarine patrol. The main armament appears to comprise four 53cm ASW or anti-ship torpedoes in single fixed tubes, a forward 25mm twin mount and a twin 57mm AA mount aft.

The first of this class was launched in 1972. About 30 are in service. Eight have been supplied to the Cuban Navy.

Later versions are equipped with semi-retractable foils permitting the overall width to be reduced, thus enabling craft to be taken alongside conventional berthing facilities.
FOILS: Single main foil of trapeze configuration set back one-third of hull length from bow. Raises greater part of hull bottom clear of the water in calm conditions at speed of about 25 knots depending on sea conditions and loading. Similar system employed earlier on Soviet 'P8' class, now retired, and on the highly successful Chinese 'Hu Chwan' class.
HULL: Standard Osa hull, welded steel construction.
POWERPLANT: Three M-504 high performance radial-type diesels, each developing 5000hp and driving variable-pitch propellers through inclined shafts.
ARMAMENT: One twin 57mm dual-purpose gun with Muff Cob radar control and one remote optical director and one twin 25mm AA mount with local control. Mounts for SA-7 Grail light AA missile launcher and four 53cm ASW or anti-ship torpedoes. Latest variants fitted with twin 30mm fully-automatic dual purpose mount forward.
Navigation radar: Pot Drum
Fire-control radar: Muff Cob
Sonar: One dipping-type
ECM/ESM: One High Pole transponder and one Square Head interrogator.
DIMENSIONS
Length: 39.3m
Beam: 7.7m
Width across foils: 12.3m
Draught, hull: 3m
    foils: 3.8m
WEIGHTS
Max loaded displacement: 250 tonnes
Standard: 200 tonnes

PERFORMANCE
Max speed foilborne: 40–45 knots

MATKA

A missile-equipped fast strike craft built at the Izhora Yard, Leningrad, Matka is designed to replace the 20-year-old Osa fast patrol boat and is based on the standard 39.3m Osa steel hull. A fixed surface-piercing trapeze foil is fitted at the bow to increase its speed in the lower Sea States and reduce its wave impact response thereby improving its performance as a weapon platform. At a speed of between 24 to 28 knots, depending on sea conditions and loading, the bow foil generates sufficient lift to raise a substantial part of the forward hull clear of the water thus reducing hydrodynamic drag and providing a 'sprint' speed of 40 to 45 knots.

The Matka prototype was launched in 1977 and series production began in the spring of 1978. At least eight are in service.
FOILS: Single main foil of trapeze configuration, set back one-quarter of hull length from bow, raises much of the hull clear of the water in relatively calm conditions at speeds of 24 to 28 knots depending on sea conditions and loading. Similar to system proven on Chinese 'Hu Chwan' class and Soviet Turya. Latest version of Turya is equipped with semi-retractable foils, thereby reducing the overall width and enabling craft to be taken alongside conventional jetties, piers and other vessels without damaging the foil tips. Matka is likely to employ similar foil arrangement.
HULL: Standard Osa hull, welded steel construction.

Matka   (Danish Defence)

Matka in Baltic Sea

POWERPLANT: Three 3700kW M-504 radial-type high-performance diesels, each driving a variable-pitch propeller through an inclined shaft.
ACCOMMODATION: Living, messing and berthing spaces for crew of 33.
ARMAMENT: Two SS-N-2C surface-to-surface missiles; one 76mm dual-purpose cannon; one six-barrelled ADMG-630 Gatling-type 30mm cannon for close-in AA defence and one mount for SA-7 Grail light AA missile launcher to counter attacks by low-flying subsonic aircraft.
CHAFF: Two 16-tube chaff launchers.
NAVIGATION RADAR: Cheese Cake.
SURFACE SEARCH: Plank Shave.
FIRE CONTROL: Bass Tilt.
ECM/ESM: One High Pole transponder and one Square Head interrogator.
COMMUNICATIONS: Cage Bear.
DIMENSIONS
Length: 39.3m
Hull beam: 7.7m
Width across foils: 12.3m
Draught, hull: 3m
    foils: 3.8m
WEIGHTS
Displacement, full load: 260 tonnes
    standard: 225 tonnes
PERFORMANCE
Max speed foilborne: 40–45 knots
Range: 750n miles at 24 knots

SARANCHA (NATO Code Name)

A fast strike missile craft, the 330-tonne Sarancha is one of the world's biggest naval hydrofoils. Designed and built at Petrovsky, Leningrad, in 1976 the craft is armed with four SS-N-9 anti-ship missiles, an SA-N-4 ship-to-air missile system and a 30mm Gatling-type rapid-fire cannon. The foil system is fully retractable to simplify slipping and docking. Autostabilisation equipment is fitted as well as an autopilot and the latest navigation, target detection and fire control systems.

Operational evaluation trials with the Soviet Navy began in the eastern Baltic in mid-1977.
FOILS: Combined surface-piercing and submerged system. The bow foil, which provides the necessary transverse stability, is of split-V surface-piercing type and carries about 60% of the load and the single fully submerged rear foil supports the remaining 40%. The rear foil is supported by two vertical struts, each of which carries a twin propeller pod assembly at its base. The struts also carry the vertical shafts and second bevel gears of the Z-drive systems which transmit power from the gas turbines in the hull to the propellers. A sonic/electronic autopilot system controls lift by

operating trailing edge flaps on the aft foil. Single rudders, which act individually for port or starboard turns, are fitted to the trailing edges of the aft foil struts. All three foil/strut units retract completely clear of the water, the two elements of the 'split V' bow foil sideways and the aft foil rearwards and upwards.
POWERPLANT: Foilborne power is believed to be provided by two NK-12MV marinised gas turbines, each delivering 12 to 15 000hp. Power is transmitted to the two propellers at the base of each strut through two sets of bevel gears and two vertical shafts to the nacelle. The central compartment of this contains the lower reduction gear which transmits power from the vertical shafts

to the propeller shafts. The power transmission system is thought to have been derived from that employed on the Typhoon commercial hydrofoil, also built in Leningrad.
ARMAMENT: Four SS-N-9 Siren anti-ship missiles on four lightweight launchers amidship, one twin SA-N-4 surface-to-air missile launcher with 15 to 20 missiles on forward deck and one 30mm Gatling-type rapid-fire AA cannon aft. The SS-N-9s are activated by a Band Stand radar, the SA-4 launcher is controlled by a Pop Group radar and the 30mm cannon has a Bass Tilt fire control. The SA-N-4 may have limited surface-to-surface capability. The craft also carries Fish Bowl fire-control radar, a Band Stand radar for air search,

Matka on patrol in Baltic Sea

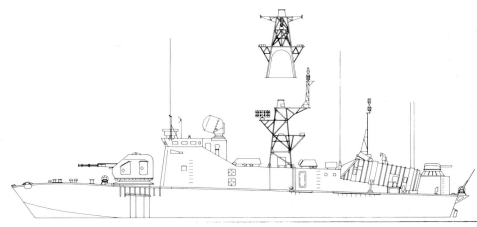
Outboard profile of Matka

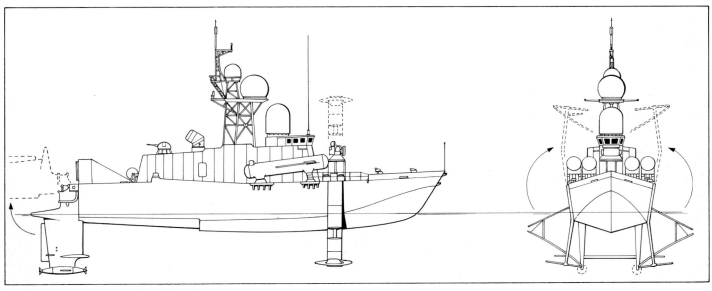
Provisional elevation and bow-on view of Sarancha

one High Pole transponder and one Square Head interrogator for ECM/ESM. A new type of navigation and surface radar is carried.

DIMENSIONS
Length overall: 45m
Length, foils extended: 51m
Width, foils extended: 23m
Hull beam: 10m
Width across foils: 24m
Draught hullborne, foils retracted: 2.5m
          foilborne: 3.5m
WEIGHT
Estimated normal take-off displacement: 330 tonnes
PERFORMANCE
Max speed foilborne: 50 knots plus

BABOCHKA (BUTTERFLY)

The world's largest and most powerful operational hydrofoil warship, this vessel is designed for anti-submarine warfare. Motive power for its foilborne propulsion system appears to comprise three NK-12MV marinised aircraft gas turbines, each delivering between 12 000 to 15 000shp.

Combustion air for the three gas turbines is fed through a large inlet occupying the aft end of the deckhouse. Exhaust discharge to atmosphere is via three angled funnels on the aft deck. If propeller driven, either V- or Z-drives are likely to have been employed so as to provide as great a clearance height as possible.

FOILS: Conventional configuration, with a surface-piercing bow foil and fully-submerged rear foil, and an automatic sonic/electronic control system operating trailing edge flaps on each foil.

ARMAMENT: Two six-barrelled 30mm Gatling-action guns for AA defence, activated by a Bass Tilt fire control radar or a remote optical director and eight 40cm AS torpedoes in two quadruple mounts immediately ahead of the superstructure between the deckhouse and the forward 30mm mount. Dipping sonar is also installed. Electronic equipment includes High Pole B IFF, Square Head and Peel Cone radar.

DIMENSIONS
Length overall: 50m
WEIGHTS
Normal take-off displacement: About 400 tonnes
PERFORMANCE
Max speed foilborne: 50 knots plus

Sarancha, 330-tonne missile armed fast attack craft   (DpA)

Outboard profile of Babochka

Stern view of Babochka

Babochka (Butterfly)

UNITED STATES OF AMERICA

BOEING AEROSPACE

This company is no longer engaged in the marketing of commercial or military hydrofoil vessels.

The Boeing Company, has licensed Kawasaki Heavy Industries Ltd for the design, manufacture, marketing, maintenance and repair of Boeing Jetfoil 929–117 hydrofoilcraft. Boeing's entry into the hydrofoil field was announced in June 1960, when the company was awarded a US $2 million contract for the construction of the US Navy's 120-ton PCH-1 *High Point*, a canard design which was the outcome of experiments with a similar arrangement in the US Navy test craft, Sea Legs.

Boeing also built a jet-driven hydroplane, the Hydrodynamic Test System (HTS), for testing foil models at full-scale velocity; the *Fresh-1*, a manned craft for testing superventilating or supercavitating foils at speeds between 60 and 100 knots, and a waterjet test vehicle, *Little Squirt*. Descriptions of *Fresh-1* and *Little Squirt* appear in *Jane's Surface Skimmers 1970–71* and earlier editions. The company also completed a highly successful waterjet-propelled gunboat, the PGH-2 *Tucumcari*, for the US Navy's Ship Systems Command. Its operational trials included several months of combat evaluation in Vietnam as part of the US Navy's coastal surveillance force. A full technical description of *Tucumcari* appeared in *Jane's Surface Skimmers 1974–75* and earlier editions. Data provided by the vessel assisted the design and development of the NATO/PHM, which is a 'scaled-up' *Tucumcari*, and the Jetfoil commercial hydrofoil.

High Point was modified by Boeing during 1972 to incorporate a new automatic control system, modified struts and foils, a new diesel for hullborne propulsion and a steerable forward strut for improved manoeuvrability. The craft was returned to the US Navy as Mod-1 configuration. In its revised form it was employed as a testbed for hydrofoil weapons compatibility.

In April 1975, the PCH was operated by the US Coast Guard for one month as part of a continuing research and development programme to evaluate high-speed water craft for the US Coast Guard. Operating in Puget Sound and around San Francisco, the craft was employed on fisheries patrol, marine environmental protection and search and rescue missions.

In 1979 the PCH-1 was selected as the research and development vehicle for demonstrating the feasibility of the US Navy's Extended Performance Hydrofoil (EPH) project.

In January 1973 the keel was laid for the first 110-ton 250-seat Model 929–100 Jetfoil passenger ferry. The hull was assembled in a former 727 assembly building at Renton, Washington, and the first craft was launched in March 1974 on Lake Washington, which is adjacent to the plant. Ten Jetfoils of this type are in commercial service. Jetfoil 0011, which was launched in June 1978, is the first Jetfoil of improved design. This version, known as the Model 929–115, has improved performance, payload and reliability. By 30 June 1986, Jetfoils had logged 1700 million passenger miles during 295 000 under way hours, with a dispatch reliability of 99 per cent.

An order for the first fast patrol craft version of the Jetfoil was placed by the Royal Navy in 1978. This was a modified commercial Jetfoil, named HMS *Speedy*, and built on the commercial Jetfoil production line. Two Allison 501-K20A gas turbines are installed in this variant for foilborne operation and two Allison 8V-92T1 diesels for hullborne operation, giving added time on-station and increased endurance. HMS *Speedy* was commissioned by the Royal Navy in June 1980 but was subsequently decommissioned in April 1982 due to defence cuts.

PHM-2 USS *Hercules*

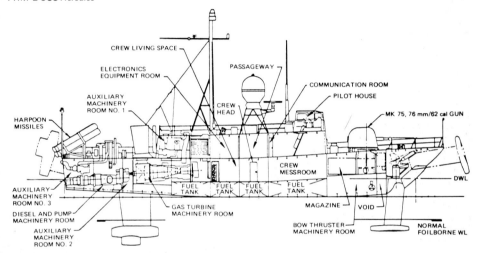

Inboard profile of PHM-3

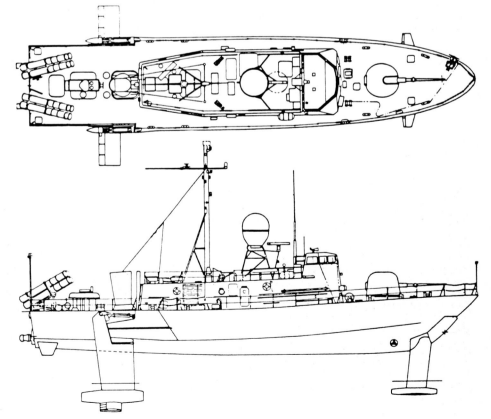

Outboard profile and deck plan of PHM-3

In April 1973 US Naval Ship Systems Command awarded the company a US $42 602 384 contract for the design and development of the 235-tonne NATO/PHM missile-equipped patrol boat, under the terms of which Boeing was to build the lead craft for the US Navy for evaluation.

The PHM was the first US Navy craft to be designed on the basis of a co-operative technical interchange between the USA and its allies within NATO.

The first PHM, *Pegasus*, was launched in November 1974. Delivery to the US Navy took place in late 1976 and the craft completed its acceptance trials at Seattle in early June 1977.

In August 1977 it was announced by the US Defense Secretary that the US Navy would receive five more PHMs, the last of which was delivered in September 1982. The five production craft and *Pegasus* are assigned to a PHM squadron operating out of Key West, Florida.

While sales efforts for commercial passenger Jetfoils have been suspended, Boeing continues to provide full service support to all existing hydrofoil operations. Both PAL of Indonesia and Kawasaki Heavy Industries of Japan have been licensed for the production of Jetfoil craft.

PCH-1 *HIGH POINT*

The PCH-1 *High Point* was accepted by the US Navy in August 1963 and used to evaluate the performance of an inshore hydrofoil ASW system. During April 1975 it was employed by the US Coast Guard in Puget Sound and off San Francisco. A full description of the craft can be found in *Jane's Surface Skimmers 1984* and earlier editions. *High Point* has been decommissioned but continues to be operated by Boeing for the David Taylor Naval Ship Research and Development Center (DTNSRDC) special trials unit.

PCH-1 *HIGH POINT* EPH FEASIBILITY DEMONSTRATOR PROJECT DESIGN

A description of this design investigation is given in *Jane's Surface Skimmers 1985* and earlier editions.

PGH-2 *TUCUMCARI*

A full technical description of this vessel appeared in *Jane's Surface Skimmers 1974–75* and earlier editions.

NATO/PHM

Craft built	Commissioned
PHM-1 USS *Pegasus*	July 1977
PHM-2 USS *Hercules*	September 1982
PHM-3 USS *Taurus*	October 1981
PHM-4 USS *Aquila*	January 1982
PHM-5 USS *Aries*	May 1982
PHM-6 USS *Gemini*	13 November 1982

The NATO Hydrofoil Fast Patrol Ship Guided Missile (NATO/PHM) originated in mid-1969 when C-in-C South presented to NATO a requirement for a large number of fast patrol boats to combat the threat posed by missile-armed fast patrol boats in the Mediterranean.

The concept of a common fast patrol boat was studied, and in September 1970 it was decided that the submerged foil craft of 140 tons proposed by the US Navy was the vessel most suited to NATO mission requirements. In October 1971 the USA indicated that it would proceed at its own expense with the design of the vessel and share the results of the studies with those nations wishing to purchase PHMs. It also offered to conduct all aspects of design and development, contracting and management in co-operation with governments entering into project membership. Costs would be reimbursed only by those nations engaged in the project.

In November 1971 the US Navy awarded Boeing a US $5.6 million contract for the pre-

PHM-3 USS *Taurus*

Wheelhouse of PHM-3 USS *Taurus*

PHM-3 USS *Taurus*

liminary design of a 230-ton craft and the purchase of mechanical and electronic components for at least two PHMs. Seventeen months later, Boeing was awarded a US $42 607 384 contract for the design and development of the PHM for NATO navies. Under the terms of the contract the first craft, the *Pegasus*, was built for the US Navy.

Pegasus was launched in November 1974 and made its first foilborne flight in February 1975. It achieved its classified designed speed, completed the Navy-conducted phase of testing its weapons and then began operational evaluation in the San Diego area in autumn 1975.

It completed its acceptance trials during the first week of June 1977 and was commissioned into service in July 1977, becoming the first hydrofoil officially designated a United States Ship (USS *Pegasus*). Rear Admiral John Bulkeley, USN, President, Naval Board of Inspection and Survey, recorded that it had demonstrated 'superb reliability throughout her trial with no major or significant breakdowns or failures'.

The first squadron of PHMs consists of the USS *Pegasus* and its five sister ships, *Taurus, Aquila, Aries, Gemini* and *Hercules,* plus the PHM Mobile Logistic Support Group (MLSG) and the Squadron Commander's staff. An interim MLSG was established to support *Pegasus* and comprised one officer and 28 enlisted personnel operating from six standard 40ft (12.1m) containers and three roadable trailers fitted to provide shop, office and training space and stowage for spares and food stores. During the second phase of the squadron build-up a converted 1178 Class LST, to be known as a Hydrofoil Support Ship (AGHS), was to be made available. This would have provided all the facilities available from the van complex plus the basic fuel and other services now provided from ashore.

However, the AGHS has been deleted from the US Navy budget and a mobile complex comprising 2.4 × 2.4 × 6m (8 × 8 × 20ft) ISO standard vans has been procured and installed at Key West. The vans are equipped to provide maintenance, workshops, equipment stores, training classrooms and on-shore messing facilities.

All of the production craft are armed with a 75mm OTO Melara dual-purpose rapid fire cannon and eight Harpoon anti-ship missiles in two four-tube lightweight canister launchers. Construction of PHM-2 *Hercules* began in May 1974 but was stopped in 1975, eventually being delivered in September 1982. All five craft were built by Boeing Marine Systems at its hydrofoil assembly plant at Renton, Washington, adjacent to Lake Washington. USS *Pegasus* was operationally assigned to the Atlantic Fleet at Key West, Florida in July 1980.

The PHM has sufficient design flexibility to allow for individual variations by any country. These variations will be primarily in the weapons systems installed, and the participating nations, current and future, can acquire the standard PHM carrying whatever combat equipment is determined necessary to meet national requirements.

PHM's potential in terms of strategic mobility was demonstrated between 30 September and 1 October 1975, when *Pegasus* completed the 1225 nautical miles from Seattle to San Diego in the record-breaking time of less than 34 hours, which included a refuelling stop at Eureka, California.

With the aid of midway refuelling the craft is capable of crossing oceans with fast carrier task groups, convoys of merchant ships and amphibious assault groups. With three under way refuellings, it can cross the Atlantic from Massachusetts to the United Kingdom at an average speed of 30 knots in 4.2 days, or it could cross from Norfolk, Virginia to Cadiz in 4.6 days with four under way refuellings.

PHM was designed to be self-supporting at sea for a period of five days although ten-day (and more) versions are routinely carried out. For extended periods, or during intensive operations,

Boeing PHM-5 USS *Aries*

it is refuelled under way with either JP-5 or Naval Distillate (DFM) by oilers, major combatants and carriers.

PHM can be adapted for such roles as antisubmarine warfare, fisheries law enforcement and the protection of offshore resources.

The standard PHM is approximately 40.5m long, has a beam of 8.6m and a full load displacement of about 241 tonnes. Foilborne range is in excess of 500n miles at speeds in excess of 40 knots in 2.4 to 3.6m seas. The hull form and size, the major structural bulkheads and decks, foils and struts, waterjets, pumps, controls and main propulsion machinery are identical. The auxiliary equipment and arrangements, deckhouse and crew accommodation are also of standard design, but variations in the latter are possible to suit the manning requirements of individual countries.

FOILS: Fully-submerged canard arrangement with approximately 31.8 per cent of the dynamic lift provided by the bow foil and 68.2 per cent by the aft foil. The aft foil retracts rearwards and the bow foil retracts forward into a recess in the bow. Bow doors preserve the hull lines when the forward foil is either fully extended or retracted. The foils and struts are in 17-4 PH martensitic, precipitation hardening stainless steel. Both forward and aft foils are welded assemblies consisting of spars, ribs, and skin. Flaps are fitted to the trailing edges to provide control and lift augmentation at take-off and during flight. The bow foil system incorporates a strut that rotates to provide directional control and reliable turning rates in heavy seas.

The shallow M or inverted double pi configuration of the aft foil is designed for improved hydroelastic and turning characteristics. The primary strut structure consists of spars, ribs and skin welded into watertight assemblies. The struts are designed as beam columns, and rigidly attached to the foil support structure at the hull.

The struts are attached to the hull with pivot pins that allow the foils to rotate clear of the water. Hydraulic actuators are used for retraction and extension, mechanical stops and position locks being employed to secure the foils in either position.

CONTROLS, FOILBORNE: The helm, throttle and an automatic control system (ACS) provide continuous dynamic control during take-off, foilborne operation and landing. Once take-off is complete, the ACS requires no attention by the crew. It controls the craft by sensing craft attitude, motion rates and acceleration, then comparing them electronically with desired values. Any deviations are processed by analogue control computer which generates electrical commands

causing hydraulic actuators to reposition the control surfaces, thus minimising detected errors. The foilborne control surfaces are trailing edge flaps on each of the foils, plus the rotating bow foil strut which acts as the foilborne rudder.

Manual controls and displays for both hullborne and foilborne conditions are concentrated at the helm station and include the wheel, a foil-depth selector, a foil-depth indicator, a ship-heading indicator and a heading holding switch.

CONTROLS, HULLBORNE: Steering control in the hullborne mode is provided by steerable nozzles which rotate electro-hydraulically in response to the wheel. An automatic heading control, similar to that employed for foilborne operation, is incorporated, together with the necessary heading reference provided by the gyrocompass.

POWERPLANT, FOILBORNE: The foilborne propulsion system comprises a single 17 000shp, coaxial two-stage, two-speed waterjet, driven through two sets of reduction gears by a single General Electric LM 2500 marine gas turbine, developed from the GE TF39, which powers the US Air Force's C-5 transport and the DC-10 Trijet.

PHM-1 uses only 16 200hp from the engine while production craft use 17 000hp. Full use of the 30 000hp potential is possible in the future, although the gearbox will have to be redesigned to absorb this power.

Both the foilborne and hullborne propulsion systems were designed by Aerojet Liquid Rocket Company, Sacramento, California, under a Boeing contract.

The single foilborne propulsion pump is capable of handling 90 000 gallons/minute and the two hullborne pumps will each operate at approximately 30 000 gallons/minute.

Engine installation and removal for overhaul is accomplished through hatches in the main deck between the deckhouse and exhaust outlet.

Normal fuel is diesel oil MIL-F-16884 (NATO F-76) or JP-5 MIL-J-5624 (NATO F-44).

POWERPLANT, HULLBORNE: Twin Aerojet waterjet pumps powered by two 800hp Mercedes-Benz 8V331TC80 diesels propel the vessel when hullborne. Each waterjet propulsor has nozzle steering and reversing buckets. The hullborne system provides long-range cruising and slow-speed manoeuvring, while the gas turbine is available when required for high-speed foilborne operation. HULL: Hull and deckhouses are all-welded structures in AL 5456 alloy.

ACCOMMODATION: Crew will average 21

officers and men, but will vary according to the armament carried up to a total of 24. Accommodation on the US Navy version is provided for five officers-the commanding officer has a separate cabin-four chief petty officers and 15 enlisted men. The superstructure accommodates the bridge, which contains steering and engine control consoles and is elevated to provide a 360-degree view. A short ladder from the bridge leads down to the command and surveillance deckhouse that accommodates the fire-control, radar, communications and navigation equipment. The size of the deckhouse provides flexibility in accommodating various national equipment requirements. The space aft of the superstructure and forward of the foilborne engine exhaust is used to erect rigging for replenishment and refuelling.

Below the main deck, about one-third of the PHM's length is devoted to crew accommodation, the forward third is occupied by the primary gun, automatic loader mechanism, ammunition storage and forward foil, and the after third is occupied by the unmanned machinery spaces.

All manned spaces are equipped with a recirculating air-conditioning system to give a maximum air temperature of 27°C at 55 per cent relative humidity in summer, and a minimum inside temperature of 18°C in winter. The officers' staterooms, crew quarters and lounge/messing area are fully air-conditioned, the temperature being controlled by individual thermostats in the spaces concerned.

SYSTEMS, ELECTRICAL: Ship's service electric plant comprises two AiResearch Ship Service Power Units (SSPUs), with ME831–800 gas turbines as prime movers driving 250kVA, 400Hz, 450V generators. Each SSPU also drives an attached centrifugal compressor for starting the LM 2500 engine and two hydraulic pumps for the ship's hydraulic system. One is capable of handling the entire electrical load, the second is provided as a standby. Through the use of static power conversion equipment, limited three-phase, 60Hz ac power and 28V dc is available for equipment requirements. In port, the craft can utilise shore power or use its own auxiliary power unit

for this purpose, as well as battery charging and emergency use of navigation and radio equipment.
HYDRAULICS: 3000psi to actuate the hullborne and foilborne controls, foil retraction and hullborne engine starting. Dual hydraulic supply is provided to each service with sub-system isolation fore and aft in the event of major damage.
FIRE EXTINGUISHING: Dry chemical equipment throughout craft, and a fixed total flooding-type Freon 1301 system.
WEAPONS/FIRE CONTROL: Either WM-28 radar and weapons control system or US model, the Mk 92 (Mod 1). Both systems embody a combined fire control and search antenna system, mounted on a single stabilised platform and enclosed in a fibreglass radome. The Italian Argo system can also be installed.
TARGETING/MISSILE WARNING: Automatic classification ESM (electronic warfare support measures) set is installed for missile warning and over-the-horizon targeting of enemy surface units.
GUNS: Standard primary gun is the OTO Melara 76mm gun, which is unmanned and automatically controlled by the fire control system. The craft can also be delivered with secondary guns. If specified two Mk 20 Rh 202 20mm AA cannon can be provided, one each, port and starboard, adjacent to the fire control antenna structure.
MISSILES: The prototype carries eight Harpoon missiles in two four-tube lightweight canister launchers, but Exocet, Otomat, Tero or any smaller missile system can be installed. Space is provided aft to accommodate the four launchers, port and starboard, in parallel pairs. The launchers are deck-fixed in elevation and azimuth.

Armament of the standard US Navy version will be eight McDonnell Douglas RGM-84A Harpoon anti-ship missiles in lightweight container launchers; one Mk 75 76mm/62cal OTO Melara gun with 400 76mm rounds, and two Mk 135, Mod 0, 4.4in launchers, together with 24 Mk 171 chaff cartridges, small arms, ammunition and pyrotechnics.
COMMAND, CONTROL AND COMMUNICATIONS: True motion navigation radar;

OMEGA navigation equipment; gyrocompass; dead reckoning tracer; Tactical and Navigation Collision Avoidance System (TANCAV); speed log; depth sounder/recorder; AN/SPA-25B repeater consoles (2); integrated intercom/announcing/exterior communications system; HF, UHF and VHF communications (teletype and voice) IFF system, ESM system.

The basic PHM design allows for a growth of approximately 5 tons in full load displacement to enhance mission capability. Areas under consideration include sonar, torpedoes, improved surface-to-surface missiles and low-light-level TV, all of which appear to be feasible without having an adverse effect on its current capabilities.

The following details apply to the model under construction for the US Navy.
DIMENSIONS
Length overall,
  foils extended: 40.5m
  foils retracted: 44.3m
Beam max, deck: 8.6m
Max width across foils: 14.5m
Draught,
  hullborne, foils retracted: 1.9m
  hullborne, foils extended: 7.1m
  foilborne, normal: 2.5m
WEIGHT
Displacement, full load including margins: 241 tonnes
PERFORMANCE
Max speed foilborne: in excess of 50 knots
Cruising speed,
  foilborne, Sea State 0/5: In excess of 40 knots
  hullborne: 11 knots
Sea State: Can negotiate 10ft seas at speeds in excess of 40 knots
Range, foilborne: Not available
  hullborne: In excess of 1000n miles

JETFOIL 929–100

This is a 110-ton waterjet-propelled commercial hydrofoil for services in relatively rough waters. It employs a fully-submerged, automatically controlled canard foil arrangement and is powered

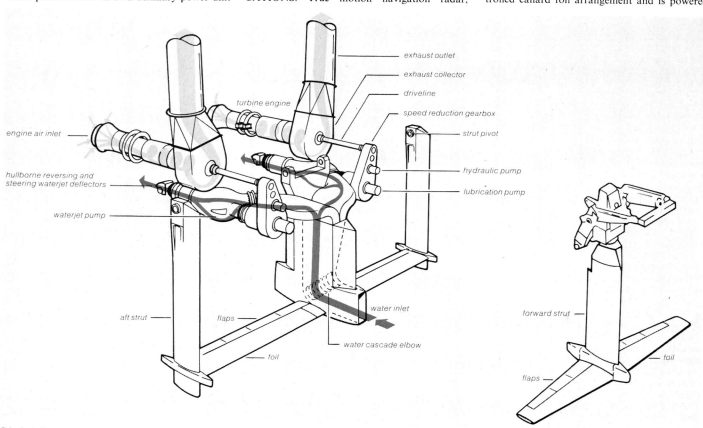

Principal elements of the Jetfoil propulsion and foil system

by two 3710hp Allison 501-K20A gas turbines. Normal foilborne cruising speed is 42 knots.

Typical interior arrangements include a commuter configuration with up to 350 seats and a tourist layout for 190 to 250 plus baggage.

Keel-laying of the first Jetfoil took place at the company's Renton, Washington, plant in January 1973 and the craft was launched in March 1974. After testing on Puget Sound and in the Pacific, the craft was delivered to Pacific Sea Transportation Ltd for inter-island services in Hawaii. High-speed foilborne tests began in Puget Sound in mid-July and it was reported that the vessel attained a speed of 48 knots during its runs.

During a rigorous testing programme to prove the boat's design and construction, Boeing No 0001 operated for 470 hours, including 237 hours foilborne. The latter phase of testing was conducted in the rough waters of the straits of Juan de Fuca and the Pacific Ocean, where it encountered wave swells as high as 9.1m, winds gusting up to 60 knots and wave chop averaging 1.8m high.

The first operational Jetfoil service was successfully initiated in April 1975 by Far East Hydrofoil Co Ltd, of Hong Kong, with Jetfoil 002, *Madeira*. Before this, the Jetfoil received its ABS classification, was certificated by the Hong Kong Marine Department and passed US Coast Guard certification trials, although a US Coast Guard certificate was not completed as the craft would not be operating in US waters.

The first US service began in Hawaii in June 1975 with the first of three Jetfoils, 003 *Kamehameha*, starting inter-island runs. By the end of the summer all five Jetfoils were in service. The tenth Jetfoil was launched in May 1977.

FOILS: Fully-submerged canard arrangement with a single inverted T strut/foil forward and a three-strut, full-span foil aft. The forward foil assembly is rotated hydraulically through 7 degrees in either direction for steering. All foils have trailing-edge flaps for controlling pitch, roll and yaw and for take-off and landing. Hydraulically driven foil flap actuators control the variation in flap positions through linkages between actuators and flap hinge points. Foils and struts retract hydraulically above the waterline, the bow foil forward, and the rear foil aft. All structural components of the foil/strut system are in 15.5PH corrosion resistant all-welded steel construction.

CONTROLS: The craft is controlled by a three-axis automatic system while it is foilborne and during take-off and landing. The system senses the motion and position of the craft by gyros, accelerometers and height sensors, signals from which are combined in the control computer with manual commands from the helm. The resulting computer outputs provide control-surface deflections through electro-hydraulic servo actuators. Lift control is by full-span trailing edge flaps on each foil. Forward and aft flaps operate differentially to provide pitch variation and height control. Aft flaps operate differentially to provide roll control for changes of direction.

The vessel banks inwardly into all turns to ensure maximum passenger comfort. The ACS introduces the correct amount of bank and steering to co-ordinate the turn in full. Turn rates of up to six degrees per second are attained within one second of providing a heading change command at the helm.

Three basic controls are required for foilborne operation: the throttle is employed to set the speed, the height command lever to set the required foil depth, and the helm to set the required heading. If a constant course is required, a 'heading hold' circuit accomplishes this automatically.

For take-off, the foil depth is set, the two throttles advanced, and the hull clears the water in about 60 seconds. Acceleration continues until the craft automatically stabilises at the command depth and the speed dictated by the throttle

Craft built (Jetfoil 929–100)

Name	Launched	Current Operator
Flores (ex *Kalakoua*, 1978 Boeing No 001)	29 March 1974	Far East Hydrofoil Co Ltd, Hong Kong
Madeira (002)	Oct 1974	Far East Hydrofoil Co Ltd, Hong Kong
Corvo (ex *Kamehameha*) (003)	Feb 1975	Far East Hydrofoil Co Ltd, Hong Kong
Santa Maria (005)	April 1975	Far East Hydrofoil Co Ltd, Hong Kong
Pico (ex *Kuhio*) (004)	June 1975	Far East Hydrofoil Co Ltd, Hong Kong
São Jorge (ex *Jet Caribe I*) (006)	Dec 1975	Far East Hydrofoil Co Ltd, Hong Kong
Acores (ex *Jet Caribe II*, 1980, ex *Oriente*, 1978) (008)	Nov 1976	Far East Hydrofoil Co Ltd, Hong Kong
Urzela (ex *Flying Princess*) (007)	May 1976	Far East Hydrofoil Co Ltd, Hong Kong
Ponta Delgada (ex *Flying Princess II*) (010)	May 1977	Far East Hydrofoil Co Ltd, Hong Kong
Okesa	Dec 1976	Sado Kisen Kaisha, Japan

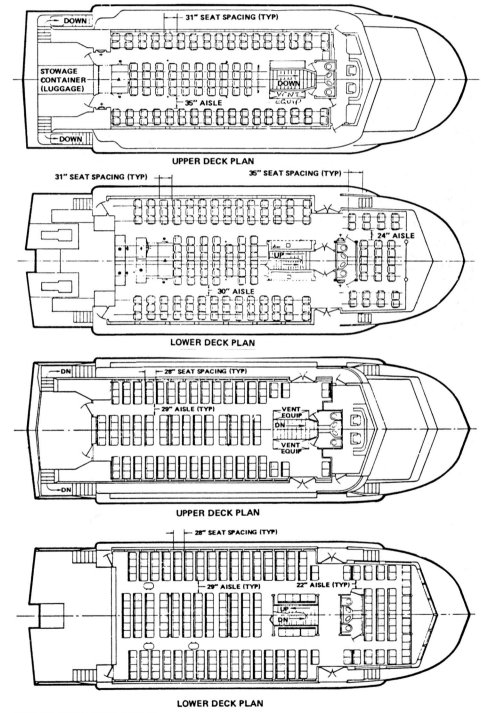

Jetfoil 929–100 interior arrangements

setting. The throttle setting is reduced for landing, the craft settling as the speed drops. The speed normally diminishes from 45 knots (cruising speed) to 15 knots in about 30 seconds. In emergencies more rapid landings can be made by the use of the height command lever to provide hull contact within two seconds.

HULL: Hull and deckhouse in marine aluminium.

The 1976-launched *Acores* Jetfoil 929–100 in service on the Hong Kong to Macau route

Aircraft assembly techniques are used, including high-speed mechanised welding processes.

POWERPLANT: Power for the waterjet propulsion system is supplied by two Allison 501-K20A free-power gas turbines, each rated at 3300shp at 27°C at sea level. Each is connected to a Rocketdyne Powerjet 20 axial-flow pump through a gearbox drive train. The two turbine/pump systems are located in their own bays, port and starboard, separated by the slot in the hull into which the central water strut retracts for hullborne operation. The system propels the craft in both foilborne and hullborne modes. When foilborne, water enters through the inlet at the forward lower end of the aft centre foil strut. At the top of the duct, the water is split into two paths and enters into each of the two axial flow pumps. It is then discharged at high pressure through nozzles in the hull bottom.

The water path is the same during hullborne operations with the foils extended. When the foils are retracted, the water enters through a flush inlet located in the keel. Reversing and steering for hullborne operation only are accomplished by reverse-flow buckets located immediately aft of the water exit nozzles. A bow thruster is provided for positive steering control at low forward speeds.

A 15 140-litre integral fuel tank supplies the propulsion turbine and diesel engines. Recommended fuel is Diesel No 2. The tank is fitted with a 5cm diameter fill pipe and fittings compatible with dockside refuelling equipment. Coalescent-type water separating fuel filters and remote-controlled motor-operated fuel shut-off valves provide fire protection.

ACCOMMODATION: Air-conditioned pass-

enger accommodation on two decks connected by a wide, enclosed stairway. Seats are track-mounted to facilitate spacing changes, removal or replacement. The cabins have 914mm (3ft) wide aisles and 2.06m (6ft 9in) headroom. In the commuter configuration $1.58m^3$ ($56ft^3$) per passenger

is provided and $1.87m^3$ ($66ft^3$) in the tourist configuration. Floors are carpeted and 61cm (2ft) seats are provided. Lighting is indirect and adjustable from the wheelhouse. Interior noise is near conversation level (below 68dB SIL) and there is a public announcement system. Each deck level

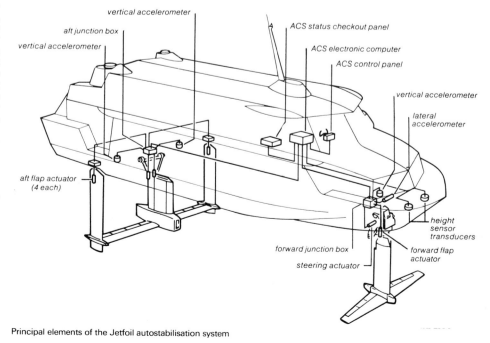

Principal elements of the Jetfoil autostabilisation system

has two wc/washbasin units. There are drinking water dispensers on each passenger deck.

Quality of the ride in the craft is comparable with that of a Boeing 727 airliner. The vertical acceleration at the centre of gravity is very low and depends on Sea State. For example, at 2 metres significant wave height the vertical acceleration is only 0.05g RMS. Lateral acceleration is substantially less than vertical. Angles of pitch and roll are less than 1 degree RMS. A structural fuse is provided which limits deceleration to less than 0.4g longitudinally and 0.8g vertically. In the event of the craft striking a major item of floating debris at full speed, the structural fuse, when actuated, allows the foil and strut to rotate backwards, protecting the system from sustaining significant damage.

Crew comprises a captain and first officer plus cabin attendants.

SYSTEMS, ELECTRICAL: 60Hz, 440V ac electrical system, supplied by two diesel-driven generators each rated at 62.5kVA. Either is capable of supplying all vital electrical power. 90kVA capacity shore connection facilities provided, and equipment can accept 50Hz power. Transformer rectifier units for battery charging provide 28V dc from the ac system.

HYDRAULICS: 210.9kg/cm^2 (3000psi) system to actuate control surfaces. Each pump is connected to a separate system to provide split system redundancy in the event of a turbine, pump, distribution system or actuator malfunctioning.

EMERGENCY: Craft meets all applicable safety regulations of the US Coast Guard and SOLAS. Hull provides two-compartment sub-division and a high degree of stability. Life rafts and life jackets are provided.

NAVIGATION: Equipment includes radar. A low-light-level television system covering potential collision zone is available as an optional extra.

DIMENSIONS
Length overall, foils extended: 27.4m
    foils retracted: 30.1m
Beam overall, max: 9.5m
Draught hullborne,
    foils retracted: 1.5m
    foils extended: 5m
WEIGHT
Displacement: 110 tons
PERFORMANCE
Max speed: 50 knots
Normal service speed: 42 knots
Turning radius at 45 knots: Less than 305m
Normal endurance at cruising speed: 4 hours
Max endurance: 8 hours
Max wave height foilborne: 3.65m

JETFOIL 929–115

The last of the Jetfoil 929–100 series was the 0010 *Flying Princess II*. The first of the improved 929–115 series, Jetfoil 0011 *Mikado*, was launched at Renton, Washington in June 1978, and is operated by Sado Kisen in the Sea of Japan.

A number of detail changes have been made in order to comply with the international craft code, but most have been made as a result of operating experience with the earlier model. The improved model Jetfoil has a lighter structure allowing an increased payload, greater reliability and is easier to maintain. Some of the modifications are listed below.

FOILS: External stiffeners on the foil struts have been eliminated and the bow foil has been changed from constant section to tapered planform for improved performance. Stress levels have been reduced for extended life.

CONTROLS: Heading hold (autopilot) installed as basic equipment. Automatic control system 'Autotrim' is improved to reduce steady state pitch and depth errors to negligible values. This reduces or eliminates the need for foil angle of incidence adjustments. A higher thrust bow-

Craft built (Jetfoil 929–115 type and conversions)

Name	Launched	Owner
Mikado (011)	June 1978	Sado Kisen Kaisha, Japan
Ginga (ex *Cu na Mara*)	Nov 1979	Sado Kisen Kaisha, Japan
Terceira (ex *Normandy Princess*)	Jan 1979	Far East Hydrofoil Co Ltd, Hong Kong
Funchal (ex *Jetferry One*)	May 1979	Far East Hydrofoil Co Ltd, Hong Kong
Horta (ex *Jetferry Two*) (016)	March 1980	Far East Hydrofoil Co Ltd, Hong Kong
Princesa Guayarmina	Nov 1980	Compañia Transmediterranea SA, Spain
Princesa Guacimara	July 1981	Compañia Transmediterranea SA, Spain
Bima Samudera I (Boeing No 0022)	Oct 1981	PT PAL, Indonesia
Princesse Clementine	Feb 1981	Regie des Transports Maritimes, Belgium
Prinses Stephanie	April 1981	Regie des Transports Maritimes, Belgium
Jet 7 (ex *Spirit of Friendship*, ex *Aries*, ex *Montevideo Jet*)	Aug 1980	Kato Kisen Co Ltd/Kansai Kisen Co Ltd
Jet 8 (ex *Spirit of Discovery*)	April 1985	Kato Kisen Co Ltd/Kansai Kisen Co Ltd
- (modified to 929–119)	Aug 1984	Indonesian Government (Navy)
- (modified to 929–119)	Nov 1984	Indonesian Government
Lilau (ex *Speedy Princess*) (shipped 1986 to Hong Kong to be modified to type 929–320)	July 1979	Far East Hydrofoil Co Ltd (FEH), Hong Kong. *(Speedy Princess* (ex British Royal Navy, HMS *Speedy*) was purchased in September 1986 by FEH (departed UK, 16 Oct 1986) and converted to a commercial passenger vessel)
- (modified to 929–120)	Jan 1986	Indonesian Government
- (modified to 929–120)	June 1986	Indonesian Government

Boeing Jetfoil 929–115 *Cu na Mara* re-named *Ginga* and in service with Sado Kisen Kaisha

Jetfoil 929–115 operated by Regie des Transports Maritimes

thruster is fitted and the navigation radar is now installed on a pedestal between the captain and first officer so that it can be swivelled for viewing from either position.

HULL: The bow structure design has been simplified to provide equivalent strength with increased payload and bulkhead 2 has been revised for decreased stress levels. Based on a seven-minute evacuation time in case of fire the following fire protection provisions have been made:

Fibreglass is used for thermal insulation where

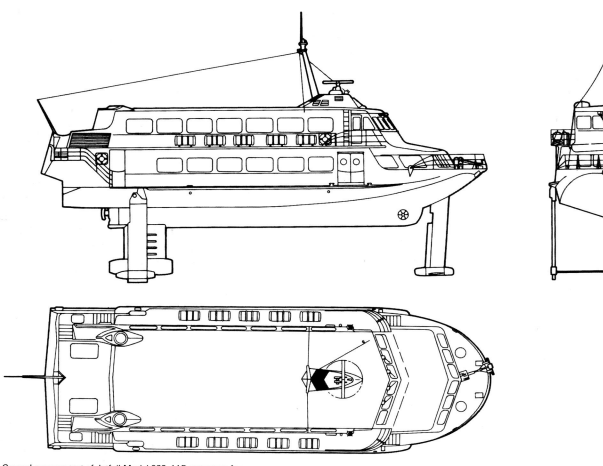

General arrangement of Jetfoil Model 929–115 passenger ferry

required throughout the passenger accommodation areas.

Aluminium ceiling panels and air-conditioner sleeves are employed throughout, together with aluminium doors and frames.

One-half inch thick Marinite is employed in machinery spaces, with US Coast Guard-type felt added wherever required for insulation to comply with 30-minute fire test.

Carpet, seat fabrics and lining materials meet low flame spread, toxicity and smoke requirements of US Coast Guard and Department of Trade, United Kingdom.

POWERPLANT: The propulsion system has been uprated to operate at 2200 maximum intermittent pump rpm with an increase of 3 tons in maximum gross weight.

ACCOMMODATION: Seats of revised design are fitted; environmental control unit has been located forward to increase payload and aid servicing, stairway to upper deck has a round handrail for better grip.

SYSTEMS, ELECTRICAL: Dc system is now in the wheelhouse to comply with new dynamically-supported craft rules. Ac panels relocated to be closer to equipment served to reduce wire runs. Redundant power sources are provided from either diesel generator for services to 24V dc emergency loads and loads essential for foilborne operation. Emergency 24V dc lights have been added in lavatories and aft machinery areas. Daylight signalling lamps with self-contained batteries are provided.

HYDRAULICS: System is consolidated with one manifold and reduced piping.

AIR CONDITIONING: Machinery moved forward to space above the main stairway and forward machinery space to improve operation and servicing.

DIESEL FUEL SYSTEM: Separate fuel systems supply the propulsion engines and diesel generators. This allows alternate fuels to be used in the turbines and greatly simplifies the plumbing system.

SEAWATER SYSTEM: Cooling water for the propulsion system has been separated from the remainder of the system. This simplifies the system and improves its reliability.

MISCELLANEOUS: Originally the hull corrosion prevention system was based on the isolation of dissimilar metals and ship-to-shore grounding. The new approach uses dockside impressed current, resistance-controlled shorting of struts and foils to the hull, additional pod anodes and electrical isolation. Other changes include a changeover to titanium seawater piping, a change in seawater pump materials and protective painting added to the hydraulic system.

DIMENSIONS
Length overall, foils extended: 27.4m
Beam, max: 9.5m
Draught,
  foils extended: 5.2m
  foils retracted: 1.7m

Height (without retractable mast),
  hullborne, above mean waterline: 12.8m
  foilborne, at 2.4m (8ft) foil depth: 15.5m
WEIGHT
Fully loaded displacement: 115 long tons
PERFORMANCE
Design cruising speed: 43 knots (80km/h; 50mph)

JETFOIL 929–117
Since 1985 Boeing has not manufactured any model of the Jetfoil. The 929–117 model, an updated version, is currently licensed for production outside the USA, with Kawasaki Heavy Industries, Ltd, Kobe, Japan and P.T. Pal Indonesia.

JETFOIL 929–320
Craft built
Speedy Princess, ex HMS *Speedy*
The Jetfoil 929–320 was delivered to the Royal Navy in June 1980 for use in fisheries patrol in the North Sea. Named HMS *Speedy*, the craft was a modified Model 929–115 commercial Jetfoil and was built on the commercial Jetfoil production line. The craft was decommissioned by the Royal Navy in April 1982 and eventually sold to the Far East Hydrofoil Co Ltd (FEH) in the autumn of 1986. The craft has been converted to passenger configuration and operates on their Hong Kong to Macao route.

WESTFOIL INTERNATIONAL
PO Box 1757, Westport, Washington 98595, USA

Telephone: (206) 268 0117

Randy Rust, *Representative*

WESTFOIL 25 METRE
Design started on the Westfoil 25-metre fully-submerged hydrofoil in the fall of 1986 with construction underway during the summer of 1987. The hull lines come from Westport Ship Yard's latest mould, for a boat designed to meet the rigours of year-round commercial service. The submerged foil and automatic control system are based on 25 years of hydrofoil experience using the latest in proven technology to provide a ride which should be better than existing hydrofoils. The ducted air propellers will provide thrust at low tip speed while the ducts will have acoustical treatment to further reduce sound.

ENGINES: Four DDA 12V-92 TA diesels with 145 type injectors, each 1080bhp max, at 2300rpm. Rpm limited to 2100.

PROPELLERS: Two ducted units by Pacific Propeller Inc with low-tip-speed variable-pitch propellers.

ACCOMMODATION
149 passengers at 81.3cm seat pitch
One galley
Four lavatories
Baggage allowance: 23kg/passenger

CAPACITIES
Fuel: 5677 litres
Fresh water: 378 litres

ELECTRICAL POWER: One 30kW Northern Lights generator providing 110V ac power with 8kW back-up. Four alternators, one on each engine, providing 12V dc and 25V dc power and power for the automatic control system (ACS). Four 8D starting batteries for mains (24V). Six deep cycle 6V batteries wired for 12V lights. One 35A 24V charger and one 80A 12V charger. Long-life battery cluster for ACS system.

AUTOMATIC CONTROL SYSTEM (ACS): The ACS includes the flaps located at the trailing edges of both the fore and aft foils, the front strut rudder, the foil flap actuation system and the automatic stabilisation and control system. The foil flaps provide control of the craft in pitch, roll and yaw to provide a smooth ride in all seas up to design sea conditions, and for take off and landing. The foil flap actuators use input from the automatic stabilisation and control system to select the angle of the foil flaps so that the wave motions are counteracted. Flaps are moved in response to helm control to turn the boat in a banked attitude. The automatic stabilisation and control system employs a computer, motion sensors, a height sensor and gyroscopes to generate the commands sent to the actuators so that the foil flaps move to maintain the desired stable attitude and foil depth.

CONTROLS: The start, idle, power management and shut down, propeller pitch, boat direction, foilborne or hullborne mode selection and strut extension/retraction controls will be located for one-man operation in the wheelhouse. In addition, hullborne controls will be located on each bridge wing. Engine instrumentation is located in the wheelhouse.

FOILBORNE STEERING: Accomplished by actuating the aft flaps differentially (in response to helm commands) to roll the boat into a turn with appropriate front strut rudder setting to maintain a co-ordinated turn. The flaps and front strut rudder settings will be maintained by the ACS in response to helm commands and motion and height sensor feedback.

HULLBORNE STEERING: Utilises an Arneson drive system for hullborne steering and reversing. A bow thruster will be installed.

FOILS AND STRUTS: Nitronic 50 stainless steel and composite structure in a canard arrangement. The front and aft foil and strut systems can be retracted independently.

ENVIRONMENTAL SYSTEMS: Air-conditioning and heating is installed.

DIMENSIONS
Length, overall (struts included): 24.39m
Beam, moulded: 7.16m
Draught, struts retracted: 1.12m
Draught, struts extended, hullborne: 4.88m
GRT: Less than 100

WEIGHT
Displacement: 71.11 tonnes

PERFORMANCE
Speed: Estimated 42 knots in Sea State 5 at full weight
Cruise power: Approximately 750bhp each at full weight

Artists' impression of Westfoil 25-meter

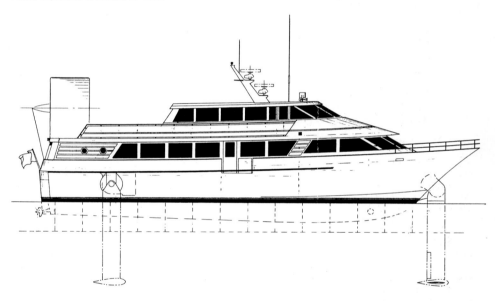

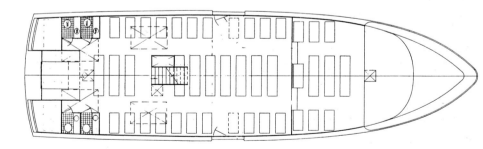

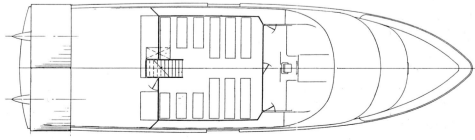

Provisional general arrangement of Westfoil 25-metre

AIR BOATS AND HYDROCOPTERS

FINLAND

KONEPAJA NILS ERIKSSON KY
SF-21630, Lielax, Parainen (Pargas), Finland

Telephone: (921) 888 086

NE 3000 AMPHIBIAN
A six-seat hydrocopter fitted with road wheels for overland use on smooth surfaces. This craft may be powered by either a Ford or Rover V6 engine. These vehicles are in use in Finland, Norway and Sweden for private use and by pilots, the Coast Guard, the military and postal services.

When driving on snow or on ice hydraulic arms can raise the hull 27cm above the surface and the craft then runs on its skis. The wheel axles are spring-mounted and the wheels can be lowered for road transportation. The vehicle may be towed behind a car but it can also be driven with the assistance of its own engine. Over snow or ice the vehicle is steered with the help of the front skis and when in water by its air rudder.

The roof of the cabin is openable by electro-hydraulic actuators. The cabin is large enough to take two stretchers.
PRINCIPAL PARTICULARS
Length: 6.1m

The Nils Eriksson Amphibian

Cabin length: 2.4m
Cabin width: 1.47m
Seats: Six
Hull: Corrosion-resistant aluminium, 2–4mm thick Buoyancy: Foam rubber-filled compartments
Speeds, over smooth ice: 100km/h
in heavy snow: 30–40km/h

Amphibian

Amphibian running over ice

FRANCE

AFR-HYDROMAR
route de Bordeaux, 24100
Bergerac,France

Telephone: (53) 570563
Telefax: (53) 632750
J.C. Simon-Beril, *Principal*

This company has developed a range of three airboats built in fibre reinforced plastic

DRAGONFLY HYDROGLIDER
This air boat can carry up to five people and has a floor cockpit area of four square metres.The

engine may be either a Citroen 650 cc or 1.3 litre VW

SWAN HYDROGLIDER
This version may carry two to three people, is 3.75m long and 1.62m in width.

THE NETHERLANDS

HOVERTRANS BV
Remenden 9, 3911 TZ Rhenen, The Netherlands

Telephone: (08376)16662/19004
Telex: 45695 NIWIN NL
Telefax: (08376) 12129

Dr. Paul Helder, *Managing Director*

PG 10 (DESIGN)
The design of the Hovertrans PG10 airboat is

aimed at providing a simple, fast craft not requiring extensive technical back up. The design meets the standards of Lloyds Register of Shipping.

The glass reinforced polyester (GRP) hull can be lengthened, which with an increase in thrust power can provide more carrying capacity. The floor area of the hull is not inhibited by fixed structures. This free area provides the feasibility of either installing individual seats or benches or leaving the entire floor area free for transportation of equipment. Two large fuel tanks with a total

capacity of 200 litres enable the airboat to be operational for a period of about 10 hours without re-fueling.

An acceptable level of sound emission according to current environmental standards has been reached by the installation of an exhaust silencer and low tip speed. Special attention has been paid to the engine bay layout and ventilation to provide optimum conditions for the air-cooled diesel engine.

The captain can watch over the safety of passengers and cargo from his position directly in front of the power unit. The simple layout of the craft provides for easy maintenance of thrust unit and engine. Moreover, the entire power – plus thrust unit can easily be removed. Due to the construction method maintenance of the hull will only require basic GRP fabricating techniques.

PRINCIPAL PARTICULARS
Length, overall: 8.00m
Beam: 2.20m
Optional: Maximum length: 10.00m
   Maximum beam: 3.00m
LOADING CAPACITY
Maximum number of passengers: 10
Crew: 1
Maximum disposable load, consisting
of fuel, passengers and cargo: 1000kg
Maximum fuel capacity is 200 litres: 170kg
Note: The assumed average weight per person is
75kg (see IMO).
PERFORMANCE
Cruising speed: 20 knots
Fuel consumption: 14 litre/hour at cruising speed
(20 knots)
Range (fuel capacity 200 l): 500km
Endurance (fuel capacity 200 l): 14 hours
ENGINE: Deutz Diesel, BF 4L 913, four cylinder

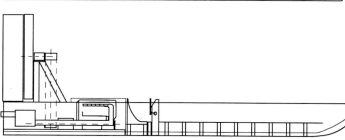

Layout of the Hovertrans PG10 airboat design

turbo charged DIN 6271 – Group 5B IOFN, delivering 74 kW (100hp) at 2300 rpm.
SYSTEMS
Propeller: two-blade Hoffman fixed-pitch, 2 metre diameter
Power transmission: drive shaft plus toothed belt

Steering system: hydraulically activated rudders
Steering rudders: two
Clutch: reversing clutch
Bilge pump: manual
Electrical system: 12V battery, 180 Ah

SWEDEN

ALBIN JOHANSSON
Nåset, S-610 24 Vikibolandet, Sweden
Telephone: (0125) 20073/20464

ARKÖ SPECIAL HYDROCOPTER
The first hydrocopter was built by Albin Johansson in 1959 and since then over 300 have been built. The craft is powered by a 43hp ILO 2-stroke engine.
PRINCIPAL PARTICULARS
Length (excluding rudder): 3.75m
Width: 1.70m
Height (propeller horizontal): 1.55m
Propeller thrust: 97kp
Propeller rpm, max: 2200
Engine rpm, max: 6200
Fuel tank capacity: 23 litres
Fuel consumption: 8 to 12 litres/h
Accommodation: 2 seats
Speed, over snow: about 150km/h
   over water: about 20 knots

Albin Johansson Arkö Special Hydrocopter

UNION OF SOVIET SOCIALIST REPUBLICS

NEPTUN CENTRAL DESIGN BUREAU (TsKB)
Moscow, USSR

Telephone: (095) 231–10–40

TSIKLON (CYCLONE)
A hydrocopter or air-propelled sledge designed for sale to the public for fishing, hunting and general purpose duties; a multi-purpose amphibian.
PRINCIPAL PARTICULARS
Length, hull: 4.30 m
Length, overall: 5.40 m
Width of central skid: 0.80 m
Height, overall, to top of duct: 2.52 m
Displacement, normal max: 1050 kg
Weight, empty: 750 kg
Load-carrying capacity in summer, for use on water: 350 kg, in winter, over snow or ice: 230 kg (3 people)

Tsiklon

Fuel tank capacity: 50 l
Engine: Moskvich 412E car engine, 49 kW, 65 hp
  at 5000 rpm
Propeller: 4-blade, fibreglass, 1.47 m diameter,
  1650 rpm, ducted, the duct providing 200 kg of
  thrust
Speed, max, full load, temp −10°C: 75 km/h over
  smooth snow. Over freshly-fallen snow, temp
  0°C, 25–30 km/h Gradient climb capability:
  7° to 8° steady climb, 15° running start
Transmission: toothed belt

It is believed that the first three craft were delivered in 1988. Their hulls are of riveted all-metal construction with the cabin and upper deck in fibreglass. The bottom and sides are of corrosion resistant AlMg-5M alloy of 1.5 to 2.0 mm thickness. The body is left unpainted in view of the severe spring and autumn conditions as well as the low-temperature winter conditions.

The design of the rudder system is covered by Soviet patent No. 1126489. When operating over snow or ice, constant contact is maintained by a 'snow rudder' with the surface over which the craft is operating; rubber shock absorbers are incorporated in this arrangement. When operating over water, a water rudder of larger surface area is fitted. Two air rudders supplement the 'snow rudder'.

The craft is fitted with an 'undersprung bottom' consisting of a light alloy sheet with riveted-on polyethylene strips which slide easily over the snow. Between this secondary bottom and the hull underside there is a layer of shock absorbing spongy rubber padding (Germit). At the expense of some 80 kg in weight, shock loads when running over rough surfaces are reduced to two-thirds.

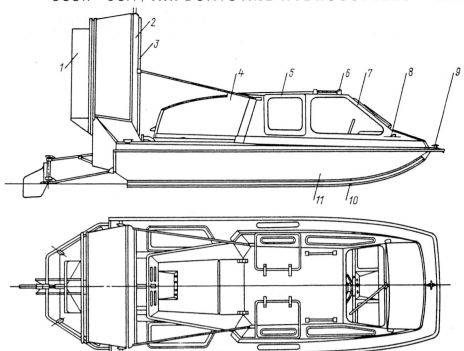

Layout and components of the hydro-snow craft. Tsiklon. 1 Air rudder; 2 Recess (cowling); 3 Safety grille; 4 Cover; 5 Door; 6 Handrail; 7 Deck cabin; 8 Navigation lights; 9 Mooring cleat; 10 Detachable bottom; 11 Body

Series of production Tsiklon is due to start in 1989 at SPO 'Vimpel' in Andropov. Budget price in 1988 was put at 7300 roubles.

UNITED STATES OF AMERICA

THE PANTHER AIR BOAT CORPORATION
300 Wilson Avenue, Cocoa, Florida 32922, USA

Telephone: (407) 632 1722
Telex: 220883TAUR

L A Bell, *President*
David L McLain, *International Sales Manager*

Panther Air Boat Corporation has developed a range of air boats capable of traversing snow, ice, rivers and swamps at speeds up to 88.5km/h. Thrust is provided by a large two-blade airscrew above the transom.

The company concentrates on the construction of craft of 3.6 to 6m long and 2.1 to 2.4m wide, built in heavy duty 4.76mm thick all-welded marine grade aluminium alloy. Craft of different dimensions and built in glassfibre can be made to order.

POWERPLANT: New General Motors automotive engines of 220hp or 300hp are normally fitted except on the 3.6m models. Four- or six-cylinder Lycoming air-cooled aircraft engines are an optional alternative. Fuel consumption, depending on payload and horsepower, varies from 18.1 to 36.3 litres per hour at cruising speed. Fuel capacity of the standard 35 US gallon aluminium tank provides an endurance of between 4½ and 9 hours and an operating range of 289.6 to 547.1km.
CONTROLS: Heading controlled by single or twin rudders in the propeller slipstream. Standard

Panther Air Boat Hunter Series 15

instrument panel includes a tachometer, hour meter, ammeter, oil pressure and either water or oil temperature gauges. An electric starter, alternator, fuel pump, in-line fuel filter and a heavy duty 70-amp/hour battery are as standard.
WEIGHTS
Payload (according to model): 680–1474kg
PERFORMANCE (according to model)
Max speed, normal load: 48–88km/h
Cruising speed: 56–64km/h

POWER PAC
A portable self-contained air drive system that bolts on to many types of small boat from flat bottom 'Jon' boats to Zodiac inflatables.
Engine: 40 or 50hp, 2-cycle
Weight: 78.2kg
Capability, depending upon hull
  payload: 270kg plus
  speed: 25mph plus
  draught: 2.5cm
Shipping dimensions: 1.95 × 1.63 × 1.63m

HIGH-SPEED CATAMARAN AND MULTI-HULL VESSELS

AUSTRALIA

ATLAY CATS SALES & SERVICE PTY LTD (COUGAR CATAMARANS)

PO Box 5344, Gold Coast Mail Centre, Queensland 4217, Australia

Telephone: (075)39 2244/3477
Telefax: (075)97 1075

Harry Roberts, *Managing Director*

WHITSUNDAY FREEDOM

A 14.6 metre, 27 knot catamaran ferry delivered in 1988 to the Whitsunday Water Taxis company. Six Cougar Catamaran boats have been delivered to this operator.

PRINCIPAL PARTICULARS
Length, overall: 14.6m
Accommodation: 60 passengers, 3 crew
Engines: two MAN 2866 LE diesels, 304 kW (408 hp) diesels
Speed, full load: 22 to 23 knots
Speed, max: 27 knots

AUSTAL SHIPS PTY LTD

126 Egmont Road, Henderson, Western Australia, Australia

John Rothwell, *Managing Director*
Christopher Norman, *Naval Architect*

36 METRE CATAMARAN

Formed in June 1987, Austal Ships secured a contract for the construction of a 36 metre, 430-passenger catamaran ferry for the Nantong High Speed Passenger Ship Company in China. Valued at A$5.5 million, the delivery will be at the end of 1990. The vessel will be fitted with two MJP water-jet units

PRINCIPAL PARTICULARS
Length, overall: 36.0m
Length, waterline: 32.4m
Beam: 11.5m
Draught: 1.3m
Depth moulded: 3.6m
Hull, superstructure and deck construction material: Marine grade aluminium alloy
Main engines: Two MTU 16V396TB83 marine diesels developing 1470kW at 1940rpm
Propulsion: Two MJP J650R water jet units
Fuel capacity: 15 000 l
Fresh water capacity: 12 000 l
Sullage: 2000 l
Speed: 30 knots
Passengers: main deck: 309
　upper deck: 429
Crew: 14

BALI HAI
36.6 METRE CRUISE CATAMARAN

Built in 1989 to run day cruises from Bali to the

The 301 passenger cruise catamaran *Bali Hai* built by Austal Ships, Pty Ltd

islands of Nusa Penida and Lembongan. The *Bali Hai* is constructed in aluminium and designed to carry 301 passengers at 22 knots.
CLASSIFICATION: DnV
PRINCIPAL PARTICULARS
Length, overall: 33.60m
Length, water line: 30.70m
Beam: 10.50m
Draught: 1.95m
Depth moulded: 3.50m

Hull, superstructure and deck construction material: Marine grade aluminium alloy.
Engines: Two MAN D2842LYE diesels developing 735kw each at 2300rpm.
Fuel capacity: 16 000 l
Fresh water capacity: 4000 l
Sullage; 6000 l
Speed: 22 knots
Passengers: 301
Crew: Eight

CARRINGTON SLIPWAYS PTY LTD

Old Punt Road, Tomago, NSW 2322, Australia

Telephone: (049) 648071
Telex: 28185 SLIPS AA
Telefax: (049) 648316/648611

D Laverick, *Managing Director*

In January 1990 it was announced that Carrington Slipways had acquired a licence from Advanced Multi-Hull Designs, a newly formed design group specialising in high-speed catamarans, for the building of their designs.

GOLEBY & BAIN MARINE ENGINEERS

61 Gillan Street, Norman Park, Brisbane Queensland, Australia

Telephone: (07) 3993477
Telefax: (07) 3956924

COMMANDER CLASS EXPOCAT

The Commander class vessel is a twin hulled semi-planning passenger ferry that was developed from a design concept by Robert Trillo of Lyming-

ton, UK. The design was adapted for the local conditions by a Brisbane designer, Rick James.

The specification called for a medium to fast vessel capable of operating for extended periods of up to 15 hours continuous running with a compliment of 100+ passengers in sheltered river waters producing low levels of noise pollution and low levels of wash. The vessel had to be simple in its construction, able to be operated by one driver and be easy to service and maintain. Fuel economy and ease of passenger loading and unloading were important.

Design implementation began in June 1987 and

the first of three identical vessels came off the production line in February 1988. The second craft followed a month later, and the third a month after that. Following trials the vessels were put into service on the Brisbane River for the start of EXPO 88 in late April 1988.

During the EXPO period of 6 months, the three vessels helped transport over 1 million passengers operating for up to 17 hours a day, seven days a week.

PRINCIPAL PARTICULARS:The vessels are made of marine grade aluminium and have three distinct sections.

Two hulls are connected together by way of four tubular spars, welded to each hull. The hulls are plated and welded using a traditional frame, stringer and bulkhead method. The cabin is built of aluminium frames and floor bearers with aluminium frames and floor bearers with aluminium sheet riveted to the frames. The whole cabin unit is then mounted onto the hulls and secured with a series of flexible couplings.

The engine space is located in each hull aft of the cabin area and contains, in each hull, a six cylinder, turbo charged, after cooled, diesel engine producing 220 horsepower (164 kilowatts) giving a speed of 18 knots under load. The engines drive a flexible shaft that leads forward to a V drive then aft through a bearing in the keel to a three-blade propeller mounted in front of a skeg supporting the shaft. Located aft of the skeg is a blade rudder.

Two fuel tanks, one in each hull, of 500 litres capacity each are located forward of the machinery space. A header tank containing fresh water is mounted on top of the cabin at the aft end above the toilets. Two toilets are located on the port side aft in the cabin where aluminium bench style seats afford seating for approximately 100 passengers. Under the local survey, an additional 10 passengers can be carried standing.

Two steering positions, port and starboard, are located adjacent to the two entry points on each side of the vessel at the forward end of the cabin. Controls are hydraulic with an electric/hydraulic steering system driven by twin hydraulic pumps mounted on each engine. All electric systems are 24 volts DC. VHF and 27 meg radios provide communications to the shore base.

DIMENSIONS
Length: 19.9 metres
Breadth: 6.5 metres
Draught: 1.2 metres
Air draught: 3.5 metres
Displacement (light ship): 11 tonnes
Displacement (loaded): 18 tonnes (approx)

INVESTMENT: Each vessel requires approximately 20 weeks construction time from acceptance of the plans by the relevant approving society. All vessels are built to the Uniform Shipping laws code and are constructed by qualified tradesmen using modern methods and machinery. Vessels can be outfitted to individual requirements to reflect operating conditions and the particular operators area. Equipment used is heavy duty commercial and all systems are designed and installed to allow maintenance by basic qualified tradesmen.

The investment cost of each vessel is governed by the standard of fitout, engine choice and level of instrumentation. As a guide however, the investment in each of the vessels built to date is approximately A$500000 per boat.

NATURAL GAS & DIESEL FUEL MIX: One of the three vessels has been recently modified to run on a blend of diesel and compressed natural gas. This innovative system is a product of joint research with the Federal Government, Allgas Energy Limited and Golden Mile Marine Limited. The vessel is identical to the others with the exception that it contains two 3208 series V-8 Caterpillar diesels producing 250 horsepower (186 kilowatts) giving a speed of 20 knots under load. Eight 90-litre cylinders containing the compressed natural gas are stored aft of the cabin in racks between the two hulls.

Commander III Expocat at the Entonine Pontoon, Brisbane, September 1988

INTERNATIONAL CATAMARAN DESIGNS PTY LTD (INCAT) [DESIGN AND DEVELOPMENT ORGANISATION]

1 Mafeking Avenue, Lane Cove, Sydney NSW Australia 2066

Telephone: (02) 427 2822
Telefax: (02) 427 7238 INCAT SYDNEY

Philip Hercus, *Director*

From 1 March 1988 the activities of International Catamarans Pty Ltd were divided in a restructuring, with Philip Hercus assuming full ownership and control of design and technology aspects under a new company name, International Catamaran Designs Pty Ltd. From the same date, Robert Clifford assumed full ownership and control of building facilities and manufacture with a licence to market and build In Cat designs worldwide, his company having the new name International Catamarans Tasmania Pty Ltd. Over 115 craft have been built or are being built to International Catamaran designs.

100 METRE WAVE PIERCER CAR FERRY (DESIGN)

As of January 1990 this design is the largest investigated by International Catamaran Designs Pty Ltd. and allows freight vehicle carriage to be considered.

PRELIMINARY PARTICULARS
HULL: Aluminium alloy
DIMENSIONS
Length, overall: 101.7m
Beam, excluding fenders: 36.2m
Beam, of hulls: 6.0m
Draught: 3.5m

ENGINES
Four Wartsila 18V32D, 7380 kW each, MCR
PROPULSION
Four KaMeWa 125 S11 water-jet units, driven via Navilus GCH 710 gearboxes
DEADWEIGHT EXAMPLE
PASSENGER/CAR FERRY
Passengers + baggage: 80 tonnes
Cars: 300 tonnes
Crew and effects: 2 tonnes
Stores, provisions: 8 tonnes
Duty-free goods: 10 tonnes
Fuel: 40 tonnes
Fresh water: 10 tonnes
Total deadweight: 450 tonnes
PASSENGER/CAR/TRUCK/COACH FERRY
By reducing car payload to 250 tonnes, 150 tonnes of trucks or coaches may be carried, giving a deadweight of 550 tonnes. Reducing the passenger payload to 35 tonnes, cars to 120 tonnes

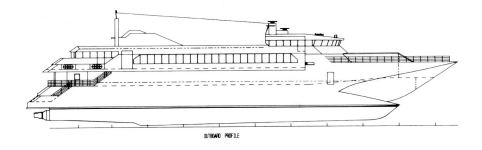

OUTBOARD PROFILE

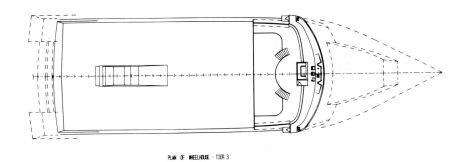

PLAN OF WHEELHOUSE - TIER 3

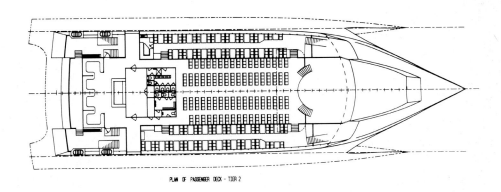

PLAN OF PASSENGER DECK - TIER 2

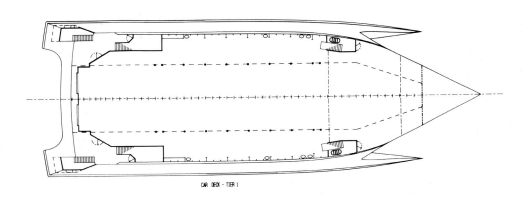

CAR DECK - TIER 1

General arrangement of 74m In Cat Wave Piercer passenger/car ferry

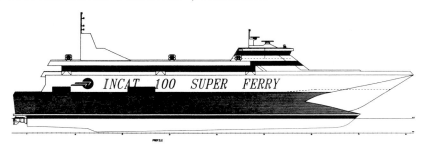

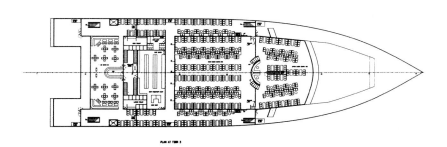

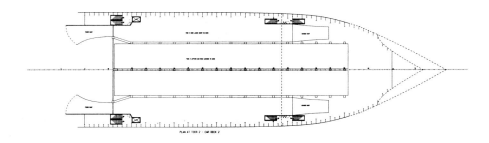

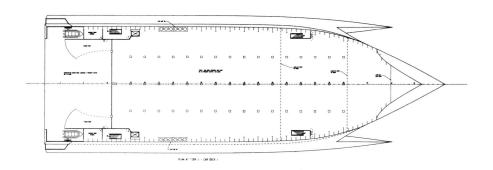

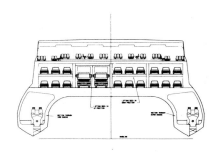

The In Cat 100 metre Wave Piercer passenger/car ferry design

and increasing trucks or coaches to 600 tonnes, a deadweight of 825 tonnes is achievable, a maximum for the design.

PERFORMANCE

Speed, max., light load: approx. 45 knots
Speed, at 90% MCR, 825 tonnes deadweight: approx. 35 knots or 38 knots at 550 tonnes.
Fuel consumption, at 90% MCR, 38 knots: 165 l/n miles.

TRIFOIL (DESIGN)

Announced by International Catamaran Designs Pty. Ltd. in January 1990, this concept involves the use of a hydrofoil system combined with a three-hull arrangement comprising a very slender deep-V centre hull and two extremely slender side hulls (of approximately half the length of the centre hull) which provide stability when the vessel is at rest or travelling at low speed. A forward hydrofoil surface is positioned beneath the main hull and two further foils are located aft, bridging the two outrigger hulls. At service speed the foil system is designed to carry about 75% of the vessel's weight. Active flaps can be fitted to the foils to augment the vessel's seakeeping ability. The Trifoil is the subject of Australian Patent Application PJ7313.

The Trifoil concept is seen by International Catamaran designs as not replacing either conventional catamarans or wave-piercing catamarans but rather being offered where the specific attributes of the concept are required.

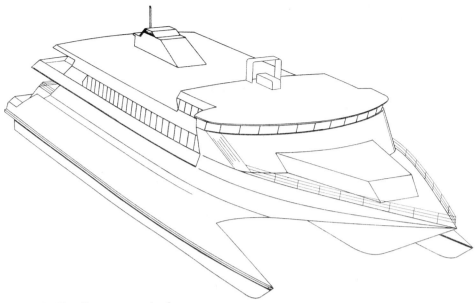

74m In Cat Wave Piercer passenger/car ferry

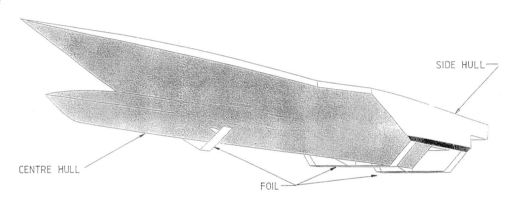

The In Cat Trifoil concept

INTERNATIONAL CATAMARANS TASMANIA PTY LTD (IN CAT)

18 Bender Drive, Moonah, Tasmania, Australia

Telephone: (002) 730677
Telefax: (002) 730932
Telefax: (002) 720072 *Engineering & Drafting*

Robert Clifford, *Director*

International Catamarans has been established over twelve years. The craft are generally of aluminium construction and the majority operate as fast passenger craft though a few of the larger ones have been built as oil rig crew/supply vessels, with a large clear deck aft.

A feature of some of the International Catamarans' vessels is the use of the company's own design of lifting rudder, which only enters the water when the helm is moved, hence reducing the resistance of the vessel. The craft also feature simple and rugged construction, as well as resiliently mounted superstructures giving the boats a high degree of reliability and comfort.

In July 1986 the 30m International Catamarans *Our Lady Pamela* undertook the longest delivery voyage of any high-speed catamaran ferry, from

The InCat *Our Lady Pamela* at the Sealink Ryde Pier terminal, Isle of Wight, England

Hobart, Tasmania to Portsmouth, UK, a distance of over 13 987 miles, arriving at Portsmouth on 30 July, 41 days 7 hours 36 minutes after leaving Hobart. All but 10 days 18 hours were spent at sea. The longest single passage covered was 2397 miles. The total fuel used was 263 700 litres, although one refuelling contained 2000 litres of salt water. For the 2138-mile passage from Gibral-

Craft built and ordered	Yard No	Completed	Max speed	Seats	Engines	Operator
18.0m *Derwent Explorer* (ex *Jeremiah Ryan*)		September 1977	26 knots	145	Two Cummins V8	
18.0m *Tropic Princess*, (ex *James Kelly I*)	002	June 1979	28 knots	100	—	Ecrolight
20.0m *Fitzroy Flyer*	004	June 1981	28 knots		—	Great Adventures
20.0m *Tangalooma*		December 1981	28 knots	200	—	Tangalooma Island Resort
15.0m *Amaroo*		December 1981	12 knots	120	—	
20.0m *Islander*, (ex *Green Islander*)	007	June 1982	28 knots	220	—	
20.0m *Quicksilver*		August 1982	28 knots	100	—	Outer Barrier Reef Cruises
29.0m *Spirit of Roylen*		December 1982	27 knots	250	—	McLeans Roylen Cruises Pty Ltd (ex Barrier Reef Holdings)
20.0m *Magnetic Northerner* (ex *Keppel Cat 2*, ex *Trojan*)		1983		200	—	Hydrofoil Seaflight Services Pty Ltd
20.0m *Keppel Cat I*		September 1984		195	—	Hydrofoil Seaflight Services Pty Ltd
27.4m WPC* *Spirit of Paradise*, (ex *Spirit of Victoria*)	016	June 1985	28 knots	—	Two DDC GM 12V 92 TA	MBM Management Ltd
30.0m *Our Lady Patricia*		March 1986	31 knots	452	Two MTU 16V 396 TC 83	Sealink British Ferries Sealink UK Ltd
30.0m *Our Lady Pamela*		July 1986	31 knots	452	Two MTU 16V 396 TC 83	Sealink British Ferries Sealink UK Ltd
31.0m WPC* *Tassie Devil 2001*	017	December 1986	30 knots	196	Two MWM TBD 234 V16	In Cat Charters
22.80m (*Starship Genesis*, ex *Genesis*)	018	July 1987	36 knots	200	Two DDC GM 16V 92 TA	In N.S.W.
31.0m WPC* *2000*	019	1988		231	—	Hamilton Island Cruises
37.2m WPC *Seaflight*	023	1988	30 knots	—	Two DDC GM 16V 149 TIB	Seaflight Ltd, New Zealand
74.0m WPC		1990	35 knots	450 + 84 vehicle spaces	Four Ruston 16 RK 270	Sea Containers, Hoverspeed†
74.0m WPC		1990	35 knots	450 + 84 vehicle spaces	Four Ruston 16 RK 270	Sea Containers, Hoverspeed†
74.0m WPC		1991	35 knots	350 + 70 car spaces	Four Ruston 16 RK 270	Tasmania Ferry Services

* Wave-piercing catamaran   † two more 74m In Cat WP catamarans ordered 26 January 1990 for Hoverspeed.

tar to Yarmouth, UK, the vessel averaged more than 22 knots.

As well as building craft at the Hobart facilities, International Catamaran Designs has licensed builders in Australia, Singapore, New Zealand, Hong Kong, USA and Great Britain.

In 1983 In Cat constructed an 8.7m test vessel conceived as a wave-piercing catamaran. This craft, *Little Devil* first underwent trials in 1984 and the results obtained allowed In Cat to proceed with a 28m wave-piercing catamaran, the *Spirit of Victoria* which has been in commercial operation since mid-1985. This craft was followed by *Tassie Devel 2001* launched in December 1986, a 31m wave-piercing catamaran of similar construction to its predecessor but with enclosed side supports and improved appearance. She operated in the rough waters off Perth during the America's Cup races. These craft are capable of higher speeds and operation in bigger waves than the conventional catamarans.

Future catamaran development is seen to concentrate on the wave-piercer concept, in which great interest has been shown. The superior sea-keeping and high performance of these craft are proving very attractive to passengers and operators alike.

74-METRE WAVE-PIERCING CATAMARAN

At the time of going to press, January 1990, five of these vessels were on order, four for Hoverspeed Limited, subsidiary of Sea Containers Ltd and one for Tasmanian Ferry Services for the Bass Strait crossing. The vessels are priced at about A\$20 million each. Of exceptional interest is the decision to employ relatively heavy medium-speed diesel engines in an advanced lightweight aluminium vessel structure with the aim of exploiting the low fuel consumption and long time between overhaul of these engines as well as avoiding the use of gearboxes. The nominal dry weight, with

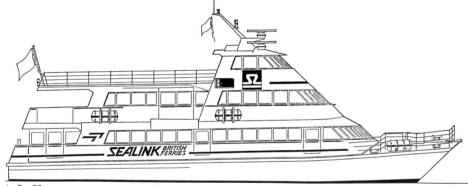
In Cat 30m catamaran as supplied to Sealink British Ferries

flywheel, of the Ruston engine to be used, the 16 RK 270, is 25.82 tonnes.

The original design conceived a vessel of 71 metres overall length and a corresponding water-line length of 55 metres. The first vessel is due to be delivered in June 1990.

CLASSIFICATION: DnV + 1A1 Light Craft Catamaran + MV R280, passenger ship, EO, car ferry A.

PRINCIPAL PARTICULARS (Sealink version)
Length, overall: 74m
Beam, overall: 25.8m
Beam of each hull: 4.4m
Draught, full load: 2.6m
Displacement: about 400 tonnes (design limit 650 tonnes)
Engines: four Ruston 16 RK 270 medium-speed diesels, each 3760 kW (5042 hp) at 720 rpm; specific fuel consumption at 90% full engine load: 201.5 g/kWh at 720 to 750 rpm, tolerance + 5%. At 1000 rpm these engines can deliver 4600 kW (6169 hp) with a s.f.c. 208.5 g/kWh at 90% full engine load.
Propulsion: Four directly-driven Riva Calzoni IRC 115 DX water-jet units, with only one on each side being equipped with steering and reversing systems.
Payload: 450 passengers plus 84 vehicles 171 tonnes
Deadweight: 198 tonnes design max 235 tonnes)
DEADWEIGHT BREAKDOWN
Passengers plus baggage: 45 tonnes
Vehicles: 126 tonnes
Crew: 2 tonnes
Stores & catering: 4 tonnes
Fuel: 16 tonnes
Lube oil: 1 tonne
Fresh water: 4 tonnes
Speed, service, full load, 90% MCR: 35 knots

30-METRE CATAMARAN
OUR LADY PATRICIA
OUR LADY PAMELA
CLASSIFICATION: Det norske Veritas + 1A1 Light Craft (CAT) R45 Passenger Ship EO UK DOT Class IV Partially Smooth Water Limits Passenger Vessel.

The first of these vessels entered service with Sealink British Ferries on 29 March 1986 and the second arrived on 30 July 1986.

HULL: Welded aluminium alloy construction (5083-H321 plating 6061-T6 sections) with the superstructure on anti-vibration mountings. There are large gangway doors on the upper deck for embarkation and disembarkation at the existing Portsmouth and Ryde Pier berthing facilities.

ENGINES/GEARBOXES: Two MTU 16V 396 TC83 diesels of 1430kW each at 1845rpm continuous rating. Gearboxes are ZF BW 750 ratio 2.548:1.

PROPULSION: Two five-blade aluminium-bronze fixed-pitch propellers.

AUXILIARY GENERATORS: Two Perkins 4108 diesels driving 26kVA alternators.

CONTROLS: International Catamarans patented hydraulically-operated lifting rudders.

NAVIGATION AND COMMUNICATIONS: Two radars, gyrocompass, two VHF radios, one echo sounder.

DIMENSIONS
Length overall: 29.60m
Length waterline: 25.50m
Beam overall (excluding fenders): 11.20m
Beam of single hull: 3.20m
Draught, loaded: 2.20m

WEIGHTS
Empty craft: 80.0 tonnes
Passengers and baggage: 37.5 tonnes
Crew and effects: 0.6 tonnes
Freshwater (500 litres): 0.5 tonnes
Fuel (two 2400-litre tanks): 4.0 tonnes
Baggage in containers: 2.4 tonnes
Total disposable load: 45.0 tonnes

PERFORMANCE
Trials speed (with disposable load of 22.5 tonnes): 31 knots

SPIRIT OF VICTORIA

This unusual 28-metre craft, Yard No 016, was launched in June 1985. The object of the design is to minimise the wave-following tendency as experienced by conventional semi-planing and planing hull craft; for this to be achieved a hull form that would cut through waves was envisaged. To explore the possibilities of this concept an 8.6-metre manned model, *Little Devil*, was constructed capable of carrying six people and powered by a 25hp outboard motor; extremely encouraging results were achieved, a speed of 16 knots being obtained at a scale displacement of

1.1 tonnes. This led to the decision to build a 28-metre version, *Spirit of Victoria*, with the backing of MBM Management Pty Ltd which was prepared to operate the boat under long term charter.

OWNER: In Cat Charters.

HULL: Welded marine-grade aluminium. Materials: 5083 H321, and 6061 T6 alloys, 5086 H32.

SURVEY: Marine Board of Victoria, Class 1C.

CLASSIFICATION: DnV + 1A 2K Light Craft R15.

ENGINES: Two DDC GM 12V-92 TA, 650bhp each, at 1980rpm continuous rating.

PROPULSION: Two five-blade, 1000mm diameter Wageningen B series propellers.

GEARBOX: Two Reintjes WVS 532 ratio 2.452:1.

GENERATOR: Deutz S2L912 diesel-driven 17.5kVA alternator 415V, 3-phase, 50Hz ac or 240V, single-phase, 50Hz ac.

NAVIGATION: 24n mile JRC radar; Wagner Mk II autopilot.

COMMUNICATIONS: Codan 8121 SSB, GME VHF, Clarion PA.

ACCOMMODATION
219 seats; 115 in main cabin, 40 in upper cabin, 22 open main deck, 42 open upper deck.

DIMENSIONS
Length overall: 27.40m
Length waterline: 25.0m
Beam overall: 13.02m
Beam, single hull: 2.22m
Draught: 1.74m

CAPACITIES
Fuel: Two 3500-litre tanks
Fresh water: One 300-litre tank

PERFORMANCE
Speed, light ship: 28 knots
Speed, full load: 26 knots

TASSIE DEVIL 2001

A developed version of *Spirit of Victoria* and the third wave-piercing catamaran to be built. The vessel is built under survey by Det norske Veritas

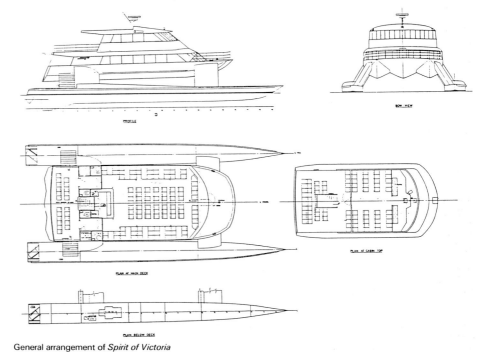

General arrangement of *Spirit of Victoria*

International Catamarans wave-piercing catamaran ferry *Spirit of Victoria* built in 1985

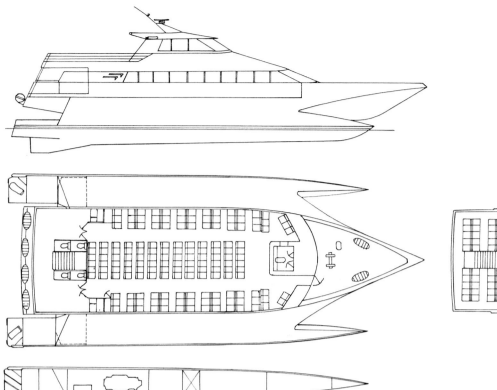

General arrangement of *Tassie Devil 2001*

Class + 1A1 Light Craft (CAT) R45. In addition the vessel is under survey by The Navigation and Survey Authority of Tasmania, Class ID, Partially Smooth Water Limits Passenger Vessel.
POWERPLANT: Two MWM 234 16V, 830kW each at 2265rpm (overload rating), 755kW each at 2200rpm (continuous light duty rating). Gearboxes ZF type BW 250, reduction ratio 3:1. Flexible couplings: Vulcan Rato S.
PROPELLERS: 5-blade modified Troost 'B' type, aluminium bronze, 1383mm pitch, 1150mm diameter, blade-area ratio: 0.89.
ACCOMMODATION: 196 passengers.
NAVIGATION: Furuno 1700 radar, Mariner log.
COMMUNICATIONS: Codan 8121 HF, President Sea Eagle 55 VHF.
DIMENSIONS
Length: 30.45m
Length waterline (excluding trim tab): 25.00m
Beam (excluding fenders): 13.00m
Draught loaded: Approx 2.0m
PERFORMANCE
Speed, max: 31 knots

STARSHIP GENESIS

An In Cat development vessel launched August 1987 for development with waterjet systems, surface-drive systems and In Cat transom drive.
POWERPLANT: Two GM DDA 16V-92 TA, 930kW each at 2300rpm. Gearboxes: Niigata MGN 332X, ratio: 2.50:1.
PROPELLERS: Aluminium bronze surface-piercing types under development.
DIMENSIONS
Length: 22.80m
Length, waterline (excluding trim tab): 18.50m
Beam (excluding fenders): 8.20m
Draught, design waterline (excluding propeller): 0.88m
PERFORMANCE: On trials speeds up to 35 knots have been reached.

38.6-METRE WAVE-PIERCING CATAMARAN

Three of these vessels were ordered by Quicksilver Connections Ltd, Port Douglas, Queens-

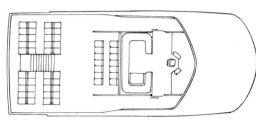

In Cat *Starship Genesis*, a 22.8m development craft

Surface-piercing propeller development on In Cat *Starship Genesis*

land and were delivered by NQEA Australia Pty Ltd in 1988 and 1989. Please see NQEA entry for details.

A notable feature of these vessels is the decision to use waterjet propulsion. This is due to the addition of a new shallow draught service to the Quicksilver Connection schedule and the company's desire to keep all vessels identical.

In addition to the Quicksilver order a USA operator ordered a similar 37m wave-piercing catamaran which was delivered in 1988. The only significant difference between this vessel and the Quicksilver craft will be the installation of more powerful engines in the USA vessel to give a

service speed of approximately 32 knots fully loaded.

Further orders followed for three wave-piercers, one 31m, one 37m and one 43m. Two of these vessels were completed in 1988 and the other in 1990.

BASS STRAIT FERRY

The original wave-piercing catamaran concept was a large vessel capable of carrying 300–500 passengers and 60–80 cars at a service speed of 35–40 knots. Such a vessel would operate a ferry service across Bass Strait, the very rough waterway between Tasmania and the Australian mainland. With the establishment of the wave-piercing concept in smaller craft, attention has again turned to the Bass Strait vessel.

Preliminary details of an In Cat proposal for a Bass Strait wave-piercing ferry were released in early 1988 and the first vessel has now been ordered.

- All-aluminium construction with passenger spaces resiliently mounted to minimise noise and vibration. This feature being in common with conventional In Cat catamarans
- Four-engine, four waterjet propulsion to maximise reliability
- Capacity for approximately 90 cars on a drive-through vehicle deck. The clear height on the

vehicle deck is 2.2m at the sides and 3.5m at the centre to suit the perceived needs for the Bass Strait service. These heights can be easily increased if necessary at the cost of the small increase in weight and a small increase in motion in the passenger spaces due to their greater height in vessel

Generous-sized passenger spaces due in part to the length of the crossing (about 4 hours) and in part to the ready availability of the required space. There are a number of survey and safety aspects which require special attention on this large wave-piercer

The vessel has access stairs in each corner of the passenger deck. In Cat believe that the best evacuation proposal will be to provide exits in the cabin side adjacent to each of the stairs and to fit inflatable slides to give access from the passenger deck to inflatable rafts. Some small changes will have to be made to the passenger deck layout to provide space for the stowage of the slides and rafts

A fire detection system will be fitted in the vehicle deck, supported by a sprinkler system for fire extinguishing. Structural fire protection will be fitted to the underside of the passenger accommodation

As the vessel has no need for buoyant spaces above the vehicle deck it is intended that the vehicle deck will be open at the aft end to facilitate ventilation. This also means that adequate arrangements can be made to drain overboard any water which might find its way onto the vehicle deck. Consequently the vessel is not vulnerable to damage of the bow door; the door is only fitted to give weather protection to the vehicles.

No major problems are foreseen in attending to the above. It is believed that other aspects of safety, eg intact and damaged stability, lifesaving appliances, fire protection, etc can be readily and adequately covered by conventional regulations such as IMO Code A.373(X).

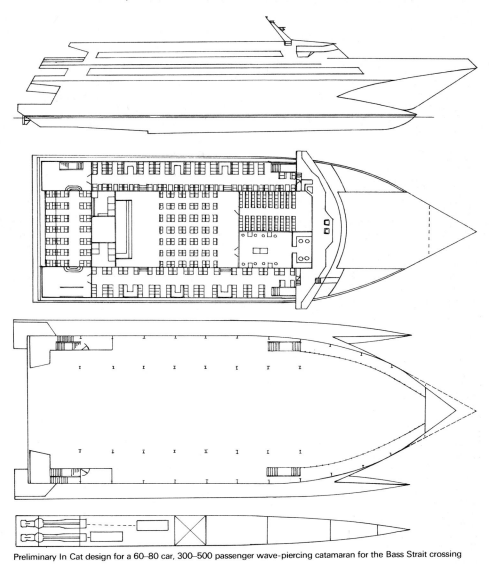

Preliminary In Cat design for a 60–80 car, 300–500 passenger wave-piercing catamaran for the Bass Strait crossing

---

LLOYD'S SHIPS HOLDINGS PTY LTD
41 Oxford Street, PO Box 121, Bulimba, Queensland 4171, Australia

Telephone: (07)399 6866
Telex: 10721378 LSHIPS AA
Telefax: (07)399 7565

This company ceased trading in late 1989. Two catamarans were built in 1988, the 25 knot, 260 passenger *Equator Dream*, and in 1989, the 20 knot, 360 passenger *Auto Batam 8*.

NQEA AUSTRALIA PTY LTD)
62–90 Cook Street, PO Box 1105, Cairns, Queensland 4870, Australia

Telephone: (070)52 7222
Telex: 48087AUS AA
Telefax: (070)51 5520/311812

D G Fry, *Chief Executive*
S Grimley, *Managing Director*
G M Steene, *Executive Director, Marketing*
A Rankine, *Executive Director, Production*
R D Rookwood, *Senior Design Engineer*
A E G Mill, *Company Secretary*

NQEA started services in 1948 from the residence of its founder with a staff of three, the principal activity being the operation of general engineering agencies, leading to general engineering manufacture and in 1964 it entered the shipbuilding industry with the construction of dumb barges. This was followed by work on many types of vessel, including Australian Navy patrol boats until in 1975 the first construction of vessels was undertaken. In 1977 NQEA was the successful tenderer for 14 'Freemantle' 42m class patrol craft,

for the Australian Navy, the first having been built by Brooke Marine in England. Taking 85 weeks to construct the craft, NQEA was delivering at a rate of one every 14 weeks.

23-METRE CATAMARAN
Early In Cat design with an all-welded aluminium hull. The superstructure is resiliently mounted to minimise noise and vibration.
SURVEYING AUTHORITY: Marine Board of Queensland, Partially Smooth Water (Class 1D), Restricted Offshore (Class 1C).
POWERPLANT: Two 800shp GM 12V-92 TA with Niigata MGN 80 reverse reduction gearbox 97:1.
PROPELLERS: Five-blade aluminium bronze.
ELECTRICAL POWER: 415V ac from shore power, or 35kVA Perkins diesel generator set 24V dc.
DIMENSIONS
Length overall: 23.0m
Length hull: 21.8m
Length waterline: 19.5m
Beam: 8.7m
Beam, single hull only: 2.5m

Draught loaded (max): 1.7m
Fuel capacity: Two 3000-litre tanks
PERFORMANCE
Speed, trial: 29 knots
Speed, cruising: 25 knots, loaded
Range: 1500 miles

28-METRE CATAMARAN
In Cat design with an all-welded aluminium hull and a resiliently mounted superstructure to minimise noise and vibration.
CLASSIFICATION: Queensland Marine Board, Class 1C, November 1983.
POWERPLANT: Two 1200shp GM 16V-92 TA high-speed diesels with ZF reverse/reduction gearbox 2.4:1.
PROPELLERS: Five-blade aluminium bronze.
ELECTRICAL POWER: 415V ac from shore power, or 80kVA GM diesel alternator set 24V dc.
DIMENSIONS
Length overall: 29.2m
Length hull: 28.0m
Length waterline: 25.0m
Beam: 11.2m
Air draught to cabin top: 8.7m

The sleek hull lines of the NQEA 37m In Cat wave-piercing catamaran, launched 12 November 1988

(Yon Ivanovic

Draught loaded (max): 1.76m
Fuel capacity: Two 5000-litre tanks
GRT: 340.43
PERFORMANCE
Speed, trial: 29 knots
Speed, cruising: 26 knots

38.6 METRE WAVE-PIERCING CATAMARAN

The first of these vessels *Quicksilver V* was completed by NQEA in November 1988 for Quicksilver Connections with a further two identical craft delivered in February and June 1989

from the same operator and a fourth vessel delivered to Yugoslavia also in June 1989
SURVEY: DnV + 1A1 R45 Queensland Department of Harbours and Marine, Class 1G.
POWER: Two GM diesel engines model 16V-149 TIB, each coupled to ZF gearbox model BU 460. Each engine will be rated 1230kW at 1800rpm.
CONSTRUCTION: All-welded aluminium generally using alloys 5083 H321 and 6061 T6. Some light plates are 5086 H32.
ACCOMMODATION: 350 passengers. Interior seats are individual armchairs with woollen upholstery. Exterior seats are moulded poly-

propelene shells. A food service area is fitted a the aft end of the lower cabin and a drinks bar in the middle of the lower cabin. Passengers spaces are air-conditioned.
WATERJETS: The vessel is fitted with two KaMeWa waterjets model 63S 62/6.
ELECTRICAL SYSTEMS: Main services are supplied by either of two diesel engine (Cummins 6BT5) driven 100kVA Stamford alternator sets These supply 415V 3ph and 415V, single phase 50Hz power. Engine starting, auxiliary and emergency services are supplied from 24V dc battery banks.

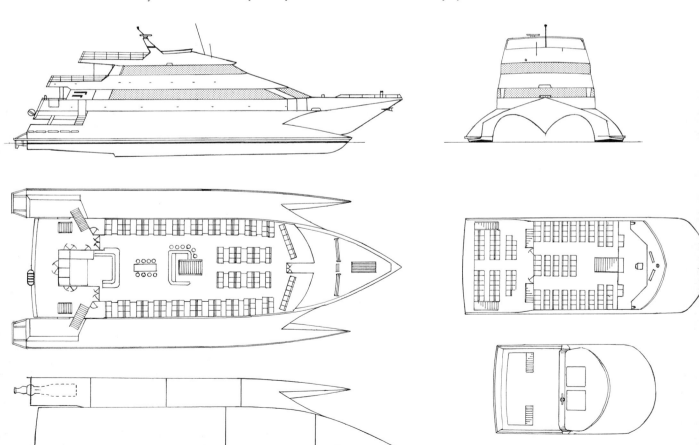

General arrangement of 37.2m In Cat wave-piercing catamaran for Quicksilver Connections Ltd

Craft built (In Cat)	Yard No	Delivered	Seats Class 1D	Class 1C	Engines	Operator
23.0m *Green Island Express*	106	June 1982	230	100		Great Adventures
23.0m *South Molle Reef* (ex *Telford Reef*)		October 1982	204			South Molle Island Resort
23.0m *Magnetic Express*	108	March 1983	240	100		Great Adventures
29.2m *South Molle Capricorn* (ex *Telford Capricorn*)		November 1983	326			Telford South Molle Island Resort
23.0m *Cougar*	113	1984	200			Great Adventures
23.0m *Reef Link*		1984	200			Reef Link Pty Ltd
24.0m *Quickcat I*		August 1984	145 to 200			Dunk Island and Barrier Reef Cruises
24.0m *Quickcat II*		1985	195			Hamilton Island Enterprises (Fantesea Cruises)
30.0m *Reef Cat*	126	May 1986	345			Great Adventures
30.0m *Quicksilver III* (ex *Quicksilver*)		October 1986	308		Two GEC Baudouin 12 P 15 SRC	In the Philippines
24.0m *Supercat II*	138	October 1988	205 +			North Shore Ferries Ltd
30.0m *Reef Link II*	147	February 1987	403			Reef Link Pty Ltd
24.0m *Taupo Cat*	148	March 1987	205			Trout Line (The Jascar Group (NZ) Ltd)
30.0m *Quicksilver IV* (ex *Quicksilver 2*)		May 1987	300		Two MWM TBD 604B V12	Philippines
30.0m *Supercat III*	125	August 1987	390			IGSA Shipping
24.0m *Roylen Sunbird*	151	August 1987	245			McLeans Roylen Cruises Pty Ltd
30.0m *Reef King*	152	December 1988	390		Two MWM TBD 604B V12	
25.3m *Wauri*		1988	—			Queensland Fisheries
26.9m *Adaire*	156	August 1988	150		Two MWM TBD 234 V16	Kuwait Public Transport Co
26.9m *Na'Aye*	157	September 1988	150		Two MWM TBD 234 V16	Kuwait Public Transport Co
38.6m WPC *Quicksilver V*	158	November 1988	252 + 66 externally		Two DDC 16V 149 TI	Quicksilver Connections
38.6m WPC *Quicksilver VI*	159	February 1989	350		Two DDC 16V 149 TI	Quicksilver Connections
38.6m *Quicksilver VII*	161	September 1989	350		Two DDC 16V 149 TI	Quicksilver Connections
39.6m WPC *Prince of Venice*	160	6 June 1989	303		Two DDC 16V 149 TA	Kompas Touristik
36.0m	163	March 1990				NSW State Transit Authority
39.0m WPC	170	May 1990	300			Nisshin Steamship Co
36.0m	172	July 1990				NSW State Transit Authority
36.0m	173	September 1990				NSW State Transit Authority

DIMENSIONS
Length overall: 38.6m
Length, waterline: 31.4m
Beam overall (excluding fenders): 15.6m
Beam hull: 2.6m
Draught, loaded: 1.6m

CAPACITIES
Passenger capacity: 340
Fuel capacity, normal: Two 2000-litre tanks
Fresh water capacity: 3000 litres

PERFORMANCE
Speed, loaded: 27 knots
Light: 30 knots

A 39 metre variation of the Quicksilver style was constructed for Kompas Touristik International, underwent an 11 000 mile delivery voyage from the builders yards to Piran in Yugoslavia, and immediately went into operation, plying between the Istrian ports and Venice. This vessel is fitted with KaMeWa water-jet units driven by DDC 16V 149 TA diesel engines.

PRINCE OF VENICE

This 39.6 metre wave-piercing catamaran is similar to those built for Quicksilver Connections Pty Ltd but is powered by up-rated DDC 16V 149 TA diesels giving 1435 kW at 2000 rpm. The vessel has a service speed of 27 knots, fully loaded and maximum speed of 30 knots at lightweight.

An NQEA 24m In Cat catamaran on trials prior to export to New Zealand for operations on Lake Taupo   *(Yon Ivanovic)*

The 39.6 metre In Cat Wave-piercing catamaran built by NQEA Australia for Yugoslavia.

The NQEA In Cat Cheetah Class patrol boat *Wauri* built for the Queensland Fisheries Department for operations in the Torres Strait

(*Yon Ivanovic*)

CLASSIFICATION
DnV + 1A1 Light Craft, R150
Jugosalvenski Registar Brodova +100 A1–3-
PU + M1-AUT3
ACCOMMODATION
Upper saloon: 91 passengers
Main saloon: 212 pasengers
Crew: 11

CHEETAH PATROL BOAT

NQEA has designed a patrol boat variant of the 23m commercial catamaran design. These boats will be identified as the Cheetah Class. One has been constructed for the Queensland Fisheries department and will be used for surveillance work in northern Australian waters. Normally operated by a six-man crew, the craft has facilities to carry an additional 12-man landing party and has extended range cruising capabilities.

DIMENSIONS
Length, overall: 25.3m
Beam, moulded: 8.7m
Beam, of each hull: 2.5m
Draught: 2.0m
Engines: Two Deutz MWM TBD 234 V12, 605kW each at 2200 rpm
Gearbox: Two ZF BW195, ratio 2.46:1.0
Propulsion: Two 5-blade, 1.0m diameter, aluminium bronze
Crew: 6
Range: 1000 miles at 20 knots
Speed, max: 25 knots

One of the 36.8 metre In Cat Wave-piercing catamaran built by NQEA Australia for the Quicksilver Connections fleet.

High-speed turn by 36.8 metre In Cat-Wave piercing catamaran.

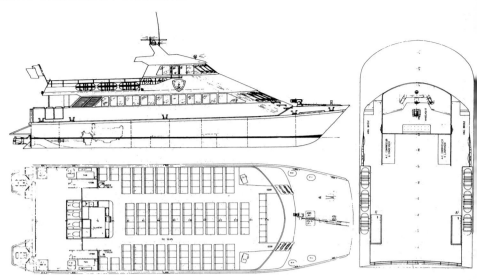

General arrangement of 150-seat NQEA In Cat catamaran
for Kuwait Public Transport Co.

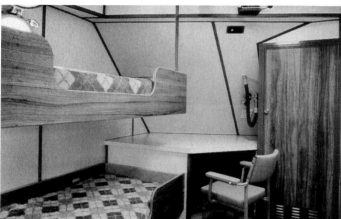

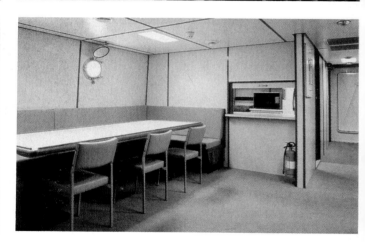

Internal views of the NQEA Cheetah Class In Cat patrol boat

PRECISION MARINE HOLDINGS PTY LTD

This company has ceased trading; please see 1989 edition for details of craft built

SABRE CATAMARANS PTY LTD
formerly
Harry Engineering
156 Barrington Road, Spearwood, Western Australia 6163, Australia

Telephone: (09) 418 3000
Telefax: (09) 364 7860

Bill Harry, *Principal*

Builder of a number of aluminium fast catamaran fishing and passenger vessels. One of the most recent is *Saladin Sabre*, a 100-passenger worker-commuter boat built for Stirling Marine Services Pty Ltd to transport construction crews from Onslow to Thevemard Island for oil field work. The boat is designed by Mark Ellis Marine Design, Freemantle, WA.

SABRE 55
SALADIN SABRE
PRINCIPAL PARTICULARS
Hull form: planing
Length, overall: 16.76m
Length, waterline: 14.95m
Beam: 7.20m
Draught: 0.72m
Engines: two DDC 8V 92T diesels
Propulsion: two Levi 800 series surface-piercing drive units
Auxiliary engine: Isuzu 17 kVA
Passengers: 100
Speed, full load: 28 knots
Speed, light-ship: 34.6 knots
Fuel tanks: two 1000 l tanks
Fresh water capacity: 500 l

SALADIN SPRINT
Built for the same purpose as *Saladin Sabre*.
PRINCIPAL PARTICULARS
Hull form: planing
Length, overall: 13.19m
Length, waterline: 11.60m
Beam: 5.40m
Draught: 0.60m
Freeboard, forward: 2.0m
Freeboard, aft: 1.30m
Engines: two Volvo Penta 357 hp, TAMD 71A turbo-charged, aftercooled diesels
Propulsion: Levi 400 series surface-piercing drive units
Passenger capacity: 40
Speed, max: 28 knots
Speed, cruising: 24 knots
Range: 350m mi
Fuel capacity: 1800 l
Fresh water capacity: 500 l

The Sabre 55 *Saladin Sabre*

The Sabre *Saladin Sprint*

SBF ENGINEERING
Waters Edge, Lot 33 Cockburn Road, South Coogee, Western Australia 6166, Australia
Telephone: (09) 4102022/2244
Telex: (09) 4101807

VICTORY III
Passenger ferry.
DESIGNER: Lock Crowther, Sydney.
OWNER: Great Keppel Island Tourist Services Pty Ltd, Rockhampton, Queensland, Australia.
LEGISLATING AUTHORITY: Queensland Marine and Harbours Department.
HULL: Catamaran hull and superstructure are

SBF Engineering *Victory III* showing bulbous bows

constructed in all-welded marine grade aluminium alloy. Each bow has a streamlined bulb on the forefoot which increases waterline length and performance. Draught of hulls forward is slightly over 1m and the craft is designed to be beached by the bow to allow passengers to embark and disembark using an SBF designed telescopic ramp lowered from the foredeck.

MAIN ENGINES: Two MWM 16-cylinder marine diesels, each producing 807kW (1082bhp).

PROPULSION: Two right handed 970mm × 1760mm propellers.

ACCOMMODATION

Passenger capacity: 448

SYSTEMS

Electrical generator: One MWM 3-cylinder generator producing 33kVA

Navigational equipment: JRC JMA 3425 colour radar; NWU 51 colour plotter; JAX2 Weatherfox; JLE 3850 satellite navigator; JFX 80 colour sounder

Communications: Codan 8121 SSB radio; Icom IC M80 VHF radio

Life saving: 450 costal life jackets; 450 flotation rafts

Firefighting: Halon gas fire extinguishers

DIMENSIONS

Length overall: 33.0m

Beam: 10.0m

Draught: 1.40m

PERFORMANCE

Speed, max: 28 knots

Speed, fully loaded: 24 knots

TROPIC SUNBIRD

Passenger ferry, but first employed as a top press and spectator boat at the 1987 Americas Cup.

DESIGNER: Lock Crowther, Sydney.

OWNER: Sunseeker Cruiser, Cairns, Queensland.

LEGISLATION AUTHORITY: Department of Marine and Harbours, Western Australia.

HULL: Catamaran hull and superstructure are constructed in all-welded marine grade aluminium alloy. The hulls incorporate bulbous bows which reduce pitching through their extra buoyancy. This craft can carry up to 600 passengers (including its external seating) and has a very shallow draught of 1.36m.

ENGINES: Two Deutz-MWM TBD 604B V12.

GEARBOXES: Two ZF BW 455.

ELECTRONICS: Koden MDC 4105 Colour radar; Koen CVS 88 Colour echo sounder; Robertson AP-40 auto pilot; Codan P121 12V radio.

DIMENSIONS

Length overall: 33.37m

Length, design water line: 30.01m

Beam: 13.00m

Draught: 1.36m

PERFORMANCE

Speed, max: 32 knots

Speed, cruise: 27 knots

QUICKCAT

Passenger ferry.

DESIGNER: Lock Crowther, Turramurra, NSW, Australia.

OWNER: Waiheke Shipping Co Ltd, Auckland, New Zealand.

LEGISLATION AUTHORITY: New Zealand Ministry of Transport.

ELECTRONICS: Koden 410 Colour radar; Raytheon echo sounder; Wagner SE autopilot; Codan 8121 24V radio.

PRINCIPAL PARTICULARS: As for *Tropic Sunbird* except that passenger cabin behind wheelhouse for *Quickcat* extends to the full width of the craft over its whole length.

Quickcat general arrangement

High-speed catamaran craft built	Seats	Operator	Route
33.0m *Victory III*	448	Great Keppel Island Tourist Services Ltd	
33.37m *Tropic Sunbird*	500 +	Sunseeker Cruises, Queensland, Australia	Cairns-Townsville-Dunk Island
33.37m *Quickcat*	500 +	Waiheke Shipping, Auckland, New Zealand	Auckland-Waiheke

The SBF catamaran *Tropic Sunbird*, a Lock Crowther bulbous-bow hull design

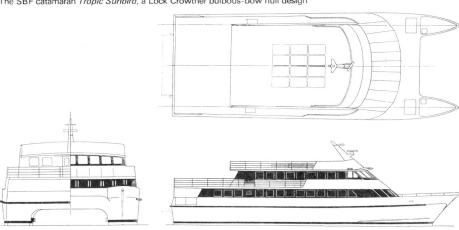

Tropic Sunbird general arrangement

The SBF *Quickcat*, a sister vessel to *Tropic Sunbird*

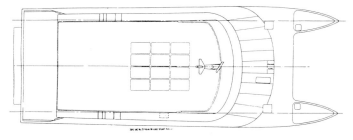

WAVEMASTER INTERNATIONAL PTY LTD

115 Egmont Road, Henderson 6166, Western Australia, Australia
Telephone: (09) 410 1422
Telex: 93356 AA
Telefax: (09) 410 2089

Trevor Kitcher, *Chairman*
Richard Patterson, *Managing Director*

Designer and builder of a number of light speed mono-hull ferries, WaveMaster International in 1989 delivered its first high speed catamaran, Yard No 020, a 32 metre fully planing vessel for the Peoples Republic of China, built in welded aluminium alloy. Operator: Sanfu Shipping Co. for the Sanfu to Hong Kong route.

YIN SHAN HU

CLASSIFICATION: Z C China Classification Society, DnV + 1A1 R45 EO.
PRINCIPAL PARTICULARS
Length, overall: 32.00m
Beam, moulded: 9.50m
Draught, max. at design water line: 1.20m
Engines: two MTU 12V 396 TB83, 1089 kW each (32^0C air, 32^0C water) MCR 1940 rpm.
Propulsion: two KaMeWa 63 S62.60 water jet units
Auxiliary power: two Mercedes Benz/Stamford alternator sets, 92 kW each.
Passengers: 252, on single main deck
Crew: 6 to 8, in upper deck quarters aft of the wheelhouse
Cargo: containerised pallets on aft upper deck for 2120 kg of luggage
Speed, full load (30 tonnes disposable load): 28 knots
Speed, light ship: 32 knots
Facilities: galley, duty-free shop, smoking room
EQUIPMENT: Full air conditioning, 72 and 48 mile colour radars, gyro compass, echo sounder, SSB and VHF radios. The mast may be lowered hydraulically.

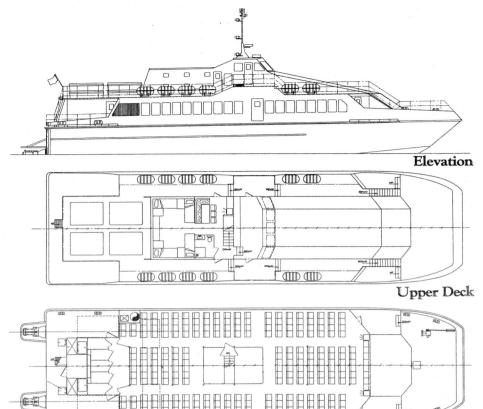

Elevation

Upper Deck

Main Deck

General arrangement of WaveMaster International 32m catarmaran *Yin Shan Hu*

WaveMaster International 252-seat *Yin Shan Hu*

WaveMaster International 252-seat *Yin Shan Hu*

FIJI

MAXLANE ENGINEERS LTD
Nakuwatu Street, Lami, Suva, Fiji

Telex: 2432 MAXLANE FJ
Telefax: Suva 300732

In 1989 it was reported that Maxlane Engineers were engaged on the bulding of a catamaran ferry for Samavest, Malaysia, powered by two 1150 kW engines driving two KaMeWa 565 water-jet units.

FINLAND

HOLLMING LTD. SHIPYARD
P.O. Box 14, SF-261 01 Rauma, Finland
Telephone: (038) 3211
Telex: 65114 HOL SF
Telefax: (038) 322124

Hollming Ltd. has undertaken the building of hulls for Marinteknik Verkstads of Sweden. Hulls for two 41 metre catamarans were built over the period 1988/89.

MXA-CONSULTING LTD OY
[DESIGNERS]
Pitkäkatu 3a D, Box 38, SF-20521 Turku, Finland

Telephone: (021) 333881
Telex: 62004TURKU SF
Telefax: (021) 331934

Matti Ahtikari, *Principal*

MXA catamarans are designed by a team of engineers under the supervision of Matti Ahtikari. This team has designed a large number of aluminium vessels for most of the Finnish shipyards, including 50m fast patrol boat for the Finnish Navy.

In 1988 MXA announced an agreement for the manufacture of their designs by Gulf Craft, Inc in the United States, in association with Scandinavian Catamarans Inc (now Scandinavian International Inc) founded in 1988 to undertake the marketing of MXA catamarans.

The licensee for MXA-Consulting Ltd Oy in the USA is:
Scandinavian International Inc, 1640 W Oakland

MXA 1700 high-speed catamaran ferry

Park Boulevard, Suite 301, Fort Lauderdale, Florida 33311, USA

MXA 1700
Designed by Matti Ahtikari, MXA-Consulting Ltd, Finland, the MXA 1700 is a 90-seat, shallow draught high-speed catamaran ferry built in marine grade aluminium. This is the first such

vessel to employ an Arneson Surface Drive propulsion system. The vessel is classified by DnV, IAI-R45 EO Light Craft. Hull construction was undertaken by Waterman Oy.

The first vessel was completed in mid-1986.
POWERPLANT/PROPULSION: Two Isuzu UM 12 PB 1 TC diesels, each 340kW at 2300rpm, fitted with ZF BW 160 gearboxes driving Arneson Surface Drive systems, type ASD 14.

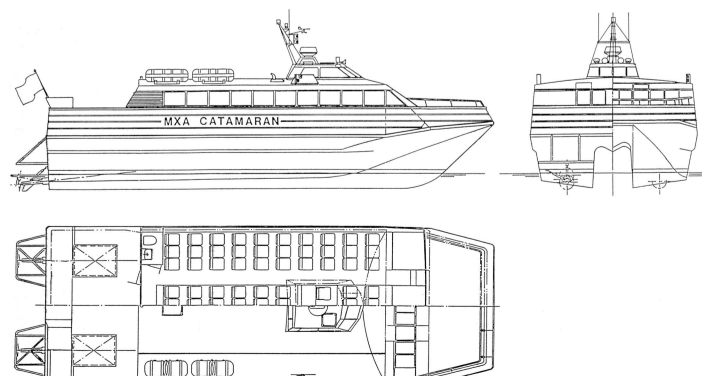

General arrangement of MXA 1700

EQUIPMENT
Hydraulics: Vickers
Navigation: Radar 16n miles Vigil 2, depth sounder VDO, two-way radio Shipmate RS 8000 F, magnetic and electric compass
Steering gear: Electric

DIMENSIONS
Length overall: 17.0m
Beam: 6.4m
Draught, max: 0.9m
WEIGHT/CAPACITIES
Passengers: About 90
Crew: 2

Displacement, max: 24.0 tonnes
Fuel tank capacity: 2000 litres
PERFORMANCE
Speed, max: 30 knots
Speed, cruising: 24 to 26 knots
Range: 300n miles
Fuel consumption: 136 litres/h

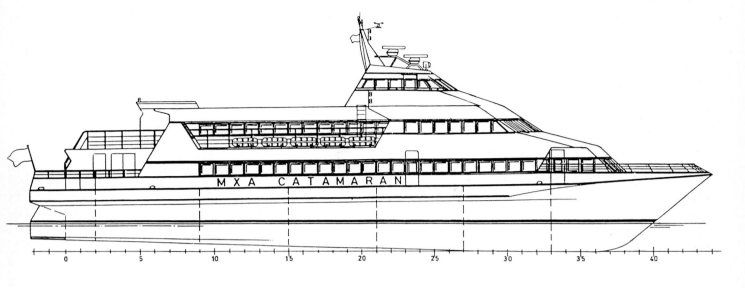

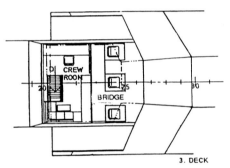

3. DECK

MXA 3900 II
CATAMARAN

L.O.A.	39,0	M
BEAM	9,6	M
DRAFT max.(WATERJET)	1,5	M
ENGINES 2 X	2040	KW
SPEED abt.	37	KN
PASSENGER	250	
CREW	4-6	

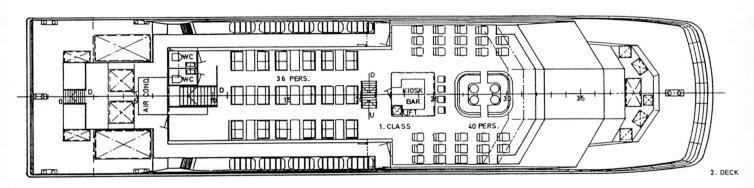

2. DECK

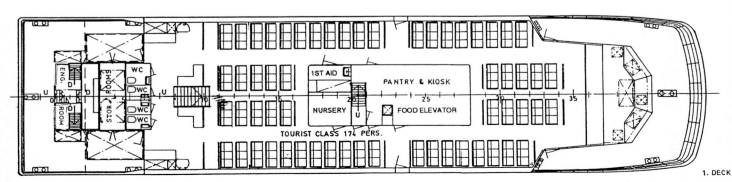

1. DECK

MXA design 3900 II

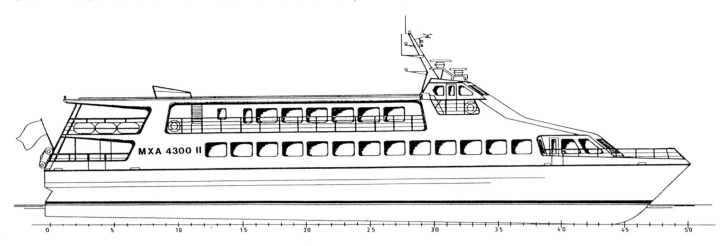

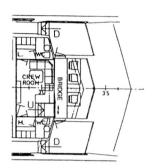

MXA 4300 II
CATAMARAN

L.O.A	43,0 M
BEAM	10,0 M
DRAFT max (Waterjet)	1,6 M
ENGINES abt. 2 x	2500 KW
SPEED abt.	37 KN
PASSENGERS abt.	450
CREW	6-8

2. DECK

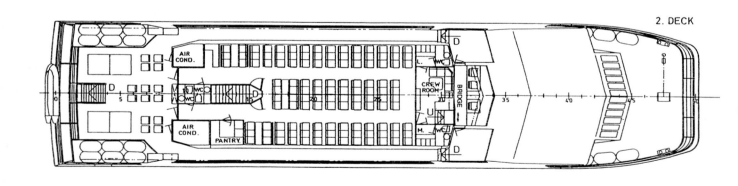

1. DECK

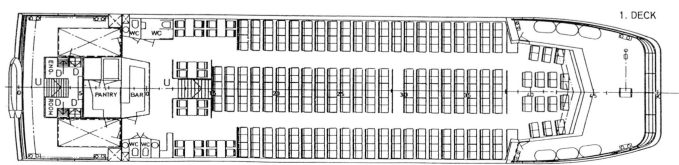

MXA design 4300 II

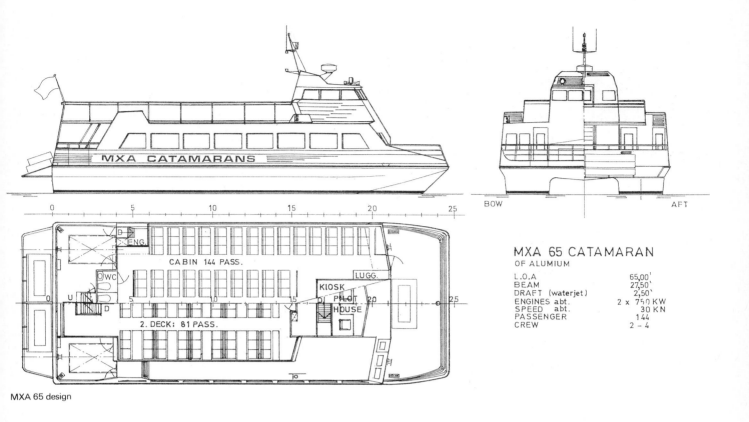

MXA 65 CATAMARAN
OF ALUMIUM

L.O.A	65,00'
BEAM	27,50'
DRAFT (waterjet)	2,50'
ENGINES abt.	2 x 750 KW
SPEED abt.	30 KN
PASSENGER	144
CREW	2 – 4

MXA 65 design

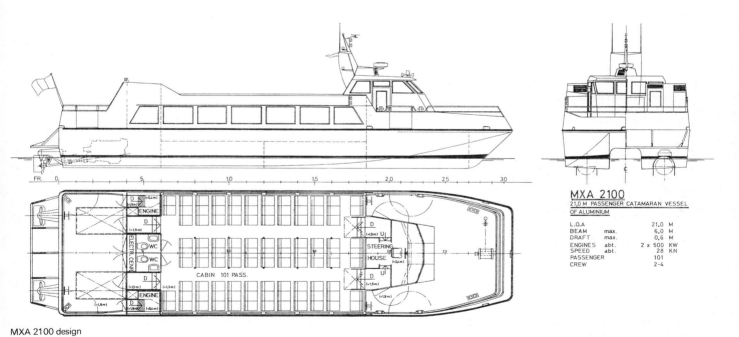

MXA 2100
21,0 M PASSENGER CATAMARAN VESSEL
OF ALUMINIUM

L.O.A		21,0 M
BEAM	max.	6,0 M
DRAFT	max.	0,6 M
ENGINES	abt.	2 x 500 KW
SPEED	abt.	28 KN
PASSENGER		101
CREW		2 – 4

MXA 2100 design

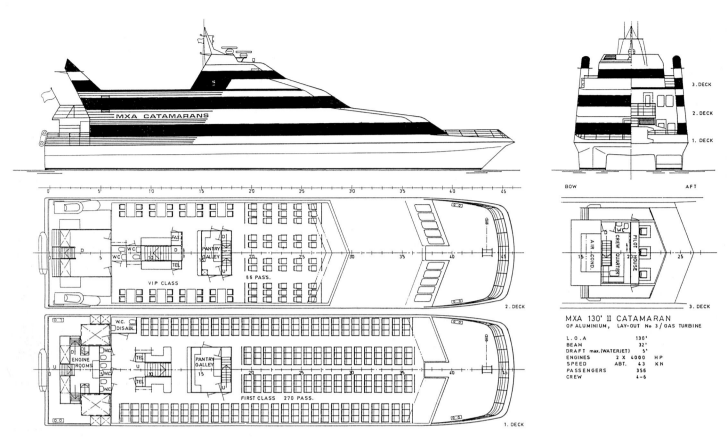

MXA 130' II design

MXA 130' II CATAMARAN
OF ALUMINIUM, LAY-OUT No 3 / GAS TURBINE

L.O.A	130'	
BEAM	32'	
DRAFT max.(WATERJET)	5'	
ENGINES	2 X 4000	HP
SPEED	ABT. 43	KN
PASSENGERS	356	
CREW	4-6	

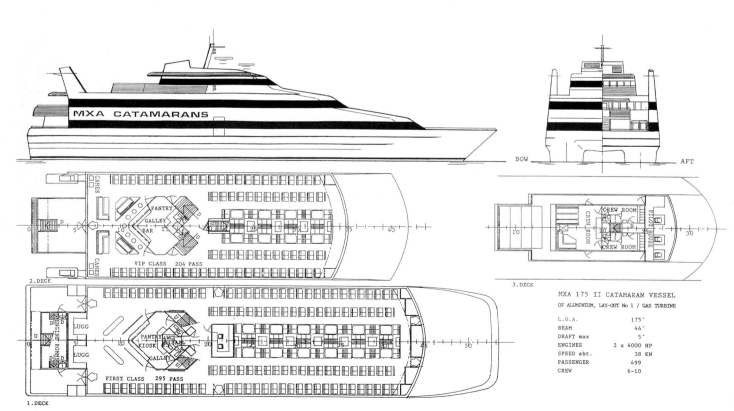

MXA 175 II design

MXA 175 II CATAMARAN VESSEL
OF ALUMINIUM, LAY-OUT No 1 / GAS TURBINE

L.O.A.	175'	
BEAM	44'	
DRAFT max	5'	
ENGINES	2 x 4000 HP	
SPEED abt.	38 KN	
PASSENGER	499	
CREW	6-10	

FRANCE

CONSTRUCTIONS ALUMINIUM NAVALES sarl

47 Avenue Maurice Chevalier, 06150 Cannes La Bocca, France

Telephone: 93473030

VILLE DE TOULON III

A 200-passenger, 20-knot vessel (length 25m, beam 8m) launched in 1987. The superstructure is of interest in that it is built up with tubular frames. Principal material of construction is aluminium AG 4 MC 5086. The craft is classified by Bureau Veritas.

Ville de Toulon III, one of three catamaran ferries built to a design by Constructions Aluminium Navales sarl

HONG KONG

A FAI ENGINEERS AND SHIPREPAIRERS LTD

861 Lai chi kok Road, Kowloon, Hong Kong

Telephone: (03) 7410981
Telex: 45517 AFES HX
Telefax: (03) 7862414

Vitus Szeto, *General Manager*

Builder of International Catamaran Designs Pty Ltd catamarans.

Li Jiang, one of nine International Catamarans 21m craft operated by People's Republic of China

Patrol boat catamaran built by A Fai Engineers and Shiprepairers Ltd

Craft built (In Cat)	Completed	Seats	Speed	Operator	Route
21.0m *Mingzhu Hu*	January 1982	150	29 knots	Guangdong Province Hong Kong Macao Navigation, PRC	Hong Kong to Jiangmen
21.0m *Yin Zhou Hu*	March 1982	150	29 knots	Guangdong Province Hong Kong Macao Navigation, PRC	Hong Kong to Jiangmen
21.0m *Liuhua Hu*	September 1982	150	29 knots	Guangdong Province Hong Kong Macao Navigation, PRC	Hong Kong to Taiping
21.0m *Li Jiang*	June 1983	150	29 knots	Kwai Kong Shipping Co Ltd, Hong Kong	Hong Kong to Wuzhou
16.0m *Kwong Fai*	June 1984	40	21 knots	Castle Peak Power Co Ltd, Hong Kong	Hong Kong
21.0m *Yue Hai Chun*	October 1984	169	29 knots	Shen Zhen Shipping, PRC	Shekou to Zhuhai
21.0m *Shen Zhen Chun*	July 1985	169	29 knots	Shen Zhen Shipping, PRC	Shekou to Zhuhai
21.0m *Zhu Hai Chun*	December 1986	169	29 knots	Shen Zhen Shipping, PRC	Shekou to Zhuhai
22.0m *Gong Bian 153*	August 1988	-	33 knots	Guang Zhou Custom Dept, PRC	Whampo & Pearl River Area (Patrol Boat)
22.0m *Ling Nan Chun*	November 1988	187	28 knots	Shen Zhen Shipping, PRC	Shekou to Zhuhai
22.0m *Nan Hai Chun*	March 1989	187	28 knots	Shen Zhen Shipping, PRC	Shekou to Zhuhai
23.0m *CA3*	June 1990	250 *(rescue places)*	28 knots	Civil Aviation Department Hong Kong Government (Airport Rescue Boat)	Hong Kong Class 1 & 2 Limit Area

JAPAN

ISHIKAWAJIMA – HARIMA HEAVY INDUSTRIES CO

New Ohtemachi Building 2–1, Ohtemachi 2-chome, Chiyoda-ku, Tokyo, Japan

MITSUBISHI HEAVY INDUSTRIES LTD

5–1, Maranouchi 2-chome, Chiyoda-ku, Tokyo, Japan

Telephone: (03) 212 3111
Telex: 22443J

HI-STABLE CABIN CRAFT (HSCC)
UKISHIRO

Completed by Mitsubishi in the autumn of 1987

AQUA DIVERS (DESIGN)

A catamaran vessel designed exclusively for scuba diving.

PRINCIPAL PARTICULARS
Length, overall: approx 23m

Breadth, moulded: approx 7.2m
Depth, moulded: approx 2.2m
Engines: two diesel
Speed, max: 30 knots
Crew: 3
Divers: 27

this prototype catamaran craft features a passenger cabin mounted on hydraulically-actuated auto-stabilising rams. The cabin is centrally mounted on top of a 200mm diameter central hydraulic jack having a stroke of one metre. This supporting member is attached by a ball and socket joint to the hulls and positions the cabin completely clear of the hulls. Four other 85mm hydraulic rams, attached with shock absorbers, support the cabin's four corners.

When motion of the basic catamaran craft

occurs in heave, yaw, surge or sway, all hydraulic rams are activated simultaneously by an on-board computer (a 16-bit personal computer) with a rapid response capability to monitoring sensors, thereby almost eliminating or minimising cabin motion. Trials have demonstrated reductions of cabin motion to one-third of the motion of the basic supporting catamaran structure.

The catamaran type was chosen as the basic vehicle because of its good stability characteristics and cabin width advantages. It is reported that

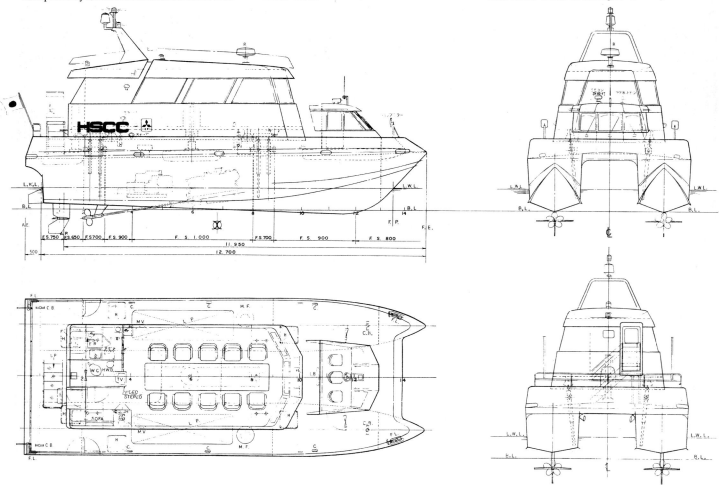

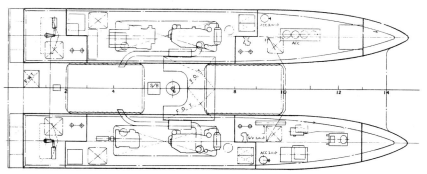

General arrangement of the Mitsubishi Hi-Stable Cabin Craft (HSCC), a research vessel designed to explore the possibilities for cabin auto-stabilisation

the computer software required for the system was developed in a five-year Y100m study programme initiated by MHI and supported by the semi-governmental Japan Foundation for Shipbuilding Advancement.

The prototype HSCC has the following characteristics:
Length: 12.70m
Beam: 5.40m
Depth: 1.80m

Accommodation: 12 passengers
GRT: 17
Speed, max: 20 knots
Engines: Two Mitsubishi 239 kW diesels
Deadweight: 1.70 tonnes
OPERATOR: Higashi Chugoku Ryoju Kosan

The Mitsubishi HSCC at sea

MITSUI ENGINEERING & SHIPBUILDING CO LTD

6–4, Tsukiji 5-chome, Chuo-ku, Tokyo 104, Japan

Telephone: (3) 544 3462
Telex: 22821J, 22924 J

See ACV section for company officials

Under a licensing agreement concluded in 1973 with Westamarin A/S, Mandal, Norway, Mitsui built three Super Westamaran CP20s. The craft, which carries up to 182 passengers, has a cruising speed of about 25 knots, is comparable to the Norwegian-built Westamaran W86 and can operate in waves 1.2 to 1.5 metres high.

In 1978 Mitsui, employing its own design team, developed the Supermaran CP20HF, seating 195 passengers and with a cruising speed of about 30 knots. This craft has been redesigned for better seaworthiness and can operate in a maximum

wave height of 2.5 metres when comfortable service can be provided with no loss of speed. Two were delivered, in March and June 1979.

The Supermaran CP30 was delivered to the Nankai Ferry Company Limited in Japan in July 1983. It carries 280 passengers at a cruising speed of 28 knots. Not only has this craft been improved for operational economy, with increased passenger capacity and comparatively less power, but also in seaworthiness. Maximum operable wave height is 3 metres and comfortable service is assured at a wave height of 2.5 metres or less with no loss of speed.

The Supermaran CP30 Mk II, *Marine Shuttle*, was introduced in service by the Tokushima Shuttle Line Co Ltd in February 1986. The vessel has a higher service speed than its predecessor the CP30, 32 knots against 28.1 knots.

A new type, the Supermaran CP10, *Marine Queen*, was delivered to the Sanzo Kigyo Co Ltd in April 1987, for cruising service in the Seto Inland Sea.

Two 280-seater Supermaran CP30 MKIIIs,

Blue Star and *Sun Rise*, entered service in 1987 with Tokushima, and a Supermaran CP30 MKIII, *Coral*, also entered service in 1988 on the coastal route of the Shikoku Island facing to the Pacific Ocean.

They have a service speed of 32 knots, and have the improved seaworthiness and the superior propulsive performance over the earlier CP20HF resulting from the improved hull form and their greater size.

CP30 MKIIIs are some of the largest high-speed catamarans built to date in the world. Mitsui has, in addition, completed other high-speed catamarans, the Supermaran CP25 *Queen Rokko*, the Supermaran CP20 *Wakashio*, the Supermaran CP25 *New Tobishima* the Supermaran CP5 *Mon Cheri* and the Supermaran CP1 *Aquajet I & II* with waterjet propulsion installed.

AQUAJET I & AQUAJET II (SUPERMARAN CP15)

These catamaran passenger ferries have waterjet propulsion and were built for Kyodo Kisen

Craft built (CP types)	Yard No	Completed	Seats	Operator
26.46m CP20 Super Westamaran (ex *Blue Hawk*)		1975	162	Showa Kaiun Co Ltd
26.46m CP20 Super Westamaran (ex *Marine Star*)	02	1976	180	Setonaikai Kisen Co Ltd
26.40m CP20 Super Westamaran (ex *Sun Beam*)		1978	188	Tokushima Kosokusen Co Ltd
32.80m CP20HF Supermaran *Sun Shine*		March 1979	195	Tokushima Kosokusen Co Ltd
32.80m CP20HF Supermaran *Blue Sky*		June 1979	195	Tokushima Kosokusen Co Ltd
40.90m CP30 Supermaran *Marine Hawk*		July 1983	280	Nankai Ferry Co Ltd
41.00m CP30 Mk II Supermaran *Marine Shuttle*		February 1986	280	Tokushima Shuttle Line Co Ltd
21.67m CP10 Supermaran *Marine Queen*	1607	April 1987	88	Ueda Kaiun KK
41.00m CP30 Mk III Supermaran *Blue Star*	1605	June 1987	280	Tokushima Kosokusen Co Ltd
41.00m CP30 Mk III Supermaran *Sun Rise*	1606	July 1987	280	Tokushima Kosokusen Co Ltd
41.00m CP30 MK III Supermaran *Coral*	1608	July 1988	250	Kochiken Marine Co Ltd
33.20m CP25 Supermaran *Queen Rokko*	1609	June 1988	250	Awaji Ferry Boat Co Ltd
19.90m CP5 Supermaran *Mon Cheri*	1610	July 1988	53	Tenmaya Marine Corporation
39.00m CP25 Supermaran *New Tobishima*	1611	May 1989	300	Sakata City
33.20m CP20 Supermaran *Wakashio*	1612	March 1989	96	Chiba Pref.
34.20m CP15 Supermaran *Aquajet I*	1613	March 1989	198	Kyodo Kisen Co Ltd
34.20m CP15 Supermaran *Aquajet II*	1614	June 1989	198	Kyodo Kisen Co Ltd

CATAMARANS	Supermaran CP5	Supermaran CP10	Super Westamaran CP20	Supermaran CP20HF
Dimensions				
Length overall	19.9m	21.67m	26.46m	32.8m
Breadth	6.0m	7.20m	8.8m	9.2m
Draught	1.1m	1.23m	1.18m	1.2m
GRT, approx	50	80	192	275
Passengers	58	88	162 to 182	195
Crew	4	3	5	5
Main engines	GM 6V-92 TA	Two GM 12V-92 TA	Two MTU 12V 331 TC82	Two Fuji Pielstick 16PA4V185-VG
Max continuous rating, each	445ps at 2170rpm	825ps at 2170rpm	1240ps at 2270rpm	2540ps at 1475rpm
Continuous rating, each	—	660ps	1125ps at 2200rpm	2280ps at 1425rpm
Max speed	approx 21 knots	26.6 knots	28.5 knots	30.7 knots
Service speed, approx	17 knots	21.8 knots	25 knots	30 knots
Endurance, approx	8 hours	20.0 hours	9 hours	9 hours

CATAMARANS	Supermaran CP30 Mk II	Supermaran CP30 Mk III	Supermaran CP25	Supermaran CP30
Dimensions				
Length overall	33.2m	40.9m	41.0m	41.0m
Breadth	9.0m	10.8m mld	10.8m	10.8m
Draught	1.4m	1.37m full load	1.39m full load	1.39m full load
GRT, approx	220	283	268	270
Passengers	250	280	280	280
Crew	7	4	4	4
Main engines	MWM TBD 604BV12	Two Fuji Pielstick 16PA4V185-VG	Two Ikegai 16V 190 ATC	Two Fuji Pielstick 12 PA4V 200 VGA
Max continuous rating, each	1714ps at 1800rpm	2540ps at 1475rpm	2750ps at 1450rpm	2630ps at 1475rpm
Continuous rating, each	—	2280ps at 1425rpm	2475ps at 1400rpm	2370ps at 1425rpm
Max speed	approx 29 knots	approx 31.1 knots	approx 34 knots	approx 35.1 knots
Service speed, approx	25 knots	28.1 knots	32 knots	32 knots
Endurance, approx	6 hours	10 hours	8 hours	8 hours

Mitsui CP30 Mk II Supermaran *Marine Shuttle*

Co. Ltd. and entered service in 1988 to ply the route between Osaka, Kobe and Awaji Island.
DIMENSIONS
Length overall: 34.2m
Beam: 8.0m
Depth: 3.2m
Draught: 1.2m
POWERPLANT: Two MTU 16V396 TB83, 1469 kW (1970 hp) each, at 1940 rpm
PROPULSION: Two KaMeWa waterjets S63
GRT: 154
SPEED
Trial: 35 knots
Cruising: 31 knots
PASSENGER CAPACITY: 198 persons

QUEEN ROKKO (SUPERMARAN CP25)

This is the catamaran double-decker cabin cruiser built for Awaji Ferry Boat Co in 1988.
DIMENSIONS
Length overall: 33.2m
Beam: 9.0m
Draught: 1.5m
Depth: 3.0m
Displacement: 217 tonnes
POWERPLANT: Two Deutz MWM604B V12 1278kW (1714 hp PS) each, at 1800 rpm
Gearboxes: two Niijata Converter MGN 433 EW with electric variable propeller speed control device. Reduction ratio 2.06:1.0
Propellers: two fixed-pitch
GRT: 220
Speed, trial: 30 knots
Speed, cruising: 25 knots
Passenger capacity: 250 persons

CORAL (SUPERMARAN CP30 MKIII)

This is a catamaran passenger ferry and the fifth one of the CP30 series built for Kochiken Marine Co Ltd in 1988.
DIMENSIONS
Length overall: 41.0m
Beam: 10.8m
Depth: 3.4m
Draught: 1.3m
POWERPLANT: two Fuji-Pielstick 12PA4V-200VGA, 1961kW (2630 hp) each, at 1475 rpm
Propellers: two fixed-pitch
GRT: 281
Speed, trial: 35 knots
Speed, cruising: 32 knots
Passenger capacity: 250 persons

Mitsui CP15 Supermaran *Aquajet I*

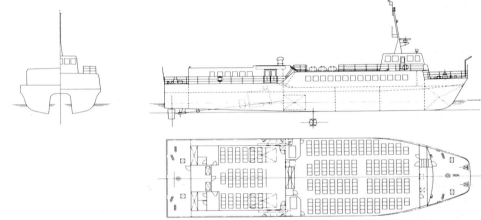

General arrangement of Mitsui CP30 Supermaran *Marine Hawk*

Mitsui's Supermaran CP30 Mk III *Coral*

SANUKI SHIP BUILDING & IRON WORKS CO LTD

Head Office: Postal code 769–11, 2112–17 Takuma, Mitoyo-gun, Kagawa-Pref, Japan

Telephone: (0875) 83–2550
Telex: 5827728SANUKI J
Telefax: (0875) 83–6287

M Yoshikawa, *Manager, Planning Division*

SEA CHATEAU

The Sanuki Ship Building & Iron Works was established in February 1942. The yard has eight berths and vessels of up to 3800 tons can be built. The company has built many kinds of aluminium high-speed passenger vessels and in 1987 launched a 30m high-speed catamaran craft very similar to the Marinteknik JC-F1 type. The Sanuki vessel is powered by two Deutz MWM TBD 604B V12 engines, 1260kW each at 1800rpm.

36 METRE CATAMARAN

A further high-speed 250-seat catamaran was built in 1989 for Fuke Kaiun for operation in Osaka Bay.

The 96-passenger Sanuki ferry *Sea Chateau*, delivered April 1988

YAMAHA MOTOR COPRORATION

(Gamagori Shipyard) 2500 Shingai, Iwata-City, Shizuoka Prefecture, Japan

Telephone: (0538) 32 1145
Telefax: (0538) 37 4250

29.1 METRE CATAMARAN TYPE 2910

Two of these vessels were delivered in March 1989 to Tokyo Blue Cruises.
Built in grp they are powered by two DDC 16V 92 TA 895kW diesels driving 5-blade propellers employing skew blades.

PRINCIPAL PARTICULARS
Length, overall: 29.1m
Beam, overall: 8.1m
Depth: 2.4m
Draught, average: 1.3m
Accommodation: 230 passengers
Weight, max: 160 tonnes

Yamaha Motor Corporation catamaran Type 2910 *Bay Bridge*

MALAYSIA

HONG LEONG-LÜRSSEN SHIPYARD BERHAD

4567 Jalan Chain Ferry, PO Box 43,
12700 Butterworth, PW, Malaysia

Telephone: (04) 347755
Telex: 47515HLYARD MA
Telefax: (04) 342424

Kwek Hong P'ng, *Director*
G Lurssen, *Director*
Darwis bin Mohammed Daek, *Director*
Quek Leng Chan, *Director*
Carl Otto Grosse-Lindermann, *Director*
James Puthucheary, *Director*
Chuah Saik Ang, *Director*
Dr G F Kohler, *Director*
Mohammed Nasir bin Abdul Samad, *Director*
Roger Tan Kim Hock, *Director*
Chuah Chuan Yong, *Deputy General Manager*
Teh Choon Meng, *Financial Controller*
Vincent Schweizer, *Project Manager*

Hong Leong-Lürssen was established in 1969 as a joint venture between Hong Leong Industries Bhd, Permodalan Nasional Bhd and Fr Lürssen Werft (GmbH & Co) of West Germany. The company engages in ship repair and shipbuilding of up to 2000-ton vessels.

ZAHARAH

This catamaran vessel (Hull No 1204) entered service in September 1984 for civil passenger transport.

Hong Leong-Lürssen-built *Zaharah*

HULL: Shipbuilding steel grade A. Longitudinal frames on web frames.
ACCOMMODATION: Crew 6, passengers 131. The vessel is air-conditioned.
POWERPLANT: Two MAN D 2542 MLE, each 625hp at 2300rpm. Fuel: Marine diesel oil, two fuel tanks, total capacity 2800 litres.
PROPELLERS: Stone Marine 850mm diameter Cunial.
SYSTEMS, ELECTRICAL: One generator, 23kW, 230V, single phase, 50Hz and 24V dc.
RADIO: One VHF Philips 828.
DIMENSIONS
Length overall: 21.75m

Beam overall: 8.0m
Draught max: 1.40m
WEIGHTS
Weight, empty: 48 tonnes
Max disposable load: 11 tonnes
PERFORMANCE
Speed, cruising: Approx 18 knots
Range: Approx 200n miles

28-METRE PASSENGER CATAMARAN (DESIGN)

Hong Leong-Lürssen Shipyard Berhad has developed its own high-speed catamaran design to meet the growing demand for high-speed craft

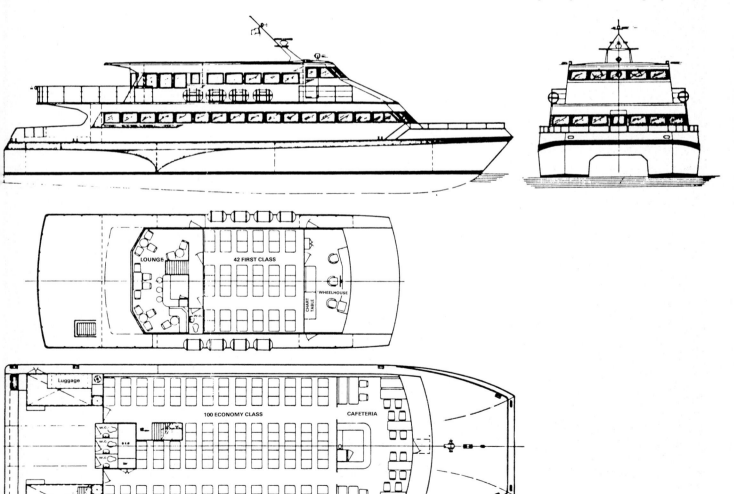

Hong Leong-Lürssen design for 28m catamaran, luxury cruise version, long range

in the Far East. Based on hard chine, symmetric hulls, the hull design has been designed and tank-tested for operating speeds of 30 to 35 knots.

The basic platform is offered with various superstructure configurations depending on the role of the craft and is suitable for both propeller and waterjet propulsion.
CLASSIFICATION: DnV 1A1 R90.

POWER PLANT: Two MWM TBD 604B V12 1714hp each at 1800rpm*, speed 33 to 35 knots or Two MTU 12V 396 TB63 1330hp each at 1650 rpm*, speed 30 to 32 knots.
(* = derated for tropical conditions.)
DIMENSIONS
Length, overall: 28.00m
Length, waterline: 26.00m

Breadth: 9.00m
Depth: 2.90m
Draught (hull): 0.95m
PERFORMANCE
Payload: 18 tonnes (for high-speed operation)
Range (at 30 knots): 250n miles

THE NETHERLANDS

ROYAL SCHELDE
bv Koninklijke Maatschappij 'de Schelde'
PO Box 16, 4380 AA Vlissingen, The Netherlands

Telephone: (01184) 82911
Telex: 37815 KMS NL
Telefax: (01184) 85010

SEASWIFT 70
70 METRE CATAMARAN (DESIGN)
Royal Shelde have developed two ferry designs based on a 70 metre catamaran hull configuration, a 500 passenger/car ferry and a 500 passenger/car/cargo ferry for which the car deck can be converted into a refrigerated cargo deck for winter cargo service.
Passenger/car version
CLASSIFICATION
DnV + 1A1 R280 Light Craft (CAT), + MV, Passenger Ship, EO Car Ferry B (PET)
PRINCIPAL PARTICULARS
Length, overall: 71.0m
Length, waterline: 60.8m
Beam, overall: 20.8m
Depth to main deck: 5.65m

Artists' impression of Royal Schelde design for Seaswift 70, a passenger/car/cargo 35 knot catamaran

Draught, off-cushion, loaded: 2.60m
ACCOMMODATION: 500 seats for passengers in single saloon, 9 cabins on upper deck for crew. Space is available on car deck for 70 cars, each of 4.5m length and 1.5 tonnes weight, in 6 lanes.

Promenade deck is fitted with 176 grp seats
Speed, service, 90% MCR: 35 knots
Range: 480 n miles at service speed
Fuel consumption: approx 75 kg/n mi at 35 knots, 208 g/kWh (+5%) at MCR

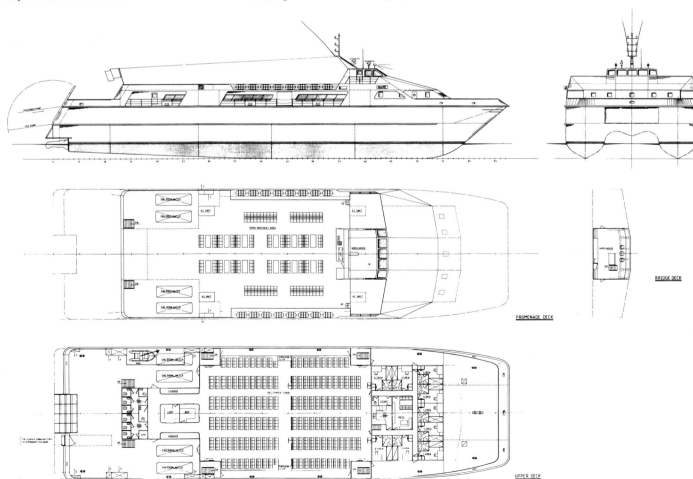

General arrangement of Royal Schelde design for Seaswift 70

ENGINES: four Ruston 12 RK 270, MCR 3440
kW each at 1000 rpm
PROPULSION: four Riva Calzoni IRC 115 DX
water-jet units. For speeds up to 20 knots, only
two engines need to be used.
Auxiliary power: Two diesel generator jets, each
350 kW
DEADWEIGHT BREAKDOWN
Passengers (500): 35 tonnes
Baggage: 15 tonnes
Cars (70): 105 tonnes
Cargo: 7 tonnes
PAYLOAD TOTAL: 162 tonnes
Crew: 2 tonnes
Fresh water: 5 tonnes
Fuel: 40 tonnes
Stores: 5 tonnes
Lube oil: 4 tonnes

ALL TOTAL: 218 tonnes

Passenger/car/cargo version:
  Details mostly as above except deadweight
would be increased to 311 tonnes, fuel load being
increased to 95 tonnes and a cargo load of 200
tonnes being possible. Speed for cargo service is
approximately 33 knots at 90% MCR.

SEASWIFT 32 (DESIGN)
  This is a design for a 33.3 metre catamaran, 230

Artists impression of the Royal Shelde Seaswift-32 catamaran ferry

passenger capacity and powered by two 1540 kW
diesel engines. Deadweight is 34 tonnes.

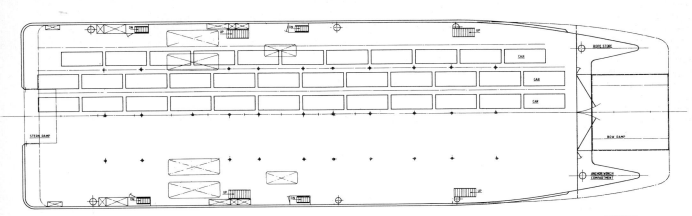

MAINDECK

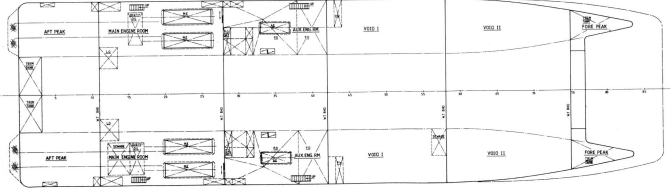

BELOW MAINDECK

Deck and hull layouts of Seaswift 70

NEW ZEALAND

INTERNATIONAL CATAMARANS (PACIFIC) LTD
Riverside Drive, Whangeri, New Zealand

Builder of two of the first International Catamarans Pty Ltd craft.

Craft built	Completed	Speed	Seats	Operator
18.0m *Tiger Lily*	December 1979	22 knots	150	
18.0m *Tiger Lily II*	January 1981	22 knots	150	

WANGANUI BOATS NEW ZEALAND LTD
PO Box 8032, Wanganui, New Zealand
Shipyard: Heads Road

Telephone: (064) 45044
Telex: 3455NZ
Telefax: (064) 45194

Douglas Wild, *Managing Director*
Chris Lendrum, *General Manager*

This company has built over 200 vessels of many types ranging from fishing vessels, workboats, dredges, tourist vessels, patrol boats, ocean-going yachts and high-speed catamaran ferries, designed by International Catamaran Designs Pty Ltd of Sydney, Australia.

TIGER LILY III
POWERPLANT: Two MWM diesels, 660hp each, at 1900rpm.
Auxiliary power unit: MWM Markon 50kVA
ACCOMMODATION: 225 seats.
DIMENSIONS
Length, overall: 23.2m
Length, hulls: 22.0m
Beam: 8.7m
Draught, full load: 1.7m
PERFORMANCE
Speed, fully loaded: 22.5 knots at 1900rpm

FIORDLAND FLYER
POWERPLANT: Two MAN V10, 450hp each at 1800rpm.
Auxiliary power unit: MWM Markon 15kVA
ACCOMMODATION: 140 seats.
DIMENSIONS
Length, overall: 19.2m
Length, hull: 18.0m
Beam: 6.5m
Draught, full load: 1.6m
PERFORMANCE
Speed, fully loaded: 22 knots

Craft built	Completed	Speed	Seats	Operator
19.2m In Cat *Fiordland Flyer*	September 1985	22 knots	140	Fiordland Travel Ltd, New Zealand
23.2m In Cat *Tiger Lily III*	December 1985	21 knots	225	New Zealand

Tiger Lily III

Fiordland Flyer

WHANGAREI ENGINEERING & CONSTRUCTION LTD (WECO)
This company is no longer trading

NORWAY

HARDING VERFT
Box 55, N-5470 Rosendal, Norway
Telephone: (054) 81322
Telefax: (054) 81934

Harding Verft became owners of the Skaalurens Skibsbyggeri A/S yard in 1989 and took over the Skaalurens catamaran project, the first vessel being the 26m *Havstril*. The *Havstril* was delivered to the Simon Møkster company, Stavanger, in June 1989 for operation between Oslo and Arendal, but later sold for PEMEX operations in the Gulf of Mexico.

HAVSTRIL
Yard No 256/2
PRINCIPAL PARTICULARS
Classification: DnV + 1A1 Light Craft Passenger Catamaran, R90
Hull: aluminium alloy
Length overall: 26.00m
Breadth: 8.00m
Draught: 1.50m
Passenger capacity, max: 200
Engines: two MWM TBD 604 B12 diesels, 1260 kW at 1800 rpm
Propulsion: Servogear VD820 propellers, 4-blade
Gearboxes: ZF
Speed, servicing, full load: 31.6 knots
Speed, max: 34.0 knots
Fuel consumption: 514 l/h
Range, at service speed: about 500n miles

28M CATAMARAN (DESIGN)
A second catamaran design is now available from the Harding Verft company.
PRINCIPAL PARTICULARS
Hull: aluminium alloy
Length, overall: 28.00m
Breadth: 8.00m
Draught: 1.50m
Passenger capacity, max: 250
Speed, service: 30 knots
Speed, max: 32 knots
Fuel consumption at service speed: 570 l/h
Range at service speed: about 500n miles
Engines: two MWM TBD 604 B12 diesels, 1260 KW at 1800 rpm
Propulsion: two c.p. propellers

The Harding 150 seat *Havstril* in service with Simon Møkster, Norway (photo: *Alan Bliault*)

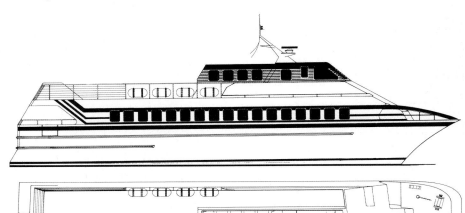

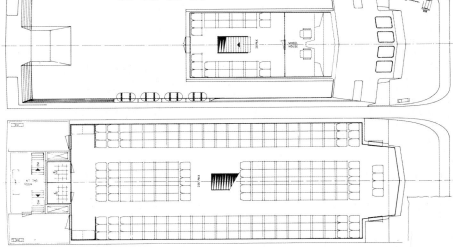

Layout of Harding design for a 28m high-speed catamaran ferry

KVÆRNER-FJELLSTRAND
N-5632 Omastrand, Norway

Telephone: (05) 55 41 00
after office hours: (90) 52455/49218/65902
Telex: 42148 FBOAT N
Telefax: (05) 55 42 44

Eirik Neverdal, *President*
Sverre O Arnesen, *Vice President*
Kåre A Hamnes, *Technical Manager*
Leidolv Berge, *Financial Manager*

In the summer of 1988 discussions began between the Fjellstrand company at Omastrand and Kvaerner Industries A/S with a view to combining their expertise and widening the international prospects for the well established and highly successful line of Fjellstrand high-speed catamaran vessels. By January 1989 agreement had been reached and the companies were merged and announced at the Kvaerner annual general meeting, 11 May 1989. This co-operative arrangement will, amongst other developments, permit the early establishment of Kvaerner Fjellstrand yards outside Norway.

Fjellstrand having achieved the most extensive and sustained export penetration of the world high-speed ferry market, both in terms of number of vessels sold and number of countries sold into, has now embarked on the development of two new main types of high-speed catamaran, the Flying Cat and the Foil Cat.

The Flying Cat type is an extension of the 38.8 metre Advanced Slender Catamaran as well as putting emphasis on a very high standard of exterior and interior design. Flying Cats are to be built in two sizes, 40 metres and 47 metres. The 47 metre Flying Cat is available in both two and three deck versions. In June 1989, Fjellstrand announced the sale of the first 40m Flying Cats for delivery in April 1990 to the Norwegian operation Fylkesbaatane i Sogn og Fjordane, owners of two of the earlier 38.8 metre catamaran ferries. A second 40 metre Flying Cat order was received 22 September 1989 from the Greek hydrofoil operator, Ceres Hellenic Shipping for delivery in November 1990. The Foil Cat takes Fjellstrand design developments a stage further in combining the advantages of the catamaran configuration with the efficiency at high-speed of advanced foil technology and a new stabilisation system for enhanced passenger comfort. These factors enable a service speed potential of over 50 knots to be offered and a fuel consumption about 50% lower than obtainable with existing high-speed catamarans.

The earlier history of Fjellstrand stems from 1928 when the company was started by Odd Oma. Wooden fishing boats were built first, then lifeboats in 1935, eventually in series production and from 1952 they were built in aluminium and later in grp. By 1962 boats up to 26m in length were being built. From 1964 Fjellstrand began to concentrate on aluminium boat building, first producing yachts, then fast work-boats, ferries and other high-speed craft for the Scandinavian market, some of catamaran form.

At the beginning of the 1980s the potential of the export market was recognised in the fields of high-speed ferries and offshore crew/supply boats.

Following the delivery of nearly 400 aluminium vessels starting in 1952, Fjellstrand built its first catamaran (25.5m) in 1976, the Alumaran 165 type. A further four vessels of this size followed up to 1981, when the first 31.5m passenger catamaran was delivered to a Norwegian operator. Between 1981 and 1985 a further twelve 31.5m catamarans were delivered worldwide for passenger ferry work and crew/supply operations in the offshore oil industry. Please see earlier editions of this book for details of the 25.5m and 31.5m catamarans. Design work on a larger 38.8m type started in 1983 and by the end of 1989, Fjellstrand had sold 33 of these vessels. The yard employs 175 people.

Craft built (31.5m) 1981–1985

Yard No	Name	Seats	Delivered	Operator/Owners
1544	Lygra	292	1981	Bergen Norhordland Rutelag, Norway
1553	Norsul Catamara	96 + 14 tonnes cargo	1982	Norsul Offshore, Brazil
1557	Anahitra	161	1983	SURF et Cie, (France) for Cameroon & Gabon
1558	Helgeland	160 + 8 tonnes cargo	September 1983	Helgeland Trafikkselskap A/S, Norway
1559	Hjørungavåg	228	1983	Møre og Romsdal Fylkesbåtar, Norway
1560	Bei Xiu Hu	291	1983	Chu Kong Shipping, China
1561	Li Wan Hu	289	March 1984	Chu Kong Shipping, China
1563	Xiu Li Hu	291	October 1984	Chu Kong Shipping, China
1564	Qiong Zhou Yi Hao	291	December 1984	Chu Kong Shipping, China
1562	Asie III	96 + 40 tonnes cargo	1984	Asie Crew Boat, Malaysia
1565	Lian Hua Hu (ex Jasarina)		1984	Chu Kong Shipping, China
1566	Yi Xian Hu	291	March 1985	Zhen Hing Enterprises Co Ltd, China
1568	Peng Lai Hu	291	July 1985	Jiang Gang Passenger Transport Co, China

The first 38.8m catamaran for Cat Lines SA, Spain, 1989

The first Fjellstrand sale to Korea the 396-seat *Dae Won Catamaran*, 1988

38.8-METRE ADVANCED SLENDER CATAMARAN (ASC)

This type is based on a broadly similar building specification to the earlier 31.5m, but has design features aimed at further improving performance, economy, space and payload. Built in marine grade aluminium alloy, designs include a ferry version with 449 seats, and an offshore vessel with a freight capacity of 40 tonnes. The hulls are of symmetrical and slim design and tunnel height has been increased to further improve seakeeping. Service speeds of up to 36.8 knots are claimed for the 38.8m catamaran fitted with MTU 16V 396 TB84 engines.

Fjellstrand offers both the 31.5m and 38.8m catamarans with KaMeWa waterjet propulsion as an alternative to Lips fixed-pitch propellers, offering an increase in speed. The vessel for Mexico was the first so equipped.

In May 1986 Fjellstrand announced the signing of a contract for ten passenger catamarans for the Istanbul Great City Municipality, Turkey. The vessels are of the 38.8m type, five with two MTU 16V 396 TB83 engines, 1510kW (at 1940rpm) each, and five with two MTU 12V 396 TB63, 1000kW (at 1800rpm) each, giving cruising speeds fully loaded of 32 knots and 25 knots respectively. The vessels have seating for 449 passengers. The value of the contract was given as between NOK 250 and 300 million. The vessels operate in the Strait of Bosphorus transporting commuters from the Asian to the European side.

The two 38.8m catamarans *Fjordprins* and *Sognekongen* embody layout and facilities giving the highest priority to passengers' needs and activities. The interiors combine extreme quietness with a very high standard of decor in terms of design, colours, materials and finishes. Facilities include a TV/video saloon, grouped seating, reclining chairs, play areas for children and refreshment services from wagons and bar. The large windows provide excellent visibility for passengers. This high level of luxury has been continued in the more recent 38.8m catamarans such as those in service with OY AW line AB.

The order by AG EMS Emden of West

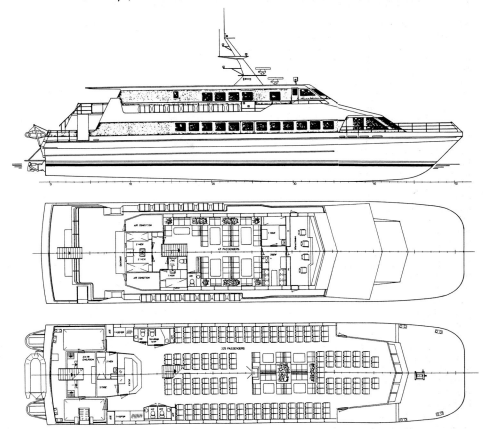

General arrangement of 38.8m catamaran for AG EMS Emden, West Germany

Germany for a 38.8m catamaran which entered service in 1989 is the first high-speed catamaran to fly the German flag, to be classified by Germanischer Lloyd and to be certified by the See-

Berufsgenossenshaft. A substantial number of German components and services have been employed in the project.

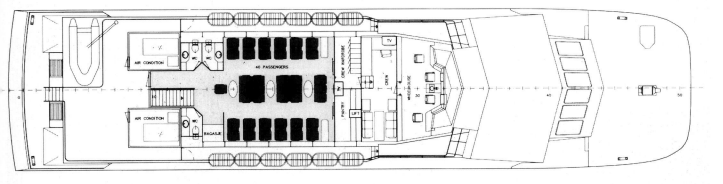

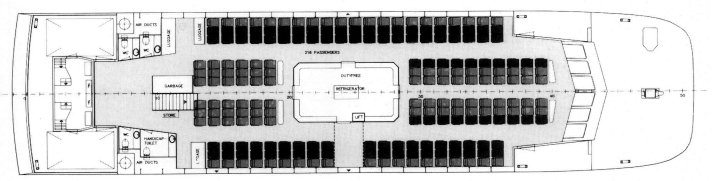

Interior of the Fjellstrand 38.8m catamaran on order for Dampskibsselskabet Øresund

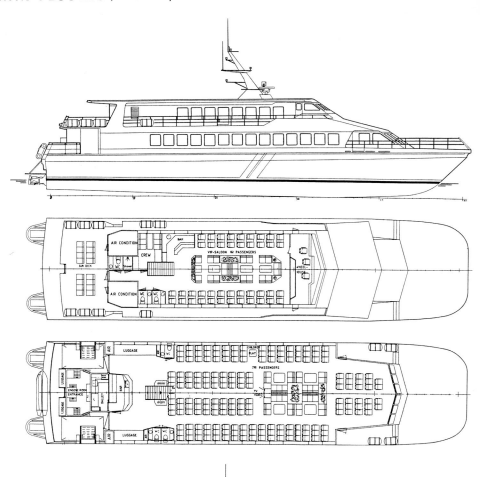

General arrangement of 38.8m catamaran for Cat Lines
SA, Spain

VICTORIA CLIPPER

CLASSIFICATION: Det norske Veritas + 1A1
R150, Light craft, passenger catamaran.
ENGINES
Main engines: Two MTU 16V 396 TB83, 1499kW
    (2010bhp) each
Auxiliary engines: Two 60kW Mercedes Benz OM
    352 A/Stamford
PROPULSION: Two KaMeWa waterjet, type
63S/62/6.
NAVIGATION: Two radars, gyrocompass, log,
echosounder and autopilot.
COMMUNICATION: Sailor SSB, Sailor VHF,
intercom/public address system, internal TV-
control from the bridge to engine room, hull side
and deck, public telephone.
DIMENSIONS
Length, overall: 38.80m
Beam: 9.40m
Depth: 3.97m
Draught, loaded: 1.51m
GRT: 420
PERFORMANCE
Passenger seats: 300 + 30 outside
Fuel consumption at service speed:
    23.9 litres/n mile
Range, at service speed: 920n miles
Fuel capacity: 22 000 litres
Fresh water capacity: 1500 litres
Speed, service, fully loaded: 31.5 knots

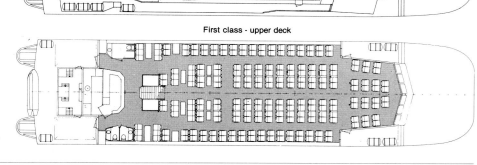

First class - upper deck

Layout of *Victoria Clipper*

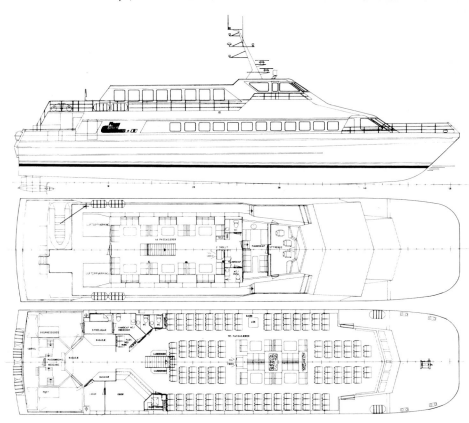

General arrangement of the Fjellstrand 38.8m catamaran
for Flaggruten, showing the Liaaen/Helix Z-drive
propeller installation

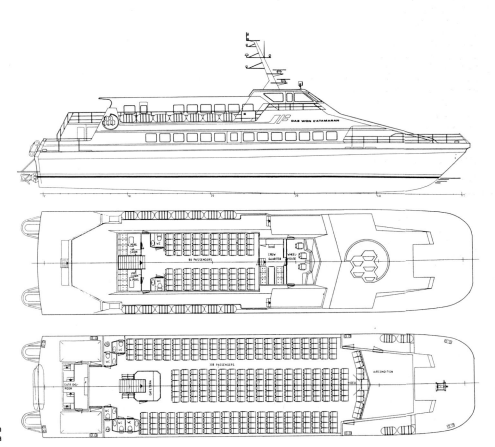

General arrangement of 38.8m catamaran for Dae Won
Ferry Co Ltd, South Korea

RECENT 38.8M CATAMARANS

Sea Cat "Baltic" class is the same as *Jetcat* "Bothnia" class except that the seating is increased to 177 on the main deck and 50 on the upper deck. Sea Cat entered service on 5 May 1988.

In the table below:
√ signifies same information is applicable as in the column for *Jetcat*.
— signifies information for the particular item as given under *Jetcat* is not specified.

	Jetcat/Blue Manta	Fjordprins & Sognekongen	Umur Bey	Mexico
NAME:				
VERSION:	"Bothnia" class			
BUILT:	1988	1987	1987–1988	1985–1986
CLASSIFICATION:	DnV + 1A1 R90, E-0 Light Craft Passenger Catamaran	DnV + 1A1 R5, E-0 Light Craft Passenger Catamaran	DnV + 1A1 R90, Light Craft Passenger Catamaran	DnV + 1A1 R150 Light Craft Passenger Catamaran
HULL:	Aluminium	√	√	
ENGINES; Main:	Two MTU 16V 396 TB84, 1835kW each at 1875rpm (90% output)	Two MTU 16V 396 TB84 2040kW each at 1940rpm (MCR)	Two MTU 16V 396 TB83 1510kW each at 1940rpm	Two MTU 16V 396 TB83 1327kW each
Auxiliary:	Two Mercedes Benz OM 352A/Stamford MSC 234S generators	√	Two 60kW Mercedes Benz/Stamford generators	Two Mercedes Benz OM 352A, 60kW each, Stamford generators
PROPULSION:	Two KaMeWa 71 S62/6 waterjets, via ZF BU 755 gear boxes	Two KaMeWa 63 S62/6 water jets	Two Lips fixed-pitch propellers, via ZF BW 750S gear boxes	Two KaMeWa 63 S62/6 water jets
DIMENSIONS				
Length, overall (m):	38.80	√	√	√
Beam (m):	9.40	√	√	√
Depth (m):	3.97	√	√	—
Draught (m):	1.58	1.55	2.50	2.40 loaded
Tonnage (GRT):	425	406	431	399
CAPACITIES				
Fuel oil:	Two 4500l tanks	Two 6000l tanks	√	Two 4500l tanks
Fresh water (l):	1800	√	1500	1500
Lube oil (l):	250	300	—	250
Bilge water (l):	1000	1000	—	—
ACCOMMODATION				
Passenger seats:	163, main deck	177, main deck	—	322, main deck
	50, upper deck	24, upper deck (conference room)	—	68 upper deck (first class)
Total seating:	213	201	449	390
Facilities:	Bar, duty-free shop, audio entertainment system: 5 channels for CD	Bar/pantry	√	√
radio and video		√	—	—
TV/video saloon		√	—	√
Slot machines		—	—	—
Hot and cold meals		√	—	—
Telephone		√	—	—
Four W.C.s + one for disabled passengers		Four W.C.s including one for disabled passengers	—	
		Children's playroom		
PERFORMANCE				
Speed, maximum:	40 knots	—	—	—
service:	36.8 knots at 27270kg disposable load	38 knots at 16000kg disposable load	32.0 knots at 33195kg disposable load	34.0 knots
				30.0 knots
Range, cruising:	—	450n miles	—	—
Fuel consumption:	—	—	—	700l/h (23.1l/n mi)
NOISE LEVELS				
Passenger cabin, main deck:	68dBA	68dBA	—	—
Passenger cabin, upper deck, middle:	66dBA	62dBA	—	—
Wheelhouse:	57dBA	58dBA	—	—
NAVIGATION:	Tranberg navigation lights	√	Aqua navigation lights	—
	Furuno radars	Two Decca radars	√	Two Decca radars
	Robertson autopilot	√		Autopilot
	Furuno echosounder	—	Hondex echosounder	Echosounder
	Anschutz gyrocompass	Robertson gyrocompass	√	Gyrocompass
	Ben Athena log	Ben log	√	Log
	Shipmate NAVTEX receiver	—	—	
COMMUNICATIONS:	Skanti MF radiotelephone	Sailor VHF radiotelephone	Sailor MF radiotelephone	Sailor SSB
	Skanti watchreceiver	—	Sailor watchreceiver	Sailor VHF
	Shipmate VHF radiotelephone	—	Sailor VHF radiotelephone	—
	NTW PA/Intercom and audio entertainment system. Hitachi closed-circuit TV	√	Skanti VHF emergency comm.set	Intercom/PA
		√	NTW PA/Intercom	Closed circuit TV
		Ericson mobile telephone	√	
OWNER/OPERATOR:	OY AW LIne AB, Finland/chartered to: Vasabaatarna AB, Finland	Fylkesbaatane i Sogn og Fjordane, Norway	The Greater City Istanbul Municipality, Turkey	Maritime World Transport Ltd
In service:	17 June 1988	September 1987 and Dec. '87	June 1987	February 1986

THERMOLINER TYPE (38.8-METRE CATAMARAN)

ANNE LINE

On 9 July 1986 Fjellstrand A/S delivered a 480m³ cargo-carrying catamaran to the Norwegian company Gods-Trans A/S, the *Anne Line*. The vessel is equipped with cooling facilities for the transport of fish to customers in Europe and for onwards shipment to the United States and on return journeys the transport of fresh vegetables, fruit and fresh-cut flowers. For such changes of cargo, a cargo deck is provided facilitating easy and efficient cleaning. A Tico Marine 35 (3t) crane and electric fork lift truck are carried on the vessel for efficient goods handling.

The *Anne Line* has a very shallow draught enabling her to pick up cargo from any fish farm along the Norwegian coast. The 30-knot speed allows the vessel to go from Stavanger to Den Helder in the Netherlands in only 13 hours. This advanced slender-hull catamaran type of Fjellstrand offers good seakeeping qualities with favourable fuel economy and high speed.

Details specifically related to *Anne Line*. Other details as under 38.8m catamaran.

CLASSIFICATION: Det orske Veritas + 1Al, R 180, EO, Light Craft Catamaran.
ENGINES: Two MTU 16V 396 TB63, 11310kW (1780bhp) each at 1650rpm, ZF gears, BW 750S. Auxiliary engines: Two 35kW Mercedes Benz/ Stamford.
PROPULSTION: Lips Fixed-pitch propellers.
NAVIGATION: Two Furuno radars, gyrocompass, log, echosounder, autopilot and Decca navigator.
COMMUNICATION: Sailor SSB, Sailor VHF, intercom, 3 mobile telephones, internal TV control from bridge of engine rooms, hull sides and cargo hold.
DIMENSIONS
Depth: 3.97m
Draught, loaded: 2.45m
Temperature controlled space: 480m³
GRT: 380
WEIGHT/CAPACITIES
Deadweight: 65 tonnes
Fuel oil tanks: 15 000 litres
Fresh water tank: 1500 litres
PERFORMANCE
Speed, service (fully loaded): 29.0 knots
Range, at service speed: 720n miles

Craft built or on order (38.8m) Advanced Slender Catamarans 1985-January 1990

Yard No	Name	Completed	Seats	Operator
	Tian Lu Hu	September 1985	326	Zhen Hing Enterprises Co Ltd, China
1570	Yong Xing	November 1985	312	Ningbo Huagang Ltd, China
1571	Mexico (ex Can Cun)	January 1986	370	Cruceros Maritimos del Caribe SA, Mexico
1572	Victoria Clipper	May 1986	330*	Clipper Navigation Inc, USA
1573	Anne Line	July 1986	Freighter	Gods-Trans A/S, Norway
1574	Caribbean Princess	31 October 1986	310	Viking Express (Bahamas) Ltd, Bahamas
1575	Bahamian Princess	February 1987	310	Viking Express (Bahamas) Ltd, Bahamas
1576	Caka Bey	February 1987	449	Istanbul Great City Municipality, Turkey
1577	Fjordprins	September 1987	201	Fylkesbaatane i Sogn og Fjordane, Norway
1578	Umur Bey	May 1987	449	Istanbul Great City Municipality, Turkey
1579	Yeditepe	May 1987	449	Istanbul Great City Municipality, Turkey
1580	Sognekongen	December 1987	201	Fylkesbaatane i Sogn of Fjordane, Norway
1581	Sarica Bey	September 1987	449	Istanbul Great City Municipality, Turkey
1582	Ulubatli Hasan	October 1987	449	Istanbul Great City Municipality, Turkey
1583	Uluc Ali Reis	January 1988	449	Istanbul Great City Municipality, Turkey
1584	Nusret	March 1988	449	Istanbul Great City Municipality, Turkey
1585	Karamürsel Bey	March 1988	449	Istanbul Great City Municipality, Turkey
1586	Sea Cat/Blue Manta	April 1988	249	OY A W Line AB, Finland
1587	Hezarifen Celebi	September 1988	449	Istanbul Great City Municipality, Turkey
1588	Cavil Bey	September 1988	449	Istanbul Great City Municipality, Turkey
1589	Sleipner	April 1989	243	Flaggruten, Norway
1590	Draupner	April 1989	243	Flaggruten, Norway
1591	Dae Won Catamaran	November 1988	396	Dae Won Ferry Co. Ltd, South Korea
1592	Nordlicht	April 1989	272	AG EMS Emden, Germany
1593	Leopardo	June 1989	290	Cat Lines SA, Spain
1594	Jetcat	June 1988	213	OY A W Line AB, Finland
1595	Eyra	August 1989	290	Cat Lines SA, Spain
1596	Nam Hae Star	October 1989	350	Nam Hae Express, S. Korea
1598	Mercury	March 1990	288	AKP Sovcomflot, USSR
1599	Solovki	March 1990	246	AKP Sovcomflot, USSR
1600	—	June 1990	164	Finnmark Fylkesrederi og Ruteselskap, Norway
1601	—	September 1990	256	Dampskibsselskabet Øresund, Denmark
1602	—	January 1992	256	Dampskibsselskabet Øresund, Denmark

* of which 30 are external

Fjellstrand *Victoria Clipper* serving Seattle and Vancouver

FLYING CAT

The new Fjellstrand design was launched in 1989 and orders were soon received from two European operators. The Flying Cat type is available in three sizes, 40 metres and 47 metres in two-deck layouts and the 47 metre also in a three-deck arrangement. The experience and best features of the Fjellstrand 38.8 metre Advanced Slender Catamaran have been incorporated in the Flying Cat together with the highest standards of interior and external design, the latter integrated with an aerodynamically enhanced configuration. A strong emphasis has been placed on the comfort and requirements of the passengers, supported by the improved seakeeping and increased speed of the Flying Cat.

PRINCIPAL PARTICULARS OF 40m BASIC TYPE
Length, overall: 40.00m
Beam, moulded: l0.00m
Draught: 1.54m
Payload: 450 passengers or 45 tonnes cargo
Speed: up to a maximum of 45 knots
Speed, cruising: 25 knots with 372 passenger load
Engines: either MTU, MWM, SACM, EM diesels or gas turbines
Propulsion: water-jet units, fixed or controllable-pitch propellers

PRINCIPAL PARTICULARS OF 47m BASIC TYPE
This version is aimed at new and longer routes and with the capability of dealing with tougher weather conditions.
Length, overall: 47.00m
Beam, moulded: 11.20m
Draught: 1.78m
Payload up to 600 passengers or 75 tonnes cargo
Speed: up to a maximum of 45 knots
Engines: either MTU, MWM, SACM, EM diesels or gas turbines
Propulsion: water-jet units, fixed or controllable-pitch propellers

Craft built or on order: 40m Flying Cat

Yard No.	Name	Completed	Seats	Operator
1597	—	June 1990	—	Fylkesbaatane i Sogn og Fjordane, Norway
—	—	November 1990	372	Ceres Hellenic Shipping, Greece

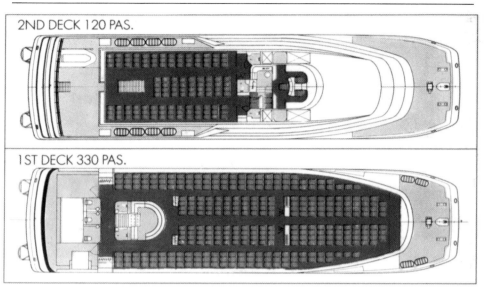

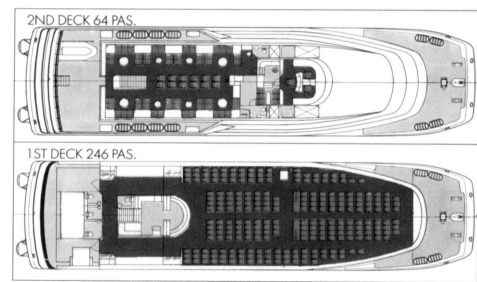

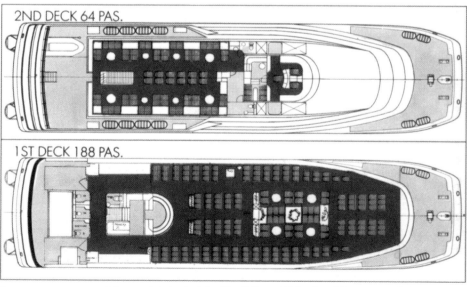

Three passenger accommodation comfort standards for 40m Fjellstrand Flying Cat: 450 passengers, 310 passengers and 252 passengers

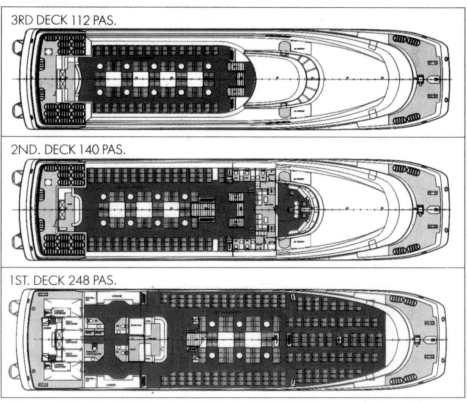

3RD DECK 112 PAS.

2ND. DECK 140 PAS.

1ST. DECK 248 PAS.

Three-deck accommodation layouts for the 47m
Fjellstrand Flying Cat

47 M FLYING CAT • 3 DECK VERSION

Artists impression of Fjellstrand 47m Flying Cats, two
and three deck versions

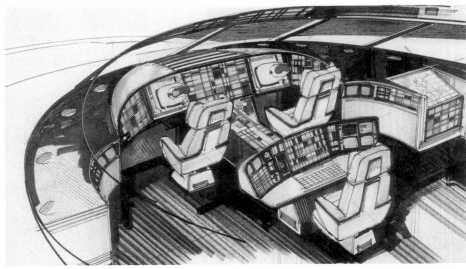

Impression of the advanced wheelhouse design for the
Fjellstrand Flying Cats

FOIL CAT

Development of this concept was undertaken with the assistance of a large-scale manned test craft enabling full-scale service speeds up to 50 knots to be explored. While the simplicity of the catamaran construction is maintained in this new concept, the addition of the lifting and stabilising foil system enables considerably higher speeds at the level of 50 knots to be achieved economically and in rougher seas. In comparison with comparable vessels of other types the transport efficiency is significantly higher, leading to fuel consumption figures 50% less than for instance conventional high-speed catamarans. In addition speed loss in waves is much reduced and vertical accelerations can be reduced to less than half those for comparable craft of other types.

Artists impression Foil Cat 50 knot ferry

Fjellstrand Foil Cat manned test craft

LINDSTOLS SKIPS & BATBYGGERI A/S

N-4950 Risr, Norway
Telephone: (041) 50 344/50 685
Telefax: (041) 52 060

22.5 M CATAMARAN

A new catamaran project on order for A/S Namsos Trafikkselskap for delivery in July 1990.

CLASSIFICATION
DnV + 1A1 RS, EO Light-Craft Passenger Catamaran
HULL
Aluminium alloy, decks and superstructure of Lindstol aluminium alloy sandwich profile.
DIMENSIONS
Length, overall: 22.50m
Breadth: 7.60m
Depth: 3.15m
Draught, loaded: 1.10m
GRT: 106
ENGINES
Two MTU 12 V 396 TE 92, 672 kW each, at 2300 rpm
Auxiliary engine: Mitsubishi/Stamford 16 kW, 20 KVA, West Power 20 M2, 1N FE
PROPULSION
Servogear c p propeller, V drive gear VD 250 B
ACCOMMODATION
87 Passengers (+ 20)
NOISE LEVELS
Saloon, medium: 68 bBA
Wheelhouse: 58 dBA
CAPACITIES
Fuel: two 1700 litre tanks
Fresh water: 400 litres
PERFORMANCE
Speed, service: 30 knots with 10.5 tonne load
Range: 440 n miles at service speed
Fuel consumption: 7.15 l/n miles

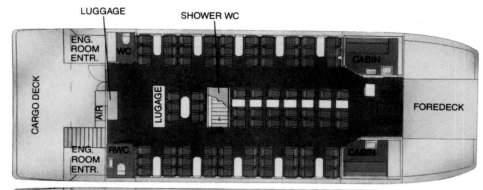

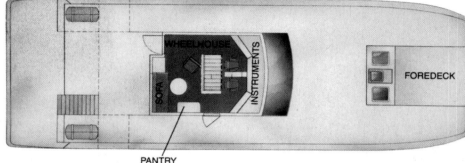

Layout of Lindstols Skips 22.5m catamaran for A/S Namsos Trafikkselskap

Artists impression of Lindstols Skips 87 passenger catamaran

ULSTEIN INTERNATIONAL A/S

Brødrene Aa a/s

N-6780 Hyen, Norway

Telephone: (057) 69 800
Telex: 42162 BRAA N
Telefax: (057) 69914

HYEN

A 25m catamaran ferry built in 1980 in glass-reinforced plastic for service with Fylkesbaatane i Sogn og Fjordane.

More recently Brødrene has built the Cirrus-designed surface-effect ships *Norcat, Ekwata* and *Ekwata II*; see the ACV section.
CLASSIFICATION: DnV + 1 IA2 K Partly Sheltered Light Craft Catamaran.
POWERPLANT: Two MTU 12V 396 TC62, each 1200bhp at 1650rpm
Gearboxes: ZF type BW-455S, ratio 1:1.509
Auxiliary power: One Mercedes Benz OM314, 42bhp, Stamford generator 35kVA
ACCOMMODATION: 156 seats.
EQUIPMENT
Radar: Furuno FRM 60, reserve, Furuno FR 240 Mk II
Gyro: Robertson SKR-80
HF: Sailor R143

Cirrus CIRR 27 R *Helgelandsekspressen* built by Brødrene Aa A/S

DIMENSIONS
Length overall: 25.0m
Beam overall: 8.4m
Draught: 2.0m
GRT: 182
PERFORMANCE
Trial speed: 25.45 knots

HELGELANDSEKSPRESSEN

Delivered to Saltens Dampskibsselskab in July 1985. This Cirrus type CIRR 27 R catamaran is classified by Det norske Veritas + 1 A1 R25 Light Craft. The vessel is of fibre-reinforced plastic/sandwich construction.
PROPULSION AND MACHINERY
Main engines: Two MTU 12V 396 TB83
Reduction gears: ZF BU 455
Auxiliary engines: Two Isuzu UM 4BBI
Generators: Two Stanford (29.5kVA, 220V, 50Hz)
Fire pumps: Vest Jet (electrical)
Bilge pumps: Six Dymatic Nova-Lens

Hydro pumps: Two Dymatic
Hydraulic gear for crane

ACCOMMODATION
Passenger lounge, 184 seats in 4 columns of 3 each
  at 85cm seat pitch
Luggage compartment aft in shelves
2.0m³ cargo room for mail and express cargo
4 toilets of which 1 for disabled and as nursery
Kiosk
Lobby for crew
Wheelhouse

DECK MACHINERY
Electrically operated anchor winch type Euro-
  drive
One 500lb Shpp anchor
One hydraulic deck-crane Tico 135 MSU
One searchlight type Noack

ELECTRICAL EQUIPMENT
220V/50Hz/3ph/two 29.5kVA. One set equipment
  on stand-by
24V emergency equipment
Shore-connection
Electrical equipment installed by Målry Electro

HEATING AND VENTILATION
Interior has two 35kW heating capacity from main
  engine cooling-water, which heats fresh air
  sucked by two centrifugal fans with a capacity
  of 2700m³/h each
Four engine room fans
Wheelhouse has separate fresh air ventilation,
  electrically heated with a capacity of approximately 500m³/h
Electric heater for shore connection

ELECTRONICS
One Decca radar RM 1070 with 4ft antenna;
  Decca radar 970 BT with 6ft antenna; gyrocompass Gyrostar NG 100; log JRC JLN 203;
  two VHF Sailor; mobile telephone (Cellnet)
  Panasonic Hand Free; econometer Ecomatic
  FC 10/20; fire alarm central board Autronic BX
  11; two tv monitors for surveillance of engine
  rooms; intercom Phonico; control panel for
  bilging, Matre; radio/cassette-player; emergency transmitter Thron 1C

Ingøy built by Brødrene Aa A/S

The Cirrus-designed *Fjørtoft* 120-seat, 30 knot ferry

(H.M. Valderhaug)

MISCELLANEOUS
Halon equipment for engine rooms, Heien-Larsen; magnet compass NOR 250; two hydraulic control systems for propellers and governor control, Hynautic; ten life-rafts, Viking 20K; pick-up boat Zodiac, equipped for 25n miles open sea; crane for launching pick-up boat; sounding system, Soundfast 800–102
DIMENSIONS
Length overall: 27.0m
Length waterline: 24.50m
Beam: 9.0m
Depth to main deck: 2.80m

Draught, max: 1.92m
GRT: 197
CAPACITIES AND WEIGHTS
Cargo: 5 tonnes
Fuel oil: two 3100-litre tanks
Potable water: 250 litres
Lubrication oil: 250 litres
PERFORMANCE
At 50% disposable load:
Contract speed at 80% MCR: 26 knots
Measured speed at 80% MCR: 30.2 knots
Measured speed at 100% MCR: 33.3 knots
100% MCR: Two engines at 1560hp

80% MCR: Two engines at 1250hp
Range, max, at service speed: 406n miles
INGØY
A 48 seat plus cargo catamaran designed by Cirrus AS and delivered to Finnmark Fylkesrederi og Ruteselskap in July 1987.
FJØRTOFT
Designed by Cirrus AS for Møre og Romsdals Fylkesrederi, the *Fjørtoft* was launched in May 1988. The vessel is powered with two 1100hp diesel engines, has seats for 120 passengers and has a speed of 30 knots.

WESTAMARIN A/S
PO Box 143, 4501 Mandal, Norway

Telephone: (043) 62222
Telex: 21514WRIN N
Telefax: (043) 62302

Westamarin A/S is part of the Swede Ship Invest AB group of companies which includes Oskarshamns Varv AB (Shipyard), Djupviks Varv AB (Shipyard) and an electrical contractor, Electro Swede AB. Westamarin A/S has an exclusive sales and production license for SES craft from AB Karlskronavarvet in Sweden for the non-military market.

Westamarin A/S was established in 1961, under the name of Westermoen Hydrofoil A/S, to produce, develop, design and market high-speed vessels for commercial and military purposes. A number of Supramar PT hydrofoil craft were built in the 1960s.

In 1970 the Westamarin type was introduced, an asymmetric-hull catamaran based on a semi-planing hull of welded marine aluminium. This design was the first high-speed catamaran to enter ferry operations. Five versions, the Westamarin 86, 95, 100, 120 and 160, have since been built totalling 47 vessels. Mono-hull vessels of type S75 and S80 have been built, as well as patrol boats for the Royal Norwegian Navy and Swedish Royal Navy.

FOIL CAT 2900
Foil Cat 2900 is a hydrofoil assisted catamaran developed by Hardanger Sunnhordlandske Dampskipsselskap (HSD), a hydrofoil and catamaran operator since 1961, and Westamarin A/S, builder of hydrofoils and catamarans since 1962. Extensive model testing has been carried out by the Norwegian Marine Technology Research Institute A/S (MARINTEK) and by the Institut fur Schiffs- und Meerestechnik, Technical University, Berlin.

The Foil Cat 2900 combines the best properties of the super slender hull catamarans with the speed capability of hydrofoil craft fitted with fully submerged foils.

Because of the very slender hulls and the stabilising effect of the foils, the comfort is excellent, even in rough seas at high speeds. With no centre-hull, and high vertical sides on both of the sharp bowed twin hulls, the craft may claim to have wave-piercing capabilities.

HSD has ordered the first Foil Cat to be built for commercial use. The vessel, to be delivered by Westamarin A/S in January 1991, will be operated on the company's routes serving Bergen.

CLASSIFICATION: DnV 1A1 R90 light craft EO
HULL: Aluminium alloy
FOILS: Stainless steel
DIMENSIONS
Length overall: 29.25m
Length waterline: 26.40m
Beam, moulded: 8.40m
Depth, moulded: 3.70m
Draught, foilborne: 1.90m

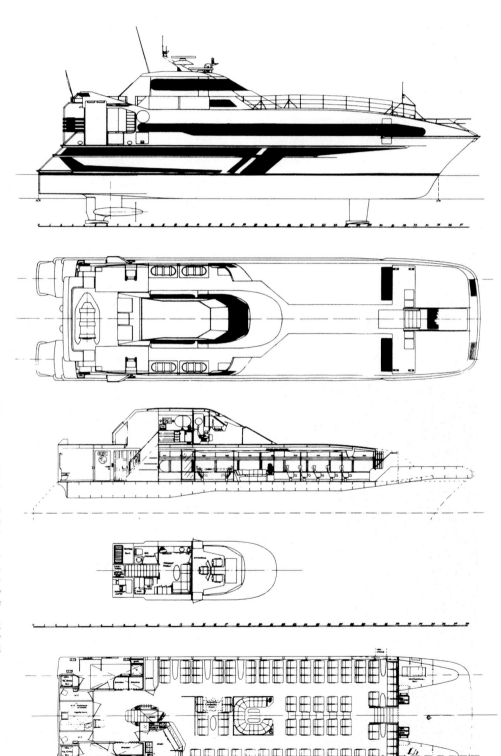

General arrangement of Westamarin Foil Cat 2900

Catamaran craft built (W86) 1971–1979

Yard No	Name	Delivered	Seats	Operator	Route
21	Fjordglytt	June 1971	140	Fylkesbaatane i Sogn og Fjordane	Bergen-Årdalstangen
22	Trident 1 (ex Belle de Dinard, ex Karmsund)	January 1972		Les Vedettes Blanches et Vertes, France	St Malo to Jersey
24	Fjordtroll	May 1972	140	Sandro, Sweden	
25	Sauda	June 1972	148		
26	Mayflower	October 1972	134	Det Stavangerske Dampskibsselskab	Stavanger-Sanneid
27	Kongsbussen	April 1973		Fosen Trafikklag A/S	Trondheim-Sula-Trondheim
28	Hertugbussen	May 1973		Fosen Trafikklag A/S	Trondheim-Sula-Trondheim
29	Tedno	June 1973	140	Hardanger Sunnhordlandske Dampskibsselskab	Bergen-Tittelsnes-Bergen
32	Koegelwieck	September 1973		BV Terschellinger Stoomboot Mij, Netherlands	Terschelling-Harlingen
34	Olavsbussen	February 1974		Fosen Trafikklag A/S	Trondheim-Sula-Trondheim
35	Tjelden (ex Haugesund)	November 1973	94 + cargo	Hardanger Sunnhordlandske Dampskibsselskab	Os-Haugesund-Os
41	Fjordbris (ex Storesund)	September 1974	165	Det Stavangerske Dampskibsselskab	Stavanger area
42	Fjordkongen II	January 1975	140	Troms Fylkes Dampskibsselskap	Tromsr area
44	Brynilen	June 1975	94 (+6 tonnes freight)	Finnmark Fylkesrederi og Ruteselskap	Hammerfest-Loppa
45	Øygar	September 1975	140	Øygarden & Sotra Rutelag L/L	Rognrysund-Bergen
46	Fjorddronningen	January 1976	174	Troms Fylkes Dampskibsselskap	Harstad-Gryllefjord-Harstad
47	Trident 2 (ex Highland Seabird)	May 1976		Les Vedettes Blanches & Vertes	
48	Fjorddrott	June 1976	167	Det Stavangerske Dampskibsselskab	Stavanger-Sauda-Stavanger
49	Fjordprinsessen	March 1977	163	Troms Fylkes Dampskibsselskap	Jrkelfjord-Skjervøy-Tromsø Gryllefjord
65	Bonholm Express (ex Steigtind)	June 1977	182	Bornholm Express	Allinge, Denmark to Simrishamn, Sweden
54	Mediteran	June 1978		Union Dalmacija-Oour Flota, Yugoslavia	
67	Marina I	July 1978		Union Dalmacija-Oour Flota, Yugoslavia	
66	Hornøy	October 1979	136	Finnmark Fylkesrederi og Ruteselskap	Måsry-Hammerfest-Srrrysundbass

PASSENGER CAPACITY: 140 to 180
ENGINES: Two MTU 16V396 TE 74L, each 2000 kW at 2000 rpm
PROPULSION/GEAR: Ulstein-Liaaen Speed Z, type CPZ 60/42 – 125 L HC
SPEED Service, fully loaded: 50 knots

WESTAMARIN W86

Twenty-three Westamarin 86s were built up to 1979. Three of the vessels operating in Norway are equipped to carry 94 to 100 passengers and up to 6 tonnes of freight. The main powerplants are two MTU 1100hp diesels.

DIMENSIONS
Length: 26.7m
Beam: 9m
Draught: 1.2m
GRT: 200
NRT: 135
PERFORMANCE
Max speed: 28 knots
Range: 235n miles

Artists impression of Foil Cat 2900

Catamaran craft built (W95) 1974–1982

Yard No	Name	Delivered	Seats	Operator	Route
36	Vingtor	May 1974		Sameiet Flaggruten, Norway	Stavanger-Bergen-Stavanger
37	Tranen (ex Sleipner)	June 1974		Sameiet Flaggruten, Norway	Stavanger-Bergen-Stavanger
38	Rapido de Formentera (ex Sunnhordland)	April 1975	180	Bormholmer Pilen, Denmark	
39	Martini Bianco (ex Amarischia)	May 1975		Aliscafi SNAV, Italy	Naples-Ischia-Capri
43	Alisur Azul (ex Westjet) (W95T)	Dec 1976		(ex Alisur SA, Spain)	Spain
51	Salem (ex Tryving) (ex Draupner)	April 1977		Dery Shipping Lines	Saudi Arabia
52	Tunen	May 1977	180	A/S Dampskibsselskabet Øresund, Denmark	København-Malmø-København
50	Pegasus	June 1977		Service Maritime Carteret, France	Carteret-Jersey-France
53	Tranen	June 1978	180	Flebasa Lines, Spain	
68	Siken (ex Tumleren)	April 1979	180	A/S Dampskibsselskabet Øresund, Denmark	København-Malmø-København
79	Azur Express (ex Alisur Amarillo (W95D))	April 1981	218	SURF, France	
80	Tromsprinsen	July 1981	210	Troms Fylkes Dampskibsselskap	Harstad-Tromsø
81	Trident 4 (ex Celestina)	June 1981	248	Vedettes Blanches et Vertes, France	St Malo-St Helier
84	Trident 3 (ex Venture 84)	July 1982		Vedettes Blanches et Vertes, France	St Malo-St Helier

WESTAMARIN W95

This longer version of the W86 can carry up to 248 passengers. The standard version has been powered by two SACM AGO 195 V12C SHR 1800hp diesels giving the 29.1m vessel a maximum speed of 32 knots. Fourteen W95s have been built before being replaced by the W100. In 1985, W95 *Sunnhordland* was fitted with MTU 12V 396 TB83 engines in place of the SACM engines and at the same time had its 0.84m diameter fixed-pitch propellers changed for 1.25m diameter controllable-pitch propellers. The gearboxes were changed from 1.103:1 to 2.54:1 ratio. Fuel consumption is 273 litres/hour.

WESTAMARIN W88

A faster but slightly smaller capacity craft than the W86 or W95 and replacing the W86, four W88s have been sold the last, *Fjordsol*, being slightly longer at 29.4m. The hull and superstructure are constructed in marine grade aluminium, AA 5083. *Skogøy*, a W88 delivered in May 1985, is classified by DnV + 1A1, R-15, light craft with approval for operation in ice.

POWERPLANT AND PROPULSION: Two MTU 12V 396 TB83, each 1150kW (1560hp) at 1940rpm

Reduction gearboxes: ZF type BW 455S, ratio 3.13:1

Propeller: Two three-blade Servogear controllable pitch

Auxiliary engines: Two Daimler Benz OM 314

Generators: Two Stamford, type MSC 234C or E, 3-phase, 230V, 50Hz

EQUIPMENT

Ventilation: Heating from main engines to all accommodation areas

Windlass: One electro-hydraulic anchor windlass

Navigation: Two radars, one gyrocompass, one magnetic compass, log and econometer

Communication: Two VHFs, intercom, mobile telephone, radio and music broadcast

Lifesaving equipment: Seven 20-person life rafts, one pick-up boat. Life preservers under seats

FACILITIES

Kiosk

Cabins for 4 crew

WCs: 3 for passengers, 1 for crew

DIMENSIONS

Length overall: 28.02m

Breadth moulded: 9.00m

Draught max: 2.20m

PERFORMANCE

Speed: 30 knots at 100% MCR

Range: 270n miles

Endurance: 9 hours at service speed

WESTAMARIN 3000 FJORDSOL

POWERPLANT: Two MTU 12V 396 TB83, 1150kW each at 1940rpm, ZF BW 455S gearboxes. Auxiliary engines: two Daimler Benz OM 352A driving Stamford MSC 234F generators, three 230V, 50 Hz.

HULL & SUPERSTRUCTURE: Aluminium AA 5083.

DIMENSIONS

Length overall: 29.4m

Length, waterline: 25.4m

Breadth moulded: 9.0m

Draught max: 2.2m

GRT: 235.0

NRT: 75.0

CAPACITIES

Passengers: 202

Cargo: 10 tonnes, one hold of 52m³

Fuel oil: two 2800-litre tanks

Fresh water: 600 litres

PERFORMANCE

Speed, service at 100% MCR, full payload: 30.0 knots

Range: 270n miles (9 hours at service speed)

Fuel consumption: 490kg/h at 100% MCR

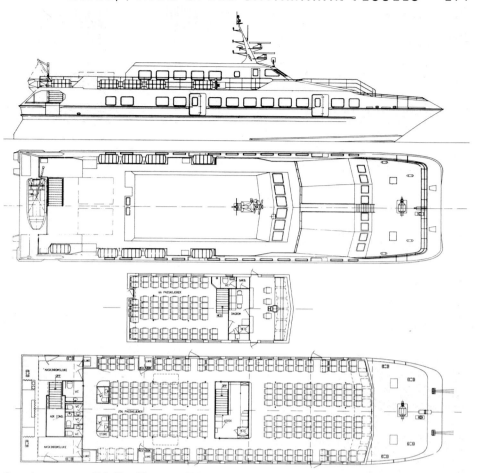

General arrangement of *Vindile,* a Westamarin 3700 S

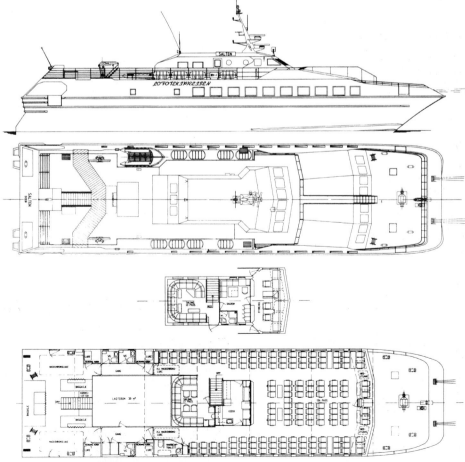

General arrangement of *Salten,* a Westamarin 3700 SC

Catamaran craft built (W88) 1981–1986

Yard No	Name	Delivered	Seats	Operator	Route
78	*Haugesund*	March 1981	180	Det Stavangerske Dampskibsselskab	Haugesund-Stavanger
82	*Midthordland*	November 1981	170	Hardanger Sunnhordlandske Dampskipsselskap	
88	*Skogøy*	May 1985	132 + 10 tonnes cargo	Ofotens Dampskibsselskap	Narvik-Svolvater
91	*Fjordsol*	June 1986	202	Det Stavangerske Dampskibsselskap	Stavanger-Ryfylke

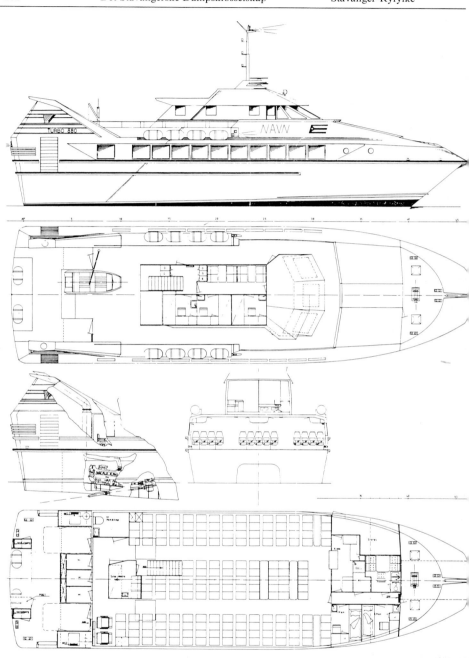

General arrangement of Westamarin W88

Westamarin W88 *Skogøy*

WESTAMARIN W100
DIMENSIONS
Length overall: 32.9m
Breadth moulded: 9.8m
Draught max: 2.0m
PERFORMANCE
Main engines: Two MTU 16V 396 TB83 or similar
Speed: 28 knots fully loaded at MCR
Capacity: Up to 300 passengers

WESTAMARIN 3700 SC
Yard No's 93 and 94)
OPERATORS
Saltens Dampskibsselskap, 1988
Ofotens Dampskibsselskap, 1988
ACCOMMODATION
Passengers: 195
Cargo: 15 tonnes in hold of 60m³
DIMENSIONS
Length overall: 36.50m
Length waterline: 31.10m
Breadth moulded: 9.50m
Draught: 1.47m
CAPACITIES
Fuel oil: Two 4000-litre tanks
Fresh water: 600 litres
PERFORMANCE
Speed, service, full payload, at 100% MCR:
35 knots
Range: 280n miles
Endurance: 8 hours at service speed
Fuel consumption: 860kg/h at 100% MCR

WESTAMARIN 3700 SC
VINDILE
(Yard No 95)
CLASSIFICATION: DnV 1A1-R45, Light Craft
Passenger Vessel.
HULL: Hulls, superstructure and deckhouse with
wheelhouse built in sea water corrosion resistant
aluminium plates AA5083 (D54S ¼H), profiles in
AA 6081 WP (B 51 SWP).
ENGINES: Two MTU 16V 396 TB84, 2040kW
each, at 1940rpm.
PROPULSION: Two KaMeWa 63S waterjet
units.
AUXILIARY POWER: Two Mercedes OM 352
driving Stamford MSC 234 E70kVA, 250V, 50Hz,
3-phase generators.

Catamaran craft built (W100) 1980–1982

Yard No	Name	Delivered	Operator
75	*Gibline I* (*W100D*) (ex *Gimle Belle*, ex *Condor 6*)	April 1980	Gibline Ltd, Gibraltar
76	*Independencia* (ex *Gimle Bird*)	September 1981	Direccao Regieonal dos Portos da Madeira, Portugal
77	*Porec* (ex *Gimle Bay*)	January 1982	Splosna Plovba Piran, Yugoslavia
83	*Nearchos* (ex *Venture 83*)	May 1982	RENATOUR SA, Greece

ACCOMMODATION
259 seats at 85cm pitch
63 seats at 90cm pitch (VIP lounge)
DIMENSIONS
Length overall: 37.00m
Length waterline: 31.10m
Breadth moulded: 9.50m
Depth moulded: 3.56m
Draught: 1.47m

WESTAMARIN 3600 (ex W120)
ZI LANG
CLASS: DnV + 1A1, R45.
HULL AND SUPERSTRUCTURE: Aluminium
AA5083.

ENGINES
Main engines: Two MTU 16V 396 TB83, each
1540kW at 1940rpm
Gearboxes: ZF BU 755S, ratio 3.07:1
Auxiliary engines: Two Mercedes OM 352 A
Generators: Two Stamford MSC 234F
ACCOMMODATION: 354 passengers, in two
cabins
DIMENSIONS
Length overall: 36.2m
Length waterline: 32.26m
Breadth moulded: 9.77m
Draught max: 2.20m
GRT/NRT: 378/140

Westamarin W3700 S *Vindile* May 1988   (*Alan Bliault*)

A Westamarin W3700 SC just before delivery to A/S Ofotens Dampskibsselskap, May 1988   (*Alan Bliault*)

PERFORMANCE

Speed: 25/27 knots fully loaded at MCR
Range: 270n miles
Fuel consumption: 650kg/h
Fuel capacity: Two 5000-litre tanks
Fresh water: 1200 litres

Westamarin W3600 *Zi Lang* commissioned January 1987 for China

WESTAMARIN 5000
ANNE LISE
(Yard No. 92)
CLASSIFICATION: DnV 1A1 R 280 Light Craft-EO.

A 49.5m thermo-cargo catamaran delivered August 1987 to the Norwegian owner, Gods-Trans A/S, Hønefoss.

This vessel is the largest of its type, dimensioned for high regularity for North Sea operations. The cargo is placed on the main deck, which consists of one cooling room of 520m^2 and one freezing room of 276m^2. The main machinery consists of the first MTU 396 TB84 2040kW engines delivered to Norway. The propeller system (including reduction gear) is of a new type, called Speed-Z propulsion system, type HST 60/40–25, delivered from AM Liaaen in Ålesund, Norway. The solution is very similar to the different Azimuth thrusters (as the Compass thrusters made by same). Windows are fitted for possible 369-seat ferry use.
HULL AND SUPERSTRUCTURE: Aluminium Aa 5083.
ENGINES: Two MTU 16V 396 TB84, 2040kW each, at 1940rpm.
REDUCTION GEARS: 2.52:1.
AUXILIARY ENGINES: Two Mercedes-Benz type OM 421, 116kW each at 1500rpm.
GENERATORS: Two Stamford type MSC 334 B.
DECK EQUIPMENT: Electro-hydraulic anchor windlass, 2600kp/3.5m.
COOLING SYSTEM
Refrigerator hold: Carrier type 5F30-C-644 E, capacity: 34 kW
Freezer hold: Carrier type 5F30-C-644 K, capacity: 14 kW
NAVIGATION: Two radars, one gyrocompass, log and econometer, depth sounder, navigator.
COMMUNICATION: VHF, radio telephone, intercom, mobile telephone, TV monitoring of engine room, cargo space and hull sides.
LIFESAVING EQUIPMENT: Four 10-person inflatable life rafts, one pick-up boat.

Catamaran craft built (W3600, ex W120) 1987

Yard No	Name	Seats	Delivered	Operator
89	*Zi Lang*	354	January 1987	Nantong Hi-Speed Passenger Ship Co, China

Catamaran craft built (W3700 SC) 1988

Yard No	Name	Seats	Delivered	Owner
93	*Salten*	195 + 30m^2 cargo hold	April 1988	Saltens Dampskibsselskab
94	*Ofoten*	195 + 30m^2 cargo hold	May 1988	Ofotens Dampskibsselskap A/S

Catamaran craft built (W3700 S) 1988

Yard No	Name	Seats	Delivered	Owner
95	*Vindile*	300	1988	Gotlandslinjen (Nordstrøm & Thulin AB)

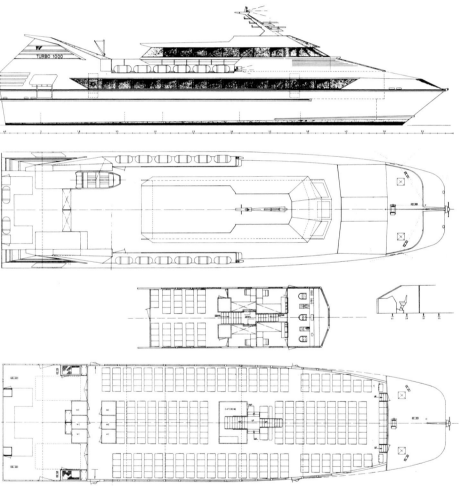

Outboard and inboard arrangement of Westamarin W3600 *Zi Lang*

The 49.5m Westamarin 5000

CREW FACILITIES: 7 cabins, single with extra pullman berth, 2 WCs, washroom, 2 showers, provisions store, one pantry and mess/dayroom.

DIMENSIONS
Length overall: 49.45m
Length: 43.6m
Breadth: 14.0m
Draught, max: 2.60m excluding propellers
    3.10m including propellers
GRT: 1057
CAPACITIES
Cargo: 200 tons
Fuel: 70 000 litres
Deadweight: 285 tonnes
Cargo space: 520m³ ± 0°C
    276m³ − 20°C

Fresh water: 2m³
Accommodation: 8 crew cabins
PERFORMANCE
Service speed: 26 knots depending on cargo load

WESTAMARIN 4100 S
Yard Nos: 103, 104, 105, 106

On May 9th, 1989 Westamarin A/S announced an order from AKP Sovcomflot for two catamaran ferries of a new type, the Westamarin 4100 S, for delivery to the Soviet Union Black Sea Shipping Company together with an option for a further two. This option was taken up in June 1989. The value of the first order was given as approximately NOK 80 million for the two vessels. Delivery of first two vessels: April 1990.

PRINCIPAL PARTICULARS
Length, overall: 42.60m (including fender and water-jet projection)
Length, design water line: 37.20m
Beam, excluding fender: 10.00m
Draught, design water line: 1.60m
Frame spacing: 0.75m
Depth, main deck: 4.07m
Propulsion: Two KaMeWa 71 S water-jet units
Passenger capacity: 298 (Yard Nos: 103, 104)
Speed: about 37 knots

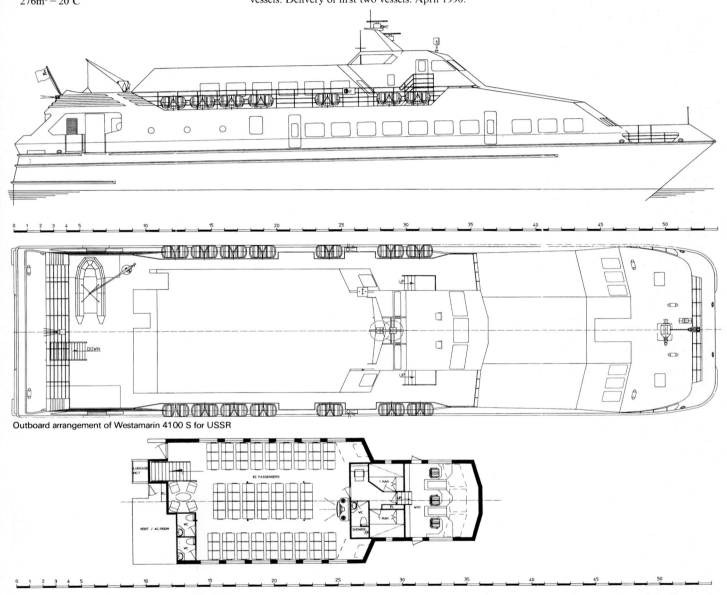

Outboard arrangement of Westamarin 4100 S for USSR

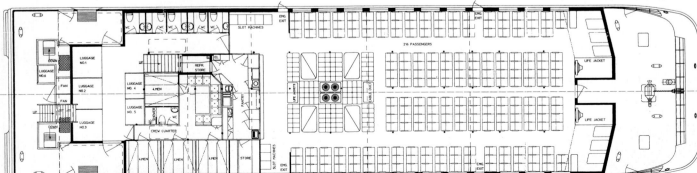

Inboard arrangement of Westamarin 4100 S for USSR

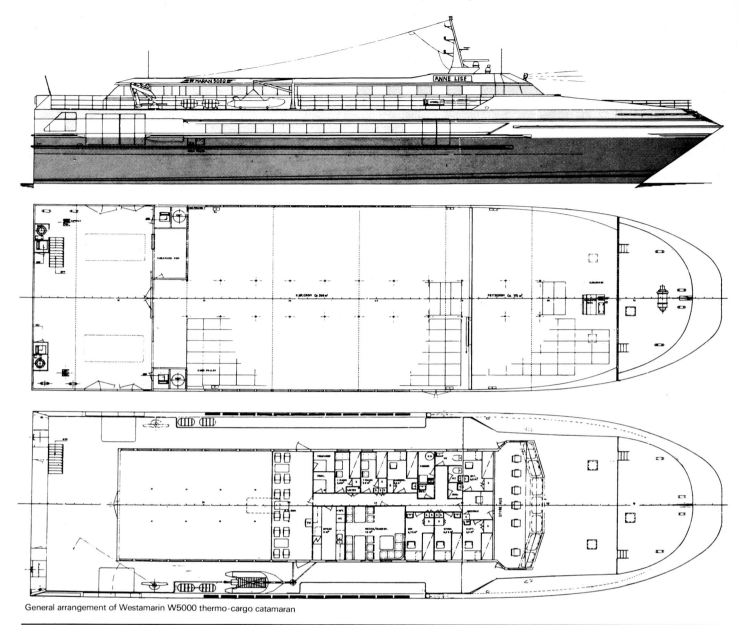

General arrangement of Westamarin W5000 thermo-cargo catamaran

SINGAPORE

ALUMINIUM CRAFT (88) PTE LTD

A Subsidiary Company of:

SINGAPORE SLIPWAY & ENGINEERING CO (PTE) LTD
(A division of Singmarine Industries Ltd)
1 Rhu Cross, Singapore 1543

Telephone: 3444698
Telex: 24050 RS
Telefax: 3343761

Wong Kog Seng, *Executive Director*
Tony Yue Kog Kuan, *General Manager*

ALUMINIUM CRAFT (88) PTE LTD

1 Rhu Cross, Singapore 1543

Telephone: 3459098/3441785
Telex: 39677 ACRAFT RS
Telefax: 3443761

Chan Seak Foo, *General Manager*
Fong Weng Meng, *Project Manager*

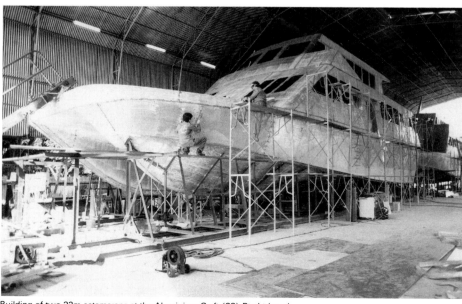

Building of two 23m catamarans at the Aluminium Craft (88) Pte Ltd yard

Aluminium Craft (88) Pte Ltd has over twenty years experience in the building and repair of aluminium craft and industrial structures. In 1989, the company received orders for two 23 metre catamaran ferries and a 27m high-speed crew boat, all three completed in that year.

FBM MARINTEKNIK (S) PTE LTD
31 Tuas Road, Singapore 2263

Telephone: 8611706/7, 8616271/2/3
Telex: 8653419MARJET RS
Telefax: (65) 8614244

Kenny Tham, *Yard Manager*
Part of FBM Marine Holdings Ltd
33/F New World Tower, 16–18 Queen's Road, Central, Hong Kong

John Warbey, *Group Sales Director*

Telephone: (5) 218302/231054
Telex: 74493HMHCO HX
Telefax: (5) 8100952

David C H Liang, *Group Chairman*
Robert Liang, *Executive Director*
Mike McSorley, *Marketing Manager*

SS23
CLASSIFICATION: GL
The first of these vessels, the *Glory of Singapore* was launched in July 1989; both are for service on the Singapore to Batam route and have seating for 130 passengers. They are powered by two

FBM Marinteknik (S) Pte Ltd (originally Marinteknik Shipbuilders (S) Pte Ltd) was formed in 1984 by the parent company Marinteknik International Ltd of Hong Kong, now Fairey Marinteknik International Ltd to build catamaran and mono-hull craft designed by Marinteknik Verkstads AB of Sweden.

HAKEEM
Designed by Marinteknik Verkstads AB of Sweden *Hakeem* is a Marinjet 34 CCB crew boat of catamaran form with symmetrical hulls with low-resistance, semi-planing characteristics. Construction of the craft in welded aluminium alloy follows the same principles as used in the Marinjet series of ferry craft. *Hakeem* has seating for 50 passengers and provision for a crew of 6.
CLASSIFICATION: Det norske Veritas R-60, Crew Boat, Light Craft.
PROPULSION
Two MTU 12V 396 TC 62 high-speed diesels, each giving 880kW at 1650rpm

671 kW high-speed diesel engines, giving a service speed of 25 knots.
The hulls of these vessels are of asymmetrical form, backed up by research and development with support from the Singapore Economic Development Board which provided a grant for the design.

Two KaMeWa 60/S62/6 waterjet units
OPERATOR: Ocean Tug Services, based at Belait, Brunei, delivered May 1985, for use by Shell Brunei.
DIMENSIONS
Length overall: 34.0m (hulls extended to provide side protection to waterjet units)
Beam overall: 9.4m
Draught full load: 1.1m
GRT: 243
NRT: 72
WEIGHTS
Disposable load: 19 tonnes
Cargo and supplies: 6.5 tonnes
Fuel capacity: 10 000 litres (8.5 tonnes)
Loaded displacement: 84.0 tonnes
PERFORMANCE
Speed cruise: 27 knots
Speed max: 30 knots
Fuel consumption: 440 litres/h
Range: 615n miles

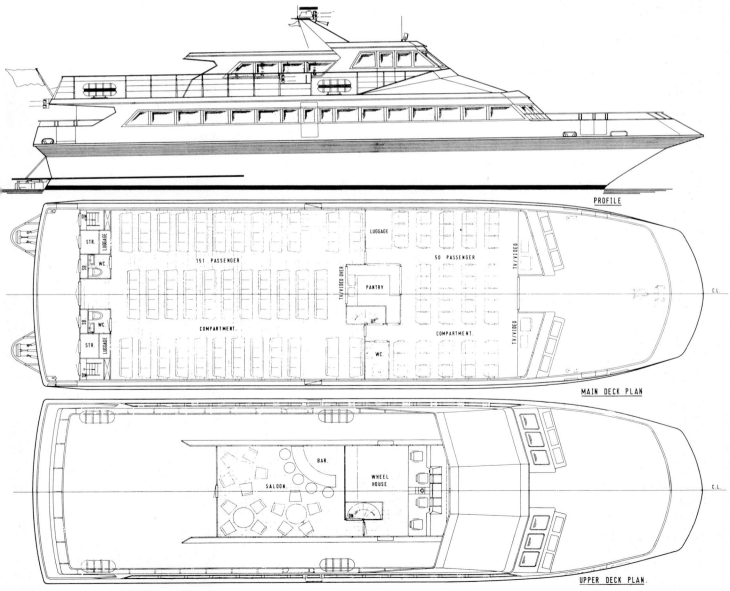

33m Marinjet passenger vessel, 33 CPV type, *Shun De*

Craft built or ordered (high-speed catamarans)

Yard No	Type	Name	Delivery or ordered	Full load cruising speed knots	Seats/cargo (tonnes)	GRT	NRT	Full load displacement (tonnes)	Operator
101	34 CCB	*Hakeem*	May 1985	27	100 + 10	243	72	84	Ocean Tug Services
103	34 CCB*	*Layar Sentosa*	May 1987	30	70 + 18	252	75	90	Shell Sarawak
105	34 CCB	*Layar Sinar*	April 1987	30	70 + 18	252	75	90	Shell Sarawak
111	35 CPV	*Airone Jet*	November 1987	35	320	320	121	125	Alilauro SpA (MEDMAR)
112	33 CPV	*Shun De*	November 1987	27	250	235	70	125	Shun Gang
115	36 CPV-D	*Condor 8*	May 1988	35	306	387	269.38	128	Condor Ltd, UK
—	41 CPV SD	*Cowes/Camoes*	1989		306	—	—	—	Hongkong Macao Hydrofoil Co Ltd
—	41 CPV SD	*Jurong/Estrela do Mar*	1989		306	—	—	—	Hongkong Macao Hydrofoil Co Ltd

*Fitting out of Marinteknik, Sweden, Yard No 61
CCB Catamaran Crew Boat

CPV Catamaran Passenger Vessel
D   Double Deck

LAYAR SINAR

The principal particulars are as follows:
ENGINES: Two MTU, 1180kW (1582bhp) each.
CLASSIFICATION: DnV R 150.
DIMENSIONS
Length overall: 34.0m
Beam: 9.4m
Draught: 1.2m
WEIGHTS
Freight: 23 tonnes
Displacement, loaded: 90 tonnes
PERFORMANCE
Speed, cruising: 30 knots
Passenger seats: 70+

CONDOR 8

Delivered to Condor Ltd, Channel Isles, UK in early May 1988.
PRINCIPAL PARTICULARS
Length, overall: 36.00m
Engines: Two MTU 16V 396 TB84
Water-jet units: Two KaMeWa 71 S62/60
Passenger: 252 in main cabin 48 in upper cabin
Duty-free shop, 5 WCs

MARINJET 41 CPV SD

For details of this type please see entry under Marinteknik Verkstads AB. Two of these vessels, *Cowes* and *Jurong* have also been named *Camoes* and *Estrela do Mar*, which will be delivered to the HongKong Macau Hydrofoil Company in 1989, joining the first, *Öregrund*, delivered by Marinteknik Verkstads AB in late 1988.

Airone Jet at Ischia harbour April 1989 (photos *Wendy Adamson*)

Shun De

SING KOON SENG
3 Benoi Road, Singapore 2262

Telephone: 8610800
Telex: 23435SKS RS

Builder of three International Catamarans Pty Ltd catamarans with welded aluminium hulls.

IPO-IPO 3001
CLASSIFICATION: ABS +A1+AMS Unrestricted Service. Panamanian flag.
POWERPLANT: Two GM 16V 149 TI 1400bhp each, at 1900 rpm.
GEARBOXES: ZF BW 455, ratio 2.529:1.
DIMENSIONS
Length overall: 30.2m
Beam (excluding fenders): 11.2m
Draught max loaded: 2.4m
Deck cargo area: 112m²
PERFORMANCE
Speed max: 27 knots
Seats: 15, aircraft type
Fire monitor: 150m³/h at 100m head

Craft built (InCat)	Completed	Passengers	Operator
29.0m *Offshore Pioneer*	1983	15*	Singapore Navy, 1986 (ex Offshore Charters of Singapore)
29.0m *Offshore Pride*	1983	15*	Singapore Navy, 1986 (ex Offshore Charters of Singapore)
30.0m *Ipo-Ipo 3001*	May 1984	15*	(ex Zadco Productions, Abu Dhabi, UAE)

* plus cargo

Sing Koon Seng In Cat *Offshore Pioneer*

SWEDEN

MARINTEKNIK VERKSTADS AB

Varvsvagen, Box 7, S-74071 Öregrund, Sweden

Telephone: (0173) 30460
Telex: 76182MARTAB S
Telefax: (0173) 30976

Hans Erikson, *Managing Director*

Marinteknik Verkstads AB co-operates with FBM Marine Holdings Ltd, Hong Kong

During the 1970s Marinteknik Verkstads AB was principally engaged in the design and building of semi-planing 16- to 18-knot 300- to 400-passenger ferries in welded aluminium. The yard was also involved in the repair, modification, design and building of other craft types in steel and aluminium up to 30m in length. In the period 1977/79 work proceeded on the design of a water-jet-propelled catamaran vessel under the type name Jetcat and construction started in November 1979. The hulls of this catamaran were of symmetrical form with a deep Vee forward leading to an almost zero deadrise aft and with a hard chine developing from the bow. Four similar boats were delivered to the HongKong Macao Hydrofoil Co in the period 1982/83 and since then another 11 catamarans have been delivered or ordered, all employing waterjet propulsion.

In addition mono-hull crew boats and ferries have been delivered or ordered, also with waterjet propulsion. See High-speed Mono-hull Craft Section.

MARINJET 33CPV (PV 2400)
NETTUNO JET
JET KAT EXPRESS
GIOVE JET
A symmetrical-hull, semi-planing, waterjet-propelled catamaran built in welded corrosion-resistant aluminium alloy employing extrusions for plating and frames.
MAIN ENGINES: Two MTU 12V 396 TB83, 1180kW, 1582bhp each at 1940rpm.
PROPULSION: Two KaMeWa 60/S62/6 waterjet units driven via ZF gearboxes type BU 455, 2.05:1 ratio.
ACCOMMODATION: 218 to 276 passengers. Three lavatories.
SYSTEMS
Fuel tank capacity: 7000 litres
Fresh water tank capacity: 500 litres.

Swedish built Marinteknik catamaran ferries in Italy, 1988

DIMENSIONS
Length overall: 33.0m
Beam overall: 9.40m
Draught, full load: 1.20m
WEIGHT
Payload: 20.5 tonnes (256 passengers)
PERFORMANCE
Speed, max: 35 knots
Speed, cruising: 32 knots
Range: 380n miles
Fuel consumption: 581 litres/h

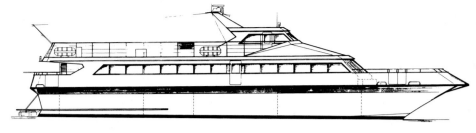

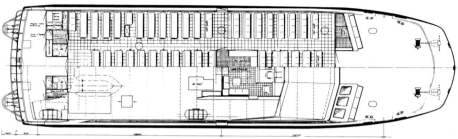

General arrangement of Marinjet 33CPV (*Jetkat 1*, *Nettuno Jet* and *Giove Jet*)

Marinjet 34 CPV *Giunone Jet*

Craft built (high-speed catamarans)

Yard No	Type	Marinteknik Designations Old	New	Engines	Craft name	Cruise speed, full load, knots	Owner/operator	Originally delivered	Application	Seats	GRT/NRT	Loaded displacement, tonnes
42	29.0m	JC-F1	-	Two MTU 12V 396 TC 82, 1175kW	*Aliterreno 1* (ex *Jaguar*, ex *Jaguar Prince*, ex *Mavi Haliç*)	27	Spain	Nov 1980	Ferry	197	251.00/173.00	85
46	29.0m	JC 3000	-	Two MTU 12V 396 TB 83, 1225kW	*Apollo Jet*	29	Hongkong Macao Hydrofoil Co Ltd	Jan 1982	Ferry	215	261.17/177.60	86
47	29.0m	JC 3000	-	Two MTU 12V 396 TB 83, 1225kW	*Hercules Jet*	29	Hongkong Macao Hydrofoil Co Ltd	1982	Ferry	215	261.17/177.60	86
48	29.0m	JC 3000	-	Two MTU 12V 396 TB 83, 1225kW	*Janus Jet*	29	Hongkong Macao Hydrofoil Co Ltd	Oct 1982	Ferry	215	261.17/177.60	86
50	29.0m	JC 3000	—	Two MTU 12V 396 TB 83, 1225kW	*Duan Zhou Hu* (ex *Triton Jet*)	29	Zhao Gang Steamer Navigation Co of China	1983/ 23 Sept 1986	Ferry	215	261.17/177.60	86
51	33.71m	PV 2400	Marinjet 33CPV	Two MTU 12V 396 TB 83, 1225kW	*Alize Express* (ex *Nettuno Jet*)		SURF, Congo	May 1984	Ferry	218	260.00/75.00	86
54	33.71m	PV 2400	Marinjet 33CPV	Two MTU 12V 396 TB 83, 1225kW	*Jet Kat Express* (ex *Jetkat I*)		A.T.E.	1984	Ferry	240	269.00/95.00	93.67
55	33.71m	PV 2400	Marinjet 33CPV	Two MTU 12V 396 TB 83, 1225kW	*Giove Jet*		Alilauro SpA	1985	Ferry	276	269.00/95.00	96
56	34.0m	PV 3100 (Jumbo)	Marinjet 34 CPV-D	Two MTU 16V 396 TB 83, 1540kW	*Lommen*	32	Dampskibssellskabet Øresund A/S	Dec 1985	Ferry	235	281.00/100.00	97.58
59	34.1m	PV 3100	Marinjet 34 CPV-D	Two MTU 16V 396 TB 83, 1540kW	*Ørnen*	32	Dampskibssellskabet Øresund A/S	July 1986	Ferry	235	285.00/101.00	97.68
60	34.1m	CV 3400	Marinjet 34CCB	Two MTU 16V 396 TB 93, 1700kW	*Emeraude Express*	40	Chambon (SURF)	Jan 1986	Crew boat	240	288.00/103.00	99.80
61*	34.0m	—	Marinjet 34CCB	Two MTU 16V 396 TB 83, 1180kW	*Layar Sentosa*	30	On charter to Shell Sarawak	1986	Crew boat	—	252.00/75.00	90.00
62	34.0m		Marinjet 34CPV-D	Two MTU 16V 396 TB 84, 1935kW	*Giunone Jet*		Alilauro SpA		Ferry	—		
69	34.0m	PV	Marinjet 34CPV	Two MTU 16V 396 TB 84, 1935kW	*Acapulco Jet*	34	Alilauro SpA	April 1989	Ferry	300		96.00
70	34.0m	—	Marinjet 34CPV	—	*Nettuno Jet*		Alilauro SpA	1988	Ferry	—		
74	41.5m	—	Marinjet 41CPV SD	Two MTU 16V 396 TB 84, 1935kW	*Öregrund*		HongKong Macao Hydrofoil Co Ltd	28 Nov 1988	Ferry	306		130.00

* Fitted out by Marinteknik Shipbuilders (S) Pte Ltd, Singapore, now FBM Marinteknik (S) Pte Ltd
SD: Single Deck

MARINJET 34 CPV-D (formerly 33CPV DOUBLE DECK) (PV 3100)
LOMMEN
ØRNEN

CLASSIFICATION: Det norske Veritas 1A1, R-45, EO Passenger.
HULL: Welded, corrosion resistant aluminium alloy, employing extrusions for plating and frames.
MAIN ENGINES: Two MTU 16V 396 TB83 diesels, 1540kW, 2065hp each, at 1940rpm.
PROPULSION: Two KaMeWa 63/S62/6 water-jet units. ZF BU 750 gears.
ACCOMMODATION
210 passengers on main deck
25 passengers in a first class saloon on the upper deck
Cabin noise level, 70dBA approx to 66dBA in some areas
Air-conditioning, television and video, stereo sound and telephone facilities
Catering and duty-free shop facilities provided.
SYSTEMS
Fuel tank capacity: 9600 litres
DIMENSIONS
Length overall: 33.71m
Beam overall: 9.40m
Draught: 1.20m (summer freeboard)
GRT: 281
NRT: 100
WEIGHT
Lightship: 78.3 tonnes
PERFORMANCE
Speed, cruising at 85% MCR, fully laden: 32 knots
Speed, max (loaded): 36 knots
Range: 320n miles
Fuel consumption: 780 litres/h (554kg/h)
Wave length limit, at cruising speed: 2.1m

MARINJET 34 CPV-D
GIUNONE JET
AIRONE JET

Two orders for this ferry type were received end of 1986, beginning 1987 for delivery to Aliscafi Alilauro del Tirreno SpA and Alilauro Italia.

MARINJET 34CCB CREW BOAT (CV 3400)
EMERAUDE EXPRESS

CLASSIFICATION: Det norske Veritas +1A1, R 50 EO.
MAIN ENGINES: Two MTU 16V 396 TB93 diesels, each 1700kW, 2280bhp MCR.
PROPULSION: Two KaMeWa 63/S62/6 water-jet units.
ACCOMMODATION
243 passengers
5 crew
Air-conditioned, video and stereo facilities
DIMENSIONS
Length overall: 34.10m
Beam overall: 9.40m
Draught: 1.20m
PERFORMANCE
Speed, max: 44 knots
Speed, cruising, full load: 40 knots

MARINJET 41-CPV-SD
ÖREGRUND

The largest Marinteknik high-speed catamaran at 41m overall length, the first of these vessels was delivered to the HongKong Macau Hydrofoil Co Ltd following its launching in Sweden on 15 November 1988. The *Öregrund* is the first Marinteknik vessel to be fitted with a pitch-damping control system, using hydraulically-activated trim tabs. The delivery trip from Öregrund to Southampton, a distance of 1116 nautical miles was undertaken in six stages in a total voyage time, including pilot-on-board time, of 33.5 hours.
The vessel is fitted with an MJP automatic manoeuvring system.
CLASSIFICATION: DnV +1A1 R 25 Light Craft EO.
MAIN ENGINES: Two MTU 16V 396 TB84,

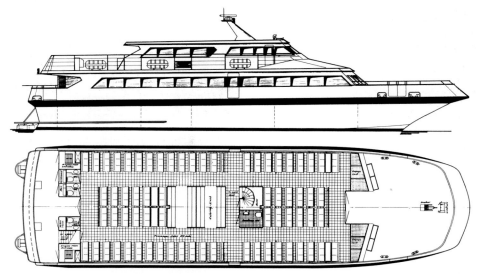

General arrangement of Marinteknik 34 CPV-D (*Ørnen* and *Lommen*)

Marinjet 34CCB crew boat *Emeraude Express*

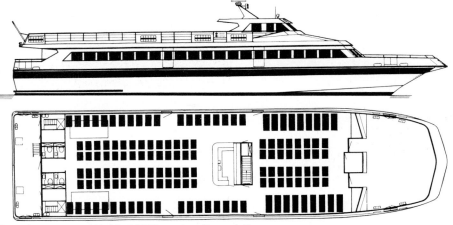

General arrangement of Marinjet 34CCB crew boat *Emeraude Express*

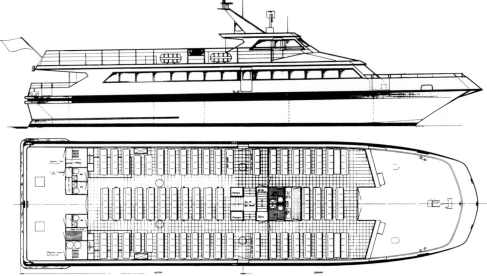

Layout of *Öregrund*

1945kW each at 1940rpm (MCR), sfc 220g/kWh.
AUXILIARY POWER: Two Mercedes OM type
with Stamford generators, 380V, 3-phase, 50Hz.
PROPULSION: Two MJP 650 waterjet units
driven via ZF gearboxes type BU 755 ratio
1.868:1.0, with disconnecting clutch.
CAPACITIES
Fuel: 7000 litres
Fresh water: 1000 litres
Lube oil: 500 litres
Hydraulic oil: 150 litres
Sewage: 1000 litres
ACCOMMODATION
Single deck: 306 passengers
Crew: 8
Six lavatories
Noise level (max) in passenger saloons: 75dBA
DIMENSIONS
Length overall: 41.5m
Breadth moulded: 11.0m
Depth moulded: 3.5m
Draught loaded: 1.2m
Air draught, to mast top, light ship: 11.5m max
PERFORMANCE
Speed, cruising: 38 knots
    lightship (97 tonnes): 42 knots
Range: 275n miles at MCR
Fuel consumption: 968 l/h
Disposable load: 40 tonnes

Forward area of passenger cabin in *Öregrund*

Öregrund on demonstration in the Solent, England, after arriving from Sweden

THAILAND

ITALTHAI MARINE LTD.

Italthai House, 11th Floor, 2018 New Petchburi
Road,
Bangkok, Thailand
Telephone: 314 6101–9/314 7578/314 7246
Telex: 21225 ITELECT TH
Telefax: 6602 3146385

See Monohull Section for details of management.

DOUMEN (Yard No. 78)
SHUN XING (Yard No. 80)
Two catamaran ferries under construction in
1989 for Yaet Hing Marine Supplies, Hong
Kong, powered by two 1250 kW high-speed diesel
engines driving KaMeWa 63 S water-jet units.

UNITED KINGDOM

ALLIANCE AGENCIES LIMITED

Unit 14–15 Cougar Quay, School Lane, Hamble,
Southampton S03 9XX, England

Telephone: (0703) 455341, 456787
Telex: 477861 G
Telefax: (0703) 455341

Alliance Agencies was formed in 1987 to design
and build the Advance range of fast grp motor
yachts and commercial craft. The company has
now extended their scope to fast catamaran aluminium ferries and patrol boats of 23 and 24
metres in length. Tank testing at the Athens Polytechnic School of Naval Architecture has been
completed on their CAT-23 passenger ferry and
the Jason 24m catamaran patrol/strike craft. The
CAT-23 has a service speed of 30 knots and is
intended for inter-island tourist services. Orders
for two CAT-23 passenger ferries have already
been placed.

CAT-23

Fast Passenger Ferry
CLASSIFICATION: Hellenic Register of Ship-
ping or other classification authorities selected by
owners.
HULL: Hulls and superstructure built in marine
grade aluminium
ENGINES: Two MTU 8V 396 TE 93
Gear Boxes: Two ZF BW 465
Propellers: Two four-blade supercavitating type
SYSTEMS
Auxiliary Engines: Two Perkins T4236
Generators: Two Ansaldo 46kW, 380V, 50Hz sets
Electrical Systems: One 380V AC 50Hz system,
one 220V AC 50Hz system and one 24V DC
system
Air Conditioning: Carrier
Navigational Equipment: One Decca/Racal
marine radar RD80 range 48n miles. One Skipper
EML123 log, one Skipper E/S 417 echo sounder.
Radio Equipment: One Skanti 3000 VHF, one
public address/entertainment system, and a TV
entertainment system.
ACCOMMODATION: 150 passengers, crew 6
DIMENSIONS
Length, overall: 23.10m
Length, waterline: 21.70m
Beam, moulded: 8.00m
Depth, moulded: 3.40m
Draught: 1.50
CAPACITIES
Fuel: 7000 l
Fresh water: 1000 l
Lube oil: 300 l
Sewage tank: 1000 l
Bilge water tank: 1000 l
PERFORMANCE
Service speed: 30 knots

JASON 24 METRE PATROL/STRIKE CRAFT (DESIGN)

The Jason 24 metre patrol/strike craft has the
CAT-23 hull, lengthened by 1 metre. The main
roles of the Jason 24 are coastal surveillance and

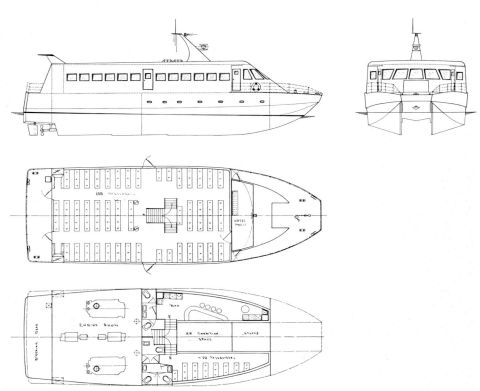

General arrangement of Alliance Agencies 23m catamaran ferry

high-speed interception. The craft is capable of
remaining at sea for a minimum of five days and
operating in weather conditions up to Sea State
5–6. The inherent stability of the catamaran hulls
enables the craft to be fitted out for a variety of
operational roles such as a missile armed strike
craft, lightly or heavily armed conventional patrol
boat, fast mine layer or as a personnel carrier
embarking up to 30 commandos and their equipment at short notice. The Jason 24 is a cost-
effective craft designed for easy maintenance
ensuring a high degree of mission readiness.
HULL: Hulls and superstructure constructed in
marine grade aluminium.
ENGINES: Depending on maximum speed
requirements, two MTU 16V 396 TE 94 or two
MTU 12V 396 TE 94 diesel engines. Loiter engine
can also be fitted.
Gear boxes: ZFBW 755 or ZFBW 465
Propulsion: Surface piercing propellers or water
jet propulsion. Loiter engine fitted with a waterjet.
SYSTEMS:
Auxiliary engines: Two 60 kW, 440V, 60 Hz gen-
erator sets
Electrical installation: One 440V AC 3 phase, 60
Hz system, one 220V AC single phase, 60 Hz
system, one 110V AC 3 phase, 400 Hz system, one
24V DC system
Air conditioning: Carrier
Navigational equipment: Radar Decca 1226, echo
sounder, gyro compass, magnetic compass,
1000W searchlight, electromagnetic speed log

Freshwater: Osmosis fresh water supply system to
supplement one tonne fresh water tank. Osmosis
water supply delivers 750 litres per day.
ARMAMENT:
Missile craft: Four surface-to-surface missiles type
Sea Skua SL on twin launchers aft, or four surface-
to-surface missiles type AS 15TT on twin launchers aft. One 30mm Oerlikon twin GCM-A03–3
mounting or one 30mm single LS30B mounting.
Two 12.7mm Browning machine guns. Two chaff
launchers SWORD and BUCK-WEGMANN
decoy systems.
Gun boat: Single or twin 30mm gun mountings
forward and aft, two chaff launchers mounted aft.
Fast minelayer: Twin 30mm mounting forward,
rails for a total of eight 960kgr mines aft, two
chaff launchers mounted aft.
Fast commando: Platoon of 30 commandos plus
weapons and equipment accommodated aft, one
30mm gun mounting forward
Communications: External communication sets
consist of one HF 250W transceiver, one
UHF/FM 50W transceiver, one HF receiver, one
UHF receiver and cryto voice equipment. Internal
communications consist of intercom to all oper-
ational and accommodation compartments.
Sound powered telephones also fitted.
COMPLEMENT: Total complement of the
missile craft is four Officers, three Chief Petty
Officers, four Petty Officers and twelve Ratings.
CAPACITIES:
Fuel: 8000 l

Fresh water: 1000 l
Lube oil: 300 l
DIMENSIONS
Length overall: 24.10m
Beam: 8.00m
Draught: 1.70m

PERFORMANCE: Speeds when fitted with MTU 16V 396 TE 94 and MTU 12V 396 TE 94 engines at full load displacement:-
MTU 16V:
Speed max: 40 knots (estimated)
Max continuous speed: 35 knots (estimated)

MTU 12V:
Speed Max: 35 knots (estimated)
Max continuous speed: 32 knots (estimated)
Range: 600n miles at 30 knots

ALUMINIUM SHIPBUILDERS LTD

Hamilton Road, Paulsgrove, Hampshire, England

Telephone: (0705) 376960
Telefax: (0705) 210406

P D P Kemp, *Chairman*
J A Davies, *Managing Director*
W R Roberts, *Production Director*
D L Stock, *Commercial Director*

Aluminium Shipbuilders Ltd is a relatively recently established manufacturing company, with a management team and skilled workforce who have long experience in shipbuilding generally and aluminium work in particular.

The company has been appointed the licensee in the UK to build the range of fast catamarans to the designs of International Catamaran Designs Pty Ltd, of Australia (qv).

RIVER 50

In August 1987, the first of a series of lightweight, high-speed passenger catamarans was delivered to Thames Line plc for operation between Charing Cross Pier and West India Dock on the River Thames. The vessel is powered by twin Volvo Penta TAMD 71A engines driving Riva Calzoni waterjets.

Five further vessels were ordered by Thames Line plc for delivery during 1988. These vessels are 17 metres long and have revised interior arrangements which allow for a spacious cabin for 62 passengers.
SURVEY: UK DOT Class V smooth water limits.
ENGINES: Volvo Penta TAMD 71A, 306bhp each at 2500rpm.
WATERJET UNITS: Riva Calzoni IRCL 39 D.
GEARBOXES: MPM IRM 301 PL-1.
CAPACITIES
Fuel capacity: Two 320-litre tanks
Fresh water capacity: 100 litres
DIMENSIONS
Length overall: 16.35m
Beam overall: 5.40m
Draught, full load: 0.60m
PERFORMANCE
Speed: 23–25 knots

The company has developed designs with its licensor of military versions of the catamarans, which will take advantage of the craft's performance and stability characteristics and significant cost-effectiveness benefits.

As well as the catamarans, ASL has received orders from the Royal National Lifeboat Institution including the first two production 13-metre all-aluminium lifeboats; this is in addition to a number of aluminium superstructures for other lifeboats. It has also been involved with the building of 20-metre fast patrol boats and 55-knot patrol/interception vessels and hovercraft, including the production of API-88 hulls for British Hovercraft Corporation, including the Canadian Coast Guard craft, all in aluminium.

CONDOR 9
49 METRE WAVE PIERCING CATAMARAN

The order by Condor Ltd for a 49m In Cat wave piercing catamaran was announced on 18 April 1989. Designed to carry 450 passengers Condor 9 will replace two hydrofoil vessels. The price of the vessel has been quoted as £5 million.

Craft built		Seats	Date
In Cat River 50	*Barclays Bank*	51	1987
In Cat River 50	*London Docklands*	62	April 1988
In Cat River 50	*Le Premier* (ex *Daily Telegraph*)	62	May 1988
In Cat River 50	*Chelsea Harbour*	62	May 1988
In Cat River 50	*Debenham Tewson and Chinnocks*	62	Aug 1988
In Cat River 50	*Harbour Exchange*	62	Aug 1988
In Cat River 50	*London Broadcasting Company*	62	1989

Aluminium Shipbuilders 62-seat River 50

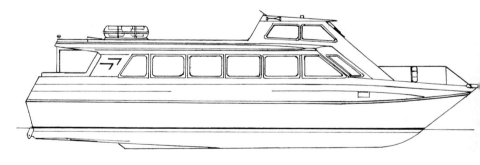

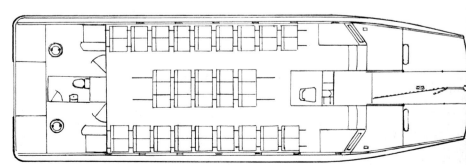

Aluminium Shipbuilders 16m In Cat ferry

CLASSIFICATION: DnV 1A1 Light Craft (CAT) R45 Passenger Ship EO
SURVEY: UK Department of Transport, Class 2, Short International Voyage vessel

PRINCIPAL PARTICULARS
HULL: Welded aluminium
DIMENSIONS
Length, overall: 48.70m

Beam, overall: 18.20m
Beam of hulls: 3.30m
Draught: 1.50m
ACCOMMODATION
Main deck: 288 seats
Upper deck: 164 seats
Crew: 15
ENGINES: Four MWM TBD 604B V 16, 1682
kW each at 1800 rpm
PROPULSION: Four MJP J650R-DD water-jet
units
CAPACITIES
Fuel: Two 7200 l tanks
Fresh water: Two 1000 l tanks
SPEED: 35 knots, service, full load

If one engine should break down a speed of 30
knots can be maintained; each engine with its
water-jet unit is entirely independent of the other
three in its operation.

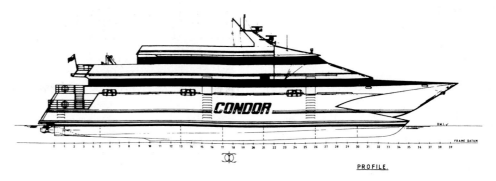

PROFILE.

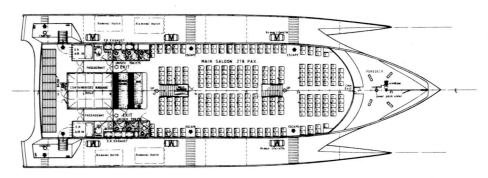

PLAN ON MAIN DECK-TIER 1.

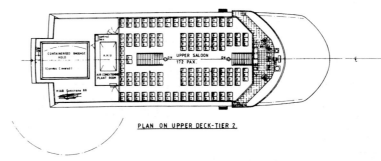

PLAN ON UPPER DECK-TIER 2.

General arrangement of the 49m InCat 450-passenger wave piercing catamaran for Condor Ltd

Artists impression of *Condor 9* built by Aluminium Shipbuilders Ltd

CAMMELL LAIRD SHIPBUILDERS LIMITED

New Chester Road, Birkenhead, Merseyside, L41 9BP, England

Telephone: (051) 647 7080
Telefax: (051) 647 7080 Ext. 2615

G.E. Howel, *Managing Director*

Aluminium Shipbuilders Ltd (ASL) of Portchester and Cammell Laird Shipbuilders of Birkenhead are setting up arrangements to collaborate in the building of very large high-speed wavepiercing ferries. The collaboration arrangements will draw on the existing expertise and experience of ASL in building catamaran vessels together with the management and production strengths of Cammell Laird in dealing with major contracts within their extensive covered construction facilities.

ASL is the UK licensee of International Catamaran Designs Pty of Australia. A 49m Wavepiercer for Commodore Shipping (Condor Ltd) is presently under construction by ASL at Portchester to enter service in 1990; this is the largest craft which can be built at Portchester. ASL have recently also delivered a number of smaller high speed catamarans to UK operators.

Cammell Laird (part of the VSEL Group) have

Artists impression of a 104 metre 750 tonne deadweight InCat passenger/vehicle catamaran.

a construction hall and other facilities capable of building and outfitting wavepiercing ferries over 100m in length and have the technical and commercial strengths and project management experience together with the capacity for dealing with multi-million pound projects.

COUGAR HOLDINGS LIMITED

Cougar Quay, School Lane, Hamble, Hampshire SO3 5JD, England

Telephone: (0703) 453513
Telex: 477229COUGAR G
Telefax: (0703) 454594

C D Curtis, *Chairman*
N E Toleman, *Director*
P Foster, *Director*
A S Hawkridge, *Director*
J P Sutcliffe, *Director*
G P Wilson, *Director*

Group Companies: Cougar Marine Ltd; Altech Marine Ltd, Hamble, UK; Asiacraft Inc, Manila, Philippines; Cougar Italia Srl, Viareggio, Italy
Cougar Holdings is part of the Toleman Group of companies.

Founded in 1969 Cougar pioneered the development of the catamaran hull form in circuit racing power boats before moving into offshore competitions and more recently high performance production and commercial boat building. The company was absorbed into the Toleman Group of companies in 1980 and builds mono-hull and catamaran craft up to 35 metres in wood, grp, Kevlar, carbon composites and aluminium alloy. Cougar's grp laminating plant is Lloyds approved. Craft can be built to Lloyds and similar authorities' classifications.

PEGASUS

Fast luxury motor yacht.
HULL AND SUPERSTRUCTURE BUILDERS: Cougar Holdings Ltd.
FIT OUT: Commercial Marine Resources Inc, 19591 Bay F, North East 10th Avenue, North Miami, Florida 33179, USA
Commercial Marine Resources commissioned Cougar to design and build a pleasure yacht capable of achieving speeds in excess of 100 knots. A catamaran hull form was chosen and research on the most suitable construction laminates was carried out by Structural Polymer Systems Ltd, Cowes, Isle of Wight, England. It is claimed that the laminates used in the hull and superstructure

Pegasus

Pegasus prior to shipment to USA

of the *Pegasus* have produced a saving of 3 tons compared with building in Kevlar Aromat/grp and 8 tons compared with a grp structure. Sea trials were planned for mid-1987.

HULL: Superstructure and hull constructed in epoxy-bonded Kevlar carbon composites, with carbon-fibre glass stiffening.

ENGINES: Two Avco Lycoming TF25 marine gas turbines, 2500shp each, at 15100rpm. Two Perkins marine diesel engines for close manoeuvring.

PROPULSION: Two ASD 14 Arneson Surface Drives, with variable trim capability, coupled to specially designed Record surface-piercing titanium propellers. Separate shafts and propellers are fitted to the Perkins manoeuvring diesels.

CONTROLS: Power steering equipment.

CAPACITY

Fuel capacity: 9463 litres

ACCOMMODATION: Spacious master stateroom aft with heads, deck level saloon forward with two berths and galley. The wheelhouse and saloon forward are enclosed but fitted with a large sliding roof to take advantage of the sun. The large amount of deck area provides sunbathing space.

SYSTEMS

Auxiliary machinery: Auxiliary diesels fitted to provide electric power, compressed air and produce hydraulic power for bar thrusters

Air-conditioning: Fitted throughout

DIMENSIONS

Length overall: 17.37m

Virgin Atlantic Challenger

Length, waterline: 13.26m
Beam, max: 4.57m
Draught, max: 1.22m
WEIGHT
Displacement, max: 18 144kg

PERFORMANCE
Speed, max: 113 knots
Fuel consumption: 1745 litres/h
Range at 112 knots: 600n miles

FBM MARINE LTD
Cowes Shipyard, Cowes,
Isle of Wight, England
Telephone: (0983) 297111
Telex: 86466FAMBRO G
Telefax: (09830 299642

Jack Barr, *Managing Director*
John Warbey, *Sales Director*
Gordon Dodd, *Manufacturing Director*
Ian Campbell, *Regional Manager*
David Codd, *Commercial Manager*
Mike McSorley, *Marketing Manager*

Patrick Methold, *Regional Manager*
Robert Milner, *Regional Manager*
Nigel Warren, *Chief Designer*

FAST DISPLACEMENT CATAMARAN (FDC 400)

This 36.4m vessel is in the form of a small-waterplane-area twin-hull configuration and details are therefore given in the SWATH section.

RTL HYDROCAT (DESIGN)

Details of this minimum wash high-speed catamaran ferry design are given in the 1989 edition of Jane's High-Speed Marine Craft and Air Cushion Vehicles.

31.5 METRE CATAMARAN (SOLENT CLASS)

In November 1989 FBM Marine Limited announced the signing of a contract with Red Funnel Ferries of Southampton for the building of two 31.5 metre, 120-seat, 32.5 knot catamaran ferries.

CLASSIFICATION

DnV + 1A1, R15, EO and UK Dept of Transport Class IV for Solent use only.

Artists impression of FBM Marine Solent Class catamaran ferry for Red Funnel Ferries

PRINCIPAL PARTICULARS

Hull: marine grade aluminium, BS 1470 N8 plate, H30 TF extrusions
Length, overall: 31.5m
Beam: 8.4m
Length/beam ratio of hulls: 12
Draught, full load: approximately 1.1m
Saloon deck height above water, loaded: 1.85m
Accommodation: 120 passengers
Speed, cruise, 70% MCR, full load: 32.5 knots
Speed, cruise, 100% MCR: 35.5 knots
Speed variation with weight: 0.25 knots/tonne
Engines: Two MTU 12V 396 TE 84, 1360kW each, 1940 rpm
Propulsion: Two MJP 650 water-jet units, driven via ZF gearboxes
Fuel consumption: 210 g/kWh; 525 l/h at 32.5/knots
Fuel capacity: 1600 l (95% full)
Deadweight breakdown example:
   120 passengers: 9.0 tonnes
   baggage: 1.8 tonnes
   payload:10.8 tonnes
   fuel: 1.36 tonnes
   water: 0.25 tonnes
   supplies: 0.25 tonnes
   crew (3): 0.225 tonnes
   deadweight 12.885 tonnes

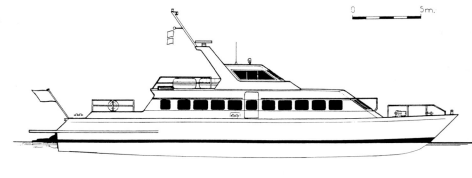

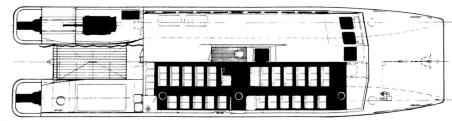

General arrangement of FBM Marine Solent Class catamaran ferry

In January 1990 FBM Marine Ltd announced that the company had been appointed licensed builders of the designs of a new Australian design team, Advanced Multi-Hull Designs of Pymble, New South Wales.

ILANFORM LTD

The Wool Hall, 12 St Thomas Street, Bristol BS1 6JJ, England

Telephone: (0272) 277510
Telex: 437287 SHARET G
Telefax: (0272) 260221

Nigel Irens, *Managing Director*

ILAN VOYAGER

The *Ilan Voyager*, is a manned test and demonstration craft designed to show in practical terms the advantages of the concept. Having particularly good stability for its size, the *Ilan Voyager* is an attractive vessel for small payload operations (up to a tonne) in rough seas. Scaled up to larger sizes the transport efficiency of the concept increases substantially as a result of the extremely high length-to-beam-ratio displacement configuration.

An interesting feature of the craft is the provision of a bow and stern thruster installation to assist manouverability.

In May 1989 *Ilan Voyager* successfully completed a Round Great Britain record-winning non-stop voyage without refuelling.

The *Ilan Voyager* concept conceived by Mark Pridie and Nigel Irens and launched in May 1988 maybe described as a high-speed displacement vessel of unusually high length-to-beam ratio and stabilised in roll by outrigger-mounted floats or secondary hulls. Of the well defined types of high-speed vessel now operating, the *Ilan Voyager* comes firmly in the category of displacement vessel. The very high length-to-beam ratio (23.3:1.0) represents a significant departure from the worlds displacement vessels. Normally such high length-to-beam ratios have not been used because of insufficient roll stability, insufficient volume for machinery and payload and a strong tendency amongst naval architects to follow proven practise.

The object of the concept is to achieve a fast vessel that will respond with the minimum of motion and accelerations to waves.

PRINCIPAL PARTICULARS

DIMENSIONS

Length, overall: 21.3m
Length, waterline: 21.2m

Ilan Voyager at speed

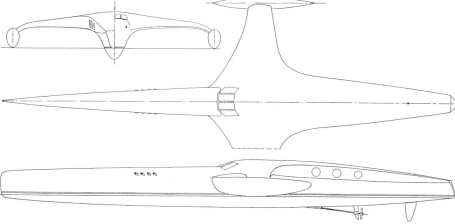

ILAN PROJECT — 21m. PROOF OF CONCEPT VESSEL

General arrangement of *Ilan Voyager*

Beam, overall: 10m
Draught (rudder): 1.1m
Displacement: 4.5 tonnes
HULL
Underwater body and foredeck: Strip planked cedar/epoxy/glass
Superstructure: AIREX PVC foam/glass epoxy sandwich
Crossbeam: Spruce booms with TAAL Plywood shearwebs
Bulkheads: TAAL plywood/epoxy/glass
ENGINES
Main engine: IVECO 8361 SEM 10 186.4kW (250hp) turbo-charged and intercooled diesel
Bow and stern thruster: IVECO M40 30kW (40hp) diesel driving water jet
Fuel: 800 l (using fixed tank only)
ACCOMMODATION
Pilot house: 4 seats
Main cockpit: 8 seats
Aft cockpit: 2 seats
Aft accommodation: 6 seats, galley
Comfortable total capacity: 8–10 persons
PERFORMANCE
Max speed: 27.5 knots
Economic cruising speed: 22–24 knots
RANGE
@ 15 knots: 700 n miles
@ 20 knots: 600 n miles
@ 25 knots: 500 n miles

Ilan Voyager

UNITED STATES OF AMERICA

ALLEN MARINE, INC
Sitka, Alaska, USA.

ALASKAN DREAM
Built in five months in 1988 for transport of miners to an island off Juneau, Alaska.

PRINCIPAL PARTICULARS
Length: 30.00m
Displacement, max: 72 tonnes
Engines: Four Caterpillar 3412 560 kW (750hp) at 2100 rpm

Propulsion: Four Hamilton 422 water-jet units, driven via a pneumatic clutch
Accommodation: 150 passengers
Crew: 3
Speed: 33 knots

ATLANTIC AND GULF BOAT BUILDING INC
It is understood that this company is no longer trading.

ATLANTIC MARINE, INC.
3500 Heckscher Drive, Jacksonville, Florida 32226, USA.

Telephone: (904) 251 3111
Telefax: (904) 251 3500

George W. Gibbs III, *Chairman of the Board*
Edward P. Doherty, *President*
Donald R. Moore, *Sales Manager*

Licensed in 1987 for the building of FBM Marine vessels.

COMMERCIAL MARINE RESOURCES INC
9591 Bay F, North East 10th Avenue, North Miami, Florida 33179, USA

Telephone: (305) 944 9144
Telex: 856276 CMR MIA

Michel J Meynard, *President*
Robert A Idoni, *General Manager*
W Harold Smith, *Project Co-ordinator*

PEGASUS
Commercial Marine Resources Inc were responsible for the above waterline design of this

craft as well as the total fit out of the vessel. The hull and superstructure have been built by Cougar Marine Ltd, UK, to plastics design and specification carried out by Structural Polymer Systems Ltd, UK. Please see Cougar Marine entry for details of this craft.

GLADDING-HEARN SHIPBUILDING

The Duclos Corporation

PO Box 300-W, One Riverside Avenue, Somerset, Massachusetts 02726–0300, USA

Telephone: (508) 676 8596
Telefax: (508) 672 1873

George R Duclos, *President*

24-METRE In Cat
MACKINAC EXPRESS
ISLAND EXPRESS
Two InCat catamaran ferries built for the Arnold Transit Co for service from Upper and Lower Peninsulas of Michigan to the resort island in the Mackinac Straits. The vessels are powered by two MWM TBD 604B V8 diesel engines.
DIMENSIONS
Length overall: 25.17m
Length, waterline: 21.50m
Beam, moulded: 8.70m
Beam of each hull: 2.50m

Draught, at design waterline: 2.10m
SEATING
Mackinac Express: 365
Island Express: 300
PERFORMANCE
Speed, cruise, full load: 31 knots

25.17 METRE InCat
VINEYARD SPRAY
Delivered September 1988 for service with Bay State Provincetown Cruises, Boston
DIMENSIONS
Length, overall; 25.17 m

Length, waterline: 21.51m
Beam, moulded: 8.70m
Beam of hulls: 2.50m
Draught, design load waterline: 2.10m
ENGINES: Two MWM 1290kW (1730hp) diesels
AUXILIARY POWER: Two 35kW Lister generators
FUEL CAPACITY: 3974 l
SPEED: 31 knots with 300 passengers

28.20 METRE InCat
JET EXPRESS

Delivered May 1989 for service with Put-in-Bay Boat Line Co, Put-in-Bay, Ohio.
PRINCIPAL PARTICULARS
Length: 28.20m
Beam: 8.69m
Draught: 1.10m
Propulsion: KaMeWa water-jet units

Craft built (InCat) or on order		Delivered	Seats	Operator
24m	InCat *Makinac Express*	1987	365	Arnold Transit Co.
24m	InCat *Island Express*	1988	300	Arnold Transit Co.
25.17m	InCat *Vineyard Spray*	September 1988	380	Bay State Cruises
25.17m	InCat *TNT Express I*	February 1989	260	TNT Hydrolines, Inc.
28.20m	InCat *Jet Express*	May 1989	380	Put-in-Bay Boat Line Co.
28.20m	InCat	1990	—	Put-in-Bay Boat Line Co.
—	InCat *Audubon Express*	1990	360	New Orleans Steamboat Co.

Licensed builder of International Catamarans Designs Pty Ltd Australia

Vineyard Spray

Jet Express

Wheelhouse controls and instruments of Gladding Hearn InCat *Jet Express*

Main deck and seating of Gladding Hearn InCat *TNT Express I*

GULF CRAFT INC

RR1 Box 395, Patterson, Louisiana 70392, USA

Telephone: (504) 395 5254/6259

R Scott Tibbs, *President*

In 1988 Gulf Craft, Inc and MXA Consulting Ltd of Finland announced an agreement for the building of MXA catamaran designs in the USA.

NATHAN I DANIEL
[PATENT HOLDER AND DEVELOPER]
948 Kailiu Place, Honolulu, Hawaii 96825, USA

Telephone: (808) 395 7373

Nathan I Daniel, *Inventor*
Howard E Daniel

SUPEROUTRIGGER

The essence of the SuperOutrigger invention is the provision of a craft with 'extended dimensions' in effective beam and length, aimed at permitting comfortable and economical operation in much rougher seas than possible with any current craft types. The efficiency of its long, thin main hull provides a substantial economic advantage over current fast craft, especially when viewed in conjunction with the SuperOutrigger's projected excellent seakeeping ability. The SuperOutrigger is aimed at combining comfortable motion, minimal speed loss in waves, good economics, simplicity and very shallow draught. There is no other craft type, mono-hull, catamaran, hydrofoil, hovercraft or SWATH, that appears to offer this combination of vital characteristics.

Following the principle of the outrigger canoe, the buoyancy of the craft is obtained from a single long thin main hull, which supports the entire payload. The cabin (or deck) is centred atop an extremely strong, light and faired triangular truss structure, which carries it high above the low-freeboard main hull, well clear of wave crests. A similarly shaped but considerably smaller outrigger hull provides stability. The outrigger hull's relatively small size (about 20% of the volume of the main hull) makes it practical to place it far to the side of the main hull, permitting overall beam dimensions several times greater than those of catamarans. As a result, the SuperOutrigger's stability against roll is greater than that of corresponding catamaran craft. It is envisaged that whereas the main hull would be two-thirds submerged in normal full-load operating conditions, the stabilising outrigger hull would be only 50% submerged, so that the effects of beam seas would be balanced, ie, would not be initially biased toward either lifting or submerging the outrigger.

Preliminary investigations in the 20- to 30-knot speed range indicate that the SuperOutrigger's power requirements, in relation to its revenue-earning work capacity, will generally be less than those for current competitive craft types. In simple terms it can be seen that replacing the two hulls of a catamaran by a single hull of the same cross-section and twice the length will cut wave drag approximately in half. In addition, frictional resistance will also decrease about 10% because of the favourable effects of increasing hull length. These very significant reductions mean that the resistance of the much smaller outrigger hull will be more than offset, while at the same time making possible a craft of much greater effective length and beam, with greatly enhanced stability.

17.68m demonstration model of the SuperOutrigger concept with Nathan I Daniel, inventor, at the controls in Honolulu harbour

This increase in stability is obtained without recourse to either a deep draught configuration or autostabilisation systems. What has become the normally accepted limitation on size for ferry craft results from the matching of the product of speed and payload to the traffic on particular routes. This almost invariably results in craft which are too small for the higher sea states in which they are to operate. The SuperOutrigger alleviates this size problem, securing the benefits of the long, slender hull in low resistance, reduced motions and minimal speed loss in waves while avoiding the lack of roll stability and insufficient payload capacity that have prevented its use in mono-hull development.

The need to provide fast, economical and sea-kindly ferry service across Hawaii's rough inter-island channels was the stimulus for the Super-Outrigger invention. Widely patented by Nathan I Daniel, the concept was first tested in simple model form in 1979 to establish basic resistance and stability characteristics in the open sea. Ocean tests indicated that a 98m craft, with a roughly 30m span between the main and outrigger hulls, would neither pitch nor roll more than 5 degrees in low Sea State 6 (4m significant wave height). A 17.68m demonstration model was launched in 1986. Capable of carrying between 3600 and 4000kg on its open deck, or up to 50 passengers, this vessel has demonstrated in Hawaiian seas that the SuperOutrigger principle is extremely effective in reducing craft motions. Presentations to the press and other interested parties are continuing, and efforts are being actively pursued to find the funding needed to build and operate 90m,

35-knot, 300-passenger craft for the Honolulu-Maui and Honolulu-Kauai routes.

Aside from its wide potential application as a ferry, it is envisaged that SuperOutriggers could also be employed as helicopter carriers, coastal patrol/search and rescue craft, crew/work boats, fishing boats and pleasure craft. The benefits are expanded upon by Nathan I Daniel in the following text.

SuperOutrigger helicopter carriers, on coastal patrol or search and rescue duty, could head quickly toward a distress call while permitting the helicopters based onboard to stay out longer, cover a wider area and/or carry increasingly heavy loads as the vessel approached its objective.

SuperOutrigger crew/work boats, faster, smoother-riding and more efficient than mono-hulls, could take over many tasks presently performed at much greater cost by helicopters.

SuperOutrigger fishing boats could get to and from fishing grounds more quickly and cheaply than other craft, resulting in lower operating costs while also beating competing vessels in delivering the catch to market. Additionally, the Super-Outrigger's smooth ride could boost crew productivity by preventing the motion-induced fatigue fishermen generally experience on conventional craft.

SuperOutrigger pleasure craft would combine the speed of conventional motorboats with the comfort and deck-room of larger, slower, costlier and more sedate vessels. The SuperOutrigger's displacement hull would not be subject to the pounding generally experienced by conventional motorboats, which rely on planing hulls for speed.

NICHOLS BROTHERS BOAT BUILDERS INC

5400 S Cameron Road, Freeland, Whidbey Island, Washington 98249, USA

Telephone: (206) 321 5500
Telefax: (206) 221 7484
Matt Nichols, *President*

Licensed builder of International Catamaran Designs Pty Ltd, Australia

22-METRE In Cat
KLONDIKE

Christened 13 June 1984 at Langley, Washington. Vessel is fitted with a bow loading structure.
ENGINES: Two Caterpillar 3412 TA diesels, 700hp each.
GEARBOXES: Niigata MGN-80.
PROPELLERS: Coolidge 5-blade.
GENERATORS: Northern Lights 40kW.
RUDDERS: Curved dipping InCat type.

DIMENSIONS
Length: 21.98m
Beam: 8.69m
Depth: 2.46m
CAPACITIES
Fuel tank capacity: 1000 US gallons
Water tank capacity: 1000 US gallons
PERFORMANCE
Seats: 210
Speed: 26 knots

Craft built (In Cat)	Delivered	Seats	Operator	Owner
22m In Cat *Klondike*	June 1984	210	Yukon River Cruises, Inc	Brad Phillips
22m In Cat *Spirit of Alderbrook*	August 1984	240	Wes Johnson, Seattle Harbor Tours	
26m In Cat *Catamarin*	May 1985	400	Red and White Fleet	Crowley Maritime Corp
26m In Cat *Gold Rush*	September 1985	400	Glacier Bat Yacht Tours	Robert Giersdorf
26m In Cat *Victoria Clipper 2* (ex *Glacier Express* & *Baja Express*)	1989 January 1986	245*	Clipper Navigation Inc	
26m In Cat *Dolphin*	August 1986	400	Red and White Fleet	Crowley Maritime Corp
30m In Cat *Executive Explorer*	June 1986	49 passengers in 25 staterooms	Glacier Bay Yachts Tours, Inc Catamaran Cruise Lines, Hawaii	
23m In Cat *Jera FB-816*	April 1988	232	US Army	US Army
36m In Cat *Catalina Flyer*	May 1988	500	California Cruisin'	Catalina Passenger Service
23m In Cat *Jelang K FB-817*	October 1988	232	US Army	US Army
37m InCat (WPC) *Nantucket Spray*	Spring 1989	400	Bay State Cruises	Bay State Cruises
22m In Cat *Martin Peña*	August 1989	167	Port of Puerto Rico	—
22m In Cat *Amelia*	November 1989	167	Port of Puerto Rico	—
22m In Cat *Covadonga*	December 1989	167	Port of Puerto Rico	—
22m In Cat *San Geronimo*	March 1989	167	Port of Puerto Rico	—
22m In Cat *Viejo San Juan*	May 1989	167	Port of Puerto Rico	—
22m In Cat *Cristobal Colón*	June 1989	167	Port of Puerto Rico	—

*400 total with outside seating

SPIRIT OF ALDERBROOK

Main dimensions as for *Klondike*.
ENGINES: Two Detroit Diesel 12V-92 TA, 800bhp each.
GEARBOXES: Niigata MGN-80.
PROPELLERS: Coolidge 5-blade.
GENERATORS: Northern Lights 30kW.

26-METRE In Cat
CATAMARIN
GOLD RUSH
VICTORIA CLIPPER 2 (ex GLACIER EXPRESS, ex BAJA EXPRESS)

ENGINES: Two Deutz BAM 16M 816C diesels, each 1346hp continuous at 1800rpm.
GEARBOXES: Reintjes WVS 832, ratio 1:2.29.
GENERATORS: Two John Deere 4275 engines and Northern Lights 50kW generators. *Glacier Express* has Pacific Diesel units.

The 400 passenger, 26m *Dolphin*

PROPELLERS: Coolidge 5-blade, 1.169m × 1.194m.

SYSTEMS
Steering: Wagner Engineering

The 500-seat, 27 knot *Catalina Flyer*

Sound and entertainment system: Harris Electric
Heating, air-conditioning: Peter Kalby Company,
    Seattle
DIMENSIONS
Length: 26.14m
Beam: 9.45m
Depth: 2.77m
Draught (full load): 2.39m
CAPACITIES
Fuel tank capacity: 20440l
Water tank capacity: 18931 *Catamarin*,
    1515l *Gold Rush, Express*
PERFORMANCE
Speed: 28 knots

36 METRE In Cat
CATALINA FLYER

The largest capacity high-speed catamaran to
be built in the United States, the 500 seat *Catalina
Flyer* (delivered May 1988) is in service between
Newport Harbor and Catalina Island in Southern
California with Catalina Passenger Service.
DIMENSIONS
Length: 36.00m
Beam: 12.20m
Draught: 2.44m
ENGINES: Two Caterpillar 3516 TA, 2000hp
    each, specially lightened diesels
GEARBOXES: Two Reintjes WS-1023, 2.538:1.0
PROPELLERS: Three-blade CuNiAl Bronze,
    1.30m diameter
SYSTEMS: Steering, Hough Marine, Seattle;
    auxiliary power, John Deere diesels, 40kW each
NAVIGATION/COMMUNICATIONS: Ross
    DR 600D flasher, two ICOM VHF radios,
    Furuno 1510D and 8030D radars, Sperry 8T
    Auto Pilot, Furuno LC-90 Loran.
AUXILIARY POWER: John Deere, two 40kW
    units
CAPACITIES
Fuel: 11355l
Fresh water: 1514l
PERFORMANCE
Speed, cruising: 27 knots
Speed, max: 30 knots

30-METRE In Cat
EXECUTIVE EXPLORER

A 31.70m cruising catamaran, built 1986 for
Alaskan and Hawaiian islands cruising.
PRINCIPAL PARTICULARS
Length, overall: 30.03m
Length, with extensions: 31.70m

Bow loading ramp operation of *Executive Explorer*

Executive Explorer built by Nichols Brothers

The 37m InCat Wave-Piercing catamaran *Nantucket Spray* built by Nichols Brothers

Beam: 11.20m
Draught, design water line: 2.51m
Speed: 22 knots
Passengers: 49
Crew: 20
Fuel (including long range tanks): 63588l
Fresh water: 19682l
Lube oil: 227l
Sewage tank: 2270l
Engines: Two Deutz BAM 816, 1004kW continuous, each, at 1800rpm
Gearboxes: Reintjes 842, 2.96:1.0
Propellers: ISO class 1, 5-blade, Nicel 1.346mx1.422m Columbia Bronze
Auxiliary power: 120kW, PDC 120 MB Mercedes-Benz W/OM-421
GRT 98

38.6 METRE InCat WPC
NANTUCKET SPRAY
This US$4 million vessel was ordered in June 1988 for service on the Californian coast but instead entered service with Bay State Cruises, Boston for service between Boston and Nantucket
CLASSIFICATION: USCG, SOLAS.

DIMENSIONS
Length, overall: 38.60m
Beam, excluding fenders: 15.60m
Beam of hulls: 2.60m
Draught: 1.30m
ENGINES: Two MWM TBD 604 V16 1768kW (2371hp) each, at 1800 rpm
PROPULSION: Two KaMeWa 63 S62/6 water-jet units
AUXILIARY POWER: Two John Deere; 55kW generators
CAPACITIES
Fuel: Two 14130 l tanks
Fresh water: 7570 l
ACCOMMODATION
Main deck: 198 seats
Wheelhouse deck: 94 seats
Flybridge deck: 75 seats
Total: 367
PERFORMANCE
Speed, cruise: 32 knots
Speed, max: 36.4 knots

22m InCat
A US $8 million order for six 167 seat vessels was placed with Nichols Bros in October 1988 by

the Port of Puerto Rico. These catamarans will be used on a 5 mile route between old San Juan and the newer metropolitan area of Puerto Rico major city.
ENGINES: Two DDC GM 12 V71, 465hp each at 1800rpm

JERA FB-816
JELANG K FB-817
Two 23.17m InCat catamarans built in 1988 for ferry service at the US Army's missile test range in the Marshall Islands. *Jera* was christened at Nichols Brothers Boat yard on 9 April 1988 and *Jelang K* on 7 October 1988.
ENGINES: Two DDC GM 16 V92 TA, 960hp each
GEARBOXES: Two ZF BW 250, 2.03:1.0 ratio
PROPELLERS: Five-blade Osborne bronze propellers, 940mm × 927mm.
SYSTEMS: Steering, Hough Marine, Seattle; starters, Klockner-Mueller. Electric power: two 50kW Northern Lights generators, John Deere 4276 engines. Air conditioning: Celcius Marine, Inc.
NAVIGATION/COMMUNICATIONS: Data Marine LX201 fathometer, Standard Com-

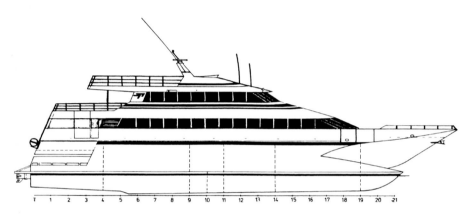

PROFILE

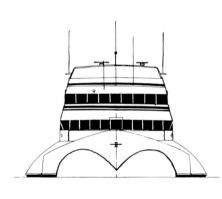

BOW VIEW

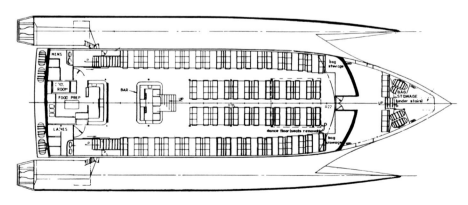

MAIN DECK
SEATS 198

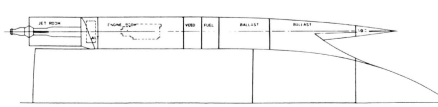

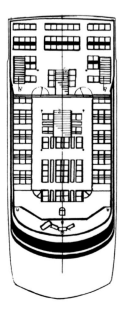

WHEELHOUSE DECK
SEATS 94

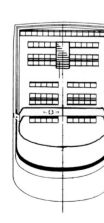

FLYBRIDGE DECK
SEATS 75

General arrangement of the 37m InCat Wave-Piercing catamaran *Nantucket Spray*

munications VHF radio, Furuno FCR 1411/6
radar, Furuno 803D radar, Data Marine LX50
speed log

DIMENSIONS
Length, overall: 23.17m *Jera*; 21.95m *Jelang K*
Beam: 8.94m *Jera*; 8.69m *Jelang K*
Draught: 1.80m

ACCOMMODATION
Seats for 232 passengers

CAPACITIES
Fuel oil: 5300 l *Jera*; 4164 l *Jelang K*
Fresh water: 946 l

PERFORMANCE
Speed: 31 knots

InCat *Jera*

InCat *Jelang K*

SMALL-WATERPLANE-AREA TWIN-HULL (SWATH) VESSELS (SEMI-SUBMERGED CATAMARANS(SSC))

AUSTRALIA

SEA MANAGEMENT CORPORATION PTY LTD
PO Box 1171, Southport, Queensland 4215, Australia

Telephone: (075) 46 2260
Telefax: (075) 46 1318

This company with shipbuilding facilities both in Caboolture, Queensland and Launceston, Tasmania has obtained a license for the sole Australian, New Zealand and South West Pacific building and marketing rights for Navatek SWATH vessel designs. Please see Navatek Ship Ltd for details of these vessels.

CANADA

EYRETECHNICS LIMITED
[CONSULTANTS/MARINE ENGINEERS]
Atlantic Region, Suite 207, 11 Morris Drive, Dartmouth, Nova Scotia B3B 1M2, Canada

Telephone: (902) 469 3372
Telefax: (902) 465 6746

Arnold P Eyre, *Chairman*
W Edwards, *Vice President*

SWATH CPV (DESIGN)

Eyretechnics have developed a design for a SWATH coastal patrol vessel for use in search and rescue, fisheries patrol, defence surveillance, MCM and other related missions in rough seas such as those that exist off the east and west coasts of Canada.

This 360-tonne all-aluminium vessel is arranged to facilitate handling and treatment of survivors by providing dedicated rescue zones, recessed into the port and starboard sides of the upper hulls. At each zone 15 square metres of deck space is provided leading to a triage area and treatment room amidships. Within the accommodation, seating and bunks are provided for up to 25 survivors. A helicopter landing pad is designed to enable landing and take-off of a Jet Ranger helicopter in up to Sea State 5 conditions. For ship external firefighting two monitors are located between the funnels with a capacity of 50% Hi-Fil.

The vessel will be driven at 15 knots in Sea State 5 head seas by two medium speed diesels developing a total of 3600hp. The main engines are located within the main-deck structure with a

SWATH CPV design by Eyretechnics Limited

mechanical transfer of drive to controllable-pitch propellers.

Accommodation, all above main deck level, provides for mixed male and female 14 person crew with officers forward and ratings aft. Stores, fuel and water requirements are designed for 15 days endurance at economical speed.

The design minimises development risks by employing standard, proven systems technology. The vessel will be built to Transport Canada regulations and classed with an international classification society.

DIMENSIONS
Length overall: 34.60m
Max beam: 15.50m
Draught (full load): 3.50m
WEIGHT
Displacement (full load): 360 tonnes
PERFORMANCE
Speed in Sea State 5: 15 knots

JAPAN

MITSUBISHI HEAVY INDUSTRIES

5–1, Marunouchi 2-chome, Chiyoda-ku, Tokyo, Japan

OHTORI

Built at the Kobe Shipyard and Engine Works of Mitsubishi Heavy Industries Ltd, the *Ohtori* was delivered to her owner, the Third District Port Construction Bureau in the Japanese Ministry of Transport on 25 March 1981. She was the first semi-submerged catamaran to be put into service.

Intended for surveying water and seabed conditions as part of a programme to purify the Seto Inland Sea, the vessel is equipped for the collection and analysis of seabed and water samples, the exploration of seabeds and the observation of sea and weather conditions.

PROPULSION: Two 1900hp diesels, 1475rpm, driving controllable-pitch propellers.

GENERATOR: 130kVA, 225V, 60Hz.

EQUIPMENT: Surveying crane, 0.99 tonne, 6.0m radius, two davits for surveying, box coner, piston coner, multi-cylinder sampler; water survey equipment (CSTD monitor, auto-analyser, turbidity meter); bottom survey equipment (ORP meter); depth and mud survey sounder (transducers); position-finding equipment (microwave position finder, Loran C receiver); data processor.

Ohtori, sea condition survey vessel

DIMENSIONS
Length overall: 27.00m
Length bp: 24.00m
Breadth (upper deck) moulded: 12.50m
Depth, moulded: 5.10m

Draught, full load, moulded: 3.40m
GRT: 251.49
PERFORMANCE
Speed, max: 20.61 knots
Complement: 20

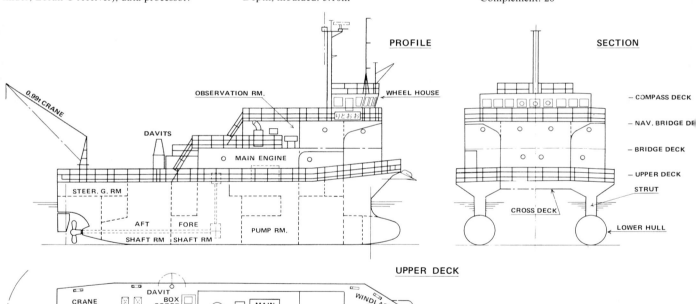

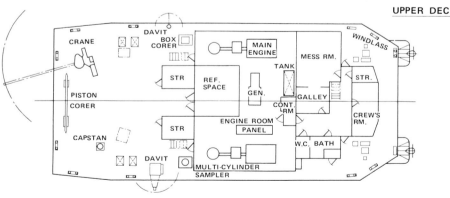

General arrangement of *Ohtori*

MITSUI ENGINEERING & SHIPBUILDING CO LTD

6–4, Tsukiji 5-chome, Chuo-ku, Tokyo 104, Japan

Telephone: (03) 544–3462
Telex: 22821/22924 MITUIZOSEN J

Kazuo Maeda, *Chairman*

Yasunosuke Ishii, *President*
Jiro Hoshino, *Executive Managing Director*
Mikihisa Komoto, *Deputy Director, General Manager, Marine Division*
Yutaka Ikeda, *General Manager, Advanced Craft Sales Dept*

Mitsui began its high-speed semi-submerged

catamaran (SSC) development programme i 1970. Since 1976, the programme has been operated in conjunction with the Japanese Marin Machinery Development Association (JAMDA In 1977 Mitsui built the experimental 18.37-tonn *Marine Ace* in order to obtain practical experienc with this hull form. In 1979 the first SSC high speed passenger vessel was launched under th

rovisional name *Mesa 80*. After extensive trials
. was completed in 1981 and renamed *Seagull*. It
as since been operated by Tokai Kisen Co Ltd
n a passenger ferry service between Atami and
)shima island. It was only the second such vessel
) be built, the first being the US Navy's SSP
aimalino range support vessel, designed to
perate in the rough seas off the Hawaiian islands.

The company has also developed and built a
SC hydrographic survey vessel, *Kotozaki*, for the
ourth District Port Construction Bureau of the
apanese Ministry of Transport. This vessel was
ompleted in 1981.

Additionally, a support vessel for underwater
xperiments, the 61.55-metre *Kaiyo* was com-
leted in 1985. This is a highly advanced semi-
ubmerged catamaran and the largest of such
essels in the world. It is not a high-speed vessel
aving a speed of 13.25 knots.

Semi-submerged catamarans can be built to suit
wide variety of applications from passenger
erries to offshore rig-support vessels.

As can be seen from the technical assistance
ontract concluded in 1985 by Mitsui with
ockheed Marine Systems Group shipyard for the
nanufacture and marketing of SSCs, continued
fforts are being made by Mitsui in opening over-
eas markets for this highly advanced shipbuilding
echnology.

MARINE ACE

Mitsui's first experimental SSC, *Marine Ace*, is
uilt in marine-grade aluminium alloy and can
perate in Sea States 2 to 3. Its automatically-
ontrolled fin stabilisers reduce ship motion in
/aves.

PROPULSION: Motive power for *Marine Ace* is
upplied by two sets of V-type four-cycle petrol
ngines, each developing 200bhp at 3700rpm.
ach drives, via a vertical intermediate trans-
nission shaft and bevel gear, a three-bladed fixed-
itch propeller; one at the end of each of the two
orpedo-like hulls.

TANK CAPACITIES
Ballast: 11.01m³ (2420 gallons)
Fuel oil: 1.45m³ (320 gallons)
AUTOMATIC MOTION CONTROL
SYSTEM: Four sets of fin stabilisers, driven by
ydraulic servo motors, reduce ship motion in
eavy seas.
DIMENSIONS
Length overall: 12.35m
registered: 11.95m
Beam max: 6.5m
at load line: 5.8m
Designed full load draught: 1.55m
GRT: 29.91*
WEIGHTS*
Full load displacement: 18.37 tonnes*
PERFORMANCE
Speed, max cruising revolutions, full load
draught: about 18 knots
*after modification in 1978

SEAGULL

Developed jointly by Mitsui Engineering &
Shipbuilding Co Ltd and the Japanese Marine
Machinery Development Association (JAMDA),
he 27-knot *Seagull* is the world's first commercial
emi-submerged catamaran. *Seagull* is in service
vith Tokai Kisen on routes linking Tokyo,
)shima island, Atami and Nii-jima island.
Despite its small size, the overall length is just
under 36m, the vessel provides a stable ride in seas
vith 3.5m waves.

During the first ten-month long commercial run
n a service between Atami and Oshima, *Seagull*
stablished an operating record of 97 per cent.
The incidence of seasick passengers was very low,
.5 per cent or less, proving the exceptional riding
omfort.
PROPULSION: Main engines are two Fuji-
SEMT marine diesels, each developing 4050hp

Craft built (SWATH)	Owner/operator	Delivered
Marine Ace 12.35m experimental SSC	Mitsui	October 1977
Seagull (ex *Mesa 80*) 35.90m ferry	Tokai Kisen Co Ltd	1979
Kotozaki 27.00m hydrographic survey	Japanese Ministry of Transport	March 1981
Kaiyo 61.55m underwater support vessel (low-speed)	Japan Marine Science and Technology Centre	May 1985
Marine Wave 15.10m pleasure cruiser	Toray Industries Inc	July 1985
Sun Marina 15.10m pleasure cruiser	San Marina Hotel	March 1987
Seagull 2	Tokai Kisen Co Ltd	December 1989

18.37-tonne *Marine Ace*, the first Mitsui SWATH, 1977

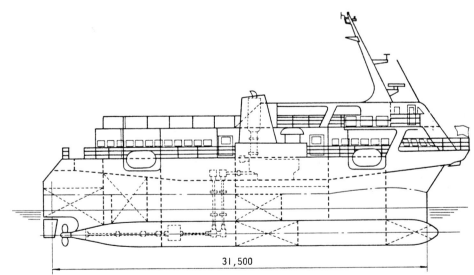

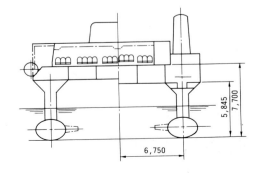

General arrangement of *Seagull*

max continuous at 1475rpm. Each drives, via a vertical transmission shaft and bevel gear, a four-blade fixed-pitch propeller. Two 206.25kVA generators provide electrical power.
HULL: Built in marine grade aluminium alloy.
ACCOMMODATION: Crew of seven. Passenger seats provided for 446.
AUTOMATIC MOTION CONTROL
SYSTEM: Four sets of fin stabilisers driven by hydraulic servo motors reduce ship motion in heavy seas.
DIMENSIONS
Length overall: 35.9m
Length, bp: 31.5m
Breadth, moulded: 17.1m
Depth, moulded: 5.84m
Designed draught: 3.15m
GRT: 672.08
PERFORMANCE
Max speed: about 27 knots

Seagull

KOTOZAKI

The world's first hydrographic survey vessel of the SSC type, *Kotozaki* is operated by the Fourth District Port Construction Bureau of the Japanese Ministry of Transport. It was delivered in March 1981.

Kotozaki provides a stable platform from which data can be gathered and its rectangular decks allow ample space for hydrographic equipment, laboratory facilities, working and living accommodation.
PROPULSION: Main engines are two Fuji-12 PA 4V 185 V6 marine diesels, each developing 1900hp at 1475rpm. Each drives, via a vertical transmission shaft and bevel gear, a controllable-pitch propeller type Kamome CPC-53F, diameter 1750mm, pitch 1400mm.
HULL: Steel catamaran hulls and aluminium alloy deck structure.
ACCOMMODATION: Complement of 20.
MOTION CONTROL SYSTEM: Controllable-pitch propellers and manually-operated fin stabilisers.
DIMENSIONS
Length overall: 27m
Length, bp: 25.0m
Beam: 12.5m
Depth: 4.6m
Designed draught: 3.2m
GRT: 253.67
PERFORMANCE
Max speed: about 20.5 knots

Kotozaki

KAIYO

The first SSC type support vessel for underwater experiments, *Kaiyo* was delivered to the Japan Marine Science and Technology Centre in May 1985. This vessel is not high-speed but is included here as it is one in the Mitsui series of SSC types and is the largest, most highly advanced semi-submerged catamaran vessel in the world.

The *Kaiyo* is fitted with a wide range of equipment including a deepsea diving system composing two submersible decompression chambers (SDC), a deck decompression chamber (DDC) and a dynamic positioning system (DPS).

The *Kaiyo* can function as an offshore testing base and is stable enough to maintain her position offshore for long periods. This stability characteristic facilitates research and development in the following areas: manned underwater work technology, deep ocean floor survey technology and new ocean monitoring systems, as well as preliminary research for manned subsea research vessels and group training and education on board.
HULL: High tensile steel for the main structure and mild steel for the superstructure.
ACCOMMODATION: Crew of 29, research personnel of 40 (limited to 50 persons on international voyages).
POWER PLANT: *Kaiyo* has a diesel-electric propulsion system.

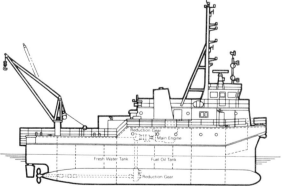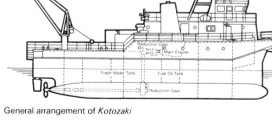
General arrangement of *Kotozaki*

Main generators: 1560kVA, 4 sets
Prime movers: High-speed marine diesel engines 1850hp, 4 sets
Main propulsive motors: 860kW, 4 sets
Propellers: Two 4-blade controllable-pitch
DIMENSIONS
Length overall: 61.55m
Breadth: 28.00m
Depth: 10.60m
Design full load draught: 6.30m
GRT: Approx 2800
PERFORMANCE
Cruising speed: Approx 13 knots
Endurance: 5100n miles

BAY QUEEN

Mitsui delivered one multi-purpose SSC (Semi-Submerged Catamaran) vessel *Bay Queen* in February 1989, and has since been awarded the contract for the construction of a high-speed SSC passenger vessel as a replacement for *Seagull*.

Bay Queen is the seventh SSC vessel built by Mitsui since 1977. She can carry a maximum of 40 passengers and has entered service for operation in inspection tours, sightseeing, crew transportation and many other purposes in Tokyo bay.

Bay Queen is the first and smallest commercialised SSC vessel in the world, made of aluminium, to a design based on the concept of

Marine Wave which was made of FRP.
ACCOMMODATION: Crew 4, luxury accommodation for 10 passenger plus 30 seats.
POWERPLANT: Two high-speed marine diesel Yanmar engine, 470hp each at 2000rpm.
TANKS
Fuel oil: 2400 litres
Fresh water: 1000 litres
GENERATOR: Yanmar 4JHL-TN diesel unit

SEAGULL 2

This higher speed SSC type passenger vessel was completed in the middle of December 1989. The new vessel is operated by Tokai Kisen Co. Ltd between Atami and Oshima as replacement of existing SSC passenger vessel *Seagull*.

Seagull proved the superior motion performance and established operating record of 97 per cent as well as seasickness ratio less than 1 per cent during the operating service time since 1981.

The new type SSC will attain more comfortable ride in sea state 5 and higher speed than *Seagull*.
ACCOMMODATION: Crew 7, two decks with 4 compartments for 410 passengers.
POWERPLANT: Four high-speed marine diesel MTU 16V396TB84 engines, 2000 kW each at 1940rpm.

SEA SALOON 15
MARINE WAVE

The first semi-submerged catamaran Sea Saloon 15 type cruiser *Marine Wave* built by MES for Toray Industries, Inc was delivered in July 1985.

Marine Wave, which is only about 15 metres in length, is relatively free from rolling and pitching by virtue of its SSC design which also allows a spacious deck to be provided and facilitates comfortable cruising. One of its most interesting features is the combination of its unusual shape with Toray's newly developed hull material incorporating carbon fibre composites. The Sea Saloon 15 has two sets of computer-controlled stabilising fins and two fixed fins.

Marine Wave is certificated by the Japan Craft

Mitsui *Kaiyo,* the largest SSC in the world

Seagull 2

General arrangement of Sea Saloon 15

Mitsui SSC high-tech cruiser Sea Saloon 15 type, *Marine Wave*, built in glass and carbon-reinforced plastic

Main particulars of the SSC vessels built by Mitsui

Ship name	Marine Ace	Seagull	Kotozaki	Kaiyo	Marine Wave	Sun Marina	Bay Queen	Seagull 2	Under const
Type	Experimental vessel	High-speed passenger ferry	Hydrographic survey vessel	Support vessel for underwater work experiments	Cabin type luxury boat	Saloon type luxury boat	Multi-purpose boat	High-speed passenger ferry	Party boat
Completion	1977	1979	1981	1985	1985	1987	Feb 1989	Dec 1989	Feb 1990
Length O.A. (m)	12.35	35.90	27.00	60.00	15.10	15.05	18.00	39.30	20.80
Length P.P (m)	11.00	31.50	25.00	53.00	11.95	11.925	15.90	33.17	15.90
Breadth (m)	6.50	17.10	12.50	28.00	6.20	6.40	6.80	1.6	6.80
Depth (m)	2.70	5.85	4.60	10.60	2.75	2.75	2.80	6.80	2.80
Draft (m)	1.55	3.15	3.20	6.30	1.60	1.60	1.60	3.25	1.60
GRT		670	250	2849	19	19	40	630	40
Payload/crew/passengers	20 personnel	402–446 passengers	approx 36 tons	—	17 personnel	33 personnel	40 personnel	410 passengers	40 passengers
Strut type	twin/single	single	single	single	single	single	single	single	single
Hull material	Al	Al	Steel/Al	Steel	FRP	FRP	Al	Al	Al
Max. speed (kts)	17.3	27.1	20.5	14.0	18.2	20.5	20	(30)	(17.5)
Main engine	two gasoline 200PS	two diesel 4050PS	two diesel 1900PS	four diesel/electric d/g 1250kW four motor 860kW	two diesel 275PS	two diesel 300PS	two diesel 470PS	four diesel 2680PS	Two diesel 370PS
Propeller	FPP	FPP	CPP	CPP	FPP	FPP	FPP	FPP	FPP
Fin control	automatic	automatic	manual	manual	automatic	automatic	automatic	automatic	automatic

Inspection Organisation for use in coastal waters. By August 1986 *Marine Wave* had operated over 860 hours including a voyage to West Japan in which she experienced waves up to 4.5m in height.
HULL: Glass reinforced plastic and carbon reinforced plastic.
ACCOMMODATION: Crew 2, luxury accommodation for 12 passengers plus 3 others.
POWERPLANT: Two high-speed marine diesel Ford Sabre 5950cc engines, 275hp each at 2500rpm, driving fixed-pitch propellers via Twin Disc MG 506 gearboxes, ratio 2.03:1.
TANKS
Fuel oil: 2000 litres
Fresh water: 300 litres
GENERATOR: Onan MDJJF-18R diesel unit.
DIMENSIONS
Length overall: 15.10m
Length, registered: 11.95m
Breadth, moulded: 6.20m
Depth, moulded: 2.74m
Draught, full load: 1.60m
GRT: 19
PERFORMANCE
Speed, max trial: about 18 knots
Speed, service: 16 knots
Endurance: about 20 hours

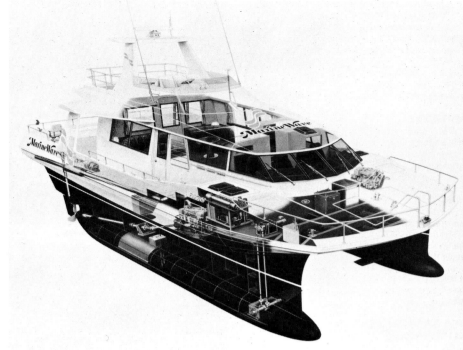

Sea Saloon 15 interior arrangements

Sun Marina

SUN MARINA
The second of Sea Saloon 15 series, *Sun Marina*

was built by Mitsui for San Marina Hotel, opened as a grand resort hotel in Okinawa in March 1987.
Sun Marina has a large luxurious party cabin which can accommodate 30 guests of the Hotel, and sails round many coral reefs from the privately owned marina of the Hotel.
ACCOMMODATION: Passengers 30; crew 3.
POWERPLANT: Two 230hp marine diesel.
TANKS
Fuel oil tank: Two 900 litres
Fresh water: 400 litres
GENERATOR: 15kW

DIMENSIONS
Length overall: 15.10m
Length registered: 11.925m
Breadth: 6.40m
Depth: 2.75m
Draught: 1.60m
WEIGHT
Gross tonnage: 19 tons
PERFORMANCE
Speed max: 20.5 knots
Speed service: 17 knots
Endurance: About 20 hours

KOREA, SOUTH

HYUNDAI HEAVY INDUSTRIES CO LTD
[SPECIAL AND NAVAL SHIPBUILDING DIVISION]
Head Office: Cheonha-Dong, Dong Gu, Ulsan, South Korea

Telephone: (0552) 32 1306/7/8
Telex: 53761/52220 HDYARD K
Telefax: (0552) 32 4007

Seoul office: 140–2, Kye-Dong, Jongro-ku, Seoul, South Korea

Telephone: 741 1142
Telex: 28361/27496 HDYARD K

H S Chae, *Vice President of Marketing and Business*
K H Jun, *Senior Manager, Special and Naval Shipbuilding Division*

27.1 METRE (DESIGN)
For several years Hyundai Heavy Industries have been investigating coastal passenger SWATH vessel designs, including ⅛th scale model testing. Among the variants investigated a 27.1 metre version was selected in keeping with the growing passenger accommodation requirements of the market.
PRINCIPAL PARTICULARS
Length, overall: 27.1m
Length, bp: 23.6m

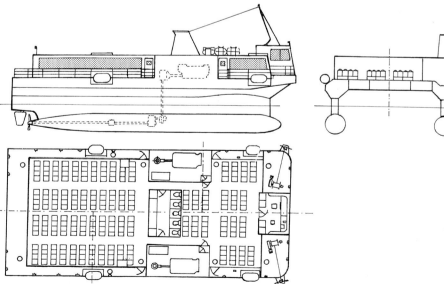

General arrangement of Hyundai 27.1m SWATH design

Beam, moulded: 12.4m
Depth, moulded: 5.3m
Lower hull length: 23.6m
Lower hull diameter: 1.8m
Lower hull length/diameter: 13.1m
Strut length: 24.6m
Strut thickness at WL: 0.75m
Distance between lower hull ℄: 10.4m

Draught, design, moulded: 2.6m approx.
Displacement, full load: approx. 132 tonnes
Engines: Two 1327kW at 1650 rpm (MCR)
Accommodation: 254 passengers
Speed: estimated as 25.3 knots at propeller rpm of 580 estimated as 24.7 knots at full load and MCR of 1327kW (1780hp)/engine

SINGAPORE

SINGAPORE SLIPWAY AND ENGINEERING CO. (PTE) LTD

No.1 Rhu Cross, Singapore 1543
a division of

Singmarine Industries Ltd

which is a division of

Keppel Corporation Ltd

Telephone: 3444698
Telefax: 3443761

W K Seng, *Executive Director*
C Y K Kuan, *General Manager*
A T K Hau, *Yard Manager*
L T Kwee, *Asst General Manager Shipbuilding*
L J Pok, *Administrative Manager*

This company has been licensed by Navatek Ships Ltd to build and market its SWATH designs in Asia. Please see entry for Navatek Ships Ltd for details of these vessels.

Singapore Slipway and Engineering Co undertook the building of the *Navatek I* partial superstructure in 1989.

First SWATH construction work by Singapore Slipway and Engineering Co, the partial superstructure of *Navatek I*

UNITED KINGDOM

FBM MARINE LIMITED

Cowes Shipyard, Cowes, Isle of Wight PO31 7DL, England

Telephone: (0983) 297111
Telex: 86466FAMBRO G
Telefax: (0983) 299642

Jack Barr, *Managing Director*
John Warbey, *Sales Director*
Gordon Dodd, *Manufacturing Director*
Ian Campbell, *Regional Manager*
David Codd, *Commercial Manager*
Mike McSorley, *Marketing Manager*
Patrick Methold, *Regional Manager*
Robert Milner, *Regional Manager*
Nigel Warren, *Chief Designer*

FDC 400
37-METRE FAST DISPLACEMENT CATAMARAN (FDC) SEAMASTER CLASS
PATRIA

In August 1988 Fairey Marinteknik, now FBM Marine Limited, announced the award of a contract for the supply of a 400-seat fast displacement catamaran to the Regional Government of Madeira, Portugal. Valued at £4 million the craft was delivered in early 1990.

First trials started in October 1989 and on 5 October the FDC 400 achieved a speed of 32.1 knots at two thirds load, some 4 to 5 knots higher than the previous maximum recorded speed for a SWATH type and therefore establishing a record.

In late January 1990 *Patria* was on trials in storm conditions and spent a total of seven hours at sea averaging 28 knots in a fully loaded condition in wave heights of 2.5 to 3.5 metres and wind speeds that seldom dropped below 70 knots and gusted at times above 90 knots.

The launch of the first FDC 400, machinery not installed 6 May 1989

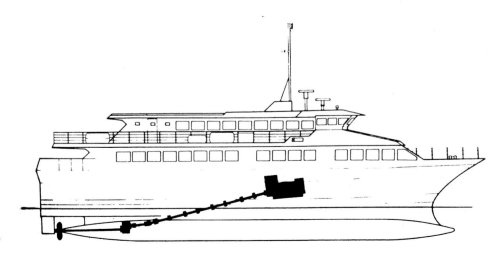

Transmission arrangement on FDC 400

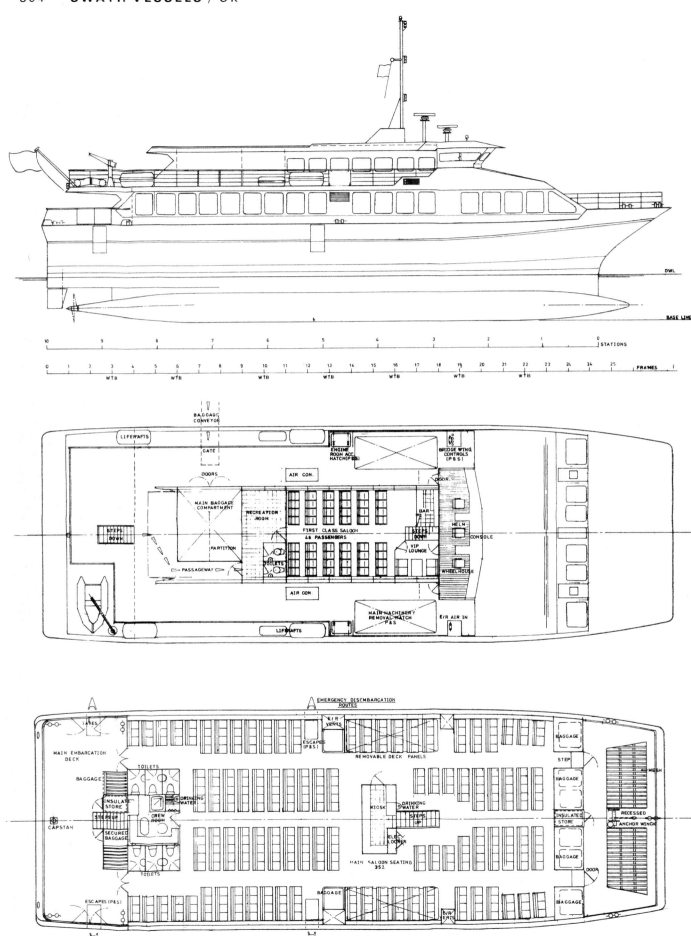

General arrangement of FDC 400

PRINCIPAL PARTICULARS
CLASSIFICATION: DnV Passenger Ship Light
    Craft
DIMENSIONS
Length overall: 36.5m
Beam: 13.0m
Draught: 2.7m
DISPLACEMENT
Full load condition: about 180 tonnes
MACHINERY
Main engines: Two MTU 16V 396 TB 84 rated at
    2040kW (25°C air, 25°C sea) 1940rpm.

Propulsion: Twin shaft and 3-blade fixed-pitch
    Lips propellers via 3.23:1.0 ZF gearboxes
Electrical: Two AC generating sets
ACCOMMODATION
Passengers: 400, Crew: 8–10
FUEL CAPACITY
17 750 l
PERFORMANCE
Speed, full load: 31.7 knots
Range: 472n miles at 30 knots
Endurance: 10 hours
Fuel consumption: 1000 litres/hour

Limiting significant wave height: 3.5m
Propulsive coefficient: 0.70
NATURAL PERIODS
Roll: 8s
Pitch: 5.5s
Heave: 5.5s
BALLAST SYSTEM
Pump: 50m³/h, 1.5kW, 380V on each of four
    ballast tanks in the platform, each of 7.5 tonnes
    capacity

The FBM Marine *Patria* on trials

The FBM Marine FDC 400 *Patria*

UNITED STATES OF AMERICA

NAVATEK SHIPS LTD

(A subsiduary of Pacific Marine)
Suite 1880, 841 Bishop St, Honolulu, Hawaii
96813, USA
Telephone: (808) 531 7001
Telefax: (808) 523 7668

Steven C H Loui, *President*
Dr Ludwig H Seidl, *Chief Scientist and Designer*
Michael Schmicker, *Vice President-Business Development*
Ken Plyler, *Director of Sales*
Dr Manfred Zapka, *Director of Engineering*
Capt Jim Cummings, *SWATH Operations*

Technology for the development of the Pacific Marine SWATH came from Dr Ludwig Seidl, Chairman of Department of Ocean Engineering, University of Hawaii. In 1977 Pacific Marine (a private corporation founded in 1944 by the late Fred H M Loui) and Dr Seidl formed the Pacific Marine Engineering Science Co. In 1979 the company was granted patent (US Patent 4174671) covering its SWATH design.

One-tenth scale models of a series of PAMESCO SWATH designs were tested in commercial model boat basins in 1978 at the Schiffbautechnische Versuchsanstalt Wien in Vienna, Austria, and in 1979 at the University of California at Berkeley. In February and March 1987, Pacific Marine returned to Vienna to finalise the prototype design with a US$250 000 test effort. Close correlation was demonstrated between computer model predictions and actual model performance, leading to the company's decision to begin construction of the prototype. Pacific Marine invested US $4.5 million to build the vessel, the hull construction being subcontracted to Thompson Metal Fabricators, Vancouver, Washington.

NAVATEK 1

The hull was launched in February 1989. *Navatek 1* is the first SWAT in the world to be classed by the American Bureau of Shipping. After being outfitted at Northwest Marine, Portland, Oregon with a partial superstructure and pilot house, sea trials commenced in May 1989. During those trials, *Navatek 1* sailed 600 miles from Portland to San Francisco, California, then 2100 miles across the Pacific to Honolulu, Hawaii. It is also the first SWATH to make the San Francisco–Honolulu, Pacific ocean transit under its own power. During the six day trip, it averaged 15 knots, its design cruising speed, through seas of 1.8 to 3.0m. It also demonstrated the ability to maintain 93% of its speed through Sea State 5. *Navatek 1* achieved a top speed of over 17 knots, and its fuel consumption was 265 l/h at 1600 rpm cruising speed. Her reduced ships motions were extremely good; waves up to 2.4m produced almost no motion.

In Hawaii, sea trials included extended runs in rough channel waters between all major islands. In July and August 1989 in the Molokai channel and Alenuihaha channels, *Navatek 1* routinely ran all headings in average seas of 3.65m, with occasional waves of just over 4.6m. The largest wave she encountered during her trials was a 5.5 to 6.1m wave set off Makapuu, Oahu. During that encounter, beer glasses sitting on tables in the forward lounge remained in place without spilling a drop.

With the successful completion of sea trials in September 1989, Hawaiian Cruises, Ltd. of Honolulu, Hawaii signed a long-term lease on the vessel for use as a 450 passenger day excursion/dinner cruise boat serving the Hawaii tourist trade, with commercial service to start in late December 1989. Due to rough waters on the cruise

Navatek 1 with partial superstructure fitted for sea trials

Navatek 1 in dry dock

Model of *Navatek 1*

route, Hawaiian Cruises will be able to offer tour
wholesalers an exclusive route no other Hawaii
vessel can operate. *Navatek l* sailed 6500 miles to
New Orleans, Louisiana via the Panama Canal in
early October 1989 where Trinity Marine installed
the rest of the two-deck superstructure. Navatek
Ships holds a US design patent on the superstructure design.

Navatek Ships Ltd. began commercial production of its SWATH designs with the lease of
Navatek 1 in September 1989. It has licensed two
shipyards outside the US to build and market its
SWATH designs: Singapore Slipway & Engineering Co. Pte., Ltd. (Singapore); and Sea Management Corp., Pty., Ltd. (Australia). It expects
to approve several additional licensees in 1990,
including at least one in Europe.

Navatek Ships Ltd. offers customers three
SWATH designs in addition to the 365-ton, day
excursion/dinner boat *Navatek 1*. They include a
200-ton, 32.9m pilot boat; a 230-ton, 37.2m fast
ferry (27/28 knots); an an 800-ton, 71.2m
casino/cruise ship.

PRINCIPAL PARTICULARS
Owner: Pacific Marine, Honolulu, Hawaii
Lessee: Hawaiian Cruises Ltd., Honolulu, Hawaii
Designer: Pacific Marine Engineering Science Co.
Construction Supervision : Pacific Marine
Hull Builder: Thompson Metal Fab, Vancouver,
Wash.
Outfitter: Northwest Marine, Portland, Ore.
Hull Launch Date: 25 February, 1989
Superstructure: Trinity Marine, New Orleans, La.
Length: 43.00m
Beam: 16.00m
Draught: 2.44 to 4.27m variable
Cruising speed: 15 knots at 1500 engine rpm
Top speed: 18 knots
Decks: two, plus observation deck
Usable deck space: main: 5l2m²; second: 445m²
  observation deck: 45.5m²; Total: 1003m²
Certified passenger capacity: 450 (luxury dinner
lounge seating)
Main engines: Twin Deutz MWM 16V-816CR
diesels, continuous rating of 1007kW each.
Engine location: lower hulls
Propulsion: direct drive with Ulstein reduction
gear and Ulstein controllable pitch four-bladed
props.
Generators: Twin Detroit Diesel 6–7l generators
rated at 99kW each

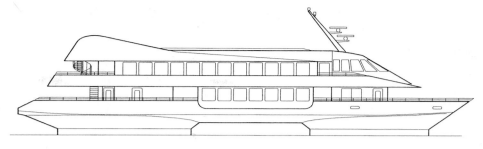
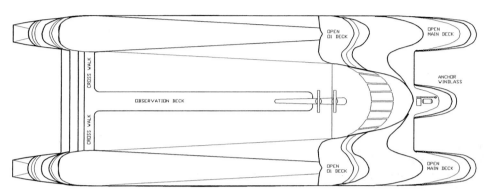
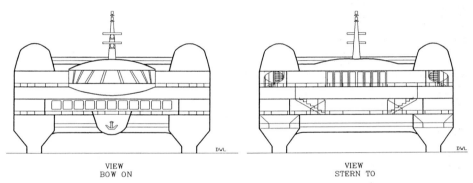

General arrangement *Navatek 1*

Launching of *Navatek 1* hull, (photo: Nat Richards)

SOME FIRSTS

Largest SWATH ever built in the United States
Largest commercial passenger SWATH in world
First SWATH in world to be classed by the American Bureau of Shipping.
First SWATH to make 2100 mile Pacific Ocean transit from San Francisco to Honolulu under own power.
US Coast Guard certification (tonnage): Subchapter T boat upon completion of superstructure in December 1989.
First service: As a luxury day excursion/dinner cruise boat in Hawaii running exclusive tour route off island of Oahu. Operating environment: seas 1.8 to 2.5m. Scheduled start of service: December 1989.

NORTHWEST MARINE IRON WORKS

Portland, Oregon, USA
    Builders of the superstructure for *Navatek I*

Superstructure being installed on deck of *Navatek 1*

SEMI-SUBMERGED SHIP CORPORATION (SSSCO)

[PATENT HOLDING AND DEVELOPMENT]
17 Loma Larga Drive, Solana Beach, California 92075, USA

Telephone: (619) 481 6417
Telefax: (619) 481 7282

Dr Thomas G Lang, *President*

SSSCO was founded by Dr Thomas G Lang, the inventor of the semi-submerged ship (S^3). Basically, the S^3 consists of two parallel torpedo-like hulls attached to which are two or more streamlined struts which pierce the water surface and support an above-water platform. Stabilising fins are attached near the after end of each hull and a pair of smaller fins are located near their forward ends.

Semi-submerged ship technology has been proved over the past fifteen years by the 190-ton SSP *Kaimalino*, a US Navy developed range-support vessel which has been operating in the rough seas off the Hawaiian islands since 1975. Following private development, Dr Lang introduced the concept into the US Navy in 1968 and holds several basic patents in the field. He led the Navy's first research work, and initiated and developed the hydrodynamic design for the stable semi-submerged platform (SSP), the world's first high-performance, open-ocean, semi-submerged ship.

The US Navy's present SWATH (Small-Waterplane-Area Twin-Hull) ship programme is based on the S^3 concept. The performance features that distinguish S^3s from conventional vessels are greatly reduced motions with sustained speed even in heavy seas, lower hydrodynamic drag and reduced power requirements at moderate to high speeds, and far superior course-keeping characteristics at all sea headings. S^3s have excellent manoeuvrability at speed, when operating in confined harbours and when station-keeping.

The control surfaces of the S^3 designs enable them to ride smoothly through the water. Controllable bow and stern fins can be operated collectively or differentially. Used together, the four fins control heave, pitch and roll. Twin rudders provide directional control at high speed. Twin screws and thrusters provide differential thrust at low speed, to help in delicate, close-in manoeuvres. The screws may have variable and reversible-pitch blades.

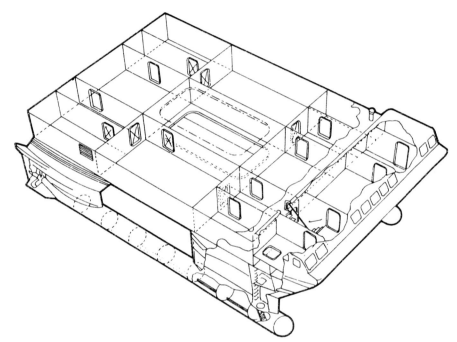

Cutaway showing basic hull configuration of SSP *Kaimalino*

A number of applications of the S^3 principle have been proposed by Dr Lang and these were described in *Jane's Surface Skimmers 1985* and earlier editions. These design proposals have included an offshore crew change vessel, a high-speed ferry, a rapid intervention vessel, supply and diving support vessels. Fishing vessel and cruise ship applications are also suggested.

KAIMALINO

Operated by the US Navy Ocean Systems Center at Hawaii the SSP *Kaimalino*, has operated from near calm conditions to beyond Sea State 6 at speeds of up to 25 knots. Its motion is small relative to a conventional mono-hull either when at rest or under way. The SSP has made smooth transits in 4.57m swells without any impacts;

SSP *Kaimalino*

however, in short, steep 3.7m waves, occasional bow impacts have occurred. No structural damage has occurred, even during storm conditions when 7.6 to 9.2m high waves were encountered.

In February 1985 ten Woods Hole Oceanographic Institution scientists participated in a series of two- and three-day cruises off Hawaii on the SWATH vessel *Kaimalino* over a two-week period to test the suitability of the SWATH design for oceanographic research.

DIMENSIONS
Length: 27m
Beam (at mid section): 14m
Height: 9.7m
WEIGHTS
Displacement: 217 tons
Max payload (including fuel): 50 tons
PERFORMANCE
Max speed: 25 knots
Range at max speed and payload: 400 n miles
REFERENCES:
SSP Kaimalino; Conception, Development History, Hurdles and Success by Thomas G Lang. ASME, Paper 86-WA/HH-4. Presented at the Winter Annual Meeting Anaheim, California, 7–12 December 1986.
SWATH Evolution: From Ideas to Ships by Thomas G Lang. AIAA paper AIAA-89-1520. Presented at Intersociety Advanced Marine Vehicles Conference, Arlington, Virginia, 5–7 June 1989.

Artist's impression of the 2529-tonne SSSCO S³ oceanographic research ship

S³ OCEANOGRAPHIC RESEARCH SHIP PROJECT DESIGN (LOW SPEED)

A design prepared for Woods Hole Oceanographic Institution to have a payload carrying capability of 420 tons.
ACCOMMODATION/SPACE
60 people in 1- and 2-person staterooms
Deck space 1280m² on three levels
Scientific storage: 223m²
Laboratory area: 281m²
Several workshops
ELECTRIC POWER
4kW Caterpillar 3516 motor/generator
DIMENSIONS
Deck length: 66.46m
Beam length: 28.96m
Draught, full load: 7.32m
Draught, full load + ½ fuel: 5.88m
WEIGHT
2529 tonnes
PERFORMANCE
Max speed: 16.5 knots at 5027shp
Continuous speed: 15.9 knots at 4446shp
Cruise speed: 15.3 knots at 3779shp
Range: 11 400n miles at 15 knots
Endurance: 40 days
Normal work conditions: Through Sea State 6
Limited work conditions: Through Sea State 7

S³ MULTI-PURPOSE VESSEL PROJECT DESIGN (LOW SPEED)

A 19.5m semi-submerged ship design suitable for cruise, fishing, diving support, hydrographic survey, oceanography, crew transport and ferry

Artists impression of the 19.5m SSSCO S³ multi-purpose vessel

work. Engines would be mounted on the lower hulls to provide more deck space and to reduce noise and vibration.
DIMENSIONS
Length: 19.51m
Beam: 10.76m
Draught: 21.6m

WEIGHT
59.85 tonnes
PERFORMANCE
Max speed full load: 15.8 knots
Speed, continuous power: 15 knots
Service speed: 14 knots at 85% max continuous bhp

SWATH OCEAN SYSTEMS, INC

979 G Street, Chula Vista, California 92011, USA

Telephone: (619) 426 2179
Telefax: (619) 426 2196

CHUBASCO

Chubasco was launched 28 March, 1987 by James Betts Enterprises of San Diego for Leonard Friedman for drift fishing. The design and building are under patents of Dr Thomas G Lang of the Semi-Submerged Ship Corporation.

HULL: Marine grade aluminium.
ENGINES: Two DDC 8V92T1 diesel, 559 kW (750hp) each, turbo-charged.
GENERATORS: Two 50kW Northern Light, one 7.5kW Northern Light.
TANKS: One 1135-litre macerator and holding tank, one 1890-litre potable water tank, four 4730-litre diesel fuel tanks with Delaval gauges, four bait tanks.
STABILISING FINS: Gyro-activated.
COMMUNICATIONS: Three VHS transceivers with ADF, two SSB radios, one Citizens Band radio, one Magnavox Satcom telephone.

NAVIGATION: One Magnavox Sat-Nav, one Furuno Loran unit, one Alden weatherfax, two Furuno 72-mile daylight radars, two Data Marine 305m fathometers, two Furuno colour fathometers, one Furuno 214m sonar unit, two water speed indicators, one wind speed indicator, one wind direction indicator, one Sperry gyrocompass and automatic pilot.
CONTROLS: Steering station at stern, steering station at each wing outside pilot house, bow thruster and controls at three stations.
ACCOMMODATION: Sleeping accommodation for nine passengers on main deck in

Chubasco

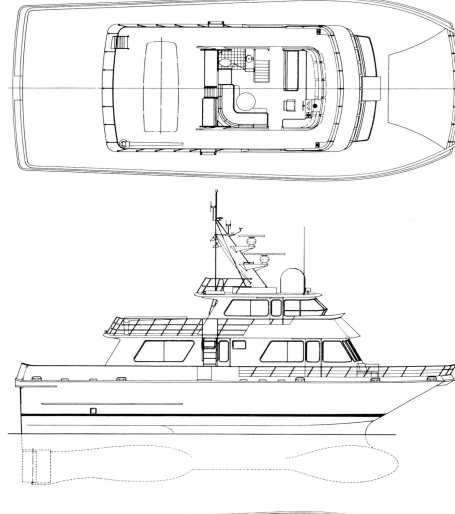

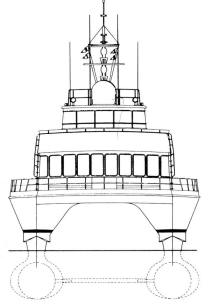

General arrangement of *Chubasco*

master stateroom, two guest staterooms, two sofa berths in saloon, plus one bunk. Pilot house berths three; all air-conditioned. Fully equipped galley.
DIMENSIONS
Length overall: 21.95m
Beam: 9.45m
Draught: 3.05m
PERFORMANCE
Speed, max: 21 knots
Speed, cruising, in 1.8m seas: 20 knots
WEIGHT: 70 tonnes
OPERATIONS: *Chubasco* is currently a demonstration vessel for SWATH Ocean Systems. She served as the official committee boat for the judges for the 1988 America's Cup Races held at San Diego.

Main deck plan, *Chubasco*

Bow thruster on *Chubasco*

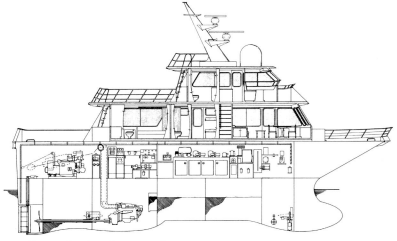

Chubasco machinery and equipment arrangements

3500 CLASS (DESIGN)

Under design January 1989, 170 tonne displacement, 25.9m overall length, 12.8m beam, aluminium construction. Passenger capacity: 350 to 400.

BETSY (ex SUAVE LINO)

Completed in 1981 for Mr Friedman as a fishing boat *Betsy* was used more recently as a tender by the Sail America Syndicate during the America's Cup defence off Fremantle, Australia.

The vessel is constructed of aluminium with a single strut configuration for each hull. Two high-speed diesels of 425hp each, mounted at deck level drive fixed-pitch propellers through bevel gears. Automatic fin control is fitted. Based in San Diego.

DIMENSIONS
Length overall: 19.20m
Length bp: 16.80m
Breadth overall: 9.10m
Draught: 2.13m
"Box" clearance: 0.70m
ENGINES
Two DDC 8V71, 317 kW (425 hp) each
WEIGHTS
Displacement: 53 tonnes
Payload: 14 tonnes
PERFORMANCE
Speed, max: 18 knots

2000 CLASS
FREDERICK G CREED

A 20.4m 80 tonne SWATH vessel launched in November 1989 and made available for the Canadian Department of Fisheries and Oceans under a lease/purchase contract for oceanographic and hydrographic service off the eastern coasts of Canada and the United States.
PRINCIPAL PARTICULARS
Length, overall: 20.40m
Beam, max: 9.75m
Draught, full load, trimmed: 2.60m
Displacement, full load: 80.26 tonnes
Displacement, lightship: 57.90 tonnes
Speed, max: 29 knots
Speed, continuous, full load: 25 knots
Speed, economical: 11 knots
Engines: Two DDC 12V92TA 805 kW diesels
Passenger capacity: 125
Natural roll period: 8.4s
Natural pitch period: 7.4s
Natural heave period: 5.1s

SWATH OCEAN 430 (DESIGN)
HIGH SPEED FERRY
PRINCIPAL PARTICULARS
Length, overall: 35.40m
Beam, max: 13.70m
Draught, full load, trimmed: 2.90m
Displacement, full load: 167.60 tonnes
Speed, continuous: 30 knots
Passenger capacity: 400
Natural roll period: 10.7s
Natural pitch period: 8.1s
Natural heave period: 5.9s

SD-60
HALCYON

RMI designed and built a 18.3m Small-Water-plane-Area Twin-Hull (SWATH) demonstrator boat, designated SD-60. *Halcyon* was launched in March 1985.

The SD-60 SWATH offers advantages over conventional craft in transporting passengers and cargo. For example, pitch and roll motions are significantly less than those of comparable small mono-hulls over the full range of anticipated sea conditions, and this will give an improved ride. Its increased speed performance in heavy seas enables it to maintain headway at design speed through and beyond Sea State 4; an important advantage in commercial service operations. The wide separation between its variable-pitch pro-

Betsy

SD-60 *Halcyon* operating in San Francisco Bay

Artist's impression of Swath Ocean 430 High Speed Ferry (Design)

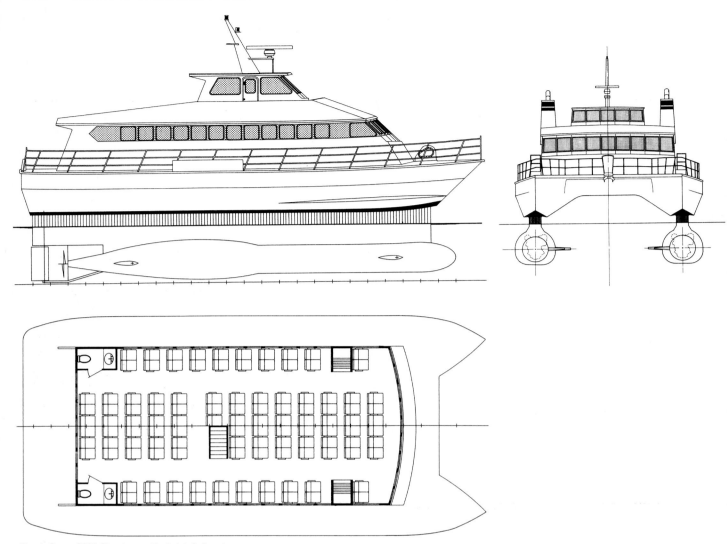

Swath Ocean 2000 Class layout, *Frederick G. Creed*

pellers allows precise manoeuvring within ports, channels and rivers, and positioning alongside ships or offshore oil platforms.

The deckhouse has a galley, head and berthing accommodation for the crew of three and space for 20 passengers. The passenger space can be converted to living quarters for nine additional crew members. The pilot house accommodates a full range of commercial communications and marine navigation systems. Microprocessor ship control systems and vessel management systems are fitted. Oceangoing ships or Lighter-Aboard-Ship (LASH) barges will be able to carry the boat on deck.

Propulsion power is by twin Caterpillar 3408 DITA marine diesels each driving, via a reduction gear and Eaton V-belt drive, a 45in diameter VPO FR-H Hundested variable-pitch propeller. The electric plant features twin Model 4.236M (25kW) Perkins marine diesel electric generator sets. The design meets USCG safety requirements and certification as a commercial passenger boat under 100 tons displacement, fully loaded.

DIMENSIONS
Length overall: 18.28m
Max beam: 9.14m
Navigational draught: 2.29m
Available cargo deck area: 54.71m²

WEIGHTS
Payload: 8 long tons
Full load displacement: 62 long tons
Light ship displacement: 52 long tons
PERFORMANCE
Max speed: 20 knots
Cruising: 18 knots
Cruising range (no fuel reserve and payload): over 800n miles
OPERATOR: US Army Corps of Engineers, Savannah, Georgia.

THOMPSON METAL FABRICATORS
Vancouver, Washington, USA

This company undertook the building of the main hull structure of *Navatek I* in 1989.

HIGH-SPEED MONO-HULL CRAFT

AUSTRALIA

AUSTRALIAN SHIPBUILDING INDUSTRIES (WA) PTY LIMITED (ASI)

Cockburn Road, South Coogee, Western Australia, Australia
PO Box 206, Hamilton Hill, Western Australia 6163, Australia

Telephone: (09) 437 0437
Telex: 93458AA
Telefax: (09) 410 2056

Name	Country	Date
HMPNGS *Tarangau*	Papua New Guinea	16 May 1987
RVS *Tukoro*	Vanuatu	13 June 1987
HMPNGS *Dredger*	Papua New Guinea	31 October 1987
MV *Nafanua*	Western Samoa	19 March 1988
RSIPV *Lata*	Solomon Islands	7 July 1988
HMPNGS *Seeadler*	Papua New Guinea	29 October 1988
CIPPB *Tekukupa*	Cook Is.	1 September 1989
HMPNGS *Basilisk*	Papua New Guinea	1 July 1989
VOEA *Neiafu*	Tonga	28 October 1989

ASI 315 PATROL BOAT

Australian Shipbuilding Industries won the contract to build patrol boats for the Pacific Patrol Boat Project. Participating countries are Papua New Guinea (4), Vanuatu (1), Western Samoa (1), Solomon Islands (2), Cook Islands (1), Tonga (3), Marshall Is. (1), and the Federated States of Micronesia (2). The craft will undertake surveillance and enforcement of the Exclusive Economic Zones of the countries concerned. The craft listed in the accompanying table have been completed and handed over.

HULL: Steel.
MAIN ENGINES: Two Caterpillar 3516 diesel engines coupled to two ZF BW 465 gearboxes.
PROPULSION: Two 123.8mm propeller shafts with 1200mm diameter propellers.

CONTROLS: Vickers Hydraulic steering gear operating twin rudders, with twin pumps.
CAPACITIES/STORES
Fuel: 27.9 tonnes
Water: 6000 litres
Water making: 3000 litres/day
Fresh/frozen provisions: 10 days
Dry provisions: 21 days
Spares: 21 days
ACCOMMODATION/CREW
Complement: Captain and two officers, two senior ratings and nine junior ratings
Layout: Captain's cabin, two-berth officer's cabin, two-berth occasional officer's cabin, officer's shower and heads, wardroom. Senior ratings two-berth cabin and mess. Twelve-berth mess deck for junior ratings plus two showers and two heads, combined galley for total crew

SYSTEMS
Auxiliary machinery: Two Caterpillar 3304 (415V 3 phase and 240V single phase), harbour generator Lister HRW3 415V 3 phase, emergency power 24V battery system; share power connection 240V single phase, 415V 3 phase
Navigational: Tokyo Keiki ES11A gyrocompass and repeats, Plaith Jupiter 73143 magnetic compass, Furuno 1011 radar with slave monitor, Furuno GP300 GPS Navigator, Furuno Fax-208A weather facsimile unit, log interface and data printer, Furuno DS-70 Doppler log distance and speed indicator, Furuno FE881 echo sounder, Rubin SHC 20L searchlight
Communications: Sailor RT144C VHF, Collins VHF (Aeronautical Mobile), VHF 20A (118–1136MHz, 20W), Collins AN/ARC UHF,

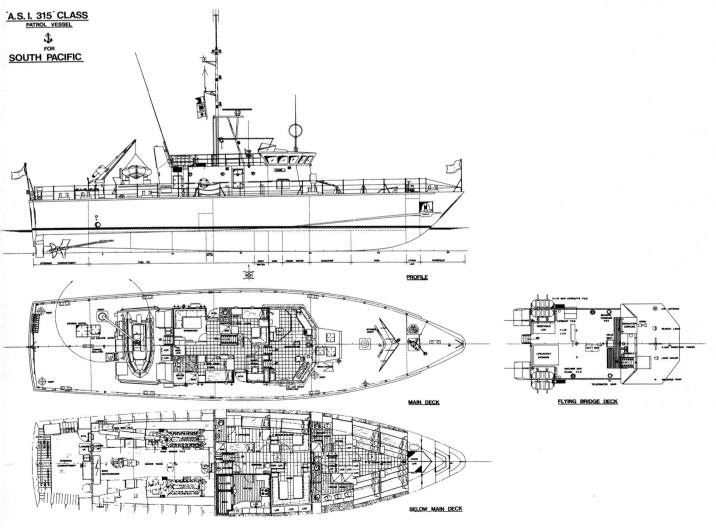

Profile and accommodation layout of ASI 31.5m patrol boat

Sailor Auto Alarm 500kHz and Sailor 2182kHz receiver distress sets, three VHF portables and one HF portable

Internal Communications: Honeywell broadcast and alarm system, eight station intercoms

Life saving: Life rafts four 16-man RFD, life-jackets 60 RFD, lifebuoys 4, EPIRB 5, Zodiac PRO 470 inflatable boat with two 30hp outboard motors plus Skanti TRP-1 hand-powered distress receiver

Ship services: Bridge pumps, two Gilkes; fuel system, one Gilkes; fresh water distribution ¾hp pressure system; ventilation, air conditioning; grey water system, overboard discharge; refrigeration five 150-litre built in cool and freezer rooms

Firefighting: Machinery space, Halon 1301 gas flooding system; magazine/lookers, water spray; throughout craft, hydrant and hose system; alarm system, heat and smoke detection; portable pump, Robin PTE 401; extinguishers, 5 BCF, 4 water, 6 foam

Desalinator: Memtec (reverse osmosis)

DIMENSIONS
Length overall: 31.50m
Length waterline: 28.60m
Beam, max: 8.21m
Draught: 2.12m
WEIGHT
Displacement (full load): 165 tonnes

31.5m ASI patrol boat

PERFORMANCE
Speed, max: 23 knots
    max sustained (full fuel): 21 knots

economical: 12 knots
minimum sustained: 7 knots
Endurance at 12 knots: 2500n miles

OCEANFAST PTY LIMITED

Lot 501, Egmont Road, Hendersen, Western Australia, Australia

Telephone: (619) 410 1900
Telefax: (619) 410 2095

John Farrell, *Managing Director*

Oceanfast specialises in high performance motor yachts and luxury cruisers. The Company's naval architect is Phil Curran and yacht design is by Jon Bannenberg Ltd. The Company is a wholly-owned subsidiary of the Western Australian based International Assets Ltd Group, with over 250 people directly employed and has a turnover in excess of A$30,000,000 per annum.

Due for completion and delivery in 1990 is Oceanfast's largest vessel to date, a 55 metre, 30 knot motor yacht. A 37 metre, 30 knot luxury cruiser will also be delivered.

OCEANFAST 4000
PARTS VI

Motor yacht.
DESIGNER: Phil Curran.
HULL: Hull and superstructure are constructed in aluminium.
MAIN ENGINES/GEARBOXES: Two MTU

12V 396 TB93, MCR 1200kW at 1975rpm, MR 1440kW at 2100rpm. One MTU 8V 396 TB93, MCR 800kW at 1975rpm, MR 960kW at 2100rpm.
PROPULSION: Three KaMeWa 63S 62/6 water-jet units.
ACCOMMODATION: Owner's stateroom on main deck; 4 guest staterooms on lower deck; crew's quarters on lower deck including captain's cabin and quarters for eight.
SYSTEMS
Auxiliary engines: Two Mercedes-Benz, driving 380V, 3-phase, 50Hz alternators at 68kVA each
Fuel capacity: 32 000 litres
Water capacity: 2000 litres supplemented by reverse-osmosis desalination capacity of 2000 litres/day
Navigational equipment: 100-mile variable range JRC colour radar, JRC auto direction finder, JRC satellite navigator, JRC automatic pilot and JRC echo sounder
Communications: 100W SSB radio with radio phone, Shipmate VHF radio with radio phone and JRC satellite communications system incorporating telephone, telex and facsimile
DIMENSIONS
Length overall: 46.69m
Length waterline: 37.47m
Beam: 8.36m

Draught: 1.25m
WEIGHT
Displacement, light ship: 140 tonnes
PERFORMANCE
Max speed, estimated: 30 knots

OPAL C

Motor yacht launched in late 1989 and delivered to Japan, April 1990.
DESIGNER: Phil Curran.
HULL: Hull and superstructure are constructed in aluminium.
MAIN ENGINES: Two MTU 6V 396 TB94, 2655kW each.
ACCOMMODATION: Owner's stateroom; 3 guest staterooms; one captains stateroom, 3 crew cabins.
SYSTEMS
Fuel tank capacity: 35 000 litres
Water capacity: 11,250-litre tank with desalinators
Navigational equipment: 72-mile range colour radar, Monochrome Radar 64 mile, Colour Echo Sounder, Satellite Navigator, Loran C, Global Positioning System, Electromagnetic Speed Log, Wind Speed/Direction Recorder, Digital Echo Sounder, Digital Speed Log, Gyro Compass/Auto Pilot Combination
Communications: HF/SSB Radio, VHF Radios,

Oceanfast 4000 *Parts VI*

Satellite Communication incl. Facsimile,
Weather Fax, Navtex, PA—Intercom System,
Audio and Visual System, CCVC/Infra Red
Security System (Specification subject to change
without notice)
DIMENSIONS
Length overall: 40.30m
Beam: 8.0m
Draught, including propellers: 1.25m
WEIGHTS
Displacement: 140 tonnes
PERFORMANCE
Speed, cruise: 30 knots
  max: 35 knots

SUN PARADISE

A 94-seat passenger luxury fast ferry launched
1987 and delivered to Ansett Transport Industries.
DESIGNERS: Phil Curran and Jon Bannenberg.
HULL: Hull and superstructure are constructed
in marine grade aluminium.
MAIN ENGINES: Two MTU 12V 396 TC82,
912kW each at 1745rpm.
PROPULSION: Two KaMeWa waterjet units,
type 56S.
ACCOMMODATION
94 passengers
5 crew
CAPACITIES
Fuel: 15 500 litres
Fresh water: 2100 litres
DIMENSIONS
Length: 34.75m
Breadth: 7.50m
Draught: 1.20m
SPEED
Max: 25 knots, cruise: 21 knots

The Oceanfast *Opal C*

Oceanfast *Opal C*

SBF ENGINEERING
Water Edge, Lot 33 Cockburn Road, South
Coogee, Western Australia 6166, Australia

Telephone: (09) 410 2022/2244
Telex: 94110AA
Telefax: (09) 410 1807

Don Dunbar, *Managing Director*

SBF Engineering builds high-speed aluminium
crew boats and passenger ferries, designed to meet
the operational needs of individual shipping companies. Apart from the vessels detailed below SBF
Engineering have also built a 54-passenger, 35-
knots, waterjet-propelled ferry, the *Fitzroy Reef
Jet*.

SATRYA EXPRESS

A 30-knot crew boat built for the Indonesian
company PT Satmarindo for operation in the
Malacca Straits.
DESIGNER: Phil Curran, 2 Edward Street, Fremantle, Western Australia 6160, Australia.
CLASSIFICATION: Built to Det norske Veritas
light craft regulations.
HULL: Hull and superstructure are constructed
in marine grade aluminium.

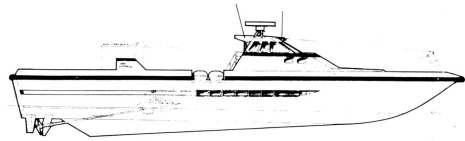

The Phil Curran-designed *Satrya Express* crew boat

SBF Engineering *Satrya Express*

MAIN ENGINES: Two MTU 12V 396 TB83 marine diesel engines producing 1260kW at 1900rpm.
CONTROLS: Vickers hydraulic steering gear.
ACCOMMODATION/CREW
Crew: 6
Passengers: 62
SYSTEMS
Fuel capacity: 12 000 litres
Electrical generators: Two 4-cylinder MWM generators producing 30kVA each
Navigational equipment: Two Furuno F240 radars, range 48 miles and Furuno FE400 echo sounder
Communications: Two AWA VHF Pilotphone 9 radios and Kodan 6801, 100W transceiver
DIMENSIONS
Length overall: 31.30m
Beam: 6.50m
Draught: 2.0m
PERFORMANCE
Speed, max: 30 knots plus
Range: 600n miles

SEA FLYTE

High-speed passenger ferry built in 1980, in service in Singapore.
DESIGNER: Phil Curran, East Fremantle.
LEGISLATING AUTHORITY: Harbour and Light Department of Western Australia, USL Code.
HULL: Hull and superstructure are constructed in marine grade aluminium.
MAIN ENGINES: Two MTU marine diesel engines developing 1050shp at 1840rpm.
PROPULSION: Two five-blade 980mm diameter, 1140mm pitch propellers by S & S Engineering, Kewdale, Western Australia.
ACCOMMODATION
Passenger capacity: 240
SYSTEMS
Electrical generators: One Ford diesel generator for air-conditioning and bar refrigeration
Navigational equipment: Kodan radar
DIMENSIONS
Length overall: 31.30m
Length waterline: 27.50m
Beam: 6.50m
Draught: 0.80m

SUNDANCER

A triple-powered high-speed ferry operated by Chuan Hup, Singapore
CLASSIFICATION: Australian USL Class 1C.
DESIGNERS: Phil Curran and Don Dunbar.
HULL: Constructed in marine grade aluminium.
MAIN ENGINES: Three MWM TBD 234 V12.
PROPULSION: Three Castoldi 07 Series waterjet units.
ACCOMMODATION: 160 passengers.
COMMUNICATIONS/NAVIGATION: Koden CVS 88 colour echo sounder, Koden MDC 410S 6ft colour radar, Robertson AP 40 autopilot, Codar 8121 12V radio.
DIMENSIONS
Length, overall: 27.5m

Sea Flyte

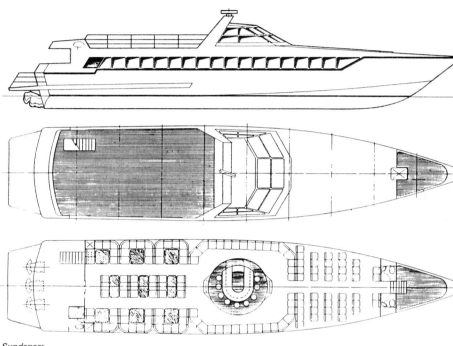

Sundancer

James Kelly II

Length, design waterline: 23.4m
Beam: 6.30m
Draught: 0.80m

PERFORMANCE
Speed, max: 36 knots
Speed, service: 32 knots

Sundancer

JAMES KELLY II

A high-speed cruising vessel designed by Phil Curran of East Fremantle, owned by Scenic Gordon & Hells Gates Charters, PO Box 38, Strahan, Tasmania 7468, Australia.

CLASSIFICATION: Passenger ferry vessel class 1B-seagoing passenger vessel for use in all operational areas including offshore operations.

HULL: Hull and superstructure built in marine grade aluminium, plating 5083-H321, extrusions 6061-T6.

MAIN ENGINES/GEARBOXES: Two GM 12V 92 marine diesels fitted with Niigata 2.38:1 reduction gearboxes and one GM 16V 92 diesel engine rated at 1100hp.

PROPULSION: Two five-blade aluminium bronze propellers powered by GM 12V 92 engines, and one Castoldi 07 waterjet powered by GM 16V 92 engine.

ACCOMMODATION/CREW
Crew: 4
Passenger capacity: 200
SYSTEMS
Fuel tank capacity: 2000 litres
Fresh water tank capacity: 200 litres
Refrigeration space: 1.5m³
DIMENSIONS
Length overall: 27.67m
Length waterline: 23.50m
Beam: 6.40m
Draught (including propeller): 1.73m
WEIGHT
Design load displacement: 49.85 tonnes
PERFORMANCE
Max speed: 34 knots

WILDERNESS SEEKER

A high-speed cruising boat owned by Scenic Gordon & Hells Gates Charters. The craft was delivered in 1985.

DESIGNER: Phil Curran.
CLASSIFICATION: Vessel class 1D.
HULL: Constructed in marine grade aluminium.
MAIN ENGINES: Two MWM TBD 234 V12 diesels, 507kW each, at MCR.
PROPULSION: Two Castoldi 07 waterjet units.
ACCOMMODATION/CREW
Crew: 2
Passengers: 100
Upper-deck viewing for 50 passengers, with bar and catering facilities in main cabin

Wilderness Seeker, a 100-seat, 30-knot cruise boat operating in Tasmania

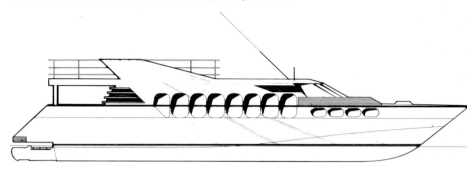

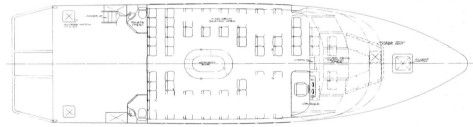

Layout of *Wilderness Seeker* designed by Phil Curran

SYSTEMS
Electrical generators: One MWM 226–3 with 30kVA alternator
Fuel capacity: 5500 litres
Fresh water: 200 litres
Refrigeration space: 0.50m³

DIMENSIONS
Length overall: 22.50m
Length waterline: 19.95m
Beam: 6.20m
Draught: 0.75m
PERFORMANCE
Speed: 30 knots

WAVEMASTER INTERNATIONAL PTY LTD

115 Egmont Road, Henderson 6166, Western Australia 6155, Australia

Telephone: (619) 410 1422
Telex: 93356 AA
Telefax: (619) 410 2089

Trevor Kitcher, *Chairman*
Richard Patterson, *Managing Director*

The company specialises in designing and building high-speed luxury ferries, with, by 1988, a range of 15 to 41 metres, and in varying passenger cargo configuration.

SEA RAIDER I, II & SEA SPIRIT

Please see 1989 edition for details of these vessels.

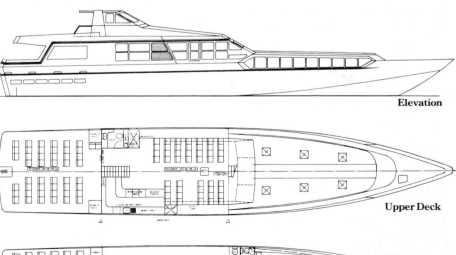

Elevation

Upper Deck

Lower Deck

Wavemaster International *Sea Raider*

BARBAROS

Launched August 1987.

CLASSIFICATION: Det norske Veritas + IAI, R45, Light Craft, SF-LC, FLC, NAUT C, NAUT B, EO-LC.

HULL: Monohedron planing type constructed in aluminium. The main deck consists of forward lounge, main lounge and aft lounge with an aft upper deck lounge and wheelhouse deck.

MAIN ENGINES: Two MTU 12V 396 TB83 series marine diesels rated at 1075kW driving custom-designed 4-blade propellers via ZF 455 2:1 reverse reduction gearboxes.

AUXILIARY ENGINE: MWM 226-TD4 four-cylinder marine diesel driving Stamford 47.5kVA 415 240V alternator.

ACCOMMODATION

Passengers: 246

Crew: 4

CAPACITIES

Fresh water: 500l

Fuel: 7000l in 3 fuel tanks

Cargo: 7 tonnes in palletised container system

NAVIGATION: Radar, Furuno 72 NM; VHF radio, Sailor 144C; HF radio, Sailor T124/R110; Watchkeeping receiver, Sailor R501; Autopilot, Wagner Mk IV.

DIMENSIONS

Length overall: 35.05m

Length, waterline: 28.70m

Beam moulded: 7.1m

Draught, max: 1.75m

WEIGHTS

Light ship: 58 tonnes

Full load: 84 tonnes

PERFORMANCE

Speed, full load, MCR: 27 knots

Speed, lightship, MCR: 30 knots

Sea Raider III, the latest ferry in the Sea Raider class

Craft built in the last six years (high-speed monohulls)

Length overall	Vessel	Launched	Current owner/operator	Area of operation
32.30m	Sea Raider I	1983	Lombardo	Hillaries-Rottnest (Perth WA)
	Gordon Explorer	1984	Morrison Tourist Services	Gordon River (Tasmania)
32.30m	Sea Raider II	1984	Palayaran Bintan Baruna Sakti	Singapore-Batam Island
32.30m	Sea Raider III ex (Sea Spirit)	1985	Palayaran Bintan Baruna Sakti	Singapore-Batam Island
34.05m	Barbaros	1987 August	Sea Bird Co Ltd	Cyprus-Turkey
30.70m	Kita Ekspres	1987 November	Kuala Perlis-Langkawi Ferry Services Sdn. Bhd.	Langkawi Island Malaysia
41.00m	Star Flyte	1988 October	Boat Torque Cruises	Fremantle-Rottnest (Perth WA)
27.00m	Suka Ekspres	1988 November	Kuala Perlis-Langkawi Ferry Services Sdn. Bhd.	Langkawi Island Malaysia
32.30m	Sea Raider III	1989	-	Rottmest
-	Senang Ekspres	1989	Kuala Perlis-Langkawi Ferry Services Sdn. Bhd.	Langkawi Island Malaysia

Barbaros built by Wavemaster International Pty Ltd for Cyprus service

KITA EKSPRES

Launched November 1987.

Designed by WaveMaster to suit the demanding operational requirements in South East Asian waters this vessel has triple waterjet units and air-conditioned accommodation for 152 passengers.

SURVEY: Australian Uniform Shipping Laws Code IC, restricted offshore service (IMO).

HULL: Monohedron planing form. Construction in aluminium. Wheelhouse forward on forward deck, lower main cabin with aft engine room.

MAIN ENGINES: Three MWM TBD 234 V12 marine diesels rated at 605kW at 2200rpm at 45°/32° ambient conditions driving Hamilton 402 waterjets via cardan shafts.

AUXILIARY ENGINES: Two MWM D226–6 marine diesels driving Stamford 55kVA alternators for 100% redundancy.

ACCOMMODATION

Passengers: 152 in main cabin
Crew: 8

CAPACITIES

Cargo: 1 tonne in hold under wheelhouse
Hand luggage stowage areas in forward main cabin
Fuel: 3750l
Water: 500l

NAVIGATION: Radar, Furuno 24 NM range; VHF radio, Uniden MC 610; HF radio, Cidan 8525S; Autopilot, Wagner SE.

DIMENSIONS

Length overall: 30.7m
Length, water line: 27.5
Beam: 6.6m
Draught: 0.75m

WEIGHTS

Lightship: 42 tonnes
Fully loaded, displacement: 60 tonnes

PERFORMANCE

Speed cruising, fully loaded: 30 knots
Speed, lightship: 33 knots

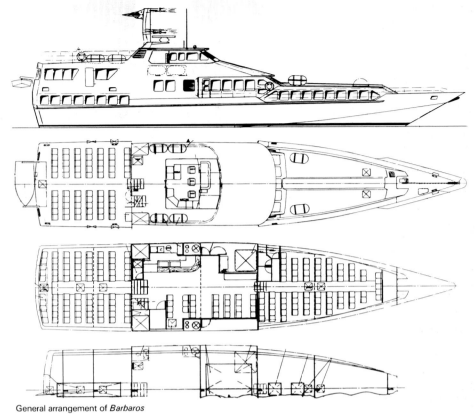

General arrangement of *Barbaros*

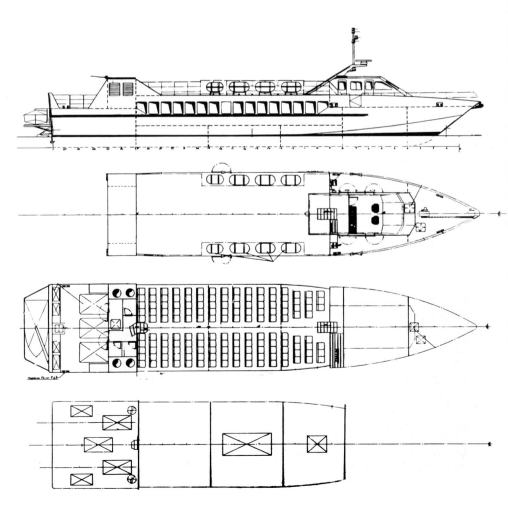

General arrangement of *Kita Ekspres*

STAR FLYTE

A Glen Williams design, delivered in October 1988.

CLASSIFICATION: Det norske Veritas + 1A1, R90 Light Craft. SF-LC, F-LC, Naut C, Naut B, ED-LG.

HULL: Monohedron planing form. Passenger accommodation on three decks. The lower passenger cabin is forward with the engine room aft of midships and cargo hold aft of engine room. The main deck has a forward passenger cabin and main cabin with a bar and bevery for all refreshments aft. The wheelhouse deck has superior passenger accommodation with a cocktail bar and hardi grass area aft.

MAIN ENGINES: Two MTU 12V 396 TB 83 marine diesel engines driving custom-designed 4-blade propellers via ZF BW 465 2.025:1 reverse reduction gearboxes.

AUXILIARY ENGINES: Two Perkins T6 3544 marine diesels driving 75kW 415/240V alternators.

ACCOMMODATION: up to 500 passengers. Crew: 6

CAPACITIES

Fresh water: 2600 l

Fuel oil: 15 400 l

Cargo:

DIMENSIONS

Length, overall: 41.00m

Length, waterline: 35.20m

Beam, moulded: 8.50m

Draught, max: 2.05m

PERFORMANCE

Speed, full load: 26 knots

Speed, light ship: 30 knots

Kita Ekspres

Elevation

Upper Deck

Main Deck

Lower Deck

Deck arrangements of Star Flyte

Star Flyte, 26 knots with up to 500 passengers

SUKA EKSPRES and SENANG EKSPRES

32 knot, 27m high-speed ferries delivered in November 1988 to Malaysia.
PRINCIPAL PARTICULARS
Length, overall: 27.00m
Length, waterline: 23.00m
Beam, moulded: 6.60m
Draught, max: 1.65m
Accommodation: 140 passengers, 4 crew
Main engines: Two MWM 8V TBD 604B
Auxiliary engine: One MWM D 226.6, 55kW
Fuel capacity: 5500l
Water capacity: 750l

SENANG EKSPRES

A 32.5 knot (at full load) mono-hull ferry built for K/Perlis Langkawi Ferry Sde Sdn Bhd, Malaysia

35 METRE JET RAIDER

A new project introduced in 1989
CLASSIFICATION: DnV 1A1 R465 EO LC
PRINCIPAL PARTICULARS
MAIN ENGINES
Two MWM 12V TBD 604, 1260kW each, MCR, 1800 rpm, 32° water ambients
PROPULSION
Two KaMeWa 56/S water-jet units
DIMENSIONS
Length, overall: 35.50m
Beam, moulded: 7.50m
Draught, max. at design water line: 1.00m
CAPACITIES
Fuel: 12 000 l
Fresh water: 15 000 l
ACCOMMODATION
Passengers: 400
Crew: 6
PERFORMANCE
Speed, full load: 30 knots
Speed, light ship: 34 knots

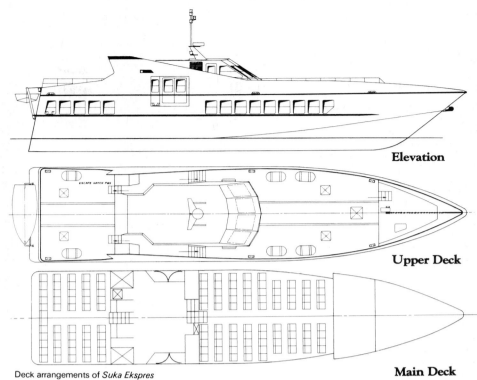

Elevation

Upper Deck

Main Deck

Deck arrangements of *Suka Ekspres*

Senang Ekspres

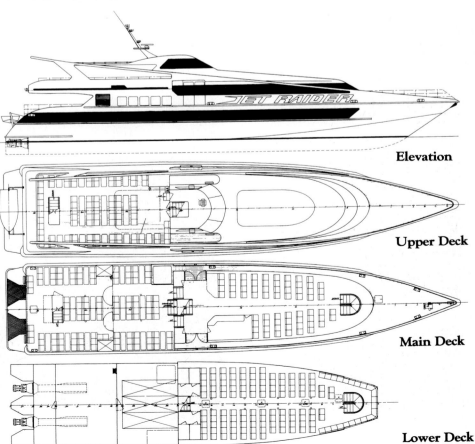

Elevation

Upper Deck

Main Deck

Lower Deck

General arrangement of the WaveMaster 35m Jet Raider

CHILE

ASTILLEROS Y MAESTRANZAS DE LA ARMADA (ASMAR)
Talcahuano, Chile

PROTECTOR CLASS PILOT LAUNCHES
LEP HALLEF
LEP ALACALUFE

Two 33metre 20 knot boats built under license from FBM Marine Ltd entered service in September 1989. These vessels have a range in excess of 1000 nautical miles and an endurance of up to 20 days and are powered by two MTU diesels. Both craft are intended to be permanently stationed in the Magellan Strait areas

One of two FBM Marine designed Chilian pilot boats

FINLAND

BÅTVARV HARRY ENGLUND
Pellinge, SF-07370, Finland

DIANA
Fast passenger ferry operating in vicinity of Helsinki.
DESIGNER: Båtvarv Harry Englund.
OWNER: Merimatkat Oy, Helsinki.
HULL: 15-degree deadrise monohedron planing hull constructed in aluminium.
MAIN ENGINES: Two MAN D 2840 10-cylinder LME engines, 618hp each.
PROPULSION: Two Hamilton Model 421 waterjet units.
ACCOMMODATION: 120 passengers.
DIMENSIONS
Length: 18.04m
PERFORMANCE
Speed, max: 35 knots lightly laden

120-passenger ferry *Diana*

WICO-BOAT
07955 Tessjö, Finland

FAST SUPPLY BOAT
A fast supply boat for evaluation by the Swedish Coastal Defence Corps.
HULL: Sandwich glass-reinforced plastics construction with Divynicell core.
ENGINES: Two Scania DS 114 diesels, 485hp each.
PROPULSION: Levi LDU 800 cowled propellers driven via ZF 1.2:1 gearboxes.
DIMENSIONS
Length: 21.8m
WEIGHTS/CAPACITIES
Displacement, empty: 20.0 tonnes
Load capacity, max: 15.0 tonnes
Liquid cargo capacity, water: 4000 litres
    fuel: 2000 litres
PERFORMANCE
Speed, lightship: 23.5 knots
Speed, 5-tonne load: 18.0 knots

The Scania-powered Wico-built Swedish defence supply boat

WÄRTSILÄ MARINE INDUSTRIES INC

HEAD OFFICE
P.O. Box1090, SF-00101 Helsinki, Finland

Telephone: (90) 1941

Telex: 126008 WMARI SF
Telefax: (90) 604 338

I Ingvesgård, *President and C E O*
K Ariaksinen, *Executive Vice President*

M Saarikangas, *Executive Vice President*
H-P Ihatsu, *Administration*
A Pankakoski, *Legal Affairs*
J Waris, *Business Development, Corporate Planning*

OY WÄRTSILÄ AB HELSINKI SHIPYARD

Box 132, SF-00151 Helsinki, Finland

Telephone: (90) 1941
Telex: 121246WHT SF

KOTKA

Wärtsilä Helsinki built four fast attack craft for the Finnish Navy. The *Kotka* is the last unit of the series. These craft are designed to function as strike and patrol boats with sea-keeping qualities for open-sea operation.
MAIN ENGINES: Power output 8000kW.
ARMAMENT
One multi-purpose 57mm gun
Two twin 23mm anti-aircraft guns
Eight surface-to-surface missiles
An electronic fire control system
DIMENSIONS
Length overall: 45.00m
Beam overall: 9.00m
WEIGHT
Displacement: 280 tonnes
PERFORMANCE
Speed: 30 knots plus

Wärtsilä *Kotka*, fast attack craft

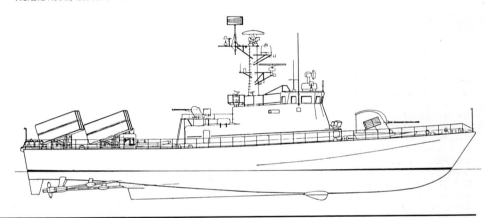
Wärtsilä 280-tonne fast attack craft

FRANCE

ALFA / NAVAL

F-83500 La Seyne, ZP de Bregaillon

Telephone: 94 945444
Telex: 404631 F

MADRAS

A 234 seat 27 knot light-alloy mono-hull ferry, with two 1119kW diesel engines . Built in 1985.

CHANTIERS NAVALS DE L'ESTEREL SA

20/26 boulevard du Midi, Boite Postale 19,
F-06321 Cannes la Bocca Cedex, France

Telephone: (93) 47 04 27
Telex: 470876ESTEREL F
Telefax: (93) 47 21 06

Amiral de Laforcade, *President*
Alain Lecerf, *Sales Manager*
Raoul Tsalichis, *Technical Manager*

Created in 1945, the yard specialises in building fast patrol boats, fast passenger boats and luxury yachts in aluminium, steel and composite resin epoxy wood.

The yard has an area of 14 000m² half of which is under cover. A 230-tonne capacity travelling gantry crane enables craft to be put into the water and to be lifted for dry docking very quickly.

By mid-1985 178 boats had been built with 109 exported to 24 countries. Eight types of fast patrol craft have been produced.

Esterel 26

ESTEREL 26

Motor yacht.
HULL: Hull and superstructure built in triple planking glued construction, resin sheathed, or in aluminium.
MAIN ENGINES: Two GM 12V 71 TI marine diesels producing a total of 1300hp.

ACCOMMODATION/CREW
Number of cabins: 4 double berth (8 persons)
Crew: 3
SYSTEMS
Fuel capacity: 6000 litres
Water capacity: 2500 litres

DIMENSIONS
Length overall: 26.0m
Beam: 5.80m
Draught: 1.45m
WEIGHT
Displacement fully loaded: 53 tonnes
PERFORMANCE
Speed, max at half load: 23 knots
Speed, cruising: 15 to 18 knots
Range at 15 knots: 650 miles

ESTEREL 27
Motor yacht.
Similar to the Esterel 26 but powered by two
MTU 8V 396 TB93 engines of 2600hp total, giving
it a maximum speed of 32 knots.

ESTEREL 29
Motor yacht.
HULL: Hull and superstructure built in triple
planking glued construction, sheathed with resin
or aluminium.
MAIN ENGINES: Two MTU 8V 396 TB93
marine diesel engines, 1300hp each.
ACCOMMODATION/CREW
Number of cabins: 4 double berth (8 persons)
Crew: 3 to 5
SYSTEMS
Fuel capacity: 11 000 litres
Water capacity: 3000 litres
DIMENSIONS
Length overall: 29.20m
Beam: 7.0m
Draught: 1.80m
WEIGHT
Displacement fully loaded: 80 tonnes
PERFORMANCE
Speed, max at half load: 23 knots
Speed, cruising: 15 to 20 knots
Range at 15 knots: 650 miles

ESTEREL 34
Motor yacht *Mes Amis* delivered July 1985.
HULL: Hull and superstructure built in triple
planking glued construction, sheathed in resin or
aluminium.
MAIN ENGINES: Two MTU 16V 396 TB93
marine diesels, 2375hp each.
ACCOMMODATION/CREW
Number of cabins: 5 or 6 double cabins (10/12
persons)
Crew: 5 to 8
SYSTEMS
Fuel capacity: 16 000 litres
Water capacity: 5000 litres
DIMENSIONS
Length overall: 34.20m
Beam: 7.80m
Draught: 2.10m
WEIGHT
Full load displacement: 135 tonnes
PERFORMANCE
Speed, max at half load: 28 knots
Speed, cruising: 15 to 25 knots
Range at 15 knots: 800 miles

ESTEREL 42
Motor yacht *Acajou* delivered June 1982.
HULL: Hull and superstructure built in triple

Esterel 29

Esterel 34 de luxe fast yacht *Mes Amis*

Esterel 42 luxury fast yacht *Acajou*

Esterel 42 prior to launching at Cannes la Bocca

planking glued construction, sheathed with resin
or aluminium.
MAIN ENGINES: Two MTU 16V 538 TB92
marine diesels, producing 3670hp each.
ACCOMMODATION/CREW
Number of cabins: 5 double berth (10 persons)
Crew: 7
SYSTEMS
Fuel capacity: 27 500 litres
Water capacity: 5000 litres

DIMENSIONS
Length overall: 42.0m
Beam: 7.80m
Draught, max: 2.10m
WEIGHT
Full load displacement: 165 tonnes
PERFORMANCE
Speed, max at half load: 34 knots
Speed, cruising: 15 to 20 knots
Range at 15 knots: 1500 miles

34-METRE HIGH-SPEED PASSENGER FERRY

Established for 46 years this builder of fast patrol boats and luxury motor yachts has entered the high-speed ferry market with a 253 passenger mono-hull vessel delivered March 1988. The design is by naval architects André Mauric and Jean-Charles Nahon and several versions of the basic design are available from 26 metres to 46 metres with passenger capacities of 150 to 450 passengers.

TROPIC

The first of the 34 metre ferries to be built *Tropic* has entered service with Société de Transports Maritimes in Guadaloupe. The vessel has air conditioning and luxury accommodation.

The Esterel *Tropic*

Wheelhouse of *Tropic*

PRINCIPAL PARTICULARS
Hull: aluminium
Class: BVI3/3
Length, overall: 34.60 m
Length, waterline: 30.80 m
Beam, overall: 7.50 m
Draught: 1.85 m
Displacement, empty: 76 tonnes
Displacement, full load: 108 tonnes
Fuel tank capacity: 11 000 l
Freshwater tank capacity: 1000 l
Engines: two MWM TBD 604B V16, each 1946 kW (2610 hp) max, 1704 kW (2285 hp) MCR
Propulsion: conventional propellers
Auxiliary power: two GM 70 kVA generating sets

Accommodation: 253 seats, 31 of which are on the sun deck
Speed, max: 32 knots
Speed, continuous: 30.5 knots

ESTEREL 105
ESTEREL OF CANNES

Delivered August 1987, hull design by André Mauric and superstructure and interior design by Paolo Caliari
PRINCIPAL PARTICULARS
Length, overall: 32.80 m
Beam, overall: 7.70 m
Draught, max: 1.83 m
Displacement: 122 tonnes

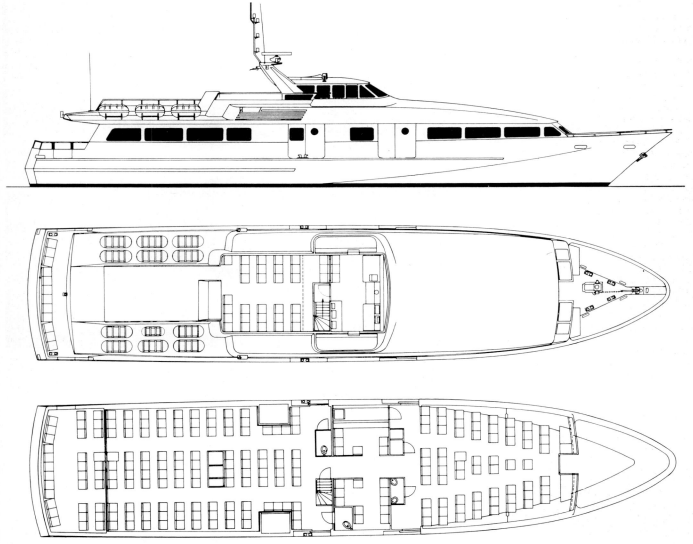
General arrangement of *Tropic*

Engines: two MTU 12V 396 TB93 each 2620 kW (3560 hp) max
Speed, max: 23 knots
Speed, cruise, trans Atlantic, full load: 12 knots-half load: 18 knots
Range at 12 knots: 3500n miles
Fuel tank capacity: 38 800 l
Fresh water tank capacity: 3000 l
Stabilisers: Naiad

Main deck: full width dining-room and saloon, including lounge, bar and TV, video, HiFi stereo, VIP guest stateroom, large bathroom
Lower deck: main stateroom, two large bathrooms and dressing room, two guest cabins, bathroom
Fly bridge: double deck saloon with bar

The Esterel 105 motor yacht *Esterel of Cannes*

CONSTRUCTIONS MÉCANIQUES DE NORMANDIE (CMN)

26 rue de Montevideo, 75116 Paris, France

Telephone: 45040877
Telex: 610097F

ERRAID, ERRACEL, EL KACED and ESSAID

Four customs patrol boats, launched 26 November 1987, for the Moroccan Customs Services. These vessels are identical to the six ships of the El Wacil class delivered by CMN to the Moroccan Navy in 1975 and 1976.
ENGINES: Two SACM diesels, 1270bhp each, at 1560rpm.
PROPELLERS: Two fixed-pitch.
DIMENSIONS
Length overall: 32.00m
Length waterline: 30.09m
Breadth, max, overall: 5.35m
Breadth, max, waterline: 4.92m
Depth, moulded, amidships: 3.00m
Draught, amidships at loaded displacement: 1.42m WEIGHTS
Displacement, full load: 88.70 tonnes
Displacement, average: 81.35 tonnes
Displacement, light: 74.00 tonnes
PERFORMANCE
Speed: 27 knots

CONSTRUCTIONS NAVALES GUY COUACH

Gujan, France

Head office: 215 avenue Francis Tonner, 06150 Cannes la Bocca, France

Telephone: (93) 47 13 17
Telex: 470737F
Telefax: (93) 48 03 66

Guy Couach are the successors to Couach Ltd who have been famous in yachting since 1897.

They have been building motor yachts in glassfibre since 1962, and they were the first to build a large motor yacht in Kevlar. They now offer a range of 35 speed boats to luxury motor yachts of 6 to 30m. The following are models offered above 20m:

The Guy Couach 2400

MODELS 2000 to 3000

Type	2000	2200	2301	2400	2402
DIMENSIONS (m)					
Length overall:	19.35	21.50	23.30	23.50	23.50
Length hull:	18.80	21.30	23.00	22.80	22.95
Beam overall:	5.40	5.40	6.28	5.40	6.30
Draught:	1.30	1.35	1.40	1.40	1.40
WEIGHTS (tonnes)					
Approx displacement, light:	24.00	30.00	35.00	32.50	35.00
full load:	31.20	37.50	42.00	39.20	42.00
MAIN ENGINES (largest installations)	Two GM 12V 92 TA 1080hp each	Two GM 12V 92 TA 1080hp each	Two DDC 12V 71 TA 1357kW each / Two DDC 16V 92 TA 2119kW each	Two GM 12V 92 TA 1080hp each	Two GM 12V 92 TA 1080hp each
PERFORMANCE					
Speed, max (knots):	31/33	28/30	24 / 32	27/29	26/28
Range at 22 knots (n miles):	490	450	400	440	450
OPTIONS*	Kevlar + LDU	Kevlar + LDU		Kevlar + LDU	Kevlar + LDU
ACCOMMODATION					
Crew:	2	2	2	2	2
Passengers:	6	8	8/10	6/8	8
SYSTEMS					
Generators:	20kW	20kW		20kW	24kW
Battery charger:	60A	60A		60A	Two 40A
Starting battery:	190Ah	190Ah		190Ah	190Ah
Servicing battery:	190Ah	190Ah		190Ah	190Ah
Fuel tank capacity:	5800 litres	5800 litres		5800 litres	6000 litres
Fresh water capacity:	1500 litres	1500 litres		1500 litres	1500 litres
Fresh water heater:	150 litres	150 litres		150 litres	200 litres
Air-conditioning, BTU:	60 000	60 000		72 000	90 000

Type	2501	2600	2801	2900	3000
DIMENSIONS (m)					
Length overall:	25.45	26.30	28.00	29.00	31.40
Length hull:	24.95	24.90	27.25	28.90	30.05
Beam overall:	6.28	6.30	6.30	7.34	6.30
Draught:	1.40	1.40	1.45	1.45	1.50
WEIGHTS (tonnes)					
Approx displacement, light:	35.00	43.00	45.00	45.00	48.00
full load:	42.00	54.00	56.00	56.00	62.00
MAIN ENGINES (largest installations)	Two DDC 12V 71 TA 1357kW each / Two DDC 16V 92 TA 2177kW each	Two DDC 12V 71 TA 1357kW each	Two DDC 16V 92 TA 2177kW each	Two DDC 12V 92 TA 1633kW each / Two DDC 16V 92 TA 2119kW each	Two MTU 12V96 TB93 1960hp each
PERFORMANCE					
Speed, max (knots):	24 / 32	24	32	25 / 29	32/33
Range at 22 knots (n miles):	400	580	580	580	580
OPTIONS*		Kevlar + LDU	Kevlar + LDU		Kevlar + LDU
ACCOMMODATION					
Crew:	4	2/3	3	3	4
Passengers:	8/10	8	10	10	12
SYSTEMS					
Generators:		32kW	32Kw		32kW
Battery charger:		Two 40A	Two 40A		Two 40A
Starting battery:		190Ah	380Ah		380Ah
Servicing battery:		190Ah	380Ah		380Ah
Fuel tank capacity:		10 000 litres	10 000 litres		12 000 litres
Fresh water capacity:		2200 litres	2200 litres		3000 litres
Fresh water heater:		200 litres	250 litres		300 litres
Air-conditioning, BTU:		120 000	120 000		144 000

* Kevlar + Levi Drive Units can increase performance by 3/4 knots approx

SOCIÉTÉ BRETONNE DE CONSTRUCTION NAVALE (SBCN)

BP 20, Hent-Croas, 29125 Loctudy, Brittany, France

Telephone: 98874271
Telex: 941356SBCN F

SBCN specialise in high-speed craft built in cold moulded plywood. The compound material is made up of very thin layers criss-crossed with hard mahogany fibres running in the same direction, vacuum-moulded in a matrix of epoxy resin. The resulting product is flexible, break-resistant and light, offers ease of maintenance and repair, good thermal and acoustic properties, avoidance of hull vibration and long term maintenance of shape. The yard has a workshop area of some 2500m². Craft delivered in 1986 and 1987 are summarised in the following paragraphs.

ATLANTE

This vessel is a high-speed passenger ferry launched in July 1985 for service with the Vedettes de L'Odet Ferry Co between Concarneau and the islands of Glénan, Brittany.
HULL: Cold moulded marine plywood.
ENGINES: Two MAN D2842 LE diesels, each 700hp.
PROPULSION: Two Hamilton Model 421 water-jet units.
PASSENGERS: 165.
DIMENSIONS
Length: 25.6m
Beam: 5.5m
Draught: 0.8m
PERFORMANCE
Speed, light, with 10% of permitted load: 30 knots
    at 31.6 tonnes displacement
    fully laden: 24 knots

TOURVILLE (ex D'ILES D'OR XVIII)

Passenger ferry, delivered 1986.
HULL: Cold moulded plywood.
MAIN ENGINES: Three MAN D 2840 LE marine diesels each 630hp.
PROPULSION: Three Hamilton 421 waterjet units.
PASSENGERS: 295.
DIMENSIONS
Length overall: 25.00m
Beam: 6.80m
PERFORMANCE
Speed, light, with 10% permitted load: 32 knots
    fully laden: 24 knots

AMIRAL DE JOINVILLE

Passenger ferry, delivered 1986.
OWNERS: Société Anonyme Atlantic Armement, for service between Noirmontier and Yeu Islands. HULL: Cold moulded plywood.
MAIN ENGINES: Two MAN D 2842 LE marine diesels each 750hp.

Amiral de Joinville, 25m passenger ferry

The waterjet-propelled *Atlante*

PROPULSION: Two Hamilton 421 waterjet units.
PASSENGERS: 195.
DIMENSIONS
Length: 25.00m
Beam: 6.70m
PERFORMANCE
Speed, light, with 10% permitted load: 31 knots
    fully laden: 24 knots

NICOLAS BOUCHARD

32m fast passenger ferry. Delivered in September 1987.
OWNERS: Société Anonyme Atlantic Armement, for service between La Baule and Belle-Ile Island.
HULL: Cold moulded plywood.
MAIN ENGINES: Two MWM TBD 234 V16 marine diesels 1200hp each.
PROPULSION: Two Sauer Engineering SE 912 waterjet units.

PASSENGERS: 270.
DIMENSIONS
Length: 32.00m
Beam: 6.80m
PERFORMANCE
Designed speed, light: 37 knots
    fully laden: 32 knots

PATRIOTE

38m patrol boat. Launched in November 1987.
OWNERS: Benin Navy.
HULL: Cold moulded plywood.
MAIN ENGINES: Three Baudouin 12P15–2 SR7 marine diesels 1200hp each.
PROPULSION: Three Sauer Engineering SE 912 waterjet units.
DIMENSIONS
Length: 38.00m
Beam: 6.90m
PERFORMANCE
Designed speed: 34 knots

SOCIÉTÉ FRANÇAISE DE CONSTRUCTIONS NAVALES (SFCN)

66 Quai Alfred Sisley, 92390 Villeneuve-la-Garenne, France

Telephone: (1) 47 94 64 46
Telex: 610998FRANCONA F

Jeanne-Marie Baudron, *Chairman and General Manager*
Charles Baudron, *General Manager*
Paul Charcusset, *Sales Director*
Jérôme Gouffier, *Purchase Director*
Christian Gaudin, *Technical Director*

Model of SFCN Marlin class patrol boat design

SFCN was founded in 1918 and for the past twenty years has specialised in the design and construction of sophisticated medium-tonnage boats (40/50m). The high performance of these conventional craft meet the demands of military applications such as light missile-launching corvettes and fast patrol boats.

To meet the demand for smaller craft with the same operational efficiency SFCN undertook hull design studies for their two new types of craft, the Espadon and Marlin class boats. The builder's claim that they have outstanding seaworthiness, perfect course and platform stability, exceptional manoeuvrability, less than 10 per cent speed loss in rough seas, low inboard diesel power, low operating cost, easy maintenance and are ideally suited for civilian and military applications.

SFCN Marlin class planing-hull fast patrol boat, type CGV 32

ESPADON 28
High-speed sea-going passenger boat.
Length overall: 27.50m
Beam: 6.40m
Draught, max: 1.85m
Displacement, full load: 70 tonnes
     light load: 50 tonnes
Engines: Two 1500hp
Max speed, full load: 25 knots
Speed cruising, with load: 22 knots
Range at 20 knots: 300 miles
Payload: 60 passengers + 7 tonnes freight
     or 150 passengers + 1 tonne freight

Regina, Espadon 28 passenger ferry operating in the Antilles

ESPADON 33
High-speed sea-going passenger boat.
Length overall: 33.0m
Beam: 6.40m
Draught, max: 1.85m
Displacement, full load: 100 tonnes
     light load: 75 tonnes
Engines: Two 1600hp
Max speed, full load: 25 knots
Speed cruising, with load: 22 knots
Range at 20 knots: 400 miles
Payload: 65 passengers + 15 tonnes freight
     or 120 passengers + 5 tonnes freight

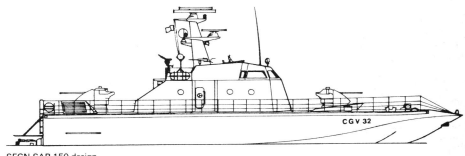

SFCN SAR 150 design

CREW BOATS (Yard Nos 841/1 and /2)
Two delivered March 1986.
Ordered by SURF & Cie in early 1985 for offshore transport from Pointe-Noire, Congo, and the offshore platforms or barges.
Length overall: 34.90m
     waterline: 28.0m
Breadth, moulded: 6.46m
Max draught, full load: 1.10m approx
Displacement: 88.70 tonnes
     light: 74.0 tonnes
Main engines: Two 1600hp
Speed: 27 knots
Passengers: 90
Crew: 5

REGINA
Passenger launch, delivered July 1984.
OWNER: M Brudey, Pointe-à-Pitre.
HULL: Hull construction is in steel with aluminium alloy superstructure.
MAIN ENGINES: Two GM 16V 149 T diesel engines, max 1350hp each at 1850rpm.
ACCOMMODATION
Passenger capacity: 150 seated
DIMENSIONS
Length overall: 27.50m
Length waterline: 23.0m
Draught: 1.85m
WEIGHT
Full load displacement: 70 tonnes

PERFORMANCE
Speed, max: 25 knots
     cruise: 22 knots

CREW BOAT
Two built, delivered 1986.
OWNER: SURF & Cie.
CLASSIFICATION: Bureau Veritas I 3/3 service special-transport (coastal transport of personnel).
MAIN ENGINES: Two engines 1600hp each.
ACCOMMODATION/CREW
Crew: 5
Passengers: 90

ESPADON CLASS FAST PATROL BOAT DESIGNS

Type	Espadon 24	Espadon 29	Espadon 34
Hull:		hull constructed in steel, aluminium alloy superstructure	
Length overall:	24.50m	29.00m	34.00m
Beam, max:	5.80m	6.50m	7.10m
Draught, max:	1.60m	1.85m	1.85m
Full load displacement:	65 tonnes	90 tonnes	110 tonnes
Main engines:	two 1200kW	two 1650kW	two 1900kW
Propulsion:		two fixed-pitch propellers	
Continuous speed, full load:	30 knots	30 knots	30 knots
Range:	300n miles	500n miles	600n miles
Complement:	7/8	10/12	18
Armament:	two 20mm guns	one twin 30mm gun	one 40mm gun
		one 20mm gun	four MM40 missiles
		one optronic fire	one search radar
		control system	one fire control radar

DIMENSIONS
Length overall: 34.90m
Length waterline: 28.0m
Beam: 6.46m
Draught: 1.10m
WEIGHTS
Full load displacement: 88.70 tonnes
Light displacement: 74.0 tonnes
PERFORMANCE
Speed: 27 knots

MARLIN 35
SAINT EUGENE V
A high-speed passenger launch, hull No. 855, delivered 8 April, 1988 to Société Anonyme d'Economie Mixte de Saint-Pierre et Miquelon.
PRINCIPAL PARTICULARS
Hull: light alloy
Length, overall: 35.00m
Length, bp: 28.00m

Breadth, moulded: 6.30m Draught, midships: 1.00m
Displacement, light: 67 tonnes
Displacement, loaded: 88 tonnes
Engines: two MWM TBD 604B v12, MCR 1268kW each max 1417kW
Propulsion: KaMeWa 63S 62/6 water-jet units
Speed: at 88 tonnes, MCR: 27 knots
Speed, max: 88 tonnes
Accommodation: 200
Crew: 6

Marlin 35 crew boats *Angelica* and *Aida* built for SURF & Cie operating off the Congo coast

SFCN CREW BOATS

Type	Marlin 30 Design	Marlin 35 *Angelica* and *Aida* hull and superstructure in aluminium alloy	Marlin 43 Design
Hull:			
Length overall:	30.00m	35.00m	43.00m
Beam, max:	6.50m	7.10m	9.10m
Draught, max:	1.10m	1.20m	1.50m
Full load displacement:	80 tonnes	95 tonnes	140 tonnes
Main engines:	two 1850kW	two 1850kW	two 1850kW
Propulsion:		two waterjets	
Weights:	15 tonnes: 150 passengers or 60 passengers plus 10 tonnes freight	23 tonnes: 250 passengers or 90 passengers plus 15 tonnes freight	32 tonnes: 400 passengers or 90 passengers plus 25 tonnes freight
Speed, continuous, full load:	40 knots	38 knots	27 knots
Range:	400n miles at 20 knots	350n miles at 20 knots	250n miles at 27 knots

Type	Espadon 24 Design	Espadon 28 steel hull with aluminium alloy superstructure	Espadon 34 Design
Hull:			
Length overall:	24.50m	27.50m	34.00m
Beam, max:	5.80m	6.40m	7.10m
Draught, max:	1.60m	1.85m	1.85m
Full load displacement:	65 tonnes	85 tonnes	110 tonnes
Main engines:	two 1200kW	two 1450kW	two 1900kW
Propulsion:		two fixed-pitch propellers	
Weights:	80 passengers	150 passengers	250 passengers
Speed, continuous, full load:	30 knots	30 knots	30 knots
Range:	350n miles at 20 knots	400n miles at 20 knots	40n miles at 20 knots

SEARCH AND RESCUE VESSEL DESIGNS

Model	SAR 150	SAR 200	SAR 300
Length overall:	38.60m	41.0m	52.20m
Beam:	6.20m	6.80m	7.15m
Max draught:	2.0m	2.10m	2.15m
Mean displacement:	150 tonnes	180 tonnes	270 tonnes
Max continuous speed (mean displacement):	with two 2200hp engines, 27 knots with two 3200hp engines, 30 knots	with two 2200hp engines, 25 knots with two 3200hp engines, 28 knots	with two 3200hp engines, 26 knots with two 5000hp engines, 30 knots
Range at 16 knots:	2000 miles	2000 miles	2000 miles
Complement (min/max):	3/5 officers 13/15 petty officers and ratings	5/7 officers 14/16 petty officers and ratings	5/7 officers 14/16 petty officers and ratings
Accommodation facilities:	12 rescued persons	15 rescued persons	20 rescued persons
Armament (optional):	one 20mm gun two 12.7mm machine guns	two 3mm twin guns two 12.7mm machine guns	one or two 20mm, 30mm or 40mm guns two 12.7mm machine guns

MARLIN CLASS FAST PATROL BOAT DESIGNS

Type	CGV 28	CGV 32	CGV 36
Length overall:	28.0m	32.0m	36.0m
Breadth, max:	6.0m	7.0m	8.0m
Draught, max:	1.65m	1.90m	1.10m
Hull:	light alloy	light alloy	light alloy
Speed:	with two 1200hp engines, 32 knots fixed-pitch propellers or waterjets or with two 1500hp engines, 35 knots variable-pitch propellers or waterjets	with two 2600hp engines, 36 knots variable-pitch propellers or waterjets	with two 3300hp engines, 36 knots variable-pitch propellers or waterjets
Range (at 16 knots):	1000n miles	1500n miles	2000n miles
Displacement:	55 tonnes	100 tonnes	120 tonnes
Complement:	2 officers 14 petty officers and ratings	3 officers 16 petty officers and ratings	3 officers 20 petty officers and ratings
Armament:	one Optronic fire control system one 20mm gun two 12.7mm machine guns	two 30mm Oerlikon guns two 12.7mm machine guns	one radar with MTI one fire control radar or Optronic fire control system one 57mm Bofors gun one twin 30mm Oerlikon gun 4 or 8 MM40 missiles one Sadral ship-to-air weapon system

Type	Marlin 26	Marlin 30	Marlin 35
Hull and superstructure:		aluminium alloy	
Length overall:	26.50m	30.00m	35.50m
Beam, max:	5.80m	6.50m	7.10m
Draught, max:	1.00m	1.10m	1.20m
Full load displacement:	50 tonnes	70 tonnes	95 tonnes
Main engines:	two 1250kW	two 1600kW	two 1935kW
Propulsion:		two waterjets	
Speed continuous, full load:	45 knots	42 knots	38 knots
Range:	600n miles	650n miles	700n miles
Complement:	7/8	10/12	18
Armament:	two 20mm guns	one twin 30mm gun one 20mm gun one Optronic fire control system	one 40mm gun four MM40 missiles one search radar one fire control radar

GERMANY, FEDERAL REPUBLIC

ABEKING AND RASMUSSEN SHIPYARD

An der Fähre 2, PO Box 1160, D-2874 Lemwerder, Federal Republic of Germany

Telephone: (0421) 6733-0
Telex: 245128AR D
Telefax: (0421) 6733112

37 METRE MOTOR YACHT
PROPULSION: Waterjet propulsion.
DIMENSIONS
Length, overall: 37.00m
WEIGHTS
Displacement about 200 tonnes
PERFORMANCE: 32.0 knots

SAR 33
Fast patrol boat.
Fourteen craft have been built and are in service in Turkey.
DIMENSIONS
Length, overall: 34.60m
Beam: 8.60m
WEIGHTS
Displacement: 160 tonnes
PERFORMANCE
Speed: 40 knots

Abeking and Rasmussen 37 metre motor yacht with KaMeWa water jets

Abeking and Rasmussen 34.6 metre search and rescue patrol boat, SAR 33

27 METRE MOTOR YACHT
DIMENSIONS
Length, overall: 27.00m
WEIGHTS
Displacement, about 95.00 tonnes
PERFORMANCE
Speed: 46.4

CGV 26
Fast patrol boat.
HULL: Built in steel with an aluminium super-structure.
DIMENSIONS
Length, overall: 26.00m
Beam: 5.80m
WEIGHTS
Displacement 75 tonnes
PERFORMANCE
Speed: 40.0 knots plus

Abeking and Rasmussen 27 metre motor yacht

Abeking and Rasmussen CGV 26, a 26 metre patrol boat

F R LÜRSSEN WERFT (GmbH & Co)
Friedrich-Klippert-Strasse 1, 2820 Bremen 70, Federal Republic of Germany

Telephone: (0421) 6604 0
Telex: 0244484AFLW D
Telefax: (0421) 6604 443

Fast motor boats, motor cruisers and motor yachts have been built from the beginning of the company's history; in 1906 the motor boat *Donnerwetter* reached a speed of 65km/h against international competition, in 1926 the Lürssen Sedan cruiser won the Blue Riband of the Rhine and in 1927 a Lürssen racing boat reached the speed of 106.3km/h. These achievements were followed by a three-engine motor yacht *Oheka II* making 32 knots in 1928 and Gert Lürssen winning the world record for diesel-driven boats in 1939 with a speed of 37 knots. Recent construction includes fast attack craft, small corvettes, mine combat vessels, and fast yachts. In 1985 the rescue craft *Hermann Helms* was built followed by the rescue craft *Alfried Krupp* in 1988.

BERLIN and STEPPKE
Rescue craft.
First of class mothership/daughter rescue craft designed and built for the West German Sea Rescue Society.
MAIN ENGINES: One MTU 12V 396 TB93 marine diesel developing 1200kW and two MWM TBD 234 V12 wing engines each rated at 574kW.
PROPULSION: One 1200mm central propeller and two 950mm wing propellers (port and starboard).
CONTROLS: Steering gear is electro-hydraulic to the three rudders each having one emergency servo device.
CAPACITIES: 500 litres of fire extinguishant.
COMPLEMENT: Crew of 8.
DAUGHTER CRAFT: Launched down stern ramp and through a hinged flap on the transom. Length 7.50m, beam 2.29m, draught 0.60m, displacement 3.10 tonnes. Power BMW D190 diesel of 121kW output, driving a fixed-pitch propeller through reduction gearing, speed 15.0 knots.
SYSTEMS
Auxiliary machinery: Two Mercedes OM352 diesels connected to Kaick generators each set rated at 50kVA
Bow thruster: ZF Herion type 70/175/320 with an output of 75kW
Firefighting: Two monitors mounted at the after end of superstructure
DIMENSIONS
Length overall: 27.50m
Beam: 6.00m
Draught: 1.63m
WEIGHT
Displacement: 100 tonnes
PERFORMANCE
Cruising speed: 24 knots

GREECE

HELLENIC SHIPYARDS CO
Skaramanga Yard, Athens, Greece

Telephone: 5572305/5573350
Telex: (Athens office) 215123
(Skaramanga yard) 215293
Telefax: 5573359

Apart from the craft described in subsequent paragraphs the yard has built six missile-firing fast patrol boats based on the Combattante 111B for the Hellenic Navy.

29-METRE FAST PATROL BOAT
Hellenic Shipyards Co has built for the Greek Government a series of 10 fast patrol boats under licence from Abeking and Rasmussen of West Germany in the period 1977–79, to be used by coast guard, customs and other authorities.

Each boat is equipped with two MTU 12V 331 TC81 diesels 1360hp each giving a speed of about 27 knots. They have a steel hull and marine type aluminium alloy superstructure and a crew of 16. The hull form is round bilge semi-displacement. The standard armament of the vessel consists of two single 20mm naval guns on the main deck.
DIMENSIONS
Length overall: 29.00m
Length waterline: 27.00m
Beam at deck: 5.00m
Depth amidships: 2.56m
Max draught: 1.62m (approx)
WEIGHT
Design displacement: 71.00 tonnes (approx)

Hellenic Shipyards 29m fast patrol boat

23-METRE FAST ATTACK BOAT
In the period 1980–81 Hellenic Shipyards Co has built two fast attack boats under licence from Panagopoulos Associates for the Hellenic Navy.

Each boat is equipped with two MTU 12V 331 TC92 diesels 1530hp each giving a speed of about 38 knots. Their structure is of all aluminium alloy and can take a crew of 6. They have a hard chine hull form with straight lines which were model tested in USA.
DIMENSIONS
Length overall: 23.00m
Length waterline: 21.00m
Beam at deck: 5.00m
Depth amidships: 2.90m
Max draught: 0.97m
WEIGHT
Design displacement: 35.00 tonnes

23m fast attack boat built by Hellenic Shipyards under licence from Panagopoulos Associates

25-METRE FAST ATTACK CRAFT (FAC-25) (DESIGN)
MAIN ENGINES: Two MTU 12V 396 TB93 engines each rated at 1398kW max, and 1152kW continuous power.
PROPULSION: Two propellers.
COMPLEMENT: 11.
ARMAMENT: One twin 30mm Oerlikon GCM-B01, two SSM launchers Penguin Mk 2, two 7.60mm light machine guns.
DIMENSIONS
Length overall: 25.00m
Breadth, moulded: 5.72m
Depth, amidships: 2.96m
Draught, full load (over propellers): 1.77m
WEIGHTS
Normal displacement (with half-filled tanks draught 1.70m): 62.90 tonnes
PERFORMANCE
Speed, sprint: 35 knots
Speed, cruising: 31 knots
Endurance: 580n miles at 30 knots, 800n miles at 20 knots

Hellenic Shipyards 25m high-speed luxury yacht

FAST ATTACK CRAFT (DESIGN)

MAIN ENGINES: Four MTU 16V TB94 each rated at 3500ps max driving through four reversible gearboxes.

PROPULSION: Four fixed-pitch propellers.

COMPLEMENT: 25.

ARMAMENT: One Bofors type Mk 2 57mm gun, one Breda-Bofors 40L/70 40mm gun, four Exocet MM40 SSM launchers, two FFV/TP 43x0 400mm torpedo tubes, two Elma system depth charge racks, two Philips type 9CM/100 Chaff/IR decoy launchers.

DIMENSIONS

Length overall: 47.00m

Length, waterline: 43.50m

Beam, max: 7.80m (approx)

Beam at waterline: 7.00m

Depth, amidships: 4.60m

Draught, normal displacement: 2.10m

WEIGHTS

Displacement, full load: 280 tonnes (approx)

Displacement, half load: 260 tonnes (approx)

PERFORMANCE

Speed, max at half load displacement: 37.00 knots

Endurance: 1500n miles (approx) at 16 knots

25 METRE MOTOR YACHT

Four of these vessels have been built

PRINCIPAL PARTICULARS

Length, overall: 25.00

Beam: 5.72m

Draught, full load: 1.09m

Displacement, full load: 60.6 tonnes

Displacement, normal: 56.3 tonnes

Engines: two MTU diesels, 1134kW each, sprint, 951kW each, continuous

Speed, max.sprint: about 32 knots

Speed, continuous, normal displacement: about 29 knots

Fuel capacity, main tank: 7000 l; spare tank: 2700 l

Fresh water capacity: 3350 l

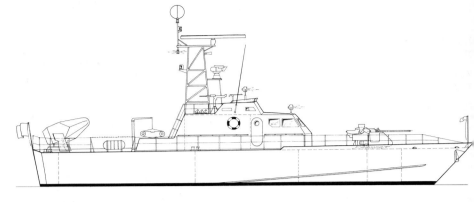

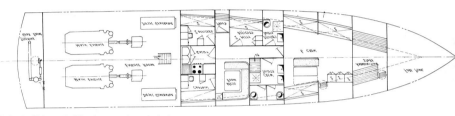

Hellenic Shipyards 25m fast attack craft design

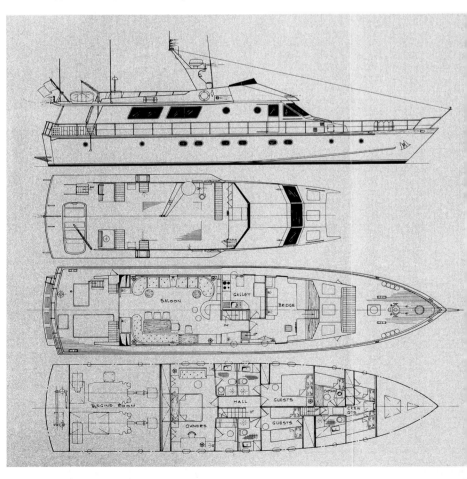

General arrangement of 25m luxury yacht

HONG KONG

CHEOY LEE SHIPYARDS LTD

863–865 Lai Chi Kok Road, Kowloon, Hong Kong, PO Box 80040 Cheung Sha Wan, Kowloon, Hong Kong.

Telephone: (3) 7437710
Telex: 56361 CLS HX
Telefax: (3) 7862873

Ken Lo, *Director*
C.H.Elliott Brown, *Technical Manager*

The company was originally founded in Shanghai over a century ago. It moved to a small yard in Hong Kong in 1937 and to a much larger yard in 1940, and was occupied with building and repairing cargo ships. It diversified into building teak sailing yachts for export in 1956 and acquired a large site for a second yard on Lantau Island in 1960. Commenced building motor yachts and building in GRP in 1961 and at present operates 3 divisions, one each for steel and composite commercial vessels, for GRP workboats and for GRP pleasurecraft. The company has built over 4000 vessels since the current records commenced in 1950.

TANJUNG BAKARANG

Harbour Inspection and Service Launch delivered in June 1988.
OWNER: Marine Department, Bandar Seri Begawan, Brunei Darussalam
CLASSIFICATION: Lloyds + 100A1 (Restricted Service) + LMC
DIMENSIONS
Length, overall: 25.84m
Length, waterline: 22.20m
Beam, moulded: 6.43m
Draught: 1.82m
CAPACITIES
Tanks, fuel oil: 13620 l
Tank, fresh water: 2630 l
WEIGHT
Displacement 55 tonnes
HULL: Moderate V bottom form with sponson chines. Construction in solid glass reinforced plastic with foam core double skin for the decks. Two tier superstructure with wheelhouse and VIP lounge on the upper deck, galley and dinette type seating on main deck. All accommodation fully air conditioned.
COMPLEMENT
8 crew plus 65 passengers
MAIN ENGINES
Two MAN D2842LXE, 662kW each driving propellers through ZF BW 190 gearboxes
SYSTEMS ELECTRICAL
Two Perkins/Stamford generator sets, 70 kVA 380V, 50Hz, 3Ph.
Two 24V 200Ah starting battery sets
Two 24V 120Ah starting battery sets
NAVIGATIONAL
One Koden MD3732T radar
One Seafarer No 700 echo sounder
COMMUNICATIONAL
One Icom IC-M700 SSB radio telephone
One Icom IC-M80 VHF radio telephone
PERFORMANCE
Speed, maximum: 23.5 knots
Speed, service: 19.0 knots

DISCOVERY BAY 17

Fast Passenger Launch delivered October 1988
OWNER: Hong Kong Resort Co. Ltd.
LEGISLATING AUTHORITY: Hong Kong Marine Department
CLASSIFICATION: American Bureau of Shipping 100 A1 + AMS
DIMENSIONS
Length, overall: 22.78m,

Tanjung Bakarang, harbour inspection and service launch

Discovery Bay 17

Length, waterline: 20.04m
Beam, moulded: 5.41m
Draught: 1.67m
CAPACITIES
Tanks, fuel oil: 5100 l
Tank, fresh water: 450 l
WEIGHT
Displacement: 36.1 tonnes
HULL
Deep V constant deadrise construction in solid glass reinforced plastics. Two tier superstructure with wheelhouse and short passenger saloon on the upper deck forward half, after half open under awning. Full length main deck passenger saloon and toilets. The closed saloons and wheelhouse fully air conditioned.
COMPLEMENT: 4 crew plus 163 passengers
MAIN ENGINES
Two Stewart and Stevenson Detroit Diesel model 16V-92MCTAB, 988 HP each driving propellers through Nico MGN 273 gearboxes
SYSTEMS ELECTRICAL
One Mercedes Benz/Stamford generator set

32.5 kVA, 380V, 50Hz, 3Ph
Two 24V 200AH starting battery sets
One 24V 120AH starting battery set
NAVIGATIONAL: One Anritsu RA-72OUA daylight marine radar
COMMUNICATIONAL: One Sailor VHF/RT 2048 compact VHF radio telephone
PERFORMANCE
Maximum speed, loaded: 25.00 knots
Service speed: 23 knots

CHEOYLEE 66

Sport Motor Yacht
DIMENSIONS
Length, overall: 20.11m, Beam: 5.79m,
Draught: 1.13m
CAPACITIES
Tanks, fuel oil: 6320 l
Tanks, fresh water: 1300 l
WEIGHT
Displacement, half fuel and water: 29.00 tonnes approx

HULL
Moderate V bottom form with sponson chines.
Hull and superstructure in glass reinforced plastics
with foam cored sandwich construction

ACCOMMODATION/CREW
Flying bridge with guests' seats
Fishing cockpit with helm and engine/gear
controls, large deck saloon/galley. Below deck,
owner's stateroom with double bed two 2-berth
guest cabins, one 2-berth crew cabin. Air conditioned throughout

MAIN ENGINES
Two Detroit Diesel Super 11V-71T1 870 HP each
driving propellers through ZF BW 195 gearboxes.
Underwater exhausts with idling by-passes

SYSTEMS ELECTRICAL
Two Westerbeke or Onan 15kW 230V 60Hz 1 Ph
generator sets with hush covers
Two 24V 180 AH starting battery sets
Two 12V 90 AH starting battery sets

PERFORMANCE
Maximum speed, half fuel 29 knots
Cruising speed 24–25 knots

Cheoy Lee 66 fast motor yacht

CHEOYLEE 66
Fast Motor Yacht
Similar to 66 Sport Yacht except no cockpit, main
deck saloon extended to transom with division.
Choice of accommodation layout either with
galley in deck saloon and five double berth cabins
below deck or galley and sauna steam and jacussi
bath rooms below deck with only three double
berth cabins.
Same machinery and performance as 66 Sport
Yacht.

CHEOYLEE 83
Cockpit Motor Yacht
DIMENSIONS
Length, overall: 25.27m
Length, waterline: 22.29m
Beam: 6.42m
Draught: 1.62m
CAPACITIES
Tanks, fuel oil: 11 355 l
Tanks, fresh water: 2650 l
WEIGHT
Displacement: 63.8 tonnes
HULL
Moderate V bottom form with sponson chines
Hull, decks and superstructure in glass reinforced
plastics with extensive use of foam cored
sandwich construction
ACCOMMODATION/CREW
Flying bridge with L settees and table for guests
Open aft cockpit with access gate to swimming
platform
Large main deck saloon with galley at forward
end
Owner stateroom with double bed and bathroom
with whirlpool bath
Below deck 2-berth crew cabin and three 2-berth
guest cabins
Air conditioned throughout
MAIN ENGINES
Two Detroit Diesel super 12V-71T1 870 hp each
driving propellers through ZF BW 195
reverse/reduction gearboxes
Underwater exhausts with idling by-passes
SYSTEMS ELECTRICAL
Two Westerbeke or Onan 15kW 230V 50Hz 1 Ph
generator sets with hush covers
Two 24V 180Ah starting battery sets
Two 12V 90Ah starting battery sets
PERFORMANCE
Speed, maximum, half fuel: 24 knots
Speed, cruising: 17–19 knots

Cheoy Lee 83

CHEOYLEE 92
Cockpit Motor Yacht
Enlarged version of 83 Cockpit Motor Yacht with
similar layout and machinery except generator
sets 25kW and more elaborate bathroom for aft
cabin

Cheoy Lee 66 sport yacht

Caterpillar 3412 1000 hp engines may be fitted at
option for maximum speed of 25 knots
DIMENSIONS
Length, overall: 28.02m
Length, waterline: 24.94m

Beam: 6.43m,
Draught: 1.37m (to keel)
WEIGHT
Displacement 67.85 tonnes

CHUNG WAH SHIPBUILDING & ENGINEERING COMPANY LIMITED

41 Yau Tong Marine Lot, Cha Kwo Ling Road, Kwun Tong, Kowloon, Hong Kong

Telephone: 85237276333
Telex: 45803WAHBU HX
Telefax: 85237727642

Wong Wah Sang, *Chairman*
Peter Man-kong Wong, *Managing Director*
Ronnie Man-chiu Wong, *Executive Director*
Alfred Pang, *Shipbuilding General Manager*
Geoffrey Robson, *Asst. Shipbuilding General Manager*
Alex N. Cowan, *Technical Consultant*

The company was established in 1940, and business covers shipbuilding, ship repairing, civil and mechanical engineering, steel structural construction, technical services and consultancy.

The shipbuilding and repair division has built and repaired marine craft in steel ranging from salvage tugs, deck container vessels, fire fighting boats, supply vessels, and cargo vessels to police patrol boats.

The company has completed a total of 34 steel police patrol launches for the Royal Hong Kong Marine Police and three cimand launches for the Customs and Excise Dept of the Hong Kong Government. The success of these craft has been due to the joint effort of Damen Shipyards (in The Netherlands) responsible for the basic design of the hull, and Chung Wah Shipbuilding and Engineering Company Ltd.

PL71, one of 15 Chung Wah-built high-speed launches for the Royal Hong Kong Marine Police

Flying bridge and coxswain console on PL71

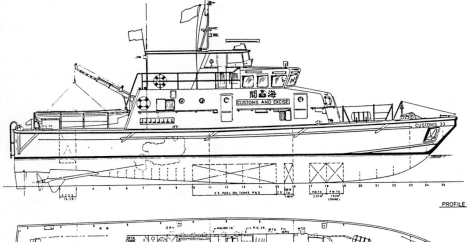

PROFILE

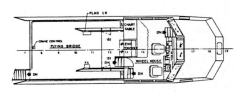

WHEEL HOUSE & FLYING BRIDGE

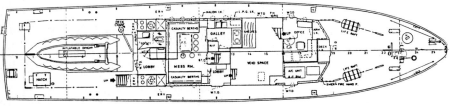

MAIN DECK

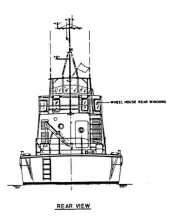

REAR VIEW

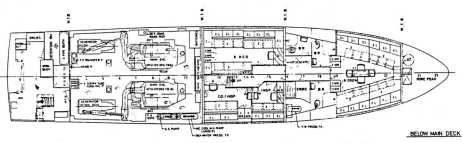

BELOW MAIN DECK

General arrangement of King class patrol boats for the Customs and Excise Department, Hong Kong

'KING' CLASS
KING LAI
Police launch.

HULL: Constructed in steel.

MAIN ENGINES/GEARBOXES: Two MTU 12V 396 TB83 each delivering 1100kW through ZF gearboxes; one Kosan 424A engine, with ZF gearbox.

PROPULSION: Two fixed-pitch propellers by SMM (MTU engines); one KaMeWa steerable waterjet (Kosan engine).

CONTROLS: Nautiservo BV electro-hydraulic steering gear.

ACCOMMODATION

Complement: 18 officers and crew

Air-conditioned

SYSTEMS

Electrical generators: Two Kosan 60kVA alternators

Navigational equipment: RM1226C 12in, with 9in slave radar and EMY1/C speed log repeater supplied by Racal Decca; one Sinrad echo sounder; one S G Brown 1000 gyrocompass and repeater

Search and rescue: One Avon sea rider launched or recovered by hydraulic crane operated from flying bridge

PERFORMANCE

Speed at operational displacement, with twin MTU engines: Over 24 knots
with twin MTU engines and Kosan engine: Over 26 knots

Kosan engine loitering speed: 9 knots

Wheelhouse of King class launch

King class police launches, built by Chung Wah

INDONESIA

P T FABRIK KAPAL INDONESIA (PERSERO)
P T PAL INDONESIA
Jakarta office:
BPPT Building, 12th Floor, JI M H Thamrin No 8, Jakarta, Indonesia

Telephone: 323774–324350
Telex: 61331APT JKT

Surabaya office:
Ujung-Surabaya, PO Box 134, Indonesia

Telephone: 291403/24139
Telex: 31223PAL SB

The company produces patrol boats in wood and aluminium designed for customs, police,

harbourmaster and naval duties. 6000 workers are employed on building and repair work.

FPB-28
Fast patrol boat.

HULL: Double planking hull construction, outer layer in teak and inner layer in red meranti. Hull frames and superstructure are in marine grade aluminium.

MAIN ENGINES: Two 1220hp diesel engines.

PROPULSION: Two three-blade fixed-pitch propellers.

SYSTEMS

Electrical generators: Two 18kVA 220/380V 50Hz 3hp generators

Batteries: 24V

Armament: One deck-mounted machine gun

Navigational equipment: One radar, one echo sounder and one magnetic compass

Communications: Internal and external

DIMENSIONS

Length overall: 28.0m

Length waterline: 26.0m

Beam: 5.40m

Draught: 1.84m

WEIGHTS

Light weight: 51.7 tonnes

Fuel displacement: 68.50 tonnes

PERFORMANCE

Max speed, continuous: 28.5 knots
intermittent: 30.0 knots

Cruising speed: 15.0 knots

Range at 28.5 knots: 1100n miles

TJETTY MARINE
Tanjung Pinang, Indonesia

BIMA EXPRESS

A high-speed ferry built in glass-reinforced plastic for the Singapore to Tanjung Pinang route, approximately 63 miles and operated by Tjetty Marine.

ENGINES: Two GM 8V 92 TI, 570hp at 2300rpm.
PROPULSION: Two Hamilton Jet Model 421, Type 38 impeller, waterjet units.
DIMENSIONS
Length: 20.0m
Beam: 4.9m
Deadrise at stern: 13°
WEIGHTS
Light: 19.0 tonnes
Loaded: 24.0 tonnes

Tjetty Marine *Bima Express* propelled by two Hamilton waterjet units, type 421

PERFORMANCE
Speed, max, light: 32.0 knots
loaded: 28.0 knots

ITALY

ALFA MARINE Srl
Via Della Scafa 135, 00054 Fiumicino, Italy

Telephone: (06) 645 3838/0355
Telex: 614580ALFAMA I

ALFA 83 25-METRE FAST CRUISER
HULL: Built in grp with V-keel with longitudinal side fins.
ENGINES/GEARBOXES: Two MTU 8V 396 TB93, 1300hp each driving propellers through BW 255 gearboxes.
SYSTEMS
Electrical: Two diesel generators 16kW, central control and distribution panel 24V, batteries 500Ah, 24V
Fuel tank capacity: 6000 litres
Trim: Hydraulically actuated flaps for longitudinal and transverse trim
Manoeuvring: Bow thruster
Navigation: 40 mg radar, echo sounder with optical plotting, Loran C, automatic pilot
Communications: VHF 25W 60-channel, SSB 1 8–28m Hz 220W
ACCOMMODATION: Master cabin with bathroom and WC, four guest cabins, with bathroom and WC, kitchen, crew quarters, 2 bunkbeds, piloting cabin, 2 seats, fly deck controls, 3 seats, fly sun deck, poop deck, lounge with bar, aft deck. Air-conditioning fitted.
DIMENSIONS
Length overall: 25.0m
Beam: 6.0m
Air draught: 3.90m
Draught: 1.50m
WEIGHTS
Displacement, empty: 40.0 tonnes
Displacement, tanks half full: 43.75 tonnes

Alfa Marine 25m, 33-knot fast cruiser

PERFORMANCE
Speed, max: 36 knots
cruising: 33 knots

ALFA 84 (DESIGN)
Fast work and weapon systems carrier.
The Alfa 84 hull has been designed to carry out a variety of commercial and naval roles. Alternative upper deck and accommodation layouts are available to meet individual operational requirements.
CLASSIFICATION: Built to ABS classification.
HULL: Grp and Kevlar hull with aluminium superstructure.
MAIN ENGINES: Two MTU 12V 396 TB93 marine diesels, 1900hp each, underwater exhaust discharge and hydrosilencers.
PROPULSION: Two waterjets, KaMeWa or Riva Calzoni Type IRC 41 DL.
CONTROLS: Pneumatic engine controls and hydraulic steering gear fitted in wheelhouse and flying bridge.
ACCOMMODATION: Living quarters for six to eight junior ratings, mess deck and heads, junior officer's three-berth cabin and commanding officer's living quarters.
ARMAMENT
Basic versions: One 20mm Oerlikon mounting forward
Gun boat version: Two 30mm Breda turrets fore and aft
Gun boat version B: Two 81mm coastal rocket launchers fore and aft
Patrol boat version: One 20mm Oerlikon mounting fore and aft, one RH60 rigid inflatable or two amphibious Gilettri Leopard eight-wheel drive vehicles
Commando boat version: One 30mm Breda turret forward plus four semi-rigid inflatables capable of carrying 24 men in total.

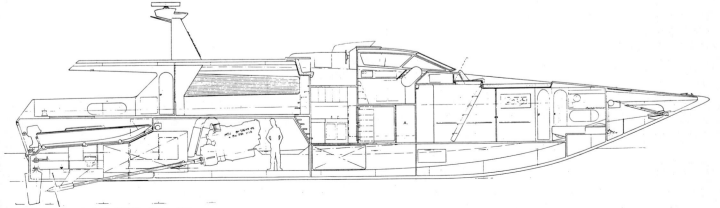

Interior arrangement of Alfa 83 25m fast cruiser

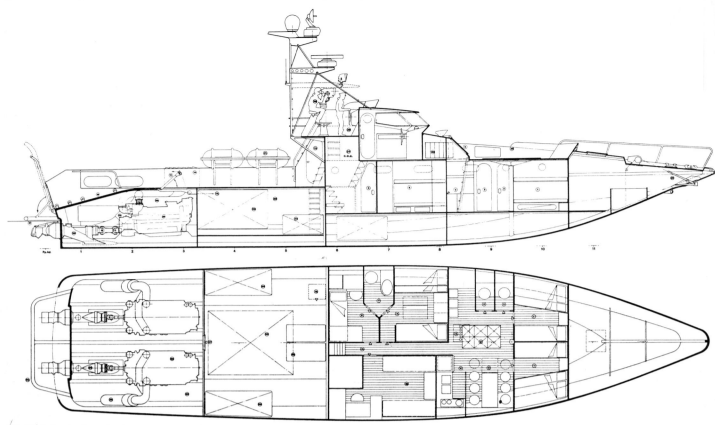

Alfa 84 design, basic version layout

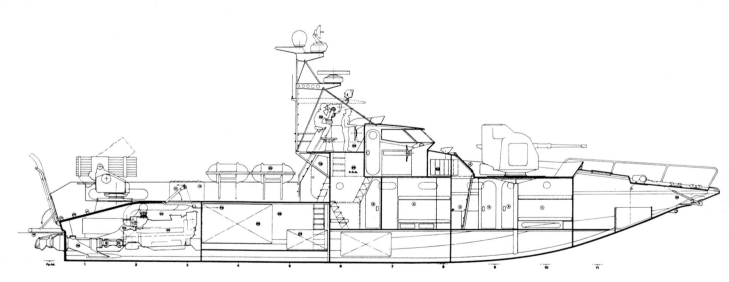

Alfa 84 design, gun boat version

Alfa 84 design, crew boat version

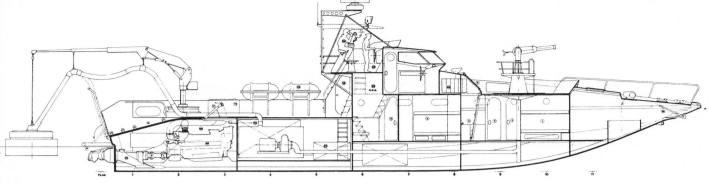

Alfa 84 design, oil recovery version

Mine-laying version: 20 anti-vessel Misar influence Manta ground mines (220kg each)
SYSTEMS
Auxiliary engines: Two 25kW diesel generators
Navigational: Automatic pilot, graphic and optic echo depth scanner, speed meterlog, radar and Loran

Communications: VHF SSB and telex
Air-conditioning: Fitted in living quarters
Searchlights: High Lux density searchlight, Galileo passive light intensification thermal telescope
DIMENSIONS
Length overall: 25.00m

Length, waterline: 20.00m
Beam: 6.00m
Draught: 1.20m
WEIGHT
Displacement: 60 tonnes
PERFORMANCE
Speed: 35 knots

AZIMUT SpA

Corso M d'Azeglio 30, 10125 Turin, Italy

Telephone: (011) 650 21 91
Telex: 220450AZITO I
Telefax: (011) 650 34 78

Dr Paolo Vitelli, *President*
Dr Ing Luciano Scaramuccia, *Technical Manager*
Dr Massimo Perotti, *Export Sales*

The company was founded in 1969 and until recently concentrated on building motor yachts in glass reinforced plastic (grp). In September 1985 Azimut took control of the Fratelli Benetti yard at Viareggio. With the acquisition of the Benetti facility craft between 35 and 50 metres may also be built in aluminium or steel.

The Viareggio yard encompasses approximately 3000m², of which 2500m² is fully enclosed; the workforce is approximately 40. In addition there are two other grp fabrication yards employing 65 in total, and a fitting out yard for the small boat division employing 20 persons.

The company has expanded into the commercial boat markets offering a range of craft; there are fast passenger ferry, crew boat and fishing boat versions available.

RIMA

Benetti 45 motor yacht.
MAIN ENGINES: Two marine diesel engines 3480hp each.
CAPACITIES
Fuel tank: 40m³
Fresh water: 8.0m³
ACCOMMODATION: Cabins for an owner's party of 14. Owner's suite consists of private bathroom, dressing room and lounge. There are six double-berth guest cabins. The galley serves a

dining room seating 12 which adjoins the main saloon. There is also an upper deck saloon leading on to the after deck which has open-air dining facilities. Crew accommodation consists of eight berths, double officer's cabin forward with the Captain's cabin and bathroom aft.
SYSTEMS: Desalinator plant producing 2150 litres/day.
DIMENSIONS
Length: 45.00m
Beam: 8.80m
Draught: 2.15m
PERFORMANCE
Speed, max: 27 knots
Speed, cruising: 24 knots
Range: 3000n miles

ATLANTIC CHALLENGER

The Azimut *Atlantic Challenger* was built to challenge the record for a transatlantic crossing but without intermediate fuelling stops. The hull was constructed at Azimut's Benetti yard in Viareggio, which was acquired by Azimut in 1985.
HULL: The hull form has a relatively shallow V aft moving gradually to a deeper V forward. Construction is in special corrosion-resistant aluminium.
MAIN ENGINES: Four CRM BR 1/2000 turbocharged and intercooled diesel engines, working in pairs, linked by means of two MAAG 1.852:1 reduction gears to two Riva Calzoni waterjet units.
Power: Four turbocharged, intercooled CRM BR 1/2000 diesel engines, maximum continuous power 1682hp at 2020rpm (Din/150) each, maximum sprint power 1850hp at 2075rpm (Din/150) each.
Transmission: Two reduction gears with dual ports, MAAG, ratio 1.853:1.

PROPULSION: Two Riva Calzoni type IRC DB2 DLX hydrojets, 1120rpm, continuous thrust at 45 knots, 6.4 tonnes each.
CAPACITIES: Seven structural, double-bottom fuel tanks fitted contain approximately 75 tons of diesel fuel. As the fuel is consumed a special open cell foam can be injected into the tanks to reduce fuel movement in the tanks in rough conditions.
ACCOMMODATION: The wheelhouse area was designed to provide accommodation for six crew members and included two helmsmen stations, a navigator and radio operator station.
DIMENSIONS
Length overall: 27.00m
Length, waterline: 24.07m
Beam, max: 7.50m
Beam, waterline: 7.10m
Height amidships: 3.55m
Deadrise aft: 13°
Deadline amidships: 22°
PERFORMANCE
Speed, max: 50 knots (approx)
Range: 3000 miles (approx)

AZ105
ATHINA R
Motor yacht.
Built 1985.
OWNER: Mme Onassis.
HULL: Hull construction is in grp.
MAIN ENGINES: Two MTU 12V TB93, 1960hp each.
ACCOMMODATION
Owner's suite: Three cabins and bathroom
Guests: Three double and one single cabins each with bathroom
Crew: Two 2-berth cabins, bathroom and crew lounge
Saloon: Formal dining for 12

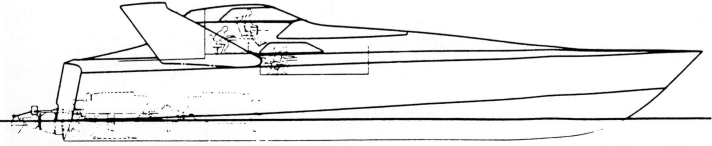

The Azimut *Atlantic Challenger* powered by four CRM BR 1/2000 diesel engines

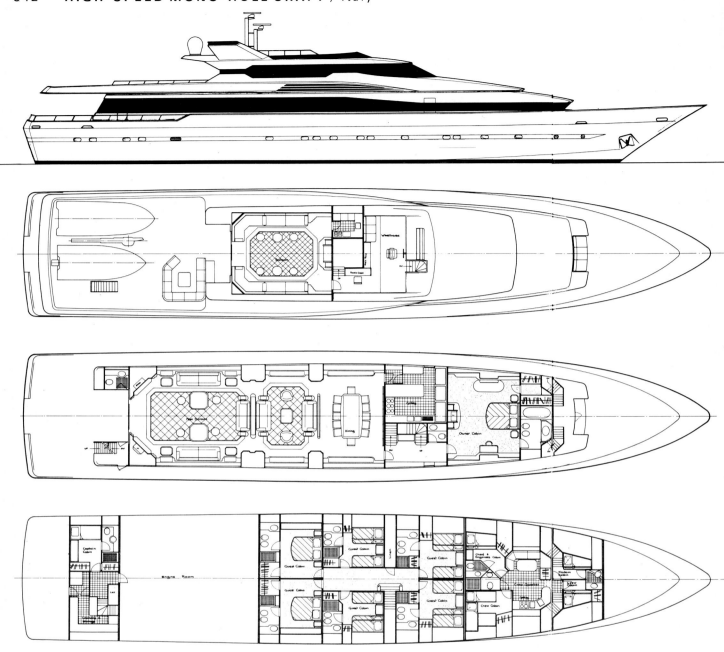

Profile and layout of the Benetti 45m motor yacht *Rima*

SYSTEMS
Television: VCR/TV system with overhead projector, pull down screen, and stereo speakers
Communications: In addition to standard sets, telephone, telex and computer interface capabilities also fitted.
Navigation: Standard equipment and a satellite navigation and communication system
DIMENSIONS
Length overall: 30.80m
Beam: 7.10m
Draught: 1.80m
PERFORMANCE
Speed, max: 27 to 31 knots

AZ105 *Athina R*

BAGLIETTO SHIPYARD SpA

Via Appia Antica 199, 00178 Rome, Italy
and
Piazza Stefano Baglietto, 17019 Varazze, Italy
Telephone: (06) 7806741 Ext 5
Telex: 625824SAMI I
Telefax: (06) 7806725

A joint venture has been formed between Alucraft and Baglietto for the design and building of motor yachts. Alucraft Consulting Inc has coordinated the design and construction of large luxury motor yachts styled by Alberto Mercati. Built in steel or aluminium in Istanbul in a joint venture with Profilo Holding these vessels are built to Lloyds specifications. In 1985 a new project was announced by Alucraft-Baglietto, the 35m Seneca 'Megajet/Cruiser' motor yacht with external design by Alberto Mercati and Baglietto shipyard handling the detailed hull, machinery and electrical plans and building at Varazze.

Four versions of Seneca are proposed:
Version A with two MTU 12V 396 TB93 engines with propellers
Version B with two MTU 12V 396 TB93 engines with KaMeWa waterjet units
Version C with two MTU 12V 396 TB94 engines with propellers
Version D with two MTU 12V 396 TB94 engines with KaMeWa waterjet units

SENECA MEGAJET/CRUISER
Version B
Preliminary specification details.
HULL: Aluminium magnesium alloy.
ENGINES: Two MTU 12V 396 TB93, derated for 32°C ambient air and 27°C sea, 1920hp (metric) each at 2100rpm, intermittent rating, or 1600hp (metric) each at 1975rpm, max continuous rating. Diesel generators, 75kVA.
CAPACITIES
Fuel tanks: 14 500 litres (can be increased to 38 000 litres)
Fresh water tanks: 4000 litres
(Fresh water daily production: Up to 1900 litres)
DIMENSIONS
Length overall: 35.0m
Length waterline (at standard displacement): 28.0m
Beam, max: 7.0m
Beam, max at chine: 5.10m
Depth amidships: 3.40m
Draught (at full load): 1.12m
WEIGHTS
Displacement, full load: 94.40 tonnes
Displacement, standard: 86.20 tonnes
Displacement, light and dry: 75.50 tonnes
PERFORMANCE
Speed, max: 28.50 knots
Speed, continuous: 26.0 knots
Range at 26 knots: 580n miles
    at 22 knots: 660n miles
    at 10 knots: 2900n miles (36 000 litres fuel)

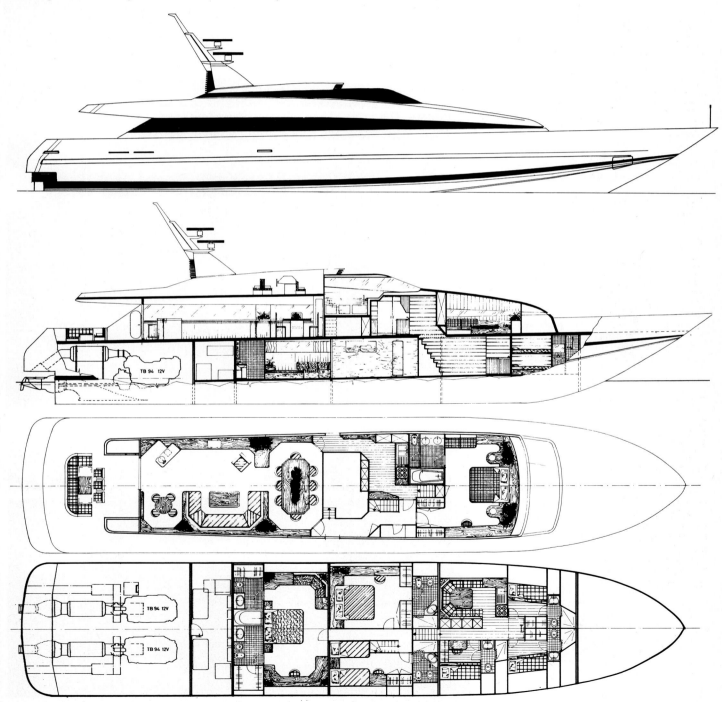

Alucraft-Baglietto 35m Seneca motor yacht

ADLER
SENECA
CHATO
LADY ANFIMAR

Three motor yachts, Yard nos 10076/11, 10079/12 and 10080/13, which were under construction in 1986, all driven by two 2130bhp KaMeWa waterjet units, type 63S62/6 and, a further motor yacht with the same power unit but fitted with KaMeWa type 50S62/6 waterjet units

which was also started in 1986 (Yard no 10103/11 and named *Lady Anfimar*), have all been delivered.

The following craft were under construction, late 1988: one 23 metre fast patrol boat powered by two MTU 12V 396 TB93 engines 1780hp each derated for 32°C ambient air and 27°C sea temperatures, one 36 metre motor yacht powered by two MTU 12V 396 TB93 engines each rated at 1920hp, one 24 metre motor yacht powered by two MAN D2840 (L) each rated at 680hp, one 24

metre fast patrol boat powered by two MTU 12V 396 TB93 engines each rated at 1780hp with water jet units, one 36 metre motor yacht powered by two MTU 12V 396 TB94 engines each rated at 2550hp, one Monostab powered by two MTU 16V 396 TB84 engines derated for 32°C ambient air and 27°C sea temperatures each rated at 2600hp.

CANTIERI NAVALI ITALCRAFT srl

Head Office: Via di Villa Emiliani 11, 00197 Rome, Italy

Telephone: (06) 875377/870981/873650
Telex: 613054ITCRAF I
Telefax: (06) 802701

Aristide Abbati, *Marketing Manager*

Italcraft, with a covered area of over 12 000m², has built more than 2500 craft since 1953. Its latest design is the M78, at 56 knots one of the world's fastest production motor yachts, a development of its original 55-knot 'Drago' class. The M78 is available in three yacht layout variations including an 'open' version with limited accommodation, named *Ultra 65*. There are also patrol craft and 100-passenger, 45-knot ferry versions. The patrol boat has a maximum speed of 52 knots and the ferry 45 knots.

M78 AEROMARINA
Fast motor yacht.
HULL: Hull and deck constructed in grp with aramidic fibre (Kevlar 49 DuPont), impregnated with isophthalic resin. The superstructure consists of grp and isophthalic resin. Four transverse bulkheads subdivide the hull.
MAIN ENGINES: Two MTU 12V 331 TC92 diesel engines. Alternatively the craft can be powered with two CRM diesel engines, 1650hp each.
PROPULSION: Two reverse/reduction gearboxes are coupled by Aquamet 22 Armco shafts to two surface-piercing Nibral propellers.
CONTROLS: A dual station hydraulic steering system is coupled to special semi-intubated rudders, of Italcraft patent. Steering positions are in the wheelhouse and flying bridge.
ACCOMMODATION
Deckhouse: Wheelhouse, main saloon and galley
Below decks: Three double cabins
Owner's heads/shower
Guest heads/shower
Crew head/shower
Double-berth crew cabin
All accommodation is air-conditioned
SYSTEMS
Auxiliary engines: One 12kW diesel generator, 220V ac 50Hz, alternative by electric equipment 60Hz standard USA
Navigational equipment: Furuno or Vigil radar, 48-mile range; Loran C; echo sounder; computerised electronic log
Communications equipment: V/HF, 55ch 25W; Navigraf radiotelephone, SSB 220W
Internal communications: Intercom between wheelhouse, flying bridge, forecastle and quarterdeck; intercom in cabins, saloon and bridge
Lifesaving: One inflatable life raft, life jackets and one semi-rigid pram dinghy with outboard
Firefighting: High pressure water pump for firefighting; portable fire extinguishers; automatic and remote control engine room fire extinguishing system
DIMENSIONS
Length overall: 21.10m
Beam: 5.45m

56 knot Italcraft M78

Cockpit and saloon of the Italcraft M78

Wheelhouse of Italcraft M78 motor yacht

Draught: 1.20m
Moulded depth: 29.915m
WEIGHTS
Full load displacement: 36.0 tonnes
Half load displacement: 34.0 tonnes
PERFORMANCE
Speed, max at half load displacement: 56.0 knots
Speed, cruise continuous power: 45.0 knots
Speed, economical cruise: 37.0 knots
Range at 45 knots: 320 miles
Range at 37 knots: 350 miles

22-METRE COAST GUARD PATROL BOAT (DESIGN)

Fast patrol boat.

A recent addition to the range of craft offered by Italcraft is their 22-metre fast patrol craft which is capable of achieving a top speed of 52 knots. One version of this craft is available, built in grp.
HULL: Constructed in grp.
DIMENSIONS
Length overall: 22.15m
Beam overall: 5.25m
Depth, moulded: 2.88m
Draught, at full load displacement: 1.29m
WEIGHTS
Full load displacement: 39.00 tonnes
PERFORMANCE
Speed, max: 51.0 knots
    High resistance: 44.0 knots
    Cruise: 27.0 knots

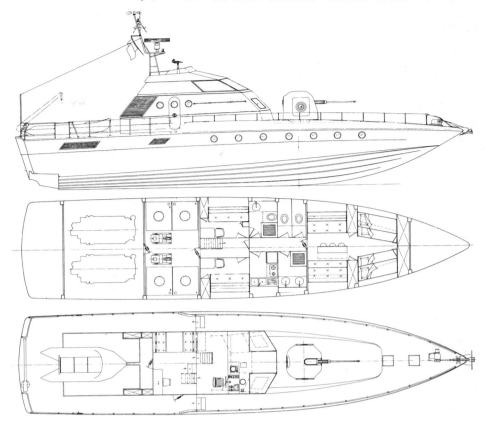

Italcraft 22m fast patrol boat design

CANTIERI NAVALI LIGURI

16037 Riva Trigoso (GE), Italy

Telephone: (0185) 44241
Telex: 270630CARIVA PPCHV I

Dr Aldo Ceccarelli, *President*

Cantieri Navali Liguri assumed their present name in 1955 from the original company Cantieri Navali Liguri di Riva Trigoso. The yard specialises in building steel-hulled craft.

CNL 35 (DESIGN)

Patrol boat.
HULL: All-welded steel hull divided into six watertight compartments, aluminium alloy superstructure.
COMPLEMENT: 20, including Commanding Officer, officers, senior and junior ratings.
ARMAMENT
Coast guard configuration: One twin 30mm gun mounting forward, two 12.5mm machine guns on upper deck

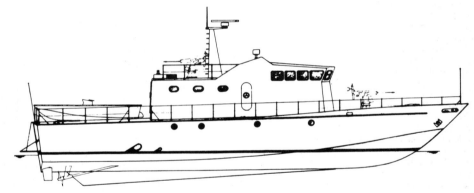

CNL 24 patrol boat design

Gun configuration: Two twin 30mm gun mountings forward and aft
Missile configuration: One twin 30mm gun mounting forward, two medium range ship-to-ship missiles in two launchers aft

DIMENSIONS
Length overall: 34.89m
Length waterline: 31.66m (130 tonnes displacement); 31.80m (160 tonnes displacement)
Beam: 8.30m
Draught: 2.40m

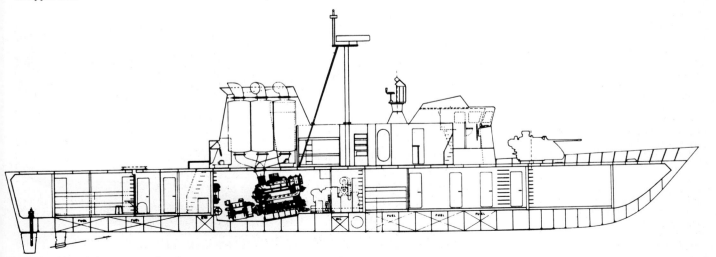

CNL 35 patrol boat design, coast guard version

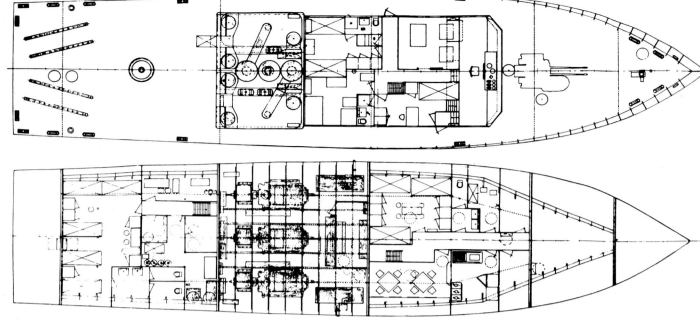

CNL 35 upper deck and lower deck accommodation layout

WEIGHT
Displacement: 130.0 tonnes to 160.0 tonnes
  depending on armament
PERFORMANCE
Speed, max: up to 34 knots
  max cruising: 28 knots
Endurance: 1.5 days at 28 knots, 3 days at 14
  knots, 6 days at 12 knots

CNL 24 (DESIGN)

  Patrol boat, designed for Middle East.
HULL: All-welded steel hull divided into six
watertight compartments, aluminium alloy super-
structure.
MAIN ENGINES: Two medium-speed diesels.
PROPULSION: Two fixed-pitch propellers.
CAPACITIES: Stores and supplies for 7 days at
sea.
COMPLEMENT: Crew of 10.
ARMAMENT: Two single 20mm guns.
DIMENSIONS
Length overall: 24.50m
Length waterline: 21.70m
Beam overall: 5.60m
Draught: 1.90m
WEIGHT
Displacement: 52.0 tonnes
PERFORMANCE
Speed, max: 26 knots
Speed, cruising: 24 knots
Endurance at 24 knots: 24 hours

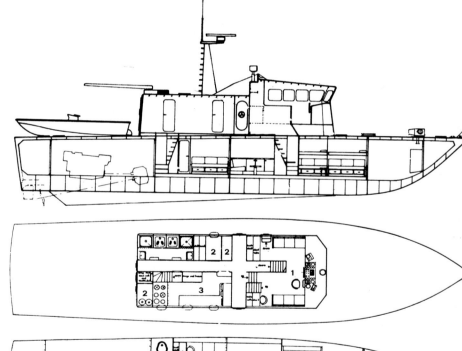

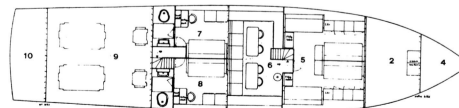

CNL 24 upper and lower deck accommodation layout

CANTIERI NAVALI PICCHIOTTI SpA
Darsena Italia 42, 55049 Viareggio, Italy

Telephone: (0584) 45345
Telex: 500328PICCHT I
Telefax: (0584) 31273

  Builder of fast patrol boats and high-speed
luxury motor yachts.

Picchiotti 18m 46-knot day cruiser

18-METRE DAY CRUISER

A recent 46-knot boat fitted with Riva Calzoni waterjet propulsion, type IRC 47 DL. Range approximately 400n miles at 39 knots.

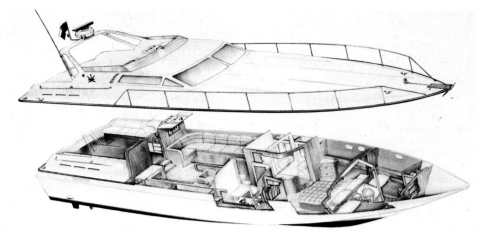

Interior of Picchiotti day cruiser

CANTIERI RIVA SpA

24067 Sarnico, Italy

Telephone: 35910202
Telex: 300183RIVA I
Telefax: 35 911059

Riva, well known for their fast motor cruisers in the 9- to 13-metre range, have now increased the size of their production craft by introducing their Riva 60' Black Corsair and Corsaro series of craft. UK agents are Lewis Marine, 59–61 High Street, Wanstead, London E11 2AE. Telephone: 01–989 2265/6.

60' BLACK CORSAIR

Length: 18.71m.
Engines: Two 1300bhp diesels.
Speed: 39 knots.

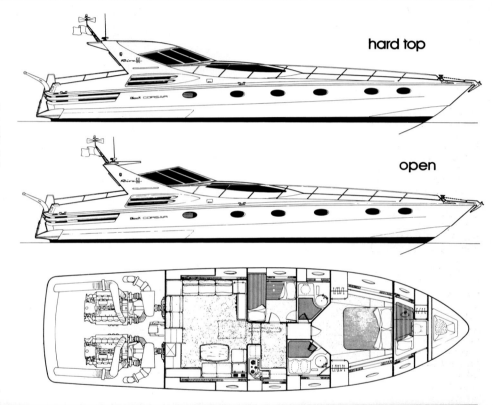

hard top

open

60' Black Corsair

Riva 60' Black Corsair

20 COSARO

A successor to the Corsaro with increased space, more power and refined lines.

PRINCIPAL PARTICULARS

Length, overall: 19.48m
Beam: 5.35m
Draught: 1.65m
Engines: Two MTU 746kW (1000hp) diesel
Accommodation: Owner plus guests, 6 + 2
    crew: 2
Speed, one third load: 32 knots
Range: 14h at 2100rpm
Fuel tank: 4150 l

Riva 60' Cosaro

Riva 20 Corsaro

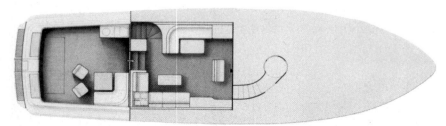

Riva 20 Corsaro

CRESTITALIA SpA

Via Armezzone 1, 19031 Ameglia (La Spezia), Italy

Telephone: (0187) 65 746/583
Telex: 283042CRESTI I
Telefax: (0187) 65 282

Liaison offices: Via Gallarate 34-D, 20151 Milan, Italy

Telephone: (02) 32 71 873

Via Ottaviano 32, 00192 Rome, Italy

Telephone: (06) 31 85 94

Crestitalia started building grp craft in 1961 at Como and moved to a new slipyard at Ameglia (La Spezia) in 1971. The company build craft in grp up to 40 metres in length and since 1961 have built approximately 20 000 craft 4 to 11m in length. The Ameglia yard has recently been equipped with a new launching deck and sheds capable of building five 40m craft simultaneously. Principal customers are the Italian Navy and Police, and overseas military and police forces.

MV100

Diving support and underwater exploration boat.

The MV100 is an enlarged version of the M85 (26m), the craft having a number of similarities in layout and equipment.
HULL: Semi-planing V-shaped hull in grp with a grp sandwich superstructure.
MAIN ENGINES: Two MTU 12V 396 TB93 marine diesels.
PROPULSION: Twin screw.
CONTROLS: Electric/hydraulic steering gear.
ACCOMMODATION: Two twin-berth officers' cabins, two crew cabins, three berths in each, and one trainee cabin with six berths.
ARMAMENT: One local control 30mm gun.
SYSTEMS
Auxiliary engines: Two Mercedes OM421 diesel generators providing 96kW each
Decompression chambers: Two, one three-person and one single Galeazzi chamber
Navigational: One magnetic compass and one Anschutz gyrocompass with two repeater compasses. One Sagem electro-magnetic log, one RN 770 Decca radar, one Noak long-range

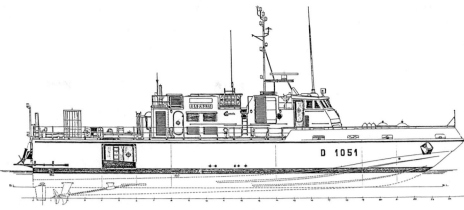

MV100 30m diving support and underwater exploration boat profile

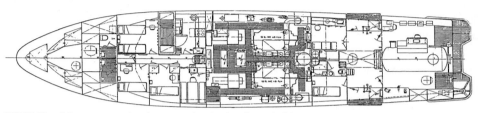

MV100 30m diving support and underwater exploration boat lower deck layout

searchlight, Elac LAZ51AT/LSE 133 echo sounder, Zeiss Orion 80B night vision telescope, and Decca Navigator Mark 21
Air-conditioning: Full air-conditioning throughout
Underwater exploration equipment: Two Pluto RCVs equipped with search and identification sensors
DIMENSIONS
Length overall: 30.00m
Beam overall: 6.90m
Draught, light displacement: 0.96m
Draught, fully loaded: 1.05m
WEIGHTS
Displacement, full load: 95 tonnes
Max displacement with load on deck: 105 tonnes
PERFORMANCE
Max speed at full load: 27 knots (approx)
Endurance: Max range at 16.5 knots with full load, 560 miles

MV88

Multi-purpose crew boat and quick deployment forces transport.
HULL: Grp.
MAIN ENGINES: Two 1600hp marine diesels.
PROPULSION: Propellers or waterjets.
CAPACITIES
Fresh water: 2600 litres
ACCOMMODATION: 250 fully equipped military personnel.
CREW: 4.
DIMENSIONS
Length overall: 27.28m
Beam overall: 6.98m
Draught: 1.10m
WEIGHT
Displacement: 82 tonnes
PERFORMANCE
Speed, max: 28 knots
cruising: 23 knots

MV100 30m diving support and underwater exploration boat

MV85

Fast patrol boat.

CLASSIFICATION: Registro Italiano Navale (RINa).

HULL: Grp.

MAIN ENGINES: Two MTU 16V 396 TB94 diesels.

Rating	Duration	rpm	Speed
Max:	one half hour out of 6 hours	2100	45 knots
Overload:	two hours out of 12 hours	2400	42 knots
Continuous:	24 hours over 24 hours	1975	40 knots

PROPULSION: Two three-bladed Nibral alloy propellers.

CONTROLS: Remote engine room controls from wheelhouse and flying bridge.

ACCOMMODATION/COMPLEMENT: Commanding Officer, four officers and eight ratings accommodated in single Commanding Officer's cabin, two double-berth officers' cabins and forward messdeck fitted with eight berths for ratings. Wardroom and galley situated in after part of wheelhouse structure.

ARMAMENT: One single 30mm Breda-Mauser mounting forward with remote FCS Elsag-Medusa control and two light machine guns on wings of flying bridge.

SYSTEMS

Auxiliary machinery: Two diesel generators of 50kW/50Hz output, each capable of providing normal full load requirements, one emergency diesel generator of 10kVA/380V

Navigational: One GEM 732 radar, one Anschutz gyrocompass, one Sagem electronic data log, one echo sounder, and one ARPA radar

Communications: One complete radio station

Air-conditioning: Provided for all living areas

DIMENSIONS

Length overall: 26.40m
Beam overall: 6.95m
Moulded depth: 3.45m
Draught, light displacement: 0.92m
Draught, half load displacement: 1.00m
Draught, full load displacement: 1.02m

WEIGHTS

Displacement, light: 61.25 tonnes
Displacement, half load: 71.57 tonnes
Displacement, full load: 79.43 tonnes

MV88 27m multi-purpose crew boat

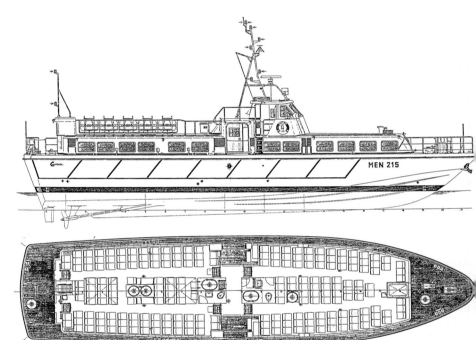

MV88 profile and interior layout

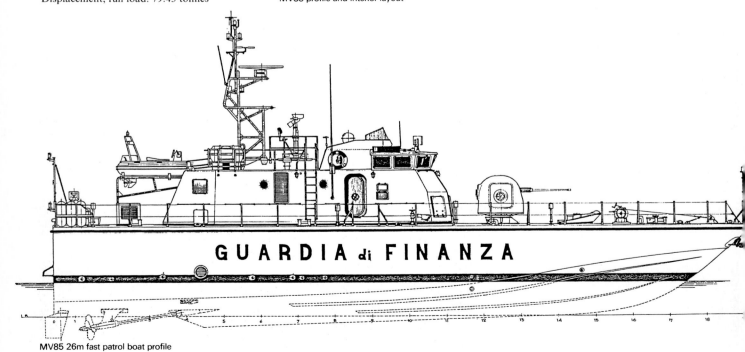

MV85 26m fast patrol boat profile

MV85 fast patrol boat

PERFORMANCE
Speed, max: 45 knots
Speed, overload: 42 knots
Speed, continuous: 40 knots
Full load endurance at 18.5 knots: 1200n miles

MV70
Fast patrol boat.
HULL: Grp.
MAIN ENGINES: Two 1400hp diesel engines.
PROPULSION: Two propellers.
CONTROLS: Mechanical remote controls to engines, hydraulic steering gear.
CREW: 12.
ARMAMENT: Twin Oerlikon 30mm.
SYSTEMS
Navigational: Radar and echo sounder
Communications: VHF-SSB-UHF
DIMENSIONS
Length overall: 21.10m
Beam overall: 5.30m
Draught: 0.90m
WEIGHT
Displacement: 40 tons
PERFORMANCE
Speed, max: 35 knots
Speed, continuous: 31 knots
Endurance at continuous speed: 17 hours

31 METRE PASSENGER FERRY
SERENA LAURO
Built in GRP 1988/89
PRINCIPAL PARTICULARS
Length, overall: 31.00m
Beam, overall: 6.90m
Draught, full load: 0.90m
GRT: less than 50
Accommodation: 350 passengers, crew 3
Engines: Two 820kW high-speed diesel
Propulsion: propeller
Speed, max, two thirds load: 24 knots
  cruising: 20 knots
Endurance: 12h

MV85 26m diving support boat

Crestitalia MV70 fast patrol boat

Serena Lauro

Freccia del Golfo

INTERMARINE SpA

19038 Sarzana, La Spezia, Italy

Telephone: (0187) 671800
Telex: 271062IMARIN I

23-METRE PATROL CRAFT

HULL: Constructed of grp, the hull is of soft round form with fine entry forward, running into a hard chine constant deadrise aft.
ENGINES: Two 1925kW diesels.
PROPULSION: Two three-blade, fixed-pitch propellers.
CREW: 11.
SYSTEMS
Generator: 43kVA
Navigation: Radar, log, echo sounder, gyro-compass
Communications: RTX VHF 60 Ch, RTX UHF, RTX HF/SSB 100W 16 Ch, RX MF/HF
Armament: One 30mm naval gun, two 7.62mm machine guns
DIMENSIONS
Length overall: 23.80m
Beam: 8.40m
Draught: 1.20m
WEIGHT
Displacement: 55.0 tonnes
PERFORMANCE
Speed, max: 40.0 knots
  max continuous: 35.0 knots
Range, at 30 knots: About 450n miles

27-METRE PATROL CRAFT

HULL: Of same material and form as the 23m patrol craft.
ENGINES: Two 2575kW diesel engines.
PROPULSION: Two three-blade, fixed-pitch propellers.
CREW: 15.
SYSTEMS
Generator: 76kVA
Armament: One 40/70 naval gun, optically stabilised fire control, one 20mm TB MG, optical sight
DIMENSIONS
Length overall: 27.27m
Beam: 6.80m
Draught: 2.10m
WEIGHT
Displacement: 85.0 tonnes
PERFORMANCE
Speed, max: 40.0 knots
  max continuous: 36.0 knots
Range, at 20 knots cruise: About 1000n miles

27 MTS PATROL CRAFT

Supplied to African navies.
HULL: Of same material and form as the 23m patrol craft.
ENGINES: Two 1925kW diesel engines
PROPULSION: Two three-blade, fixed-pitch propellers.
CREW: 11
SYSTEMS
Generator: 43kVA, radar, log, echo sounder, gyrocompass, communication
Armament: One 30mm naval gun, two 7.62 machine guns
DIMENSIONS
Length overall: 23.80m
Beam: 8.40m
Draught: 1.20m
WEIGHT
Displacement, 55.0 tonnes
PERFORMANCE
Speed, max: 40 knots
  max continuous: 35 knots
Range, at 30 knots: About 450n miles

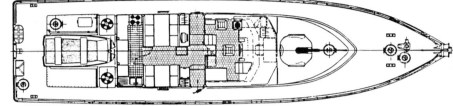

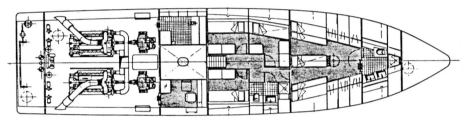

Intermarine 23m patrol boat

Intermarine 27 MTS patrol craft

Intermarine 27m patrol craft

RODRIQUEZ CANTIERI NAVALI SpA

Via S Raineri 22, 98100 Messina, Italy

Telephone: (090) 7765
Telex: 980030RODRIK I
Telefax: (090) 717358

Please see entry under Hydrofoils section for company information.

MONOSTAB

This is a new patented concept for a stabilised mono-hull vessel matching the characteristics of a semi-planing hull with two automatically controlled surface-piercing foils, the object being to achieve a better overall performance than obtainable with a pure mono-hull, especially at Froude Numbers near unity.

If waterjet propulsion is used for a semi-planing mono-hull it is almost inevitable that with engines and auxiliary machinery also being at the stern, the vessel will have a far aft centre of gravity with subsequently large changes in centre of gravity position from full load to light condition. Such machinery location also allows however for a hull shape with very fine entrance angles providing reduction in bow wave generation and good seakeeping performance especially in head seas.

The Monostab concept reduces the difficulties of an excessively rear centre of gravity position by the provision of a pair of surface-piercing foils connected to moving arms, manually- or automatically-controlled and positioned at the rear of the craft. The effect is to allow for a true dynamic relief of weight-load from abaft thereby reducing the amount of craft weight supported by the combined buoyant/planing lift of the hull and effecting a planing trim reduction substantially equivalent to a forward shifting of the craft centre of gravity. This in turn is expected to lead to an improvement of cruising performance because of the higher efficiency of foils in relation to hull efficiency in the range of speeds under consideration and because of the indirect advantage of being able to trim the craft correctly for any load condition. Further, with a considerable improvement in directional stability, with the dihedral effect of the foils generating correct banking in turns and the possibility of regulating the planing trim angle of the craft in head seas to reduce slamming, a large reduction of the hull bottom deadrise can be obtained, leading in turn to a better hydrodynamic efficiency of the hull.

Additional advantages of the concept, if trimmable foils are used, is that a strong roll and pitch damping effect is obtained together with an increase in the transverse stability of the basic hull. These effects allow for a reduction in the waterline beam, improving hydrodynamic efficiency and rough water performance. With automatic control actuation of the moving arms a considerable increase in rough water performance can be obtained without involving unduly fast arm movements.

The first craft to be built according to the above principles was launched in 1989.
ENGINES: Two MTU 16V 396 TB84, 2040 kW diesels.
PROPULSION: Two Riva Calzoni IRC82DLX waterjet units.
ACCOMMODATION: 350.
DIMENSIONS
Length overall: 36.00m
Length waterline: 30.00m
Breadth, moulded: 7.50m
Draught: 0.90m
WEIGHTS
Useful load: 35 tonnes
PERFORMANCE
Speed, cruising: 35 knots

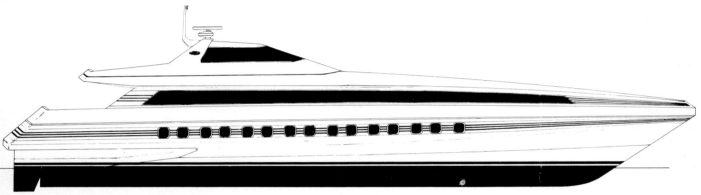

The Rodriquez Monostab project

Monostab on trials 1989

TECNOMARINE SpA

Central Services, Via dei Pescatori 56, 55049
Viareggio, Italy

Telephone: (0584) 384466, 3801
Telex: 500487TECNO I
Telefax: 584–387630

Ms Anna Maria Patini, *President*
Marco M. Pinna

Tecnomarine was established in 1973 staffed with skilled labour and technicians from Picchiotti. The yard builds fast craft in wood, grp, aluminium alloy and steel from 14 to 120 metres and is now one of the largest builders of luxury yachts in the world. Tecnomarine has a design staff of 45 and has long standing working relationships with Sparkman and Stephens on engineering design, Paola D. Smith & Associates on interior design and Tommaso Spadolini (Design Studio Spadolini) on styling. The total area of the company's various yards is 16752m².

TECNOMARINE 118

Motor yacht.
HULL: Construction in aluminium alloy or grp.
MAIN ENGINES: Two MTU 16V 396 TB93, 2600hp at 2100rpm each.
CAPACITIES
Fuel: 14000 litres
Fresh water: 4000 litres
DIMENSIONS
Length overall: 36.00m
Length waterline: 31.16m
Beam, max: 7.33m
Draught, max: 2.25m
PERFORMANCE
Speed, max: 29 to 30 knots
Range: 1000n miles

TECNOMARINE T62

Motor yacht.
HULL: Constructed in grp
MAIN ENGINES: Two GM 12V 71 TA 671kW (900hp) each, at 2300rpm each coupled to V.
CAPACITIES
Fuel: 4000 litres
Fresh water: 1200 litres
DIMENSIONS
Length, overall: 18.35m
Length, waterline: 14.80m
Beam, max: 5.22m
Depth, moulded: 2.30m
Draught: 1.50m
WEIGHTS
Displacement, full load: 29.30 tonnes
Displacement, light load: 24.30 tonnes
PERFORMANCE
Speed, max (half load): 37 knots
Speed, cruise: 32 knots
Range at cruise speed: 400n miles

Some Tecnomarine craft built up to the end of 1987

Length	Construction	Power	Max speed
16m	grp	two GM 870hp each	33.0 knots
24m	wood or grp	two GM 1080hp each	29.5 knots
28m	wood or grp	two MTU 1600hp each	30.0 knots
36m	light alloy or grp	two MTU 2610hp each	29–30 knots

T118 accommodation layout

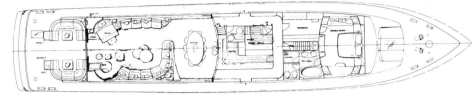

T118 upper deck layout

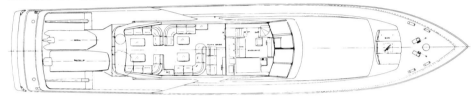

T118 sun deck layout

Tecnomarine T118 motor yacht *Longitude Zero*

Tecnomarine T62

TS163

A new megayacht project by Tecnomarine in the planning stage in late 1989. The vessel is to be powered by two General Electric LM1600 gas turbines, 13125kW (17600hp) each, in combination with two 1530kW (2052hp) diesels in a CODOG arrangement. Propulsion will be by water-jet units. A maximum speed of 70 knots is predicted, and, on diesel engines alone, 17 knots. Range is given as 3000 nautical miles at 10 knots.

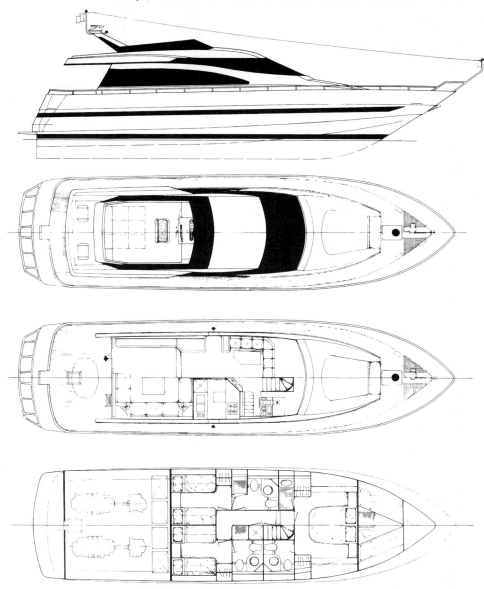

General arrangement of T62

The TS163 Tecnomarine gas turbine powered megayacht

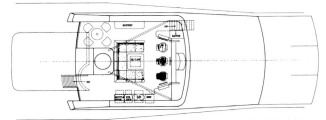

FLY BRIDGE

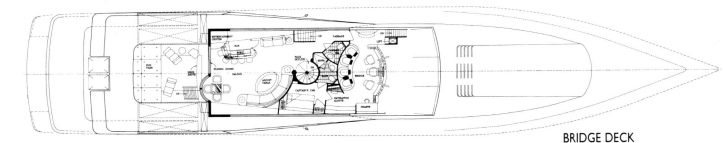

BRIDGE DECK

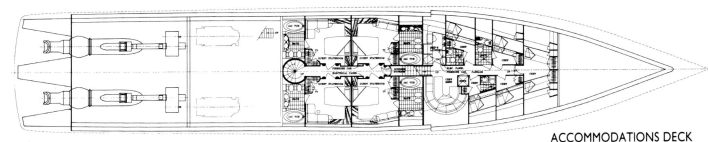

MAIN DECK

ACCOMMODATIONS DECK

General arrangement of TS163

CANTIERE NAUTICO VERSILCRAFT Srl

Via dei Pescatori 64, Viareggio(LU), Italy

Telephone: (0584) 384946
Telex: 624198VERSIL I

Marketing
Versil Marine SA
Hinterbergstrasse 21,CH-6330 Cham-Zug, Switzerland

Telephone: (042) 418044
Telex: 865328 VEMA CH
Telefax: (042) 416723

Versil Marine France
64, La Croisette, Palais Mirimar, 06400 Cannes, France

Telephone: (93) 435666
Telex: 970836VERSIL F

73ft CHALLENGER
HULL: Grp.
MAIN ENGINES: Three GM 12V 92 TI.

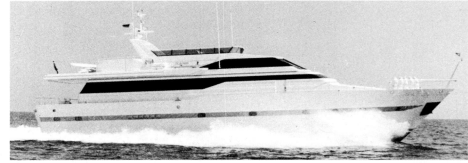

Versilcraft 73ft Challenger

ACCOMMODATION
Crew: 2 berths
Passengers: 6 to 8 berths
CAPACITIES
Fuel tank: 9988 litres
Water tank: 1614 litres
DIMENSIONS
Length, overall: 22.26m

Beam, overall: 6.10m
Draught: 1.83m
WEIGHTS
Displacement, normal load: 40 tonnes
Displacement, fully loaded: 45 tonnes
PERFORMANCE
Speed, normal displacement, max: 26 knots
Speed, normal displacement, cruising: 23 knots

83ft SUPER CHALLENGER
MARCALEC
HULL: Grp.
MAIN ENGINES: Three GM 12V 92 TI diesel engines.
ACCOMMODATION
Crew: 2 to 3
Guests/passengers: 6 to 8 berths
CAPACITIES
Fuel tank: 10 000 litres
Water tank: 1600 litres
DIMENSIONS
Length overall: 25.40m
Beam overall: 6.09m
Draught: 1.83m
Height above waterline to deck: 3.05m
WEIGHTS
Displacement, empty: 40.0 tons
    normal: 45.0 tons
    fully loaded: 50.0 tons
PERFORMANCE
Speed, max, normal displacement: 25.0 knots
    cruising, normal displacement: 22.0 knots
Range at economical speed: 572 miles

VERSILCRAFT 66'
EARL GREY
PRINCIPAL PARTICULARS
Length,overall:19 80m
Beam:5.60m
Draught:1.50m
Displacement,no load:29.00 tonnes
Displacement,average load:32.00 tonnes
Engines:two MAN 597kW diesels
Fuel:5000 l
Water:800 l
Accommodation:6 to 8
Crew:1 to 2

25-knot Versilcraft motor yacht Super Challenger *Macalec*

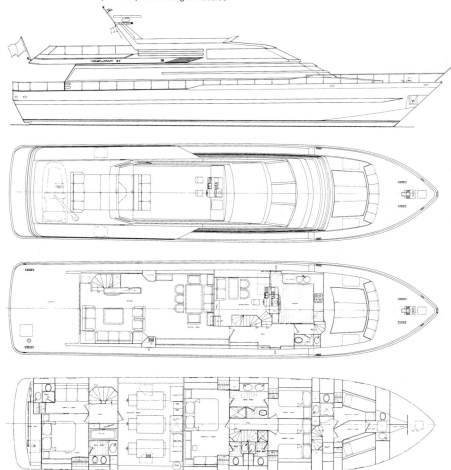

Versilcraft 83ft Super Challenger

The Versilcraft 66'

JAPAN

BINAN SENKAPO KOGYO

Builder of 26metre, 87 passenger monohull ferry *Auto Batan II*.

Auto Batan II

MITSUBISHI HEAVY INDUSTRIES LTD (MHI)

5–1, Marunouchi 2-chome, Chiyoda-ku, Tokyo 100, Japan

Telephone: (03) 212 3111
Telex: 22443J

SHIMONOSEKI SHIPYARD AND ENGINE WORKS

16–1 Enouni-cho, Hikoshima, Shimonoseki, Japan
Telephone: (66) 2111
Telex: 0682284J

SEAHAWK

Built in 1977 (hull 784, Shimonoseki Shipyard) and in service with Koshikijima Shosen Co.
PRINCIPAL PARTICULARS
Length, pp: 45.00m
Beam: 7.80m
Depth: 3.90m
Draught: 1.25m
GRT: 388
Main engines: Two Ikegai MTU 6V652, 1644kW (2205hp)
Seats: 290
Speed: 26.5 knots

Seahawk

MARINE STAR

Built in 1983 and in service with Oki Kisen Co. Ltd.
PRINCIPAL PARTICULARS
Length, overall: 48.50m
Breadth: 8.20m
Depth: 3.90m
GRT: 286
Main engines: Two 1805kW (2420hp) high-speed diesels
Seats: 351
Speed, max. rated: 30.7 knots

Marine Star

30 METRE FISHERY PATROL BOAT
PRINCIPAL PARTICULARS
Length, overall: 31.50m
Beam: 6.30m
Depth: 3.10m
GRT: 92
Main engines: Two 1160kW (1520hp) at 1840 rpm
Speed, max: 31 knots
Crew: 12

SUNLINE
This interesting vessel was completed in October 1986. The *Sunline* high-speed passenger ship incorporates a new feature in naval architecture, a semi-submerged bow (SSB) designed to suppress intense pitching and rolling in rough weather. The aft part of the vessel is of conventional high-speed ship form. *Sunline* is owned by Nippon Koun Kaisha Ltd of Ehime Prefecture.
ENGINES: Two 746kW (1000hp), at 2170rpm.
DIMENSIONS
Length overall: 26.76m
Beam: 5.80m
Depth: 2.67m
GRT: 71
PERFORMANCE
Passenger capacity: 70
Speed, max: 28.1 knots

30m Fishery Patrol Boat

Mitsubishi semi-submerged bow (SSB) *Sunline*

Mitsubishi 70-passenger, 28-knot *Sunline*

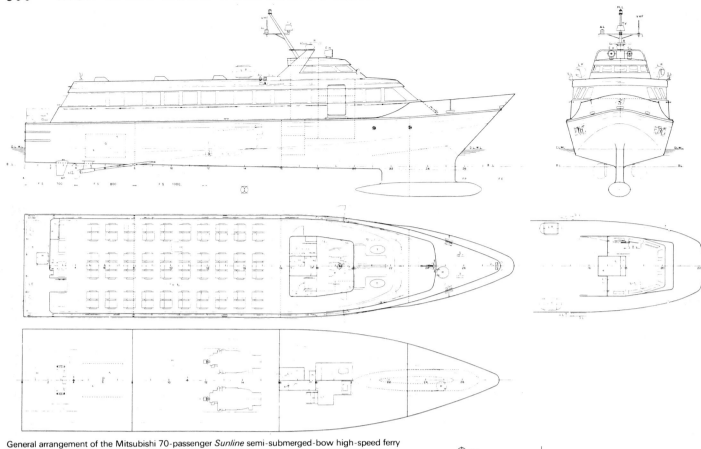

General arrangement of the Mitsubishi 70-passenger *Sunline* semi-submerged-bow high-speed ferry

HIGH-SPEED FISHING BOAT
NS2–10200

A 26.03-metre fishing boat capable of 30.6 knots.

ENGINES: Two GM DDA 16V-149 TI, MCR: 1675hp each at 1900rpm.

PROPULSION: Two 3-blade, fixed-pitch, 920mm diameter, 1180mm pitch, aluminium bronze.

COMPLEMENT: Nine.

DIMENSIONS

Length: 26.03m
Length, bp: 23.48m
Breadth, moulded: 5.73m
Depth, moulded: 2.84m
Draught, design: 1.05m
Draught, extreme: 1.09m
GRT: 56.0

PERFORMANCE

Fuel consumption: 160g/hph

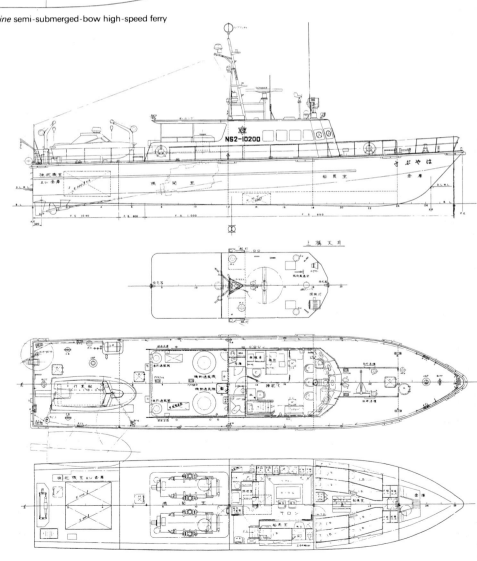

General arrangement of Mitsubishi NS2–10200

Mitsubishi 30.6-knot fishing boat NS2–10200

MITSUI ENGINEERING AND SHIPBUILDING CO LTD (MES)

6–4 Tsukiji 5-chome, Chuo-ku, Tokyo 104, Japan

Telephone: (03) 5443462
Telex: 22821/22924 J

Kazuo Maeda, *Chairman*
Yasunosuke Ishii, *President*
Yutaka Ikeda, *General Manager, Advanced Craft Sales Dept.*

SEABULLET 27-M

A revolutionary Seabullet hull form for planing craft has been developed by Mitsui Engineering & Shipbuilding Co Ltd, designed to achieve a combination of high-speed performance and riding comfort. Unlike conventional mono-hull planing craft, the Seabullet has a triple-support hull form with three planing surfaces, a form previously used only in racing boats. This hull form, adapted for commercial purposes, makes the Seabullet a high-performance craft with not only high-speed stability and high seaworthiness but also an unprecedented ability to withstand impacts.

The Seabullet 27-M has been built to take full advantage of this new hull form. With a new, aesthetically attractive streamlined shape, she is designed as a pleasure boat or sightseeing craft.

Taking advantage of the excellent characteristics of the Seabullet hull form, MES plans to produce a series of diverse pleasure boat models, and to market them actively for both commercial and recreational uses.

The Seabullet was jointly developed by MES and the Japan Marine Machinery Development Association (JAMDA) with financial support from the Japan Shipbuilding Industry Foundation.

Features claimed by MES for the Seabullet hull form are:

Mitsui Seabullet 27-M experimental craft

The planing surface is divided into three parts and three-point support is maintained even at high-speeds; the craft can run smoothly and stably in its entire speed range.

Even during high-speed running, the Seabullet boat is unusually immune to impacts from waves; riding comfort is thereby doubly ensured.

Highly seaworthy, she excels both in wave-plowing and wave-riding performance.

The vessel is less susceptible to side skidding, and is superior in turning performance and man-oeuvrability.

As the hull form allows greater breadth, a correspondingly larger deck area can be secured.

HULL MATERIAL: Frp.

ENGINE AND DRIVING SYSTEM: Gasoline engine, stand drive.
Engine output: Two 200hp engines
DIMENSIONS
Length overall: 7.95m
Breadth: 3.2m
Height overall: About 3.4m (excluding mast)
Depth: 1.3m
PERFORMANCE
Plying limit and route: Limited coastal waters
Speed: 35 knots
Fuel oil tanks: Two 180-litre tanks
Max complement: 13 persons
Equipped with toilet and basin, and air-conditioned

MOKUBEI SHIPBUILDING COMPANY

Otsu, Biwa Lake, Japan

Dr M Ikeda, *Chief Naval Architect*

LANSING

A waterjet-propelled sightseeing tourist boat built in 1982 for operation by the Biwa Lake Sightseeing Co on the very shallow Biwa Lake. Built in aluminium, the vessel has seating for 86 passengers and 2 crew. The fully-laden power-to-weight ratio is 41.5hp/tonne.

POWERPLANT: Two MAN 254 MLE V12 diesels rated at 540hp each, at 2230rpm.
WATERJETS: Two Hamilton Model 421 type directly driven from engine flywheel via torsionally-flexible coupling and Cardan shaft.
AUXILIARY POWER/CONTROLS: The vessel is fitted with an auxiliary diesel ac generator which enables ac motor driven hydraulic powerpacks to be used for the waterjet unit controls. A tandem pump hydraulic powerpack is used for the reverse ducts while a single pump hydraulic powerpack operates the steering. At the helm, control for steering is via a wheel; the reverse is operated via a single electric joystick and two position indicators

Stern of *Lansing* showing the Hamilton waterjet units

are fitted, one for the steering deflector angle and
the other for the reverse duct position.
DIMENSIONS
Length overall: 22.0m
Length waterline: 19.80m
Beam: 4.0m
Draught: 0.55m
WEIGHT
Displacement, max: 26 tonnes
PERFORMANCE
Speed, max at 26 tonnes displacement: 27 knots
Speed, partially loaded: 30 knots

23.5-METRE FERRY

A twin-engine waterjet-propelled shallow
draught craft.
DESIGNER: Dr M Ikeda.
ENGINES: Two Yanmar 6LAAM-UT1, 500hp
each, at 1850rpm.
PROPULSION: Two Hamilton Jet 421 waterjet
units.
ACCOMMODATION: 50 passengers.
DIMENSIONS
Length overall: 23.50m
Length waterline: 21.15m
Beam: 4.78m
Draught: 0.61m

Mokubei *Lansing*

WEIGHT
Weight, full load: 34.57 tonnes
PERFORMANCE
Speed, max: 26.50 knots
Speed, full load: 21.6 knots
Fuel tanks: Two 980-litre

ESCOURT BOAT
KAIYO

A 25.5-metre, 21.5-knot steel-hull firefighting
boat equipped to carry foam liquid, launched 19

February 1986 and owned by Sanyo-kaiji Co Ltd
and Nihon-kaiji-kogyo Co Ltd.
DESIGNER: Dr M Ikeda.
ENGINES: Two Yanmar 12LAAK-UT1, 1000hp
each, at 1850rpm.
PROPULSION: Two fixed-pitch, 3-blade, aluminium bronze, 1000mm diameter, 1000mm
pitch, developed blade-area ratio: 0.90. Propeller
shaft diameter: 99mm, length 6500mm.
REDUCTION GEAR: NICO-MGN 332, shaft
output MCR: 1000hp at 907rpm.
COMPLEMENT: Nine.

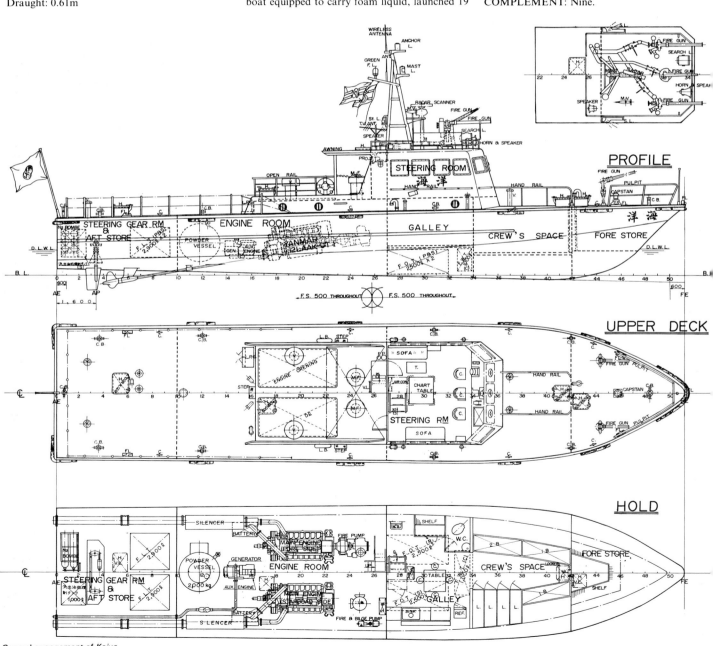

General arrangement of *Kaiyo*

DIMENSIONS
Length overall: 25.50m
Breadth, moulded: 5.60m
Depth, moulded: 2.70m
Draught, design: 1.10m
WEIGHT
Lightweight: 54.85 tonnes
GRT: 49.0
PERFORMANCE
Fuel consumption: 221g/kWh

MIZUSUMASHI II
Water quality research boat delivered 31 March, 1989.
PRINCIPAL PARTICULARS
Length, overall: 23.50m
Length, pp: 22.90m
Beam, moulded: 4.80m
Depth, moulded: 2.25m
Displacement, full load: 39.12 tonnes
Complement: 30
Speed, 100% MCR: 28 knots
Main engines: Two DDC 16V92TA, 1007kW each, MCR, 2300 rpm
Reduction gear: NICO MGN 332E, ratio: 1.42:1.00
Propulsion: Two 5-blade, 700mm dia., 884mm pitch, developed area ratio: 1.0

Kaiyo

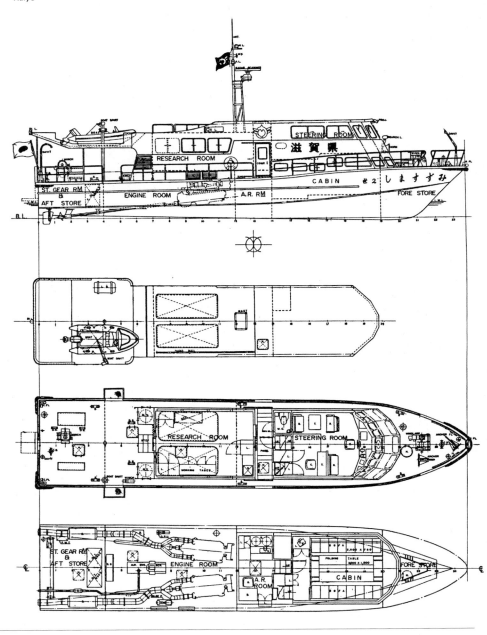

Mizusumashi

SHINJU SHIPBUILDING COMPANY
Kyushu Island, Japan

Telephone: (0944) 54 2117/9

TROPICAL QUEEN
A waterjet-propelled sightseeing tourist boat for inter-island services from the island of Ishigaki, *Tropical Queen* was delivered in July 1982. The vessel was designed by the Yamaha Motor Co Ltd and is built in glass-reinforced plastic sandwich construction.
MAIN ENGINES: Two GM 12V 92 TI diesels, 730hp each at 2135rpm.
PROPULSION: Two Hamilton Model 421, type 56 impeller waterjet units.
CONTROLS: At the helm the steering is power assisted and the reverse bucket is controlled by a 24V dc electric joystick switch. The hydraulic powerpack for steering is belt-driven off one main engine while separate 24V dc electro-hydraulic powerpacks, activated by the single powerpack switch, power-operate the reverse buckets.
DIMENSIONS
Length overall: 27.3m
Length waterline: 23.49m

Beam: 5.3m
Deadrise: 5°
WEIGHTS/CAPACITIES
Displacement, max: 37 tonnes
Fuel: 2000 litres
PERFORMANCE
Speed, fully laden, 37-tonne displacement: 27
    knots at 2000rpm, corresponding to 600hp
    input per engine
Speed, fully laden, max: 29 knots

150-passenger *Tropical Queen*

Tropical Queen

Tropical Queen

Interior of *Tropical Queen*

KARIUSHU

Passenger ferry.
HULL: Fibre-reinforced plastic.
MAIN ENGINES: Two GM 8V 71N, 395hp each at 2170rpm.
PROPULSION: Two ALBC$_3$ propellers.
ACCOMMODATION: Air-conditioned accommodation for 95 passengers and 3 crew.
SYSTEMS
Fuel tank capacity: 2000 litres
Electrical generator: One Mitsubishi M14H, 10hp at 2200rpm
DIMENSIONS
Length overall: 20.80m
Length, Japanese Registered: 19.50m
Breadth: 4.80m
Depth: 2.30m
GRT: 65
Japanese gross tonnage: 40
PERFORMANCE
Speed, max: 23.14 knots
  cruising: 19.0 knots

Hamilton waterjets, model 421, type 56 impeller, on stern of *Tropical Queen*

SEA ANGEL

Pleasure motor yacht.
HULL: Fibre-reinforced plastic.
MAIN ENGINES: Two MAN D 2542, 540hp each at 2170rpm.
PROPULSION: One ALBC$_3$ propeller.
ACCOMMODATION: Air-conditioned accommodation for 12 passengers and 8 crew.
SYSTEMS
Fuel tank capacity: 4000 litres
Electrical generator: One Oman MDEH-15R, 40hp at 1800rpm
Navigation: One 48-mile radar
DIMENSIONS
Length overall: 20.0m
Length, Japanese Registered: 19.24m
Breadth: 5.20m
Depth: 2.0m
GRT: 70
Japanese gross tonnage: 42
PERFORMANCE
Speed, max: 24.0 knots
  cruising: 22.0 knots

Shinju *Kariushu* passenger ferry

SHIMABARA

Passenger ferry.
HULL: Fibre-reinforced plastic.
MAIN ENGINES: Two GM 12V 92 TI, 700hp each, max continuous at 2170rpm.
PROPULSION: Two ALBC$_3$ propellers.
ACCOMMODATION: Air-conditioned, for 96 passengers and 3 crew.
SYSTEMS
Fuel tank capacity: 2400 litres
Navigation: One 48-mile radar
DIMENSIONS
Length overall: 23.80m
Length, Japanese Registered: 22.50m
Breadth: 4.80m
Depth: 2.30m
GRT: 80
Japanese gross tonnage: 51
PERFORMANCE
Speed, max: 28.0 knots
  cruising: 22.0 knots

Shinju *Sea Angel* motor yacht

YUKIKAZE 8

Fishing pleasure boat.
HULL: Fibre-reinforced plastic.
MAIN ENGINES: One Yanmar 12LAAK-DT, 800hp at 1800rpm.
PROPULSION: One ALBC$_3$ propeller.
ACCOMMODATION: Room for 12 passengers and 8 crew.
SYSTEMS
Fuel tank capacity: 4500 litres
Electrical generator: One Yanmar 3HMK, 27hp at 3200rpm

Shinju *Shimabara* passenger ferry

DIMENSIONS
Length overall: 19.79m
Length, Japanese Registered: 17.65m
Breadth: 4.0m
Depth: 1.80m
GRT: 32
Japanese gross tonnage: 19

Shinju *Yukikaze 8* fishing pleasure boat

KOREA, SOUTH

MIWON TRADING AND SHIPPING CO LTD

1–15, 2 KA Chung Hak-Dong, Yongdo-ku, Busan, South Korea

Telephone: 4844114
Telex: 24592MITRA K
Telefax: (02) 784 7857

28-METRE PASSENGER CRAFT

A sightseeing boat built in grp for the Jung Ahang Express Co. six have been built.

CHUNG JU 1, 2, 3, 5, 6 & 7
Length, overall: 28.00m
Length, waterline: 24.00m
Beam: 5.10m
Deadrise angle: 5°
Draught, static: 0.65m
Displacement, unladen: 34 tonnes
Displacement, max: 45 tonnes
Engines: Two DDC 12V71TI, 649kW at 2300 rpm, 544kW at 2180 rpm
Propulsion: Two Hamilton water jets, Model 421

Miwon Trading 27-knot sightseeing craft

Speeds: 37.2 tonnes displacement; 30.2 knots at 2280 rpm, 27.8 knots at 2180 rpm
Accommodation: 120 passengers and crew

MALAYSIA

CHIONG BROTHERS SHIPYARD

and other yards Sibu, Malaysia

One of a number of builders of fast river ferries for Malayasian river services.

64 SEAT RIVER FERRY
PRINCIPAL PARTICULARS
Length, overall: 27.44m
Beam, waterline: 2.74m
Beam, overall: approx. 3.20m
Displacement: 15 to 16 tonnes, depending upon engine type fitted
Cabin skin: 1.5mm galvanised steel

Frames: 3mm steel strip
Plating: 3mm steel, 6mm below engine room
Fuel capacity: 600 l
Hull weight of steel: 10 tonnes
Engine: can be MAN, 260kW (350hp), cruise 2200 rpm, 87.5% of full power
Accommodation: 64 in 16 rows, central aisle
Speed: 32 knots

Coral Express: a fast ferry completed in Malaysia 1989 *(M.Daley)*

High-speed steel mono-hull ferry under construction at Chiong Brothers Shipyard

Various types of 30–32 knot ferries on the Sareki/Sibu route, Sarawak *(M. Daley)*

NETHERLANDS

SCHEEPSWERF PORSIUS BV

Kruysbaken 10, 1505 HS Zaandam, Netherlands

Telephone: (075) 158652
Telex: 19316PORS NL

Scheepswerf Porsius is a yacht builder and in early 1986 built a 33-metre aluminium motor yacht designed by MPS Engineering of Lemwerder, West Germany.

33-METRE MOTOR YACHT

HULL: Welded aluminium construction in marine grade aluminium AlMg 4.5Mn. All tanks are integrated in the bottom structure of the hull. Three watertight bulkheads divide the engine room, owner's and guest area, crew area and fore-ship section.

MAIN ENGINES: Two MTU 12V 396 TB94 engines.

CONTROLS: Twin rudders, two stabilisers and one bow thruster hydraulically operated.

SYSTEMS

Auxiliary engines: Two generators, each delivering at least 50kW

Soundproofing: All machinery resiliently mounted. Main exhaust under water with sound dampened bypass above water for the idling condition

Sanitary system: US Coast Guard approved sewage plant connected to a vacuum system and holding tank

Air-conditioning: System installed to reach a temperature difference outside to inside of 8°C and humidity difference of 35%

32.90m motor yacht built by Porsius

DIMENSIONS
Length overall: 32.90m
Length waterline: 28.20m
Beam overall: 7.40m
Max draught under rudder: 1.65m
Draught amidships: 1.40m

WEIGHTS
Full load weight incl max fuel capacity: 135.0
  tonnes
Half load weight with 7.5 tonnes of fuel: 109.5
  tonnes
Empty weight: 97.5 tonnes

PERFORMANCE
Max speed: 32 knots
Range: Approx 3000n miles with 30.50 tonnes of
  fuel and speed of 12 knots

32.90m MPS Engineering-designed motor yacht built by Scheepswerf Porsius

NORWAY

BÅTUTRUSTNING A/S

Termetangen, N-5420 Rubbestadneset, Norway

Telephone: (05)427111
Telefax: (05)427602

Builder of many mono-hull vessels, Båtu-
trustning A/S were engaged in the construction of
a 26m 45 knot ferry in January 1989.

ASKEPOTT

Designed by Teknisk Modellcenter A/S this
three-engine 118 passenger 40 knot ferry was
delivered to Per Vold in 1989. The vessel has an
unusually high maximum speed capability of 47
knots.

Askepott (photo Alan Bliault)

PRINCIPAL PARTICULARS
Hull: GRP sandwich construction
Length, overall: 25.30m
Length, waterline: 21.45m
Breadth, waterline: 5.50m
Breadth: 6.00m
Engines: Three MWM TBD 234V16, each 872kW max, 780kW continuous
Gearboxes: Three ZF BU250
Propulsion: Three KaMeWa water-jet units, type 40S
Fuel capacity: 6.000 l
Speed, service: 40 knots
Speed, max: 47 knots
Range, max: 420 n miles

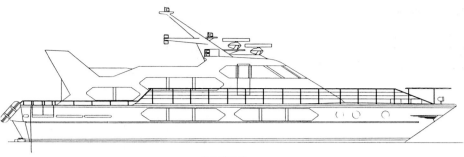

PROFIL

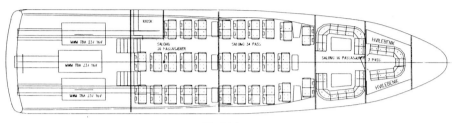

PLAN

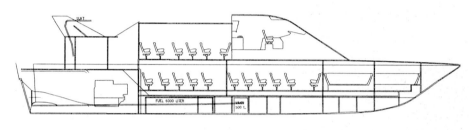

SNITT

OVERBYGG

General arrangement of *Askepott*

KVAERNER FJELLSTRAND A/S
N-5632 Omastrand, Norway

Telephone: (05) 55 41 00
Telex: 42148FBOAT N
Telefax: (05) 55 42 44

Details of mono-hull vessels built by the Fjellstrand company over the period 1977 to 1982 are given in the 1989 edition.

ULSTEIN INTERNATIONAL A/S
N-6065 Ulsteinvik, Norway
BRØDRENE AA A/S
N-6780 Hyen, Norway

Telephone: 5769800
Telex: 42162 BRAA N
Telefax: 5769914

EIKEFJORD MARINE A/S
N-6940 Eikefjord, Norway

Telephone: (057) 49100
Telefax: (057) 49168

Builders of fast mono-hull ferries as well as SESs.

GARSØY
Combined patrol and personnel vessel built in 1988 for the Royal Norwegian Navy. Design by Cirrus A/S.
PRINCIPAL PARTICULARS
Length, overall: 34.00m
Breadth: 7.00m

Garsøy

Draught: 1.80m
Engines: Two MWM TBD 604 BV8, 840kW each

Reduction gears: Two ZF BU250
Propulsion: Two Servogear VD780B propellers

HØYDALSFJORD

A 100-seat, 32 knot ferry built by Brødrene Aa.
PRINCIPAL PARTICULARS
Length, overall: 22.50M
Length, waterline: 19.l0m
Beam: 5.80m
Engines: Two 559kW at 1800 rpm
Speed, cruising, full load: 32 knots

Høydalsfjord

SINGAPORE

FBM MARINE (S) PTE LTD

31 Tuas Road, Singapore 2263

Telephone: 8611706/7, 8616271/2/3
Telex: 53419MARJET RS
Telefax: 8614244

FBM Marine Limited is part of FBM Marine Holdings Ltd, 33/F New World Tower, 16–18 Queen's Road, Central, Hong Kong.

Telephone: (5) 218302
Telex: 74493 HMHCO HX
Telefax: (5) 8100 952

John Warbey, *Group Sales Director*
Kenny Tham, *Yard Manager*

David C H Liang, *Group Chairman*
Robert Liang, *Executive Director*
Mike McSorley, *Marketing Manager*

As well as building catamaran ferries and crew boats to Marinteknik design, this yard has built a total of seven mono-hull ferries and crew boats. The hulls of two of the vessels completed have been built in the Öregrund yard of Marinteknik Verkstads AB, Sweden.

35-METRE PASSENGER FERRY

A number of 35-metre passenger ferries have been built to differing operational requirements.
OWNER: Yuet Hing Marine Supplies.
CLASSIFICATION: Germinisher Lloyds + 100 A4K MCA and IMO code A373(x).
HULL: Deep V forward and flat V with flat chines aft. Constructed in marine grade aluminium T profile extrusions and plates welded by Robot MIG fully automatic welding machines. Provision is made for the main engines to be removed through two bolted access hatches.
MAIN ENGINES: Two MTU 12V 396 TB83 marine diesels, 1180kW at 1940rpm continuous each.

PROPULSION: Two KaMeWa type 63/S62/60 waterjet propulsion units.
CAPACITIES
Fuel: 6000 litres
Water: 1000 litres
Lube oil: 250 litres
Hydraulic oil: 150 litres
Sewage holding tank: 500 litres
ACCOMMODATION
Passengers: 265 and 3.12 tonnes of luggage
Complement: Officer/crew 14
DIMENSIONS
Length overall: 35.00m
Beam, moulded: 7.70m
Depth, moulded: 2.84m
Draught, light: 1.05m (mean)
Draught, loaded: 1.25m (mean)
PERFORMANCE
Speed, max: 30 knots
Speed, cruising: 27 knots

Craft built (high-speed mono-hull)

Designation	Yard No	Craft name	Owner/operator	Delivered	Engines	Classification	Payload	Speed
30MCB (CV900)	102	*Hamidah**	Ocean Tug Service	1985	Two MTU 6V 396 TC62	DnV R-30 Crew boat, light craft	50 passengers + 6.8 tonnes	19 knots cruise
31MCB	104	*Zakat*	Black Gold (M), Sdn Bhd, Malaysia	1986	Two MTU, 440kW each	GL + 100A2, 30 miles	38 passengers + 13.38 tonnes	37 knots
31MCB	106	*Amal*	Black Gold (M), Sdn Bhd, Malaysia	1986	Two MTU, 440kW each	GL + 100A2, 30 miles	38 passengers + 13.38 tonnes	
35MPV	107*	*Discovery Bay 12*	Discovery Bay Co	April 1987	Two MWM TBD 604B V8, 840kW each	HK Navy Dept, Cl2, Protected Waters	256 passengers	25 knots
35MPV	108	*Discovery Bay 15*	Discovery Bay Co	May 1987	Two MWM TBD 604B V8, 840kW each	HK Navy Dept, Cl2, Protected Waters	256 passengers	25 knots
35MPV	109	*Discovery Bay 16*	Discovery Bay Co	June 1987	Two MWM TBD 604B V8, 840kW each	HK Navy Dept, Cl2, Protected Waters	256 passengers	25 knots
35MPV	110	*Wu Yi Hu*	Jiangmen Jiang Gang Passenger Traffic Co, China	1987	Two MTU 12V 396 TB83, 1180kW each		265 passengers + 3.12 tonnes	27 knots contract
40MPV-D	116		Alilauro SpA	1988	Two MTU, 1940kW each	RINA/DnV	27 tonnes	35 knots
40MPV-D	-	*Celestina*	Linea Lauro	1988	-	-	265 passengers	27 knots

*hull built by Marinteknik Verkstads AB, Sweden and fitted out by Fairey Marinteknik Shipbuilders (S) Pte Ltd, Singapore, now FBM Marine (S) Pte Ltd.

The 265-seat, 27-knot *Celestina*

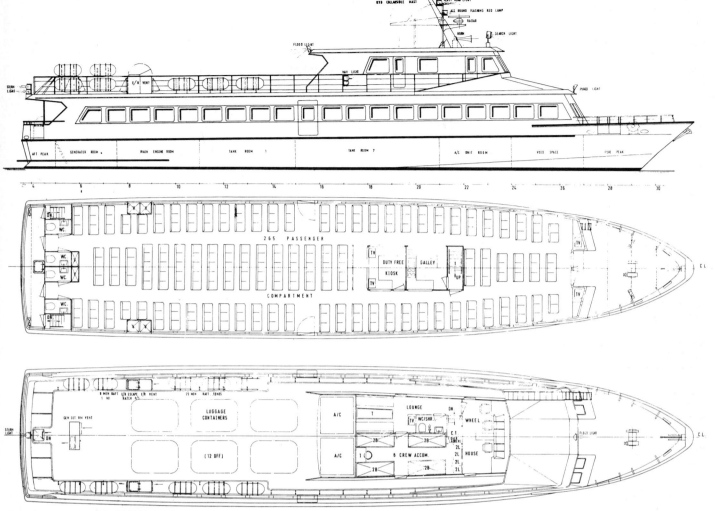

General arrangement of the FBM Marine (S) *Wu Yi Hu*

Discovery Bay 15 built by FBM Marine (S) Pte Ltd

SINGAPORE SHIPBUILDING AND ENGINEERING LTD (SSE)

7 Benoi Road, Singapore 2262

Postal address: PO Box 138, Jurong Town Post Office, Singapore 9161

Telephone: 8612244/6844
Telex: 21206SINGA RS
Telefax: 8613028

George Chow, *General Manager*
Boon Swan Foo, *Senior Manager (Design & Engineering)*
Wong Kin Hoong, *Senior Manager (Marketing and Business Development)*
See Leong Teck, *Senior Manager (Design and Engineering)*
Tan Pheng Hock, *Senior Manager (Yard)*

Singapore Shipbuilding and Engineering Ltd (SSE) was established in 1968 as a specialist shipyard. Current areas of expertise include the building of specialised commercial vessels, military engineering equipment fabrication and the reconstruction and modernisation of old vessels. SSE is located in a 30-acre site at the mouth of the Benoi Basin. In addition to the Swift class patrol boat described below SSE have built or have on order over 30 of their PT class patrol boats (14.54m, 30 knots), 19 for the Singapore Marine Police, two for Singapore Customs and Excise Dept and seven for the Royal Brunei Police Force, this latter order to be completed by the end of 1987.

SSE have also completed (1983) a luxury motor yacht, 14.13m, delivered to a Singapore owner.

In 1986 SSE completed their first air cushion vehicle, an Air Vehicles Tiger 40.

SWIFT CLASS PATROL BOAT

A fast patrol boat, 12 of which were built over the period 1979 to 1980 (Yard Nos 152 to 163) for the Singapore Navy.

HULL: Hard chine planing form, welded aluminium.

ENGINES: Two Deutz SBA 16M 816 diesels, 1330hp each, at 2000rpm or two MTU 12V 331 TC92 diesels, 1475hp each, at 2300rpm.

AUXILIARY POWER: Two diesel generating sets, each 440V, 60Hz, 3-phase, can sustain 100% ship's load.

CAPACITIES

Main fuel tanks: 7000 litres
Reserve tanks: 1600 litres
Fresh water tank: 2000 litres

CREW: 12 (1 CO, 2 Officers, 3 Petty Ratings, 6 Ratings).

ARMAMENT: Two bridge wing general purpose machine guns or half-inch Browning guns. Missile system with two or three launchers aft depending on type of missile.

DIMENSIONS

Length overall: 22.70m
Length waterline: 20.00m
Beam, extreme: 6.20m
Depth, amidship: 3.00m
Draught, at design waterline: 1.60m

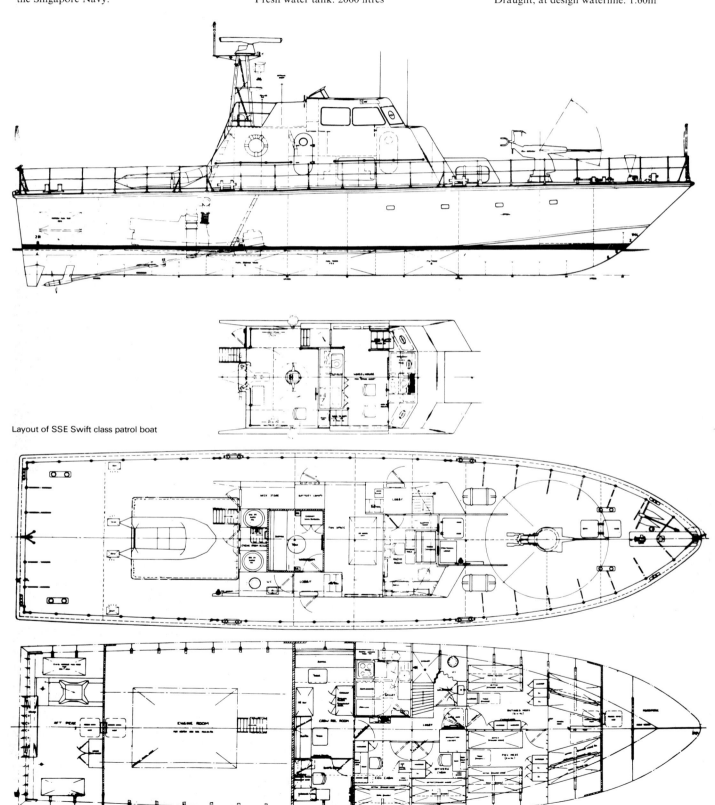

Layout of SSE Swift class patrol boat

Layout of SSE Swift class patrol boat

WEIGHTS
Displacement, half load (with missile): 47 tonnes
Displacement, half load (without missile): 43 tonnes
PERFORMANCE
Speed, max: 33 knots (Deutz), 35 knots (MTU)
Speed, max continuous: 31 knots (Deutz), 31 knots (MTU)
Range, at 10 knots: 900n miles
Range, at 20 knots: 550n miles

Swift class patrol boat

SWEDEN

DJUPVIKS VARV AB
S-440 64 Rönnäng, Sweden

Telephone: 30462230
Telex: 21298DVA S
Telefax: 30462500

About two years ago Djupviks Varv became a member of the Swede Ship Group. The yard was founded in 1894 and since 1937 nearly all the Swedish Coast Guard vessels have been built by Djupviks Varv. The yard started building in aluminium in 1950 and have built about 100 craft in this material to date. During 1980 the building programme was extended to include deliveries of pilot boats, passenger vessels, high-speed catamarans and luxury yachts.

COAST GUARD 280 CLASS
Fast patrol boat. To date Djupviks Varv has delivered every craft in this class to the Swedish Coast Guard.
HULL: All-welded aluminium hull and superstructure.
MAIN ENGINES: Two Cummins marine diesels of 1100hp each.
SYSTEMS: Comprehensively equipped with navigational aids.
DIMENSIONS
Length overall: 21.00m
Beam: 5.00m

Swedish Coast Guard 280 class patrol boat

PERFORMANCE
Speed, max: 27 knots

MARINTEKNIK VERKSTADS AB
Varvsvagen, Box 7, S-74071 Öregrund, Sweden

Telephone: 17330460
Telex: 76182MARTAB S
Telefax: 17330976

Hans Erikson, *Chairman & Managing Director*

Marinteknik Verkstads AB co-operates with FBM Marine Holdings Ltd, Hong Kong.

Following the pioneering by Marinteknik of high-speed waterjet-propelled catamaran ferries, the same form of propulsion was applied in 1985 to a mono-hull crew boat design. The first such craft were built at the company's yard at Öregrund and fitted out and delivered at the Marinteknik Singapore (now FBM Marine (S) Pte Ltd) yard in 1985. Since then Marinteknik Verkstads AB have built a further five mono-hull craft for ferry operations in Hong Kong, Sweden and Italy, and are engaged in the design and building of small mono-hull cruise vessels.

Europa Jet

Craft built (high-speed mono-hull)

Designation	Yard No	Craft name	Owner/Operator	Delivered	Engines	Payload	Speed
30 MCB (CV900)	58	*Hamidah**	Ocean Tug Service	1985	Two MTU 6V 396 TC82	50 passengers + 6.8 tonnes cargo	19 knots cruise
MPV	64	*Discovery Bay 15*	Discovery Bay	April 1987	Two MTU, 840kW each	22 tonnes	25 knots
41 MPV	65	*Cinderella*	Rederi AB Marinteknik/City Jet Line	1987	Four Scania DSI 14 300kW each	450 passengers	22 knots cruise
38 MPV	66	*Cosmopolitan Lady*	Private Cruise International I Ltd	1989	Two MTU, 880kW each	12 passengers	20 knots
41 MPV	68	*Europa Jet*	Alilauro SpA	1987	Two MTU, 770kW each	350 passengers	22 knots
41 MPV	71	*Rosario Lauro, (ex Aurora Jet)*	Alilauro SpA	1988			
41 MPV	—	*Rosaria Lauro*	Alilauro SpA	1988	—	—	—
41 MPV	72	*Cinderella II*	City Jet Line	1989	Two MTU 12V 396 TB83	450 passengers	28 knots
41 MPV	76	*Iris*	Kvarner Express	1989	Two MTU 12V 396 TB83	350 passengers	28 knots
41 MPV	78	*Cinderella III*	City Jet Line	1990	Two MTU 12V 396 TB83	—	28 knots

*Fitted out by Fairey Marinteknik Shipbuilders (S) Pte Ltd, Singapore, now FBM Marine (S) Pte Ltd.

MARINJET 30MCB (CV900)
HAMIDAH
For details of this craft please see 1989 edition of this book

CINDERELLA
A 41.9m fast passenger ferry/day cruise ship operating in Stockholm Archipelago.
OWNER: City Jet Line, Stockholm, Sweden.
CLASSIFICATION: Sjöfartsverket, Sweden.
HULL: Constructed in aluminium. Internal design by Lennart Janson.
MAIN ENGINES: Four Scania DSI 14 marine diesels, cruising power 300kW each at 1800rpm (MCR)
PROPULSION: Two MJP J550R-DD waterjet units, belt driven
CAPACITIES
Fuel: 5000 litres
ACCOMMODATION: Payload of 450 passengers, with 85-seat restaurant on the upper deck and a cafeteria in the main saloon.
SYSTEMS
Auxiliary engines: One Scania DN11 108kW generator and one Perkins 4236 25kW generator
Air-conditioning: Fitted throughout

Rosaria Lauro built at Öregrund

The Marinteknik Verkstads *Öregrund* and *Cinderella* at Stockholm winter 1988/89

DIMENSIONS
Length overall: 41.90m
Breadth: 7.70m
Draught, full load: 1.10m
PERFORMANCE
Speed, cruise (fully loaded, 35 tonnes disposable load): 22 knots
Range: 450n miles
Fuel consumption: 170 litres/h (tank: 7000 litres)

CINDERELLA II & III

The second and third vessels for City Cruise Line are fitted with two MTU 12V396 TB83 engines giving a maximum speed of 28 knots. Fuel consumption is 570 l/h and cruise speed with 35 tonnes disposable load is 27 knots at MCR of 1150kW (each engine) at 1940 rpm. MJP 650R-DD water-jet units are fitted.

40 METRE MINI-CRUISE VESSEL
COSMOPOLITAN LADY

This 40 metre Marinteknik 20 knot mini-cruise vessel is a semi-planing, diesel-powered waterjet-propelled monohull vessel with V-shaped lines and very shallow draught designed for cruising in restricted areas (280 nm) or alternatively world-wide service. The vessel is constructed according to applicable classification rules and the latest international rules. It fulfills the damage stability requirements with one damaged compartment.

The vessel is equipped with 6 double cabins, all with private bathroom, WC/shower unit, accommodating 12 passengers. All the cabins are well equipped, situated outside with their own sea view. There are large common areas for the passengers, including dining room, two lounges and an entrance foyer with a cocktail bar. The fully equipped galley, with large provision stores, is suitable for making a gourmet cuisine. The vessel is equipped with accommodation for a crew of 7.

The hull is divided into seven watertight compartments and constructed with salt-water-resistant aluminium profiles designed and developed by Marinteknik, producing a light craft that is both extremely strong and durable and with proven high reliability.

The waterjet propulsion system gives the 40 metre mini-cruise vessel a high degree of manoeuvrability at all speeds, a great advantage when the vessel is operating in busy harbours and narrow waterways. Other advantages of the waterjet system for this vessel are shallow draught, minimal wash and wake signatures, high propulsive efficiency at all speeds and, with the protected impeller, little chance of damage from water-borne debris, very low vibration and noise levels.

PRINCIPAL PARTICULARS
Classification: DnV + 1A1 Light Craft, R280 EO
Length, overall: 40.00m
Length, pp: 31.50m
Breadth: 7.90m
Engines: Two MTU 12V396 TB93, 880kw each driving two MJP J650R propulsion water-jet units, via ZF BU 255 gearboxes
Speed: up to 20 knots

Layout of Marinteknik Verkstads *Cinderella*

Cinderella

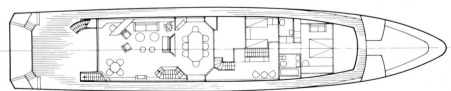

Layout of the Marinteknik mini-cruise vessel

The Marinteknik Verkstads 40m mini-cruise vessel
Cosmopolitan Lady

OSKARSHAMNS VARV AB

Box 2, S-57201 Oskarshamn, Sweden

Telephone: (0491) 170 80
Telex: 4963OSKYARD S

Located on the east coast of Sweden Oskarshamns Varv specialise in building aluminium and steel motor yachts and military craft. The company is part of the Swede Ship Group. Craft are built in construction halls 90 × 31.5m, 83 × 19.0m and 40 × 31.5m with overhead cranes, lifting capacity 80 metric tons. There are also machine shop and repair facilities with two floating docks for vessels up to 30 000 dwt. Number of employees is about 170.

24-METRE SPORT FISHERMAN

Fast motor yacht. The first of this class of motor yacht has been delivered.
CLASSIFICATION: Hull certificate, Det norske Veritas.
HULL: Construction of hull and superstructure is in aluminium.
MAIN ENGINES: Two MTU 12V 396 TB93 marine diesel engines 1600bhp each. Electrical trawling motors also fitted.
PROPULSION: Two CP propellers.
CAPACITIES
Fuel: 15 000 litres (approx)
Fresh water: 1000 litres (approx)
SYSTEMS
Auxiliary engines: Two G & M 60kW diesel generators
Navigational: Magnuavox Sat Nav system, Raytheon speed log and depth sounder, Foruno ADF, Decca colour radar, Loran C, Robertson autopilot and a Plath gyrocompass
Communications: Sailor SSB, Sailor VHF, Airphone intercom, Foruno Weatherfax Polaris Regency VHF back-up and Inmarsat satellite communications
DIMENSIONS
Length overall: 24.10m
Breadth: 7.20m
Draught: 1.75m
GRT: 75 tons (approx)
PERFORMANCE
Speed, service: 27 knots

Oskarshamns Varv 24m Sport Fisherman

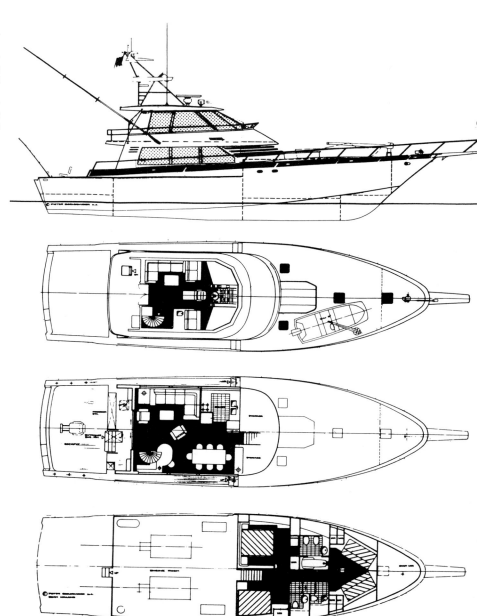

24m Sport Fisherman profile and accommodation layout

SMUGGLER MARINE AB

Malmvägen 15, 115 41 Stockholm, Sweden

Telephone: (08) 6613799
Telex: 10651NAVPROD S
Telefax: (08) 66734 35

Hans Lindgren, *Director*

Smuggler Marine UK LTD

PO Box 39, Lymington, Hampshire, England

Telephone: (0590) 683261
Telefax: (0590) 79124

Smuggler Marine traces its origins to the 1950s, when four Swedish airline pilots began to develop and build racing boats. They subsequently established a firm called Weedo Båtar, selling pleasure craft at the same time as they notched-up big competition successes with their sports boat Weedo GT.

In 1964 the firm was divided into two arms of which one, Smuggler Boat, concentrated on the further development of fast racing hulls while the other, Weedo Båtar, started the successful development of advanced offshore rescue craft.

Weedo Rescue Boats are now in two versions, one complying with SOLAS rules for MOBs (Man Overboard Boats) and the other with offshore rules. The boats are approved by authorities such as the Norwegian Maritime Directorate, Britain's Department of Trade and the Australian authorities, as well as the Swedish authorities. There are about 20 Weedo boats stationed around the Swedish coasts, some 60 boats are employed in the North Sea offshore industry and about 40 boats have been sold elsewhere.

Co-operation with the product development consultants, Naval Production, started in 1971 in connection with what was then an advanced project, the building of a 45ft patrol craft in sandwich glassfibre-reinforced plastic. Successful prototype trials were soon followed by orders from, among others, the Swedish Navy and the Indian Coastguard, as well as private buyers.

Naval Production has wide international experience of product development in a variety of other fields, such as advanced propulsion systems, including waterjets, and hydraulics and involvement with the Swedish Jetcat project.

In 1985 Smuggler Boat was acquired by Intrade Invest AB and Naval Production and Smuggler Marine AB was established. Weedo Båtar was taken over in 1986. Naval Production's activities are now fully integrated with Smuggler Marine.

Intensive development work is currently proceeding on a completely new range of hulls to be built mainly with highly advanced composite materials. The prototype for this production, the diesel waterjet driven Smuggler 384, has for nearly two years undergone extensive tests with the Swedish Navy.

Several larger boats are in design at the same time as Smuggler Marine and SP Systems are further developing design and production technology.

SMUGGLER 80 HIGH SPEED
(DESIGN)
LEADING PARTICULARS
Length, overall: 25.0m
Length, over deck: 25.0m
Beam, max: 6.6m
Draft, at full load: 1.4m
Displacement empty: 35m³
Disposable load: 20 tons
PROPULSION MACHINERY
Engines: Two MTU 16V 396 TB94
Power: 2560kW (3480bhp) each at 2100rpm

Prototype of the Smuggler 384

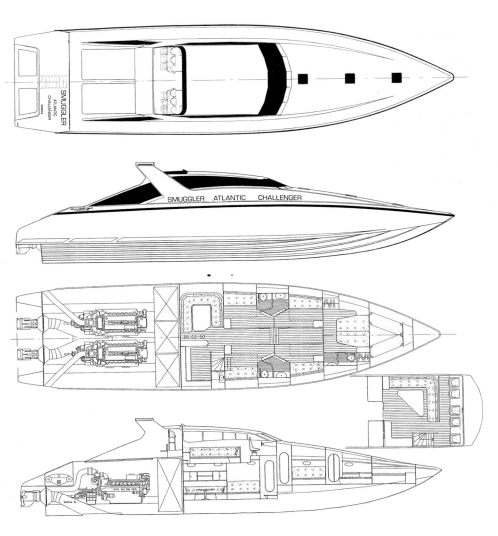

Waterjet Unit: Two KaMeWa NP 52 Twin Jet
(Patent pending)
PERFORMANCE
Speed max at 10% provisions: 60+ knots

Speed cruising at full load: 45 knots
Speed max at full load: 50+ knots
Range at cruising speed: 980n miles
Range at maximum speed: 820n miles

TAIWAN

HI-STAR MARINE CO LIMITED

50, Ta Yeh S Road, Kaohsiung, Taiwan

Telephone: 78715286
Telefax: 78715280

Charles Chang, *General Manager*
Tim Juan, *Marketing Manager*

HI-STAR 70

A luxury motor yacht, the first boat has been delivered and is cruising between the European countries.
ENGINES: Two GM 8V-92 TA, 735bhp each at 2300rpm.
DIMENSIONS
Length overall: 21.34m
Length waterline: 17.98m
Beam: 5.64m
Draught: 1.17m
Freeboard, forward: 2.26m
Freeboard, aft: 1.96m
Design waterline to freeboard height: 4.80m
CAPACITIES
Fuel: 1200 to 1800 gallons
Water: 400 gallons
DISPLACEMENT: Approx 38 tonnes
PERFORMANCE
Speed: 22 to 30 knots

Hi-Star 70

THAILAND

ITALTHAI MARINE LIMITED

Italthai House, 11th Floor, 2013 New Petchburi Road, Bangkok, Thailand

Telephone: 3146101–9/314 7578/314 7246
Telex: 21225ITELECT TH
Telefax: 66023146385

Dr Chaijudh Karnasuta, *Chairman*
Angelo Gualtieri, *Managing Director*
Papit Gualtieri, *Executive Director*
Vice Admiral Chob Sirodom, *Assistant to Managing Director*
Suwit Khandawit, *Marketing Manager*

Italthai Marine was formed in 1978 by the amalgamation of the Italian-Thai Development Corporation, Italthai Holding Co Ltd, and Oriental Marine and Laminates Ltd. There are approximately 450 employees and the shipyard occupies about 56 000m² with workshops, fabrication shops and a shipway length of 190 metres with 250 metres in length of main building berths. There is also a floating dry dock of 100 metres with a lifting capacity of 6000 tons for repairing medium size sea-going vessels. The yard constructs and repairs small to medium size craft and vessels in steel, grp and aluminium.

50.14-METRE PATROL GUN BOAT

Built for the Royal Thai Navy.
HULL: Aluminium alloy/steel.
DIMENSIONS
Length overall: 50.14m
Breadth, moulded: 7.25m
Draught: 1.68m
WEIGHT
Load displacement: 300 tons
PERFORMANCE
Speed, max continuous: 24 knots

High-speed craft built

Year	Type	Length	Max speed	Main engines	Hull	No	Owner
1980-1981	Patrol Craft Fast (PCF)	19.59m	25 knots	MTU 6V 396 TC 82	Aluminium alloy	6	Royal Thai Navy
1982	Patrol Craft Fast (PCF)	20.80m	25 knots	MTU 6V 396 TC 82	Aluminium alloy	5	Royal Thai Navy
	Patrol Gun Boat (PGB)	50.14m	24 knots	MTU 16V 538 TB 91	Aluminium/steel	1	Royal Thai Navy
1983	Patrol Craft Fast (PCF)	20.80m	25 knots	MTU 6V 396 TC 82	Aluminium alloy	3	Royal Thai Navy
1984-1986	Patrol Boat	27.43m	25 knots	Deutz MWM SBA 16M 816 CR	Aluminium alloy	1	Police Department
	Patrol Gun Boat (PGB)	50.14m	24 knots	MTU 16V 538 TB 91	Aluminium/steel	5	Royal Thai Navy

Italthai 50.14m patrol gun boat delivered to the Royal Thai Navy

27.43-METRE PATROL BOAT
Built for Marine Police Division, Thai Police Department.
HULL: Aluminium alloy.
ENGINES: Deutz MWM SBA 16M 816 CR.
DIMENSIONS
Length overall: 27.43m
Beam: 5.60m
PERFORMANCE
Speed: 25 knots

19.59-METRE FAST PATROL CRAFT
Built for Royal Thai Navy.
HULL: Aluminium alloy.
DIMENSIONS
Length overall: 19.59m
Moulded breadth: 5.30m
Draught: 1.52m
WEIGHT
Displacement: 35.56 tonnes
PERFORMANCE
Max continuous speed: 25 knots

Italthai 27.43m patrol boat delivered to Thai Marine Police

Italthai 19.59m fast patrol boat, one of six delivered to Royal Thai Navy

TECHNAUTIC INTERTRADING CO LTD
44/13 Convent Road, Silom, Bangkok 10500, Thailand

Telephone: 2340730/9368
Telex: 87650TECO TH

Capt Nirun Chitanon, *Director and General Manager*
The Technautic shipyard employs 150 people, has a total area of 7944m², the main building occupying 2076m². Over 52 craft in the 8- to 26-metre range have been delivered, mainly patrol boats and work boats.

P86 (26-METRE PATROL BOAT)
Fast patrol boat.
DESIGNER: C Raymond Hunt Associates Inc, 69 Long Wharf, Boston, Massachusetts 02110, USA
Telephone: (617) 742 5669, Telex 294116 BOSTUX (Attn: Hunt Associates)
HULL: Grp sandwich with Airex pvc foam core.
MAIN ENGINES: Three Isotta Fraschini ID 36 8VSS, total 3150hp at 1900rpm.
PROPULSION: Three Castoldi 07 waterjets.
CAPACITIES
Fuel: 18 050 litres
Water: 2545 litres
ACCOMMODATION
Officers: Captain's cabin, 2 officers' cabins, heads, wardroom and galley
Ratings: Forward messdeck, accommodation for four ratings; after messdeck, accommodation for seven ratings, heads and washrooms
DIMENSIONS
Length overall: 26.20m
Length waterline: 22.60m
Beam: 6.30m
Draught: 1.10m

Technautic 26m fast patrol boat built to the C Raymond Hunt P86 design

P86 Patrol boat

WEIGHTS
Displacement, light: 220 500kg
Displacement, half load: 264 600kg
Displacement, full load: 308 700kg

PERFORMANCE
Speed, max: 30 knots
cruising: 27 knots

UNITED KINGDOM

AILSA-PERTH SHIPBUILDERS LIMITED

Harbour Road, Troon, Ayrshire, KA10 6DN
Scotland UK

Telephone: (0292) 311311
Telex: 778027AILSA G
Telefax: (0292) 317613

Gregory Copley, *Chairman*
Peter G Waymouth, *Managing Director*
Tom Jenkins, *Director and Naval Architect*

The Ailsa shipyard was privatised in February 1987 when it was taken over from British Shipbuilders by Ailsa-Perth. The yard has a covered building hall capable of constructing two vessels at a time of up to 114 metres in length with a beam of up to 20.50 metres. There are also two dry docks, fitting-out and repair jetties, also 5852 square metres of steel and outfit production shops. Ailsa-Perth have introduced three new naval designs, their 62-metre Highlander class corvette and the Cobra and Crescent class 34-metre patrol boats in addition to their 25-metre craft.

In September 1989 Ailsa-Perth announced the signing of an agreement with Vosper International Ltd. under which the yard will market and build Vosper's designs from 21m patrol boats upwards. Also in September 1989 Ailsa-Perth acquired the facilities and designs of Montrose Marine Ltd., based in Scotland. This acquisition provides capability for building in GRP.

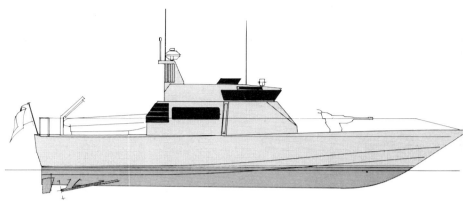

Profile of Ailsa-Perth 25m patrol boat design

25-METRE PATROL BOAT (DESIGN)

Fast patrol boat.
DESIGNER: Alistair R Cameron, Camarc Ltd, Worthing, Sussex, England.
HULL: Superstructure and hull constructed in aluminium.
MAIN ENGINES: Two diesel engines varying in type up to 3000shp driving through U-drive gearboxes or V-drive units. Engine layout can incorporate a small waterjet for loiter use.
ARMAMENT: Dependent on operational requirements, typical layout would be 20/30mm cannon forward, two 7.20mm general purpose machine guns mounted on bridge with a Sea Skua missile aft.
DIMENSIONS
Length overall: 25.00m
PERFORMANCE
Dependent on engine installation, payload and endurance requirements: 25 to 39 knots

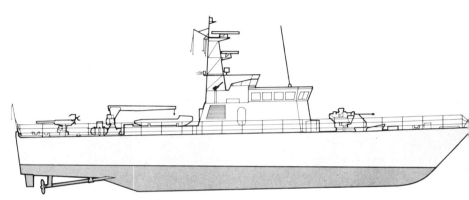

Profile of Ailsa-Perth Crescent and Cobra class designs

CRESCENT AND COBRA CLASS (DESIGN)

Patrol and general surveillance craft.
DESIGNER: Ailsa-Perth.
HULL: Steel.
MAIN ENGINES: Two Paxman Valenta 16CM each developing 2500kW at 1500rpm.
ARMAMENT: One 30mm Oerlikon twin mounting type GCMA 03–2 forward, one 20mm mounting aft, Cossor Naval Transponder Type IFF 2750, one Racal Decca Type 2459F surveillance radar.
COMPLEMENT: 21 consisting of commanding officer, two officers, nine senior ratings and nine junior ratings. The complement can be increased by a further three persons if required.

SYSTEMS
Electrics: 440V/3ph/60Hz, two main generator sets at 80kW per set
Navigational: Racal Decca type AC 1690/6 radar
DIMENSIONS
Length overall: 34.00m
Length, waterline: 30.90m
Breadth, moulded: 6.75m
Draught, moulded: 1.70m
WEIGHT
Displacement, half load: 146.25 tonnes
PERFORMANCE
Speed, sprint: 34 knots
Speed, max continuous: 29 knots
Range at 16 knots: 800km
Range at 14 knots: 1000km

ATLANTIC SPRINTER LTD

1, The Square, Bagshot, Surrey, GU19 5AX, England

Telephone: (0276) 71010
Telex: 858334 HAMMAIR G
Telefax: (0276) 71270

Richard Noble, *Principal*

ATLANTIC SPRINTER

In the past year a number of changes have taken place concerning the project as first described in the Addenda of the 1989 edition of Jane's High Speed Marine Craft. Construction is due to start in May 1990 and launching is timed for 28 February, 1991 following which the vessel will be delivered to Portsmouth for trials prior to arriving in New York in July for the record attempt. The vessel is expected to make the attempt on the Blue Riband Atlantic crossing record in the period

Impression of *Atlantic Sprinter (Painting by Wilf Hardy G.Av.A. copyright 1989)*

July/August 1991; the great circle distance between the Ambrose Channel Light, New York and the Bishop Rock Lighthouse, the Scilly Isles, being 2948 n miles. The vessel is being designed to achieve its record run in Sea State 4 conditions.

The design team is now as follows:

Hull: Hydro Engineering Systems of Geneva, Chief Designer, Erbil Surter

Structural consultants: Ove Arup and Partners

Tank testing: HSVA Hamburg Ship Model Basin

Co-ordinating designer: Martin Francis Naval Architects, Antibes, France

The intention is that *Atlantic Sprinter* will be built on the Tyne on a riverside site allocated by the National Garden Festival at Gateshead, work to start early in 1990 and the boat to be built in full view of the public visiting the Garden Festival. With further support from the Newcastle Initiative, Tyne Tees Television and the Newcastle Chronicle and Journal, the decision has been taken to build the *Atlantic Sprinter* on the Tyne, birthplace of the Blue Riband liner *Mauretania*.

A subsidiary company is being formed by Atlantic Sprinter Ltd. to build the boat. The equity in this subsidiary is to be handed on to the workforce on completion, to enable Tyne-based marine building development to continue.

PRINCIPAL PARTICULARS

Some confirmed and revised details as at January 1990 are as follows:

Engine: Rolls Royce RB-211, 24600kW (33000hp)

Displacement: 360 tonnes

Speed, target: 60 knots

Range: 3600 n miles

Starting fuel: 250 tonnes

Atlantic crossing time, target: 49 h

BERTHON BOAT COMPANY LTD

The Shipyard, Lymington, Hampshire SO41 9YL, England

Telephone: (0590) 673312
Telex: 477831 BERTHN G
Telefax: (0590) 679811

D O May, *Director*
B J May, *Director*
J G Hemingway, *Director*

BERTHON 80
DALVINA

Completed June 1st, 1989, this luxury motor yacht was designed by Laurent Giles Ltd of Lymington and the all-aluminium hull built by Congar Holdings of Hamble to Lloyds approval and supervision.

A special feature of this vessel is the fitting of a hydraulically actuated MVS 2000 Koop Nautic roll stabilising system. With this system on *Dalvina* a mass of 1.14 tonnes can be moved athwartships across a 5 m horizontal track at up to 3.66 metres per second. The movement is controlled by a computer that anticipates roll motion both underweigh and when stationary.

Another interesting feature of this vessel is that the superstructure is mounted on an aluminium frame fixed to the hull structure by rubber bushes. This approach for reducing noise and vibration on this vessel was introduced by the Southampton Wolfson Unit.

PRINCIPAL PARTICULARS

Length, overall: 24.30m

Length, waterline: 21.25m

Beam: 6.40m

Draught: 1.80m

Displacement: 75 tonnes

Engines: Two MTU 8V396TB93 969kW max., each

Fuel capacity: 13620 l

Freshwater capacity: 2043 l

Speed, cruising, continuous: 19.5 knots
    max: 22 knots

Range, cruising: over 2000 n miles

Berthon 80' *Dalvina*

Berthon 80' *Dalvina*

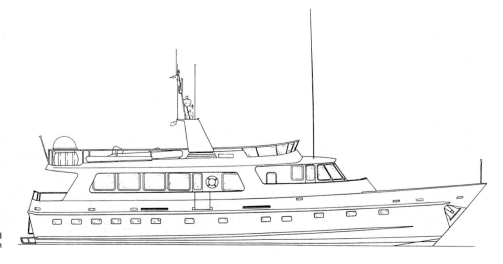

Profile of Berthon 80' designed by Laurent Giles Ltd of Lymington

BROOKE YACHTS INTERNATIONAL LIMITED

Heath Road, Lowestoft, Suffolk NR33 9LZ, England

Telephone: (0502) 517151
Telex: 975665
Telefax: (0502) 514663

Anthony de Kerdrel, *Managing Director*
David Semken, *Production Director*

VIRGIN ATLANTIC CHALLENGER II

DESIGNERS: Peter Birkett and Sonny Levi.

The *Virgin Atlantic Challenger II* was designed and built in 21 weeks to break the Atlantic Blue Riband record set 34 years ago. The craft completed the 2949n mile passage from Ambrose Light to Bishop Rock on 29 June 1986 with a total run time of 3 days, 8 hours, 31 minutes and 35 seconds thus improving on the current Blue Riband time by 2 hours, 9 minutes and 35 seconds.
HULL: All-welded corrosion-resistant aluminium alloy. The wheelhouse is constructed separately and riveted and glued to the main frame.
ENGINES: Two MTU 12V 396 TB93 turbocharged diesels, each producing 2000hp at 2000rpm.
PROPULSION: Two Sonny Levi drive units driving Italian built surface-piercing five-bladed propellers.
SYSTEMS
Fuel tanks: Four Marston tanks mounted midships, 3.13 tonnes capacity each

Trim: One trimming tank of 1.20 tonnes in the bows
Safety: An Auto Marine buoyancy bag system is provided to prevent the boat from sinking in the event of major trouble
Navigation: Two Racal Decca 170 BT radars with enclosed randome scanners. The scanners can be connected to either radar display by means of switching connecting wires; two MNS 2000 Racal Decca, one Trimble combined Loran/GPS, one Lokata portable RDF working on MF frequencies, one Racal Decca CVP 3500 video plotter (the antenna on the two MNS 2000 are interchangeable between the receivers. Each MNS 2000 has a log and compass input. The colour plotter is connected to the main Racal Decca MNS 2000), one Marine Data steering display, one Marine Data fluxgate compass, one Thomas Walker electromagnetic log, one Cetrek 7000 autopilot, one Cetrek fluxgate compass, two Ritchie high-speed magnetic compasses. (The Marine Data display has log and compass inputs as well as connection to the MNS 2000. The Cetrek autopilot is capable of obtaining heading information from either fluxgate compass.
Communication: Two Skanti HF SSB type TRP 8250 radios, one Sailor VHR radio type RT 2047 (Racal Decca supply), two Icom portable VHF radios on marine band, one Icom portable VHF radio on aircraft band, one Argos beacon, three Racal Decca EPIRBs

All equipment operates directly from a 24V dc supply, and is fitted to absorb pounding at sea.

DIMENSIONS
Length overall: 22.02m
Beam, max: 5.82m
Cabin width: 4.0m
Cabin length: 5.0m
PERFORMANCE
Speed, max: In excess of 55 knots
Speed at full load, with 13.7 tonnes of fuel: 46.5 knots
Speed at half load: 51.6 knots

G WHIZ
33-METRE HIGH-SPEED MOTOR YACHT

Completed for delivery in March 1989 for an order in the USA.
DESIGNERS: Renato Sonny Levi with styling and interiors by Jon Bannenberg.
HULL: Hull and superstructure constructed in marine grade aluminium alloy with Kevlar forward superstructure with tanks for fuel oil, fresh water and sewage built into double bottom.
MAIN ENGINES: Two MTU 16V 396 TB94 marine diesel engines rated at 2700hp each at 1975rpm operating through ZF 1.479:1 gearboxes
PROPULSION: Two Levi Drive units LDU 3000TL
CAPACITIES
Fuel: 13.00 tonnes
Fresh water: 2.00 tonnes
ACCOMMODATION: Two guest staterooms with bathrooms, crew in one double/one twin cabins and two bathrooms.
SYSTEMS: G & M 50kW 208V, three phase, 50Hz diesel generator

Virgin Atlantic Challenger II

G WHIZ

DIMENSIONS
Length overall: 33.00m
Length waterline: 24.00m
Beam, max: 7.30m
Draught, max: 1.14m
WEIGHTS
Displacement: 80.00 tonnes
PERFORMANCE
Speed (at 80 tonnes displacement): 45 knots
Range: 450 n miles approx at cruising speed
PRINCIPAL ELECTRONIC EQUIPMENT
Magnavox MX2400 Satcom with Sharpe FO210
telefax
Furuno FSN 70 Radar
Furuno Weather fax
Chartnav system interfaced to GPS and Robertson AP9 autopilot
2 Trimble 10X combined GPS/LORAN
ICOM M700 SSB Radio
S/P Radio 'Sailor' VHF
Mitel SX10E PABX telephone system, 8 extensions, 4 trunk lines, facility for shoreline connection, Panasonic KXT 2204 telephones.
ENTERTAINMENT
Main Saloon: Sony five-way Compact Disc Player, Quad 306 stereo power amplifier, VHS

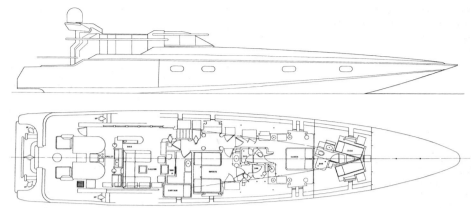

33m high speed motor yacht *G-WHIZ*

multistandard video, Barco MCD 2640 26' super quad colour TV.
Wheelhouse: Sony radio/cassette player
Owners cabin: Sony combined radio/cassette complete with multi Compact Disc Player
Guest cabin: Sony combined radio/cassette complete with multi Compact Disc Player

Captain and crew cabin: Sony car radio/cassette player
GALLEY: Fully operational to include range, fridges, freezer and ice-maker
The boat is fully air conditioned

FBM MARINE LIMITED

Cowes Shipyard, Cowes, Isle of Wight PO31 7DL, England

Telephone: (0983) 297111
Telex: 86466FAMBRO G
Telefax: (0983) 299642

J Barr, *Managing Director*
John Warbey, *Sales Director*
T Liu, *Financial Director*
Gordon Dodd, *Manufacturing Director*
David Codd, *Commercial Manager*
Mike McSorley, *Marketing Manager*
Robert Milner, *Regional Manager*
Patrick Methold, *Regional Manager*
Ian Campbell, *Regional Manager*
Nigel Warren, *Chief Designer*

The company name was changed in 1988 from Fairey Marinteknik (UK) Ltd to FBM Marine Ltd. The company has expertise in the design and production of ferries, patrol boats, special service craft, workboats and lifeboats.

'TRACKER' CLASS

Twenty-eight of these 20m patrol craft are in service with security forces and customs in eight countries.
HULL: The Tracker hull is of hard chine form with a fine entry and pronounced topside flare providing a dry, seakindly hull that will operate economically at high cruising speeds. A skeg enhances directional stability and gives some protection to the twin propellers and rudders.

Hull, deck and superstructure are of high quality hand lay-up grp. Hull and deck scantlings, construction and materials are approved by Lloyd's Register of Shipping and each hull is provided with a Lloyd's Construction Certificate.

The hull has close pitch transverse frames and deep full-length longitudinal engine girders. All fuel oil and fresh water is carried in integral centreline tanks formed between the inner longitudinals. The deck and superstructure are of sandwich type construction.

Full cathodic protection by zinc anodes for minimum 1 year life.
MAIN ENGINES/GEARBOXES: Two Detroit Diesel GM 12V-71 TI, turbocharged, aftercooled, fresh water heat exchanger-cooled marine diesels with ZF BW190 2:1 reverse/reduction gearboxes.

20m Tracker fast patrol boat

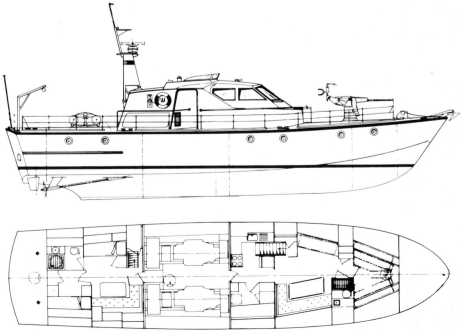

FBM 20m Tracker fast patrol boat

Each engine is maximum rated at 750shp (560kW) at 2300rpm.

PROPULSION: Monel K500 63.5mm diameter propeller shafts running in replaceable water-lubricated rubber bearings. Five-blade propellers and 'P' brackets are in nickel aluminium bronze.

CONTROLS: Two station hand hydraulic steering system operating twin balanced nickel aluminium bronze rudders. Emergency tiller provided.

ACCOMMODATION: Spacious accommodation is provided below decks for 6 crew and 2 petty officers forward of the engine room and for 2 officers and the captain aft. The accommodation is furnished and equipped, and is fully air-conditioned throughout. Watertight bulkheads divide the hull into 6 compartments: the forepeak (anchor chain locker); focsle with berths for 4 crew; forecabin with crew's mess area, berths for 2 crew, cabin for 2 petty officers, galley, dry food store and toilet/shower; engine room; aft cabin with wardroom, berths for 2 officers, captain's cabin and toilet/shower; aft peak (steering gear and general stowage).

Above decks, the enclosed wheelhouse has a centreline steering position together with separate navigator's and radio operator's stations. It is fully air-conditioned and large enough to be used as an operations room and to allow the installation of comprehensive navigation and communication systems. Aft of the wheelhouse is an open bridge deck equipped with a centreline steering position.

SYSTEMS

Electrical: 24V dc insulated return; 2 banks of batteries charged by main engine alternators and by transformer/rectifier from 240V ac system. 240V ac supplied by two 15kW diesel generators or shore supply and powering air-conditioning system, engine room fans, galley equipment, domestic water heater and main lighting

Bilge/fire: Electrically powered main bilge pump with suctions to each watertight compartment and piped to supply fire/deckwash hydrant in superstructure. Back-up manual bilge pump in main bilge circuit

ARMAMENT: A single 20mm cannon can be mounted on the foredeck and two 12.7mm machine guns on the bridge wings.

DIMENSIONS

Length, overall: 20.0m
Beam: 5.18m
Draught: 1.45m
Fuel capacity: 5460 litres
Fresh water capacity: 1365 litres

WEIGHT

Empty: 30 tonnes (approx)

PERFORMANCE

Speed, max: 25.5 knots
        continuous: 23.0 knots
Range at 20 knots: 450n miles

FBM 33m Protector fast patrol boat; three delivered to the Royal Bahamas Defence Force, 1986

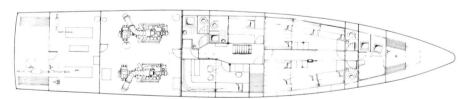
FBM 33m Protector fast patrol boat

'PROTECTOR' CLASS

Three Protector 33m patrol boats were delivered to the Royal Bahamas Defence Force in 1986. These vessels are intended for long endurance patrol missions (fisheries protection and EEZ security duties).

Two further Protector class boats have been built under license in Chile.

HULL: The Protector hull is designed to combine good seakeeping with fuel efficiency at all operational speeds. The full-length topsides knuckle enhances stability and with the forward spray rail, gives a stable, dry and seakindly hull. Optional roll damping fins can replace the standard bilge keels.

The hull is divided into watertight compartments and meets strict one compartment flooded damage stability criteria.

The hull and major bulkheads are of all-welded mild steel construction with deep transverse frames and closed spaced longitudinals. Integral double bottom tanks are provided, 3 for fuel, 1 for fresh water. Deck and deckhouse are of all-welded marine aluminium with Kelocouple bi-metallic connection to hull at gunwale edge. All ladders, deck hatches, watertight and weathertight doors are of aluminium. Rectangular section plastic fendering around gunwale.

Full cathodic protection provided by zinc anodes for minimum 1 year life.

MAIN ENGINES/GEARBOXES: Two Paxman Valenta 8RP 200–1-CM fresh water heat exchanger-cooled marine diesel engines each maximum rated at 2000bhp (1492kW) at 1600rpm driving through ZF BWK 458 2:1 reverse/reduction gearboxes.

Alternative machinery such as twin MTU 16V 396 or triple Detroit Diesel GM 16V-149 can be installed to suit particular requirements.

PROPULSION: Monel K500 115mm diameter propeller shafts running in replaceable water-lubricated rubber bearings in steel stern tubes and 'P' brackets. Twin, 3-blade fixed-pitch nickel aluminium bronze propellers.

CONTROLS: Two station hydraulic power-assisted steering system operating twin balanced hollow steel fabricated rudders. Hand hydraulic emergency steering position in aft peak.

ACCOMMODATION: Fully air-conditioned accommodation is provided for 19 permanent crew plus 7 spares. Two messes, one either side forward c/w berths, wardrobes, lockers, mess tables and seats, toilets and wash places house 14 ratings, with 4 spare berths and lockers further forward. Two cabins amidships accommodate 2 NCOs and 2 officers, each with one spare berth. Separate washplaces and toilets are provided. Adjacent is spacious wardroom for officers and NCOs and containing a spare settee berth. The CO's cabin is in the deckhouse aft of the wheelhouse and includes a shower cubicle. The deckhouse also houses the radio room and galley. The wheelhouse has fully equipped stations for the helmsman, OOW and navigator and has access aft to the open bridge with its second helmsman's station.

SYSTEMS

Electrical: 24V dc insulated return; 2 banks of batteries charged by main engine alternators and by transformer/rectifier from 240V ac system. Two 44kW diesel generators or shore supply provide 240/110V ac 60Hz single phase power for all major craft electrical power requirements including galley, laundry, air-conditioning and lighting

Butyl insulated wiring with heat, oil resistant and flame retardant outer sheath to BS6883

Bilge/fire: Two electrically powered bilge/fire pumps discharge seawater to hydrants for fire-fighting and deck washing or bilge via a bilge manifold with suctions to each watertight compartment. Fire detection and Halon 1301 extinguishing equipment is installed in machinery rooms

ARMAMENT: Foredeck deck ring for up to 30mm single gun mount. Spigots for GPMGs on

bridge wings. Ammunition store below decks forward.

CAPACITIES

Fuel capacity: 16.0 tonnes
Fresh water capacity: 2.5 tonnes

DIMENSIONS

Length overall: 33.0m
Beam: 6.73m
Draught: 1.95m

WEIGHT

Empty: Approx 95 tonnes

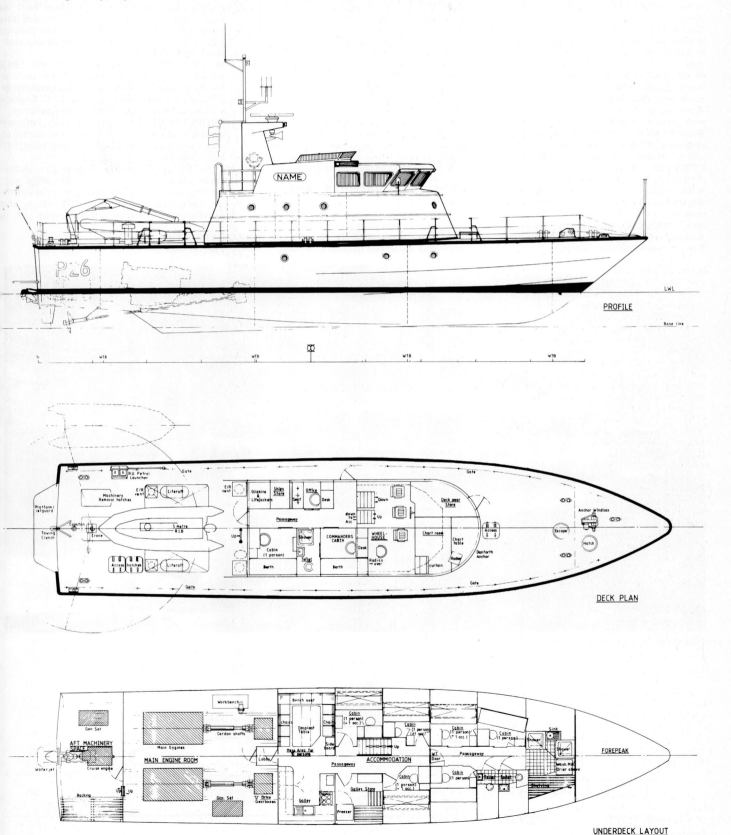

PERFORMANCE
Speed, max: Up to 33 knots depending upon machinery installed
Range at 15 knots: 1200n miles

PROTECTOR 26
Customs and Excise cutter.

UK Customs and Excise Marine Branch placed an order for three 26m Protector fast patrol cutters for entry into service during 1988. The craft are a development of the 33m Protector class, designed to meet the needs of HM Customs and Excise for operation anywhere round the coastline of Great Britain.

HULL: Hull, deck and superstructure in welded marine grade aluminium, with integral alloy fuel tanks.

MAIN ENGINES: Two Paxman 12 SET CW marine diesels of 1440bhp each with ZF BW 460S gearboxes. One single Perkins T63544 marine diesel engine of 213shp driving a Hamilton 361 waterjet unit for cruise/loiter speeds.

PROPULSION: Two fixed pitch propellers coupled to ZF BW 460S gearboxes via a V-drive, and one Hamilton 361 waterjet unit.

CONTROLS: Power-assisted hydraulic steering system operating twin-linked balanced aerofoil spade rudders. Primary controls are from the wheelhouse, with a secondary position on the open bridge.

ACCOMMODATION: Single cabins for commanding officer and seven crew. Four cabins are fitted with pipe-cots for visitors.

SYSTEMS
Auxiliary engines: Two 30kW (continuous) diesel driven 240V single phase 50Hz generator sets and engine driven alternators

Electrical system: 24V dc and 240V, 50Hz single phase

Navigational: Equipment includes two navigational radars, one with ARPA plotter, gyro with repeaters, Decca Navigator Mk 53, direction finder, log, echo sounder, and autopilot

Communications: One HF set and one marine 2182Khz UHF set, telex, navtex and internal communications.

Crane: An hydraulic knuckle boom crane mounted on main deck for launch and recovery of rigid inflatable boarding boat

DIMENSIONS
Length overall: 25.70m
Beam overall: 6.20m
Draught (approx): 1.70m

PERFORMANCE
Speed, max: 25 knots
Speed, loiter (waterjet only): 8 knots
Endurance: At economical speed of 11 knots craft can patrol for five days, assuming thirty six hours on loiter/cruise engine at 7 knots.

41-METRE PASSENGER FERRY
CAPRI JET
CAPRI JET II

Capri Jet a 41m passenger ferry was completed in 1988 and operates on the Naples/Capri route improving the service frequency by 50%.

A second similar vessel Capri Jet II was ordered in May 1989 and will be delivered in 1990.

DESIGNER: Marinteknik Verkstads AB/FBM Marine Ltd.

OWNERS: Navigazione Libera Del Golfo SpA, Italy.

CLASSIFICATION: Built to rules of the Code of Safety for Dynamically Supported Craft comparable to the SOLAS and Load Line Conventions, class notation RINa is *100-A (UL) 1.1-Nav. S-TP.

HULL: Superstructure and hull are built in welded marine grade aluminium, sub-divided into seven watertight compartments. A semi planing hull with a deep-V forward progressing to a shallow-V aft with hard chines.

MAIN ENGINES: Two MTU 12V 396 TB83 marine diesels giving minimum 1180kW each at MCR, 1940rpm at ambient air temperature of 27°C and sea water temperature at 27°C. Engines are coupled to ZF marine reduction gearboxes.

PROPULSION: Two waterjet units, steering deflection angle is 30 degrees port and starboard with an estimated reverse thrust of approximately half of the forward gross thrust.

CONTROLS: All controls and machinery instruments are within reach of the helmsman's seat. Steering and reversing buckets for the waterjets are controlled electro-hydraulically from the wheelhouse. A retractable bow thruster unit is fitted.

CAPACITIES
Fuel oil: 7000 litres

FBM Marine *Capri Jet* operating between Naples and Capri

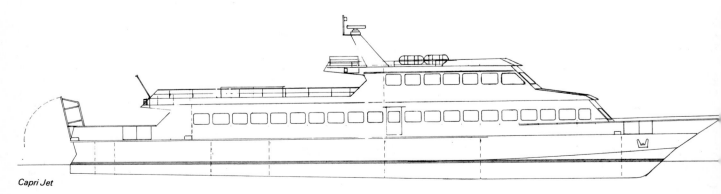

Capri Jet

Lubrication oil: 200 litres
Fresh water: 1000 litres
ACCOMMODATION: Two passenger saloons can seat up to 480 passengers, with clearance to carry 350 passengers by the Italian classification authority Registro Italiano Navale on the Naples/Capri route. The main passenger saloons are air-conditioned and trimmed to a high level of comfort. Noise and vibration levels are low due to the waterjet propulsion system.
SYSTEMS
Auxiliary engines: Two diesel generators each driving a 30kVA alternator
Electrical supplies: 380V ac, 50Hz three phase, 220V ac, 50Hz single phase, 24V dc, shore supply connection
DIMENSIONS
Length overall: 41.00m
Beam: 7.80m
Draught: 1.10m
Typical disposable load: 35 tonnes
PERFORMANCE
Speed, max light: 33.5 knots
Speed, max loaded: 30.0 knots

HALMATIC LIMITED
Havant, Hampshire PO9 1JR, England

Telephone: (0705) 486161
Telex: 86461HALMAT G
Telefax: (0705) 453217

R H Hunting, *Chairman*

A G Hopkins, *Managing Director*
C G Dove, *Director*
P G Jones, *Director*

A member of Hunting Associated Industries, Halmatic build a range of commercial, leisure and patrol craft in grp. They also mould hulls for other builders to complete. Hulls are constructed under Lloyds Survey and can be completed to Lloyds, DTI, Bureau Veritas for France, RINa for Italy or equivalent classification. The company is also approved to the British Ministry of Defence Quality Assurance Standard 05/21.

HARGRAVE 85
MARIOLA
Designed by Jack Hargrave, the 85ft (25.91m) hull is a development of the Hargrave 64ft (19.51m) hull and uses the latest advances in grp design. The hull is of semi-displacement form designed for speeds up to 20 knots. Considerable hull volume is provided allowing comfortable coastal or world-wide operation.
DIMENSIONS
Length overall: 25.91m
    waterline: 23.24m
Beam: 5.87m
Draught, max: 1.57m
WEIGHTS
Displacement: 70 to 80 tonnes
Hull weight: 13 607kg
PERFORMANCE
Speed, max: 20 knots

Mariola, a 20-knot motor yacht with Halmatic grp hull

McTAY MARINE
Port Causeway, Bromborough, Wirral, Merseyside L62 4TP, England

Telephone: (051)346 1319
Telex: 627459
Telefax: (051)334 0041

P. Aaron, *Divisional Managing Director*

CHARTWELL
A high-speed survey vessel for hydrographic survey duties in the Thames and Thames estuary. The vessel has a longitudinally framed steel hull with an aluminium superstructure. The hull form is based on the NPL high-speed, round bilge series. The survey duties include echo sounding, sonar sweeping, wire sweeping, marking obstructions, tidal stream observations, together with search and rescue.
PRINCIPAL PARTICULARS
Length, overall: 26.58m
Length, b.p: 23.94m
Beam: 5.84m
Depth: 3.05m
Engines: Two Paxman Diesels 12 SETCWM, 1074kW each, 1500 rpm.

Chartwell

Propulsion: Two fixed-pitch 3-blade Brunton propellers, driven via ZF BW460 gearboxes, ratio 1.509:1.0. One PP Jets PP170 water-jet unit (for improved control at low speed) driven by Volvo Penta AMD121D diesel, 283kW, 1800 rpm.
Speed, trial, main engines only: 22 knots

SOUTER SHIPYARD LIMITED
Admiralty Gate, Thetis Road, Cowes, Isle of Wight PO31 7JD, England

Telephone: (0983) 294711
Telex: 86520SOUTER G
Telefax: (0983) 299842

B Williams, *Chairman*
E J Webster, *Chief Executive*
J F McIntosh, *Director*
K Downer, *Director of Marketing*
K O Olson, *Financial Controller*
J Tucker, *Production Manager*
K Newnham, *Purchasing Manager*

T Collins, *Quality Manager*
H Cresdee, *Design Office Manager*

Founded in 1942 Souter Shipyard Ltd builds high-speed patrol craft, passenger carriers and VIP yachts. Construction is in glass reinforced plastic (grp), aluminium or steel from 5m to 35m in length. Affiliated companies are Souter Copland Composites Limited and Sims Fabrications Limited.

WASP 30-METRE PATROL CRAFT
Design began in early 1984 and trials of the first craft were completed in October 1985.
The hull is of semi-displacement soft chine form with raked stern and a flat, raked or vertical transom. The beam is slightly more than that of conventional craft of this size, which results in a slightly lower maximum top speed, but provides superior sea-going qualities with respect to crew fatigue and efficiency over a period of several days in bad weather. The craft is fully equipped with navigational aids and communication equipment. Accommodation layout is for a normal operational complement of three officers and six crew, enabling the craft to run on a continuous watch system.
HULL: The hull is constructed in grp and is subdivided by transverse bulkheads and frames. Scantlings are approved to Lloyds or similar

marine standard agencies. The deck is of grp and integrally bonded to the hull. Superstructure is of marine grade aluminium alloy.

MAIN ENGINES/GEARBOXES: Two GM 16V-149 TI diesel engines, 1550shp each at 1900rpm with 2:1 ratio gearboxes.

PROPULSION: Two Lips Ltd, 1000mm diameter nickel aluminium bronze propellers.

CONTROLS: Hydraulic steering and engine controls.

ACCOMMODATION/CREW
Complement: 3 officers and 6 ratings
Crew spaces air-conditioned and ventilated

SYSTEMS
Auxiliary engines: Two G & M 47MDP4–63R marine diesel generators, 240V, 50Hz, single-phase giving a maximum output of 47kVA
Fuel tank capacities: Five aluminium tanks, total 17 200 litres
Refuelling points on main deck, port and starboard
Fresh water capacity: 2540 litres
Electrical: 240V ac and 24V dc
Navigational: Gyrocompass, autopilot Decca 450, Sat Nav Furuno FS70, Radar Furuno 1401, Video Plotter GD200
Communications: RT Sunair GSB900MF/HF, Motorola VHF/FM
Life saving: DOTI safety equipment

DIMENSIONS
Length overall: 30.0m

The Souter Wasp 30m patrol boat

Length waterline: 27.0m
Beam overall: 6.70m
Draught, max including propellers: 1.70m
Air draught, max (waterline to highest mast/aerial): 12.0m
Air draught to cabin top: 7.0m

WEIGHTS
Empty weight (without fuel, crew, payload or provisions): 88 tonnes

Max disposable load (fuel, crew, payload and provisions): 17 tonnes
Design max displacement: 105 tonnes

PERFORMANCE
Speed, cruise: 22.0 knots
max: 25.0 knots
Range: 500n miles at 22 knots

VOSPER THORNYCROFT (UK) LIMITED

Head Office: Victoria Road, Woolston, Southampton SO9 5GR, England

Telephone: 0703445144
Telex: 47682VTWOOL G
Telefax: 0703 421539

Vosper Thornycroft (UK) Ltd continues the shipbuilding business established over a century ago by two separate companies, Vosper Ltd and John I. Thornycroft & Co. Ltd. These Companies merged in 1966, were nationalised in 1977, returned to the Private sector in 1985, and floated on the London Stock Exchange in 1988. The Company has designed, built and repaired warships of all sizes, and has always specialised in high speed craft. Since the early 1970s it has also developed the use of glass reinforced plastic (grp) for warships, particularly Mine Countermeasures Vessels.

Vosper Thornycroft has also built a variety of non-military fast craft, including hovercraft, hydrofoils, and monohull ferries. *Gentry Eagle*, the 1989 Transatlantic Speed Record breaker, which they built, exemplifies their capabilities in the high speed market.

Diversified engineering work is also undertaken, including ship design consultancy for overseas builders, support services, and the design and manufacture of roll damping fins and electronic control systems for marine and industrial use.

Current fast patrol craft designs range from 13 metres to ocean capable vessels in excess of 80 metres. Designs to meet most requirements can be produced with minimal development from proven warships.

30 METRE FAST PATROL BOAT HAWK CLASS

The 30 metre Hawk Class patrol boat is designed for prolonged operation at speed in EEZ

Vosper Thornycroft 30m patrol boat on trials

offshore roles. Two of the three craft on order for a Middle Eastern country have been completed and the third will be delivered in 1990.

HULL: The hull is grp and the superstructure is marine grade alloy both constructed to Lloyds approved standards. Hull shape is hard chine with a moderately high deadrise, fine entry forward, and generous freeboard.

MAIN ENGINES: Two high speed turbo charged marine diesels coupled to reverse reduction gear boxes

PROPULSION: Two fixed pitch propellers, other configurations are optional.

COMPLEMENT: Typical complement is three officers, two petty officers and eleven junior ratings.

ARMAMENT: A typical armament would be one twin 30mm BMARC GCM A-02 power operated gun mounting forward and one single hand operated 20mm mounting aft. Bridge mountings for GPMGs. Wallop Stockade decoy launching system. Radar, electronic warfare and communications sets to suit operational requirements.

DIMENSIONS
Length, overall: 30.45m
Length, between perpendiculars: 26.55m
Breadth, moulded: 6.87m
Depth, moulded: 4.20m

WEIGHTS
Half load displacement: 95.0 tonnes

PERFORMANCE
Speed, max continuous: 28 knots

34 METRE FAST PATROL BOAT

Originally based on a 31 metre Vosper Thornycroft design which was exported to many navies, the 34 metre Fast Patrol Boat has been developed using simplified construction techniques to reduce costs and enable relatively inexperienced shipyards to build on effective craft and develop their own technology.

Thirty-seven of these craft have been built under license by Bollinger Machine Shop and Shipyard, Louisiana, USA, for the US Coastguard and a further 12 are on order.

HULL: All welded steel with longitudinal construction and five watertight bulkheads. The superstructure is all welded marine grade aluminium alloy.

MAIN ENGINES: Two high speed marine diesel engines, each driving forward into reverse reduction gearboxes with U drives.

PROPULSION: Two fixed pitch skew blade propellers.

COMPLEMENT: Typical complement: three officers and twelve ratings.

ACCOMMODATION: Air conditioned cabins and mess decks with a centralised galley.

ARMAMENT (Typical): Two single 30mm gun mountings.

SYSTEMS: (Typical) Three diesel generators. Two navigational radars with Racal CANE automatic plotting and information system, satellite navigator, electronic surveillance system, communication sets, gyro compass, log and repeaters. Fire fighting water pump with foam generators. Fresh water by reverse osmosis plant.

DIMENSIONS
Length, overall: 34.00m
Length, waterline: 31.00m
Beam, max: 9.00m
Draught, amidships: 1.25m
PERFORMANCE (Typical)
Speed, max: 37 knots
Speed, max continuous: 34 knots
Range: 1600n miles
Endurance: 6 days

GENTRY EAGLE

In early 1987 Mr Tom Gentry placed an order with Vosper Thornycroft for a challenger for the Transatlantic Speed Record established by Richard Branson in his *Virgin Atlantic Challenger*. This boat too was designed by Peter Birkett. Construction started in May 1987 and trials began in March 1988.

Mr. Gentry and his team made their first attempt on the record in 1988, but were defeated by abnormally bad weather. Although the boat and crew were making good time in high seas, it was decided that the single refuelling stop required would be impossible in the conditions, and Mr Gentry wisely gave up the attempt. On the way back to the United States, the boat was damaged in an accident which prevented a further attempt that year.

A second attempt on the record was made in 1989. Shortly before 4 am on Thursday 27th July *Gentry Eagle* successfully completed the fastest ever Atlantic crossing by sea, arriving in Britain 62 hours and 7 minutes after leaving New York; an average speed of 48 knots which was 18 hours and 23 minutes less than the previous record. Mr Gentry afterwards said that the conditions in mid Atlantic were at least as rough as those encountered by the previous record holder.

Gentry Eagle's experience demonstrates the extreme difficulty of the Atlantic crossing and the great versatility of the deep-Vee monohull in seakeeping, load carrying and high speed.

OWNER: Tom Gentry, Honolulu, Hawaii.
DESIGN
Hull and Project Management: Peter Birkett
Engineering: Peter Downie
Electrical: Ian Starr

34m Vosper Thornycroft designed US Coastguard patrol boat

Gentry Eagle

HULL: An all welded aluminium hull, with rivetted and glued aluminium superstructure. Hard chine V bottom with three watertight bulkheads.
MAIN ENGINES: Two MTU 16V 396 TB94 sequentially turbo charged marine diesels, 3480hp (2560kW) each, at 2100rpm driving through two ZF BU 755 1.87 reduction gear boxes. One Allison gas turbine.
PROPULSION: Two KaMeWa 63 waterjets connected to diesel engines, incorporating steering and reverse gear. One Arneson retractable surface drive propeller connected to gas turbine.
CAPACITIES: Combination of double bottom tanks and flexible cells, with a total capacity of 45 tonnes
ACCOMMODATION
Wheelhouse: Dual driving station including engine and JPs controls, trim flap controls, magnetic and electronic compasses and autopilot,

rpm, helm and log readouts. Navigation station including primary radar, electronic chart and navigation system, electronic compass and log repeaters. SSB and UHF radios. Engineers station includes all engine instruments, fuel gauges and No 2 radar, switching for fuel valves and pumps. Off duty seating accommodation for six.
Below decks: Shower, heads, keyhole bunks for eight, access to fore deck.
SYSTEMS
Firefighting: Manually operated Halon fire extinguisher system
Life saving: Argos beacon, two eight-man life rafts, survival suits, EPIRBS.
DIMENSIONS
Length, overall: 33.50m
Beam, max: 7.30m
Deadrise, aft: 18°

UNITED STATES OF AMERICA

ALUMINIUM BOATS INC (TRINITY MARINE GROUP)
Crown Point, Louisiana, USA

77-FOOT ALUMINIUM FERRY BOAT
The first of these craft, to a design by J B Hargrave, Naval Architects, was built in 1979 and a sister vessel was completed in 1986. The vessels are operated by Sheplers Inc of Mackinaw City, Michigan, and operated on the Mackinaw City to Mackinac Island route. Two earlier fast ferries designed by J B Hargrave but built by Camcraft were the 18.3m *The Welcome* and the 17.1m *Felicity* with carrying capacities of 120 and 150 passengers respectively.

THE HOPE
ENGINES: Three GM 12V-71 TI diesels, V-drive induction gears.
ACCOMMODATION: 265 passengers.
DIMENSIONS
Length overall: 23.48m
    waterline: 21.34m
Beam: 6.10m
Draught: 1.61m
PERFORMANCE
Speed, light: 24 knots
    loaded: 20 knots

STERLING
Fast passenger ferry.
OWNERS: Boston Harbour Commuter Service.
The *Sterling* is a converted crew boat, ex *Sterling Fryou*, built in 1980 by Camcraft Inc for Bailey Marine service. The craft operates on 9.8-mile ferry run from Hingham Shipyard to Rowes Wharf, Boston.
MAIN ENGINES: Two Detroit Diesel 12V-71 TI diesel engines developing 510hp each at 2100rpm.
ACCOMMODATION: 150 passengers. Main cabin on the main deck seats 80 served by a small galley providing refreshments. Below the main deck there is seating for 39 plus lounge tables. The outer upper deck is certified for 100 passengers.
SYSTEMS
Auxiliary machinery: Two 40kW Detroit Diesel 371 engines with Delco generators
Navigational: Two radars
Communications: Crew boat communications sets retained
DIMENSIONS
Length: 30.48m
Beam: 7.31m
Draught: 1.52m
PERFORMANCE
Speed: 26 knots

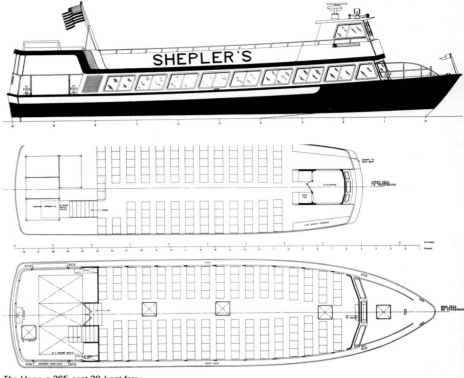

The Hope, a 265-seat 20-knot ferry

Sterling, a converted crew boat passenger ferry

BLOUNT MARINE CORPORATION
461 Water Street, Warren, Rhode Island 02885, USA

Telephone: (401) 245 8300

Luther H Blount, *President*
Marcia L Blount, *Executive Vice President*
Ronald Baer, *Works Manager*
Brian Dolph, *Sales Assistant*

Blount Marine Corporation was formed in 1952 and as of December 1989 had designed and built 283 vessels ranging in size from 5 to 80m. Among the many types built has been the world's first small stern trawler and a significant number of all types of passenger/commuter vessels including mini-cruise ships, making Blount Marine one of the best known small passenger-boat builders in the USA. The Hitech composite hull was invented by Luther Blount.

HITECH EXPRESS
Hull No 251, Design No P452.
A multi-purpose craft design started in 1983 and built in 1984. The vessel has been granted USCG Certification for 149 passengers. Two smaller versions have been built.
Hitech Express has been engaged in demonstrating reliable, fast economical commuting service in the USA. It has made 5 runs to New York City from Warren, Rhode Island, a distance of 150 miles, in just over 5 hours (November 1984, May 1985, June 1985). It has made the run from the Battery, New York, to Staten Island fully loaded in 10 minutes, against 28 minutes via conventional ferry; also crossed the Hudson at mid-Manhattan in 2 minutes 46 seconds (in November 1984 and June 1985).

POWERPLANT: Two GM 12V-71 TI, 510shp at 2300rpm (each).
PROPELLERS: Two 711mm diameter, 622mm pitch Columbian Bronze.
FUEL TANK: Integral 1923-litre.
FUEL: No 2 diesel.
CONTROLS: Throttle and clutch controls Morse MD-24 single lever type using sprockets, roller chain, ss cable, aluminium fairleads and Morse Instrument control unit mounted on each engine. Steering through Wagner hydraulic system. Trim tabs manually adjusted type.
HULL: Aluminium structural frames, bulkheads and decks with polyurethane foam sprayed over and a layed up glassfibre skin $1/4$ to $1/8$ thick forming the outer hull covering.
ACCOMMODATION/CREW
Wheelhouse: Full-width console, engine instrument panel and engine alarm panel
Crew: One licensed operator and one deckhand

Passenger accommodation: Men's and women's toilet space, carpeting, or non-skid decking, fixed or movable seating, superstructure insulation, interior finish work, sound insulation, air-conditioning, heating, portable bar, and PA system optional. Cabin has aluminium framed and plated interior with fixed and sliding cabin windows and life preservers stowed in overhead racks. Ventilated through door and windows, air-conditioning and heat optional

SYSTEMS

Emergency exits and safety equipment: Life preservers, one ring buoy, one rescue ladder, flares, four fire extinguishers, one fire axe, 100ft fire hose, fire and bilge pump, first aid kit and anchor, all as required by USCG

Electrical: Two 60A alternators, one on each main engine providing 32V dc power throughout vessel. Engine room area available for optional generator

Communications and navigation: Radio: One Regency MT-5500 VHF or equal, standard equipment. Radar: One Furuno FR-240 or equal, standard equipment. Compass, horn and searchlight

DIMENSIONS

EXTERNAL DIMENSIONS

Length overall: 23.48m
Length waterline: 22.66m
Beam overall: 6.10m
Draught (max, including propeller(s)): 1.12m
Air draught, max (waterline to highest mast or aerial): 7.16m
Air draught to cabin top: 3.05m

INTERNAL DIMENSIONS

Cabin, length: 15.24m
   max width: 5.64m
   max height: 2.11m
   floor area: 68.28m²
Doors, forward and aft: 0.91 × 1.98mm
Freight deck area, exterior aft: 27.87m²

WEIGHTS

Empty weight: 23.87 tonnes
Max payload: 15.00 tonnes
Max disposable load (fuel, crew, payload and provisions): 15.00 tonnes
Design max displacement: 56.39 tonnes
GRT: 65.59

PERFORMANCE (at max displacement)

Max speed, calm water (max power): 27.8 knots
Cruising (service) speed, calm water (max continuous power): 24.3 knots
Turning circle diameter starting at cruising speed: 60m
Rate of turn starting at cruising speed: Approx 15°/s
Crash stop, stopping distance: 24m
Time to accelerate to cruising speed: 15–20 seconds
Max permissible Sea State: 1.5m to 4–5 Beaufort
Range at cruising speed: 250/300 miles

Blount Marine *Hitech Express*

BOLLINGER MACHINE SHOP & SHIPYARD INC

PO Box 250, Lockport, Louisiana 70374, USA

Telephone: (504) 532 2554/1–800–888–3894
Telex: 584127

Richard Bollinger, *President*
George Bollinger, *General Manager*
Donald T Bollinger, *Chairman & C.E.O.*

Founded in 1946, Bollinger expanded from a machine shop/repair facility to building offshore work boats for the oil industry. In August 1985, the company was awarded a contract to build 16 of the "Island" Class patrol boats for the US Coast Guard. The hull is the well proven 33.50m patrol boat design by Vosper Thornycroft (UK) Ltd and the superstructure has been adapted to meet US Coast Guard operational requirements. All 16 vessels were successfully delivered by the end of June 1987.

In February of 1987, Bollinger was awarded an additional 21 "Island" Class (B-Class) patrol boats for the US Coast Guard. The eighteenth vessel of the 21 vessel order was delivered in September of 1989, and the remaining vessels delivered at 35 day intervals. A further twelve vessels are now on order (at January 1990).

'ISLAND' CLASS 33-METRE PATROL BOAT

HULL: Designed by Vosper Thornycroft (UK) Ltd and built in steel with an aluminium superstructure.
MAIN ENGINES/GEARBOXES: Two Paxman

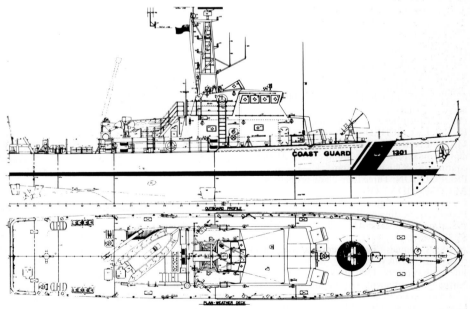

General arrangement of *Farallon*

Valenta 16RP 200M V type; 3000bhp at 1500rpm (max), 2910shp at 802rpm (max). Engines are coupled to Zahnradfabrik (ZF) gearboxes, ratio 1.87:1.
PROPULSION: Two Vosper Thornycroft five-blade (skewed) propellers, 1257mm diameter, 1066–1549mm pitch (0.7R).
CONTROLS: Vosper Thornycroft steering system. Paxman engine controls.

ACCOMMODATION

Complement: 18
SYSTEMS
Auxiliary engines: Two Caterpillar 3304T, 99kW generators
Fresh water tank capacity: 6661 litres
Fuel oil (95%) tank capacity: 39 295 litres

ARMAMENT: One 20mm Mk-16 gun and two M-60 machine guns.
DIMENSIONS
Length overall: 33.52m
Beam overall: 6.40m
Depth, moulded, deck amidships: 3.35m
Draught, mean to design waterline: 1.98m
WEIGHTS
Design displacement: 167.76 tonnes
Displacement, light: 117.50 tonnes
PERFORMANCE
Speed, max sustained cruising: 26.0 knots (half load)
Speed, economical cruising: 12.8 knots
Speed, max: In excess of 26 knots
Max range at economical speed: 3380n miles

NAMED 'ISLAND' CLASS 33-METRE PATROL BOATS

Thirty-seven of these Vosper Thorneycroft (UK) designed boats have now been named:

Bollinger built *Aquidneck*, the ninth of the 49 patrol boats built or on order for the US Coast Guard

1301	Farallon	1312	Sanibel
1302	Manitou	1313	Edisto
1303	Matagorda	1314	Sapelo
1304	Maui	1315	Matincus
1305	Monhegan	1316	Nantucket
1306	Nunivak	1317	Attu
1307	Ocracoke	1318	Baranof
1308	Vashon	1319	Chandeleur
1309	Aquidneck	1320	Chincoteague
1310	Mustang	1321	Cushing
1311	Naushon	1322	Cuttyhunk
		1323	Drummond
		1324	Key Largo

1325	Metomkin
1326	Monomoy
1327	Orcas
1328	Padre
1329	Sitkinak
1330	Tybee
1331	Washington
1332	Wrangell
1333	Adak
1334	Liberty
1335	Anacapa
1336	Kiska
1337	Assateague

BREAUX'S BAY CRAFT INC

PO Box 306, Loreauville, Louisiana 70552, USA

Telephone: (318) 229 4246/7
Telefax: (318) 229 8332

Roy Breaux, Sr, *President*
Roy J Breaux, *Vice-President*
Royce E Breaux, *Vice-President*
Hub Allums, *Sales*
Jerry Lagrange, *Sales*

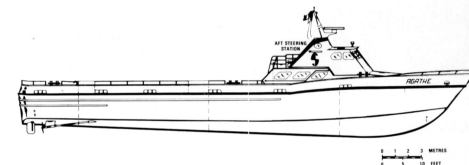

AGATHE

Crew boat.
OWNER: Compagnie des Moyens de Surfaces Adaptes à L'Exploitation des Océans (SURF), serving ELF offshore Cameroun fields 5 times weekly since 1982.
CLASSIFICATION: Bureau Veritas I3/3-Special Service-coastal waters.
HULL: Constructed in aluminium.
BUILT/LAUNCHED: 1979.
MAIN ENGINES: Three GM 16V-92 marine diesels, maximum rating 730hp each at 2150rpm; continuous 680hp at 2000rpm
PROPULSION: Three four-blade propellers.
ACCOMMODATION
Crew: Captain, engineer and seaman/cook
Passengers: Seating on deck level: 22
    Seating below deck: 43
SYSTEMS
Auxiliary engines: Two generators type Delco-GM 3L 71, 30kW
Fuel tank capacity: 1300 litres
Navigation equipment: Two radars, one autopilot and one echo sounder
Communications: One SSB radio and two VHF radios
Air-conditioning: Fully air-conditioned
Lifesaving: In accordance with Solas regulations. One Zodiac inflatable and outboard
DIMENSIONS
Length overall: 34.90m
Beam: 7.32m
Draught: 1.93m
Air draught, max: 7.62m
Air draught to cabin top: 6.10m
GRT: 190.72
NRT: 139.50

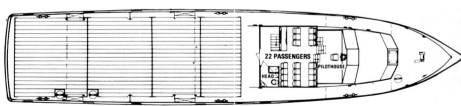

Agathe built by Breaux's Bay for SURF

WEIGHTS
Empty weight: 65.0 tonnes
Payload: 25 tonnes on deck
Max disposable load: 33 tonnes
Designed max displacement: 100 tonnes
PERFORMANCE
Speed, max: 24 knots (light ship)
    cruising: 22 knots (half load)
Range at cruising speed: 1000n miles (48 hours)

MISS PEGGY ANN

Owner: John E. Graham & Sons, Bayou LaBatre, Alabama, serving the oil fields of the Gulf of Mexico 365 days a year
Classification: U.S.C.G. Certified for 200 miles offshore A.B.S. Load-Line Assignment
PRINCIPAL PARTICULARS
Hull: All-welded aluminium construction with transverse non-floating frames

Main Engines: Four DDC 12V-71TI 1521kW (2,040hp) at 2100 rpm
Gears: Twin Disc MG514 with 2.5:1.0 reduction
Shafts/Propellers: 88.9mm Aquamet No.17 Stainless steel and Michigan Nibral Dina Quad propellers 96.5cm × 88.9cm
Auxiliary Power: Two 40kW Detroit Diesel/Kato generator sets
Accommodation: Seating for 64 passengers. Berths for ten crew. Fully air conditioned
DIMENSIONS
Length, overall: 39.63m
Beam: 8.00m
Draught: 1.37m
Air draught: 9.15m
Air draught cabin top: 7.01m
Deck area: 21.34m × 6.86m
Cargo capacity: 86.4 tonnes
Fuel capacity: 363336l
Water capacity: 70969l
PERFORMANCE
Range: Approx. 2,160 miles (90 hours)
Speed, light, cruise: 23.5 knots
Speed, half-load, cruise: 20.75 knots
Electronics: Radars: Two Furuno FR-810D. SSB: Stephens SEA 222. VHF: Cybernet CTX 2050. LORAN: Furuno LC-90. Depth Indicator: Datamarine 3000. Loud Hailer: Apelco HXL 1000

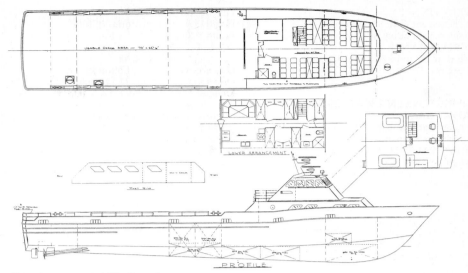

General arrangement of *Miss Peggy Ann*

Miss Peggy Ann

CHRISTENSEN MOTOR YACHT CORPORATION

4400 Columbia Way, Vancouver, Washington 98661, USA

Telephone: (206) 695 7671
Telex: 754607CHRISTENSEN
Telefax: (206) 695 6038

David H Christensen, *President*

The company builds production motor yachts of double Airex cored grp construction; Kevlar and carbon fibre materials are also used in areas of high stress. A standard mould is used for building hulls from 29m to 39m in length, which can be widened for different lengths and engine power requirements. Alternative superstructures are installed to meet individual owners' requirements. Unless otherwise specified Christensen yachts are built under ABS standard inspections.

The company established a 6500m²(70,000ft²) building facility in 1986 and by March 1989 had built fifteen yachts and were employing 150 people working for customers in Italy, Japan and the United States.

CHRISTENSEN CXV

Pilot house motor yacht.
HULL: Double Airex cored grp and Kevlar construction.

MAIN ENGINES: Two Caterpillar 3412 marine diesel engines 605shp continuous rating at 1800rpm, 813shp intermittent at 2100rpm coupled to Twin Disc MG 514 marine gearboxes. Optional MTU, Cummins and GM engines available to attain speeds exceeding 35 knots.
CONTROLS: Hydraulic steering system and single lever air clutch and throttle controls fitted in pilot house.
CAPACITIES
Fuel: 26 495 litres
Motor oil: 416 litres
Used oil: 227 litres
Holding tank: 1892 litres
Fresh water: 3406 litres
Hot water: 250 litres
ACCOMMODATION: Owners' double cabin plus two separate bathrooms, galley, pantry, dining room and saloon are situated on the main deck. Three double guest cabins, two bathrooms and accommodation for Captain and crew of six with requisite heads and showers situated on lower deck. Alternative layout available for Captain's cabin to be fitted abaft the pilot house on the boat deck.
SYSTEMS
Auxiliary engines: Two Northern Lights 1800rpm 60kW generator sets
Bow thruster: Optional extra
Stabiliser system: Optional extra
Air-conditioning: Two-stage air-conditioning and heating system, Aqua-Air or equivalent

Finishing of a Christensen composite plastic hull

DIMENSIONS
Length overall: 36.57m
Length waterline: 32.30m
Beam: 8.15m
Draught: 1.82m

WEIGHTS
Displacement light: 88.30 tonnes
Displacement heavy: 120.31 tonnes
PERFORMANCE
Speed, max: 10 to 30 knots depending on hp of
    engines

CHRISTENSEN 130FT (39.6 METRE)
ROYAL OAK
Launched October 1988, a pilot house motor
yacht for a Japanese owner.
PRINCIPAL PARTICULARS
Length, overall: 39.60m

Length, waterline: 35.70m
Length, less swim platform: 38.10m
Beam: 8.20m
Draught: 1.80m
Freeboard, forward: 4.20m
Displacement, light: 131.5 tonnes
Displacement, heavy: 172.3 tonnes
Engines: Two DDC 16V92TA, model 8162–7400,
    dry weight 3538kg, each 1044kW at 2300 rpm
    (gross power), 932kW at 1950 rpm cruising
    power
Speed: at a displacement of 150 tonnes, Royal
    Oak will cruise at 20 knots on approximately
    2090kW

Fuel capacity: 30280l
Water capacity: 5677l
Base Price, July 1989: US $5,895,000

FURTHER CURRENT DESIGNS
As at July 1989 the following additional designs
were available
32.6 metre raised pilot house motor yacht, base
    price US $3,350,000
32.6 metre flush deck motor yacht, base price US
    $3,150,000
36.6 metre pilot house motor yacht, base price US
    $4,795,000

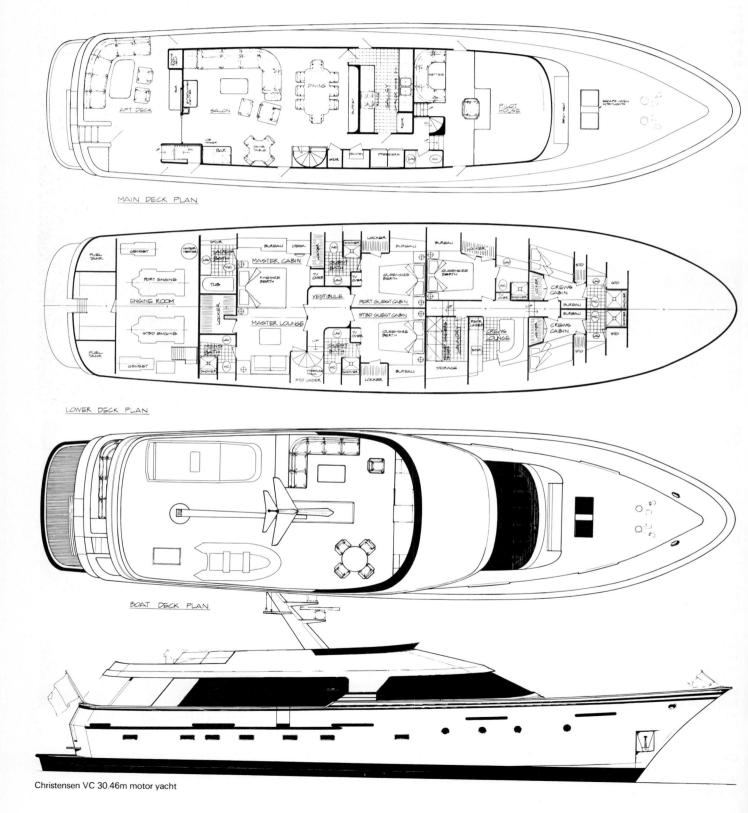

MAIN DECK PLAN

LOWER DECK PLAN

BOAT DECK PLAN

Christensen VC 30.46m motor yacht

Royal Oak

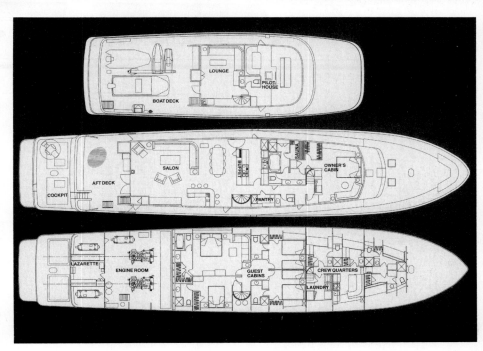

Deck layout of *Royal Oak*

Side elevation *Royal Oak*

Side elevation 32.6m raised pilot house motor yacht

CHRISTENSEN VC

Motor yacht.

HULL: Double Airex cored grp and Kevlar construction.

MAIN ENGINES: Two Caterpillar 3412 marine diesel engines 605shp continuous rating at 1800rpm, 813shp intermittent yacht rating at 2100rpm coupled to Twin Disc MG 514 marine gearboxes. Optional MTU, Cummins and GM engines available to attain speeds exceeding 35 knots.

CONTROLS: Hydraulic steering system and single lever air clutch and throttle controls fitted in pilot house.

CAPACITIES

Fuel: 26 495 litres
Motor oil: 416 litres
Used oil: 227 litres
Holding tank: 1892 litres
Fresh water: 3406 litres
Hot water: 250 litres

ACCOMMODATION: Owner's cabin and suite, two double guest cabins plus two separate bathrooms, Captain's cabin and crew accommodation in two double cabins situated on lower deck. Galley dining saloon, lounge area and pilot house are on the main deck with a seating area above on the boat deck.

SYSTEMS

Auxiliary engines: Two Northern Lights 1800rpm 60kW generator sets
Bow thruster: Optional extra
Stabiliser system: Optional extra

FLYBRIDGE PLAN

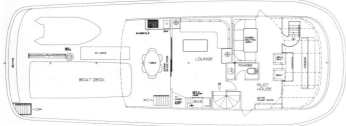

BOAT DECK PLAN

ALTERNATE BOAT DECK

MAIN DECK PLAN

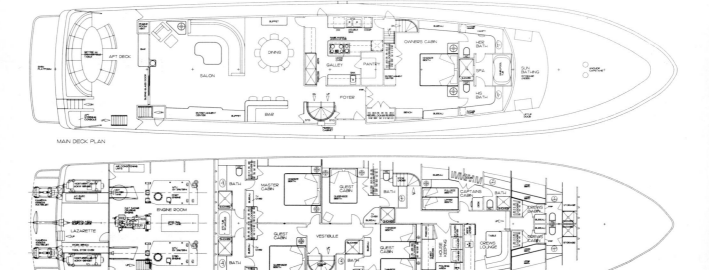

Christensen CXV 36.57m motor yacht

Air-conditioning: Two-stage air-conditioning and
heating system, Aqua-air or equivalent
DIMENSIONS
Length overall: 30.48m
Length, waterline: 25.60m
Beam: 7.62m
Draught: 1.82m
WEIGHTS
Displacement, light: 77.18 tonnes
Displacement, heavy: 104.42 tonnes
PERFORMANCE
Speed, max: 10 to 30 knots depending on hp of
engines fitted

Side elevation 32.6m flush deck motor yacht

107' Flush Deck Motor Yacht

Side elevation 36.6m pilot house motor yacht

120' Pilot House Motor Yacht

DENISON MARINE INC
750 North East 7th Avenue, PO Box 805, Dania,
Florida 33004, USA

Telephone: (305) 920 0622/4011
Telex: 316387DENSHIP
Telefax: (305) 920 6553

Kit Denison, *President*
Joseph Langlois, *Vice President of Engineering*
Carl Bischoff, *Vice President of Production*

Denison Marine Inc specialises in the design
and construction of aluminium motor yachts from
20 to 50m in length. At its inception in 1983, the
company integrated modern automation technologies in shipbuilding with traditional crafts-
manship and attention to detail. Both
conventional and modern yachts are manufactured in the US.

Denison Marine has pioneered the use of waterjet propulsion in yachts over 30.5m that exceed 34
knots. High performance hulls from 23.8 to

38.7m, capable of speeds beyond 50 knots, are
presently under construction.

FOR YOUR EYES ONLY
Raised bridge motor yacht, built December
1985, hull No 103, fitted with trim tabs and bow
thrusters.
HULL: Welded aluminium.
MAIN ENGINES: Two MTU 12V 396 TB93,
1439kW (1930bhp) each, at 2100rpm, fitted with
ZF BW 455, 2.27:1 reduction gears.

Denison motor yacht production in 1987

Hull No	Name	Length overall (m)	Beam (m)	Draught (m)	Type of motor yacht	Displacement full load (tonnes)	Engines	Propulsion units	Berths	Speed max (knots)
103	*For Your Eyes Only*	30.48	6.71	1.22	Raised bridge	94.48	Two MTU 12V 396 TB93 1930bhp each at 2100rpm	KaMeWa 63 waterjets	8 + 4 crew	34
112	*Nena VIII*	33.22	7.62	1.98	Raised bridge	132.06	Two MTU 16V 396 TB93 2570bhp each at 2100rpm	KaMeWa 71 waterjets	8 + 5 crew	35
116	*Quest*	31.39	6.71	1.22	Raised bridge	101.59	Two MTU 12V 396 TB93 1930bhp each	KaMeWa 63 waterjets	10 + 5 crew	37
114	*Thunderball*	33.53	6.71	1.22	Raised bridge cockpit	113.78	Two MTU 16V 396 TB94	KaMeWa 72 waterjets	8 + 6 crew	46
120	*Haggis II*	24.48	5.79	1.07	High-performance deep-Vee	50.79	Two MWM 12 604B 1930bhp each at 1800rpm	Arneson Drive ASD 16	6 + 2 crew	46

Recent motor yachts completed

	Dynamo V	Lady Anna	Big Bad John	Patricia	Astra Dee
Launch date:	Winter 1989	Summer 1990	Summer 1990	Fall 1990	Winter 1990
Hull:	Raised-bridge cockpit m. yacht	Al. sports fisherman	Raised-bridge cockpit m. yacht	Raised-bridge cockpit m. yacht	Flush bridge m. yacht
Length, overall, m:	35.06	36.89	33.23	32.32	28.35
Beam, m:	6.71	7.62	6.71	6.71	6.71
Draught, m:	1.37	1.75	1.83	1.83	1.22
Engines:	Two MTU 12V 396 TB83 1439kW each	Two MWM TBD 604B 1919kW each	Two DDC 16V 149 1790kW each	Two MWM TBD 604BV 12 1439kW each	Two DDC 16V 149 1790kW each
Propulsion:	Two KaMeWa S63 water-jet units	Two turned propellers	Two turned propellers	Two turned propellers	Two Arneson ASD-16 units
Displacement, tonnes:	102	102	102	96.5	86.4
Berths	8 + 3 crew	6 + 4 crew	6 + 3 crew	8 + 3 crew	6 + 6 crew
Speed, knots:	34	32	32	30	36

PROPULSION UNITS: Two KaMeWa type 63 waterjet units.

ACCOMMODATION/EQUIPMENT: Sleeps eight in four staterooms, four berths for crew. The three guest staterooms have twin or queen-size berths, hanging lockers, drawers and heads with showers. Flybridge lounge area has over 8m of seating, Mar Quipt hydraulic crane, 4.6m Bayliner tender with 85hp outboard, and lighted helicopter landing pad. Push-button, automatic fold-forward mast to clear helicopter rotor blades. Fully equipped galley.

ELECTRONICS: Anschutz autopilot; VHF, Standard USA; SSB Furuno/Skanti TRP-8258; Radar, Furuno FCR-1411 colour; Satnav, Furuno FSN-700; speed log, Datamarine 3000W/S100KL Remote; two VHF ICOM 80C; CB, Cybernet CTX 40 + 4; Cellular Telephone, NEC M 5000 R; Loran, Northstar 800 Loran C; two depth sounders, Datamarine 3000W/3030 remote; Mentor Fuel Management Computer.

PERFORMANCE
Speed, cruising: over 30 knots

QUEST

A bridge motor yacht completed in 1987, hull no 116.

MAIN ENGINES: Two MTU 12V 396 TB93 1930bhp each.

PROPULSION: Two KaMeWa 63 water jets

CAPACITIES
Fuel: 28387.5 litres
Water: 5677.5 litres

ACCOMMODATION: Ten guests and fire crew.

SYSTEMS: Two Northern Lights 55kW and one Northern Lights 12kW diesel generators.

DIMENSIONS
Length, overall: 31.39m
Beam: 6.71m
Draught: 1.22m

WEIGHTS
Displacement: 101.59 tonnes

PERFORMANCE
Speed, max: 36 knots

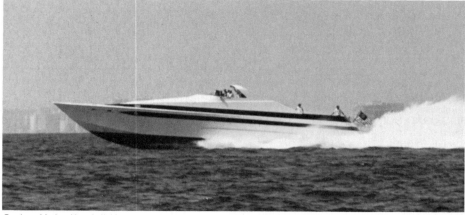

Denison Marine *Haggis II* driven by two Arneson surface drive units, type ASD 16

For Your Eyes Only

For Your Eyes Only

Quest

THUNDERBALL

Raised bridge motor yacht launched in August 1988 hull no 114.
HULL: Marine grade aluminium
MAIN ENGINES: Two MTU 16V 396 TB94 marine diesels
PROPULSION: Two KaMeWa 72 water jets
CAPACITIES
Fuel: 38985.5 litres
Water: 3785 litres
ACCOMMODATION: Eight guests and six crew
DIMENSIONS
Length, overall: 33.53m
Beam: 6.71m
Draught: 1.22m
WEIGHTS
Displacement 113.78 tonnes
PERFORMANCE
Speed, max: 46 knots

Thunderball

MISS TURNBERRY ex (MONKEY BUSINESS II)

Raised pilothouse cockpit motor yacht under construction, launch date spring 1990, hull no 115.
HULL: Constructed in marine grade aluminium.
diesel engines 2800bhp each
PROPULSION: Two Arneson ASD-18 drives
CAPACITIES
Fuel: 60560 litres
Water: 7191.50 litres
ACCOMMODATION: 11 guests and six crew
SYSTEMS: Two Northern Lights 100kW diesel generating sets
DIMENSIONS
Length, overall: 42.67m
Beam: 7.62m
Draught: 1.83m
WEIGHTS
Displacement 152.38 tonnes
PERFORMANCE
Speed, max: 30 knots

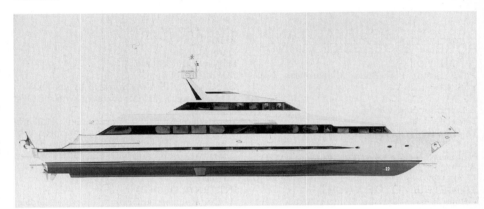

Miss Turnberry

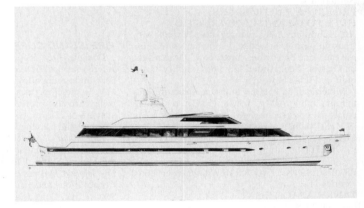

Patricia

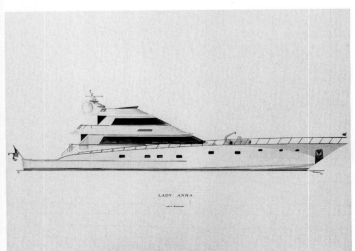

Lady Anna

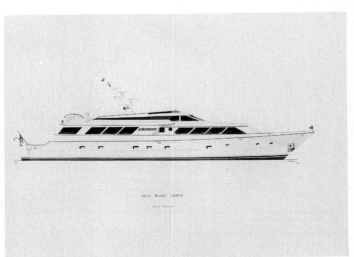

Big Bad John

ROBERT E DERECKTOR OF RHODE ISLAND INC

Tom Derecktor, *Vice President*

There are three shipyards in the group and the craft covered in this entry will appear under the appropriate yard. The group have built over 250 boats up to 36 metres in length.

DERECKTOR SHIPYARD
(Rhode Island)

Coddington Cove, Middletown, Rhode Island 02840, USA

Telephone: (401) 847 9270
TWX: 710 387 6305
Telefax: (401) 846 1570

Bob Derecktor, *President*

DERECKTOR SHIPYARD AND ROBERT E. DERECKTOR, INC
(New York)

311 E Boston Port Road, Mamaroneck, New York 10543, USA

Telephone: (914) 698 5020
Telex: 646904
Telefax: (914) 698 4641

Paul Derecktor, *Vice President*

31-METRE MOTOR YACHT

Built in early 1989 this 31 metre luxury yacht was designed by DIANA Yacht Design BV, the Netherlands.
PRINCIPAL PARTICULARS
HULL FORM AND CONSTRUCTION
All aluminium fully planing deep-V hull with transom stern, trim wedge, 3 spray rails and chine rail each side on bottom, flared bow, 3 water tight bulkheads. Fuel, water, oil and sanitary tanks built in double bottom.

Material of hull plating and superstructure: aluminium alloy AlMg 4.5Mn (5083); remaining parts of construction to be aluminium alloy AlMgSi1 (6082).
MAIN ENGINES: Two diesel engines MTU 16V 396 TB84, rating to ISO 3046/i; 2040kW (2775)hp) each
PROPULSION: Two KaMeWa waterjet units series 71
TANK CAPACITIES
Fuel oil: 25 000 litres
Fresh water: 6000 litres

Derecktor 35m patrol boat design

DIMENSIONS
Length, overall: 31.0m
Length waterline: 26.0m
Beam: 7.5m
Draught: 1.4m
Displacement: 120 tons
EQUIPMENT
GENERATORS: Two Northern Lights 40kW
J D Nall "Agua Air" Air condition with soft start controls
Two 40hp thrusters, by Cramm (Holland) mounted in engine room for low speed propulsion and manoeuvring, Schottel Bow Thruster, two deck cranes by Cramm, two Steen Anchor Windlass, windows supplied by WIGO, Holland
INTERIOR DESIGN
By Dee Robinson Interiors of Fort Lauderdale, Florida in co-operation with DIANA Yacht Design BV.

FIRE ISLAND CLIPPER

Designed by Roper Associates, this vessel entered service 9 December 1979. She is built in 5086 aluminium alloy and powered by three GM 12V-71 diesel engines. The tunnel installed propellers are also protected by skegs. The craft has a length of 22.87m, beam 6.71m and a draught of 1.07m. A full passenger load of 350 can be carried.

Fire Island Clipper is believed to be the first all-aluminium high-capacity fast ferry to be built in the United States. There are nine sister vessels. *Fire Island Clipper* is owned by Wayfarer Leasing Corporation and is leased to Sayville Ferry Service, Inc, Long Island, New York.

See Operators' section for photograph of this vessel.

DERECKTOR GUNNELL, INC
(Florida)

775 Taylor Lane, Dania, Florida 33004, USA

Telephone: (305) 920 5756
TWX: 99 0116
Telefax: (305) 925 1146

Skip Gunnell, *Director*

Three high-performance luxury yacht designs are offered by this yard, the QED 50ft, 61ft and 70ft.

TRIDENT 105
LADY FRANCIS

A high-speed waterjet-propelled motor yacht built in 1987, to American Bureau of Shipping Maltese Cross A1 for Yachting Service.
DESIGNERS: Sparkman & Stephens Inc, 79 Madison Avenue, New York, NY 10016, USA.
HULL: Aluminium alloy, 5086 series welded aluminium, 6061 aluminium extrusions, teak main deck and boat deck.
MAIN ENGINES: Two MTU 12V 396 TB93 diesel engines 1462kW (1960hp) each.
PROPULSION: Two KaMeWa series 63 waterjet units.
CAPACITIES
Fuel: 22 710 litres
Water: 6056 litres
Holding tanks (fibreglass): 2271 litres
Sump tanks (fibreglass): 378.5 litres
ACCOMMODATION
Sun deck: Pilothouse, saloon, boat deck with settees, seats and Jennaire electric barbecue

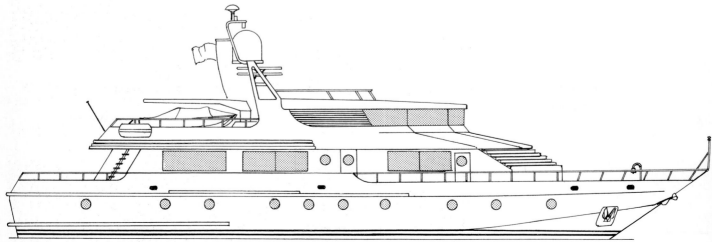
31m (DIANA Yacht Design BV) water-jet luxury motor yacht built by R E Derecktor Shipyard

Main deck: Master state room and bathroom, entertainment centre with TV, VCR and radio, galley, main saloon entertainment centre

Lower deck: Two double-berth cabins and bathrooms, one cabin with two twin-size berths and bathroom. Captain's stateroom with double-berth and bathroom, double crew cabin with heads and shower, crews lounge and kitchenette

SYSTEMS

Auxiliary machinery: One 75kW Northern Lights generator and one 30kW slow speed Northern Lights night generator

Bow thrusters: Richfield 400mm retractable hydraulic bow thrusters with two control stations

Air-conditioning: Three 60 000Btu J D Nall water chiller units for air-conditioning throughout including engine room

Fresh water: Two Sea Recovery 2271 litres/day reverse osmosis water makers

Hot water: Two 170-litre hot water heaters with circulating pumps

Navigational: One Raytheon NGR and one Raytheon 3710 radar, one Raytheon SNA9–8 colour charting IBM PC planning terminal, one Furuno F5N-70 satnav system, one North Star 800X loran system, one Robertson-Shipmate Commander autopilot, one Raytheon weather fax system and Brookes and Gatehouse system instruments

Communications: VHF Incom Sailor, SSB Furuno Skanti TRP 82585, 250W, one Aiphone intercom system, Kenwood Bang & Olfson stereo system, and ACR-EPIRB

Tender: One Zodiac 5m hard bottom launch with 90hp Evinrude outboard

DIMENSIONS

Length overall: 32.00m

Length waterline: 27.66m

Beam: 7.01m

Draught: 1.22m

PERFORMANCE

Speed, long range cruising: 15 to 16 knots

Speed, fast cruising: 25 knots

Speed, max: 31 knots

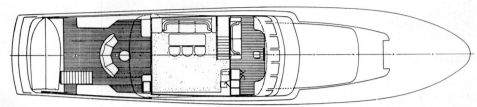

Trident 105 32m motor yacht

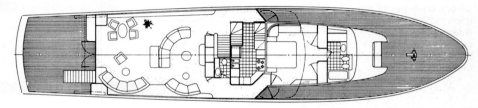

Trident 105 sun deck level

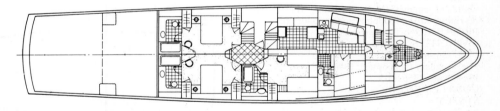

Trident 105 main deck

Trident 105 cabin plan

The Derecktor Trident 105 *Lady Frances*

DERECKTOR 66
WICKED WITCH III
High-speed motor yacht.
OWNER: Donald Ford.
HULL: Aluminium alloy, stepped surface hull form, skeg on centreline.
MAIN ENGINES: Two GM 12V-71 T marine diesels 870hp each coupled to 195 ZF, V-drive gearboxes; propeller shaft angle: 7°.
DIMENSIONS
Length overall: 20.11m
Length waterline: 16.38m
Beam, max: 5.41m
Beam, waterline: 4.80m
Draught: 1.67m
WEIGHT
Displacement: 29.51 tonnes
PERFORMANCE
Speed, max: 33 knots

DILLINGER 74
This vessel, completed in the Spring of 1990 is designed by Frank Mulder, the Dutch naval architect designer of *Octopussy*. *Dillinger 74* is built in advanced carbon-fibre pre-impregnated materials. A weight saving of between 2700 and 3200 kg over aluminium construction was expected.
PRINCIPAL PARTICULARS
Length, overall: 22.66m
Length, waterline: 18.50m
Beam: 5.24m
Draught: 1.09m
Engines: Two MTU 12V396 TB93
Propulsion: Two KaMeWa S45 water-jet units
Capacities, fuel: 7570l
water: 1893l
Speed: 60 knots

23-METRE PATROL BOAT
HULL: Aluminium alloy.
MAIN ENGINES: Two GM 12V-92 MTI marine diesels maximum rating 975bhp each at 2300rpm coupled to ZF reverse/reduction V-drive 2:1 ratio. Optional engines Mercedes-Benz MTU 331 maximum rating 1600bhp each at 2340rpm.
PROPULSION: Twin propellers.
CAPACITIES
Fuel: 15 140 litres
Fuel auxiliary (helicopter): 1890 litres
Fresh water: 756 litres
COMPLEMENT: 10.
SYSTEMS
Auxiliary machinery: Ac power provided by GM 2150 diesel generator 35kW 110/220V 3-phase powered by GM 2–71 diesel engine. Dc power provided by Constavolt La Marche A-5–60, 24V batteries six lead acid type, Surett 12V
Fresh water: Reverse osmosis fresh water maker
DIMENSIONS
Length overall: 23.44m
Length waterline: 21.35m
Beam, max: 4.88m
Depth, amidships: 3.05m
Draught, max: 1.93m
WEIGHTS
Displacement, light: 31.75 tonnes
Displacement: 43.09 tonnes
PERFORMANCE
Speed, max with GM 12V-92 MTI engines: 28.5 knots
Range at 22 knots: 1100 miles
Speed, max with MTU 331 engines: 40 knots
Range at max speed: 1000 miles

Artists impression of the 60 knot *Dillinger 74*

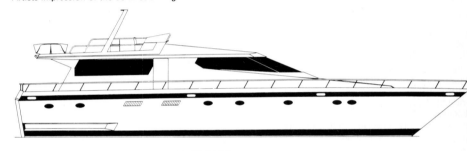

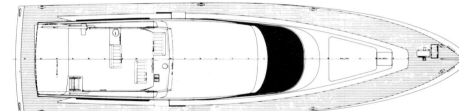

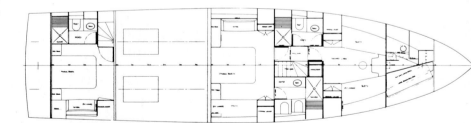

Derecktor 66, profile deck plan and accommodation

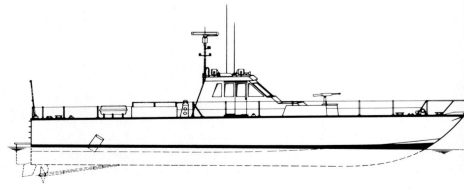

23m patrol boat outboard profile

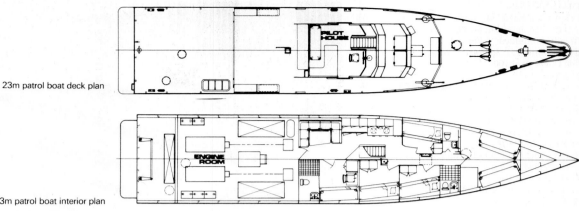

23m patrol boat deck plan

23m patrol boat interior plan

EQUITABLE SHIPYARDS, INC
TRINITY MARINE GROUP
Industrial Canal, PO Box 8001, New Orleans, Louisiana 70182, USA.

Telephone: (504) 286 2500
Telefon: (504) 286 2554

KALAMA & SKAGET
34.15 METRE FERRY

A contract valued at US $5.0 million was placed with Equitable Shipyards in 1988 for the supply of two air-conditioned 25 knots, 250 commuter passenger vessels for the Washington State Department of Transportation for service in 1989 between Vashon Island, Bremerton and down town Seattle.

The vessels were delivered in October 1989 but due to budget constraints they did not immediately enter service with Washington State Ferries but were chartered to the California Department of Transportation for use between San Francisco and the East Bay.

PRINCIPAL PARTICULARS
CERTIFICATION
USCG, sub-chapter T, ABS, under 100 GRT
HULL: Aluminium

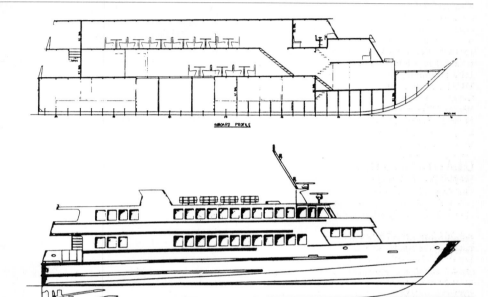

25 knot ferry for Washington State Ferries

Skaget at speed

DIMENSIONS
Length, moulded: 34.07m
length, at main deck: 34.49m
Breadth, moulded: 7.49m
Depth, moulded: 3.37m
GRT: less than 100
Draught: 2.13m
ENGINES: Four DDA GM 16V 92TA, 716kW
    each, at 2100rpm
GEAR BOXES: Four ZF, ratio 2.5:1.0
GENERATORS: Two Detroit Diesel 4.71 diesel
    engines driving two 60kW generators
PERFORMANCE
Speed, cruising: 25 knots, full load displacement
CAPACITIES
Fuel: approx 151140 l
Freshwater: approx 2650 l
Ballast: approx 64345 l

CARIBE TIDE
An air-conditioned 232 passenger ferry deliv-
ered in 1988 for serving cruise ship passengers in
the US Virgin Islands.
PRINCIPAL PARTICULARS
CERTIFICATION: USCG
HULL: aluminium
DIMENSIONS
Length: 25.91m
Beam: 7.32m
Draught: 1.68m

Artist's impression of Equitable Shipyards 25 knot, 280 passenger ferry for Washington State Department of Transportation

ENGINES: Four Cummins KT 19M, 380kW
    each, at 2100rpm
GEAR BOXES: Twin Disc MG514, ratio 2.0:1.0

GLADDING-HEARN SHIPBUILDING

The Duclos Corporation
One Riverside Avenue, Box 300, Somerset, Massachusetts 02706–0300, USA

Telephone: (617) 676 8596
Telefax: (617) 672 1873

George R Duclos, *President*

SANDY HOOK
Pilot boat for Port of New York.
DESIGNERS: C Raymond Hunt Associates Inc,
    69 Long Wharf, Boston, Massachusetts 02110,
    USA
Telephone: (617) 742 5669
Telex: 294116 BOSTLX (Attn Hunt Associates).
OWNERS: Sandy Hook Pilots Association of
    New York and New Jersey.
HULL: Constructed in aluminium alloy.
MAIN ENGINES: Two MAN-B&W 12V D 2452
    diesels developing 545bhp each at 1800rpm
    operating through L & S Marine reverse/
    reduction gearboxes with a ratio of 2:1.
PROPULSION: Twin Columbian Tetradyne pro-
    pellers.
CAPACITIES
Fuel: 56 775 litres
Fresh water: 757 litres
Water ballast: 3785 litres
ACCOMMODATION/CREW
Complement: Six pilots and four crew
Accommodation: 12 recliner seats, a television
    and dinette in deckhouse. Below decks hull is
    divided into four watertight compartments, fore
    peak, galley/sleeping quarters, engine room,
    and steering Lazorette
SYSTEMS
Generators: Two Northern Lights diesel gen-
    erators
Engine controls: Cobelt
Bow thruster: Hynautic
Navigation: Two Furuno radars, two depth soun-
    ders, Northstar Loran, a survey grade Ray-
    theon for sounding docks and approaches
Communications: Three Shipmate VHF sets
DIMENSIONS
Length overall: 19.50m
Beam: 5.18m
Draught: 1.67m

Sandy Hook 24-knot pilot boat, designed by C Raymond Hunt Associates

Twin screw motor yacht *Silver Ghost*

PERFORMANCE
Speed, max: 24 knots
    cruising: 21 knots

SILVER GHOST
Flying bridge diesel yacht
DESIGNER: C Raymond Hunt Associates Inc,

69 Long Wharf, Boston, Massachusetts 02110,
USA
Telephone: (617) 742 5669
Telex: 294116 BOSTLX (Attn Hunt Associates).
HULL: Constructed in welded aluminium tra-
ditional style cruiser with a deep-V hull with work
boat scantlings, watertight subdivisions and ABS
grade collision tank.

MAIN ENGINES: Two GM Detroit 8V-92 TI marine diesels, each 585shp at 2300rpm coupled to Allison MH 1.97:1 reduction gearboxes.
PROPULSION: Two propellers.
CAPACITIES
Fuel: 4920 litres
Water: 1249 litres (plus water maker)
ACCOMMODATION: Large owners' state room forward with guest and crew cabins amidships. Saloon with galley and lower steering position over engine room, cockpit aft and flying bridge over saloon.
SYSTEMS
Auxiliary engines: One 20kW and one 8kW generator sets
DIMENSIONS
Length overall: 18.48m
Length waterline: 16.38m
Beam: 1.63m
Draught, hull: 0.99m
Draught, skeg: 1.53m
WEIGHT
Displacement: 27.18 tonnes
PERFORMANCE
Speed, max: 25 knots
Speed, cruise: 20 knots
Range at 20 knots: 500n miles

CHELONIA
Twin screw motor yacht.

Multi-purpose yacht intended for ocean passages to Bermuda and Caribbean, sports fishing, diving and marine biological research trips. Equipped and constructed to commercial standards.
DESIGNER: C Raymond Hunt Associates Inc, 69 Long Wharf, Boston, Massachusetts 02110, USA
HULL: Welded aluminium.
MAIN ENGINES: Two GM Detroit 8V-92 TI marine diesels each developing 585shp at 2300rpm coupled to Allison MH 1.97:1 reduction gearboxes.
PROPULSION: Two propellers.
CAPACITIES
Fuel: 6813 litres (three tanks)
Water: 1135 litres (two tanks)
ACCOMMODATION: Cabin for two crew forward, guest cabin portside amidships with two berths, owner's cabin consists of double berth, heads and separate shower. Saloon consists of semi-enclosed galley, large desk, U-shaped dinette and lounge seating. After cockpit fitted with wide transom door/diving platform. Engine room is below the saloon situated in superstructure, enclosed bridge fitted above the saloon.
SYSTEMS
Auxiliary engines: One 20kW and one 8kW generator sets
DIMENSIONS
Length overall: 18.59m
Length waterline: 16.54m
Beam: 5.11m
Draught (hull): 0.99m
Draught (skeg): 1.52m
WEIGHT
Displacement: 27.18 tonnes
PERFORMANCE
Speed, max: 24 knots
Speed, cruise: 21 knots

Stern of twin screw motor yacht *Silver Ghost*

Twin screw motor yacht *Chelonia*

Chelonia enclosed bridge layout

GULF CRAFT INC
RR1 Box 395, Patterson, Louisiana 70392, USA

Telephone: (504) 395 5254/6259

R Scott Tibbs, *President*

Gulf Craft Inc is a builder of high-speed aluminium conventional hull passenger ferries and crew boats. The *Caleb McCall* is a 44-metre crew boat with a maximum speed of 27 knots. An interesting feature of this craft is that there are five engines which the owner claims gives better manoeuvrability and makes engine replacement or repair easier.

CALEB McCALL
Crew boat.
OWNER: McCall Boat Rental, Cameron, Louisiana, USA
CLASSIFICATION: USCG approved Gulf of Mexico, 200 miles offshore.
HULL: Superstructure and hull are built in aluminium. Hull plating is in 5086 grade, 15.8mm thick over the propellers, the remainder of the bottom is 12.7mm thick with 8.4mm side plating, superstructure is in 4.8mm plate.
MAIN ENGINES/GEARBOXES: Five Cummins KTA 19M diesel engines coupled to Twin Disc MG518, 2.5:1 reduction gearboxes.
PROPULSION: Five three-blade Columbian Bronze FP propellers.
CONTROLS: Orbitrol/Charlynn steering and

Kobelt engine controls. Duplicate engine controls also fitted on the upper bridge allowing operator to face aft with a clear view while working cargo at rigs and oil platforms.

CAPACITIES
Passengers: 75
Diesel: 45 420 litres (12 000 US gallons)
Water: 75 700 litres (20 000 US gallons)

ACCOMMODATION: Three two-berth cabins, galley and mess room.

SYSTEMS
Auxiliaries: Two Cummins 6B5.8, 56kW generators
Deck equipment: McElroy windlass
Navigational equipment: Raytheon/JRC colour and Furuno FR 8100 radars, Si-Tex Koden Loran, Datamarine sounder, Decca 150 autopilot
Communications: Motorola Triton 20 SSB, Raytheon 53A VHF

DIMENSIONS
Length overall: 44.20m
Beam, moulded: 8.50m
Depth: 3.50m
Draught: 2.40m
Deck area (working): 25m × 7.3m
GRT: 70
NRT: 48

WEIGHT
Deck load: 150 tons

PERFORMANCE
Speed, light: 27 knots
Speed, loaded: 23 knots (approx)

ANNABETH McCALL
NORMAN McCALL

Two of four very large crew boats delivered in 1989 to McCall Boat Rentals of Cameron, Louisiana. These boats combine increase in size (48.78 metre length) for improved sea-keeping with reasonably high speed around 25 knots.

PRINCIPAL PARTICULARS
Length: 48.78m
Beam: 9.15m
Engines: Six Cummins KTA19-M2 diesels, each 507kW, giving a total power of 3042kW
Cargo capacity: 190 tonnes

BLAIR McCALL

The previous world's largest crew boat of 47.25m in length and powered by five Cummins diesels of 507kW each. Payload: 92 passengers plus 190 tonnes cargo. Speed: up to 23 knots.

HALTER MARINE INC

6600 Plaza Drive, Suite 500, New Orleans, Louisiana 70127, USA

Telephone: (504) 246 8900
Telex: 6821246HALMAR

Jack Edwards, *President*
Archie Dunn, *President, Trinity Marketing*
Harvey Walpert, *Vice President, Contracts*
James Rivers, *Vice President, International Sales*
Ed Shearer, *Vice President, Business Development*
John Moreau, *Engineering Manager*
Barry Heaps, *Equitable/Halter, Yard Manager*

Formed in 1957, Halter Marine Inc has built over 1200 vessels since 1957 and has designed and built more high-speed vessels than any other shipyard in the USA. The yard specialises in aluminium and high strength Corten steel hulls. The parent company is Trinity Industries of Dallas, Texas and the sister company is Equitable Shipyard.

The following craft descriptions represent some of the principal types of high-speed craft designed and built by Halter Marine Inc, having lengths of approximately 20m or over with speeds of over 20 knots.

HALMAR 65 (CREW BOAT TYPE)

This is a crew boat design but is also available in the following variants: customs launch, tanker service launch, pilot boat, ferry, communications launch, work boat and ambulance launch. The first of the type was designed and built in 1964 and by August 1985 112 had been built, with production continuing. The craft have been classified by various authorities including USCG, ABS and Lloyds. Most are in service with the offshore oil industry.

HULL: Corten steel, longitudinally framed; aluminium 5086, transverse framed.
MAIN ENGINE: Various options, the most popular being two GM 12V-71 TI, producing 510hp each at 2100rpm.
PROPULSION: Two Columbian Bronze propellers, 813mm diameter, in Nibral.
CONTROLS: Morse MD-24, manual, two stations. Steering hydraulic, 600lb/in².
ACCOMMODATION: 49 passengers and 2 crew (1 captain, 1 deckhand/engineer).
SYSTEMS
Fuel: One integral fuel tank: 3596 litres, diesel fuel No 2
Hydraulic: Steering and anchor windlass, 600lb/in², 41bar
Electrical: 110/220V ac, 60Hz, generator 2–71 GM, 20kW
DIMENSIONS
Length, moulded: 19.66m
Width, moulded: 5.90m

Halmar 65 20-knot crew boat, one of over 120 built

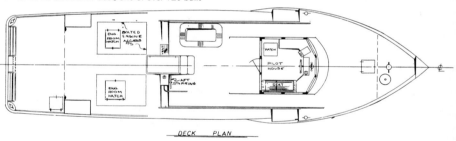

DECK PLAN

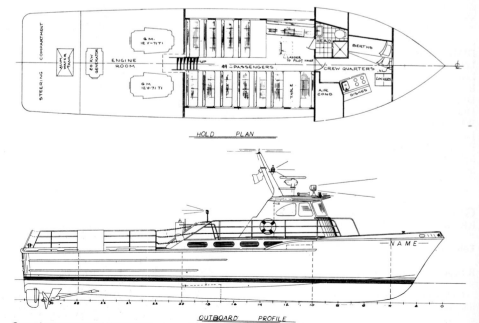

HOLD PLAN

OUTBOARD PROFILE

General arrangement of Halmar 65 type crew boat

Draught, max: 1.12m
Air draught to cabin top: 3.66m
Air draught, max: 5.79m
Freight deck area: 4.57 × 6.10m
PERFORMANCE
Speed, max: 21 knots, aluminium hull
18 knots, steel hull
Speed, cruising: 19 knots, aluminium hull
16 knots, steel hull
Turning circle diameter: 49m
Crash stop distance: 30m
Time to accelerate to cruising speed: 50s
Max permissible Sea State for operation: 3 to 4

HALMAR 65 (PATROL BOAT TYPE)

Main particulars as for the Halmar 65 crew boat type but with the following differences:
MAIN ENGINES: Most popular, two GM 12V-71 TI, 675hp each at 2300rpm.
PROPULSION: Two Columbian Bronze propellers, 838mm diameter, in Nibral.
ACCOMMODATION: For captain, 2 officers and 4 crew.
SYSTEMS
Fuel: One integral tank containing 4546 litres, diesel fuel No 2
WEIGHT
Displacement at designed load waterline: 34.54 tonnes
PERFORMANCE
Speed, max: 26 knots, aluminium hull
21 knots, steel hull
Speed, cruising: 22 knots, aluminium hull
18 knots, steel hull
Time to accelerate to cruising speed: 45s

HALMAR 78 (PATROL BOAT TYPE)

As for the Halmar 65 this design is built for various applications. The first Halmar 78 was completed in 1982 and 23 had been built by August 1985; Classification Lloyds Class 100 A-1, November 1982.
HULL: Corten steel, longitudinally framed.
MAIN ENGINES: Two GM 12V-71 TI, producing 675hp each at 2300rpm.
PROPULSION: Two Columbian Bronze propellers, 864mm diameter, in Nibral.
CONTROLS: Morse MD-24, manual, 2 stations.
ACCOMMODATION: For captain, 2 officers, 8 crew. Below the main deck there are 4 staterooms, 3 heads and a galley.
SYSTEMS
Fuel: Two integral tanks, total capacity of 10 607 litres, diesel fuel No 2
Hydraulic: Steering and windlass, 600lb/in², 41bar
Electrical: 220/440V ac, 50Hz, generator 2–71 GM, 20kW
Communications and navigation: Sailor RT-144 VHF and Decca 150 radar
DIMENSIONS
Length overall: 23.78m
Beam overall: 5.64m
Draught, max: 1.43m
Air draught to cabin top: 4.73m
Air draught, max: 7.0m
WEIGHTS
Empty: 42.67 tonnes
Max disposable load: 14.02 tonnes
PERFORMANCE
Speed, max: 22 knots
Speed, cruising: 20 knots
Turning circle diameter: 52m
Crash stop distance: 34m
Time to accelerate to cruising speed: 45s
Max permissible Sea State: 4 to 5
Range: 745n miles
Endurance: 38 hours

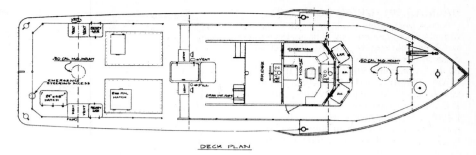

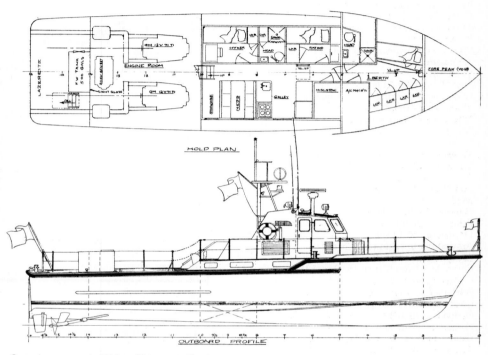

General arrangement of Halmar 65 type patrol boat

Halmar 65 type patrol boats

Halmar 78 crew boat *Oil Conveyor II*

HALMAR 101 (CREW BOAT TYPE)

A crew boat design available in a full range of variants. Designed and built first in 1977/78, 37 had been delivered by August 1985, classified either by USCG or ABS.

HULL: Aluminium 5086, transverse framed.

MAIN ENGINES/GEARBOXES: Three GM 12V-71 TI, 510hp each at 2100rpm, driving via twin disc 2.0:1 reduction gears.

PROPULSION: Three Columbian Bronze propellers, 864mm diameter, in Nibral (one vessel is fitted with three Rocketdyne waterjet units; two 406.4mm diameter driven by two GM 16V-92 TI diesel engines and one 609.6mm diameter driven by one Allison 501 gas turbine).

CONTROLS: Kobelt, pneumatic, 2 stations.

ACCOMMODATION/CREW

Passengers: 55

Crew: 6 (2 captains, 2 deckhands, 1 cook, 1 engineer)

SYSTEMS

Fuel: Two integral tanks, total 9092 litres

Hydraulic: Steering and anchor windlass, 600lb/in², 41bar

Electrical: Two generators, GM 3–71, 30kW each 110/220V ac, 60Hz

Communications and navigation: VHF, Sailor 144, SSB, Motorola, Radar, Decca D-150 36-mile range

Air-conditioning: Three units Freon, water-cooled

DIMENSIONS

Length overall: 31.0m

Beam overall: 6.48m

Draught, max: 1.68m

Air draught to cabin top: 4.67m

Air draught, max: 7.16m

Cargo deck (wood) area: 16.77 × 5.18m

GRT: Under 100

WEIGHTS

Empty: 55.88 tonnes

Payload: 30.48 tonnes

Disposable load: 40.43 tonnes

Deck load capacity: 30.48 tonnes

MAIN DECK

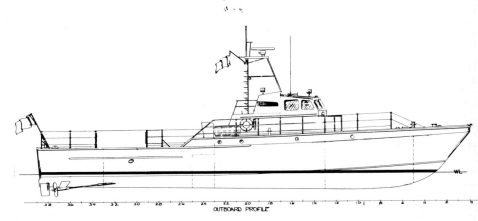

HOLD PLAN

General arrangement of Halmar 78 corten steel patrol boat

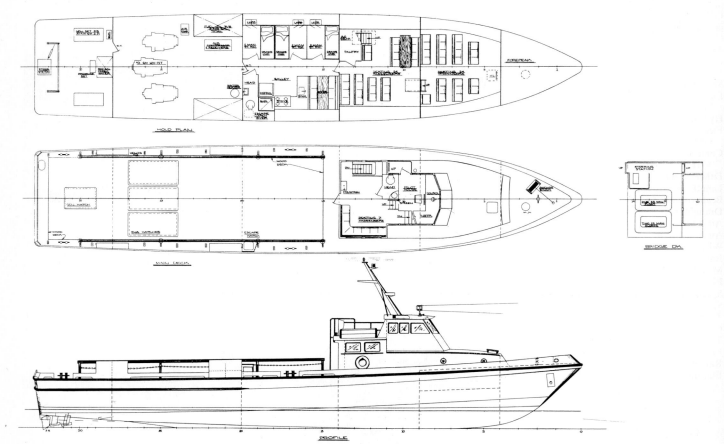

General arrangement of Halmar 101

PERFORMANCE
Speed, max: 22 knots
Speed, cruising: 20 knots
Turning circle: 55m
Crash stop distance: 37m
Time to accelerate to cruising speed: 45s
Max permissible Sea State: 5
Range: 500n miles
Endurance: 24 hours

HALMAR 112 (CREW BOAT TYPE)
A crew boat design available in a full range of variants. Designed and built first in 1981, five had been delivered by August 1985, classified by the ABS, and are in service in the Middle East, India and the Far East.
HULL: Aluminium 5086, transverse framed.
MAIN ENGINES: Four GM 12V-71 TI, 510hp each at 2100rpm.
PROPULSION: Four Columbian Bronze propellers, 864mm diameter, in Nibral.
CONTROLS: Kobelt; pneumatic, 2 stations.
ACCOMMODATION: For 92 passengers and 5 crew (2 captains, 1 engineer, 1 cook, 1 deckhand). Accommodation is air-conditioned and heated.
SYSTEMS
Fuel: Two integral tanks, total 28 413 litres, diesel No 2
Hydraulic: Steering and anchor windlass, 600lb/in², 41bar
Electrical: Two GM 3–71, 40kW generators 110/220V ac, 60Hz
Communications and navigation: VHF, Sailor, SSB, Motorola and Decca radar
DIMENSIONS
Length overall: 34.15m
Beam overall: 7.62m
Draught, max: 1.83m
Air draught to cabin top: 2.44m
Air draught, max: 7.72m
Cargo deck area: 17.38 × 6.10m
GRT: Under 100
WEIGHTS
Empty: 66.04 tonnes
Payload: 60.96 tonnes
Max disposable load: 62.48 tonnes
PERFORMANCE
Speed, max: 22 knots
     cruising: 20 knots

Halmar 101 crew boat

Halmar 112 crew boat

Halmar 112 crew boat type Sea Shuttle

Turning circle diameter: 55m
Crash stop distance: 40m
Time to accelerate to cruising speed: 45s

Max permissible Sea State: 5
Range: 1200n miles
Endurance: 54 hours

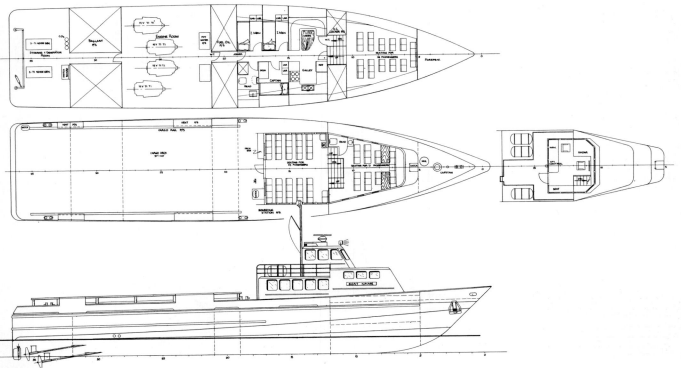
General arrangement of Halmar 112

HALMAR 115 MOTOR YACHT

A high-speed motor yacht designed and built in 1984 to ABS Class.

HULL: Double chine, aluminium 5086, transverse framed.

MAIN ENGINES: Four GM 12V-92 MTI, 1000hp each at 2300rpm.

PROPULSION: Four Columbian Bronze propellers, 1016mm diameter, in Nibral.

CONTROLS: Kobelt, pneumatic, engine control, Bennett Trim, hydraulic.

ACCOMMODATION/CREW
Guests: 8
Crew: 5, captain, stewards, deckhands
Main deck: Pilot house, saloon, galley, bar
Lower deck: Crew's quarters, owner's cabin, 4 guest rooms, 6 heads, engine room, generator room
Flybridge: Flybridge station, jacuzzi, barbecue, boat deck lounge
Air-conditioned

SYSTEMS
Fuel: Five integral tanks, total 43 566 litres, diesel No 2
Hydraulic: Boat crane, 1000lb/in², 68 bar. Bennett Trim
Electrical: Two 62.5kW generators, 220/440V ac, 50Hz
Communications and navigation: Two VHF Sailor, one SSB Sailor, two Decca radars, one satnav, one navigator, two fathometers, one autopilot

DIMENSIONS
Length overall: 35.06m
Beam overall: 7.62m
Draught, max: 1.60m
Air draught to cabin top: 5.18m
Air draught, max: 8.0m

WEIGHTS
Empty: 85.0 long tons
Max disposable load: 40.0 long tons

PERFORMANCE
Speed, max: 32 knots
    cruising: 29 knots
Turning circle: 56m
Crash stop distance: 30m
Time to accelerate to cruising speed: 35s
Max permissible Sea State: 5
Range: 2100n miles
Endurance: 65 hours

Halmar 115 32-knot motor yacht

HALMAR 122 (CREW BOAT TYPE)

A large crew boat designed and completed in 1985 having a 70-ton cargo capacity. Built to ABS Class A1, this design, as for the Halmar crew boats, is available for a wide range of applications.

HULL: Aluminium 5086, transverse framed.

MAIN ENGINES: Four GM 12V-71 TI, 510hp each at 2100rpm.

PROPULSION: Four Columbian Bronze propellers, 864mm diameter, in Nibral.

CONTROLS: Kobelt, pneumatic, 2 stations.

ACCOMMODATION: For 92 passengers and 5 crew (2 captains, 1 engineer, 1 cook, 1 deckhand).

SYSTEMS
Fuel: Four integral tanks, total capacity of 4660 litres, No 2 diesel
Hydraulic: Steering, capstan and anchor windlass, 600lb/in², 41bar
Electrical: Two GM 3–71, 40kW generators 110/220V ac, 60Hz
Communications and navigation: One VHF, Sailor 144, one SSB, Motorola and one Decca D-150 36-mile range radar
Water, potable: 3714 litres
    ballast: 64 400 litres

DIMENSIONS
Length overall: 37.20m
Beam overall: 7.62m
Draught, max: 1.83m
Air draught to cabin top: 5.49m
Air draught, max: 7.72m
Cargo deck area: 20.12 × 6.10m
GRT: Under 100

WEIGHTS
Empty: 73.15 tonnes
Payload: 71.12 tonnes (deck load capacity)
Max disposable load: 75.65 tonnes

PERFORMANCE
Speed, max: 21 knots
Speed, cruising: 19 knots

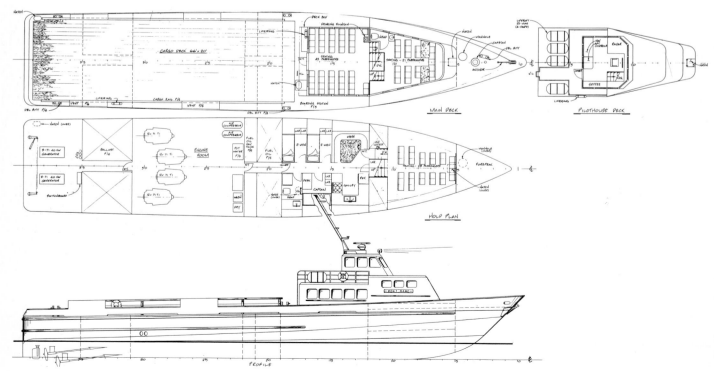

Turning circle diameter: 56m
Crash stop distance: 41m
Time to accelerate to cruising speed: 45s
Max permissible Sea State: 5
Range: 1700n miles
Endurance: 88 hours

CARIBE TIDE

Delivered at the end of 1988 for Transportation Services of St John, Inc for operations from cruise ships in the Virgin Islands.

PRINCIPAL PARTICULARS
Length: 19.82 m
Beam: 7.32 m
Draught: 1.68 m
Depth, moulded: 2.90 m
Engines: four Cummins KT19M, 380 kW each, at 2100 rpm
Gearboxes: Twin Disc MG514, ratio 2:1
Air conditioning: 10 tonnes (185% over capacity)
Accommodation: 240 passengers

HEBAH MARWA & DAINA sister vessels)

The first of three all-aluminium crew boats for Marine and Transportation Services, Saudi (Ltd) Damman, Saudi Arabia, delivered Ocober 1988

PRINCIPAL PARTICULARS
Length: 33.74 m
Beam: 6.61 m
Depth, moulded: 2.89 m
Accommodation: 25 passengers plus 25 tons of cargo
Engines: three Detroit Diesel 12V71TI, 380 kW (510 hp) each, at 2100 rpm
Gearboxes: Twin Disc MG 514, ratio 2:1
Fuel tank capacity: 12 870 l
Freshwater tank capacity: 3785 l
Ballast water capacity: 17 410 l
Freshwater maker: 1135 l/day

Halmar 122 deep-Vee hull crew boat

The 21.7 knot 240 passenger *Caribe Tide*

The ATCO *Hebah*, 25 passenger, 25 tonne cargo, crew boat built by Halter Marine, Inc

HUCKINS YACHT CORP INC
Florida, USA

HUCKINS 78
PRINCESS PAT
Motor yacht.
HULL: Grp/airex core construction.
MAIN ENGINES: Two MAN diesel engines rated at 760shp at 2300rpm each connected to ZF 2.5:1 gearboxes.
PROPULSION: Two Arneson Surface Drives Model ASD 14, coupled to 1.07m diameter, four-bladed Nibral surface-piercing propellers.
DIMENSIONS
Length overall: 23.77m
Length waterline: 19.81m
Beam: 6.09m
Draught: 1.14m
WEIGHT
Displacement, full: 44.39 tonnes
PERFORMANCE
Designed speed: 23 knots

Huckins 78, a 23m aft cockpit motor yacht

KNIGHT AND CARVER YACHTS
3650 Hancock Street, San Diego, California 92110, USA

Telephone: (619) 295 3115

Joe Fole, *Designer*

SPORTS YACHT (DESIGN)
HULL: Composite.
MAIN ENGINES: Two MTU 12V 396 TB94 marine diesels, 2550hp each.
PROPULSION: Two KaMeWa 63 waterjets.
CAPACITIES
Fuel: 5565 litres
Water: 742 litres
ACCOMMODATION: Owners suite, state room with bath, also lounge and galley, pilot station and after sunpad.
SYSTEMS
Auxiliary machinery: One 8kW generator
Communications: Radio telephone and telex, computer interface, television, VCR, TV and stereo
Navigation: Standard equipment

DIMENSIONS
Length overall: 21.34m
Beam: 5.79m
Draught: 0.67m
WEIGHTS
Displacement, dry: 23.58 tonnes
Displacement, full: 30.38 tonnes
PERFORMANCE
Speed, max, light load: 71 knots
Speed, max, full load: 62 knots

PANJANDRUM
Motor yacht built 1987.
HULL: Grp composite, coring material is Airex for the hull and Divinycell for the decks.
MAIN ENGINES: Two MTU 12V 396 TB94 diesel engines 2550hp each.
CAPACITIES
Fuel: 24 983 litres
Water: 2649 litres
ACCOMMODATION: Owner's suite includes two bathrooms, a jacuzzi, bar and desk area with a computer terminal. Two double guest staterooms each with a bath, saloon bar and film theatre, formal dining for eight and galley. Crews' quarters

consist of Captain's stateroom and bath, double cabin, crew bathroom, galley and lounge.
SYSTEMS
Auxiliary machinery: Two 33kW generators and one 12kW generator
Navigational: Standard equipment and a satellite navigation system
Communications: Standard telephone sets, telex, computer interface capability and satellite communications
Television: VCR/TV/electronic telescopes
Stabilisers: Koop rotary retractable stabilisers
DIMENSIONS
Length overall: 29.60m
Beam: 7.31m
Draught, full load: 0.88m
WEIGHTS
Displacement, dry: 45.80 tonnes
Displacement, half: 58.50 tonnes
Displacement, full: 71.20 tonnes
PERFORMANCE
Speed max, light load: 52 knots
Speed max, full load: 46 knots
Speed, continuous, light load: 35 knots
Speed, continuous, full load: 39 knots
Range at 12 knots approx: 3450 miles

Artist's impression of *Panjandrum* built by Knight and Carver Yachts

LANTANA BOATYARD INC
808 N Dixie Highway, Lantana, Florida 33462, USA

Telephone: (305) 585 9311
Telex: 513480

Elliot R Donnelley, *Chairman of Board*
Alexander Stalker, *President*

David M Conway, *Chief Financial Officer & Treasurer*
Michael W Gore, *Director, International Sales*

Formed in 1965, Lantana Boatyard began construction of military boats in 1980. It is situated on a 10-acre site 12 miles south of the Port of Palm Beach.

GUARDIAN
Four of these 34-knot capability patrol boats have been built. The design was started in February 1982 and trials of the first boat completed in October 1983.
HULL: All-welded aluminium alloy 5086 construction longitudinally formed over transverse bulkheads and web frames. Modified V hull with single hard chine.

MAIN ENGINES: Three MTU 8V 396 TB93, 1200shp each.
PROPULSION: Three Columbian Bronze propellers, 1067mm diameter, cast Nibral, fixed-pitch.
CONTROLS: Hydraulic power steering and pneumatic engine controls.
ACCOMMODATION: Enclosed wheelhouse forward with open bridge above. 19 crew. Commanding Officer's quarters on deck behind wheelhouse. Six officers below midships and twelve crew below deck forward. All accommodation is air-conditioned.
SYSTEMS
Fuel tank capacity: 24 603 litres
Hydraulic: Steering, two pumps 81.6 bar, 1200lb/in^2
Electrical: Two GM 4–71 diesel generators, 3-phase, 50kW each. 120/208V ac, 24V dc. Engine start with dc emergency power
Navigation and communication: Depth sounder, satnav, magnetic compass, Sperry gyrocompass, Sunaire SSB radio, VHF radio, Furuno radar
Lifesaving: One rigid/inflatable boat, two 10-person inflatable liferafts on deck
DIMENSIONS
Length overall: 32.32m
Length waterline: 30.49m
Freeboard, amidships: 1.96m
Beam overall: 6.25m
Draught, max: 2.10m

HMJS *Paul Bogle*, the Lantana-built 30-knot-plus patrol craft of the Jamaica Defence Force Coast Guard commissioned September 1985

Air draught to cabin top: 5.49m
Air draught, max: 9.76m
WEIGHTS
Empty: 49 tonnes
Max disposable load: 27.2 tonnes
Design max displacement: 76.20 tonnes
PERFORMANCE
Speed, max: 34.0 knots
Speed, cruising: 30.0 knots

Turning circle diameter: 333m
Rate of turn, starting at cruising speed: 246°/minute
Crash stop distance: 115m
Time to accelerate to cruising speed: 137s
Max permissible Sea State for operation: Strong Gale Force 9
Range: 1200n miles
Endurance: 48 hours at 25 knots

MAGNUM MARINE CORPORATION

2900 Northeast 188th Street, North Miami Beach, Florida 33180, USA

Telephone: (305) 931 4292
Telex: 6811630
Telefax: (305) 931–0088

F M Theodoli, *President*
Mrs Katrin Theodoli, *Managing Director*

Magnum Marine specialises in the construction of high performance, offshore pleasure and patrol craft from 8m to 21m in length. In this range its standard designs are:
Magnum 27, an 8.33m grp fast coastal patrol boat
Magnum 40, an 12.19m grp fast open or flybridge patrol craft
Magnum 45, a 13.60m grp open patrol boat
Magnum 53, a 16.13m grp open or flybridge patrol boat
Magnum 63, a 19.20m grp/Kevlar patrol and pleasure craft
Magnum 70, a 21.22m grp/Kevlar patrol and pleasure craft
Magnum patrol craft are in service with the US Marine Patrol, US Customs, US Coast Guard and many other non-US agencies.

Magnum 63 flybridge

MAGNUM 63

This boat is built in accordance with the requirements of Lloyd's Register of Shipping and the American Bureau of Shipping. As of August 1989 a total of 14 have been built, the first was completed in 1985. In August 1986 the Magnum 63 won the 370 mile Miami-Nassau-Miami offshore race. In 1987 a new and faster version of this Magnum 63 was developed and Magnum again won the race. The craft can be fitted out as a patrol boat. A flybridge version was shipped to Japan in November 1987.
HULL: The boat is basically a four-piece construction consisting of a hull, deck, forward inner liner and cockpit liner, all laminated in grp or for additional weight saving the lamination can be of Dupont Kevlar. Interiors may be built of Kevlar and Nomex honeycomb composite materials. Deadrise aft is 24°.
ENGINES: Two DD 16V92TA, 1440hp each
PROPULSION: Two Arneson Surface Drive SP2000 propeller units.

CAPACITIES
Fuel: 4320 litres
Fresh water: 720 litres
CREW: Nine.
SYSTEMS
Electrical: Eight 12V, 200Ah batteries, four for each engine; 60A engine driven alternators; 12V and 24V dc system; 100/220V 60Hz ac system; two automatic 60A converters; Onan diesel generator, 7.5kW
Firefighting: Manual and automatic firefighting equipment
DIMENSIONS
Length overall: 19.20m
Length waterline: 16.31m
Breadth overall: 5.28m
Draught, static: 0.91m (with Arneson Surface Drive)
PERFORMANCE
Speed, max: 52 knots
Range: 400 to 500n miles at continuous speed

1987 version of Magnum Marine 63, *Maltese Magnum*, winner of the 1987 Miami-Nassau-Miami Sea Race at an average of 51 knots over 314.77n miles

MAGNUM 63 (1987 VERSION)
MALTESE MAGNUM
HULL: Constructed in Dupont Kevlar, super-structure to suit individual requirements.
MAIN ENGINES: Two CRM marine diesels, 1850hp each at 2075rpm coupled to two Arneson drives via 1.18:1 reduction gearboxes.
PROPULSION: Two five-blade Nibral propellers, 838mm dia, 1143mm pitch.

CAPACITIES
Fuel: 4542 litres
Fresh water: 946 litres
ACCOMMODATION: 6 to 10.
DIMENSIONS
Length overall: 19.20m
Beam, max: 5.18m
Draught, static: 0.91m
Draught, running: 0.46m

PERFORMANCE
Speed, max: 65.80 knots

MAGNUM 70
Fast patrol craft launched in December 1988.
DESIGNER: Pininfarina
HULL: Grp/Kevlar
DIMENSIONS
Length, overall: 21.34m

PACIFICA by KIPPER YACHTS
3595 Frankford Avenue, Panama City, Florida 32405, USA

Telephone: (904) 769 8976

Bill Jahn, *Production/Quality Manager*

CONVINCER
Sport fishing, built in 1987.
HULL: Frp.
MAIN ENGINES: Two 1330bhp marine diesel engines.
PROPULSION: Two KaMeWa 50S62/6 waterjet units.

DIMENSIONS
Length overall: 21.33m
Beam: 6.29m
Draught: 1.21m
WEIGHT
Displacement: 45 tonnes
PERFORMANCE
Speed: 34 knots

PALMER JOHNSON INC
61 Michigan Street, Sturgeon Bay, Wisconsin 54235, USA

Robert Boler, *Vice President*
William Parsons, *Executive Vice President*

TIME
Built in 1986 for Atwood, Rockford, USA, this motor yacht is driven by two 2145bhp KaMeWa waterjet units, type 71S62/6.

SWIFTSHIPS INC
PO Box 1908, Morgan City, Louisiana 70381, USA

Telephone: (504) 384 1700
Telex: 586453
TWX: 819 950 5700 SWIFT INC MGCY

Holding Company: UNC Resources, Falls Church, Virginia, USA.
Subsidiaries: Mangone Swiftships Inc, Houston and Champion-Swiftships, Pass Christion, Mississippi, USA.

Swiftships produces aluminium alloy craft up to 38 metres and steel vessels from 45 to 76 metres in length. Swiftships employs about 900 personnel and apart from their fast crew boats have supplied fast aluminium patrol craft ranging in size from 8 to 45 metres in length, in service with US armed forces, naval coastguard, and police forces in some 20 countries throughout the world.

Swiftships 65 patrol boats

65 PATROL BOAT
Patrol boats supplied to governments of Antigua, Dominica and St Lucia.
HULL: Superstructure and hull constructed in aluminium alloy.
MAIN ENGINES: Two GM 12V-71 TI marine diesel engines coupled to Twin Disc MG 514C reverse/reduction gearboxes.
PROPULSION: Two Columbian crew boat propellers.
CONTROLS
Engine controls: Ponish
Steering system: Vickers/Charlynn
CAPACITIES
Fuel: 4542 litres
Water: 1892 litres
SYSTEMS
Auxiliary machinery: 20kW Detroit Diesel/International Electric generator set
DIMENSIONS
Length overall: 19.81m
Beam: 5.56m
Draught, full load: 1.52m

115 CREW BOAT
Fast supply/crew boat.
CLASSIFICATION: USCG Sub-Charter T Requirements and certified for ocean service, limited to 200 miles offshore.

HULL: Superstructure and hull constructed in aluminium alloy.
MAIN ENGINES: Three MTU 8V 396 TC82 marine diesels providing 800shp each at 1845rpm through ZF BW 255 2:1 reduction gearboxes.
PROPULSION: 101mm diameter Aquamet 17 stainless steel shafts coupled to three four-bladed bronze 96mm × 1016mm Columbian propellers.
CONTROLS
Engine controls: Wabco air controls
Steering: Two Hydreco hydraulic pumps with Charlynn Orbitrols
CAPACITIES
Fuel: 14 004 litres
Industrial water (transferable): 49 432 litres
Ballast: 49 432 litres
Potable water: 3785 litres
Lube oil: 302 litres
Hydraulic oil: 151 litres
Sewage holding tank: 3406 litres
Transfer tank (fuel or water): 1324 litres
ACCOMMODATION
Crew: 6 persons in 3 double cabins
Passengers: Seats for 49 persons. Two heads and one shower
SYSTEMS
Auxiliary machinery: Two 30kW generators driven by Detroit Diesel 3-71 diesel engines at 1200rpm
Air compressors: Two Quincy F-325, two-stage

type and driven by 5hp three-phase electric motors and 302-litre air receivers
Air-conditioning: Two central type cooling units servicing galley, staterooms, passenger spaces and pilot house. Heat provided by duct-mounted strip heaters
Firefighting: Two fire stations on main deck (port and starboard) with hoses and nozzles. Optional Akron Model No 508 fire monitor can be installed on top of main cabin
Transferable liquid system: Barnes Model 15CCE 76mm industrial water transfer pump driven by 7.5hp drip proof electric motor. Fuel transfer pump is a Barnes Model 15CCE 76mm, driven by a 7.5hp drip proof electric motor
Navigational: Danforth Constellation compass, two Perko 254mm searchlights, Konel Furuno FR-711 radar, Raytheon F720D fathometer, Loran C-Texas Instruments TI-9900, one EPIRB
Communications: Drake TRMI-SSB radio, and Drake MRT-55 UHF radio
Lifesaving: 54 life jackets, three ring buoys, three liferafts (two 25-man, one 10-man), fire extinguishers, one fire axe and two hoses
DIMENSIONS
Length overall: 35.05m
Beam: 7.62m
Draught, max: 2.20m
Clear main deck area: 5.48m × 16.45m

WEIGHT
Deck cargo: 75.22 tonnes
PERFORMANCE
Speed, normal load: 23 knots
Range: 750n miles

Inboard Arrangement

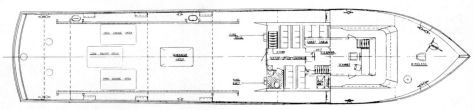

Main Deck Arrangement

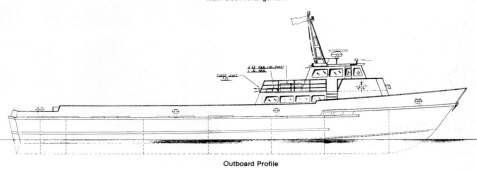

Swiftships 115 crew/supply boat profile, main deck and inboard layouts

Outboard Profile

TRINITY YACHTS INC
at
EQUITABLE SHIPYARDS, INC.

See entry for Equitable Shipyards, Inc. for address details.

LEDA
29.57 METRE MOTOR YACHT

The formation of Trinity Yachts Inc. was announced in July 1989 and at the same time the building of its first luxury motor yacht *Leda*. This vessel designed by MPS Gilgenast is built in aluminium and is powered by two MTU 8V396 TB93 diesel engines, 960kW each, driving two four-skew-blade propellers through ZF BW255 gear-

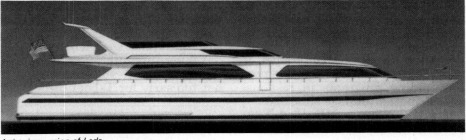

Artists impression of *Leda*

boxes. Moulded beam is 7.01 metres and draught 1.4 metres. Half-load cruising speed is 22.5 knots.

The vessel is built to ABS standards and certified ABS + A-1, AMS Circle yacht service.

TEMPEST YACHTS, INC.

3333 N.E. 188th St. North Miami Beach, FL 33180

Telephone: 3059374400
Telefax: 3059373752
Telex: 9103806795

Tempest Yachts, Inc. has established a reputation as an innovative manufacturer of high quality, diesel-powered vessels for a wide variety of applications. The Company, with its new headquarters, is located in North Miami Beach, Florida where it produces currently, 17 models ranging from 9.75m-25.9m in length. The Tempest product line offers a combination of style, performance, luxury, sophisticated technology, outstanding seaworthiness and total safety.

Tempest Yachts is a high-tech oriented, growing company and as such it is constantly developing the state-of-the-art technology required. Its technology is complimented with extensive offshore experience which enables Tempest to produce vessels that are comfortable, practical and well designed for their particular application.

Due to its capabilities, Tempest Yachts was

selected from among all American boat builders to design and construct an offshore Fast Coastal Interceptor (FCI) craft for the United States Coast Guard. These patrol boats, 13.4m in length, are currently operated in various areas in most weather conditions for a variety of applications ranging from rescue missions to anti-drug warfare.

TEMPEST 60

High-speed offshore performance craft available in both pleasure and commercial applications.
PRINCIPAL PARTICULARS
HULL AND DECK: FRP, ABS class
DIMENSIONS
Length over all: 18.29m
Beam: 4.80m
Draught: 1.07m
Displacement: 22.68 tonnes
ENGINES: Two Caterpiller 3412 TA diesels, 783 kW (1050 hp) each
PROPULSION: Tempest's own T-Torque (patent pending) surface piercing drive system
CONTROLS: Kobelt mechanical engine controls, single station hydraulic power steering system

SYSTEMS
Auxiliary power: 15 kW Westerbeke generator
Fuel system: 3785 l (1000 US gallons)
Water system: 1060 l (280 US gallons)
Electrical system: 220 Vac, 110 Vac, 24 Vdc, 12 Vdc
Communication and navigation: VHF, Loran, radar, auto pilot, depth sounder
Fire extinguishing system: Halon 1301
Maximum speed: 50 knots

TEMPEST 85

Ocean-going Raised Pilot House Motor Yacht also available in various commercial applications.
PRINCIPAL PARTICULARS
HULL: FRP, ABS class
DECK: Aluminium 5086
DIMENSIONS
Length over all: 25.91m
Beam: 6.40m
Draft: 1.52m
Displacement: 61.22 tonnes
ENGINES: Two Caterpiller 3412 TA diesels, 7.83 kW (1050 hp) each
PROPULSION: 4 blade Nibral propellers
CONTROLS: Kobelt Pneumatic, two stations,

hydraulic power steering system, hydraulic bow thruster

SYSTEMS

Auxiliary power: Two Northern Light 35 kW generators

Fuel system: 13248 l (3500 US gallons)

Water system: 2650 l (700 US gallons)

Electrical system: 220 Vac, 110 Vac, 24 Vdc, 12 Vdc

Communication and navigational systems: VHF, Loran, radar, auto pilot, depth sounder, Sat-Nav, Sat-Comm, Facsimile, SSB

Fire extinguishing system: Halon 1301

Maximum speed: 30 knots

Tempest 60 sport yacht

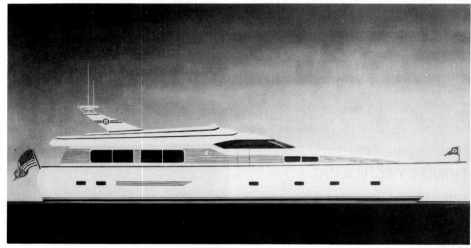

Tempest 85 raised pilot house motor yacht

TRINITY MARINE GROUP

14055 Industrial Seaway Road, P.O. Box 3029, Gulfport, Mississippi, U.S.A.

Telephone: (601)864 0029
Telex: 6821246
Telefax: (601)867 1666

The Trinity Marine Group is owned by Trinity Industries, Inc. (NYSE:TRN) Dallas, Texas and includes Equitable Shipyards, Inc., Halter Marine, Inc., Moss Point Marine, Inc., Gretna Machine and Iron Works, Inc., Aluminum Boats, Inc., HBC Barge, Inc., and Trinity-Beaumont.

Details of high-speed vessels built in this group are given under the entries for the relevant shipyards

WESTPORT SHIPYARD INC

PO Box 308, Westport, Washington 98595, USA

Telephone: (206) 268 0116

Randy Rust, *Proprietor*

Westport Shipyard was established in 1964 and sold to the present owners in 1977. The yard has a workforce of 80 and consists of 5110M² (70,000ft²) of covered building sheds and workshops plus 4 acres of fenced storage space. The range of craft built is from 10.4 to 36.6 metres in length. Hulls of the larger craft are built with a sandwich type construction of Airex pvc and grp, which the builder claims yields a tougher and lighter hull than an all-grp type. Hull moulds are adjustable for length and beam enabling craft to be built in the following length ranges: 16.15 to 19.80 metres, 19.80 to 29.0 metres and 27.4 to 36.6 metres. The company has built some 50 vessels to USCG 'S' classification since 1977. Since 1981 a further eleven craft built to USCG 'L' classification have been delivered.

Glacier Spirit

AVALON EXPRESS
GLACIER SPIRIT
OWNERS: Stan Stephens Charters, USA.

DESIGNER: Jack Sarin, Bainbridge Island, Washington, USA.
HULL: Construction in grp/Airex foam core.

MAIN ENGINES/GEARBOXES: Twin Lugger L-8955A diesels 4 cycle, V-8 TA, 555hp each at 2100rpm coupled to Twin Disc MG-514 2.5:1 gearboxes.

PROPULSION: Two three-bladed 1016mm × 914mm Michigan propellers.

CONTROLS: Marol, MSSB electronic/hydraulic power steering system, with Marol autopilot.

CAPACITIES

Fuel: 5678 litres

Water: 757 litres

ACCOMMODATION: 150 passengers.

SYSTEMS: One Northern Lights, 20kW M-854 diesel generator and one Northern Lights, 10kW hydraulically powered generator, Wesmar bow thrusters.

DIMENSIONS

Length overall: 24.38m

Beam: 6.70m

Draught: 1.52m

WEIGHTS

Light: 45 tons

Loaded: 60 tons

PERFORMANCE

Speed, max: 22 knots

Catalina Express

CATALINA EXPRESS
TWO HARBORS EXPRESS

OWNERS: Catalina Channel Express Lines, San Pedro, California, USA.

DESIGNERS

Hull lines: Edwin Monk Jr, Bainbridge Island, Washington, USA

Fit out: Jack Sarin, Bainbridge Island, Washington, USA

HULL: Construction in grp/Airex foam core.

MAIN ENGINES/GEARBOXES: *Catalina Express* has two DD 12V-92 TA water-cooled Pacific diesels developing 850shp each at 2100rpm, coupled to Twin Disc/Niigata MGN 80–1, 1:1.97 gearboxes. *Two Harbors Express* is fitted with Deutz MWM SBAM 12M 816 engines as for *Glacier Seas*.

PROPULSION: Two Michigan Wheel 965mm × 864mm three-bladed Nibral propellers.

CONTROLS: Arnot pneumatic engine controls, and Wagner Engineering steering gear.

ACCOMMODATION: 149 passengers accommodated in main cabin, and VIP lounge fitted abaft the wheelhouse. The top deck features open seating.

SYSTEMS

Electrics: M843, 12kW Northern Lights diesel generator

Bow thruster: Wesmar 25hp

Hydraulic system: Spencer Fluid Power with Cessna 421 variable displacement pump

Stabilisers: Naiad Roll Control system

Navigational: Micrologic ML-3000 Loran C, Wagner Mk 4 autopilot, Wagner Rudaler Angle Indicator, Impulse 530 Depth Sounder, Impulse 580 SLT (speed/log/trim) indicator, Furuno FR360 Mk II radar, Furuno FR240 M3 radar, Ritchie Power damp compass

Communications: Horizon USA II standard VHF, Aiphone internal communications

Lifesaving: 9in Buoy liferings, Model 1280 automatic water lights, Model 1618 buoyant apparatus (4- and 16-person 'wafers')

Firefighting: Badger-Powhaton fire hydrant and hose

DIMENSIONS

Length overall: 27.43m

Beam: 6.40m

Draught: 1.37m

PERFORMANCE

Speed, max: 27 knots

Subsequently two sister ships to the *Catalina Express* have been built fitted with two Deutz SBAM 12M 816 engines.

Catalina Express passenger cabin

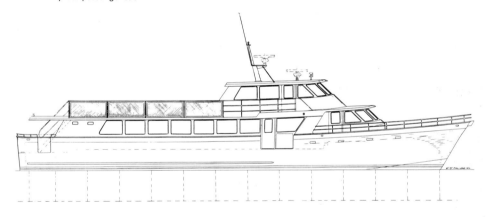

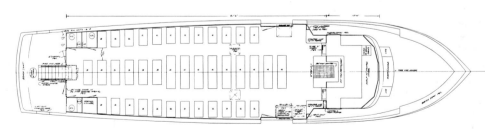

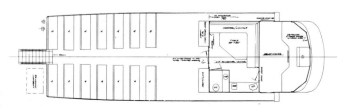
Catalina Express layout

GLACIER SEAS

Fast tour boat.

OWNERS: Chuck and Marguerite West, Traverse Pk, Alaska, USA.

DESIGNER: Jack Sarin, Bainbridge Island, Washington, USA.

HULL: Construction in Airex/frp.

MAIN ENGINES/GEARBOXES: Twin Deutz SBAM 12M 816 marine diesel engines, each at 694kW (930hp) at 1800rpm coupled to Reintjes reduction gearboxes.

PROPULSION: Two four-bladed Coolidge 1066.8mm × 914.4mm Nibral propellers.

ACCOMMODATION: Licensed to carry 130 passengers. The craft is equipped with bars on both enclosed decks and a galley for preparation of hot meals. Half of the seating is in dinette type benches and tables, the remainder consists of individual chairs.

SYSTEMS: 35hp Wesmar bow thruster.

DIMENSIONS
Length overall: 27.43m
Beam overall: 6.90m

PERFORMANCE
Speed, service: 21 knots

SUPER EXPRESS

Two of these 28.96m vessels have been ordered. With a beam of 6.91m, they are licensed to carry 149 passengers in coastwise service, but have seating for 152 passengers inside and 40 outside.

The vessel includes three passenger lounges with bar services, plus a VIP stateroom with a bar. With a full load of passengers, the vessel cruises at 30.5 knots and with a light load, the cruise speed increases to approximately 32 knots.

HULL: FRP with double-cored Airex bottom and single-cored Airex sides. All of the laminates are of military specification fire-retardant resin. The entire superstructure is of all-composite type construction (i.e. only the main sole and bulkheads are of wood construction). Extensive use of high strength materials was incorporated into the design to control weight.

ENGINES: Two Detroit Diesel 16V92T diesels rated at 1175 kW 1575 continuous s.h.p. at 1900 rpm with ZF BW470 marine gear having a 3.04:1 reduction. Shafts are 10.16 cm Aquamet 17. The engines heat exchange cooling, air starts and wet exhaust. Five-blade propellers, 54 × 63 are fitted.

ENGINE CONTROLS: Air controls with shaft brakes, primarily. Kobelt and Wabco components, three stations.

STEERING SYSTEM: Wagner hydraulic with Wagner Mark IV pilot. Rudders were a cast urethane foil section.

GENERATORS: 12kW Northern Lights and 8kW hydraulic.

STABILISERS: Naiad 403 system with 0.557m² fins.

CLOSED CIRCUIT TV: Panasonic cameras in engine room and main salon with the monitor in the pilot house. Intercom and background music system by Aiphone.

SEATING: Yacht 400 type supplied by Ralph Ekness Co. of Norway.

BAGGAGE COMPARTMENT CONVEYOR: Hydraulic with doors on each side.

BAR SYSTEM: Multiple brand pop and liquor system with ice storage and refrigerated storage.

TANKAGE
Fuel capacity: 7570 l (2000 US gallons)
Water capacity: 379 l (100 US gallons)

ELECTRONICS
Radar: FR 810 DS Furuno
Radar: FR 1800
Micrologic: ML 8000 Loran
VHF: Standard Titan and Standard 768
Speed and depth log: B & G HS 921
Compass: Aximath 100 Digital
Telephone: Cellular

Super Express

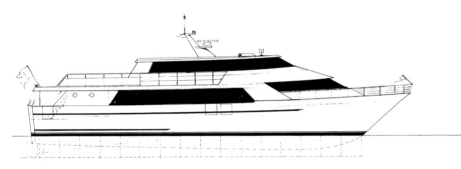

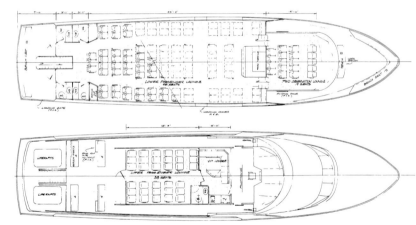
General arrangement of *Super Express*

Super Express interior

AIR-LUBRICATED-HULL CRAFT

AUSTRALIA

STOLKRAFT SOUTH QUEENSLAND PTY LIMITED
[LICENSEES, DESIGNERS AND DEVELOPERS]

Head Office: Tall Trees, 11 Marina Court, Mudgeeraba, QLD 4213, Australia

Telephone: (03)61–75–304441
Telefax: (03)61–75–304441

John D Aitkenhead *Director*
N V Aitkenhead *Director*
John A Lund, *Naval Architect*

North American Office:
Stolkraft High Speed Hulls Ltd, 3036, 11th Avenue, Vancouver, British Columbia, Canada V6K 2M6

Telephone: (604) 731 2790

Leo D Stolk's Stolkraft concept of optimising the benefits of air lubrication on a planing hull can be summarised as follows: at speed, an appreciable amount of aerodynamic lift is built up by a ram-air cushion at the bow and this creates a second ram-air cushion and lifts the craft so as to reduce frictional resistance.

A feature of the concept is the absence of trim variation. The craft rises bodily, parallel to the surface, and has no tendency to porpoise. At speed it creates neither bow-wash nor hull spray outward. The aerodynamic lift reduces fuel consumption.

Tests have been undertaken with a 2.4m model at the Netherlands Ship Model Basin (NSMB), Waganingen, Netherlands. The performance of this model was monitored in the high-speed tank and actual sea tests with 4.95m and 8.45m vessels provided additional data. During the tank tests speeds of up to 80 knots were simulated with no performance problems.

These and further NSMB tests in 1980 confirmed that the final design has a speed/power characteristic more favourable than the high-speed catamaran, planing craft and surface-piercing hydrofoils and in terms of total operating and capital costs, the Stolkraft is significantly more economical at higher speeds than air cushion vehicles and other high-speed vessels.

Details of the prototype Stolkraft, Inceptor II SK.16 Mk I and the Stolkraft Mk III 14-seat test craft are given in *Jane's High-Speed Marine Craft and Air Cushion Vehicles 1986, Jane's Surface Skimmers 1985* and earlier editions.

In late 1989, Ports of Auckland Ltd placed an order for a 12.9 metre Stolkraft pilot vessel. This vessel is powered by two MAN 2866 LE engines each developing 304 kW (408 hp) and driving Arneson ASD 10 surface-drive propulsion units.

STOLKRAFT 10.3-METRE FAST FERRY

The first commercial order for Stolkraft was placed in 1986 for two 41-passenger, 10.3-metre fast ferries. These vessels entered service in January 1987 with the Gold Coast Water Bus Co at Australia's Gold Coast, south of Brisbane. Important factors for the ferry operator were high speed, minimal wash and wake and low capital and operating costs.
HULL: Glass-reinforced plastic in sandwich construction.
ENGINE: Volvo twin 270hp diesels with Hamilton waterjets (first boat) and Arneson surface drives (second boat).

Stolkraft Inceptor II SK.16 Mk I

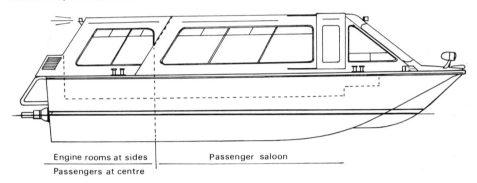
Engine rooms at sides — Passenger saloon — Passengers at centre

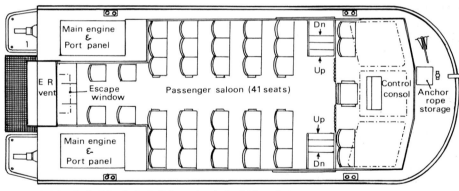
Layout of 10.3m Stolkraft fast ferries built for services in the Brisbane area

Hull form of 10.3m Stolkraft

10.3m Stolkraft waterbus in service at Gold Coast, Queensland

ACCOMMODATION: 41 passengers.
DIMENSIONS
Length: 10.3m
Beam: 4.3m
Depth: 1.7m
Draught: 0.7m
PERFORMANCE
Operating speed: 30 knots

FUTURE DESIGNS

Stolkraft have proposed designs for several applications of the concept as follows:
Firefighting/rescue boat
    Length, overall: 18.00m
    Beam: 7.5m
    Draught: 1.0m
    5 monitors
    Speed: 40 to 45 knots

10.3m Stolkraft waterbus at speed

Passenger ferry
    Length, overall: 20.5m
    Beam: 8.5m

Draught: 1.5m
120 passengers
Speed: 40 to 45 knots

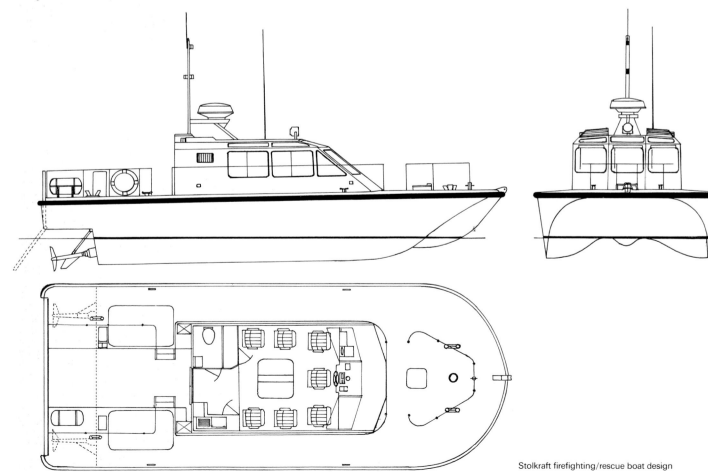

Stolkraft firefighting/rescue boat design

Patrol boat
 Length, overall: 22.0m
 Beam: 8.0m
 Draught: 1.3m
 Speed: 45 to 50 knots

BATAM EXPRESS III
Delivered to Sinba Shipping, Singapore, in 1988.
PRINCIPAL PARTICULARS
Length, extreme, including stern platforms:
 11.40m
Length, datum waterline: 9.10m
Breadth, moulded: 4.56m
Depth, moulded: 1.70m
Draught, mean: 0.70m
Passengers: 45
Engines: Two Isotta Fraschini ID 3Z SS 6LM
 each at 270 kW (362 bhp) 3000 rpm
Gearboxes: Twin Borg Warner model 73C
 reduction ratio 2:1
Propulsion: Twin Arneson model ASD 10 Surface
drives.

Speed: Loaded with weights equivalent to 45 passengers a speed in excess of 30 knots was achieved. However, the average of two runs in each direction through a measured mile with a load in excess of the fully loaded condition provided 27.5 knots.
Equipment: Air conditioning, radar, 240V generator, refrigerator, stereo, video, TV , liferafts.
Classification: Det norske Veritas.

FAST FERRY – Port MacQuarrie
This vessel was supplied in 1988 and is currently in service as a fast tourist vessel at Port MacQuarrie. The owners have reported that the vessel has been operated as far as 27 miles along the coast from Port MacQuarrie in open sea and the seakeeping qualities are exceptional.
PRINCIPAL PARTICULARS
Length overall (hull): 7.50m
Length datum waterline: 6.60m
Breadth (moulded): 3.30m
Depth (moulded):1.30m

Engines: Two 119 kW (150 hp) Yamaha outboard engines.
Passengers: 24
Crew: 1
Speed: Light 41 knots
Speed: Fully laden 36 knots

LEO D STOLK
This vessel is currently operating as a charter vessel and ferry on the Gold Coast. Because it is fitted with water jets it has the versatility to operate in areas of the Gold Coast waterways where shallow draft is essential. This craft has high speed capabilities with up to 25 passengers, although it does seat 40 at slower speeds.
The specifications of this vessel are as follows:
Length: 10.30m
Length datum waterline: 9.10m
Breadth: 4.55m
Speed: Light 30 knots
Seating: 40

FRANCE

ALFA/NAVAL
Zone Industrielle de Bregaillon, 83500 La Seyne-sur-Mer, France

Telephone: (94)945444
Telex: 404631 F

B S Anjuel, *Principal*

TURBO CAT 27
BARAKA 2
An air-lubricated-hull boat originally referred to as an SES. Built in marine-grade aluminium, launched December 1988, initially for SARL Guadeloupe but was in service off French west coast operating to Ile d'Yeu from St. Jean de Monts in 1989.
CLASSIFICATION: Bureau Veritas Class 3 passenger rules
PRINCIPAL PARTICULARS
Length: 27.00m
Breadth: 7.10m
Draught: 1.10m
Engines, for propulsion: Two MWM BAM 816

Baraka 2

CR diesels, 1070kW each
 for air lubrication: one Deutz BFL 413 diesel
Propulsion: Two KaMeWa 50 S water-jet units, driven via flat belt transmissions

Accommodation: 230 passengers including external seating
Speed: up to 35 knots

SOCIÉTÉ FRANÇAISE DE CONSTRUCTIONS NAVALES (SFCN)
66 Quai Alfred-Sisley, 92392 Villeneuve-la-Garenne, France

Telephone: (47) 94 6446
Telex: 610998 FRANCONA F

Directors: See entry for SFCN in the High-speed mono-hull section

MARLIN 21 CLASS AIR-LUBRICATED HULL CRAFT
Details of these vessels in their basic form are given in the SFCN entry in the High-speed mono-hull section. The Marlin design is now completed with an exclusive air lubrication system for the

hull giving a considerable maximum speed increase. A French patent was applied for in October 1984.
The first vessel to be fitted with air lubrication, a Marlin 21, was launched 27 November 1986.
ENGINES: Two MWM TBD 234 V6, 489bhp each.
PROPULSION: Two Riva Calzoni waterjet units.
HULL: Aluminium alloy AG 4 MC.
DIMENSIONS
Length, overall: 21.75m
Beam, extreme: 4.10m
Draught: 0.65m
GRT: 39
WEIGHT
Displacement, full load: 15.10 tonnes
PERFORMANCE
Speed, without air lubrication: 33 knots with air lubrication: 40 knots

SFCN Marlin 21 class boat fitted with air lubrication system

THE NETHERLANDS

LE COMTE-HOLLAND BV

Stuartweg 4, 4131 NJ Vianen, P.O. Box 24, 4130
EA Vianen, The Netherlands

Telephone: (0903473)71904)
Telex: 40475 LECOM N

Also: A. le Comte Co., Inc., 101 Harbor Lane
West, New Rochelle, New York, USA

Telefax: (914)636 1359

AIR-LUBRICATED VESSELS

A new development by le Comte, employing a unique bow form designed to induce a degree of air lubrication beneath the hull. Two inwardly directed side Vee bows are joined by a central third bow of short length and of less depth. The working of this configuration is described by le Comte as follows:

'By 17 knots the bow starts to lift, the little inner bow creating a vacuum and the two outer bows with the shape of the wide bow forces the air in between. With the vacuum created by the little bow this process is maximised forcing the air underneath the entire bottom. The stern section is of the Vee bottom type and when the hull is lifted she actually rides on the two outer hulls and the protruding Vee of the aft section. She now has air between the water surface and the hull surface. Depending on the speed this layer of air becomes a cushion of air and at high speed she is an excellent sea boat as the air cushions the boat. That is particularly obvious when one stands near the bow; in say 1.3 metre waves at 30–35 knots, the g factor is hardly noticeable, while for the same speed and size one cannot stay near the bow of a deep Vee boat in such waves.'

A further benefit claimed is that the concept creates very little spray or wake.

Le Comte has drawn up a number of designs for their air lubricated vessels of lengths of between 11.75 and 23.75m. The power required for achieving 35 knots in Sea States 1 to 2 has been found to be half that of an equivalent deep Vee hull vessel with 24° to 26° deadrise.

Bow configuration of le Comte air-lubricated-hull vessels

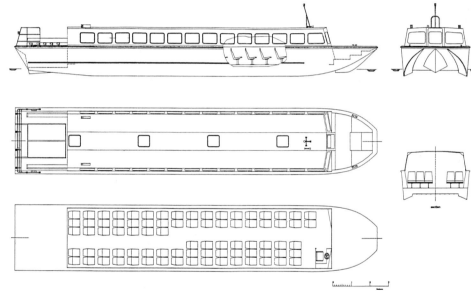

le Comte 19.75m air-lubricated-hull passenger vessel

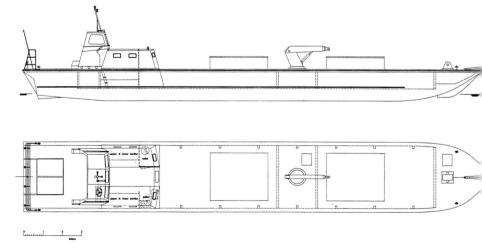

le Comte 23.75m air-lubricated-hull cargo vessel

le Comte 13.75m patrol boat

le Comte 13.75m patrol boat at 35 knots

UNION OF SOVIET SOCIALIST REPUBLICS

MOSCOW SHIPBUILDING AND SHIP REPAIR YARD
[MINISTRY OF THE RIVER FLEET]
Exporter: V/O Sudoexport, Chaikovsky St.11, Moscow, 123231
Telephone: (095) 255 1813
Telex: 411116

GHOST
Built in Leningrad and due to be launched in 1990, this 70-seat air lubricated mono-hull vessel is reported to be powered by a single 1044kW MTU diesel engine.

ZARIA (DAWN)
Experiments with high-speed waterbuses, capable of negotiating the many shallow waterways in the Soviet Union, began in 1961.

The object was to develop a vessel for services on shallow waters, with depths of only 0.5m, at speeds of at least 21.5 knots. The prototype Zaria, called the Opytnye-1 (experimental), was put into experimental operation on the river Msta in 1963. During trials the craft attained a speed of 42km/h and proved to have a turning radius of 40–70m. The craft runs bow-on to any flat, sloping bank to embark passengers.

Built with a strong aluminium alloy hull and equipped with a well protected waterjet, the craft is unharmed by floating logs, even when they are encountered at full speed.

Zaria

Variants include models with a flat load deck in place of the passenger cabin superstructure amidships, and used as light freight vessels. A total of 149 units of the first model of the Zaria were built.

Zaria was designed by a team at the Central Design Office of the Ministry of the River Fleet, Gorki, working in conjunction with the Leningrad Water Transport Institute. Series production is under way at the Moscow Shipbuilding and Ship Repair Yard of the Ministry of the River Fleet.

Given the design prefix P83, Zaria conforms to Class P of the RSFSR River Register.

The latest model is distinguished by its trimaran

Zaria

bow configuration, which gives improved performance in waves and enables the craft to be routed on major waterways. Apart from the large number of Zarias in service in the USSR, a number have been supplied to Czechoslovakia, Poland and the German Democratic Republic.

PROPULSION: Power is provided by a single M401A-1 four-stroke, water-cooled, supercharged, 12-cylinder V-type diesel with a normal service output of 870–900hp at 1450–1500rpm and a maximum output of 1000hp. It has a service life of 3000 hours before the first overhaul. It has a variable-speed governor and reversing clutch and drives a single 0.7m diameter variable-pitch, four-bladed waterjet impeller. Fuel consumption is 155kg/h. Lubricating oil consumption at continuous cruising speed is 5kg/h.

The waterjet is of single-stage type with a semi-submerged jet discharge. The brass four-blade, variable-pitch impeller, diameter 693mm, sucks in water through an intake duct which is covered by a protective grille. The discharged water flows around two balanced rudders which provide directional control. Two reversal shutters, interconnected by a rod and operated by cable shafting, reverse the craft or reduce the waterjet thrust when variations in speed are necessary.

A localised ram-air cushion, introduced by an upswept nose and contained on either side by shallow skegs, lifts the bow clear of the water as the craft picks up speed. The airflow also provides air/foam lubrication for the remainder of the flat-bottomed hull.

CONTROLS: Irrespective of load, the radius of turn is between 30 to 50m with the rudder put hard over at an angle of 30 degrees. This turning radius can be decreased by throttling down the engine or closing the valves of the reversing system. At slow speed the craft is capable of pin-wheeling. The time required to stop the vessel is 8 to 10 seconds, the coasting distance being between 50 and 60m. The craft is able to navigate small winding rivers with waterways of 12 to 15m wide with the radii of windings varying between 40 and 70m without slowing down.

The vessel can easily pull into shore without landing facilities, providing the river bed slope is no steeper than 3 degrees. The time required for pulling in, embarking passengers, then leaving, averages 90 seconds. Steps for access are at the bow, port and starboard, and lowered by a control in the wheelhouse.

HULL: Hull and superstructure are of all-welded aluminium alloy plate construction, the constituent parts being joined by argon-shielded arc welding. Framing is of mixed type, with transverse framing at the sides and the main longitudinal elements within the hull bottom. The outside shell and bottom plating is 5mm thick, except for the base at the bow where it is 6mm thick. The wheelhouse is in moulded glass-reinforced plastic. The waterjet duct and nozzle are in grade Cr3 steel and are riveted to the hull.

ACCOMMODATION: Three transverse bulkheads and two recesses divide the hull into six compartments. Behind the forepeak and wheelhouse (frames 0–3) is the passenger cabin (frames 3–27) and aft of this is a compartment housing a small bar and toilet (frames 27–30). A soundproof cofferdam (frames 30–31) follows, aft of which is the engine room (frames 31–41) and steering compartment (frames 41 to stern). The raised wheelhouse, located at the bow, gives 360-degree visibility. The latest export model of the Zaria seats 63 in the passenger cabin, plus another four, without luggage, in two recesses. On routes of up to 45 minutes duration an additional 24 standing passengers can be carried. Life jackets for passengers are stowed in lockers in the baggage compartment and under seats at the rear of the cabin.

The crew off-duty room contains a sofa, table, wall-mounted cupboard, folding stool and a mirror. The toilet contains a wash basin, a bowl, mirror and soap tray.

The wheelhouse has rotating seats for the captain and engineer, two sun visors and there are two windscreen wipers.

The passenger cabin and wheelhouse are heated by warm air produced by hot water from the closed circuit main engine cooling system. Warm air is admitted into the passenger cabin and wheelhouse through a perforated chamber at the bulkhead. The engine room is heated by two 1.2kW electric heaters and the crew room by a 0.6kW electric heater.

SYSTEMS, ELECTRICAL: Main engine-driven 3kW, 28V dc generator charges the storage batteries and meets the demands of 24V circuits while the vessel is under way. Four lead-acid batteries

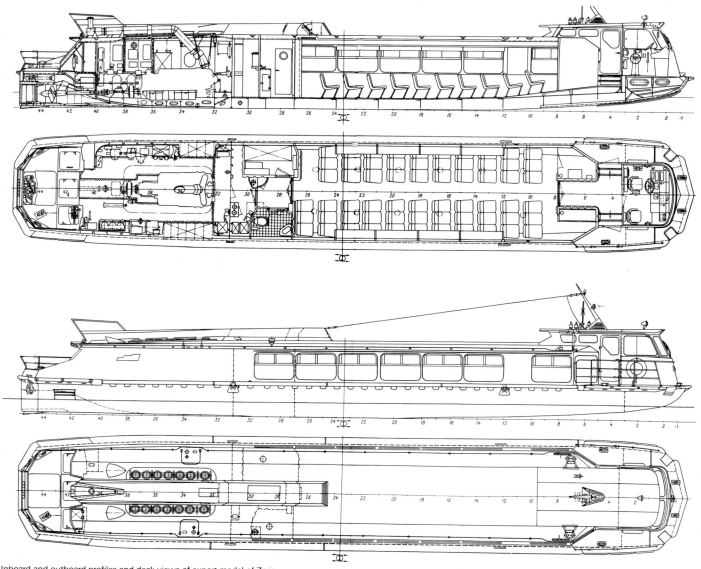

Inboard and outboard profiles and deck views of export model of Zaria

type 6TCT-132 EMC 12V, 132Ah each are used to supply electric power for the lighting system, signal lights and radio equipment at anchorage as well as the priming unit and heater. The storage batteries are coupled to form a series-multiple connection yielding 24V and respective current intensity.

Current consumers operating at anchorage as well as the battery charger, electric water and oil heaters, heaters in the engine room and service spaces are fed single-phase ac 220V current.

FIREFIGHTING: Two tanks containing fire-extinguishing compound and hoses for fighting an outbreak in the engine room. System can be brought into operation either from the engine room or from the wheelhouse. Engine room is also provided with two portable carbon dioxide fire extinguishers. Another of the same type is provided in the wheelhouse and two foam fire extinguishers are standard equipment in the main cabin.

FUEL: Craft is refuelled through a filling hose and a neck on the port side of the superstructure. Fuel is fed to the main engine from a service tank with a capacity of $4.13m^3$, sufficient to enable a vessel to cruise for 8 hours without refuelling. In addition, there is a 400-litre storage tank which contains a two-hour reserve to be used in an emergency. The same tank supplies fuel to a water heater.

COMPRESSED AIR: Starting system for main engines comprising three 45-litre air-cylinders, valves (safety, shut-off, pressure reducing and starting) and piping. Pressure $75-150kgf/cm^2$. Two cylinders in operation, one standby.

ACCOMMODATION
Seats in lounge: 63
Seats in recesses (with luggage): 4
One washroom/WC
DIMENSIONS
Length overall: 23.9m
Beam overall: 4.13m

Freeboard up to undetachable parts at mean draught of 0.44m; 3.2m
Depth: 1.20m
Mean draught, light: 0.44m
loaded: 0.55m
WEIGHTS
Empty: 16.68 tonnes
Weight with 60 passengers and stores for 8-hour trip: 24.78 tonnes
Max weight of cargo stowed in luggage recesses: 1 tonne
Fuel capacity: 3.8 tonnes
PERFORMANCE
Speed (in channel of 0.8m depth): 40km/h, 21.6 knots
Range: Suitable for service distances of 150km (93 miles) and above
Endurance at cruising speed: 8 hours
Max wave height, allowing full speed: 0.70m

UNITED STATES OF AMERICA

ALLEN JONES & WALTER A MUSCIANO

[PATENT HOLDERS, DESIGNERS AND DEVELOPERS
5028 Lauderdale Avenue, Virginia Beach, Virginia 23455, USA
and
100 Church Street, Suite 1940, New York, NY 10007, USA

Telephone: (804) 464 0768/(212) 732 2800

Capt Allen Jones, Jr. *Principal, FASTCO, Fast American Ship Transportation Co, Virginia Beach, Virginia*
Walter Musciano, *Chief Designer*

WAVE-FORMING KEEL HIGH-SPEED HULL (DESIGN)

The inventor of the Wave-Forming Keel (WFK) concept is Capt Allen Jones, USN (Rtd) who has been granted an original patent, US Patent No 4048939, believed to be the only original patent granted for hull design this century.

The WFK concept builds on the idea of the stepped planing hull by employing a novel method of introducing air to the step by using water to pump air to the planing surfaces to form a lubricating film of micro bubbles or sea foam/froth and thereby reduce frictional resistance. This result is achived by incorporating longitudinal V or flat-bottom V section, free-flooding, free-breathing, planing structures on the hull bottom, the wave-forming keels. Two or three of these longitudinal structures can be fitted. Each keel can in turn be divided into two or three sections, the spaces between the sections forming steps which function as mixed-fluid venturi pumps.

Originally the proposed designs for using the concept were based on rather conventional hulls but more advanced hull designs have now been developed expressly for use with Wave-Forming Keels. Tests have been conducted with a variety of WFK designs for speed and sea keeping ability with and without wave-forming keels. The principal objective of the proposed evaluation is to monitor operation of a craft equipped with wave-formers and collect sufficient performance data to evaluate its comparative improvement over current state-of-the-art planing craft in the 50- to 100-knot speed range.

A fixed wave-former may be designed to be

Wave-forming keel high-speed commuter ferry design with surface-piercing propellers

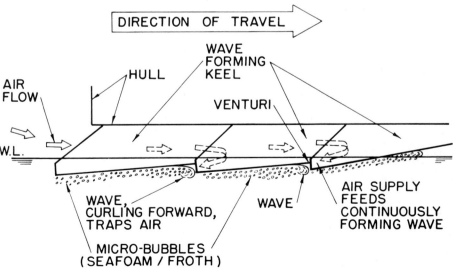

Principle of wave-forming keels providing air lubrication

optimum for specific performance criteria or it may be designed for broader objectives or adjustable wave-formers may be applied.

For this project, three wave-former design variations will be applied to the same craft to demonstrate the broad range of performance that can be obtained from a single craft configuration and the ease with which the inherent speed and

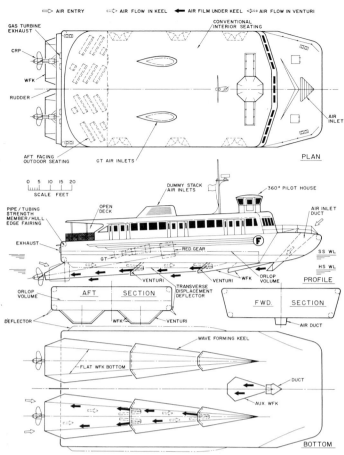

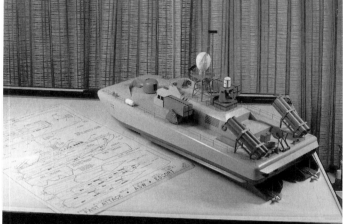

Wave-forming keel concept applied to a high-speed commuter ferry design

Radio-controlled model of fast-attack craft employing the wave-forming keel concept

Configuration of wave-forming keel (3 sections) on manned test craft

Underside of bow, looking aft, manned test craft

sea keeping characteristics of the same craft can be altered over a broad range.

The WFK is flooded when the craft is in its buoyant state (at rest or moving very slowly), therefore the resistance is very high at low speeds and the vessel is extremely stable in this state. As speed increases, the craft begins to plane on the WFK and sea water begins to leave the flooded WFK. The mixed fluid pump action of the sea water on the venturi step then draws air into the WFK, via the rear opening. This air moves forward in the WFK, exits through the venturi openings and lubricates the WFK. Each design has specific ranges which allow for optimum operation of the venturi. As speed is reduced, the planing lift is reduced and the water flows into and fills the WFK as the craft returns to the buoyancy-supported condition.

The WFK increases the length of the trough built up aft of the hull, thus decreasing resistance by giving longer effective length to the Wave-Forming Keel. Typically, the merits of the WFK are fully realised at speeds over 36 knots when about 75 per cent of buoyancy is replaced by dynamic lift at higher speeds.

The planing craft speed and ride quality are closely related, and are determined by the WFK design, location and arrangement. Performance in a seaway can be expected to be superior to conventional planing hull craft because the impact area presented by the WFK is considerably less than a conventional planing hull craft.

Further refinements of the WFK concept have now been proposed by the developers. Hull and venturi forms optimised for calm sea use and for rough sea use are available as well as further detailed optimisation leading to improved efficiency.

WING-IN-GROUND-EFFECT CRAFT

CHINA, PEOPLE'S REPUBLIC

CHINA SHIP SCIENTIFIC RESEARCH CENTER (CSSRC)

Wuxi, Jiangsu, People's Republic of China

Telephone: Wuxi 668012
Telex: 36216 CSSRC CN

RAM-WING VEHICLE 902

A single-seat test vehicle.

The research plan behind the development of the 902 was begun in 1979 and a programme of theoretical and wind-tunnel experimental research was carried out which provided solutions for the particular problem of longitudinal stability encountered by such craft when operating in and out of ground effect. The 902 was built in 1983 and it first flew on 12 November 1984.

PRINCIPAL PARTICULARS

Length, overall: 9.55m
Span, overall: 5.80m
Weight, max: 385kg
Weight, empty: 280kg
Disposable load: 105kg
Engines: two HS-350A, 15kW each, aircraft piston engines
Propellers: two fixed-pitch, aircraft type
PERFORMANCE
Speed, take-off: 40.5 knots
Speed, cruise: 65.0 knots
Take-off distance: 150m
Landing distance: 100m
Lift/drag ratio, max: 20.0

Take-off can be achieved in waves up to 0.4 to

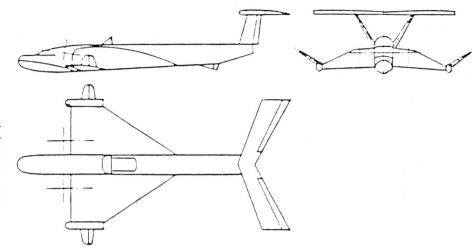

Wing-in-ground-effect craft built by China Ship Scientific Research Centre

0.5 metres with winds of Beaufort 6 to 7. The craft can be flown in and out of ground effect and in the surface effect region of 0.6 to 8.0 metres altitude it can fly safely without any automatic stabilising device.

XTW-1

Following the success of the 902 a larger ram wing craft was built, the XTW-1, for lake and river communications duties. This craft has a weight of 920kg and is powered by two 30kW piston engines

giving it a cruise speed of 70 knots, with four people on board. A retractable undercarriage is incorporated for slipway handling.

XTW-2

With the experience gained with the 902 and XTW-1 a much larger project was embarked upon in 1988. The XTW-2 will have a weight of 2500kg and will be powered by two 150kW piston aircraft engines giving it a speed of 97 knots carrying 12 to 15 passengers.

XTW-1 on trials over Lake Tai

MARINE DESIGN AND RESEARCH INSTITUTE OF CHINA (MARIC)

314 Sichuan Road, Central, PO Box 3053, Shanghai, People's Republic of China

Telephone: 215044
Telex: 33029MARIC CN
Cable: 5465

Yun Liang, *Deputy Chief Engineer*

For further information on MARIC work please see Air Cushion Vehicles section.

PAR WIG TYPE 750

This two-seat experimental PAR/WIG craft was completed in 1985, and over the period March 1985 to June 1987 over 40 trial flights were performed, exploring various operating conditions.
HULL: Built in grp with aircraft construction techniques.

MARIC PAR WIG Type 750 coming ashore

MARIC PAR WIG Type 750 showing its considerable clearance height above the water

LIFT AND PROPULSION: Four 30hp piston engines driving four ducted propellers type DT-30.
DIMENSIONS
Length overall: 8.47m
Beam overall: 4.80m
Height overall: 2.34m
WEIGHTS
Max take-off weight: 745kg

Payload: 172kg
PERFORMANCE
Speed, max, calm water at 0.5m altitude: 71.0 knots
Range: 70n miles
Take-off distance: in Beaufort 4 to 5 wave height 0.5m: about 160m
Take-off time, approx: 30s
Take-off speed: 24 knots

Over-water behaviour: can take off and fly steadily in wave height conditions of 0.5 to 0.7 metres with Beaufort 4 to 5 and gust 6 wind conditions. In horizontal flight, average pitch is 0.3 degrees and roll, 0.53 degrees.
Max. impact deceleration on water landing is about 1.54g.

GERMANY, FEDERAL REPUBLIC

BOTEC ENGINEERING SOCIETY LTD

Odenwaldring 24, D-6101 Gros-Bieberau, Federal Republic of Germany

Telephone: (06162) 1013
Telefax: (06162) 1014 (AIRFOIL FLAIR BOATS)

Günther W Jörg, *Proprietor*
Ingrid Schellhaas

In 1987 Günther Jörg established this company for the design, development and construction of Airfoil-Flying Boats (aerodynamic ground-effect vehicles of all sizes). Construction was immedi-ately put in hand with a small 2-seat craft, the Sport-fly, and first trials started in the second week of December 1987. Serial production 1989.

A second company was also formed by Günther Jörg in 1987, **Airfoil Sales Company for Ground Effect Vehicles**, with the same address as above.

SPORT-FLY (JÖRG II, TAF VIII-1)

A two-seat craft designed to achieve 67 knots with a 100hp petrol engine, built in aluminium alloy and grp materials.
ENGINE: 4-cylinder, 2-cycle air-cooled, 100hp.
PROPELLER: 3-blade adjustable pitch, diameter 1.5m.

DIMENSIONS
Length: 8.30m
Width, max: 3.42m
Width for transporting: 2.25m (special trailer available)
WEIGHTS
Weight, empty: 480kg
Payload: 180kg
PERFORMANCE
Speed, take-off: 38 knots
Speed, cruising: 67.5 knots
Range: 108n miles with 25 litres normal tank or 270n miles with additional tank
Surface clearance height: 0.2m to 0.3m
Buoyancy: Ten water-tight compartments

AIRFOIL GmbH
GÜNTHER W JÖRG
[DESIGNER, DEVELOPER AND PATENT HOLDER]
Odenwaldring 24, 6101 Gros-Bieberau, Federal Republic of Germany

Telephone: (06162) 3624/1013
Telefax: (06162) 1014

Günther W Jörg was for a number of years a constructor, works manager and development engineer for various West German vertical take-off and landing (VTOL) projects. He sees his Aerodynamic Ground Effect Craft (AGEC) concept as a means of providing fast, economical and comfortable long-distance travel. His experiments began in the 1960s with a series of radio-controlled models. Wind-tunnel tests were also undertaken and the results were checked by a computer. The first Günther Jörg ram wing, a two-seater powered by a modified Volkswagen engine, was designed in 1973, and first flew in 1974. After an extensive test programme, Jörg II

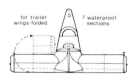

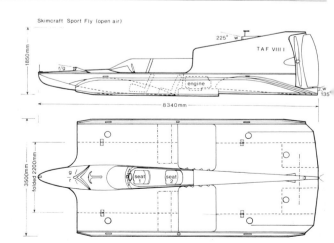

Skimcraft Sport Fly (open air)

was designed, performing its first flight in 1976. This incorporated more than 25 design improvements and has travelled more than 10 000km. During 1978 and 1979, Jörg designed a glassfibre-hulled four- to six-seater, Jörg III, which would

have been put into series production in Poland had it not been for political tension. The first prototype was completed in 1980. Designs are being prepared for larger and faster craft capable of carrying heavier loads over greater distances.

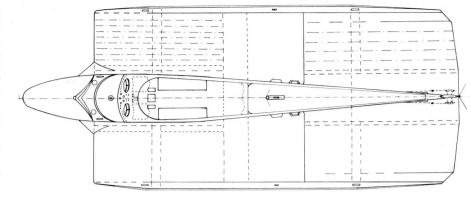

Stabilisation about the pitch and roll axes and maintaining the flying height of the AGEC can be regulated independently by the ground/water surface reaction and therefore requires only a simple steering control for movement around the vertical axis. This basic requirement led to the development of a tandem wing configuration, the handling characteristics of which were first tested on models and then on two-seat research craft. Tests showed that the tandem wings had good aerodynamic qualities, even above turbulent water, with or without water contact.

AGEC's have ample buoyancy and are seaworthy, even while operating at low speed (cruising in displacement condition). After increasing speed the craft lifts off the surface of the water and the resulting air cushion reduces the effects of the waves. After losing water contact the boat starts its ram wing flight at a height of 4 to 8 per cent of the profile depth. A two-seater with a wingspan of 3.2m and a profile length of 3.05m will have a flying height above the water surface of 102 to 203mm at a speed of 96.6km/h. The low power requirement of this type of craft is achieved through the improved lift/drag ratio of a wing-in-ground-effect as compared to free flight.

The exceptionally high lift/drag ratio of these craft keep the thrust requirements per kilogram of weight low, thus transport efficiency is high. The ratio of empty weight to payload for the test craft is 2:1, but calculations already show that it will be 1:1 with more advanced designs; large transport craft might be 1:2. A craft of more than 300 tons would have a wing chord of 36m and fly under ground effect conditions at between 3.5 and 7m. It would have a wing span of 40m and a length of 100m, requiring engine thrust of 55 000hp (40 000kW). Cruising speed would be 250km/h from 10 000hp (7350kW) and craft of this size could travel all-year-round over 90 per cent of the world's sea areas.

The main components of an Aerodynamic Ground Effect Craft are: forward main wing; aft wing; vertical stabiliser and rudder; longitudinal tip fence/float; fuselage for passengers and/or cargo and the powerplant. The latter comprises an engine with propeller or ducted propeller, which can be mounted as a pod on the rear wing or as a unit integrated with the rear fuselage.

Additional equipment might include a retractable undercarriage, which would enable the craft, under its own power, to run on to dry land or move from land to water for take-off. Towing connections can be provided for water-skiing and an electrically operated anchor winch can be fitted.

The following operational possibilities are foreseen:

INLAND WATERWAYS AND OFFSHORE AREAS: Suitable for rescue boats, customs, police, coast guard units, patrol boats, high-speed ferries, leisure craft.

COASTAL TRAFFIC: Large craft would be operated

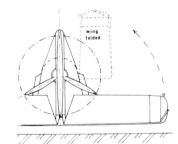

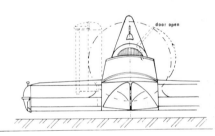

Jörg IV Skimmerfoil

Jörg IV at 145km/h

as fast passenger and passenger/car ferries and mixed-traffic freighters.

OVERLAND: Suitable for crossing swamps, flat sandy areas, snow and ice regions. Another poss-

ible application is as a high-speed tracked skimmer operating in conjunction with a guide carriage above a monorail.

Small craft, displacing 1 ton or more, can travel over the supporting surface at a height of 304mm or more at a speed of 96.6 to 144.8km/h.

Larger craft, weighing 10 to 50 tons will be able to fly at a height of 914mm to 1.98m at a speed of 129 to 177km/h.

Coastal craft displacing more than 100 tons will fly at a height of 3.04m or even higher.

The basic advantage of the AGEC is its ability to transport passengers and freight far quicker than conventional ship, rail or road transport. The ratio between empty weight and service load is about 2:1 but can certainly be improved. Fuel consumption is 80 to 85 per cent lower than that

Construction of TAF VIII-4S

Jörg V (TAF VIII-4S) on ground test, September 1986

of a boat of similar construction. A high degree of ride comfort is achieved with these craft.

The Airfoil-Flairboats of Jörg design are designed in accordance with Aircraft International Standards Part 1, Definitions, May 23rd, 1974, p. 11, Annex 8, para. 3. No special F.A.A. Certificate is required for the operation of Flairboats in any country.

JÖRG I
Total wingspan: 4.1m
Length overall: 6.2m
Wing profile length: 2.5m
Max take-off weight: 700kg
Passengers: 2
Cruising speed: 100km/h
Installed power: 70hp
Average cruising height: 0.1m
Max flying height: 0.5m
Year of construction: 1973–74
Construction: Grp/wood
Range: 300km

JÖRG II SPORT-FLY
(PROTOTYPE)
A 2-seat test boat for series production, it was built in 1976 and is owned by Günther Jörg.
Total wingspan: 3.28m
Length overall: 8.3m
Wing profile length: 3m
Max take-off weight: 770kg
Passengers: 2
Cruising speed: 135km/h
Installed power: 70hp
Average cruising height: 0.12m
Max flying height: 1m
Construction: Wood
Range: 500km
(with long-range tanks, more than 1000km)

JÖRG II-2
TAF VIII-1
PRODUCTION VERSION OF JÖRG II
First flights of this craft were undertaken in December 1987.
Total wingspan: 3.42m
Length overall: 8.30m
Height, max: 1.90m

The Jorg 2 seat TAF VIII-1 on road trailer. Total time for loading and unloading: half an hour

Weight, empty: 480kg
Payload: 180kg
Engine: 4-cylinder, 2-cycle air-cooled, 100hp
Propeller: 3-blade, adjustable pitch, 1.5m diameter
Speed, take-off: 38 knots
Speed, cruising: 67.5 knots
Fuel tank: 25 litres
Range: 108n miles
  (with additional tank: 270n miles)
Cruising height over surface: 0.20 to 0.30m
  over waves: higher
Hull: Aluminium and glassfibre, ten water-tight sections
Trailer width, max: 2.25m

JÖRG III
A glassfibre 4- to 6-seater, 11.3m in length, built in Poland in 1980.

JÖRG IV
Craft built
1st craft: Skimmerfoil

Owner: G Jörg held at University of Stellenbosch, Cape Town, South Africa, built 1981
2nd craft built in 1983
In March 1985 a Jörg IV achieved an average speed of 158km/h over a distance of 145km at high ambient air temperatures in the Arabian Gulf.
Total wingspan: 5m
Length overall: 11m
Wing profile length: 3.9m
Max take-off weight: 1500–1700kg
Passengers: 4
Cruising speed: 127km/h
Installed power: 320hp (3.5-litre BMW car engine)
Average cruising height (calm water): 0.17m
Max flying height: 1.2m waves
Year of construction: 1981/82
Construction: Aluminium
Range: 500–600km
Endurance: 4–4.75 hours

JÖRG V
TAF VIII-4S
This new Jörg craft underwent its first ground

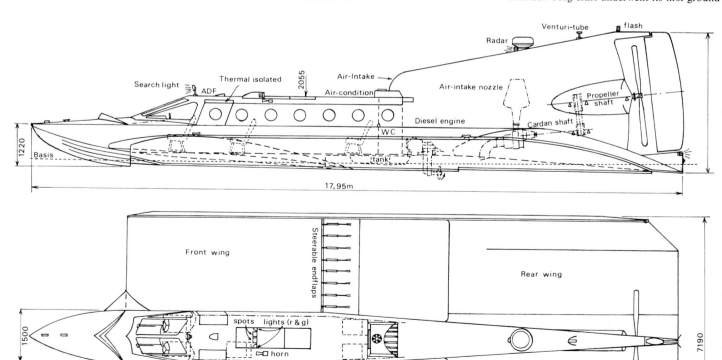

Layout of the Jörg Aerodynamic Ground Effect Craft TAF VIII-4S

TAF VIII-4S during ground test

tests in September 1986. Open sea tests in the North Sea started in September 1987.
Length overall: 17.95m
Speed: 80–165km/h (45–90 knots)
Passengers: 5–8
Weight: 3.5 tonnes
Flying height, calm water: 0.6m, higher over waves
Engines: One 650hp Textron Lycoming LTX 101 turboshaft with water-methanol injection available for 10 per cent power increase for take-off. One diesel engine driving a retractable marine propeller
Propeller: MT-P 4-blade, 2.9m diameter, cable/hydraulically controlled
Transmission: 9 V-belts (Optibelt, Höxter, W Germany)
Range: Up to 500km

PROJECT DESIGNS

Details of three project designs with passenger capacities of 15, 135 and 400 are given in *Jane's Surface Skimmers 1985*.

A new project design for 1990's development is the 19.8m Flairboat TAF VIII-5

A Jörg Airfoil Flairboat at high speed

FLAIRBOAT TAF VIII-5 (DESIGN)

Intended for river and inter-island traffic.
PRINCIPAL PARTICULARS
Length, overall: 19.80m
Width: 8.50m

Height: 4.65m
Draught: 0.40m
Hull: aluminium and composite plastics
Engines: two 634kW + diesel engine for manoeuvring

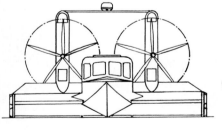

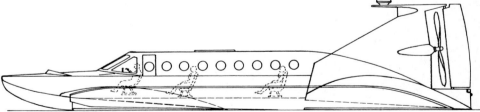

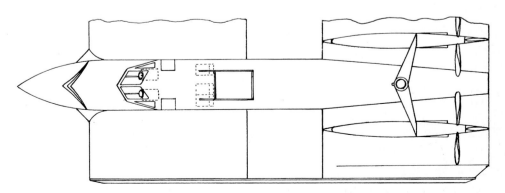

General arrangement of Jörg TAF VIII-5 Flairboat

Accommodation: passengers 12 to 15, crew 2
Speed, max: 108 knots
Speed, cruise: 95 knots
Range:200n miles
Weight: approx. 9200kg

Payload: 1.5 tonnes
Reference: For further information on Jörg Aerodynamic Ground Effect Craft please see paper: *History and Development of the Aerodynamic Ground Effect Craft (AGEC) with tandem wings*

by Dipl Ing G W Jörg. Proceedings of Ram Wing and Ground Effect Craft Symposium, Royal Aeronautical Society, London, 19 May 1987.

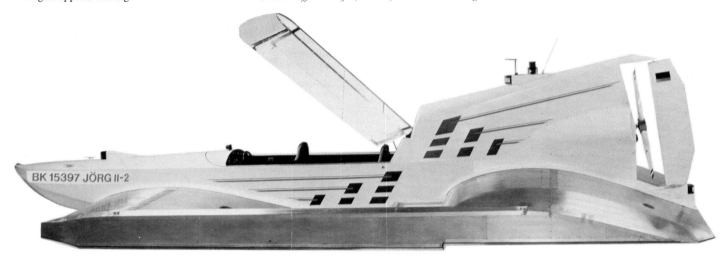

RHEIN-FLUGZEUGBAU GmbH (RFB)
[SUBSIDIARY OF MESSERSCHMITT-VÖLKOW-BLOHM]
Head Office and Main Works: Flugplatz, Postfach 408, D-4050 Mönchengladbach 1, Federal Republic of Germany

Telephone: (02161) 682–0
Telefax: (02161) 682200

Other Works:
Flugplatz, D-2401 Lübeck-Blankensee, Federal Republic of Germany

Dipl-Ing Alfred Schneider, *President*

RFB is engaged in the development and construction of airframe structural components, with particular emphasis on wings and fuselages made entirely of glassfibre-reinforced resins. Research and design activities include studies for the Federal German Ministry of Defence.

RFB X-113 Am during flight demonstration over Wattenmeer

Current manufacturing programmes include the series production of Fantrainer 400/600 and components and assemblies made of light alloy, steel, glass- and carbonfibre-reinforced resins for aircraft and quantity production. Manufacturing and maintenance of ejection seats and energy-absorbing armoured seats for helicopters. Emergency overhead oxygen boxes for airliners.

As a result of Dr Lippisch's work on the wing-in-ground-effect machine X-112 in the USA, RFB bought several of his patents and further developed the wing-in-ground-effect technology in close co-operation with Dr Lippisch.

After elaborate towing and wind tunnel tests supplemented by radio-control model tests, the X-113 was derived, a 1:1.7 scaled down version of

The RFB Airfish FF-2 showing its inflated wing structure

a four-seat craft. This single-seat trimaran-type craft, built of composite materials in a special sandwich construction developed by RFB, successfully underwent tests on Lake Constance in October 1970.

During additional trials, which were performed in autumn 1972 in the Weser estuary and the North Sea coastal region over rough water, the X-113's design and the chosen composite construction method proved fully effective.

The flight performance measurements confirmed the analytically expected improvements with respect to lift and drag resulting in gliding angles of 1:23 close to the surface. Even flights out of ground effect were successfully performed with gliding angles of 1:7 because of the low aspect ratio during this flight phase.

The X-113 showed inherent stabilities even with respect to altitude keeping. Speeds of 97 knots (180km/h) were achieved with a power of 28kW (38hp) in ground effect. The ability to achieve bank attitudes permits very small curve radii and excellent manoeuvrability. Remarkably good sea behaviour was shown from the outset. Take-offs and landings in wave heights of about 0.75m presented no problem.

AIRFISH FF2

Further application of the ground-effect technology resulted in a new two-seat sports vehicle, the Airfish FF2. This craft was developed and tested by Fischer Flugmechanik, Kiekenstrasse 88.2156, Willch 4, Proprietor Hanno Fischer, who at the same time is Technical Director of Rhein-Fluzeugbau GmbH (RFB). A license agreement exists with the aim of introducing the technology into operational use. This craft is powered by a 22kW (30hp) Rotax engine driving a shrouded fan. By means of a reduction gear low blade speed is achieved resulting in very low noise emission.

The light-weight vehicle with a mass of 260kg needs only small power. During the testing phase, which started in summer 1988, 11kW (15hp) showed sufficient for a 56 knot (100km/h) forward speed using the self-stabilising ground effect with automatic altitude keeping through the surface ram effect.

By virtue of its specific aerodynamic layout the vehicle always stays close to the ground allowing solely dynamic jumping over obstacles. This is possible using the stored kinetic energy which, however, does not permit continued free flight out of the ground effect. Thus the vehicle, like a hovercraft, can be defined as a boat without the necessity to apply aircraft regulations and to have a pilot licenced for its operation.

The current test programme is targeted to complete a vehicle for quantity production in 1989.

RFB X-114 AND -114H AEROFOIL BOATS

Evolved from the X-113, this six- to seven-seater has a maximum take-off weight of 1500kg and is fitted with a retractable wheel undercarriage, enabling it to operate from land or water.

Power is provided by a 200hp Lycoming IO-360 four-cylinder horizontally-opposed air-cooled engine driving a specially-designed Rhein-Flugzeugbau ducted fan. Range, with 100kg of fuel, is more than 1000km. Operational speed is 75 to 200km/h.

An initial trials programme was successfully completed in 1977. A new series of trials is now being undertaken after hydrodynamic modifications that included the fitting of hydrofoils beneath the sponsons, raising maximum take-off weight to 1750kg. In this configuration it is known as the X-114H.

The vehicle is designed to operate over waves up to 1.5m in ground effect and can therefore be

RFB X-114 Aerofoil boat with hydrofoils extended

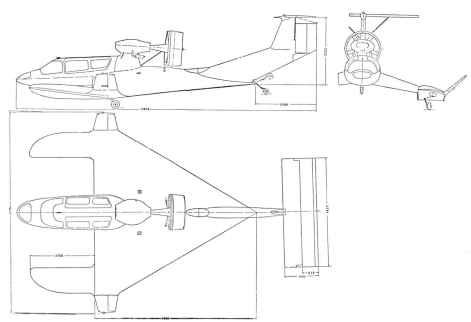

General arrangement of RFB X-114

Airfish FF2

used without restriction during 80 per cent of the year in the Baltic Sea area and 60 per cent of the year in the North Sea. In high seas of more than 1.5m, take-off and landing takes place in waters near the coast. Flying is virtually unrestricted, providing due allowance is made for the loss in economy.

Fuel consumption costs, while flying in ground

effect, are lower than those for cars. RFB states that its economics cannot be matched by any other form of transport aircraft.

Although built primarily as a research craft to extend the experience gained with the X-113 Am single-seater, Aerofoil boats of the size of the X-114 are suitable for air-taxi work along coastlines, the supervision of restricted areas, patrol, customs and coastguard purposes, and search and rescue missions.

Without any significant new research the construction of a vehicle with a take-off weight of approximately 18 000kg is possible. On a vehicle of this size, the ratio of empty weight to take-off weight is less than 50 per cent.

DIMENSIONS
Length overall: 12.8m
Wing span: 7m

Height overall: 2.9m
WEIGHTS
Max take-off
  X-114: 1500kg
  X-114H: 1750kg
Payload: 500kg
PERFORMANCE
Max cruising speed: 200km/h
Cruising speed in ground effect: 150km/h
Max flight range: 2150km

AIRFISH 3 (FLARECRAFT)

The latest wing-in-ground-effect project by RFB. Built from composite plastics, metal and fabric, an interesting feature of this craft is the incorporation of a retractable water rudder integrated with an electrically-driven propeller with two forward and one reverse gears.

PRINCIPAL PARTICULARS
Empty weight: 425kg
Crew: 160kg
Baggage: 30kg
Fuel: 35kg
Lift off weight: 650kg
Range: 200 miles
Endurance 2.5 h
Speed, lift off: 39 knots
Speed, taxi speed in hull step: 22 knots
Speed, cruise speed (in flare condition): 65 knots
Speed, max: 78 knots
Height above surface, in flare mode: 0.1 to 1.0m
Jump height: 4.5m
Jump distance: 90m

ITALY

RODRIQUEZ CANTIERI NAVALI SpA

Via S Raineri, 22–98100 Messina, Italy

Telephone: (090)7765
Telex: 980030 RODRIK I
Telefax: (090)775294

In September 1989 it was reported that the Rodriquez and Dornier companies were engaged in a joint venture to produce by the end of the 1990s a revolutionary high-speed 'ground effect' craft travelling at ten to twenty metres above the water that could compete with aircraft for medium-distance travel.

UNION OF SOVIET SOCIALIST REPUBLICS

CENTRAL LABORATORY OF LIFESAVING TECHNOLOGY (CLST)

Moscow, USSR

Yury Makarov, *Chief Engineer*
A W Gremyatsky, *Project Leader*
Evgeniy P Grunin, *Designer*
N L Ivanov, *Designer*
S Chernyavsky
Y Gorbenko
A Kuzakov, *Consultant*
V Shavrov, *Consultant*
A Baluyev, *Director of Flight Trials*

ESKA-1

The Central Laboratory of Lifesaving Technology (CLST), a division of the Rescue Organisation for Inland Waters (OSVOD), has designed a small aerodynamic ram-wing machine, capable of 140km/h, which will be used to answer distress calls on the Soviet lakes, rivers and canals. The Ekranolyetny Spasatyelny Kater-Amphibya (ESKA), surface-effect amphibious lifeboat is available in several versions. It has been referred to as the Ekranolet and the Nizkolet (skimmer).

Apart from meeting emergency situations on waterways, the craft, which is amphibious, is capable of operating in deserts, tundra, arctic icefields and steppeland. Derivatives are to be employed as support vehicles for geologists, communications engineers and construction groups.

In Soviet publications emphasis has been given to the potential value of such craft in opening up the mineral wealth of Siberia, the Soviet far-east, far-north and other virgin territories.

As with the X-113 Am and other machines of this type, the vehicle operates on the principle that by flying in close proximity to the ground, the so-called image flow reduces induced drag by about 70 per cent. Flight-in-ground-effect inhibits the downwash induced by wing lift, thus suppressing the induced drag. Whereas an average aircraft at normal flight altitude carries about 4kg per hp of engine output, the wing-in-ground-effect machine, on its dynamic air cushion carries up to 20kg, an improvement of more than 400 per cent. 'Weight

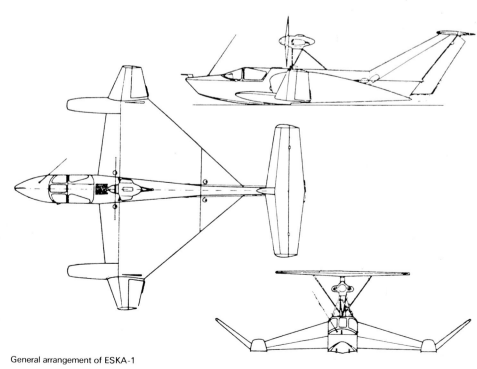

General arrangement of ESKA-1

efficiency' of the craft (ratio of useful load to all-up weight) is 25 to 50 per cent depending on size.

At angles of attack of 2 to 8 degrees near the ground, its lift is 40 to 45 per cent greater than when flying out of ground effect. In addition the supporting surface hinders the vortex flow from the lower wing surface to the upper surface which decreases induced drag.

Control of the ESKA is said to be easy and pilots require no special training. Within ground effect it is no more complicated to control than a car.

The design, which has been strongly influenced by the Lippisch 'aerofoil boat' concept, employs an almost identical short span, low aspect ratio reversed delta wing with anhedral on the leading edge, dihedral tips and wing floats. A description of ESKA-1 follows, together with illustrations of other aerodynamic machines designed at the CLST, including the saucer-shaped E-120 single-seater; the An-2E, which incorporates the fuselage, engine and cabin of the Antonov An-2W seaplane, and a two-seater powered by a 210hp Walter Minor engine.

One of the Ekranoplan's designers has been quoted as saying: 'Craft of this type are destined to become, in the not-too-distant future, as popular as hydroplanes, hovercraft and helicopters'.

ESKA-1

Research on aerodynamic ram wings began at CLST during 1971. During 1971–72 a series of small scale models were built, followed by the construction of five different full-size craft, including one with a circular planform.

The initial design of the ESKA-1 was prepared by Evgeniy Grunin between September and December 1972. In December 1972 the CLST section specialising in the provision of transport rescue facilities gave the design its full approval and accepted it for construction without additions or alterations.

Several free-flying models of the design were built and tested. In February 1973, A Gremyatsky was nominated leader of the project, and test-flew the first prototype in August of that year. Flight tests were subsequently undertaken by A A Baluyev.

Keynotes of the design were low cost, the use of advanced technology wherever possible and overall reliability in operation. In addition the craft had to be easily broken down for storing and transport by road. Analysis of these and other requirements and conditions led to the decision to build the craft in wood, using 1mm thick aviation ply, plastic foam, glassfibre, glues and varnishes. The resulting machine operated for more than four years in various conditions.

The designers state that although the ESKA-1 is similar aerodynamically to the late Dr Alexander Lippisch's X-112, X-113 Am and X-114, the basis of ensuring longitudinal stability and the hydrodynamics at take-off differ. They add, 'In the absence of data on the results of tests for those designs, we relied on our own experience and used the results obtained in our own experiments with model ram wings'.

Practical help in the preparation of the initial design was given by A Kuzakov, designer of the MAK-15 glider, and the late V B Shavrov (1899–1976), designer of the Sh-2. Another well-known Soviet aircraft designer, V B Gribovsky acted as a consultant in solving the design problems presented by certain joints and structural members.

The basic aerodynamic design and construction of ESKA-1 has provided sufficient data for it to be recommended as a rescue/patrol and communications craft for certain national assignments. The test results show a case for continuing development work on two or three ESKA-1 prototypes, built with modern materials. It has shown considerable operational potential.

POWERPLANT: Single 32hp M-63 four-stroke

ESKA-1

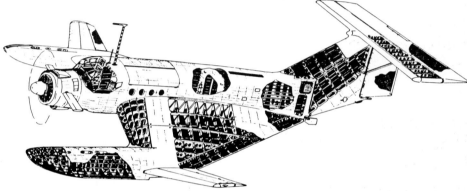

Cutaway of CLST ESKA adaptation of Antonov An-2W

two-cycle motorcycle engine drives, via a two-stage reduction gear, a wooden SDW-2 series 1.6m diameter constant pitch propeller. Engine is mounted on tubular steel tripod in dorsal position behind the cockpit. ST-4 electric starter mounted on engine block and driving the camshaft via a gear mounted on the extension shaft.

HULL: Built mainly of pinewood frames and longerons, with a box keel in plywood. Structure covered in aviation plywood with exterior clad in glass cloth saturated with ED-6 epoxy resin. Finished with white emulsion and synthetic varnish.

ACCOMMODATION: Cabin contains two aircraft seats in tandem with safety belts and space for parachutes. Rear seat for passenger or observer is placed close to centre of gravity so that no additional trimming is necessary when flying without a passenger.

WINGS: Cantilever shoulder-wing monoplane. Wooden monospar construction with leading edge covered in 1mm ply to form torque box. Dihedral tips each carry a wooden slotted aileron.

TAIL UNIT: Trapezium-shaped, strutted T-tail-plane mounted on top of fin by sheet metal fixtures. All-wooden single box spar structure. Fixed-incidence, single full-span elevator. Elevator and tailplane covered with AST-100 glass cloth. Wooden rudder secured to fin at two points.

LANDING GEAR: Wing-tip floats are made in pvc foam and covered with a single layer of ASTT3b/-S1 glass cloth. Each is attached to wing by four steel bolts.

CONTROLS: Single aircraft-type control column, incorporating engine throttle, located in the centre of cockpit ahead of pilot's seat. Conventional foot-operated bar to control rudder.

TESTING AND RECORDING EQUIPMENT:

In addition to basic aircraft-type instrumentation, the prototype ESKA-1 carried the following test equipment to record pitch and bank angles of up to 40 degrees: K12–51 oscilloscope; GS-6W equipment to measure pitch and angles of bank; synchronising equipment and an electrical supply pack, comprising an SAM28 27V battery and a PT-0.125–36/100 3F alternator.

RADIO: A modified portable 21 RTN-2-4M transmitter receiver provides a continuous radio link between ESKA-1 and the shore up to a distance of 2.5–3km.

DIMENSIONS

Wing span overall: 6.9m

Length: 7.55m

Height: 2.5m

Wing area: 13.85m²

Tail area: 3m²

WEIGHTS

All-up weight: 450kg

Empty: 230kg

Useful load: 220kg

Weight efficiency: 48.879%

PERFORMANCE

Speed, displacement condition: 30–40km/h
  planing on water: 50–60km/h
  ram flight at a height of 0.3–3m: 100–140km/h
  at altitude, 100–300m: 120–130km/h
  take-off: 55km/h
  landing: 50–55km/h

Take-off run from water: 80–100m
  from snow: 50–60m

Landing run on water (without braking parachute): 40m

Most effective flying height in surface effect: 0.3–1.5m

Max altitude, with 50% load, for obstacle clearance: Up to 50m

Range with full fuel supply: 300–350km
Wing loading: 32.5kg/m²
Power loading: 15kg/hp
Limiting weather conditions: Can operate in
Force 5 winds

CLST ANTONOV An-2E

This adaptation of the An-2 multi-duty 12-seat
biplane was built in 1973 to the design of E P
Grunin. It incorporates several major components
of the Soviet-built floatplane version, the An-2W,
including the forward fuselage, cabin and engine-
a 1000hp Shvetsov ASh-621R nine cylinder radial
air-cooled engine, driving a four-bladed variable-
pitch metal propeller.

The craft is intended for a range of utility appli-
cations in addition to carrying passengers and
freight. Like the RFB X-114, which is undergoing
trials in the German Federal Republic, the
An-2E has a retractable wheeled undercarriage
for operation from land as well as rivers, lakes
and coastal waters.
DIMENSIONS
Span: 15.75m
Length: 18.65m
Height: 8.1m
Lift area: 94m²
WEIGHT
All-up weight: 7000kg

CLST EKRANOLET E-120

No technical details have been released concerning this circular planform WIG single-seater.
One of a number of experimental wing-in-ground-
effect machines designed by the CLST, it was built
in 1971.

PARAWING EKRANOPLANS

The originator of the idea of applying Rogallo-
type flexible delta wings to light ekranoplans is
Evgeniy Grunin, one of the designers of the
ESKA-1. The parawing is well known for its outstanding aerodynamic qualities and stability and
is convenient for transport and storage. Grunin,
assisted by S Chernyavsky and N Ivanov, fitted a
flexible wing to the fuselage of the Czechoslovak
Let L-13J Blanik, a powered version of the well
known two-seat, all-metal sailplane. Power is supplied by a 42hp Jawa M-150 piston-engine driving
a 1.1m diameter Avia V210 propeller on a tripod
mounting aft of the cockpit, an arrangement
almost identical to that employed on ESKA-1.
The craft was designated the E-0773 Shmiel
(Bumblebee). Profiting from the encouraging
results of the flight trials, the team has designed a
number of small ekranoplan projects incorporating flexible wings, including a modified
version of the An-2W, the floatplane version of the
Antonov An-2, single-engine general-purpose
biplane.

R-1001 MANTA

In 1974 the Central Laboratory of Lifesaving
Technology developed a two-seater ekranoplan
for light liaison duties with the Soviet fishing fleet.
Visually the craft shows the influence of the late
Dr Alexander Lippisch's design studies for a 300-
ton Aerofoil boat, a major departure from the
Lippisch concept being the asymmetrically
located cabin jutting ahead of the broad aerofoil-
shaped hull on the port side. Reports suggest that
in building the wings and hull extensive use was
made of grp laminate reinforced with carbon
fibres.

Power is supplied by a 210hp Walter Minor

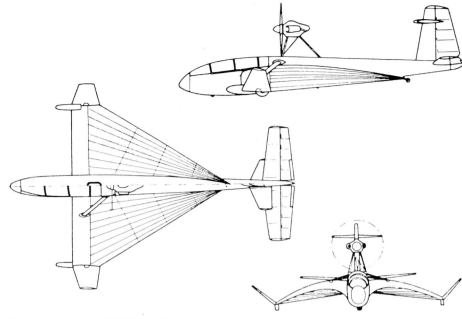

General arrangement of E-0773 Bumblebee 1

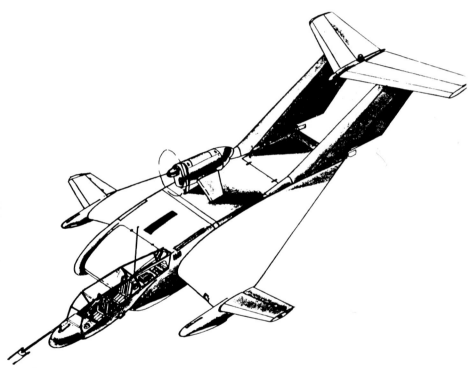

R-1001 Manta

VI engine of Czechoslovak manufacture, and the
craft has an all-up weight of 1460kg.

Dynamic models were used to gather design
data on stability, manoeuvrability and performance.

CLST ESKA EA-06

A developed version of ESKA-1, believed to
be a four-seater, began trials in September 1973,
one month after ESKA-1 made its first flight.
Photographs of a radio-controlled model of the

EA-06 indicate that its lines are similar to those
of ESKA-1, major differences being a wider
cabin with a full-view windscreen and an aft fuselage angled upwards to support the fin and
high-mounted tailplane well clear of the water.

The dynamically similar model was built to ¼
scale and had a wing span of 1.75m. Power was
supplied by a two-cylinder motor, developing
1.8hp at 12 500rpm, and driving a 300mm diameter laminated airscrew. Laminated balsawood
construction was employed.

OPERATORS

CIVIL OPERATORS OF HIGH-SPEED CRAFT

The following abbreviations are used in this section:

ALH	Air-lubricated hull craft
CAT	Catamaran vessel
F CAT	Foil-Catamaran vessel
HOV	Hovercraft, amphibious capability
HYD	Hydrofoil, surface piercing foils, fully immersed foils
MH	Mono-hull vessel*
SES	Surface effect ship or sidewall hovercraft (non-amphibious)
SWATH	Small-waterplane-area, twin-hull vessel

*Apart from a few exceptions only craft exceeding 20m are covered.

ANTIGUA

Caribbean Link

High-speed craft operated

Type	Name	In service
CAT Westamarin W86	Carib Link	1987

Routes operated
Antigua to Barbuda
Antigua to Montserrat
Antigua to Guadeloupe-Dominica

ARGENTINA

Alimar SA
Avenida Cordoba 1801 (Esq Callao), Codigo Postal 1120, Buenos Aires, Argentina

Telephone: 41–6919, 41–5914
Telex: 0121510ALMAR AR

High-speed craft operated

Type	Name	Seats	Delivered
HYD Rodriquez PT 50	Flecha de Buenos Aires	125	1962
HYD Rodriquez PT 50	Flecha de Colonia	125	1962
HYD Rodriquez PT 50	Flecha del Litoral	125	1963

Routes operated
Buenos Aires to Colonia, Uruguay (32n miles) and on by coach to Montevideo

AUSTRALIA

Ansett Transport Industries
Hayman Island, Queensland, Australia

Head Office: 501 Swanston Street, Melbourne, Victoria 3000, Australia

Telephone: (03) 6681334
Telex: 30085AA

High-speed craft operated

Type	Name	Seats	Delivered
MH Wavemaster International Ltd 35m	Sun Goddess Mk II	60	1984
MH Oceanfast 34.75m	Sun Paradise	96	1987

Boat Torque Cruises Pty Ltd
2nd Floor Suite 9, 23 Richardson Street, South Perth, Western Australia, Australia

High-speed craft operated

Type	Name	Seats
MH WaveMaster (Phil Curran) 32.3m	Sea Raider I	250
MH WaveMaster (Glen Williams) 41.0m	Star Flyte	506
MH WaveMaster (Glen Williams) 32.3m	Sea Spirit	250

Operation
Perth and Freemantle to Rottnest Island

Dignum Pty Ltd
Perth, Western Australia, Australia

High-speed craft operated

Type	Name	Seats	Delivered
MH SBF Engineering 27.50m	Sundancer V	160	1987

Route operated in 1987
Cairns to Port Douglas to Cooktown, 195n miles round trip. Craft now based in Brisbane

Fitzroy Island Resort
c/o Great Adventures Pty Ltd, PO Box 898, Cairns, Australia

Telephone: (070) 51 5644
Telex: 48284AA

K L Reddicliffe, *Manager, Cruise Operations*
John Kerr, *Resort Manager*

High-speed craft operated

Type	Name	Delivered
CAT International Catamarans Pty Ltd (Hobart)	Fitzroy Flyer	June 1981

Routes operated
Cairns to Green Island and Fitzroy Island

International Catamarans Pty Ltd *Fitzroy Flyer* at Cairns, March 1983

Gold Coast Water Bus Co Pty Ltd

12 Capri Commercial Centre, Isle of Capri, Gold Coast, Queensland 4217, Australia

Telephone: (075) 317951/920335

John Aitkenhead, *Managing Director*

High-speed craft operated

Type	Name	Seats	Delivered
ALH Stolkraft 10m	*Leo D Stolk*	41	January 1987
ALH Stolkraft 10m	*Lady Susan*	41	9 September 1987 (launched)

Routes operated

Shuttle service between Paradise Points and Nerang, Gold Coast, to be extended later to Brisbane via Sanctuary Cove

The first Stolkraft to enter service with the Gold Coast Water Bus Co

Gordon River Cruises Pty Ltd

PO Box 40, Strahan, Tasmania 7468, Australia

Telephone: (004) 71 7187/7281
Telex: 59284AA
Telefax: (004) 717317

R F Kearney, *Proprietor*
J A Kearney, *Proprietor*

High-speed craft operated

Type	Name	Seats	Delivered
MH SBF Engineering (Phil Curran)	*James Kelly II*	200	1983
MH WMI Engineering (Phil Curran)	*Gordon Explorer*	250	1985
MH SBF Engineering (Phil Curran) 19.95m	*Wilderness Seeker*	100	1986

Operations

High-speed cruising in Macquarie Harbour and Gordon River World Heritage area, 4½ hour trips
The three vessels have been carrying 90 000 passengers annually to the Gordon River

James Kelly II

Gordon Explorer

Wilderness Seeker

Great Adventures Pty Ltd

PO Box 898, Cairns, Australia

Telephone: (070) 515 644
Telex: 48284 GRTADV AA
Telefax: (070) 517 556

K L Reddicliffe, *Cruise Manager*
N W Langdon, *General Manager*

High-speed craft operated

Type	Name	Delivered
CAT NQEA InCat 23m	*Green Island Express*	June 1982
CAT NQEA InCat 23m	*Reef Adventure*	March 1984
CAT NQEA InCat 30m	*Reef Cat*	June 1986
CAT NQEA InCat 30m	*Reef King*	December 1987

Routes operated

Cairns to Green Island
Cairns to Michaelmas Cay (via Green Island)
Cairns to Outer Barrier Reef-Norman Reef (via Green Island)

Reef King, operated by Great Adventures Pty Ltd

Great Keppel Island Tourist Services Limited

(previously operating as Hydrofoil Seaflight Services Pty Ltd)
168 Denison Street, Rockhampton, Queensland, Australia

Telephone: (079) 336744/272948

Claude Diehm, *Director*
Claude Diehm (Jr), *Director*
David Diehm, *Director*
Andrew Diehm, *Director*
Helen Jackson (Mrs), *Director/Secretary*

High-speed craft operated

Type	Name	Seats	Delivered
CAT SBF Engineering	*Victory III*	448	1985
MH SBF Engineering	*Aqua Jet*	48	1985
CAT Precision Marine 35.6m	*Capricorn Reefseeker*	350	October 1987

Routes operated

Rosslyn Bay (Yeppoon) to Great Keppel Island
Rosslyn Bay (Yeppoon) to Carricornia Section, Great Barrier Reef, 90 min

Hamilton Island Enterprises

CNR Broadwater Avenue, Shute Harbour, Shute, Queensland, Australia

Telephone: (079) 466858
Telex: 46793AA

High-speed craft operated

Type	Name	Seats	Delivered
CAT NQEA InCat 24m	*Quickcat II*	195	1985
CAT InCat 31m WPC*	*2000*	-	Early 1988

* Wave-piercing catamaran leased for 3 months from Easter 1987

Route operated

Shute Harbour to Hamilton Island

Hayles Magnetic Island Pty Ltd

PO Box 411, Townsville, Queensland 4810, Australia
Telephone: (071) 71 6927

High-speed craft operated

Type	Name	Delivered
CAT NQEA InCat 22m	*Magnetic Express*	March 1983

Route operated

Townsville to Magnetic Island

Stern view of NQEA *Magnetic Express*

Hover Mirage

1st Floor, 12 Short Street, Southport 4215, Queensland, Australia

A member of the Quintex Group.

Gold Coast Terminal, Marina Mirage, 74 Seaworld Drive, Broadwater Spit, Main Beach, Qld. 4217

Brisbane Terminal, Dryandra Road, Brisbane Domestic Airport, Eagles Farm, Qld. 4007

Cpt D B Cranwell, *General Manager*
Cpt P Morrison, *Operations Manager*
I Leadbeater, *Engineering Manager*
B. Spencer, *Marketing Manager*

Telephone: 075 913144
Telex: 075 913389

High-speed craft operated

Type	Name	Seats	In service
HOVNQEA AP1–88	*Hover Mirage*	70	15 August 1987
HOV NQEA AP1–88	*Hover Mirage II*	70	12 September 1987

Hover Mirage and *Hover Mirage II*   (Yon Ivanovic)

NQEA AP1–88 *Mirage*

Routes operated

From 31 October 1988:
Marine Mirage (Gold Coast) to Brisbane Airport via Moreton Bay Islands and Wildlife National Park, A$74 single, A$98 return, 1h 40min.
Tour packages are also undertaken by Hover Mirage.
Also 2h trips from Marina Mirage through the Broadwater to Jumpinpin Bar and 1½h trips taking in South Stradbroke Island.

Incat Charters/MBM Management Pty Ltd

Melbourne, Victoria, Australia

High-speed craft operated

Type	Name	Seats	Delivered
CAT InCat (Hobart) 28m	*Spirit of Victoria**	217	1985
CAT InCat (Hobart) 31m	*Tassie Devil 2001**	200	1986
CAT NQEA InCat 18m	*Incat II* (ex *James Kelly I*)		1986
CAT NQEA InCat 20m	*Tassie Devil* (ex *Keppel Cat I*)		1986

*wave-piercing catamarans

Route operated

Hobart to Port Arthur
Tassie Devil 2001, first at Perth for the America's Cup 1986/87, then to Barrier Reef Island services

Tassie Devil 2001   (ZF AG)

Kalford Pty Ltd

Redcliffe, Queensland, Australia

High-speed craft operated

Type	Name	Seats	Delivered
CAT NQEA InCat 22m	*Cougar*	200	1984

Route operated

Moreton Bay to Brisbane

Low Island Cruises

Now operating under new company name: Quicksilver Connections Ltd. See entry on page 375.

Morrison Tourist Services

Tasmania, Australia

High-speed craft operated

Type	Name	Seats	Delivered
MH WaveMaster International	*Gordon Explorer*	-	1984

Route operated
Gordon River

Roylen Cruises

A Division of McLean's Roylen Cruises Pty Ltd
Harbour Road, Mackay Harbour, PO Box 169, Mackay,
Queensland, 4740 Australia

Telephone: (079) 553066
Telex: 48515 AA
Telefax: (079) 553186

Barry J Dean, *Manager*

High-speed craft operated

Type	Name	Seats	Delivered
CAT InCat (Hobart)	*Spirit of Roylen*	240	1982
CAT InCat (NQEA)	*Roylen Sunbird*	240	1987

Routes operated
Mackay to Great Barrier Reef (140km return)
Mackay to Hamilton Island (120km return)
Mackay to Lindeman Island (90km return)
Mackay to Brampton Island (40km return)

Peel's Tourist and Ferry Service Pty Ltd
P.O Box 197, Lakes Entrance 3909, Victoria, Australia

Telephone: (051) 551246/551527

Barrie Peel, *Proprietor*
Wayne Peel, *Proprietor*

High-speed craft operated

Type		Name	Seats	Delivered
CAT InCat (Hobart) } Bulls Marine Pty Ltd }	20.4m	*Thunderbird*	190	December 1984

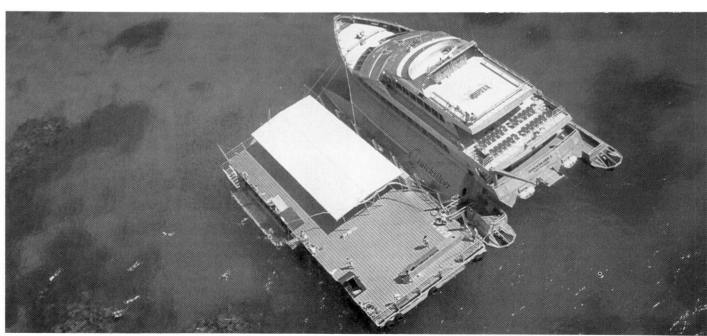

Peels InCat *Thunderbird*

Routes operated
Lakes Entrance to Paynesville and nearby lakes, channels and creeks

P & O Heron Island Resort

Queensland, Australia

High-speed craft operated

Type	Name	Seats	Delivered
CAT Precision Marine 30m	*Reef Adventurer II*	130 + 10t cargo	1987

Route operated
Heron Island to Gladstone

Queensland Government

Department of Harbours, Marine Boating and Fisheries Patrol, Thursday Island, Queensland

High-speed craft operated

Type	Name	Delivered
CAT NQEA InCat, 22m Cheetah Class	*Wauri*	1988

Quicksilver Connections Ltd

PO Box 171, Port Douglas, North Queensland, Australia 4871

Telephone: (070) 985373
Telex: 48969LOWISL AA
Telefax: (070) 985772

Jim Wallace, *Managing Director*
Jo Wallace, *Director*
Mike Burgess, *General Manager*
John F Lergessner, *Operations Manager*

A Quicksilver Connections wave-piercing catamaran engaged in reef viewing trip

High-speed craft operated

Type	Name	Seats	Delivered
CAT InCat (Hobart) 20.0m	*Quicksilver II (ex Low Isles Reef Express)**	153	June 1982
CAT InCat 30.0m WPC	*Quicksilver IV*	193	August 1985
CAT InCat 37.2m WPC	*Quicksilver V*	340	November 1988
CAT InCat 37.2m WPC	*Quicksilver VI*	340	February 1988
CAT InCat 37.2m WPC	*Quicksilver VII*	340	September 1989

The NQEA InCat *Quicksilver III* was sold to an operator, and *Quicksilver IV* was up for sale at the end of 1989.

Routes operated
*Port Douglas to Low Isles, 8 n miles, 25 min
Port Douglas to Cooktown, 62 n miles, 2h 30 min
Port Douglas to Agincourt Reef North, 39 n miles, 1h 30 min
Port Douglas to Cairns, 36 n miles, 1h 10 min, A$ 15

Reef Link Pty Ltd
197 Flinders Street, Townsville, Queensland 4810, Australia

Telephone: (077) 725733
Telex: 47381REEFCT AA

Douglas Tarca, *Managing Director*

High-speed craft operated

Type	Name	Seats	Delivered
CAT NQEA InCat 22m			
CAT NQEA InCat 30m	*Reef Link*	190	1983

Reef Link 2 cabin was largely destroyed by electrical fire in the middle of 1987 but was subsequently re-built and back in operation in January 1988.

Route operated
Townsville to John Brewer Reef

Roylen Cruises
A Division of McLean's Roylen Cruises Pty Ltd
Harbour Road, Mackay Harbour, PO Box 169,
Mackay,
Queensland, 4740 Australia

Telephone: (079) 553066
Telex: 48515 AA
Telefax: (079) 553186

Barry J Dean, *Manager*

High-speed craft operated

Type	Name	Seats	Delivered
CAT InCat (Hobart)	*Spirit of Roylen*	240	1982
CAT InCat (NQEA)	*Roylen Sunbird*	240	1987

Routes operated
Mackay to Great Barrier Reef (140km return)
Mackay to Hamilton Island (120km return)
Mackay to Lindeman Island (90km return)
Mackay to Brampton Island (40km return)

Scenic Gordon & Hells Gates Charters
See entry under Gordon River Cruises Pty Ltd under which name the company now operates

South Molle Island Resort
South Molle Island, Queensland, Australia

Telex: 48132AA

S G McMullen, *General Manager*
Jock Collins, *Marine Manager*

High-speed craft operated

Type	Name	Seats	Delivered
CAT NQEA InCat 23.0m	*Telford Reef*	204	October 1982
CAT NQEA InCat 29.2m	*Telford Capricorn*	326	November 1983

State Transit Authority of New South Wales
Ferry Division, 6th Floor, 19 Pitt Street, Sydney, New South Wales 2000, Australia

Telephone: 2413734
Telex: 177609AA
Telefax: 2514149

O P Eckford, *General Manager, Ferry Services*
N Hornsby, *Technical Services Manager*

High-speed craft operated

Type	Name	Seats	Delivered
HYD Rodriquez PT 50	*Long Reef*	140	1969
HYD Rodriquez RHS 140	*Curl Curl*	140	January 1973
HYD Rodriquez RHS 160F	*Manly*	235	1984
HYD Rodriquez RHS 160F	*Sydney*	235	1985
CAT NQEA 36.0m InCat	—	—	March 1990
CAT NQEA 36.0m InCat	—	—	July 1990
CAT NQEA 36.0m InCat	—	—	September 1990

Dee Why and *Fairlight* sold for scrap, 1988

Route operated
Sydney (Circular Quay) to Manly (7n miles), 15 min
Fare, single: A$4.00

Long Reef approaching Manly terminal

Tadolan Pty Ltd
Cairns, Queensland, Australia

High-speed craft operated

Type	Name	Seats	Delivered
MH SBF Engineering 15.0m	*Fitzroy Reef Jet*	54	1987

Tangalooma Island Resort Ltd
Moreton Island, Queensland 4004 and Cnr.Kingsford Smith Drive & Harvey Street, P O Box 1102, Eagle Farm, Queensland, 4007 Austrailia

Telephone: (075)2686722
Telefax: (07)2686106 AA

Brian Osborne, *Director*

High-speed craft operated

Type	Name	Delivered
CAT International Catamarans Pty Ltd (Hobart) 20.0m	*Tangalooma*	December 1981

Route operated
Brisbane to Moreton Island, 26 n miles, 1h 10min
In period 1 July 1988 to 30 June 1989 43300 passengers were carried each way on the Brisbane to Moreton Island route.In addition approximately 980 tonnes of cargo were carried

Tasmanian Ferry Services
This company will take delivery of a 74m International Catamarans WPC in December 1990. This vessel will carry 350 passengers and 70 cars and will operate between George Town, Tasmania and Port Welshpool, Victoria across The Bass Strait. Trip time will be 4h 10 min.

AUSTRIA

Donau-Dampfschiffahrts-Gesellschaft (DDSG)
Reisedienst, Handelskai 265, A-1021 Vienna, Austria

Telephone: (222) 266536
Telex: 131698A

Hans Kreuzer, *Director*
Dr Helmut Zolles, *General Manager*
Dr Leopold Vavra, *General Manager*

High-speed craft operated

Type	Name	Seats	Delivered
SES Vosper Hovermarine HM 221	*Donaupfeil*	80	February 1986

Route operated
Vienna to Budapest (180n miles)

Vosper Hovermarine HM 221 80-seat *Donaupfeil*　　　　　(DDSG)

BAHRAIN, STATE OF

Coastguard Directorate
Ministry of the Interior, Public Security, PO Box 13, Bahrain

Telephone: 700000
Telex: 9572CGD BN

Col Abdul Aziz A Al-Khalifa, *Director*

High-speed craft operated
HOV Air Vehicles Tiger

Operations
General purpose search and rescue

BELGIUM
Eurosense Technologies NV
Nervierslaan 54, B-1810 Wemmel, Belgium

Telephone: (02) 460 7000
Telex: 26687B
Telefax: (02) 460 4958

E Maes, *Managing Director*
J Van Rensbergen, *Project Manager*

High-speed craft operated

Type	Name	Delivered
BHC SR.N6–1S (converted by Hoverwork to a survey craft)	*Beasac** (ex *Freedom*)	April 1984

*BELFOTOP-Eurosense Acoustic Sounding Air Cushion platform

Operation
BELFOTOP (Belgian Fotographic Topology) employs a Hoverwork-converted BHC SR.N6–1S for Belgian coast hydrographic survey and remote sensing work. The craft is based at Zeebrugge on behalf of the Ministry of Works.

Beasac hydrographic survey platform engaged in high-speed near-shore bathymetric surveys

Règie voor Maritime Transport (RTM)
Belliardstraat 30, B-1040 Brussels, Belgium

Telephone: (02) 2300180
Telex: 23851REMATB B
Telefax: (02) 2311480

Ir P Muyldermans, *General Director* (5 Natiënkaai, B-8400 Ostend, Belgium)
E Depraetere, *Commercial Director* (30 Belliardstraat , B-1040 Brussels, Belgium)
F Engelen, *Marketing Director* (30 Belliardstraat, B-1040 Brussels Belgium)

High-speed craft operated

Type	Name	Seats	Delivered
HYD Boeing Jetfoil 929–115	*Princesse Clémentine*	280	May 1981
HYD Boeing Jetfoil 929–115	*Prinses Stephanie*	280	1981

Route operated
Ostend to Dover (64n miles, 1 hour 40min)
Passengers carried in 1988: 302 815

Boeing Jetfoil 929–115 *Princess Clementine* of RTM

BOLIVIA

Crillon Tours SA
PO Box 4785, Avenida Camacho 1223, La Paz, Bolivia

Telephone: 350363; 374566/67; 372970
Telex: 2557CRITUR BV

Darius Morgan, *President*
Elsa Morgan, *General Manager*
Helmut Kock, *Hydrofoil Designer and Consultant*

　　Crillon Tours SA was founded in 1959 by Darius Morgan and started its hydrofoil services on Lake Titicaca in 1966. Their first craft was the *Inca*

Arrow, an Albatross type built by the Ludwig Honold Manufacturing Co. Three more hydrofoils were added in the next ten years, followed in 1976 by the first Bolivian hydrofoil, the *Bolivia Arrow.* A sister operation is undertaken on Lake Itaipu in Paraguay by Darius Morgan's other company, Aliscafos Itaipu SA.

High-speed craft operated

Type	Name	Delivered
HYD Ludwig Honold Manufacturing Co	*Inca Arrow*	1966
HYD Ludwig Honold Manufacturing Co	*Bolivia Arrow*	1976
HYD Ludwig Honold Manufacturing Co	*Andes Arrow*	
HYD Ludwig Honold Manufacturing Co	*Copacabana Arrow*	
HYD Ludwig Honold Manufacturing Co	*Titicaca Arrow*	
HYD Ludwig Honold Manufacturing Co	*El Sol Arrow*	
HYD Seaflight SpA H.57	*Sun Arrow*	1976

Route operated
Lake Titicaca, serving La Paz, Huatajata, Sun Island, Copacabana, Juli, Puno, Tiahuanacu, Guaqui, Pako

Five hydrofoils of the Crillon fleet on Lake Titicaca

Hovermarine Titikaka Transport
PO Box 3371, St Yanacocha No 300 of No 1, La Paz, Bolivia

Telephone: 343354/350339/352547/354945
Telex: 5490BX

High-speed craft operated

Type	Name
SES Vosper Hovermarine HM 218	*Rey del Titikaka*
SES Vosper Hovermarine HM 218	*Reina del Titikaka*

Not operating since 1985

Route previously operated (Bolivia to Peru)
La Paz to Copancara to Sun Island to Juli to Puno

BRAZIL

Aerobarcos do Brasil, Transportes Maritimos e Turismo SA (TRANSTUR)
Avenida Amaral Peixoto 71, 11° Andar, Niterói 24020 RJ, Brazil

Telephone: 7197070

Hamilton Amarante Carvalho, *Director President*
Luiz Paulo Amarante Carvalho, *Technical Director*
Vicente Oliveros Perez, *Financial Director*
Tse Min Hsu, *Administrative Director*

High-speed craft operated

Type	Name	Seats	Delivered
HYD Rodriquez PT 20	*Flecha do Rio*	83	1970
HYD Rodriquez PT 20	*Flecha de Niterói*	83	1971
HYD Rodriquez PT 20	*Flecha das Ilhas*	83	1972
HYD Rodriquez PT 20	*Flecha de Itaipú*	83	1972
HYD Rodriquez RHS 110	*Flecha de Angra**	150	1976
SES Hovermarine HM 216	*Gávea*	65	1976
SES Hovermarine HM 216	*Gragoatá*	65	1976
SES Hovermarine HM 216	*Guaratiba*	65	1976
HYD Rodriquez PT 20	*Flecha de Ipanema*	85	1978
HYD Rodriquez PT 20	*Flecha de Icaraí**	85	1978
HYD Rodriquez PT 20	*Flecha da Ribeira**	85	1978

*These three craft are ex *Flying Phoenix,* ex *Flying Kingfisher* and ex *Flying Heron,* previously with Hongkong Macao Hydrofoil Co 1978. Only one believed to be operating.

Routes operated	Passengers in 1986
Rio de Janeiro-Niterói (5 mins, 2.8 miles)	2371 159
Rio de Janeiro-Ribeira (Ilha do Governador) (12 mins, 5.5 miles)	212 425*
Rio de Janeiro-Paquetá Island (20 mins, 9.2 miles)	216 678

* temporarily stopped

TRANSTUR RHS 110 *Flecha de Angra* ex Hongkong Macao Hydrofoil Co
(TRANSTUR)

TRANSTUR Rodriquez PT 20

Norsul Offshore SA
Av Augusto Severo 8, Rio de Janeiro, Brazil

Telephone: (021) 292 0122
Telex: (021) 22115

Delmas Abreu Penteado, *Managing Director*
Aristido Reichert, *Administrative/Financial Manager*
Julio Cesar G de Andrade, *Operations Manager*
Oswaldo Thielmann Jnr, *Contracts Manager*
Rufo Belligotti *Technical and Maintenance Manager*

High-speed craft operated

Type	Name	Seats	Delivered
MH Swiftships	*Parintins*	39	1972
MH Swiftships	*Parati*	39	1972
MH Swiftships	*Penedo*	39	1972
MH Breaux's Bay	*Palmares*	36	1975
MH Breaux's Bay	*Pelotas*	36	1975
MH Breaux's Bay	*Penalva*	36	1975
MH Breaux's Bay	*Piracicaba*	36	1975
CAT Fjellstrand	*Norsul Catamarã*	96 +	1982
		15 tonnes cargo	

Fjellstrand *Catamarã* belonging to Norsul Offshore SA

Operation
Offshore support along Brazilian coast with bases in Macaé, Natal, Fortaleza, Aracajú and Belém

BRUNEI

Brunei Shell Petroleum Company Sendirian Berhad
Seria, Negara Brunei Darussalam

Telephone: (673) 3 73999
Telex: 3313BU

High-speed craft operated

Type	Name	Seats	Delivered
CAT Marinteknik Shipbuilders (S) Pte Ltd Marinjet CV 1800	*Hakeem*	50 (light cargo)	1985

Owner: Dart Marine Offshore SA
Charterer: Brunei Shell Petroleum Co Sdn Bhd
Operator: Ocean Tug Services (Sdn Bhd), Jasra Group

Marinteknik Marinjet CV 1800 crew boat *Hakeem*

Operations
Delivered to the Brunei Shell Marine Department for a 5-year charter mainly for transportation services to the Fairley and Ampa offshore oil fields, *Hakeem* is based at Kuala Belait

BULGARIA

Navigation Maritime Bulgare (NAVIBULGAR)
Varna, Bulgaria

High-speed craft operated

Type	Name	GRT	Delivered
HYD S Ordzhonikidze	*Kometa 1*	127	1965
HYD S Ordzhonikidze	*Kometa 2*	127	1966
HYD Sormovo	*Kometa 3*	142	1966
HYD Sormovo	*Kometa 6*	136	1973
HYD S Ordzhonikidze	*Kometa 7*	142	1974
HYD S Ordzhonikidze	*Kometa 8*	142	1974
HYD Sormovo	*Kometa 9*	136	1975
HYD Sormovo	*Kometa 10*	142	1975
HYD Sormovo	*Kometa 11*	147	1975
HYD Sormovo	*Kometa 12*	142	1976

CAMEROON

SURF SA
See entry under France.

CANADA

Canadian Coast Guard Hovercraft Units
The Canadian Coast Guard (CCG) operates two Hovercraft Units, administered from CCG Headquarters in Ottawa, with operational tasking controlled by the Region in which they are based.

Headquarters Administration: Fleet Aviation Office, Fleet Systems Directorate, Canadian Coast Guard, (CCG), 8th Floor, Tower 2, Canada Building, 344 Slater Street, Ottawa, Ontario K1A 0N7, Canada

Telephone: (613) 998 1617
Telefax: (613) 995 4700

T F Melhuish *Manager*

Canadian Coast Guard SR.N6 (086) at Vancouver Airport, 2 October1986

West Coast Canada
Canadian Coast Guard Hovercraft Unit: PO Box 23968, AMF, Vancouver International Airport, British Columbia V7N 1T9, Canada

Telephone: (604) 273 2556

J McGrath, *Officer in Charge*

This Unit also has a sub-base:
PO Box 2410, Parkesville, British Columbia V0R 2S0, Canada

Telephone: (604) 248 2724

J Palliser, *Officer in Charge*

The Canadian Coast Guard Hovercraft Unit in Vancouver was formed in 1968 for hovercraft evaluation in search and rescue and other coast guard duties.

High-speed craft operated

Type	Commissioned
HOV BHC SR.N6, serial No 039, CH-CGB, purchased from BHC	1977
HOV BHC SR.N6, serial No 031, CH-CGD, rebuilt by unit	1981
HOV BHC SR.N6, serial No 030, CH-CCG, rebuilt by unit	April 1986
(HOV BHC SR.N5, serial No 021 was retired and scrapped in April 1986)	

Operations
Patrol area is the Straits of Georgia and Gulf Islands (500 square miles), although search and rescue duties are undertaken outside this area. The average patrol distance is 80 miles.

The Unit commenced operations with SR.N5 021 in 1968 in the search and rescue role quickly establishing itself and within 5 years was responding to over 900 calls per year. The craft's speed and versatility made it ideal for other CCG roles, amongst which are light station servicing, buoy maintenance, ship inspections, shore patrols, pollution control, and emergency work with other agencies. In 1977, the additional work justified a second craft, and SR.N6 039 was purchased. Soon afterwards, new fishing fleet activities resulted in a northward extension of the SAR cover provided, and in 1980–81, the first of two old SR.N6 craft previously purchased was completely rebuilt and commissioned by Unit personnel, enabling a sub-base at Parkesville, some 90km north of Vancouver to be built and equipped with one SR.N6, becoming operational early 1982. By 1984, the SR.N5 was reaching the end of her economical life, and the second old SR.N6 began to be rebuilt, finally commissioning in April 1986, when 021 was retired.

All the craft are comprehensively equipped with sophisticated communications and navigation equipment, Night-sun searchlights (65 million candle power), auxiliary fuel tanks, firefighting equipment, and a full range of medical equipment, with stretchers, and oxygen equipment. The craft are on operational call 24 hours a day.

Eastern Canada
Laurentian Region ACV Unit
850, Nun's Island Boulevard, Nun's Island, Quebec H3E 1H2, Canada

Telephone: (514) 283 5841

D L'Heureux, H Goulet, *Craft Captains*

High-speed craft operated

Type	Name	Commissioned
HOV BHC AP1–88/200, serial No 006, CH-CCG, serial No 201	*Waban-Aki*	Sept 1987

Textron Marine Systems (ex Bell Aerospace) Voyageur, serial No 002, CH-CGA, commissioned in 1974 was finally sold for scrap in 1988

Operations
This Unit started operations by evaluating the potential of hovercraft in the Montreal District of the Laurentian Region, and in 1980 was integrated into the CCG Fleet operating in that region. In 1974–75, the Voyageur demonstrated remarkable capabilities for ice-breaking in the St Lawrence and its tributaries, and has been used extensively every winter to break and manage ice in shallow water, and for flood relief.

Voyageur was replaced in September 1987 with a BHC AP1–88/200 designed with a forward well-deck equipped with an easily removable crane, together with a hydraulic capstan and winch. As well as icebreaking in the winter, *Waban-Aki* maintains marine aids to navigation along some 350 miles of the St Lawrence river and also responds to SAR incident calls.

Ice Control Enterprises Inc
40 Forest Avenue, Hamilton, Ontario L8N 1X1, Canada

Telephone: (416) 528 4283
Telefax: (416) 529 7097

D S Schroeder, *President*

and

Jones, Kirwan and Associates
Box 4406, Station D, Hamilton, Ontario L8V 4L8, Canada

This company owns the Air Trek Systems Ltd Air Trek 140 which was used for commercial ice-breaking work during the winters of 1985/86 and 1986/87 in a number of locations in Ontario and Quebec.

CARIBBEAN

Oy AW Line AB, chartering for Caribbean operation

High-speedcraft operated

Type	Name	Seats	In Operation
CAT Fjellstrand 38.8m	*Blue Manta (ex Sea Cat)*	230	1989

Routes operated
Martinique, Granada, St Vincent, St Lucia, Dominique, Guadeloupe, Antiqua, St Bartholomew, St Martin

CHINA, PEOPLE'S REPUBLIC

Changjiang Shipping Administration Bureau
Shanghai, People's Republic of China

High-speed craft operated

Type	Delivered
SES Vosper Hovermarine HM 218, serial No 129*	1983
SES Vosper Hovermarine HM 218, serial No 130*	1983
*purchased from The Hong Kong & Yaumati Ferry Co Ltd	

Routes operated
Shekou (China) to Pearl River and Aberdeen (Hong Kong)

China Air Cushion Technology Development Corporation (CACTEC)
Head Office: 9 Qi Xiang Nan Li, Binhu Road, Tianjin, People's Republic of China

Telephone: 331859/333339
Cable: 3333

Branch Office: 171 Gaoxion Road, Shanghai, People's Republic of China

Telex: 770539

Formed in 1984, CACTEC, subordinated to China State Shipbuilding Corporation (CSSC), is a specialised business corporation. Jointly with MARIC the corporation deals with a wide variety of applications of the air cushion principle, and lays emphasis on the research, development, design and production of both amphibious hovercraft and sidewall hovercraft.

High-speed craft operated

Type	Seats	Delivered
SES MARIC 7203	81	September 1982
SES MARIC 719	186	1984
HOV MARIC 716 II	32	1985

Chong-Qing Ship Transportation Co
Shi Chuan Province, People's Republic of China

High-speed craft operated

Type	Name	Seats	Delivered
SES Dong Feng MARIC 717 III	Min Jiang	54–60	September 1984
SES Dong Feng MARIC 717 III	Jin Sha Jiang	54–60	1987
SES Dong Feng MARIC 717 III	Jin Ling Jiang	54–60	1987

Operation
Chong Qing to Yi Bin, 200 n miles
Chong Qing to Lu Zhou, 135 n miles

Chong-Qing Ferry Boat Company
Shi Chuan Province, People's Republic of China

High-speed craft operated

Type	Name	Seats	Delivered
SES Dong Feng MARIC 717 II	Chong Qing	70	October 1984
SES Dong Feng MARIC 717 II	Yu Xiang	70	

Route operated
Yangtze River between Chong Qing and Fu Ling, 65 n miles

Yu Xiang, delivered in September 1989 operates from Hang Zhou to Chong Qing, 1512 n miles along the Great Canal and Yangtze River through the spectacular 'Three Gorge' area.

Chu Kong Shipping Co Ltd (CKS)
see Zhen Hing Enterprises Co Ltd

Geophysical Surveys Inc USA)

High-speed craft operated

Type	Delivered
HOV Griffon Hovercraft 1000 TD	1985
HOV Griffon Hovercraft 1000 TD	1985
HOV Griffon Hovercraft 1000 TD	1985

Operation
Survey contract in China

Government Panyu County Branch

High-speed craft operated

Type	Name	Seats	Built
HYD Hitachi PT50	Guia*	126	1964

* Class withdrawn 31 July 1987

Guangdong Province Hong Kong Macau Navigation Co

High-speed craft operated

Type	Name	Seats	Delivered
CAT A Fai Engineers and Shiprepairers InCat 21.9m	Mingzhu Hu	150	1982
CAT A Fai Engineers and Shiprepairers InCat 21.9m	Yin Zhou Hu	150	1982
CAT A Fai Engineers and Shiprepairers InCat 21.9m	Liuhua Hu	150	1982

Routes operated
Taiping and Jiangmen to Hong Kong

Guangdong San Fu Passenger and Cargo Transport Associate Co

High-speed craft operated

Type	Name	Seats	Delivered
CAT A Fai Engineers and Shiprepairers InCat 21.0m	Jin Shan Hu	150	September 1984

Hue Yang Ao Tougang Industrial Ltd
People's Republic of China

High-speed craft operated

Type	Name
SES Korea Tacoma Marine Industries Ltd 18m	Tacoma II

Route operated
Hong Kong to Chinchun

Jian Gang Passengers Transport Co
c/o Chu Kong Shipping, 28 Connaught Road West, 7th floor, Hong Kong

High-speed craft operated

Type	Name	Seats	Delivered
CAT Fjellstrand 31.5m	Peng Lai Hu	291	1985

Route operated
Jiangmen to Kowloon (Hong Kong)

Jiangmen Jiang Gang Passenger Traffic Co
85 Dizhong Road, Jiangmen, Guangdong, People's Republic of China

Telephone: 32421/32438

Li Bai, *Manager*

High-speed craft operated

Type	Name	Seats	Delivered
MH Marinteknik Singapore, 35m (Yard No 110)	Wu Yi Hu	265	1987
CAT WaveMaster International	Zhen Xing	310	1990

Route operated
Jiangmen to Hong Kong (81n miles)

Nantong High Speed Passenger Ship Co
Nantong, People's Republic of China

High-speed craft operated

Type	Name	Seats	Delivered
CAT Westamaran 120 (ex W88)	Zi Lang	354	1987
CAT Austal Ships 36m		430	1990

Route operated
Shanghai to Nantong

Ningbo Huagang Ltd
No 2–2 86 Lane, Bai Sha Road, Ningbo, People's Republic of China

High-speed craft operated

Type	Name	Seats	Delivered
CAT Fjellstrand 38.8m	Yong Xing	312	November 1985

Route operated
Ningbo to Shanghai

Fjellstrand 38.8m *Yong Xing*

Sanfu Shipping China

High-speed craft operated

Type	Name	Seats	Delivered
CAT A Fai Engineers & Shiprepairers Ltd InCat 21.0m	Jin San Hu	150	1985
CAT Wave Master 32.0m	Yin Shan Hu	252	July 1989

Shanghai Municipality

People's Republic of China

High-speed craft operated

Type	In service
SES Wu-Hu Shipyard MARIC 719 II	August 1988

Route operated

Shanghai to Zhon Ming Island

MARIC 719 II 257 seat, 28 knot SES built by Wu-Hu Shipyard

Shen Zhen Shipping

People's Republic of China

High-speed craft operated

Type	Name	Delivered
CAT A Fai Engineers and Shiprepairers InCat 21.0m	Yue Hai Chun	1984
CAT A Fai Engineers and Shiprepairers InCat 21.0m	Shen Zhen Chun	1985
CAT A Fai Engineers and Shiprepairers InCat 21.0m	Zhu Hai Chun	December 1986

Shenzou Transport Company

People's Republic of China

High-speed craft operated Type

SES Hovermarine HM 218

Shun Gang Passenger Corporation Co Ltd

c/o The Foreign Economics and Trading Committee of Shun De District, Shun De, Guangdong, People's Republic of China

High-speed craft operated

Type	Name	Delivered
CAT FBM Marinteknik (S) Marinjet 33CPV (Yard No 112)	Shun De	November 1987

Wuzhou Navigation Co

High-speed craft operated

Type	Name	Seats	Delivered
CAT A Fai Engineers & Shiprepairers Ltd InCat 21m	Lijiang	150	1983

Route operated

Wuzhou to Hong Kong

Yuet Hing Marine Services

People's Republic of China

High-speed craft operated

Type	Name	Seats	Delivered
CAT Precision Marine 39.70m	Xin Ning	280	1988

Route operated

Pearl River estuary area

Zhao Gang Steamer Navigation Company

Harbour Building, Oong Nong Road North, Zhaoqing, Guangdong, People's Republic of China

High-speed craft operated

Type	Name	In service
CAT Marinteknik JC-3000	Duan Zhou Hu (ex Triton Jet)	September 1986

Route operated

Zhaoqing to Hong Kong, 143n miles, 5 hours. One single trip per day.

Zhen Hing Enterprises Co Ltd

c/o **Chu Kong Shipping**, 28 Connaught Road West, 7th floor, Hong Kong

High-speed craft operated

Type	Name	Seats	Delivered
CAT Fjellstrand 31.5m	Bei Xiu Hu	289	1983
CAT Fjellstrand 31.5m	Li Wan Hu	289	1984
CAT Fjellstrand 31.5m	Xiu Li Hu	291	1984
CAT Fjellstrand 31.5m	Qiong Zhou Ui Hao*	291	1984
CAT Fjellstrand 31.5m	Yi Xian Hu	291	1985
CAT Fjellstrand 38.8m	Tian Lu Hu (ex Jasarina)		1985
CAT WaveMaster 32.0m	Yim Shan Hu	252	April 1989
CAT WaveMaster 32.0m			April 1990

Route operated

Zhong Shan to Kowloon (Hong Kong)

Fjellstrand 31.5m Xiu Li Hu

Fjellstrand 38.8m catamaran Tian Lu Hu

CZECHOSLOVAKIA

Ckeskoslovenská Plavba Dunajská (Czechoslovak Danube Navigation)

Ulica Cervenej Armády 35, 815 24 Bratislava, Czechoslovakia

Telephone: (7) 572 71
Telex: 92338CSPD C
Telefax: (7)58801
Juraj Pavelek, *General Manager*
Pavel Sestak, *Manager Technical*
Ivan Kucik, *Manager of Navigation*

High-speed craft operated

HYD Voskhod
HYD Meteor

Routes operated

Vienna to Bratislava, 1 hr, fare 115 ATS (US $8.20)
Bratislava to Vienna, 1 hr 15 min, fare 115 ATS (US $8.20)
Bratislava to Budapest, 4 hr 30 min, 467 ATS (US $33.30)
Budapest to Bratislava, 4 hr 30 min, 467 ATS (US $33.30)

DENMARK

Bornholm Express
Nordbornholms Turistbureau, Hannershusvej 2, Sandvig, DK-3770 Allinge, Bornholm, Denmark

High-speed craft operated

Type	Name	Seats	In service
CAT Westamarin W86	*Bornholm Express* (ex *Steigtind*)	182	June-August 1986 June onwards 1987

*includes upper deck accommodation for 24

Route operated
Simrishamn (Sweden) to Allinge (Bornholm), Denmark, 1 hour

Bornholmerpilen A/S
The following boats were chartered April to October 1989.
Westamarin Catamarans:
  Sundhordland, Midthorland and *Vindile* for the Ronne to Kastrup route, 2.5h

A/S Dampskibsselskabet Øresund (DSØ)

Flyvebådene,	Flygbåtarna
Havnegade 49, DK-1058 Copenhagen K, Denmark	Box 563, S-20125 Malmö, Sweden
Telephone: (33) 12 80 88	**Telephone:** (040) 10 39 30
Telex: 27502SUNDET DK	**Telex:** 32708S
Telefax: (33) 93 33 10	**Telefax:** (40) 12 04 84

High-speed craft operated

Type	Name	Seats	Delivered
CAT Westamarin W95	*Tunen* (Yard No 52)	180	May 1977
CAT Westamarin W95	*Tranen* (Yard No 53)	180	June 1978
CAT Westamarin W95	*Siken* (ex *Tumleren*) (Yard No 68)	180	April 1978
CAT Marinteknik Marinjet	*Lommen* (Yard No 56)	235	December 1985
CAT Marinteknik Marinjet	*Ørnen* (Yard No 59)	235	June 1986
CAT Fjellstrand 38.8m		256	September 1990
CAT Fjellstrand 38.8m		256	January 1992

Route operated
Copenhagen to Malmö (45 min, 17n miles). Ordinary single fare, economy class, DKr 80, SEK 70; 1st class, DKr 114, SEK 100, to 30 April 1990, mostly hourly departures between 06.00 and 24.00 from Copenhagen, departures between 06.00 and 00.45 from Malmö, with some additional departures on the half hour on Saturdays and Sundays and during the summer season.
Copenhagen to Ven

A/S Dampskibsselskabet Øresund (DSØ)
Hovercraft Division
Postbox 150, 2770 Kastrup, Copenhagen, Denmark

Telephone: 01521930/513111

Niels Riechers, *Managing Director*
Poul Bendtsen, *Operation Manager*

AP1–88 *Freja Viking* at Malmö

Karlskronavarvet Westamarin Jet Rider 3400 *Jet Princess* of JKL Shipping A/S

DSØ service AP1-88 operated for SAS between Kastrup Airport, Copenhagen and Malmő, Sweden, crossing the Øresund during the very cold winter of 1984/85

Service introduced June 1984, craft leased to Scandinavian Airlines System (SAS).
Annual traffic: approx 200 000

High-speed craft operated

Type	Name	Seats	Delivered
HOV British Hovercraft Corporation AP1-88	Liv Viking	81	May 1984
HOV British Hovercraft Corporation AP1-88	Freja Viking	81	May 1984
HOV British Hovercraft Corporation AP1-88 (003)	Idun Viking	81	December 1988

Route operated
Copenhagen Airport, Kastrup, Denmark to Malmő, Sweden (13n miles, 35 min). By October 1988 DSØ had carried over 776 000 passengers since starting services with its two API-88s in June 1984.

Scanjet Ferries
JKL-Shipping A/S
See entry under Norway for company details

High-speed craft operated

Type	Name	Seats	In service
SES Karlskronavarvet Westamarin Jet Rider 3400 37.0m	Jet Princess (ex Draupner)	292	June 1988
SES Karlskronavarvet Westamarin Jet Rider 3400 37.0m	Jet Prince (ex Sleipner)	292	June 1988
CAT* – 37.0m	—	—	January 1989
SES Westamarin 39.0m	—	—	June 1989
SES Westamarin 39.0m	—	—	June 1989

Routes operated
Copenhagen to Helsingborg, 1h 15min
*Copenhagen Airport to Malmő
Copenhagen to Gothenburg

The Fjellstrand Sea Cat while in temporary Norwegian service with Flaggruten in 1988

FINLAND

Alva Line, joint company of
Vaasanlaivat & Oy AW Line AB
Norra Esplanden 1A, 22100 Mariehamn, Åland, Finland

Telephone: 358 28 17271

High-speedcraft operated

Type	Name	Seats	In Service
CAT Fjellstrand 38.8m	Jet Cat	230	17 June 1988

Route operated
Vaasa (Finland) to Umeå (Sweden) 2h 0 min. Single fare, SEK 132 to 174 (Mariehamn to Norrtälje, May to September 1988)
Helsinki to Tallinn (USSR) Spring 1990

Lake Saimaa Waterway Authority
Finnish National Board of Navigation, Helsinki, Finland

High-speed craft operated

Type	Delivered
HOV Finn-Leiju	1984

Operation
Trial operations began in 1984 with a Finn-Leiju 387 hovercraft for the maintenance and inspection of navigation lights and buoys in the Saimaa lake district. Two Finn-Leiju 387 hovercraft are now operated by the Lake Saimaa Waterway Authority

FRANCE

Société Anonyme Atlantic Armement
See Navix S.A. entry for fleet previously operated by this company.

Chambon Group
See SURF SA

Société Anonyme d'Economie Mixte Maritime de Sainte-Pierre et Miquelon
France

High-speed craft operated

Type	Name	Delivered
MH SFCN 35m	St Eugene 5	March 1988

Emeraude Lines
From Saint-Malo:
Gare Maritime, BP 16, 35401 Saint Malo Cedex, France

Telephone: (99) 40 48 40
Telex: 950271 F
Telefax: (99) 812873

From Granville:
1 rue Lecampion, 50400 Granville, France

Telephone: (33) 50 16 36
Telex: 170002 F
Telefax: (33) 518871

Westamarin W95 Trident 3 in service with Emeraude Lines

High-speed craft operated

Type	Name	Seats	Delivered
CAT Westamarin W86	*Trident 2**	170	
CAT Westamarin W95	*Trident 3*	205	
CAT Westamarin W95	*Trident 4**	218	May 1988

Routes operated

Saint Malo to Saint Helier, Jersey
        to Saint Peter Port, Guernsey
        to Sark
 *Granville to Saint Helier, Jersey
        to Saint Peter Port, Guernsey
        to Sark

IFREMER
Institut Français de Recherche Pour L'Exploitation de la Mer
Centre de Brest, BP 337, 29273 Brest Cedex, France

Telephone: (98) 22 40 40
Telex: 940627OCEAN F
Telefax: (98) 05 04 73

Philippe Marchand, *Head of Department*

IFREMER has given financial and technical support for the development of the ADOC 12 which it owns and of the NES 24 which is under construction.

High-speed craft operated

Type	Name	Delivered
HOV Aeroplast ADOC 12	*Jean-Pierre*	1985

Navix S.A.
8 rue de la Boetie, Paris 75008, France

Telephone: (1) 47 42 57 02
Telex: 280170
Telefax: 42 66 29 78

High-speed craft operated

Type	Name	Seats	Delivered
MH SBCN 25m	*Amiral de Tourville*	220	1986
MH SBCN 25m	*Amiral de Joinville*	195	1986
MH SBCN 32m	-	-	

Routes operated

Noirmoutier and Yeu Island (*Amiral de Tourville* and *Amiral de Joinville*). La Baulle and Belle-Ile using the new 32m SBCN craft

Service Maritime de Carteret
Boite Postale 15, 50270 Barneville-Carteret, France

Telephone: (33) 538721
Telex: 170477CARSEY F

High-speed craft operated

Type	Name	Seats	Delivered
CAT Westamarin W95 (Yard No 50)	*Pegasus* (ex *Gimletun* (1978), ex *Ta Yue Shan* (1977))	181	June 1977

Route operated

Carteret to Gorey, Jersey (30 min), March to November

Compagnie Morbihamaise de Navigation
France

High-speed craft operated

Type	Name	Max Speed (knots)	Seats	In Service
CAT Fjellstrand 25.5m	*Børtind*	26	194	1987
CAT Fjellstrand Alumaran	*Gourinis*		165	1987

Routes operated

Quiberon to Sauzon, Sauzon to Le Palais to Houat

SURF SA
(Cie des Moyens de Surfaces Adaptes a l'Exploitation des Oceans)
148 rue Sainte, 13007 Marseilles, Boite Postale 48, 13262 Marseilles Cedex 7, France

Telephone: (91) 54 92 29
Telex: 401042SURF F
Telefax: (91) 33 85 70

Westamarin W95 *Pegasus* in service with Service Maritime de Carteret

High-speed craft operated

Type	Name	Max speed (knots)	Seats	Delivered
CAT Fjellstrand 31.5m	Anahitra*	30	161	1983
CAT Marinteknik 34CCB 34.1m	Emeraude Express	44	240	February 1986
MH SFCN 34.9m	Aida	31.5	90	April 1986
MH SFCN 34.9m	Angelica	31.5	90	April 1986

*Transport to the Ekoundou and Kole oil fields

Operations

Offshore support, off Congo coast, Pointe Noir to Emeraude North and South oilfields and to the Likouala oilfield

SURF's *Angelica* and *Aida*

Anahitra operated by SURF

Vedettes Armoricaines

1er Eperon, Boite Postale 88, 56 rue d'Aiguillon, 29268 Brest Cedex, France

Telephone: (98) 80 70 15
Telex: 940210NAVIPAM F

High-speed craft operated

Type	Name	Seats	Built
HYD S Ordzhonikidze	Kometa 1	-	1970
MH Tecimar	Jaguar	300	1980

Routes operated

Guernsey and Sark to St Helier, Jersey
St Helier to St Malo, Jersey (1 hour 25 min) and Granville

Vedettes Blanches et Vertes

Gare Maritime de Carteret, 50270 Barneville-Carteret, France

Telephone: (33) 53 81 17
Telex: 170002F

High-speed craft operated

Type	Name	Seats	Delivered
CAT Westermoen W86	Ar Vro (ex Trident 1 '87, ex Belle de Dinard '86 Karmsund '76)	140	January 1972
CAT Westamarin W86	Trident (ex Highland Seabird)		May 1976

Route operated

Carteret to Gorey to Saint Peter Port (summer service only)

Vedettes de L'Odet Ferry Company

Concarneau, Brittany, France

High-speed craft operated

Type	Name	Seats	Delivered
MH Société Bretonne de Construction Navale	Atlante	165	July 1985

Route operated

Concarneau to Iles de Glénan

Vedettes Vertes Granvillaises

1–3 rue le Campion, 50400 Granville, France

Telephone: (33) 50 16 36
Telex: 170002F

High-speed craft operated

Type	Name
CAT Westamarin W95	Trident 2

Route operated

Carteret to St Helier, Jersey (40 min)

Trident 2 (ex *Highland Seabird*) and *Pegasus* at Guernsey, May 1985   (A S Hands)

GABON

K/S A/S Gabnor
Gabon Ferry Services

Gabon

High-speed craft operated

Type	Name	Seats	Delivered
SES Brødrene Aa Båtbyggeri A/S CIRR 105P	Ekwata	290	September 1986
SES Brødrene Aa Båtbyggeri A/S CIRR 120P	Ekwata II	330	1988

Route operated

Libreville to Port Gentil, 85n miles

GERMANY, DEMOCRATIC REPUBLIC

Fahrgastechiffahrt Straisund
Democratic Republic of Germany

High-speed craft operated

Type	Name	Delivered
HYD S Ordzhonikidze Kometa	*Stoertebeker I*	1974
HYD S Ordzhonikidze Kometa	*Stoertebeker II*	1974
HYD S Ordzhonikidze Kometa	*Stoertebeker III*	1974

GERMANY, FEDERAL REPUBLIC

AG Ems Reederei
Post Box 1154,
Am Borkumkai, D2970 Emden,
Federal Republic of Germany

Telephone: 04921 890722
Telex: 27838
Telefax: 04921 890746

High-speed craft types operated

Type	Name	Seats	Delivered
CAT Fjellstrand 38.8m	*Nordlicht*	272	March 1989

Route operated
Emden to Borkum and inter-island(Frisian islands)

Köln-Düsseldorfer Deutsche Rheinschiffahrt AG (KD)
Frankenwerft 15, D-5000 Cologne 1, Federal Republic of Germany

Telephone: (0221) 20880
Telex: (08) 882 723

High-speed craft operated

Type	Name	Seats
HYD Sormovo Raketa	*Rheinpfeil (Rhine Arrow)*	64

Route operated
Cologne to Koblenz to Bingen to Mainz and many intermediate stops, 13 April to 28 October

Raketa, *Rheinpfeil,* operated by Köln-Düsseldorfer (KD) German Rhine Line

GIBRALTAR

Gibline Ltd (management)
6/1 Engineer's Lane, Gibraltar

Telephone: 75749
Telex: 2279 SEAGLE GK

Herman Bergshaven, *Chairman*
Joseph Gaggero, *Director*
Jan Lindberg, *Director*

General Sales Agents for Gibline Ltd:
Seagle Travel Ltd, 98 George's Lane, PO Box 480

Telephone: 71415, 76763
Telex: 2279GK
Telefax: 75160

J A Vinent, *Chairman*
D Vinent, *Director*
H L Llufrio, *Managing Director*

High-speed craft operated

Type	Name	Seats	Delivered*
CAT Westamarin 100D	*Gibline 1*	244	1985
	(ex *Gimle Belle* '85,		(built 1981)
	ex *Condor 6* '81)		
	(Yard No 75)		

16 reserved for Commodore Class on certain sailings
*to Gibline Ltd

Routes operated (22 April to 31 October 1987)
Gibraltar to Tangier (1 hour 10 min)
Gibraltar to M'Diq (1 hour 10 min) Thursday only, summer only

Fares: Normal one way, £17.00, (1989/90); normal return, £28.00, (1989/90)

Westamarin 100D *Gibline 1* at speed across the Strait of Gibraltar

GREECE

Dodecanese Hydrofoils

High-speed craft operated

Type	Name	In service
HYD S Ordzhonikidze Kometa	*Alkyonis 1*	1981
HYD S Ordzhonikidze Kometa	*Alkyonis 2*	1981

Routes operated
Between islands in the Greek Dodecanese

Ceres Flying Hydroways Limited
8 Akti Themistokleus, Freattys, Piraeus, Greece

Telephone: 4531716–17
Telex: 213606SHPC GR; 212257 CHSE GR

Services started in 1977 with the Piraeus to Hydra route

High-speed craft operated

Type	Name	Seats*	Delivered
HYD S Ordzhonikidze Kometa-M	*Flying Dolphin I*	116	1975
HYD S Ordzhonikidze Kometa-M	*Flying Dolphin II*	116	1975
HYD S Ordzhonikidze Kometa-M	*Flying Dolphin III*	116	1976
HYD S Ordzhonikidze Kometa-M	*Flying Dolphin V*	116	1976
HYD S Ordzhonikidze Kometa-M	*Flying Dolphin VI*	116	1976
HYD S Ordzhonikidze Kometa-M	*Flying Dolphin VII*	116	1976
HYD S Ordzhonikidze Kometa-M	*Flying Dolphin IV*	116	1977
HYD S Ordzhonikidze Kometa-M	*Flying Dolphin VIII*	116	1977
HYD S Ordzhonikidze Kometa-M	*Flying Dolphin IX*	116	
HYD S Ordzhonikidze Kometa-M	*Flying Dolphin X*	116	1978
HYD S Ordzhonikidze Kometa-M	*Flying Dolphin XI*	116	1979
HYD S Ordzhonikidze Kometa-M	*Flying Dolphin XII*	116	1979
HYD S Ordzhonikidze Kometa-M	*Flying Dolphin XIV*	116	1981
HYD S Ordzhonikidze Kometa-M	*Flying Dolphin XV*	116	1981
HYD S Ordzhonikidze Kometa-M	*Flying Dolphin XVI*	116	1981
HYD S Ordzhonikidze Kolkhida	*Flying Dolphin XVII*	155	1984
HYD S Ordzhonikidze Kolkhida	*Flying Dolphin XVIII*	155	1984

High-speed craft operated (contd)

Type	Name	Seats	Delivered
HYD S Ordzhonikidze Kolkhida	*Flying Dolphin XIX*	155	1986
HYD S Ordzhonikidze Kolkhida	*Flying Dolphin XIX*	155	1990
CAT Fjellstrand Flying Cat	—	372	1990

(*Flying Dolphin's IV, V* and *XII* are owned by Ceres Hydrofoils Shipping and Tourism SA. *Flying Dolphins IX, X* and *VIII* are owned by Ceres Hydrocomets Shipping and Tourism SA. *Flying Dolphins VI, VII* and *XI* are owned by Ceres Express Ways Shipping and Tourism SA. *Flying Dolphins XIV, XV, XVI* and *XVII* are owned by Ceres Hydrolines Shipping Co)
*MTU engines are being fitted to all Ceres Kometas enabling them to be fitted with 136 seats

Routes operated
Aghios Konstantinos to Volos to Skiathos to Glossa to Skopelos to Aionissos
Piraeus (Zea) to Poros to Hydra to Eranioni to Spetsai to Porto Heli to Leonidi to Kiparissi to Monemvassia

Part of the Ceres 15-craft Kometa fleet   *(Page Beken Ltd/Wilson Walton)*

Nearchos Shipping Co
(ex Psiloritis Maritime)
56 El Venizelou, Athens 10678, Greece

Telex: 215284/219706 GR

High-speed craft operated

Type	Name	Delivered
HYD S Ordzhonikidze Kometa	*Marilena*	1981
HYD S Ordzhonikidze Kometa	*Tzina*	1981

Both certificated by ABS.

Rethimniaki Naftiliaki Touristiki (RENATOUR SA)
250 Arkadiou Rethymno, Crete, Greece

Telex: 291226GR

High-speed craft operated

Type	Name	Seats	Delivered
CAT Westamarin W100D	*Nearchos* (ex *Venture 83*, launched as *Rosario*)	245	May 1982

Route operated
Réthimnon to Santorini (Thira)

Sonia Shipping, Melina Trading

High-speedcraft operated

Type	Name	Seats	In Service
CAT Westamarin W95T	*Karmen (ex Alisur Azul)*		1989

Operations
African Coast

GUADELOUPE

Société de Transports Maritimes Brudey
Pointe-à-Pitre, Guadeloupe

High-speed craft operated

Type	Name	Seats	Delivered
MH Société Française de Constructions Navales (SFCN) 27.50m	*Regina*	150	July 1984
MH Chantiers Navals de L'Esterel 34.6m	*Tropic*		1988

Trans Antilles Express (A.T.E)
A.T.E.
Quai Gatine, Gare Maritime, 97110 Pointe a Pitre, Guadeloupe

Telephone: 590 83 12 45/91 13 43
Telefax: 590 91 11 05

with:
SURF
148, rue Sainte, 13007 Marseille, France

Telephone: 91 54 92 29
Telex: 401042 SURF F
Telefax: 91 33 85 70

High-speed craft operated

Type	Name	Max speed knots	Seats	Delivered
MH Alfa Naval	*Madras*	25	234	1985
MH Breaux 34.4m	*Agathea*	22	150	1979
CAT Marinteknik Verkstads 33 CPV	*Jetkat* (ex *Jetkat 1*)	31	240	1984
CAT Westamarin	*Azur Express* (ex *Nettuno Jet*)	26	218	1981

Operations
High speed sea transport of passengers or interisland connections within the West Indies

Alfa Naval *Madras* operated by ATE

Marinteknik Verkstads AB *Jet Kat Express* operated by ATE

Marinteknik Verkstads AB *Alize Express* operated by ATE

HONG KONG

Castle Peak Power Co Ltd

High-speed craft operated

Type	Name	Seats	Delivered
CAT A Fai Engineers and Shiprepairers Ltd InCat 16.0m	Kwong Fai	40	June 1984

Chu Kong Shipping

Hong Kong
See **Yuet Hing Marine Supplies,**
Hong Kong **Customs and Excise Department**
8th Floor, Harbour Building, 38 Pier Road, Central, Hong Kong

High-speed craft operated

Type	Name
MH Chung Wah Shipbuilding and Engineering Co Ltd King Class Yard No 204	Customs 6 Sea Glory
MH Chung Wah Shipbuilding and Engineering Co Ltd King Class Yard No 205	Customs 5 Sea Guardian
MH Chung Wah Shipbuilding and Engineering Co Ltd King Class Yard No 206	Customs 2 Sea Leader

Hong Kong *Customs 6 Sea Glory* built by Chung Wah Shipbuilding and Engineering Co Ltd

Discovery Bay Transportation Services Ltd
Hong Kong Resort Company

2nd floor, Jardine House, Central, Hong Kong

Telephone: (5) 249181
Telex: 65179HKRCL HX

High-speed craft operated

Type	Yard No	Name	Seats	Originally delivered
SES Hovermarine HM 218	466	(ex RTS 101)		
SES Hovermarine HM 218.	468	(ex RTS 102)		
SES Hovermarine HM 218	471	(ex RTS 103)		
SES Hovermarine HM 218 (HM 2 Mk IV)	446	(ex HYF 108)	92	1976
SES Hovermarine HM 218 (HM 2 Mk IV)	447	(ex HYF 109)	92	1979
SES Hovermarine HM 218 (HM 2 Mk IV)	448	(ex HYF 110)	92	1979
MH Marinteknik Sweden/Singapore 35MPV*	64/107	Discovery Bay 12 250		1987
MH FBM Marine (S) 35MPV	108	Discovery Bay 15 256		May 1987
MH FBM Marine (S) 35MPV	109	Discovery Bay 16 256		June 1987
MH FBM Marine (S) 35MPV	122	Discovery Bay 19 250		1990
MH FBM Marine (S) 35MPV	125	Discovery Bay 20 250		1990
MH Cheoy Lee 22.8m	-	Discovery Bay 17 163		October 1989

* hull built in Sweden

Route operated

Discovery Bay, Lantau to Central, Hong Kong, 9 n miles, 25min
Approx 300,000 passenger trips per month

Discovery Bay 15

Hong Kong Hi-Speed Ferries Ltd (HSF)

13/F, V Huen Building, 138 Queens Road, Central, Hong Kong

Telephone: (5) 8152789
Telex: 89846 HKHPF HX
Telefax: (5) 430324

Dr Stanley Ho, *Chairman*
Capt P N Parashar, *General Manager*

High-speed craft operated

Type	Name	Speed	Seats	Entered service
MH Vosper Thornycroft 62.5m	Cheung Kong	26 knots	659*	May 1985
MH Vosper Thornycroft 62.5m	Ju Kong	26 knots	659*	May 1985

* plus 30 external seats

Ju Kong which was owned by New Hey Ltd is now owned by Ibarrola Co. Ltd *Cheung Kong* which was owned by Nuirhill Ltd is now owned by Gandiage Co. Ltd. The new owners are owned by S T D M Macau.

Route operated

Hong Kong to Macau, public holidays: HK $48 to 60; weekends, weekdays HK $38 to 50 excluding embarkation fee of HK $18
Seven departures daily from Hong Kong, 1 hour 30 mins

Traffic carried

1.141 million passengers in 1987
1.106 million passengers in 1988

Cheong Kong

Hongkong Macao Hydrofoil Co Ltd (HMH)

New World Tower, 33rd floor, 16–18 Queen's Road, Central, Hong Kong

Telephone: (5) 218302
Telex: 74493HMHCO HX

Kenny Tham, *Deputy General Manager*

This company started hydrofoil service in 1964 with two Rodriquez Supramar PT 20, 68-seat craft operating between Hong Kong and Macau. It now operates a fleet of eight hydrofoil and four waterjet catamaran ferries and is operating an additional route, Hong Kong to Zhuhai in China.

High-speed craft operated

Type	Name	Seats	Entered service
HYD Rodriquez PT 50	Flying Albatross	125	December 1964
HYD Rodriquez PT 50	Flying Skimmer	125	April 1965
HYD Rodriquez PT 50	Flying Condor	126	March 1966
HYD Rodriquez RHS 140	Flying Dragon	125	June 1971
HYD Rodriquez RHS 140	Flying Egret	125	February 1972

High-speed craft operated (contd)

Type	Name	Seats	Entered service
HYD Rodriquez RHS 140	*Flying Sandpiper*	125	January 1973
HYD Rodriquez RHS 140	*Flying Swift* (ex *Flying Goldfinch*)	125	December 1973
HYD Rodriquez RHS 140	*Flying Ibis*	125	December 1974
CAT Marinteknik Verkstads	*Apollo Jet*	215	January 1982
CAT Marinteknik Verkstads	*Hercules Jet*	215	June 1982
CAT Marinteknik Verkstads	*Janus Jet*	215	December 1982
CAT Marinteknik Verkstads 41 CPV	*Oregrund*	306	28 January 1989
CAT FBM Marinteknik (S) Pte Ltd	*Camoes/Cowes*	306	1989
CAT FBM Marinteknik (S) Pte Ltd	*Estrela do Mar/Jurong*	306	1989

The Marinteknik *Triton Jet* was sold in 1986 to the Zhao Gang Steame Navigation Company and re-named *Duan Zhou Hu*

Routes operated

Of the 12 vessels in current operation, one Marinteknik catamaran, *Hercule Jet*, operates between Hong Kong and Zhuhai, a special economic zone in China on the Pearl Estuary, a route of 35n miles; two vessels operate betweei Kowloon and Macau and the remaining vessels between Hong Kong and Macau, a distance of 36n miles.

HMH Rodriquez PT 50 *Flying Condor*   (HMH Co Ltd)

Apollo Jet the first Marinteknik catamaran to enter regular service with the Hongkong Macao Hydrofoil Co Ltd   (HMH Co Ltd)

Marinteknik Verkstads *Oregrund* delivered to Hongkong Macao Hydrofoil company, January 1989

The Hong Kong & Yaumati Ferry Co Ltd

Central Harbour Services Pier, 1st Floor, Pier Road, Central District, Hong Kong

Telephone: (5) 423081
Telex: 83140HYFCO HX
Telefax: CCITT G II & Gill (5) 423958

C K Lau, *Chairman*
H M Leung, *Managing Director*
David C S Ho, *General Manager*

The world's largest operator of sidewall hovercraft (SES).

High-speed craft operated

Type	Yard No	Name	Seats	Delivered
SES Hovermarine HM 216 (HM 2 Mk III)	328	*HYF 103*	74	1975
SES Hovermarine HM 216 (HM 2 Mk III)	329	*HYF 104**	60	1975
SES Hovermarine HM 218 (HM 2 Mk IV)	435	*HYF 105*	100	1976
SES Hovermarine HM 218 (HM 2 Mk IV)	443	*HYF 106*	100	1976
SES Hovermarine HM 218 (HM 2 Mk IV)	445	*HYF 107*	100	1976
SES Hovermarine HM 218 (HM 2 Mk IV)	457	*HYF 111*	100	1979
SES Hovermarine HM 218 (HM 2 Mk IV)	458	*HYF 112*	100	1979
SES Hovermarine HM 218 (HM 2 Mk IV)	459	*HYF 113*	100	1980
SES Hovermarine HM 218 (HM 2 Mk IV)	462	*HYF 114*	74	1980
SES Hovermarine HM 218 (HM 2 Mk IV)	463	*HYF 115*	100	1980
SES Hovermarine HM 218 (HM 2 Mk IV)	464	*HYF 116*	74	1980
SES Hovermarine HM 218 (HM 2 Mk IV)	469	*HYF 117*	100	1980
SES Hovermarine HM 218 (HM 2 Mk IV)	470	*HYF 118*	74	1980
SES Hovermarine HM 218 (HM 2 Mk IV)	473	*HYF 119*	74	1980
SES Hovermarine HM 218 (HM 2 Mk IV)	474	*HYF 120*	100	1980
SES Hovermarine HM 218 (HM 2 Mk IV)	475	*HYF 121*	74	1980
SES Hovermarine HM 218 (HM 2 Mk IV)	476	*HYF 122*	100	1980
SES Hovermarine HM 218 (HM 2 Mk IV)	477	*HYF 123*	74	1980
SES Hovermarine HM 218 (HM 2 Mk IV)	478	*HYF 124*	74	1980
SES Hovermarine HM 218 (HM 2 Mk IV)	479	*HYF 125*	100	1980
SES Hovermarine HM 218 (HM 2 Mk IV)	480	*HYF 126*	100	1980
SES Hovermarine HM 218 (HM 2 Mk IV)	481	*HYF 127*	100	1980

*laid up
HYF 101, 108, 109, 110, 128, 129 and *130* had been sold as of July 1986.
HYF 102 had been sold as of October 1986 to W & Y International Ltd, Hong Kong

Routes operated

	Annual traffic		
	1984	1985	1986
Hong Kong-Shekou, China 22.5n miles	173 000	163 910	178 754
Hong Kong-Whampoa, China 70n miles	55 000	59 796	36 857
Hong Kong-Zhoutoujui, China 80n miles	115 000	121 293	107 281

Hue Yang Ao Tougang Industrial Ltd

High-speed craft operated

Type	Name
SES Korea Tacoma Marine Industries Ltd 18m	*Tacoma II*

Route operated
Hong Kong to Chinchun

Kwai Kong Shipping Co Ltd

High-speed craft operated

Type	Name	Delivered
CAT A Fai Engineers and Shiprepairers InCat 21.0m	*Li Jiang*	June 1983

The Royal Hong Kong Police Force, Marine Region

25 Salisbury Road, Tsim Sha Tsui, Kowloon, Hong Kong

Telephone: 3692261
Telex: 65367HX
Telefax: 33115564

R L J Macdonald, *Regional Commander, Assistant Commissioner*
B J Deegan, *Deputy Regional Commander, Chief Superintendent*
Lionel LAM Kin, *Chief Staff Officer, Chief Superintendent*

High-speed craft operated

Type	Speed, knots	Name
MH Vosper Thornycroft Singapore 23.8m	22	*PL 50 Sea Cat*
MH Vosper Thornycroft Singapore 23.8m	22	*PL 51 Sea Puma*
MH Vosper Thornycroft Singapore 23.8m	22	*PL 52 Sea Leopard*
MH Vosper Thornycroft Singapore 23.8m	22	*PL 53 Sea Eagle*
MH Vosper Thornycroft Singapore 23.8m	22	*PL 54 Sea Hawk*
MH Vosper Thornycroft Singapore 23.8m	22	*PL 55 Sea Lynx*
MH Vosper Thornycroft Singapore 23.8m	22	*PL 56 Sea Falcon*
MH Chung Wah Shipbuilding and Engineering Co Ltd 26.3m, Yard No 178, Mark II Patrol	25	*PL 57 Mercury*
MH Chung Wah Shipbuilding and Engineering Co Ltd 26.3m, Yard No 179, Mark II Patrol	25	*PL 58 Vulcan*
MH Chung Wah Shipbuilding and Engineering Co Ltd 26.3m, Yard No 180, Mark II Patrol	25	*PL 59 Ceres*
MH Chung Wah Shipbuilding and Engineering Co Ltd 26.5m, Yard No 166, Mark I Patrol	23	*PL 60 Aquarius*
MH Chung Wah Shipbuilding and Engineering Co Ltd 26.5m, Yard No 167, Mark I Patrol	23	*PL 61 Pisces*
MH Chung Wah Shipbuilding and Engineering Co Ltd 26.5m, Yard No 168, Mark I Patrol	23	*PL 62 Argo*

High-speed craft operated (contd)

Type	Speed, knots	Name
MH Chung Wah Shipbuilding and Engineering Co Ltd 26.5m, Yard No 169, Mark I Patrol	23	PL 63 Carina
MH Chung Wah Shipbuilding and Engineering Co Ltd 26.5m, Yard No 170, Mark I Patrol	23	PL 64 Cetus
MH Chung Wah Shipbuilding and Engineering Co Ltd 26.5m, Yard No 171, Mark I Patrol	23	PL 65 Dorado
MH Chung Wah Shipbuilding and Engineering Co Ltd 26.5m, Yard No 172, Mark I Patrol	23	PL 66 Octans
MH Chung Wah Shipbuilding and Engineering Co Ltd 26.5m, Yard No 173, Mark I Patrol	23	PL 67 Vela
MH Chung Wah Shipbuilding and Engineering Co Ltd 26.5m, Yard No 174, Mark I Patrol	23	PL 68 Volans
MH Chung Wah Shipbuilding and Engineering Co Ltd 26.5m, Yard No 189, Mark III Patrol	25	PL 70 King Lai
MH Chung Wah Shipbuilding and Engineering Co Ltd 26.5m, Yard No 190, Mark III Patrol	25	PL 71 King Yee
MH Chung Wah Shipbuilding and Engineering Co Ltd 26.5m, Yard No 191, Mark III Patrol	25	PL 72 King Lim
MH Chung Wah Shipbuilding and Engineering Co Ltd 26.5m, Yard No 192, Mark III Patrol	25	PL 73 King Hau
MH Chung Wah Shipbuilding and Engineering Co Ltd 26.5m, Yard No 193, Mark III Patrol	25	PL 74 King Dai
MH Chung Wah Shipbuilding and Engineering Co Ltd 26.5m, Yard No 194, Mark III Patrol	25	PL 75 King Chung
MH Chung Wah Shipbuilding and Engineering Co Ltd 26.5m, Yard No 195, Mark III Patrol	25	PL 76 King Shun
MH Chung Wah Shipbuilding and Engineering Co Ltd 26.5m, Yard No 196, Mark III Patrol	25	PL 77 King Tak
MH Chung Wah Shipbuilding and Engineering Co Ltd 26.5m, Yard No 197, Mark III Patrol	25	PL 78 King Chi
MH Chung Wah Shipbuilding and Engineering Co Ltd 26.5m, Yard No 198, Mark III Patrol	25	PL 79 King Tai
MH Chung Wah Shipbuilding and Engineering Co Ltd 26.5m, Yard No 199, Mark III Patrol	25	PL 80 King Kwan
MH Chung Wah Shipbuilding and Engineering Co Ltd 26.5m, Yard No 200, Mark III Patrol	25	PL 81 King Mei
MH Chung Wah Shipbuilding and Engineering Co Ltd 26.5m, Yard No 201, Mark III Patrol	25	PL 82 King Yan
MH Chung Wah Shipbuilding and Engineering Co Ltd 26.5m, Yard No 202, Mark III Patrol	25	PL 83 King Yung
MH Chung Wah Shipbuilding and Engineering Co Ltd 26.5m, Yard No 203, Mark III Patrol	25	PL 84 King Kan

Sealink Ferries Ltd

Central Harbour Services Pier, 1/F, Pier Road, Central District, Hong Kong

Telephone: (5) 423081/433298
Telex: 83140HYFCO HX

This company was formed in 1981 to operate on the Kowloon-Macau route. Services began in September 1983 with four Vosper Hovermarine HM 527s. It became a wholly owned subsidiary of The Hong Kong & Yaumati Ferry Co Ltd on 30 June 1986.

High-speed craft operated

Type	Name	In service
SES Vosper Hovermarine HM 527 (501)	Tejo	September 1983
SES Vosper Hovermarine HM 527 (502)	Douro	1983
SES Vosper Hovermarine HM 527 (503)	Sado	1984
SES Vosper Hovermarine HM 527 (504)	Mondego	1984

Route operated

	Annual traffic	
	1984	1986
Kowloon to Macau, 1 hour 10 mins, 40n miles	550 000	850 000

One craft (503) has been leased for short periods to the Hong Kong & Yaumati Ferry Co. for use on the route Kowloon to Canton.

Shun Tak Enterprises Corporation Ltd (STEC)
Far East Hydrofoil Co Ltd

Penthouse, 39th Floor, Shun Tak Centre, 200 Connaught Road, Central, Hong Kong

Telephone: (5) 8593111
Telex: 74200SEDAM HX
Telefax: (5) 596471

Stanley Ho, *Group Executive Chairman*
David Hill, *General Manager*
Andrew Tse, *Manager, Financial Control*
Jenning Wang, *Engineering Manager*
W K Chan, *Fleet Operations Manager*

The company started hydrofoil service in 1963 with a PT 20 and gradually built up to a total of 14 surface-piercing hydrofoils. It started the world's first commercial Jetfoil service in April 1975. Subsequently the Jetfoils took over the bulk of the traffic due to passenger demand and the surface-piercing hydrofoils were gradually phased out and additional Jetfoils purchased. All surface-piercing hydrofoils were removed from service by end 1983 and subsequently sold. In 1989 STEC Jetfoils carried 66.7% of all Hong Kong-Macau passenger traffic with 36 277 passages and 7.97 million passengers. STEC Jetfoils have carried a total of 62 563 628 passengers up to June 30th 1989. Each jetfoil has a seating capacity of 268.

High-speed craft operated

Type	Name	Seats	Entered service with STEC
HYD Boeing Jetfoil 929–100	Madeira		1975
HYD Boeing Jetfoil 929–100	Santa Maria		1975
HYD Boeing Jetfoil 929–100	Flores (ex Kalakaua '78)	260	1978
HYD Boeing Jetfoil 929–100	Corvo (ex Kamehameha)		1978
HYD Boeing Jetfoil 929–100	Pico (ex Kuhio)		1978
HYD Boeing Jetfoil 929–100	São Jorge (ex Jet Caribe I '80, ex Jet de Oriente '78)		1980
HYD Boeing Jetfoil 929–100	Acores (ex Jet Caribe II)		1980
HYD Boeing Jetfoil 929–100	Ponta Delgada (ex Flying Princess II)		1981
HYD Boeing Jetfoil 929–115	Terceira (ex Normandy Princess)		1981
HYD Boeing Jetfoil 929–100	Urzela (ex Flying Princess)		1981
HYD Boeing Jetfoil 929–115	Funchal (ex Jetferry One '83)	250	1983
HYD Boeing Jetfoil 929–115	Horta (ex Jetferry Two)		1983
HYD Boeing Jetfoil 929–115*	Lilau (ex HMS Speedy)		1987

*converted 929–320

Routes operated

Hong Kong-Macau and Kowloon-Macau, distance 38–40n miles. 24 hour service since March 1989. Services 3 times per hour each way during daylight hours and 2 times per hour from sunset until 2 am, and then hourly from 2 am till 7 am.

Funchal, Jetfoil Model 929–115

W & Y International Ltd

42–44 Granville Road, 8C, Kowloon, Hong Kong

High-speed craft operated

Type	Name
SES Hovermarine HM 216	ex HYF 102*

*purchased from The Hong Kong & Yaumati Ferry Co Ltd, 1987

Yuet Hing Marine Supplies
Hong Kong

High-speed craft operated

Type	Name	Seats	Delivery
CAT Precision Marine 38.0m	Xin Ning	280	August 1988
CAT Precision Marine 38.0m	—	—	1989

HUNGARY

MAHART (Magyar Hajózási Részvénytársaság)
Apaczai Csere Janos utca 11, 1366 Budapest V, Pf58, Hungary

Telephone: 1181 743/1181 704
Telex: 225412 MAHART H
Telefax: 1187 740

MAHART carries between 30 000 and 35 000 passengers a year with their high-speed craft fleet and total journeys come to 15 million passenger km/year.

High-speed craft operated

Type	Name	Seats	Built
HYD Sormovo Meteor	Sólyom	108	1975
HYD Sormovo Voskhod	Vöcsök I	62	1977
HYD Sormovo Voskhod	Vöcsök II	62	1986
HYD Sormovo Voskhod	Vöcsök III	62	1987
HYD Sormovo Voskhod	Vöcsök IV	62	1987
HYD Sormovo Meteor	Solyom II	104	1988

Routes operated
Budapest to Vienna, 282km, 5 hours, April to October
In 1989 Mahart Tours introduced a scheduled inland hydrofoil trip between Budapest and Esztergom, 'The Danube Bend'. The new route has been a great success as it covers the most beautiful part of the Danube in Hungary. Operation is from June to September, Friday to Sunday.

Sormovo Meteor *Sólyom* operated by MAHART

INDIA

Anklesaria
Bombay, India

High-speed craft operated
Type
SES Hovermarine HM 216

Operation
Crew boat

INDONESIA

Palayaram Binton Baruna Sakti
Batam Islands, Indonesia

High-speed craft operated

Type	Name	Seats	Delivered
MH Wave Master International	Sea Raider II	250	1984

PT Hover Maritim Semandera
Jalan Gondangdia Lama 26, Jakarta 10350, Indonesia

Telephone: 325608(5 lines), 310–3358
Telex: 45746SHARCO IA
Telefax: (62) 21 310 3357

Air Marshal (Rtd) Suharnoko Harbani, *Chairman*
H M Suharnoko, *Vice Chairman*
H Wijaya, *Commissioner*
Ir A W Suharnoko, *President Director*
Lt Col (Navy) Tri Suwojo, *Director Operations*
Isamaya P Asrah, (Acc) *Director Finance*

High-speed craft operated

Type	Name	Seats	Delivered
SES Vosper Hovermarine HM 218 Mk IV	Semandera Satu	78	1986
SES Vosper Hovermarine HM 218 Mk IV	Semandera Dua	78	1986

Routes operated
Tanjung Priok (Port of Jakarta) to P.Kotok Besar and P.Antuk Timur (Holiday resort islands northwest of Jakarta), distance 40–45n miles, trip time 1 hr 20 min, commercial service started February 1987, one and occasionally two trips per day, four days per week, departures: Jakarta 07.00, Islands 16.00, contract with resort operator (subsidiary of Japan Airlines). Fare US$22.50 single.
Hover Maritim Semandera is also offering a two-day cruise package to the Ujung Kulon National Park from Jakarta, distance 135n miles, trip time 4 hr 25 min, service started September 1987, major holidays only, departures: 07.00 from Jakarta. Package fare US$300.00 per person.
Since November 1989 the Company is providing off-shore crew transfer services for Atalantic Richfield Indonesia Inc.(Subsidiary of ARCO) on one year charter basis. The service is expected to be expanded with the addition of ten 20 metre fast monohull personnel carrier vessels to be delivered by an Australian shipbuilder.

Vosper Hovermarine HM 218 Mk IV *Semandera Satu*

PT PELNI (Pelayaran Nasional Indonesia)/PT PAL Indonesia/P Seribu Paradise Travel Agent
Indonesia

High-speed craft operated

Type	Name	Seats	Delivered
HYD Boeing Jetfoil 929–115/0022	Bima Samudera I	255	1982
HYD Boeing Jetfoil 929–115	Bininda II*		1986

*Navy owned

Routes operated
Tanjung Priok, Jakarta to Pandang, Lampung (Srengsan) on Mondays, Wednesdays and Saturdays. Fare US$42 single
Tanjung Priok, Jakarta to Palau Putri, P Seribu on Sundays

PT Satmarindo
Indonesia

High-speed craft operated

Type	Name	Seats	Delivered
MH SBF Engineering (Phil Curran design)	Satrya Express	62	1985

Crew boat with capacity for two 8-tonne deck containers.

Operation
Servicing of the Hudbay Oil Lalang oil and gas fields in the Strait of Malacca

IRAN

Islamic Republic of Iran Shipping Lines
Khorramshahr and Bandar Abbas, Iran

High-speed craft operated

Type	Name
HYD USSR Feodosiya Shipyard Kometa	Iran Resalat (ex Arya Ram) Yard No S-34
HYD USSR Feodosiya Shipyard Kometa	Iran Tareeghal (ex Arya Baz, ex Kometa S-26)

ITALY

Adriatica di Navigazione SpA
Zattere 1411, Palazzo Sociale, 30123 Venice, Italy

Telephone: (041) 704322/781611
Telex: 410045ADRNAV I

High-speed craft operated

Type	Name	Seats	Delivered
HYD Rodriquez PT 50	Nibbio	125	1964
HYD Rodriquez RHS 160	Diomedea (launched as Flying Phoenix)	160	1975
HYD Rodriquez RHS 160F	Monte Gargano	210	1989

Routes operated
1988 Schedule May to September:
Nibbio: Ortona to Tremiti, 1 hour 50 min, fare 159 000 lira one way
Vasto to Tremiti, 1 hour 10 min, fare 9500 lira one way
Vieste to Tremiti, 1 hour, fare 18 000 lira one way
Diomedea: Termoli to Tremiti, 45 min, fare 14 400 lira (July and August): other times 6700 lira one way

Agip SpA
20097 S Donato Milanese, Milan, Italy

Telephone: 5201
Telex: 310246ENI I

High-speed craft operated
HYD Rodriquez PT 20
HYD Rodriquez PT 50

Alilauro SpA
Head Office: Via Caracciolo 11, 80 122 Naples, Italy

Telephone: (81) 7611004
Telex: 720354ALILAR I
Telefax: (81) 667327

Capt Salvatore Lauro, *President*

Associated company:
Medmar SRL (Linee Mediterranee Marittime ed Aeree s.r.l.)
Rome Office:
Via Ofanto 18

Telephone: (6) 8419057
Telefax: (6) 8451989

High-speed craft operated

Type	Name	Seats	Delivered
HYD Rodriquez PT 50	Alimarte (ex Alivit)	140	1969
HYD Sormovo Kometa M	Aliapollo (ex Alitunisi, 1984 ex Alispan Secondo, 1980 ex Atalanta, 1971)	116	1971
HYD Sormovo Kometa M	Alivulcano (ex Alispan Primo, 1977 ex Lepa Vida, 1970)	116	1972
HYD Sormovo Kometa M	Alivenere (ex Aligiglio)*	116	1972
HYD Sormovo Kometa M	Alisorrento*	116	1972
HYD Sormovo Kometa M	Alivesuvio*	116	1973
HYD Sormovo Kometa M	Alirug	140	1969
CAT Marinteknik Marinjet 33 CPV	Giove Jet	282	April 1985
HYD S Ordzhonikidze Kolkhida	Aliatlante	155	June 1986
HYD S Ordzhonikidze Kolkhida	Alieolo		July 1986
MH Marinteknik Verkstads AB 34 MPV	Europa Jet (ex Europa 1 '87)		September 1987
CAT FBM Marinteknik Shipbuilder (S) Pte Ltd Marinjet 34 CPV	Acapulco Jet	300	1988
CAT Marinteknik Verkstads AB	Nettuno Jet		
CAT Marinteknik Verkstads AB 34 CPV	Giunone Jet		
MH Marinteknik Verkstads AB 41 MPV	Rosaria Lauro		
CAT Marinteknik Verkstads 36 CPV	Airone Jet		
HYD Kolkhida	Alikenia	115	1986
HYD Kolkhida	Aliflorida	115	1988
HYD Kometa	Alieros	116	1973
HYD Kometa	Alisaturno	116	1972
HYD Kometa	Alischia	116	1977
HYD Kometa	Alicapri	116	1983

*These Kometas were fitted with MTU 8V 396 TB83 engines in the order shown in 1984, 1985 and 1986
The first *Nettuno Jet* was bought back by Marinteknik Verkstads AB and sold to SURF, France, 1987.
The first Marinteknik JC-F1 JetCat, *Alitirreno I* was sold to a Spanish operator in 1989.

Nettuno Jet, in service with the Alilauro company, Linea Jet

Routes operated

Naples to Ischia Porto
Naples to Forio
Naples to Sorrento
Sorrento to Capri
Sorrento to Fiumicino
Capri to Ischia
Salerno to Amalfi to Positano to Capri
Naples to Capri and the ports of the Cilento coast
Flumicino to Palau (Sardinia) to Porto Vecchio (Corsica)
Naples to Positano
Formia to Ischia to Capri to Sorrento to Napoli
Sorrento to Ischia
Flumicino to Ponza to Ventotene to Ischia to Capri to Sorrento

Aliscafi SNAV SpA
(Societa di Navigazione Alta Velocita)

Head Office: Cortina del Porto, Via San Raineri 22, 98100 Messina, Italy

Telephone: (90) 773722
Telex: 980030RODRIK I

Terminal (main): Via Caracciolo 10, 80122 Naples, Italy

Telephone: (81) 660444
Telex: 720446SNAVNA I

High-speed craft operated

Type	Name	Seats	Built
HYD Rodriquez PT 20 (laid up)	Freccia del Sole	72	1956
HYD Rodriquez PT 20	Freccia delle Eolie	72	1957
HYD Rodriquez PT 20	Freccia del Tirreno	72	1957
HYD Rodriquez PT 50	Freccia d'Oro	130	1959
HYD Rodriquez PT 50	Freccia di Messina	125	1959
HYD Rodriquez PT 20	Freccia dello Stretto	72	1960
HYD Rodriquez PT 20	Freccia di Reggio	72	1961
HYD Rodriquez PT 20	Freccia del Peloro	72	1961
HYD Rodriquez PT 50	Freccia di Sicilia (ex Condor 1)	125	1964
HYD Rodriquez PT 20	Freccia del Vesuvio	72	1966
HYD Rodriquez PT 50	Freccia delle Isole	125	1966
HYD Rodriquez PT 50	Freccia Atlantica (ex Sirena '67)	125	1960
HYD Rodriquez PT 50	Sun Arrow	125	1968
HYD Rodriquez PT 50	Freccia Adriatica	125	1969
HYD Rodriquez PT 20	Freccia dello Ionio		
HYD Rodriquez PT 20	Freccia di Posillipo		
HYD Rodriquez PT 20	Freccia di Procida		
HYD Rodriquez PT 50	Freccia del Sud (ex Princefoil '78 ex Vingtor '74)	105	1960
CAT Westamaran W95	Martini Bianco		1975
HYD Rodriquez RHS 160	Alijumbo	180	1979
HYD Rodriquez RHS 200	Superjumbo	254	1981
HYD Rodriquez RHS 150F	Dynasty	161	1984

High-speed craft operated (contd)

Type	Name	Seats	Built
HYD Westermoen Hydrofoil A/S PT 50	Freccia del Lipari (ex Alicapri '77, ex Flipper '69, ex Westfoil '67, ex Alei-Gal '65, ex Westfoil '63)	125	1961
HYD Westermoen Hydrofoil A/S PT 50	Freccia del Mediteraneo	125	1963
HYD Rodriquez RHS 150M			
HYD Rodriquez RHS 150M			

RHS 160F *Alijumbo Eolie* was transferred to Spain in 1988 to Navieva Mallorquina

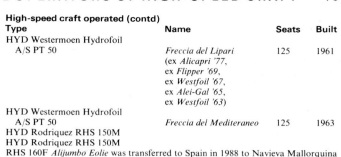

Rodriquez PT 20 *Freccia di Sorrento* in service with the Italian Ministero dei Mercantile Marine for anti-pollution work

Aliscafi SNAV PT 50 *Freccia di Sicilia* (built in 1964) at the Lipari terminal, October 1987

Westamaran W95, built in 1975, operated by SNAV   (*photo: Mike McSorley*)

Routes operated (1987) for various periods in the year

Anzio to Ponza to Ventotene to Ischia to Naples

Reggio Calabria to Messina to Porto Levante to Lipari to Santa Marina to Panarea to Ginostra

Naples to Capri

Palermo to Cefalu to Filicudi to Rinella to Santa Marina Salina to Vulcano to Lipari

Naples to Ustica to Favignana to Trapani

Messina to Reggio Calabria to Messina to Vulcano to Lipari to Santa Marina Salina to Panarea to Stromboli

Rimella (Is Salina) to Santa Marina (Is Salina) to Lipari (Is Lipari) to Porto di Levante (Is Vulcano) to Lipari (Is Panarea) to Stromboli to Naples

Vibo Valenta to Stromboli to Panarea to Vulcano to Lipari to Vulcano

Trapani to Pantelleria to Kelibia

Messina (Sicily) to Reggio Calabria to Messina to Stromboli to Panarea to Santa Marina Salina to Lipari to Vulcano

Capo d'Orlando (Sicily) to Vulcano to Lipari to Capo d'Orlando to Vulcano to Lipari

Milazzo (Sicily) to Is Vulcano to Lipari to Santa Marina (Is Salina) to Rimella (Is Salina) to Santa Marina to Is Panarea to Is Stromboli to Is Panarea to Is Filicudi to Is Alicudi to Is Filicudi to Rinella to Santa Marina (Salina) to Lipari to Vulcano to Milazzo

Casamicciola to Procida to Naples

Alivit Due Srl

See Alilauro SpA entry for craft previously listed under this Alilauro subsidiary

CAREMAR
(Compania Regionale Marittima SpA)
Molo Beverello 2, 80133 Naples, Italy

Telephone: (081) 5515384
Telex: 720054

High-speed craft operated

Type	Name	Seats	Delivered
HYD Rodriquez RHS 140	Albireo	140	1977
HYD Rodriquez RHS 160	Algol	180	1978
HYD Rodriquez RHS 160	Alioth	180	1979
HYD Rodriquez RHS 160F	Anilam	210	1986
HYD Rodriquez RHS 160F	Aldebaran	210	1986

Routes operated

Naples to Capri
Naples to Ischia Porto
Naples to Procida
Formia to Ponza/Ventotene

CAREMAR'S *Algol*

Covemar Eolie
Via Capp M Scala 21, Milazzo ME, Sicily, Italy

High-speed craft operated

Type	Name	Seats
HYD Rodriquez PT 50S	Star Capricorn (ex Springeren, 1967)	117
HYD Rodriquez PT 20	Freccia della Salina	—

Route operated

Lipari to Milazzo

Ministero dei Mercantile Marine

In 1987 a Rodriquez PT 50 hydrofoil was adopted for anti-pollution work. The vessel was previously operated by Aliscafi SNAV SpA.

High-speed craft operated

Type	Name	Built
HYD Rodriquez PT 50	Freccia di Sorrento (ex Freccia di Reggio '70, ex Freccia del Caribe '64)	1959

Navigazione Libera del Golfo SpA
Naples, Italy

High-speed craft operated

Type	Name	Seats	Delivered
MH FBM Marine 41.0m	Capri Jet	353	July 26, 1988
MH FBM Marine 41.0m	Capri Jet II		June 1990

Route operated

Naples to Capri, 40 min

Ministero dei Trasporti
Via L Ariosto 21, 20145 Milan, Italy

Telephone: (02) 48 120 86/4816230
Telex: 311294NAVIGE I

Dott Ing Pietro Santini, *Government Manager*

The Italian Ministry of Transport has three subsidiary hydrofoil operating companies which run services on Lake Como, Lake Garda and Lake Maggiore as detailed below. Passengers carried in 1988 totalled 6674108

Navigazione Alta Italia SpA
Via Corsica 19/s, 16128 Genoa, Italy
Telephone: (010) 56331
Telex: 270181 NAI I

This company has purchased two PT20 hydrofoils (one of which was *Porto Corsini*) from Agip

Navigazione Lago di Como
Via Rubini 22, 22100 Como, Italy

Telephone: 273324/26 02 34

Dott Ing F Parigi, *Director*

High-speed craft operated

Type	Name	Seats	Built
Rodriquez PT 20	Freccia del Lario	80	1964
Rodriquez PT 20	Freccia delle Azalee	80	1967
Rodriquez RHS 70	Freccia delle Betulle	80	1974
Rodriquez RHS 70	Freccia delle Gardenie	80	1976
Rodriquez RHS 150SL	Freccia delle Valli	180	1981
Rodriquez RHS 150SL	Guglielmo Marconi	180	1983
Rodriquez RHS 150FL	Stendhall	200	1989
Rodriquez RHS 150	Voloire	200	1989

The *Capri Jet* built by FBM Marine, Isle of Wight, UK for Navigazione Libera del Golfo SpA

Rodriquez RHS 150SL 180-seat *Guglielmo Marconi* operated by Navigazione Lago di Como

Routes operated
Como-Argegno-Lenno-Tremezzo-Bellagio-Menaggio-Varenna-Bellano-
Dongo-Gravedona-Domaso-Colico
Bellagio-Mandello-Lecco

Navigazione Sul Lago di Garda
Piazza Matteotti 2, 25015 Desenzano del Garda, Italy

Telephone: (030) 914 1321/3
Telex: 303114NAVIGA I

High-speed craft operated

Type	Name	Seats	Built
Rodriquez PT 20	*Freccia del Garda*	80	1958
Rodriquez PT 20	*Freccia degli Ulivi*	72	1965
Rodriquez RHS 70	*Freccia del Benaco*	71	1974
Rodriquez RHS 70	*Freccia del Gerani*	71	1976
Rodriquez RHS 150SL	*Freccia delle Riviere*	200	1981
Rodriquez RHS 150SL	*Galileo Galilei*	200	1982
Rodriquez RHS 150FL	*Goethe*	200	1988

Routes operated
Peschiera-Desenzano del G.-Sirmione-Bardolino-Garda-Salò-Gardone
Riviera-Maderno-Torri del Benaco-Gargnano-Castelletto-Malcesine-
Limone-Torbole-Riva del Garda

Navigazione Lago Maggiore
Viale F Baracca 1, 28041 Arona, Italy

Telephone: 032246651
Telex: 200248NAVIMA I
Telefax: 032257365

Dott Ing Paolo De Pascale, *Director*

High-speed craft operated

Type	Name	Seats	Built
Rodriquez PT 20	*Freccia del Verbano*	80	1964
Rodriquez PT 20	*Freccia del Ticino*	80	1968
Rodriquez RHS 70	*Freccia delle Camelie*	80	1974
Rodriquez RHS 70	*Freccia delle Magnolie*	80	1975
Rodriquez RHS 150SL	*Freccia dei Giardini*	176 + 20	1981
Rodriquez RHS 150SL	*Freccia Enrico Fermi*	200	1984
Rodriquez RHS 150FL	*Goethe*	200	1988
Rodriquez RHS 150FL	—	200	—

Routes operated
Arona-Angera-Belgirate-Stresa-Baveno-Pallanza-Intra-Luino-Brissago-
Porto Ronco-Ascona-Locarno

SIREMAR
(Sicilia Regionale Marittima SpA)
Via Principe di Belmonte, 1/C-90139 Palermo, Sicily, Italy

Telephone: (091) 582688
Telex: 910135SIRMAR I

High-speed craft operated

Type	Name	Seats	Built
Rodriquez PT 50	*Freccia Atlantica* (ex *Sirena*)	125	1960 leased from Aliscafi SNAV SpA
Rodriquez PT 50	*Pisanello*	130	1961
Rodriquez PT 20	*Pinturicchio*	70	1968
Rodriquez RHS 160	*Donatello*	184	1980
Rodriquez RHS 160	*Botticelli*	184	1980
Rodriquez RHS 160F	*Masaccio*	210	1987
Rodriquez RHS 160F	*Mantegna*	210	1989
Rodriquez RHS 160F	*Giorgione*	210	1989
Rodriquez RHS 140	*Duccio*	140	1977

Routes operated
Milazzo to Eolie
Trapani to Egadi
Palermo to Ustica
Milazzo to Stromboli
Milazzo to Alicudi

SIREMAR'S *Botticelli*

TOREMAR SpA
(Toscana Regionale Marittima SpA)
Scali del Corso 5, 57100 Leghorn, Italy

Telephone: (586) 22772
Telex: 590214I

High-speed craft operated

Type	Name	Seats	Built
HYD Rodriquez RHS 140	*Fabricia*	140	1977
HYD Rodriquez RHS 160F	*Masaccio*		1987
HYD Rodriquez RHS 160F	*Duccio*		1988

Routes operated
Portoferraio to Cavo to Piombino (Elba to mainland)

Vetor srl
Italy

High-speed caft operated

Type	Name	Delivered
HYD Feodosiya Kometa	*Vetor 944*	1984

JAPAN

Awaji Ferry Boat Co
Japan

High-speed craft operated

Type	Name	Seats	Delivered
CAT Mitsui CP25 Supermaran	*Queen Rokkou*	250	June 1988

Mitsui catamaran ferry *Queen Rokko* operated by Awaji Ferry Boat Co

Awashima Kisen Co. Ltd
3 Awashimaura-mura, Iwafune-Gun, Niigata-Ken 958–01, Japan

High-speed craft operated

Type	Name	Speed	Seats	Delivered
MH Sumidagawa Zosen Co Ltd	*Iwayuri*	24 knots	144	May 1979

Route operated
Awashima to Iwafune

Biwako Kisen Co Ltd
(Biwa Lake Sightseeing Company)
1–5-24 Hamaotsu, Otsu-City 520, Shiga Prefecture, Japan

High-speed craft operated

Type	Name	Speed	Seats	Delivered
MH Mokubei Shipbuilding Co Ikeda 22m (Hamilton Jet waterjet-propelled)	*Lansing*	27 knots	86	Aug 1982

Route operated
Biwa Lake, sightseeing

Designed by Dr M Ikeda, the Mokubei Shipbuilding Company waterjet-propelled *Lansing*

Boyo Kisen Co. Ltd
134–6 Yanai, Yanai-City 742, Japan

High-speed craft operated

Type	Name	Speed	Seats	Delivered
HYD Hitachi Zosen PT 20	*Shibuki No 2*	32 knots	66	June 1969
HYD Hitachi Zosen PT 50	*Shibuki No 3*	34 knots	123	October 1973

Route operated
Yanai to Mitsuhama

Daitohmaru Kanko Co. Ltd
461 Watakano, Isobe-Cho, Shima-Gun, Mie-Ken 517–03, Japan

High-speed craft operated

Type	Name	Speed	Seats	Delivered
MH New Japan Marine Co Ltd	*Daitohmaru No 12*	23 knots	56	December 1977

Route operated
Wadakano to Anagawa

Enoh Kisen
Japan

High-speed craft operated

Type	Name	Speed	Seats	Delivered
MH New Japan Marine Co Ltd	*Edajima No 2*	23.9 knots	60	February 1975
MH New Japan Marine Co Ltd	*Edajima No 3*	23.7 knots	60	January 1976
MH New Japan Marine Co Ltd	*Edajima No 5*	23.4 knots	74	November 1982

Route operated
Ujina to Fujinowaki

Ezaki Kisen Co. Ltd
2286 Ushibuka-machi, Ushibuka-City 863–19, Japan

High-speed craft operated

Type	Name	Speed	Seats	Delivered
MH Garuda KK	*Garuda No 1*	23 knots	82	October 1972
MH Toei	*Garuda No 2*	23 knots	96	March 1976
MH Toei	*Garuda No 5*	23.9 knots	96	October 1979

Route operated
Ushifuka to Minamata

Fuke Kaiun Co. Ltd
3–3-25 Hon-machi, Sumoto-City 656, Japan

An HM 216 purchased from Hovermarine Pacific Co Ltd in July 1981.

High-speed craft operated

Type	Name	Speed	Seats	Launched
SES Hovermarine Transport Ltd HM 216	*Sea Hope* (ex *Hovstar*)	33 knots	63	September 1976
CAT Sanuki 36m	*Sea Chateau*	—	250	April 1988

Route operated
Fuke to Sumoto

Geibi Shosen Co. Ltd
1–11–23 Ujinakaigan, Minami-Ku, Hiroshima-City 734, Japan

High-speed craft operated

Type	Name	Speed	Seats	Launched
MH Miho Zosenjyo Co Ltd	*Chidori No 5*	24 knots	70	March 1979

Route operated
Nakamachi to Ujina

Goto Ryokaykusen Co. Ltd
5–35 Matsugaeda-machi, Nagasaki-City 850, Japan

High-speed craft operated

Type	Name	Speed	Seats	Launched
MH Nankai	*New Gotoh*	23 knots	193	June 1984

Route operated
Gonokubi to Fukue

Habu Shosen Co. Ltd
1899–31 Habu-Cho, Innoshima-City 722–23, Japan

High-speed craft operated

Type	Name	Speed	Seats	Launched
MH Kiso Zosen Tekko Co Ltd	Innoshima No 2	25 knots	68	April 1976
MH Kiso Zosen Tekko Co Ltd	Innoshima No 3	26 knots	70	July 1979
MH Kiso Zosen Tekko Co Ltd	Innoshima No 5	26.5 knots	70	March 1981

Route operated
Habu to Mihara

Hankyu Kisen Co. Ltd
45 Harima-machi, Chuo-Ku, Kobe-City 650, Japan
Kobe, Hyogo Prefecture, Japan

Telephone: (78) 3315191

Asaziro Katsumata, *Maritime Director*

High-speed craft operated

Type	Name	Speed	Seats	Launched
HYD Hitachi Zosen PT 50	Zuihoh	35 knots	123	January 1972
HYD Hitachi Zosen PT 50	Houo	35 knots	123	March 1972
HYD Hitachi Zosen PT 50		35 knots	123	February 1974
HYD Hitachi Zosen PTS 50 Mk II	Housho	38 knots	123	January 1983

Routes operated
Kobe to Kameura (Naruto)
Kobe to Tokushima

Hayatekaiun Co. Ltd
148–15 Maesatosoe, Irabu-cho, Miyako-Gun, Okinawa-ken 906–05, Japan

High-speed craft operated

Type	Name	Speed	Seats	Delivered
MH Setouchi Craft Co Ltd	Hayate No 11	25 knots	70	March 1984

Route operated
Sarahama to Hirara

Higashi Chugoku Ryoju Kosen
Japan

High-speed craft operated

Type	Name	Speed	Seats	Delivered
CAT Mitsubishi HSCC	Ukishiro	—	12	1987

Hiroshima Imabari Kosokusen Co. Ltd
853 Miyajima-cho, Saeki-Gun, Hiroshema-Ken 739–05, Japan

High-speed craft operated

Type	Name	Speed	Seats	Delivered
MH Miho Zosenjyo Co Ltd	Waka	25 knots	84	July 1984
MH Miho Zosenjyo Co Ltd	Seto	25 knots	84	August 1984

Route operated
Ujina to Imabari

Horai Kisen Co. Ltd
2235–17 Minato-machi, Mihara-City 723, Japan

High-speed craft operated

Type	Name	Speed	Seats	Delivered
MH Fuji Yacht	Hikari No 2	23 knots	139	March 1978
MH Kanda Zosen	Hikari No 3	23 knots	69	November 1979

Route operated
Mihara to Setoda

Imabari Kosokusen Co. Ltd
1–2 Katahara-cho, Imabari-City 794, Japan

High-speed craft operated

Type	Name	Speed	Seats	Delivered
MH Miho Zosenjyo Co Ltd	Kamome No 2	24 knots	52	November 1973
MH Miho Zosenjyo Co Ltd	Kamome No 5	25 knots	80	May 1976
MH Miho Zosenjyo Co Ltd	Chidori No 7	24 knots	70	January 1980
MH Miho Zosenjyo Co Ltd	Kamome No 7	25 knots	93	April 1982

Routes operated
Imabari to Iguchi
Imabari to Onomichi

Iriomote Kanko Kaiun Co. Ltd
2 Misaki-Cho, Ishigaki-City 907, Japan

High-speed craft operated

Type	Name	Speed	Seats	Delivered
MH Sumidagawa Zosen Co Ltd	Marine Star	24 knots	141	March 1979

Route operated
Ishigaki to Funaura

Ishizaki Kisen Co. Ltd
1–4-9 Mitsu, Matsuyama-City 791, Ehime Prefecture, Japan

Telephone: (899) 510 128

High-speed craft operated

Type	Name	Speed	Seats	Launched
HYD Hitachi Zosen PT 20	Kansei*	34 knots	66	1962
HYD Hitachi Zosen PT 50	Kosei	34 knots	125	1969
HYD Hitachi Zosen PT 20	Myojo	34 knots	66	1970
HYD Hitachi Zosen PT 20	Kinsei	34 knots	68	1972
HYD Hitachi Zosen PT 50	Saisei	34 knots	126	1974
HYD Hitachi Zosen PT 50	Shunsei	34 knots	123	1975
HYD Hitachi Zosen PT 20	Ryusei	34 knots	69	1981

*Spare craft

Routes operated
Matsuyama to Hiroshima (PT 50s)
Matsuyama to Onomichi (PT 20s)
Matsuyama to Mihara (PT 20s)

Iwakuni Hashirajima Kosokusen Co. Ltd
Iwakuniko 4, Shinminato-machi, Iwakuni-City 740, Japan

High-speed craft operated

Type	Name	Speed	Seats	Delivered
MH Kiso Zosen Tekko Co Ltd	Suisei	22 knots	96	November 1982

Route operated
Iwakuni to Hashirashima

Izu-Hakone Railways Co. Ltd
300 Daiba, Mishima-City 411, Japan

High-speed craft operated

Type	Name	Speed	Seats	Delivered
MH Sumidagawa Zosen Co Ltd	Cobalt Arrow 2	22 knots	132	March 1975
MH Sumidagawa Zosen Co Ltd	Cobalt Arrow 3	22 knots	144	December 1978

Route operated
Numazu to Matsuzaki

Japanese National Railways
Koko-tetsu Building, 1–6-5 Marunouchi 1-chome, Chiyoda-ku, Tokyo 100, Japan

Telephone: (03) 212 3587

The Mitsui MV-PP5 Mk II hovercraft *Tobiuo* was withdrawn from service in April 1988 following the construction of the road and rail bridge between Shikoku and Honshu islands

Japan Ocean Cruise Line
Japan

High-speed craft operated

Type	Name	Speed	Seats	Launched
HYD Kawasaki Jetfoil 929–117	Nagasaki	45 knots	180	September 1989

Kagoshima Shosen Co Ltd
Japan

High-speed craft operated

Type	Name	Speed	Seats	Delivered
HYD Kawasaki Jetfoil 929–117	Toppy	45 knots	265	June 1989

Kansai Express Ferry. Co Ltd
1–3 Tamamo-cho, Takamatsu-City 760, Japan

High-speed craft operated

Type	Name	Speed	Seats	Delivered
MH Suzuki Zosen Co Ltd	*Phoenix 1*	23.27 knots	88	February 1975
MH Suzuki Zosen Co Ltd	*Phoenix 2*	23.00 knots	88	April 1975

Routes operated
Tonosho to Takamatsu
Takamatsu to Tonosho

Kasumigaura Jet Line KK
Japan

High-speed craft operated

Type	Name	Delivered
MH Yamaha Motor Co Ltd	*Kasumi Jet*	1984

Kato Kisen Co Ltd/Kansai Kisen Co Ltd
Japan

High-speed craft operated

Type	Name	Launched
HYD Boeing Jetfoil 929–115	*Jet 7* (ex *Spirit of Friendship*)	August 1980
HYD Boeing Jetfoil 929–115	*Jet 8* (ex *Spirit of Discovery*)	April 1985

Operation
Started 1987, Seto Inland Sea

Kochiken Marine Co. Ltd
6–10–23 Sanbashidori, Kochi-City 780, Japan

High-speed craft operated

Type	Name	Seats	Completed
CAT Mitsui CP30MK Supermaran	*Coral*	250	July 1988

Koshikijima Shosen Co. Ltd
Nomotochisaki, Kushikino-City 896, Japan

High-speed craft operated

Type	Name	Speed	Seats	Launched
MH Mitsubishi	*Sea Hawk*	26.5 knots	290	January 1977

Route operated
Kushikino to Koshikijima

Kyodo Kisen Co. Ltd
5 Kaigandori, Chuo-Ku, Kobe-City 650, Japan

1–5–24 Hama-Ohtsu, Ohtsu 520, Shiga Prefecture, Japan

High-speed craft operated

Type	Name	Speed	Seats	Delivered
MH Miho Zosenjyo Co Ltd	*Hamakaze*	25 knots	136	February 1976
MH Miho Zosenjyo Co Ltd	*Asakaze*	25 knots	135	August 1977
MH Miho Zosenjyo Co Ltd	*Oikaze*	25 knots	136	September 1978
MH Miho Zosenjyo Co Ltd	*Sachikaze*	25 knots	136	December 1978
MH Miho Zosenjyo Co Ltd	*Urakaze*	25 knots	136	November 1979

Routes operated
Osaka to Sumoto
Kobe to Sumoto

Kyushu Shosen Co. Ltd
16–12 Motofune-cho, Nagasaki-City 850, Japan

High-speed craft operated

Type	Name	Speed	Seats	Delivered
HYD Kawasaki Jetfoil 929–117	*Pegasus*	45 knots	282	March 1990

Kyūshū Yusen Co Ltd
1–27 Kamiya, Hakata, Fukuoka 812, Japan

High-speed craft operated

Type	Name	Speed	Seats	Launched
MH Mitsubishi	*Sea Ace*	28 knots	231	May 1980
HYD Kawasaki Jetfoil 929–117	—	45 knots	263	March 1991

Route operated
Hakata to Iki

Maruto Kisen Co. Ltd
2235–17 Minato-machi, Mihara-City 723, Japan

High-speed craft operated

Type	Name	Speed	Seats	Delivered
MH Tohkai Boat Co Ltd	*Queen Romance*	27 knots	115	June 1976
MH Hayami Zosen Co Ltd	*Queen Romance No 2*	29 knots	126	April 1982

Route operated
Setoda to Mihara

Meitetsu Kaijo Kankosen Co. Ltd
18–1 Sanbonmatsu-cho, Atsuta-Ku, Nagoya-city 456, Japan

High-speed craft operated

Type	Name	Speed	Seats	Delivered
MH Suzuki Zosen Co Ltd	*Ohtoki*	22 knots	97	February 1981
MH Suzuki Zosen Co Ltd	*Ohtoki 2*	22 knots	97	July 1981
MH Suzuki Zosen Co Ltd	*Ohtoki 3*	22 knots	97	March 1982
MH Suzuki Zosen Co Ltd	*Kaien 5*	22 knots	61	March 1982
MH Suzuki Zosen Co Ltd	*Kaien 6*	22 knots	79	July 1982

Routes operated
Shinojima to Kohwa
Gamagohri to Toba

Mihara Kanko Kisen Co Ltd
2235–17 Minato-machi Mihari-City 723,Japan

High-speed craft operated

Type	Name	Speed	Seats	Delivered
MH Setouchi Craft Co Ltd	*Nishi Nikko No 3*	26 knots	150	October 1976
MH Setouchi Craft Co Ltd	*Nishi Nikko No 5*	26 knots	81	February 1981
MH Setouchi Craft Co Ltd	*Nishi Nikko No 8*	26 knots	81	October 1981

Route operated
Mihara to Setoda

Mikatagoko Yuransen
1–5 Hayase Mihama-Cho Mikata-Gun Fukui-Ken 919–11, Japan

High-speed craft operated

Type	Name	Speed	Seats	Delivered
MH Ohtani	*Suisei No 3*	22 knots	50	July 1975
MH Ohtani	*Suisei No 5*	22 knots	50	July 1975
MH Ohtani	*Suisei No 6*	22 knots	50	August 1976
MH Ohtani	*Suisei No 7*	22 knots	50	August 1976
MH Ohtani	*Suisei No 8*	22 knots	50	May 1981

Route operated
Hayase to Mikatasanbashi

Ministry of Transportation
Maritime Safety Agency, Japan

High-speed craft operated

Type	Name	Delivered
MH Mitsubishi Heavy Industries Ltd 26.01m	*Iseyuki*	1975
MH Mitsubishi Heavy Industries Ltd 26.01m	*Hamazuki*	1976
MH Mitsubishi Heavy Industries Ltd 26.01m	*Hatagumo*	1976
MH Mitsubishi Heavy Industries Ltd 26.01m	*Isozuki*	1977
MH Mitsubishi Heavy Industries Ltd 30.99m	*Asagumo*	1978
MH Mitsubishi Heavy Industries Ltd 30.99m	*Hayagumo*	1979
MH Mitsubishi Heavy Industries Ltd 26.01m	*Hanayuki*	1981
MH Mitsubishi Heavy Industries Ltd 26.01m	*Awagiri*	1983
MH Mitsubishi Heavy Industries Ltd 30.99m	*Asagari*	1983

Operation
Patrol vessels

Third District Port Construction Bureau
Japan

High-speed craft operated

Type	Name	Delivered
SWATH Mitsubishi 27.01m	*Ohtori*	March 1981

Nankai Ferry Co Ltd
6–5 Chikkoh, Wakayama 640, Wakayama Prefecture, Japan

High-speed craft operated

Type	Name	Speed	Seats	Launched
CAT Mitsui CP30	*Marine Hawk*	28.5 knots	280	July 1983

National Institute of Polar Research
9–10 Kaga 1-chome, Itabashi-ku, Tokyo 173, Japan

Telex: 2723515 POLRSCJ
Telefax: (03) 963 0166

K Ishizawa, *Logistics Section, National Institute of Polar Research*

The Mitsui MV-PPO5A air cushion vehicle is used only for collecting performance data on sea ice near Syowa Station.

High-speed craft operated
Type	Speed	Seats	Delivered
HOV Mitsui MV-PP05A	30 knots	3	1980

MV-PPO5A on sea ice near Syowa Station

Nihon Koun Kaisha Ltd
Eime Prefecture, Japan

High-speed craft operated
Type	Name	Seats	Delivered
MH Mitsubishi Heavy Industries Ltd 26.76m	Sunline	70	September 1986

Nomi-cho Kotsu Office
1–13–13 Ujinakaigan Minami-Ku Hiroshima City 734, Japan

High-speed craft operated
Type	Name	Speed	Seats	Delivered
MH Miho Zosenjyo Co Ltd	Chidori No 6	22 knots	76	June 1981

Route operated
Nakamachi to Ujina

Ohmi Marine
11–12 Yasukiyo-Cho, Hikone City 522 Japan

High-speed craft operated
Type	Name	Speed	Seats	Delivered
MH Mokubei	Wakaayu	22 knots	64	February 1972
MH Mokubei	Wakaayu No 2	22 knots	88	August 1973
MH Mokubei	Wakaayu No 5	24 knots	160	March 1983
MH Mokubei	Wakaayu No 8	24 knots	62	March 1984
MH Mokubei	Wakaayu No 6	24 knots	100	July 1984

Routes operated
Hikone to Chikubushima
Imazu to Chikubushima
Iiura to Chikubushima

Ohmishima Ferry
6762 Inokuchi Kamiura-Cho Ochi-Gun Ehime-Ken 794–14, Japan

High-speed craft operated
Type	Name	Speed	Seats	Delivered
MH Miho Zosen Co Ltd	Ohmishima No 3	23.8 knots	70	May 1978

Route operated
Mihara to Iguchi

Oita Hover Ferry Co Ltd
1–14–1 Nishi-shinchi, Oita shi Oita ken, Japan

Telephone: (0975) 58 7180

Hiroshi Ono, *President*
Keiichiro Isayama, *Vice President*
Kitoshi Iwai, *General Director*

Oita Hover Ferry Co Ltd was established in November 1970 and began operating in October 1971.
Annual traffic: Approx 360 000

High-speed craft operated
Type	Name	Speed	Seats	Launched
HOV Mitsui MV-PP5 Mk 2	Hakuchyo No 3	45 knots	75	June 1970
HOV Mitsui MV-PP5 Mk 2	Hobby No 1	45 knots	75	May 1971
HOV Mitsui MV-PP5 Mk 2	Hobby No 3	45 knots	75	September 1971
HOV Mitsui MV-PP5 Mk 2	Angel No 5	45 knots	75	April 1975
HOV Mitsui MV-PP5	Hobby No 6 (ex Akatombo 51 and stretched)	45 knots	75	
HOV Mitsui MV-PP5	Hobby No 7 (ex Akatombo 52)		51	

Routes operated
Oita to Oita Airport (15.6n miles, 24 min)
Beppu to Oita Airport (6.5n miles, 10 min)

Oita Hover Ferry MV-PP5   *(K Isayama)*

Oki Kisen KK
Nakamachim, Saigo-cho, Okigun, Shimane Prefecture, Japan

Telephone: (85) 1221122
Telex: 628966J
High-speed craft operated
Type	Name	Speed	Seats	Launched
MH Mitsubishi 48.5m	Marine Star	28 knots	351	December 1983

Route operated
Sakai to Oki

Ryobi Unyu
1–1-8 Bancho Okayama City, Japan

High-speed craft operated
Type	Name	Speed	Seats	Delivered
MH Miho Zosen	Princess Olive	24 knots	94	July 1981
MH Miho Zosen	Queen Olive	24 knots	94	October 1981

Route operated
Okayama to Tonosho

Sado Kisen Kaisha
9–1 Ban Bandaijima, Niigata City 950, Japan

Telephone: 0252(45) 2311

S Nakamura, *Jetfoil Manager*

Passengers carried in 1984: 465 000.

High-speed craft operated
Type	Name	Speed	Seats	In service
HYD Boeing Jetfoil 929–100	Okesa	42 knots	282	May 1977
HYD Boeing Jetfoil 929–115	Mikado	42 knots	286	1978
HYD Boeing Jetfoil 929–115	Ginga (ex Cu na Mara)	42 knots	257	1986
HYD Kawasaki Jetfoil 929	Tsubasa	45 knots	266	March 1989
HYD Kawasaki Jetfoil 117	—	45 knots	266	April 1991

Route operated
Niigata Honshu Island to Ryotsu, Sado Island (36.3n miles, 1 hour)

Sanyo Kisen Co Ltd
2418–8 Kasaoka, Kasaoka City 714 Japan

High-speed craft operated

Type	Name	Speed	Seats	Delivered
MH Suzuki Zosen Co Ltd	Silver Star	23 knots	90	March 1972
MH New Japan Marine Co Ltd	New Sanyo	22 knots	79	January 1973
MH Setouchi Craft Co Ltd	Setoji	24 knots	75	August 1982

Routes operated
Fukuyama to Marugame
Kasaoka to Sanagi

Sanyo Shosen Co Ltd
1030–23 Takehara-Cho, Takehara City, Japan

High-speed craft operated

Type	Name	Speed	Seats	Delivered
MH Miho Zosenjyo Co Ltd	Hayabusa No 5	24 knots	58	March 1975
MH Miho Zosenjyo Co Ltd	Chidori No 3	22 knots	52	June 1975
MH Miho Zosenjyo Co Ltd	Hayabusa No 7	24 knots	58	July 1975
MH Miho Zosenjyo Co Ltd	Hayabusa No 8	24 knots	58	April 1977
MH Miho Zosenjyo Co Ltd	Hayabusa No 10	24 knots	70	October 1977
MH Miho Zosenjyo Co Ltd	Hayabusa No 11	24 knots	70	March 1979

Routes operated
Nikata to Imabari
Mihara to Ohcho
Takehara to Namikata

Sanyu Kisen Co Ltd
Japan

High-speed craft operated

Type	Name	Speed	Seats	Delivered
MH New Japan Marine Co Ltd	Wakamaru	22.4 knots	60	March 1976

Route operated
Ujina to Akashi

Seiun Kisen Co Ltd
2-5-12 Sakaeminato-machi, Uwajima City 798, Japan

High-speed craft operated

Type	Name	Speed	Seats	Delivered
MH Miho Zosenjyo Co Ltd	Chidori	24 knots	46	September 1972
MH Miho Zosenjyo Co Ltd	Hayakaze	25 knots	52	July 1974
MH Miho Zosenjyo Co Ltd	Shiokaze	25 knots	80	February 1976

Route operated
Tsunoura to Uwajima

Setonaikai Kisen Co Ltd (Seto Inland Sea Lines)
1–12–23 Ujinakaigan, Minami-ku, Hiroshima 734, Japan

Telephone: (082) 255 3344
Telex: 653–625 STSHRM J
Telefax: (082) 251 6743

Toshihiro Yoshii, *Sales Director* (Hoshi Building 3F, 1-6-11 Kamiyacho, Nakaku, Hiroshima, Japan)

Setonaikai Kisen Co has been operating transport services linking the islands in the Inland Sea for many years and now has a fleet of 38 vessels, operating regular services along nine routes between Hiroshima and Shikoku, including a main route between Hiroshima and Matsuyama.

High-speed craft operated

Type	Name	Speed	Seats	Launched
HYD Hitachi Supramar PT 20	Ohtori No 2*	34 knots	113	February 1970
HYD Hitachi Supramar PT 20	Ohtori No 3*	34 knots	113	October 1972
HYD Hitachi Supramar PT 20	Hikari No 2*	34 knots	123	March 1975
HYD Hitachi Supramar PT 50	Condor*	34 knots	121	June 1972
HYD Hitachi Supramar PT 50	Ohtori No 5	34 knots	113	May 1973
HYD Hitachi Supramar PT 50	Condor No 2	34 knots	121	April 1974
HYD Hitachi Supramar PT 50	Condor No 3	34 knots	121	August 1974
MH Miho Zosenjo	Marine Star 2	25 knots	103	November 1979
MH Miho Zosenjo	Marine Star 3	25 knots	120	January 1983
Setouchi Craft MH	Akinada	27 knots	125	May 1989

*spare craft

Routes operated
Miyajima to Hiroshima to Omishima Island (Port of Miyaura) to Setoda (*Akinada*)
Hiroshima to Matsuyama 1 hour (*Condor, Condor No 2, Condor No 3 and Ohtori No 5*), some services stopping at Kure, then 1 hour 10 min (*Hikari No 2*)
Mihara to Imabari 1 hour (*Marine Star 2, Marine Star 3*), some services stopping at Setoda, then 1 hour 7 min

Akinada, introduced into service by Setonaiki Kisen in May 1989

Shikoku Ferry Company (Bridge Line)
10–32 Tamamo-cho, Takamatsu City 760, Japan

High-speed craft operated

Type	Delivered
CAT Sanuki Shipbuilding and Iron Works 30m *Sea Chateau*	1988

Shikoku Railway Company (JR Shikoku)
1–10, Hamano-cho, Takamatsue-shi, Kagawa-ken, 760, Japan
This company took over the Shikoku part of the business of Japan National Railways. The hovercraft *Tobiuo* was taken out of service April 9 1988 and sold.

High-speed craft operated

Type	Name	Speed	Seats	Launched
MH	Shiokaze	27 knots	140	July 1987

Route operated
10–8 miles, trip time, 29 miles

Shiokaze

Shimabara Kanko Kisen
7 Shimokarishiri-machi, Shimabara City 855, Japan

High-speed craft operated

Type	Name	Speed	Seats	Delivered
MH Shinju Zosen Kohgyo Co Ltd	Hamayuu	23 knots	86	January 1974
MH Toei	Garuda No 3	22 knots	83	September 1978

Route operated
Shimabara to Ohmuta

Shodoshima Kosoku
10–32 Tamamo-cho,Takamatsu City 760,Japan

High-speed craft operated

Type	Name	Speed	Seats	Delivered
MH Miho Zosenjyo	*Hikari*	25 knots	90	December 1974

Route operated
Takamatsu to Tonosho

Showa Kaiun Co Ltd
1–2 Katahara cho,Imabari 794, Ehime Prefecture, Japan

High-speed craft operated

Type	Name	Speed	Seats	Delivered
HYD Hitachi Zosen PT 20	*Hayate No 1*	33.5 knots	67	April 1962
CAT Mitsui Super Westamarin CP20	*Blue Hawk*	25 knots	162	

Routes operated
Matsuyama to Mihara *(Hayate No 1)*
Mihari to Imabari *(Blue Hawk)*

Tenmaya Marine Co Ltd
Japan

High-speed craft operated

Type	Name	Seats	Completed
CAT Mitsui CP5 Supermaran	*Mon Cheri*	58	May 1988

Tokai Kisen
1-9-15 Kaigan, Minato-ku, Tokyo 105, Japan

Telephone: 03–432–4551

High-speed craft operated

Type	Name	Speed	Seats	Launched
SWATH Mitsui	*Seagull* (ex *Mesa-80*)	25 knots	402	July 1979
MH Mitsubishi Heavy Industries Ltd	*Seahawk 2*	26.5 knots	401	February 1980
SWATH Mitsui	*Seagull 2*	22 knots	420	December 1989

Routes operated
Seagull
Atami to Ohshima
Tokyo to Ohshima*
Tokyo to Niijima*
Ohshima to Tokyo
Seahawk 2
Inatori to Ohshima
Ito to Ohshima
Atami to Ohshima*
*summer services only

Tokushima Kosokusen Co Ltd (Tokushima Highspeed Boat Co)
3-1-3 Sannomiya-cho, Chuo-ku, Kobe, Japan
Hiromu Harada, *President*

High-speed craft operated

Type	Name	Speed	Seats	Launched
CAT Mitsui Supermaran CP30 Mk III	*Blue Star*	32 knots	280	21 June 1987
CAT Mitsui Supermaran CP30 Mk III	*Sun Rise*	35 knots	280	20 July 1987

Route operated
Osaka to Tokushima, Shikoku Island

(Tokushima Shuttle Line Co Ltd)
3–11–10 Chikkoh, Minato-ku, Osaka, Japan

Hiromu Harada, *President*

High-speed craft operated

Type	Name	Speed	Launched
CAT Mitsui Supermaran CP30Mk II *Marine Shuttle*		32	February 1986

Route operated
Wakayama to Tokushima, Shikoku Island

Tokushin Co Ltd
345–1 Yamauchimen Tabira-cho, Kitamatsuura-Gun, Nagasaki-Ken 859–48,Japan

High-speed craft operated

Type	Name	Speed	Seats	Delivered
MH Toei	*Cobalt No 1*	23 knots	95	January 1977
MH Toei	*Cobalt No 2*	23 knots	95	March 1977

Route operated
Hirato to Kashimae

Ueda Kaiun KK
Japan

Charterer of Mitsui Supermaran CP10 from KK Seto Naikai Cruising formed in 1987 as a joint venture of MES, the Chutetso Group and the Ueda Group.

High-speed craft operated

Type	Name	Seats	Delivered
CAT Mitsui CP10	*Marine Queen*	88	April 1987

Operation
Cruising on the Seto Island Sea

Wakasawan Kanko Co Ltd
1-3-2 Kawasaki, Obama City 917, Japan

High-speed craft operated

Type	Name	Speed	Seats	Delivered
MH Obama Zosen	*Wakasa*	22 knots	180	April 1973

Route operated
Obama to Sodohmon

Yaeyama Kanko Ferry Co
1–3 Misaki-cho, Isigaki-City 907, Okinawa, Japan

Telephone: 0980825010
Telex: 792681K

High-speed craft operated

Type	Name	Speed	Seats	Delivered
MH Miho Zosenjyo Co Ltd	*Hayabusa*	27 knots	88	December 1974
MH Shinju Shipyard Co Ltd 27.3m	*Tropical Queen*	30 knots	150	July 1982
MH Suzuki Zosen Co Ltd	*Hirugi 2*	28 knots	96	February 1986

Route operated
Ishigaki to surrounding islands

Mitsui Supermaran CP30 Mk III *Sun Rise*

Model of *Tropical Queen* designed by Yamaha Motor Co

Yasuda Sangyo Kisen Co Ltd
(Yasuda Ocean Group) Airport Line
5–35 Matsugaeda-machi, Nagasaki, Japan

High-speed craft operated

Type	Name	Speed	Seats	Delivered
MH Higashi Kyushu	Ohmura	23 knots	77	April 1976
MH Sakamoto	Ryuyo	23 knots	55	Ausust 1976
MH Shinju	Ohmura 3	23 knots	71	September 1976
MH Shinju	Ohmura 5	23 knots	71	December 1976
MH Shinju	Mishima	22 knots	139	December 1979
MH Shinju	Nagasaku 5	23 knots	22	April 1980
MH Shinju	Nagasaki 7	23 knots	22	July 1980
MH Fantom Marin Ishijima	Airport Liner 1	30 knots	12	March 1985
MH Fantom Marin Ishijima	Airport Liner 3	30 knots	12	July 1985
MH Nankai	Genkai 3	23 knots	95	March 1982
MH Nankai	Genkai 3	23 knots	95	March 1982
MH Nankai	Genkai 5	23 knots	104	May 1983
MH Nankai	Erasumus	25 knots	123	October 1984
MH Nankai	Airport Liner 5	30 knots	44	July 1985
MH Nankai	Airport Liner 7	25 knots	66	March 1986
MH Nankai	Airport Liner 8	25 knots	66	March 1986
MH Nankai	Airport Liner 10	27 knots	66	December 1986
MH Nankai	Airport Liner 11	27 knots	66	February 1987
MH Nankai	Airport Liner 13	27 knots	66	April 1987
MH Nankai	Airport Liner 15	27 knots	66	June 1987
MH Nankai	Airport Liner 17	27 knots	66	June 1987
MH Nankai	Nagasaki 8	25 knots	39	June 1987
MH Nankai	Nagasaki 10	25 knots	39	August 1987
MH Nankai	Taiyo	25 knots	231	March 1988
MH Shinju	Toliton	23 knots	150	June 1986
MH Shinju	New Nagasaki	24 knots	120	December 1973
MH Uehara	Ocean Liner 1	27 knots	88	April 1988
MH Euhara	Ocean Liner 3	27 knots	88	September 1988
MH Uehara	Ocean Liner 5	27 knots	97	February 1989
MH Nankai	Ocean Liner 7	27 knots	97	February 1989
MH Nankai	Ocean Liner 8	27 knots	97	February 1989
SES Brødrene Aa CIRR 120P	—	43 knots	320	September 1990

Routes operated
Nagasaki Airport to Ohmura and Simabara
Nagasaki Airport to Ohkusa
Nagasaki Airport to Togitsu and Nagasaki
Nagasaki Airport to Nagasaki Holland Village and Hirado and Sasebo and Higashi Sonogo and Ureshino

---

JORDAN

Port of Aquaba Authority
Aquaba, Jordan

High-speed craft operated
Type
SES Hovermarine HM 218

KOREA, SOUTH

Daeheung Sang-sa
South Korea

High-speed craft operated

Type	Name	Seats	Built
HYD Hitachi Zosem	Dae Heung (ex Tobiuo No 1 '81)	133	1973

Dae Won Ferry Co Ltd
Pohang
South Korea

High-speed craft operated

Type	Name	Seats	Built
CAT Fjellstrand 38.8m	Dae Won Catamaran	396	November 1988

Route operated
Mukho to Ullung-do, 85n miles, 3 hours

Dong-Bu Co Ltd
Chongro 2 GA 9, Changro Gu, Seoul 110, South Korea

Telephone: (02) 720 6811/9
and
Chung-peong Lee 205–3, Puck-san meun, Chun Sung Kun, Kang-Won Doo, South Korea

Telephone: (0361) 2–6488

High-speed craft operated

Type	Name	Seats
SES Korea Tacoma Marine Industries Ltd 12m	Que-Ryoung	56
SES Korea Tacoma Marine Industries Ltd 17m	Que-Ryoung II	72

Route operated
Soyang River (Yang gu)-In Jae

Dong-Hae Kosokchun Co
South Korea

High-speed craft operated

Type	Name	Seats
CAT Mitsui CP20	Dong-hae Kosok 1	182

Route operated
Imwon to Chodong

Ge-Jae Gaebal
5 Ga 16, Jung-Ang Dong, Jung Gu, Pusan City 600, South Korea (terminal)

Telephone: 4630354

K S Kim, *President*

High-speed craft operated

Type	Name	Seats
SES Korea Tacoma Marine Industries Ltd 18m	Phinex	60

Route operated
Pusan to Gejae Island

Government

High-speed craft operated

Type	Name	Delivered
HOV Korea Tacoma Industries Ltd Turt IV type, 12m	Eagle II	1984

Han Ryeo Development Co Ltd
9F Suhrin Building, 88 Suhrin Dong, Chongru-Gu, Seoul, South Korea

Telephone: (734) 5638/9
Telex: 24856HANRYEO K
Telefax: (739) 4349

High-speed craft operated

Type	Name	Delivered
HYD Rodriquez PT 20	Angel I	
HYD Hitachi PT 20	Angel III	
HYD Rodriquez RHS 110	Angel VII	
HYD Hyundai PT 20	Angel IX	January 1985

Route operated
Busan to Yeosu

Sea trial of Hyundai PT 20 *Angel IX*, January 1985

Jeo-Kyung Ferry Co.
5 Ga 16, Jung-Ang Dong, Jung Gu, Pusan City 600, South Korea

Telephone: 445994

J S Park, *President*

High-speed craft operated

Type	Name
SES Korea Tacoma Marine Industries Ltd 18m	*Air Ferry*

Route operated
Pusan to Gejae Island

Korea Tacoma 18m SES *Golden Star* entering Pusan Harbour

Jung Ahang Express Company
South Korea

High-speed craft operated

Type	Seats	Delivered
MH Miwon Trading and Shipping Co 28m	20	August 1986
MH Miwon Trading and Shipping Co 28m	128	September 1986

Operation
A four-craft fleet operates on the man-made Choong Joo Dam where it is engaged in sightseeing tours.

Ministry of Health and Social Affairs
South Korea

High-speed craft operated

Type	Name	Seats
HOV Korea Tacoma Marine Industries Ltd Turt IV Mk 1	*Jun-Nam 540*	9

Nam Hae Express Co.
Mokpo, South Korea

High-speed craft operated

Type	Name	Seats	Built
CAT Kvaerner Fjellstrand 38.8m —		—	1989

Semo Co. South Korea
High-speed craft operated

Type	Name	Seats
SES Korea Tacoma Marine Industries Ltd 23m	*Young-Kwang I*	158
SES Korea Tacoma Marine Industries Ltd 23m	*Young-Kwang II**	158

*modified 28m SES

Route operated
Pusan to Gejae Island (Okpo, Changsungpo and Dumo)

Shin Young Shipbuilding & Engineering Co
789 Woodoo-ri, Tolsan-up, Yeochun Kun, Junham, South Korea

Telephone: (0662) 2–1251–6
Telefax: (0662) 63–1256

Jang-Yeon Shin, *President*

High-speed craft operated

Type	Name	Seats
SES Korea Tacoma Marine Industries Ltd 26m	*Tacoma III*	158

Route operated
Yeosu to Gemun Island

Wha-Sung Haewoon
5 Ga 16, Jung-Ang Dong, Jung Gu, Pusan City 600, South Korea (terminal)

Telephone: 442063

W K Shin

High-speed craft operated

Type	Name	Seats
SES Korea Tacoma Marine Industries Ltd 18m	*Golden Star*	60

Route operated
Pusan to Gejae Island

KUWAIT

Kuwait Public Transport Co
(ex Touristic Enterprises Company (KSC))
PO Box 23310 Safat, Kuwait

Telephone: 412060
Telex: 22801TENCO KT

High-speed craft operated

Type	Name	Seats	Delivered
SES Vosper Hovermarine HM 218	*Auhah*	82	February 1983
SES Vosper Hovermarine HM 218	*Umn Al Maradam*	82	1983
SES Vosper Hovermarine HM 218	*J/Kubbar*	82	1984
CAT NQEA InCat 26m	*Adaire*	150	August 1988
CAT NQEA InCat 26m	*Na'ayem*	150	November 1988

Route operated
Ras Al-Ardh Terminal, Kuwait City to Failaka Island (10n miles, 25 min)

MADEIRA
See Portugal

MALAYSIA

Asie Crewboat Sdn Bhd
10th Floor Menara Apera ULG, 84 Jalan Raja Chulan, 50200 Kuala Lumpur, West Malaysia

Telephone: (03) 2610831/2610935
Telex: 30531 AHSB MA

Khalil Akasah, *Chairman*
Kamaruzaman Akasah, *Executive Director*
Capt Mohd Nasir Ahmad, *Operations Manager*

High-speed craft operated

Type	Name	Seats	Delivered
MH Halter Marine Sea Shuttle 34.1m	*Asie I*	60 (+ 80 tons cargo)	1982
MH Halter Marine Sea Shuttle 34.1m	*Asie II*	60 (+ 80 tons cargo)	1982/83
CAT Fjellstrand 31.5m	*Asie III*	96 (+ 40 tons cargo)	March 1984
MH Halter Marine Sea Shuttle 31.0m	*Asie IV*	52 (+ 30 tons cargo)	February 1985
MH Halter Marine Sea Shuttle 31.0m	*Asie V*	52 (+ 30 tons cargo)	March 1985
MH Halter Marine Sea Shuttle 31.0m	*Asie VI*	52 (+ 30 tons cargo)	July 1985
MH Halter Marine Sea Shuttle 31.0m	*Asie VII*	52 (+ 30 tons cargo)	February 1985

Operation
For Esso Production Malaysia Inc (EPMI), Sarawak Shell Bhd, Union Oil of Thailand and others
Offshore support, Malaysia, Thailand, Indonesia, South China Sea, and Singapore, transport of cargo and passengers, inter-fields offshore of Trengganu. Area of operation to include offshore Southern Thailand, Sabah & Sarawak waters.

Associated Marine Sdn Bhd

Kuching, Sarawak, Malaysia

High-speed craft operated

Type	Yard No	Name	Seats	Originally delivered
SES Hovermarine HM 216				
(HM2 Mk III)	326	(ex *HYF 101*)	60	1974

(laid up in Kuching, November 1986)

Black Gold (M) Sdn Bhd

151A Jalan Aminuddin Baki, Taman Tun Dr Ismail, Kuala Lumpur, Malaysia

High-speed craft operated

Type	Name	Delivered
MH Fairey Marinteknik Shipbuilders (S) MCB 31m	*Amal*	1986
MH Fairey Marinteknik Shipbuilders (S) MCB 31m	*Zakat*	1986

Hover Travel Sdn Bhd

1st Floor, 60 Market Place, Sibu, Sarawak, Malaysia

High-speed craft operated

Type	Name	Delivered
HOV Slingsby SAH 2200	*Challenger No 1*	1987

Kedah & Perlis Ferry Service Sdn Bhd

81 Dindong Kuah, Langkawi, Kedah, Malaysia

Telephone: (4) 749291

High-speed craft operated

Type	Name	Seats	Entered service
SES Vosper Hovermarine HM 218	*Kijang Mas*		February 1984
MH WaveMaster 30.7m	*Kita Ekspres*	150	1987
MH WaveMaster 27.0m	*Suka Ekspres*	130	1988
MH WaveMaster 27.0m	*Sinar Ekspres*	130	February 1989

Route operated

Kuala Perlis to Langkawi Island (45 mins)

Vosper Hovermarine HM 218 *Kijang Mas* operated by Kedah & Perlis Ferry Service Sdn Bhd

Malaysian Government

High-speed craft operated

Type	Name	Seats	Delivered
CAT Hong Leong-Lürssen Shipyard Bhd	*Zaharah*	131	September 1984

Malaysian International Shipping Corporation (MISC)/Amsbach Marine

No 2 Jalan Conlay, 50450 Kuala Lumpur 04–09, Malaysia

Telephone: (03) 2428088
Telex: 30325NALINE MA, 30428 MA, 31057 MA, 31058 MA

Arriffin Alias, *Managing Director*

High-speed craft operated

Type	Yard No	Name	Seats	Delivered
34m crew boat	103/61*	*Layar Sentosa*	70 (+ 12 tons cargo)	June 1987
34m crew boat	105	*Layar Sinar*	70 (+ 12 tons cargo)	June 1987

*hull built in Sweden

Operation

On time charter to a multinational oil company in coastal waters off Malaysia

MISC crew boat *Layar Sentosa*

Pomas Sdn Bhd

Hovermarine Wharf, Bintawa, Kuching, Sarawak, Malaysia

High-speed craft operated

Type	Name	Seats	Entered service
SES Hovermarine HM 218	*Pomas No 1*	95	April 1986

Route operated

Kuching to Sarikei to Sibu (daily) (90n miles)

Rawa Safaris

Mersing Tourist Centre, Jalang Ismail, Mersing Jahore, Malaysia

Tengku Alang

High-speed craft operated

Type	Name	In service
HYD Vosper Singapore PT 20B Mk II	*Rawa Bird*	1987

Operation

Mersing, Pulau Rawa and Pulau Tioman (not in monsoon season)

MALTA

Gozo Channel Co Ltd

Sa Maison Wharfe, Valleta, Malta

Lino Kuereb, *Managing Director*
J Engerei, *Operational Director*
Joseph Borg, *Engineer and Technical Director*

High-speed craft operated

Type	Name	Seats	In service
SES Hovermarine Int'l HM218	*Calypso*	84	May 1988

Route operated

Malta to Gozo services:
Ferries to Mgarr, 25min
Mgarr to Bugibba, 15 min
Mgarr to Sa MaIson, 26 min
Also services to Sliema to Mgarr (Gozo Island) and to Marsalform and Comino Island

Virtu Rapid Ferries Limited (A joint venture between The Virtu Steamship Co. Ltd. (Malta) and Fekete & Co. A/S (Norway)

'Virtu', 3 Princess Elizabeth Terrace, Ta'Xbiex, Malta

Telephone: 317088, 317071, 316766
Telex: 1214 & 1667 SHIPAZ MW
Telefax: 314533

Michael Kamsky, *General Manager*

High-speed craft operated

Type	Name	Seats	In service
SES Brødrene Aa Cirrus 120	*Santa Maria*	330	1988
SES Eikefjord Marine A/S Cirrus 120	*San Pawl*	330	1989
SES Eikefjord Marine A/S Cirrus 120	*San Pietro*	330	1989

Routes operated

Valetta (Malta) to Pozzallo,52 n miles, 1 hour 30 min
Valetta (Malta) to Catania,113 n miles, 3 hours
Larnaca to Jounieh (Lebanon), 3 hours
Valetta to Tunisia, 1990

Santa Maria in Mediterranean operation, 1989

MEXICO

Cruceros Maritimos del Caribe SA de CV
Calle 6 Nte No 14, Cozumel, Mexico

Telephone: (987) 21508/88

Venado 30, m18, SM 20, Cancún, Mexico

Telephone: 44211/22 44

Jose Trinidad Molina Caceres, *Chairman of the Board*
Rogelio Molina Caceres, *General Manager*
Javier Guillermo Clausell, *Manager*

High-speed craft operated

Type	Name	Seats	Delivered
CAT Fjellstrand 38.8m	*Mexico*	390	February 1986

Operation

Mexican Caribbean area tourist service
Cancún to Cozumel, 43 miles, fare approx US $15.0, August 1987
Cozumel to Playa del Carmen, 9 miles, fare approx US $3.0, August 1987

Fjellstrand 38.8m *Mexico*

Petroleos Mexicanos (PEMEX)
Tampico, Mexico

High-speedcraft operated

Type	Name	Seats	In Service
CAT Harding Verft A/S 26.0m	*Havstril*	200	January 1990

This vessel was purchased from Simon Møkster by the US company Daysland.

Operation

Transport of oil workers in Gulf of Mexico

Secretaria de Turismo
Avenida Presidente Masarik 172, Mexico 5, DF, Mexico

Telephone: 2508555

The Rodriquez hydrofoils, RHS 150 *Xel-Há* and RHS 160 *Nicte-Há*, operated by the Secretaria de Turismo, were laid up in 1986 in Veracruz.

MOROCCO

Cie Maritime des Hydrofoils Transtour (Transtour SA)
4 rue Jabha al Ouatania, Tangiers, Morocco

Telephone: 34004/5
Telex: 33608M

All craft laid up 1988

Kometa *Sindibad* when operated by Transtour SA

NETHERLANDS

BV Rederij G Doeksen en Zonen
West Terschelling, Netherlands

Telephone: (5620) 6111

J. A. Luycks, *Managing Director*
J Doeksen, Jnr, *Operational Manager*

High-speed craft operated

Type	Name	Seats	Delivered
CAT Westamarin W86	*Koegelwieck*	176	1973
CAT Harding Verft A/S 28.0m	*Stuifdijk*	250	June 1990

Route operated

Harlingen to Terschelling (45 mins)
Harlingen to Vlieland

Rotterdam Port Authority (Havenvan Rotterdam)
Galvanistraat 15, 3002 AP Rotterdam, Netherlands

Telephone: (010) 489 6911
Telex: 23077ALGEMEEN

High-speed craft operated

Type	Name	Delivered
SES Vosper Hovermarine HM 218	*Havendienst 1*	1979
For disposal		
Laid up		
SES Vosper Hovermarine HM 218	*Havendienst 7*	1979
SES Vosper Hovermarine HM 218	*Havendienst 10*	1979
SES Vosper Hovermarine HM 218	*Havendienst 9*	1980

Operation

Havendienst 1 in service for special operations

NEW ZEALAND

Fiordland Travel Ltd NZ
Milford and Doubtful Sounds, South Island, New Zealand

High-speed craft operated
Type	Name	Seats	Delivered
CAT Wanganui Boats (NZ) InCat 19.2m	Fiordland Flyer	140	September 1985

Fullers Captain Cook Cruises Ltd
Division of Fullers Corporation Ltd
PO Box 145, Maritime Building, Paiha, Bay of Islands, New Zealand

Telephone: 27421
Telex: 2613NZ
Telefax: 27831

PO Box 448, Auckland, New Zealand

Telephone: 394901
Telefax: 370636

Harry L Julian, *Chairman*
Peter B Smith, *Joint Managing Director, Bay of Islands*
Lance Julian, *Joint Managing Director, Auckland*
Karl Andersen, *Director*
Paul von Dorsten, *Director*
Frederick Mills, *Director*
Barry Fenton, *Director*
John Kane, *General Manager, Group Marketing*
Niall Allock, *Company Secretary*

Well-established interests in the marine transport field were merged in 1986 to form the Fullers Captain Cook Group. Fullers vessels have plied the Bay of Islands water since 1886. A wide range of vessels and vehicles are involved in the company's operations including an 18-metre, 40-passenger underwater viewing craft. Their first high-speed vessels were acquired in 1986 and 1987.

High-speed craft operated
Type	Name	Seats	Delivered
CAT NQEA InCat 24.0m	Supercat II	250	October 1986
CAT NQEA InCat 30.0m	Supercat III	450	August 1987

Operation
Bay of Islands, Auckland Harbour, Kawau Harbour

Golden Sands Charter Cruises
Auckland, New Zealand

This organisation purchased the Auckland Airport SR.N6 rescue hovercraft in February 1986 for NZ $157 000. In February 1987 it was reported to be operating in the Hauraki Gulf area, North Island.

Gulf Ferries Ltd (Waiheke Shipping Co Ltd)
5th Floor Endeans Building, 2 Queen St, Auckland, PO Box 1346, New Zealand

Telephone: (09) 33 380/733 776/779 260
Telefax: (09) 792 084
Douglas Hudson, *General Manager*

Supercat 2 passing Auckland Harbour

High-speed craft operated
Type	Name	Seats	Entered service
CAT SBF Engineering 33.37m	Quickcat	500+	March 1987
CAT NQEA 24.0m	Supercat II	180+	October 1988

A new high-speed vessel is contemplated for delivery at the end of 1990

Routes operated
Auckland to Waiheke Island, 30 min, Waiheke to Pakatoa Island, 1 hour commuter service. *Supercat* also operates along a route to the Great Barrier

Hydrofoil Cruises Ltd
PO Box 58, Queenstown, New Zealand

High-speed craft operated
Type	Name	Delivered
HYD Supramar PT 4	Meteor III	1970

Operation
30 min lake cruises from Central Queenstown

Hovercraft Adventures
PO Box 656, Queenstown, New Zealand

Telephone: 28034

Ewen J Mc Cammon, *Owner*

High-speed craft operated
Type	Delivered
HOV Hovercraft Manufacturers (NZ) Riverland Surveyor 8	1984

Operation
Half-hour tourist trips over mud flats, sand banks and river rapids in Queenstown area

The Mount Cook Group Ltd
The marine interests of this company have been sold to Fuller Captain Cook Cruises Ltd

Troutline of New Zealand
Jascar Group (NZ) Ltd
Lake Taupo, New Zealand

High-speed craft operated
Type	Name	Seats	Delivered
CAT NQEA InCat 24.0m	Taupo Cat	247	March 1987

Operation
Scenic cruising on Lake Taupo

Seaflight Ltd
Auckland, New Zealand

High-speedcraft operated
Type	Name	Seats	Delivered
CAT InCat Tasmania 37.2m	—	—	1988

Wanaka Lake Services Ltd
PO Box 20, Wanaka, New Zealand

Telephone: (02943) 7495
Telefax: (02943) 7805

Bruce Miller, *Director*

High-speed craft operated
HOV Riverland Surveyor 8-originally operated by Airborne Hovercraft Services

Operation
Half-hour tourist trips over farm land and in river and lake areas of Lake Wanaka, Ram Island, Matukituki River and Glendhu Bay

NIGERIA

Federal Ministry of Transport (Ind)
19th floor, Western House, Broad Street, Lagos, Nigeria

High-speed craft laid up

Type	Name	Delivered
SES Vosper Hovermarine HM 218	*Innovator I*	1977
SES Vosper Hovermarine HM 218	*Innovator II*	1977
SES Vosper Hovermarine HM 218	*Innovator III*	1977

Police

High-speed craft operated

Type	Delivered
HOV Air Vehicles Ltd Tiger	1983

Operation
Lagos Harbour patrol duties

NORWAY

A/S Bergen-Nordhordland Rutelag A/S (BNR)
Lars Hilles gt. 26, PO Box 4204
Nygårdstangen, 5028 Bergen, Norway

Telephone: (05) 318110
Telefax: (05) 317403

Oddvar Vigestad, *Commercial Director*

High-speed craft operated

Type	Name	Seats	Delivered
CAT Fjellstrand Aluminium Yacht Alumaran 165	*Manger*	189	1979
CAT Fjellstrand 31.5m	*Lygra*	292	1981

Route operated
Bergen to Frekhaug to Narvik to Frekhaug to Bergen. Round trip 1 hour 40 min to 1 hour 45 min

An early Fjellstrand catamaran *Manger* operated by Bergen Nordhordland Rutelag

Elkem-Spigerverket A/S
Lillebukt Stjernry, N-9543 Stjernsund, Norway

Mr Martinsen, *Director*

High-speed craft operated

Type	Name	Seats	Delivered
MH Fjellstrand 26m	*Nefelin IV*	84 (+ 32m³ cargo)	1980

Fjellstrand *Nefelin IV* operated by Elkem-Spigerverket

Finnmark Fylkesrederi og Ruteselskap
Havnegt 3, N-9600 Hammerfest, Norway

Telephone: (084) 11655
Telex: 64257N
Telefax: (084) 12773

John P Petersen, *Managing Director*

High-speed craft operated

Type	Name	Seats	Delivered
CAT Westamaran W86	*Brynilen* (Yard No 44)	94	June 1975
CAT Westamaran W86	*Hornry* (Yard No 66)	136	October 1979
MH Brødrene Aa Båtbyggeri	*Tanahorn* (Yard No 182)	49	1986
CAT Brødrene Aa Båbyggeri 25.5m	*Ingøy (Yard No 183)**	48 + cargo (incl 4 cars)	July 1987
Cat K. Fjellstrand 40.0m Flying—Cat		164 + cargo (incl 3 cars)	April 1990

Routes operated
Masry to Hammerfest to Soroysundbass
*Masry to Havrysund to Hammerfest
Kirkenes to Murmansk (USSR) summer service

Cars being carried on *Ingøy*, owned by Finnmark Fylkesrederi og Ruteselskap on the most northerly high-speed ferry operation in the world

The passenger/car ferry *Ingøy* at speed

Flaggruten
Please see Samiet Flaggruten

Fosen Trafikklag A/S
Fosenkaia, PO Box 2554, N-7002 Trondheim, Norway

Telephone: (07) 525540

High-speed craft operated

Type	Name	Delivered
CAT Westamarin W86	*Kongsbussen* (Yard No 27)	April 1973
CAT Westamarin W86	*Hertugbussen* (Yard No 28)	May 1973
CAT Westamarin W86	*Olavbussen* (Yard No 34)	February 1974

Routes operated
Trondheim to Brekstad to Storfosna to Hestvika to Fjellvoer to Fillan to Ansnes to Knarrlagsund to Sistranda to Mausundvoer to Vadsoysund to Bogoyvoer to Sula
Trondheim to Vanvikan (25 min)

Fylkesbaatane i Sogn og Fjordane

Postbox 354, 6901 Florø Norway
Strandavegen 354, 6900 Florø Norway

Telephone: (057) 43 200
Telex: 42674
Telefax: (057) 43 760

Arne Dvergsdal, *Director*

High-speed craft operated

Type	Name	Seats	Delivered
CAT Westamarin W86	*Fjordglytt* (Yard No 21)	140	May 1971
CAT Westamarin W86	*Fjordtroll* (Yard No 24)	140	May 1972
MH Westamarin S75	*Solundir*	80	1972
MH Brødrene Aa Båtbyggeri A/S	*Hyen*	156	1980
CAT Fjellstrand 38.8m	*Fjordprins*	201	October 1987
CAT Fjellstrand 38.8m	*Sognekongen*	201	December 1987
CAT Fjellstrand 40.0m Flying Cat	—	—	June 1990

Routes operated

*Bergen to Årdalstangen
Bergen to Målry

Gods-Trans A/S

Hønefoss, Norway

High-speed craft operated

Type	Name	Cargo	Delivered
CAT Fjellstrand 38.8m	*Anne Line*	480m³ cooled volume	July 1986
CAT Westamarin W5000 49.5m	*Anne Lise*	950m³ cooled + refrigerated volume (270 tonnes)	August 1987

Operation

In 1986 *Anne Line* operated weekly trips linking Norway, England and the Netherlands, shipping salmon for eventual dispatch from London Airport to the USA. Return journeys were used to ship fruit and flowers to Norway. *Anne Lise* is involved in cod transport, Iceland to Holland, fruit and vegetable transport and can carry a payload of 300 tonnes at 26 knots service speed

Hardanger Sunnhordlandske Dampskipsselskap (HSD)

PO Box 2005, N-5024 Nordnes, Bergen, Norway

Telephone: (05) 325070
Telex: 42607HSD N
Telefax: (05) 324555

Arne Dvergsdal, *Managing Director*
Birger Skår, *Director, Shipowning Division*
See also Sameiet Flaggruten

High-speed craft operated

Type	Name	Seats	delivered
CAT Westamarin W86	*Tedno* (Yard No 29)	140	June 1973
CAT Westamarin W95	*Sunnhordland* (Yard No 38)	180	April 1975
CAT Westamarin W86	*Teisten* (ex *Øygar*)	140	September 1975
CAT Westamarin W88	*Midthordland* (Yard No 82)	170	November 1981
F CAT Westamarin Foil Cat 2900		140	January 1991

The HSD Westamarin W88 *Midthordland*

Routes operated

Bergen to Tittelsnes
Bergen to Leirvik
Bergen to Ølen

Helgeland Trafikkselskap A/S

Postboks 603, N-8800 Sandnessjøen, Norway

Telephone: (086) 43066
Telefax: (086) 40256

Gunnar A Larsen, *Chairman of the Board*
Torleif Gaard, *Managing Director*
Jarle Dalen, *General Manager*

High-speed craft operated

Type	Name	Speed	Seats	Delivered
CAT Fjellstrand 31.5m	*Helgeland*	27 knots	160 +8 tonnes cargo	1983
CAT Fjellstrand Alumaran 165 25.6m	*Traena*	24 knots	128 + 6 tonnes cargo	1976
MH Fjellstrand 25.9	*Råsa*	24 knots	93 + 4 tonnes cargo	1979
MH Fjellstrand 18.6m	*Tuva*	20 knots	42 +2 tonnes cargo	1981
MH Fjellstrand 18.6m	*Sanna*	30 knots	37 (no cargo)	1988

Routes operated

The traffic area operated is Ytre Helgeland in the northern part of Norway, and consists of numerous islands. The high-speed craft operate from Sandnessjren serving a large number of towns in the islands and coastline. Almost 140 000 passengers were carried in 1987 and about the same number was expected for 1988.

Helgeland

Hovertransport A/S

PO Box 6, 1335 Snaroya, Norway

Jan Bjølgerud, *Administrative Director*

Following the leasing in 1987 of an AP-88 hovercraft which was terminated in November 1987, Hovertransport A/S chartered an HM218 in mid 1989 for a six month period. Based at Horten the craft served Tofte, Drøbak, Fagerstrand, Fornebu and Oslo

HM2 *Hover Express* operating near Oslo 1989 (photo Alan Bliault)

JKL-Shipping A/S

PO Box 7, 1361 Billingstadsletta, Norway
JKL Building, Stasjonsveien 18, Billingstad, Norway

Telephone: (02) 848590
Telex: 76113JKL N
Telefax: (02) 848383

Jann K Lindberg, *Managing Director*

Please see entry under Denmark for details of Copenhagen to Gothenburg SES operation.

Møre og Romsdal Fylkesbåtar
Fylkeshuset, N-6400 Molde, Norway

Telephone: (072) 52411
Telex: 40287N

Olav Smørdal, *Commercial Director*
Harald Ekker, *Assistant Director*
Olav Saunes, *Technical Manager*
Håkon Lorentzen, *Maritime Manager*
Kåre Sandøy, *Nautical Personnel Manager*

High-speed craft operated

Type	Name	Seats	In service
CAT Fjellstrand 31.5m	Hjørungavåg	250	1983
CAT Brødrene Aa Båtbyggeri CIRR 265P	Fjørtoft	123	June 1988

Route operated
Ålesund to Valderøy to Hareid, 286 000 passengers in 1988
Ålesund to Nordøyame, 80 passengers in 1988

Hjørungavåg

A/S Namsos Trafikkselskap
PO Box 128, D-S Kaia, N-7801 Namsos, Norway

Telephone: (77) 72433
Telex: 55492NTS N
Telefax: (77) 72467

High-speed craft operated

Type	Name	Delivered
MH Westamarin S75	Juvikingen	June 1973
CAT Lindstøl Skip 22.5m	—	July 1990

Route operated
Namsos to Rørvik

A/S Ofotens Dampskibsselskap
PO Box 57, 8501 Narvik, Norway

Telephone: (082) 44090
Telex: 64040

Per Bjerke, *Managing Director*

High-speed craft operated

Type	Name	Seats	Delivered
CAT Westamarin W88 (Yard No 88)	Skogøy	132 + 10 tonnes cargo	May 1985
CAT Westamarin W3600SC (Yard No 94)	Ofoten	195 + 30m² cargo hold	May 1988

Route operated
Narvik to Svolvaer

Oygarden og Sotra Rutelag A/S
5353 Straume, Norway

Telephone: (05) 33 0310

Bjørn Ove Børnes, *Managing Director*

This operator sold its Westamarin W86 *Øygar* at the end of 1986 to Hardanger Sunnhordlandske Dampskibsselskap. See 1987 edition, p 346

Saltens Dampskibsselskab A/S
PO Box 312, N-8001 Bodø, Norway

Telephone: (081) 21020
Telefax: (081) 20835

High-speed craft operated

Type	Name	Seats	Delivered
MH Fjellstrand 26m	Rødøyløven		1977
MH Fjellstrand 23m	Tysfjord		1981
MH Fjellstrand 25.5m	Oykongen		1982
MH Fjellstrand 25.5m	Oydronningen		1982
CAT Brødrene Aa Båtbyggeri CIRR 27P	Helgelandsekspressen	184	June 1985
CAT Westamarin 3600SC	Salten	186 + 65m³ cargo	1988
MH Brødrene Aa 23m	Rorstad		1984

Route operated
Bodø to Skutvik via Hellnessund, Nordskott, Holkestad and Bogøy
Bodø to Narvik via Svolvøaeør
Bodø to Sandnessjøn

Sameiet Flaggruten
Owned by:
Det Stavangerske Dampskibsselskab (45%) with Sandnes Dampskibs-Aktieselskab and Hardanger Sunnhordlandske Dampskibsselskab (25%)

High-speed craft operated

Type	Name	Seats	Delivered
CAT Westamarin W95	Vingtor		May 1974
CAT Westamarin W95	—		June 1974
CAT Westamarin W95	—		April 1977
CAT Fjellstrand 38.8m	Sleipner	243	1989
CAT Fjellstrand 38.8m	Draupner	243	1989

Route operated
Stavanger to Bergen

The Flaggruten Fjellstrand *Sleipner* at the Stavanger Fast Boat Terminal *(photo Alan Bliault)*

Simon Møkster
PO Box 108, Skogstrstraen 37, N-4001 Stavanger, Norway

High-speed craft operated

Type	Name	Built
MH Fjellstrand 26m	Veslestril	1981
HYD Rodriquez PT50	Stilprins (ex Teisten)	1970

For the summer of 1989 Simon Møkster bought the Harding catamaran *Havsdril*, carried 12000 passengers between Oslo and Arendal then sold the boat to Daysland, Texas USA for a contract with PEMEX.

The 25-knot Fjellstrand *Veslestril* owned by Simon Møkster

Det Stavangerske Dampskibsselskab
Børehaugen 1, N-4001 Stavanger, Norway

Telephone: (04) 520020
Telex: 33032N

Ansgar Johannssen, *Technical Superintendent*

High-speed craft operated

Type	Name	Seats	Delivered
CAT Westamarin W95	*Vingtor* (Yard No 36)*		May 1974
CAT Fjellstrand 38.8m	*Sleipner*		1989
CAT Westamarin W86	*Fjordbris* (Yard No 41) (ex *Storesund*)	165	September 1974
CAT Westamarin W86	*Fjorddrott* (Yard No 48)	167	June 1976
CAT Fjellstrand 38.8m	*Draupner*		1989
CAT Westamarin W88	*Haugesund* (Yard No 78)	180	March 1981
CAT Westamarin W88	*Fjordsol* (Yard No 91)	202	June 1986
MH Båtutrustning TMS 25m	*Askepott*	—	1988
CAT	—	150	1990
CAT	—	150	1990

Routes operated
Stavanger to Judaberg to Jelsa *(Mayflower)*
Stavanger to Judaberg to Helgoysund to Eik to Nedstrand to Vikedal to Sandeid *(Fjorddrott)*
Stavanger to Judaberg to Jelsa to Hebnes to Marvik to Sand to Sauda *(Fjordsol)*
Stavanger to Sør-Bokn to Brrey to Tuftene *(Fjordbris)*
Stavanger to Føresvik to Kopervik to Haugesund *(Haugesund)*
* operate the Sameiet Flaggruten service

W86 *Mayflower* (built in 1972) operated by Det Stavangerske Dampskibsselskab
(Alan Bliault)

A/S Torghatten Trafikkselskap
PO Box 103, N-8900 Brønnøysund, Norway

Telephone: (086) 22311
Telex: 55089N
Telefax: (086) 21719

High-speed craft operated

Type	Name	Seats	Delivered
MH Brødrene Aa Båtbyggeri 27m	*Torgtind*	-	1981
CAT Brødrene Aa Båtbyggeri 25m	*Heilhorn*	48 + cargo (incl 4 cars)	1987

Routes operated
Brønnrysund to Vega to Tjøtta
Bindalsfjorden

Troms Fylkes Dampskibsselskap
Kirkegt 1, N-9000 Tromsø, Norway

Telephone: (083) 86088
Telex: 64457
Telefax: (083) 88710

William Petersen, *Managing Director*
Jan M Leinebø, *Financial Manager*
Edvard Molund, *Technical Manager*
Karstein Jensen, *Operating Manager*

High-speed craft operated

Type	Name	Seats	Delivered
CAT Westamarin W86	*Fjorddronningen*	174	January 1976
CAT Westamarin W86	*Fjordprinsessen*	163	March 1977
CAT Westamarin W95	*Tromsprinsen*	210	June 1981
MH Brødrene Aa Båtbyggeri	*Gapøy*	43	June 1980
MH Djupviks Varv	*Reinfjord*	49	June 1984
SES Brødene Aa Båtbyggeri CIRR 105P	*Fjordkongen*	268	1987

Operations
Fjordkongen, reserve craft
Fjorddronningen, *Fjordprinsessen* and *Gapøy* operate Hardstadarea, *Tromsprinsen*, Tromso-Harstad, and *Reinfjord*, Skjervøy area

PAKISTAN

Pakistan Water and Power Development Authority
WPDA Offices Complex, Husseinabad, Giddu Road, Hyderabad, Pakistan

High-speed craft operated

Type	Name	Seats	Delivered
HOV Griffon Hovercraft Ltd 1000 TD-008 (GH 9456)	—	—	1987

Giffon Hovercraft 1000 TD (008) supplied to Pakistan WPDA

PARAGUAY

Aliscafos Itaipu SA
Yegros 690, Asunción, Paraguay

Main harbour: Hernandarias, Alto Panama, Paraguay
Telephone: 063 479

Telephone: 95–112
Telex: 264IE PY

Darius Morgan, *President*
Erminio Gatti, *Vice President*

High-speed craft operated

Type	Name	Seats	Entered service
HYD Ludwig Honald Mfg Co Albatross	*Flecha Guarani**	22	June 1985
HYD Ludwig Honald Mfg Co	*Flecha de Itaipu*	22	June 1985

*built 1964, overhauled and re-engined in Miami

Operation
Tourist use on Itaipu Lake on the border between Brazil and Paraguay
Puerto Hernandarias-Puerto Guarani

One of the boarding points for Aliscafos Albatross hydrofoils operating on Lake Itaipu in Paraguay *(Darius Morgan)*

PERU

Ministry of Health
Peru

The two Mark 3 River Rover craft used by the Joint Services Expedition to Peru in 1982, and working with the Amazon Trust River Medical Service based at San Francisco near Ayacucho, have been moved to other locations in Peru. This move was dictated by increased terrorist activity in the area and the withdrawal of the British funded Amazon Trust and the closure of the service.

River Rover 305 started operations in May 1984 at Puerto Bermudez on the River Pichis. Medical service involving doctor, nurse, health promoter and occasionally a dentist is provided to remote Campa Indian communities in the three rivers feeding the River Pichis. The rivers have extensive shallow areas making conventional boat travel slow, difficult and hazardous.

River Rover 303 is based at Iscozacin on the River Palcazu (an adjacent valley to the Pichis) and is also taking medical aid to remote Amuesha Indian communities as well as mixed race settlers in the area. The area is one of fast flowing, shallow rivers with many rocky outcrops and shingle banks. Boat transport is at best difficult, and in the dry season impossible in some areas. The medical team are reaching areas hitherto only visited on foot through the jungle.

Both craft are totally run, maintained and managed by the Peruvian Ministry of Health in conjunction with a Special Integrated Development Project of the Central Jungle.

PHILIPPINES

Bataan Manilla Ferry Services
Sea Express Services
Hoverferry Terminal, CCP Complex Rozas Boulevard, Metro-Manila, Philippines

Telephone: 8323653
Telex: 66927SEA PN

High-speed craft operated
Type	Name
SES Vosper Hovermarine HM 216	*Sea Express 101**
SES Vosper Hovermarine HM 216	*Sea Express 102**
SES Vosper Hovermarine HM 216	*Sea Express 103**

Route operated
Manila to Corregidor to Mariveles
*only one believed to be operational

POLAND

Przedsiebiorstwo Usiug Turystycznych "Pomerania"
Szczecin, Poland

High-speed craft operated
Type	Name	Built
HYD S Ordzhonikidze Meteor	*Adriana*	1973

Zegluga Gdanska
Ul Wartka 4, Gdansk, Poland

Telephone: 31-19-75

High-speed craft operated
Type	Name	Built
HYD Sormovo Kometa	*Poszum*	1973
HYD Sormovo Kometa	*Poweiw*	1973
HYD Sormovo Kometa	*Poswist*	1975
HYD Sormovo Kometa	*Poryw*	1976
HYD Sormovo Kometa	*Pogwizd*	1977
HYD Sormovo Kometa	*Polot*	1977

Routes operated
Gdynia to Hel (25 min)
Gdansk to Hel (55 min)
Gdynia to Jastarnia (25 min)
Sopot to Hel (25 min)
Gydnia to Sopot (10 min)
Gydnia to Hel to Wladyslawowo

Zegluga Szczecinska
Ul Energetyka 55, 70-656 Szczecin, Poland

Telephone: 45561, 470 51
Telex: 0422158PL

Michal Bardasz, *Director*

High-speed craft operated
Type	Name	Built
HYD Sormovo Kometa	*Lida*	1971
HYD Sormovo Kometa	*Kalina**	1973
HYD-Kometa	*Maria*	1973
HYD-Kometa	*Wanda*	1973
HYD S. Ordzhonikidze	*Daria* (ex *Kometa 4* '76)*	1975
HYD Sormovo Kometa	*Liwia**	1978

Route operated
Szczecin to Świnoujście (1 hour 15 min)
*operating en route Kolobrzeg to Roenne/Bornholm, Denmark, 2 hours 30min

PORTUGAL

Direcĉao Regional de Portos da Madeira
Av Arriaga No 50, 9000 Funchal, Madeira, Portugal

Telephone: 21041/2
Telex: 72290 DIPMAD P

Antonio Silverio de Freitas, *Regional Port Director*

High-speed craft operated
Type	Name	Seats	Delivered
CAT Westamarin W100	*Independencia* (Yard No 76) (ex *Gimle Bird*)	250	September 1981
SWATH FBM Marine FDC400	*Patria*	400	March 1990

Route operated
Funchal to Porto Santo Island, 44n miles

Patria

PUERTO RICO

Antilles Shipping Co & SNAV
San Juan, Puerto Rico

Telephone: (809) 724 2971/776 7787

Capt Giovanni Schironni (SNAV)

High-speed craft operated
Type	In service
HYD Rodriquez RHS 200	1986
HYD Rodriquez RHS 160	1986

Route operated
Round trip: San Juan, Puerto Rico (Crown Bay) and Charlotte Amelia, St Thomas, US Virgin Islands. One trip per day, four days per week, started May 1986. The service is operated and managed by SNAV
Journey time: Approx 2 hours, US$65.0 return

Puerto Rico Ports Authority
San Juan, Puerto Rico

High-speed craft operated

Type	In service	Name	Built
CAT Nichhols Bros InCat 22m	September 1989	*Martin Peña*	August 1989
CAT Nichhols Bros InCat 22m	October 1989	*Amelia*	November 1989
CAT Nichhols Bros InCat 22m	January 1990	*Cavadonga*	December 1989
CAT Nichhols Bros InCat 22m	February 1990	*San Geronimo*	March 1989
CAT Nichhols Bros InCat 22m	June 1990	*Viego San Juan*	May 1989
CAT Nichhols Bros InCat 22m	July 1989	*Cristobal Colón*	June 1989

ROMANIA

Intreprinderea de Exploatare a Floti Maritime (NAVROM)
Galatz, Romania

High-speed craft operated

Type	Name	Delivered
HYD S Ordzhonikidze Kometa	*Poseidon*	1970

SAUDI ARABIA

Saudi Arabian Coastal and Frontier Guard
Ministry of the Interior, Airport Road, Riyadh, Saudi Arabia

High-speed craft operated

Type	Delivered
HOV BHC SR.N6 Mk 1	
HOV BHC SR.N6 Mk 1	
HOV BHC SR.N6 Mk 1	
HOV BHC SR.N6 Mk 1	
HOV BHC SR.N6 Mk 1	
HOV BHC SR.N6 Mk 1	
HOV BHC SR.N6 Mk 1	
HOV BHC SR.N6 Mk 8	1981
HOV BHC SR.N6 Mk 8	
HOV BHC SR.N6 Mk 8	
HOV BHC SR.N6 Mk 8	
HOV BHC SR.N6 Mk 8	
HOV BHC SR.N6 Mk 8	1982
HOV BHC SR.N6 Mk 8	

Operation

Craft are based at Jeddah and Aziziyah for patrol, contraband control, search and rescue and liaison duties.

SINGAPORE

Dino Shipping Pte Ltd
&
Garuda Jaya Trading Co
BIK 334 Kreta Ayer Road No 02–08, Singapore 0208

Telephone: 2200555/27849
Telex: 33988 JAYACO RS
Telefax: 2250525

High-speed craft operated

Type	Name	Seats	Built
MH SBF Engineering	*Sea Flyte*	225	1980
MH Tjetty Marine	*Bintan I*	80	—
MH Tjetty Marine	*Bintan II*	80	1984
MH Tjetty Marine	*Bintan III*	—	—
MH Wavemaster International	*Sea Raider II*	200	1988
MH Wavemaster International	*Sea Raider III*	—	1989

Routes operated

Singapore to Tanjang Pinang (Bintan, Indonesia)
Singapore to Sekopang (Batam Island, Indonesia)

Igsa Transport
International Plaza 35–09, Anson Road, Singapore 0105

Telephone: 2221500

High-speed craft operated

Type	Name	Built	
SES Hovermarine HM 216	*Batam Express Dua*	60	
CAT NQEA InCat 30m	*Supercat III*	358	1989
CAT Fjellstrand	*Asie III* (short charter)	159	1984

Inasco Enterprises Pte Ltd
63 Robinson Road, Singapore 0106

Telephone: 2216421, 22449797

High-speed craft operated
Type
CAT Precision Marine 31m

Route operated
Singapore to Tanjung Pinang, Batam Island (Indonesia)

J & N Cruise
24 Raffles Place, 26–02 Clifford Centre, Singapore 0104

Telephone: 533 2733

High-speed craft operated

Type	Name	Delivered
CAT Lloyd's Ships 35.6m	*Equator Dream*	August 1988

Routes operated (cruise operations)
Clifford Pier, Singapore to Kusu Island and Pulau Sakeng

Equator Dream cruise vessel

Shell Eastern Petroleum (Pte) Ltd
PO Box 1908, Pulau Bukom, Singapore 9038

Telephone: 2294150
Telex: 21251RS

Capt M J Whichelow, *Marine Manager*

Operator: **Straits Shipping Pte Ltd**
15 Hoe Chiang Road, Singapore

Telephone: 2250788

High-speed craft operated

Type	Name	Seats	Entered service
SES Vosper Hovermarine 218	*Bukom Deras*	90	1983
SES Vosper Hovermarine 218	*Bukom Pantas*	90	1983
SES Vosper Hovermarine 218	*Bukom Lekas*	90	1983
SES Vosper Hovermarine 218	*Bukom Maju*	90	1983
SES Vosper Hovermarine 218	*Bukom Jaya*	90	1983

Route operated
Pasir Panjang to Pulau Bukom refinery

Sinba Shipping
High-speed craft operated

Type	Name	Seats	Delivered
ALH Stolkraft	*Batam Express III*	45	1988

Tai Tong Shipping
High-speed craft operated

Type	Name	Seats	Delivered
MH SBF Engineering 27.5m	*Sundancer*	160	1988

Tan Pia Law

High-speedcraft operated

Type	Seats	Delivered
CAT Aluminium Craft SS23	130	July 1989
CAT Aluminium Craft SS23	130	July 1989

Tian San Shipping Pte Ltd

Singapore

Operator of three 28 metre, 28 knot ferries

Yang Passenger Ferry Service

407 Jalan Besar, Singapore 0820

Telex: 56408YANGFE RS

Yong Kian Chin, *Director*

High-speed craft operated

Type	Yard No	Name	Seats	Delivered
SES Vosper Hovermarine HM 218	472	*Auto Batam 1*	84	1982

(previously owned by Auto-Shipping, Singapore and Union Hydraulic Jack (Pte) Ltd)

MH Binan Senkapu Kogyo —		*Auto Batam 2*	87	1982
CAT Lloyds Ships 36.5m —		*Auto Batam 8*	—	1989

Route operated

Singapore to Batam Island (Indonesia)

Auto Batam 1 in Singapore harbour November 1989 *(photo: M Daley)*

SOLOMON ISLANDS

Fisheries Protection

High-speed craft operated

Type	Delivered
MH Agnew Clough (C Raymond Hunt) 25m P-150	1981

Solomon Islands Navigation Services

O Box 59, Honiara, Solomon Islands

Roy Clements, *Proprietor*

High-speed craft operated

Type	Seats	In service
HOV Griffon 1500 TD*	17	1987

*Previously operated in Australia

SPAIN

Alisur SA (Alisur Caribe)

La Esperanza 1–1 Dcha, Arrecife de Lanzarote, Canary Islands, Spain

Telephone: 814272, 81 49 01
Telex: 96327ALSR E

Bruno Hitz, *President*
Gennaro Doria, *Director*

The Westamarin W95T *Alisur Azul* was sold in June 1986.

High-speed craft operated

Type	Name	Delivered
CAT Westamarin W95D	*Alisur Amarillo* (Yard No 79)	April 1981

Route operated

St Maarten to St Barths 30 min, to Anguilla 30 min, to Saba 60 min, to Statia 75 min, to St Kitts 90 min (Netherlands Antilles)

Alisur Amarillo operating in the Netherlands Antilles

Cat Lines SA

Valencia, Spain

High-speed craft operated

Type	Name	Seats	Delivered
CAT Fjellstrand 38.8m	*Leopardo*	290	June 1989
CAT Fjellstrand 38.8m	*Eyra*	290	September 1989

Routes operated

Leopardo: Villanova (Barcelona area) to Mallorca, 100n miles, 3 hours
Mallorca to Menorca, 26n miles, 1 hour
Eyra: Javea (Valencia/Alicante area) to Ibiza, 55n miles, 2 hours Ibiza to Mallorca, 62n miles, 2 hours

Compañia Naviera Mallorquina (subsidiary of Compañia Transmediterranea)

Spain

High-speed craft operated

Type	Name	Seats	In service
HYD Rodriquez RHS 160F	*Pez Volador* (ex *Alijumbo Eolie*)	220	1 June 1988 to 30 September 1988

Route operated

Alicante to Ibiza, 2 hours 45 min

HYD S Ordzhonikidze Kolkhida	*Tiburon*	May 1988

Route operated

Ibiza to Palma, 2 hours

Compañia Transmediterranea SA

Plaza Manuel Gómez Moreno s/n, Edificio Bronce-Centro Azca, Apartado de Correos 982, 28020 Madrid, Spain

Telephone: 4550049, 4560009
Telex: 27666TRASM E

Boeing Jetfoil 929–115, *Princesa Guayarmina*, operated by Compañia Transmediterranea

High-speed craft operated

Type	Name	In service
HYD Boeing Jetfoil 929–115	*Princesa Guayarmina*	1981
HYD Boeing Jetfoil 929–115	*Princesa Guacimara*	1981
HYD Rodriquez RHS 160F	*Barracuda*	April 1989
HYD Rodriquez RHS 160F	*Marrajo*	1990
HYD Kawasaki Jetfoil 929–117	—	1990

In 1989 the Rodriquez RHS 200 hydrofoil *San Cristobel* was leased.

Route operated

Las Palmas, Grand Canaria to Santa Cruz de Tenerife (1 hour 20 min)
Las Palmas to Morro Jable (1 hour 30 min)

Flebasa Lines
Spain

High-speed craft operated

Type	Name	In service
HYD Rodriquez RHS 140	*Rapido de Ibiza (ex Viggen)*	1988
CAT Westamarin W95	*Tranen*	1989

Hovercraft Espania
Spain

High-speed craft operated

Type	Name	Seats	Delivered
HOV BHC SRN6 MKI 027	*Phoenix*	—	January 1989

Route operated

La Linea

Yasmin Line
Spain

High-speed craft operated

Type	Name	Seats	Delivered
CAT Marinteknik Verkstads 34m	—	—	1989

Iselena de Navegacion SA
Avenida Virgen del Carmen, No. 3 & 5, Algeciras, Spain

Telephone: 652000/652950/652561
Telex: 78132

V S Lopez, *President*

High-speed craft operated

Type	Name	Seats	In service
CAT Fjellstrand 38.8m	*(ex Caribbean Princess)*	310	1990
CAT Fjellstrand 38.8m	*(ex Bahamian Prince)*	310	1990

Real Maritima de Cruceros SA
Spain

High-speed craft operated

Type	Name	Seats	In service
HOV NQEA BHC AP1–88	*Benidorm (ex Courier)*	81	1989

Route operated
Malaga to Ceuta

SWEDEN

City Jet Line
PO Box 537, S-18500 Vaxholm, Sweden

Telephone: (0764) 32804/30882, (08) 606102

Capt Bjørn Justine

High-speed craft operated

Type	Name	Seats	Delivered	In service
MH Marinteknik Verkstads 41m	*Cinderella*	450	15 May 1987	12 June 1987
MH Marinteknik Verkstads 41m	*Cinderella II*	450	1989	—
MH Marinteknik Verkstads 41m	*Cinderella III*	450	1990	—

Route operated
Stockholm to Möjaström (60n miles) and outer islands

Marinteknik *Cinderella* in operation, Stockholm 1987

TAIWAN

Tien Peng Yang Hovertravel Corporation
High-speed craft operated

Type	Name	Seats	Delivered
HOV NQEA BHC AP1–88	*Tienpengyang I*	94	November 1989
HOV NQEA BHC AP1–88	*Tienpengyang II*	101	November 1989
HOV NQEA BHC AP1–88	*Tienpengyang III*	101	November 1989

TANZANIA

Zademarine Ltd
P O Box 5455, Dar Es Salaam, Zanzibar, Tanzania

Telephone: (051)33965/35700

High-speed craft operated

The Brødrene Aa SES *Virgin Butterfly* was operated for a period from 1 February 1989 between Dar Es Salaam, Zanzibar, Tanga and Mombasa

TURKEY

Istanbul Great City Municipality
Istanbul, Turkey

Ten Fjellstrand 38.8m, 449-passenger catamarans were purchased to provide a ferry service for commuters across the Strait of Bosphorus. Five have a 24-knot cruise speed capability and five, 32 knots

High-speed craft operated

Type	Name	Seats	Delivered
CAT Fjellstrand 38.8m			
(MTU 16V 396 TB83)	*Umer Bey*	449	April 1987
CAT Fjellstrand 38.8m			
(MTU 16V 396 TB83)	*Sarica Bey*	449	August 1987
CAT Fjellstrand 38.8m			
(MTU 16V 396 TB83)	*Ulir Ali Reis*	449	January 1988
CAT Fjellstrand 38.8m			
(MTU 16V 396 TB83)	*Nusret*	449	March 1988
CAT Fjellstrand 38.8m			
(MTU 16V 396 TB83)	*Hezarifen Celebi*	449	September 1988
CAT Fjellstrand 38.8m			
(MTU 12V 396 TB63)	*Caka Bey*	449	February 1987
CAT Fjellstrand 38.8m			
(MTU 12V 396 TB63)	*Yeditepe*	449	May 1987
CAT Fjellstrand 38.8m			
(MTU 12V 396 TB63)	*Ulabatli Hasan*	449	September 1987
CAT Fjellstrand 38.8m			
(MTU 12V 396 TB63)	*Karamursel Bey*	449	March 1988
CAT Fjellstrand 38.8m			
(MTU 12V 396 TB63)	*Cavli Bey*	449	September 1988

Routes operated

Bostanci to Kabatas, 10n miles, 18 min, TL 1000, 1987
Bostanci to Karakoy to Atakoy, 39 min round trip
Kabatas to Buyukada

Naviga
Turkey

High-speed craft operated

Type	Name	Delivered
SES Hovermarine Int'l. HM218	*Klassis*	1989

UNION OF SOVIET SOCIALIST REPUBLICS

Azcherryba
Taganrog, USSR

High-speed craft operated

Type	GRT	Delivered
HYD S Ordzhonikidze Kometa-*M*	142	1977

Azov Shipping Co
89, Admirala Lunina Pr, Zhdanov 341010, USSR

Telex: 412601/2, 115156

High-speed craft operated

Type	GRT	Delivered
HYD Kometa *19*	136	1973
HYD Kometa *22*	136	1974

Black Sea Shipping Company
1 Lastochkina Str, 270026 Odessa, USSR

Telex: 232711, 412677

High-speed craft operated

Type	GRT	Delivered
HYD S Ordzhonikidze Kometa *13*	127	1968 (Odessa)
HYD S Ordzhonikidze Kometa *16*	142	1969 (Odessa)
HYD S Ordzhonikidze Kometa *27*	136	1975 (Yalta)
HYD S Ordzhonikidze Kometa *32*	142	1977 (Yalta)
HYD S Ordzhonikidze Kometa *37*	142	1978 (Odessa)
HYD S Ordzhonikidze Kometa *40*	142	1979 (Yalta)
HYD S Ordzhonikidze Kometa *41*	142	1979 (Yalta)
SES Sosnovka, 30 delivered Rassvet	(80 seat)	
HYD-Tsiklon	250	November 1987
CAT Westamarin W 4100 S	—	April 1990
CAT Westamarin W 4100 S	—	April 1990

Routes operated

Daily services, Odessa to Ochakov, Kherson and Nikolaev
Black Sea Kometas carry over 1.5 million passengers a year and are mostly based in the ports of Sochi, Tuapse, Novorossiysk, Yalta, Odessa and Izmail

Kolkhida craft at Odessa

Caspian Shipping Co
Astrakhan, USSR

D Gashumov, *President*

High-speed craft operated

Type	GRT	Delivered
HYD Kometa *21*	136	1974
HYD Kometa *28*	136	1975

Far Eastern Shipping Co.
Vladivostok, USSR

High-speed craft operated

Type	Name	Seats	Delivered
CAT Kvaerner Fjellstrand 38.8m	*Mercury*	286	March 1990

Routes operated

Vladivostok–Nakhodka–Preobrazhemie–Olga–Rudnaya Pristan (264 n miles)
Vladivostok–Slavyanka (60 n miles)

Murmansk Shipping Co
Murmansk, USSR

High-speed craft operated

Type	GRT	Delivered
HYD Kometa *30*	142	1976

Northern Shipping Co.
Arkhangelsk, USSR

High-speed craft operated

Type	Name	Seats	Delivered
CAT Kvaerner Fjellstrand 38.8m	*Solovki*	230	March 1990

Routes operated

Archangelsk to Pertominsk to Solovetskiy, 188 n miles
Archangelsk to Solovetskiy, 166 n miles

Soviet Danube Shipping Co
2, Pr Suvorova, Izmail 272630, USSR

Telex: 412699, 232817

High-speed craft operated

Type	GRT	Delivered
HYD Kometa *34*	142	1977
HYD Kometa *35*	142	1978
HYD Kometa *36*	142	1978

Volga-Don Shipping

In 1987 it was reported that 33 high-speed diesel-powered vessels were in the fleet comprising 40% of the passenger vessels. Of 29 in the Rostov sector, 14 are to be replaced. There are seven Meteors, seven Raketas, four Voskhod and two Zarya vessels, serving 12 routes.

Other Kometas delivered in the USSR

High-speed craft operated

Type	GRT	Delivered
Kometa 10	127	1967 (Sochi)
Kometa 12	127	1967 (Sochi)
Kometa 17	127	1970 (Yalta)
Kometa 23	136	1974 (Yalta)
Kometa 24	136	1975 (Sochi)
Kometa 33	142	1978 (Sochi)
Kometa 38	142	1978
Kometa 1	142	1980
Kometa 43	142	1980
Kometa 46	142	1980
Kometa 47	142	1980
Kometa 48	142	1981
Kometa 49	142	1981
Kometa 51	142	1981
Kometa 21	142	1982
Kometa 53	142	1982
Kometa 54	142	1982
Kometa 55	142	1982
Kometa 57	142	1983

UNITED ARAB EMIRATES

Zadco Productions

Abu Dhabi, United Arab Emirates

High-speed craft operated

Type	Name	Seats	Delivered
CAT Sing Koon Seng Pte InCat 30m	Ipo Ipo 3001	15 + 60 tonnes cargo	1984

UNITED KINGDOM

Condor Ltd

Commodore House, Bulwer Avenue, St Sampson's, PO Box 10, Guernsey, Channel Islands, United Kingdom

Telephone: (0481) 46841
Telex: 4191289CMDR G
Telefax: (0481) 49543

David Norman, *Managing Director*
Lionel Frampton, *Marine Superintendent*
Andrew Way, *Assistant Marine Superintendent*
Richard Sumner, *Operations Manager*

Condor Ltd started in 1964 with one hydrofoil, *Condor 1*, a PT 50 and now has three Rodriquez hydrofoils, *Condor 4*, *Condor 5*, *Condor 7* and an FBM Marinteknik(S) 37m catamaran. Condor Ltd now has in addition a 49m wavepiercing catamaran designed by International Catamaran Designs Pty Ltd, and has been built by Aluminium Shipbuilders of Porchester, Portsmouth, UK. The new Wavepiercer will carry 450 passengers at 35 knots and will be the largest passenger-only wavepiercing catamaran built.

The traffic is seasonal and the craft do not operate from New Year to mid March.

High-speed craft operated

Type	Name	Seats	Delivered
HYD Rodriquez RHS 140	Condor 4	136	1974
HYD Rodriquez RHS 160	Condor 5	180	1976
HYD Rodriquez RHS 160F	Condor 7	200	1985
CAT FBM Marinteknik(S)	Condor 8	300	June 1988
CAT Aluminium Shipbuilders InCat Wavepiercer 49m	—	450	June 1990

Routes operated

Condor Ltd operates a fast passenger network between St Malo in France and Jersey, Sark, Guernsey, and Weymouth in the UK. The company carries 430 000 passengers per annum.
St Malo to Jersey 38n miles (1h 10min)
Jersey to Sark 27n miles (45min)
Jersey to Guernsey 28n miles (50min)
St Malo to Guernsey 57n miles (1h 35min)
Guernsey to Weymouth 70n miles (2h)

Artists impression of Incat 450 seat 35 knot Wavepiercer operated by Condor Ltd

(John Howard Wright)

Hoverspeed Limited

The International Hoverport, Dover, Kent CT17 9TG, England

Telephone: (0304) 240101/240540
Telex: 965915G
Telefax: (0304) 240099

N Tatham, *Chairman*
R Wilkins, *Managing Director*
R S Adams, *General Sales Manager*
K Hilditch, *Personnel Manager*
C W Hunt, *Technical Manager*
P C Walker, *Company Secretary*
D Wise, *Operations Manager*

Hoverspeed was formed as a result of a merger between the two cross-Channel operators, British Rail Hovercraft Limited (Seaspeed) and Hoverlloyd. Operations began in October 1981. The history of the operations and company development is given in the 1989 and previous editions of this book. In May 1990 Hoverspeed will take delivery of its first catamaran craft, a 74 metre International Catamaran Designs Wave Piercing Catamaran capable of carrying 80 cars and 450 passengers. This vessel and its sister ship which will be delivered in July 1990 will be delivered by sea from the builder, International Catamarans Tasmania Pty. Ltd., Moonah, Tasmania. They will be operated on the route from Portsmouth to Cherbourg.

Hoverspeed SR.N4 Mk II *Swift*   *(Hoverspeed Ltd)*

High-speed craft operated

Type	Name	First entered service	Payload
HOV BHC SR.N4 Mk 1 modified to Mk 3 in 1979	*The Princess Margaret* (GH 2006)	1968 Seaspeed	424 passengers 55 cars
HOV BHC SR.N4 Mk 1 modified to Mk 3 in 1978	*The Princess Anne* (GH 2007)	1969 Seaspeed	424 passengers 55 cars
HOV BHC SR.N4 Mk 1 modified to Mk 2 in 1973	*Swift* (GH 2004)	1969 Hoverlloyd	278 passengers 34 cars
HOV BHC SR.N4 Mk 1 modified to Mk 2 in 1974	*Sir Christopher* (GH2008)	1972 Hoverlloyd	278 passengers 34 cars
HOV BHC SR.N4 Mk 2	*The Prince of Wales* (GH 2054)	1977 Hoverlloyd	278 passengers 34 cars
CAT InCat Tasmania 74m WPC	*Christopher Columbus*	July 1990 Hoverspeed	450 passengers + 80 cars
CAT InCat Tasmania 74m WPC	—	July 1990 Hoverspeed	450 passengers + 80 cars

Note:
SRN4 Mk 2 *Sure* was broken up in 1988

Routes operated
Dover to Calais (23n miles)
Dover to Boulogne (27n miles)
Portsmouth to Cherbourg, 2 h 40 min

Traffic carried:

	Passengers	Vehicles
1985	1 645 000	238 000
1986	1 575 000	257 000
1987	1 587 600	287 200

Hovertravel Limited

Head Office: 12 Lind Street, Isle of Wight, Hampshire PO33 2NR, England

Telephone: (0983) 65181
Telex: 86513 HOVERWORK G
Telefax: (0983)812859
Terminal offices: Quay Road, Ryde, Isle of Wight (Tel: 0983 65241); Clarence Pier, Southsea (Tel: 29988)

C D J Bland, *Chairman and Managing Director*
E W H Gifford, *Director*
J Gaggero, *Director*
A C Smith, *Director*
R G Clarke, *Director*
R Box, *General Manager (Solent Services)*
G M Palin, *Company Secretary*

Hovertravel Limited was formed in 1965 to operate two SR.N6 Winchester hovercraft across the Solent between Ryde, Isle of Wight and Southsea and Gosport. The Gosport route was discontinued after a brief period.

Journey time is about 9 minutes on the Ryde to Southsea route. Approximately 600 000 passengers are carried each year on the route together with many tons of mail and freight parcel packages. By September 1989 the cumulative total number of passengers carried exceeded 10 million.

Launching in Tasmania of the hull of the first 74m wave piercing catamaran for Hoverspeed Portsmouth to Cherbourg route

High-speed craft operated

Type	Name	Seats	Delivered
HOV BHC AP1–88 GH 2087	*Tenacity*	80	1983
HOV BHC/HW AP1–88 GH 2107	*Double O Seven*	100	April 1989

AP1–88 GH 2100 *Perseverance* which was delivered to Hovertravel late in June 1985 was sold to Textron Marine in 1988 for sale to the US Navy for training purposes as was *Resolution* in 1989.

Route operated

Portsmouth (Southsea Promenade) to Ryde (3.85n miles, time under 10 mins, fare below 5 return)

Capacity on route from June 1990 will be 8000 passengers per day

Tenacity and *Double O Seven* nearest to camera at Ryde terminal (photo Alan Bliault)

Hoverwork Limited

12 Lind Street, Ryde, Isle of Wight, Hampshire PO33 2NR, England

Telephone: (0983) 65181
Telex: 86513HOVERWORK G

C D J Bland, *Managing Director*
E W H Gifford, *Director*
A C Smith, *Director*
R G Clarke, *Director*
G M Palin, *Secretary*

Hoverwork Limited, a wholly-owned subsidiary of Hovertravel Ltd, was formed in 1966. The company provides crew training and charter facilities for all available types of ACVs, thus bridging the gap between the operators and manufacturers.

High-speed craft operated

)Hoverwork Limited has access to all craft owned by Hovertravel Limited

Operations

The company has trained over 50 hovercraft captains and has received some 40 charter contracts, including film sequences and the operation of the SR.N6 craft for mineral surveys throughout the world. The company operated the hovercraft passenger service during Expo' 67 at Montreal and a service at the 1970 and 1976 Algiers Expositions.

Hoverwork is the largest international operator of hovercraft, having access to Hovertravel's SR.N6s, and its AP1–88 80-seat passenger craft. Hoverwork has undertaken operations in areas from the Arctic to the equator, including logistics exercises in the northern part of Svalbard and in equatorial parts of South America. To date Hoverwork has operated in the following areas: Canada, South America, Mexico, Brunei, Netherlands, Bahrain, Kuwait, the United Arab Emirates, Saudi Arabia, Algeria, Tunisia, English North Sea, Spitzbergen, Australia, Iraq and Egypt.

London City Airport Ltd

King George V Dock, Silvertown, London E16 2PX

Telephone: 01 4745555
Telex: 264731

High-speed craft operated

Type	Name
CAT Aluminium Shipbuilders InCat	*Le Premier* (ex *Daily Telegraph*)

Route operated

London City Airport to Charing Cross

Le Premier operated by London City Airport Ltd on the River Thames

Red Funnel Ferries

12 Bugle Street, Southampton, Hampshire SO9 4LJ, England

Telephone: 0703333042
Telex: 47388CHAMCON G
Telefax: (0703) 639438

T E P Thornycroft, *Managing Director*
R C Shepherd, *Secretary and Finance Director*
M E R Collis, *Commercial Manager*
J Day, *Group Chief Accountant*
R A Marshall, *Technical Manager*
Capt H Middleton, *Ferry Operations Manager*

High-speed craft operated

Type	Name	Seats	Delivered
HYD Rodriquez RHS 70	*Shearwater 3*	67	1972
HYD Rodriquez RHS 70	*Shearwater 4*	67	1973
HYD Rodriquez RHS 70	*Shearwater 5*	67	1980
HYD Rodriquez RHS 70	*Shearwater 6*	67	1982
CAT FBM Marine 31.5m	—	120	1991
CAT FBM Marine 31.5m	—	120	1991

Route operated

Southampton to West Cowes, Isle of Wight (10.8n miles, 20 min)
Single fare: £4.00, return: £6.00 (1988)

Passengers carried

1984:411 000
1985:436 200
1986:466 700
1987:529 188

The Red Funnel *Shearwater 5*

Sealink British Ferries
(Sealink UK Ltd)

Isle of Wight Services, Gunwharf Road, Portsmouth PO1 2LA

Telephone: (0705) 812011
Telex: 86 440 G

Isle of Wight Services
Portsmouth Harbour, Portsmouth, Hampshire PO1 2LA, England

Telephone: (0705)812011
Telex: 86440 SELINK G
Telefax: (0705)855257

W E D Gibbons, *General Manager*
Maelor Jones, *Ship Manager*

High-speed craft operated

Type	Name	Seats	Delivered
CAT International Catamarans Pty Ltd (Hobart) 30.0m	*Our Lady Patricia*	440	March 1986
CAT International Catamarans Pty Ltd (Hobart) 30.0m	*Our Lady Pamela*	440	August 1986

Route operated
Portsmouth Harbour (Station) to Ryde Pier, Isle of Wight (15 min)
Summer season service operates via Clarence Pier, Southsea
Clarence Pier to Ryde Pier, 12 min
Single adult fare: 3.50 (1990), cheap day return 5.00

Our Lady Pamela

Thames Line plc
The Chambers, Chelsea Harbour, Lots Road, London SW10 0XF, England

Telephone: 01–376 3676
Telefax: 01–376 4708

High-speed craft operated

Type	Name	Seats	Delivered
CAT Aluminium Shipbuilders Ltd 17.5m River 50	*Barclays Bank*	62	April 1988
CAT Aluminium Shipbuilders Ltd 17.5m River 50	*London Docklands*	62	May 1988
CAT Aluminium Shipbuilders Ltd 17.5m River 50	*Debenham Tewson and Chinnocks*	62	August 1988
CAT Aluminium Shipbuilders Ltd 17.5m River 50	*Harbour Exchange*	62	August 1988
CAT Aluminium Shipbuilders Ltd InCat 17.5m River 50	*London Broadcasting Company*	62	1989

Route operated
Thames, Charing Cross Pier to West India Dock

Thames Line InCat *Barclays Bank*

UNITED STATES OF AMERICA

Alderbrook Marine Inc
Hood Canal, Washington, USA

High-speed craft operated

Type	Name	Seats	Delivered
CAT Nichols Bros Boat Bldrs InCat 22m	*Spirit of Alderbrook*	200	1984

Route operated
Catalina to San Pedro

American Skimmer Inc
Massapequa Park, New York, USA

Shashi Tejpau, *Owner*
Nancy Sutherland, *Operations Manager*

High-speedcraft operated

Type	Name	Seats	In Service
SES Hovermarine (US) HM216	*American Skimmer*	62	1989

Route operated
Glen Cove Marina, Glen Cove, Long Island to Pier 11, Wall Street, Manhattan

Arcorp Properties
Port Imperial Ferry
Pershing Road, Weehawken, New Jersey 07087, USA

Telephone: (201)902 8700/564 3130
Arthur E Imperatore, *President*

High-speed craft operated

Type	Name	Seats	In service
MH Blount Marine Corporation Hitech 23.5m	*Port Imperial*	149	1986
MH Gulf Craft	*Port Imperial Manhattan*	350	1988
MH Gulf Craft	*Port Imperial New Jersey*	350	1988

Route operated
Weehawken, New Jersey to 38th Street and 12th Avenue, Manhattan, every 15 min from 6.45 am to midnight. A rush hour service is also run to Slip 5 in Lower Manhattan

The 350 passenger 24 knot *Port Imperial Manhattan*

Arnold Transit Co
Box 220, Mackinac Island, Michigan 49757, USA

Route operated
Hingham Shipyard to Rowes Wharf (9.8 miles, under 30 min)

Telephone: (906) 847 3351

Robert Brown, *General Manager*

High-speed craft operated

Type	Name	Seats	In service
CAT Gladding-Hearn InCat 25m	*Mackinac Express*	350	1987
CAT Gladding-Hearn InCat 25m	*Island Express*	300	1988

Routes operated
Mackinaw City to Mackinac Island
St. Ignace to Mackinac Island, 14 min, May to November

Arnold Transits' *Mackinac Express*

Bay State Provincetown Cruises (Bay State-Spray & Provincetown Steamship, Inc)

20 Long Wharf, Boston, MA 02110

Telephone: (617) 723 7800

Joseph G. Pallotta

High-speed craft operated

Type	Name	Seats	In service
CAT Gladding-Hearn InCat	*Vineyard Spray*	322	June 1988
CAT Nichols Bros InCat	*Nantucket Spray*	367	May 1989

Route operated
Commonwealth Pier, South Boston Harbor to Vineyard Haven (Martha's Vineyard) 3 hours, 72 min, via Cape Cod canal, US$50 return, daily round trip.

Blue and Gold Fleet

Box Z-2, Pier 39, San Francisco, California 94133, USA

Telephone: (415) 781 7890

The Nichols Bros InCat *Gold Rush* was sold in 1988 to Catamaran Cruise Lines.

Boston Harbor Commuter Service (BHCS)

One Range Road, Nahant, Massachusetts 01890, USA

Telephone: (617) 599 7620/740 1253

Dana Goodell, *President*

The BHCS operates under the aegis of the Massachusetts State Water Transportation System and the Massachusetts Bay Transit Authority.

High-speed craft operated

Type	Name	Seats	Delivered
MH Camcraft crew boat converted by Aluminium Boats Inc	*Chimera*		1984
MH Camcraft crew boat converted by Aluminium Boats Inc	*Sterling* (ex *Sterling Fryou*)	150	1986

The two Trinity Marine Group 25 knot ferries chartered in 1989 by the California Department of Transportation.

Bottom Time Adventurers
Fort Lauderdale, Florida, USA

A J Bland, *Director*

High-speed craft operated

Type	Name	Seats	Delivered
CAT Atlantic & Gulf Boat Bldg 23.8m InCat	*Bottom Time II*	32 (16 staterooms)	August 1986

Operation
Diving expeditions, naturalist research expeditions, film company support vessel

California Department of Transportation
San Francisco, California, USA

Chartered the two Trinity Marine Group (Equitable Shipyards Inc) 250 passengers 25 knot ferries from Washington State Ferries following the San Francisco earthquake of 1989.

Catalina Channel Express Lines
PO Box 1391, San Pedro (Berth 95), California 90733, USA

Telephone: (213) 519 1212/7971

Doug Bombard, *President*
Greg Bombard, *Vice President and General Manager*
Audrey Bombard, *Secretary/Treasurer*
Tom Rutter, *Vice President Operations*
Elaine Vaughan, *Vice President Marketing*

High-speed craft operated

Type	Name	Seats	Delivered
MH Westport 56	*Channel Express*	60	1981
MH Westport 80	*Avalon Express*	80	1983
MH Westport Shipyard Inc 27.44m 90	*Catalina Express*	149	1984
MH Westport Shipyard Inc 27.44m 90	*Two Harbors Express*	149	1986
HYD Westport Shipyard Inc	*Catalina Foil*	149	1989
MH Westport 95	*Super Express*	149	1989
MH Westport 95	*Avalon Super Express*	149	June 1990

Route operated
San Pedro to Avalon, Santa Catalina Island, fare US $13.85, 1989

Two Harbors Express, of Catalina Channel Express Lines

Westport International 25m hydrofoil project for Catalina Channel Express Lines

Catalina Passenger Services

High-speed craft operated

Type	Name	Seats	Delivered
CAT Nichols Bros InCat	*Catalina Flyer*	500	May 1988

Route operated
Newport Beach to Catalina Island, 26n miles, 75 min.

Clipper Navigation Inc
2701 Alaskan Way, Pier 69, Seattle, Washington 98121, USA

Telephone: (206) 443 2560
Telex: 329473 attn CLP 954
Telefax: (206) 443 2583

1000.A Wharf St, Victoria, British Columbia V8W 1T4, Canada

Telephone: (604) 382 8100
Telex: 329473attn CLP-954
Telefax: (604) 382 2152

Merideth Tall, *President*
Leonard Tall, *Executive Vice-President*
Darrelle Bryan *Vice-President General Manager*

High-speed craft operated

Type	Name	Seats	In Service
CAT Fjellstrand 38.8m	*Victoria Clipper*	300	April 1986
CAT Nichols Bros InCat	*Victoria Clipper II* (ex *Express*)	—	1989

Operation
Seattle to Victoria, British Columbia, Canada, from July 1986 (2 hours 30 min). Fare: US $36.0 one way or US$59.0 round trip 19 September 1989 to 11 May 1990 ; US$42.0 one way or US$69.0 round trip 12 May to mid September 1990

Victoria Clipper departing Seattle

Stern of Fjellstrand *Victoria Clipper*

Department of Transportation, United States Coast Guard
2100 Second Street SW, Washington DC 20593–0001, USA

Telephone: (202) 267 2997
Telefax: (202) 267 0025

M M Rosecrans *Lieutenant Commander, US Coast Guard Chief, Ship Design Branch Marine Technical and Hazardous Materials Division*

High-speed craft operated (Sea Bird class)

Type	Name	In service
SES Bell Halter Model 522A (110 Mk 1)	*Sea Hawk* (WSES-2)	October 1982
SES Bell Halter Model 522A (110 Mk 1)	*Shearwater* (WSES-3)	October 1982
SES Bell Halter Model 522A (110 Mk 1)	*Petrel* (WSES-4)	June 1983

Operations
Based at Key West, Florida and engaged in anti-drug smuggling patrols in the Caribbean Sea

Glacier Bay Yacht Tours Inc (Catamaran Cruise Lines)

Seattle, USA

Robert Giersdorf, *President*
Bert Nordby, *Vice-President*

High-speed craft operated

Type	Name	Seats	In service
CAT Nichols Brothers Boat Builders InCat 30m	*Executive Explorer*	25 st:te-rooms*	October 1986
CAT Nichols Brothers Boat Builders InCat 30m	*Hawaii Express*	400	6 December 1986
CAT Nichols Brothers Boat Builders InCat	*Gold Rush* (ex *Glacier Express*, 1985)	220	1988 (built 1985)

*49 passengers

Operation

Summer months (June to mid-September): Alaska, based in Juneau, *Executive Explorer* calls at Skagway, Haines/Pt Chilkoot, Glacier Bay Lodge, Sitka and Ketchikan.
Hawaii Express operates one day excursions out of Maui's Maalaea harbour to Molokai and Lanai and to Molokini Island, started early 1987.

InCat 220-seat catamaran *Gold Rush* now operated by Catamaran Cruise Lines

Golden Gate Ferry

Golden Gate Bridge, Highway and Transportation District, 101 East Sir Francis Drake Blvd, Larkspur, California 94939, USA

Telephone: (415) 457 8800

Robert Stockwel, *President*
James R Bronkema, *1st Vice President*
Richard D Spotswood, *2nd Vice President*
Carney J Campion, *General Manager*
Eric A Robinson, *Division Manager*
Carl D Harrington, *Operations/Maintenance Superintendent*

The Ferry Division was formed in 1970 to operate waterborne mass transit on San Francisco Bay, operating between Marin County and San Francisco. In 1976, service was expanded with three semi-planing, triple gas turbine, 25-knot, waterjet-propelled vessels. For economic reasons these three vessels have now been re-powered with twin diesel engines using conventional propellers and rudders and with a resulting speed of 20.5 knots. The last of the three vessels modified was delivered in its new form in October 1985. See High-Speed Mono-Hull Craft Section.

The Golden Gate Ferry vessel *Sonoma*

High-speed craft operated

Type	Name	Seats	Originally entered service
MH Campbell Industries Spaulding S-165 50.3m	*Marin*	partially open deck 118 open deck 42 enclosed decks 372	December 1976
MH Campbell Industries Spaulding S-165 50.3m	*Sonoma*	partially open deck 118 open deck 42 enclosed decks 372	March 1977
MH Campbell Industries Spaulding S-165 50.3m	*San Francisco*	partially open deck 118 open deck 42 enclosed decks 372	September 1977

Route operated

San Francisco to Larkspur, Marin County. Time 42 to 43 min

Grundstad Maritime Overseas/Crown Cruise Line

2790 North Federal Highway, Boca Raton, Florida 33431–0900, USA

Telephone: (305) 394 7450
Telex: 159067GO-GO
Telefax: (305) 392–5917

Lars-Johan Hagerup, *Vice President, Operations*

Owner of three Westamarin Supramar PT 150 hydrofoils. These three vessels have been converted into luxury diving vessels for operation in the Caribbean; their foils have been removed. For details of the PT 150 hydrofoil, please see page 153 of the 1987 edition

High-speed craft operated

Type
HYD Westamarin PT 150 *Crown Pearl* (ex *Princess of the Waves*, *Princess of the Lakes* (1984), ex *Princess of the Waves* (1979))
HYD Westamarin PT 150 *Crown Diver* (ex *Prince of Niagara*, *Prince of the Waves* (1979), ex *Norfoil* (1973), ex *Scandia* (1970), ex *Hydroliner* (1969), ex *Expressan* (1969))
HYD Westamarin PT 150 *Crown Islander* (ex *Queen of Toronto*, *Queen of the Waves* (1979))

PT 150, one of three converted into luxury diving craft but with foils removed

Maryland Natural Resources Police

Tawes State Office Building, Annapolis, Maryland 21401, USA

Telephone: (301) 974 3170/3187
Telefax: (301) 974 3189

High-speed craft operated

Type	Seats	Delivered
Slingsby Aviation Hovercraft SAH 2200	16	August 1987

Operation

The craft is used on a multi-mission basis to include law enforcement patrol, emergency medical transport, search and rescue and icebreaking. In addition,

Slingsby Aviation SAH 2200 in service with the Maryland National Resources Police

the unit is called upon to perform all other missions that are difficult or impossible for conventional patrol craft or light aircraft. This includes search and rescue during inclement weather and transport of US Coast Guard personnel over pack ice to service aids to navigation as needed.

The Slingsby 2200 became fully operational in September 1987 and is being used on a multi-mission basis to include law enforcement patrol, emergency medical transport, search and rescue and icebreaking. In addition, the unit may be called upon to perform all other missions that are difficult or impossible for conventional patrol craft or light aircraft. This includes search and rescue during inclement weather and transport of personnel over pack ice. A primary mission of this craft is the provision of emergency medical services and medical transport. For these purposes the craft will be staffed with Emergency Medical Technicians and a Cardiac Rescue Technician with all the necessary equipment to meet the requirements of an advanced life support unit.

Put-In-Bay Boat Line
South Bass Island, Lake Erie, Ohio, USA

High-speedcraft operated

Type	Name	Seats	In Service
CAT Gladding Hearn	Jet Express	380	June 1989

Route Operated
Put-in-Bay to Port Clinton, 13 n miles, 22min
US$15 return fare

Red and White Fleet, Crowley Maritime Corporation
Pier 41, San Francisco, California 94133, USA

Telephone: (415) 546 2800

Russ Johnson, *General Manager*
Shirley Kohlwes, *Operations Manager*

High-speed craft operated

Type	Name	Seats	Delivered
CAT Nichols Brothers InCat 26m	Catamarin	274	1985
CAT Nichols Brothers InCat 26m	Dolphin	274	1986

Operation
Marin County area commuter and cruise services
Catamarin and *Dolphin* operating (1986) ferry services between San Francisco and Sausalito, Tiburon, and Vallejo on San Francisco Bay. Also used on cruise service to Marineworld Africa USA in Vallejo from San Francisco

Saltair Marina
Salt Lake City, Utah, USA

Operation started 1983.

High-speed craft operated

Type	Name	Seats	Built
HYD Ludwig Honald Mfg Co	Albatross (ex Victory II)	21	1964

Routes operated
20-min sightseeing trips: from south shore of the Great Salt Lake, tour of Salt Lake City and the lake. Variable schedule.

Sayville Ferry Service Inc
Brown's River Road, PO Box 626, Sayville, Long Island, New York 11782, USA

Telephone: (516) 589 0810

Capt Kenneth Stein, *President*

Sayville Ferry Service have a total fleet of 10 vessels with passenger capacity from 6 to 350. Most of them are operated at between 15 and 20 knots but the *Fire Island Clipper* can cruise at 26 knots at full load.

High-speed craft operated

Type	Name	Seats	Built
MH Derecktor Shipyard	Fire Island Clipper	350	1979

Operation
Sayville, Long Island (South Shore) to Fire Island, 5n miles, serving two summer communities, stops at Cherry Grove and Fire Island Pines. In 1988 a total of 447 372 passengers were carried.

Sayville Ferry Services *Fire Island Clipper*

Sea World Inc
This organisation no longer operates the three Ludwig Honald Albatross hydrofoil craft in the Mission Bay area, San Diego.

Shepler's Inc
Mackinaw City, Michigan, USA

High-speed craft operated

Type	Name	Seats	In service
MH Camcraft Boats Inc (Hargrave) 18.30m	The Welcome	120	
MH Camcraft Boats Inc (Hargrave) 17.10m	Felicity	150	
MH Aluminium Boats Inc (Hargrave) 23.78m	Captain Shepler	265	1986

Route operated
St Ignace (Upper Peninsula) to Mackinaw City (Lower Peninsula) and Mackinac Island, Michigan

Tidewater Marine Service Inc
1440 Canal Street, Suite 2100, New Orleans, Louisiana 70112, USA

Telephone: (504) 568 1010
Telex: 0460050

Richard M Currence, *President, Tidewater Marine Service Inc*
John P Laborde, *Chairman and Chief Executive Officer, Tidewater Inc*

In November 1985 it was announced by Tidewater Inc that its subsidiary, Tidewater Marine Service, Inc, had taken delivery of the Bell Halter Model 212B 110 Mk II *Speed Tide* on a long-term charter with a purchase option from the owner, Bell Halter Inc of New Orleans.

With the addition of *Speed Tide*, the Tidewater fleet numbered 268 vessels of all major classes in worldwide service. Of these, April 1985 listing showed 16 to be crew boats, a number of which would be in the high-speed category.

High-speed craft operated

Type	Name	Seats	Delivered
SES Bell Halter 212B, 110 Mk II	Speed Tide	119	November 1986

Operation
The vessel is working in the Gulf of Suez, for the Gulf of Suez Petroleum Company, a venture of Egypt's national oil company and Amoco, delivering support crews and supplies to drilling rigs and production facilities located within a 50-mile radius in the Gulf of Suez.

Bell Halter Model 212B (110 Mk II) *Speed Tide* on long term charter with Tidewater Marine Service, Inc   *(Donlen)*

TNT Hydrolines, Inc
65, Willowbrook Blvd.,
Wayne, New Jersey 07470, USA

Telephone: (201) 785 9560
(212) 244 4770
Thomas E Bruyere, *President*
John R Arwood, *Chairman*

High-speed craft operated

Type	Name	Seats	In service
MH Gladding-Hearn Shipbuilding	*TNT Express 1*	265	February 1989

Route operated
Bayshore area NJ to Wall Street, 45 min

Tri-State Marine Transport, Inc
Richmond Hill, Queens, New York, USA

F Ardolino, *Vice President*

High-speed craft operated

Type	Name	Seats	Delivered
SES Avondale Air Ride 109	—	400	Spring 1989
SES Avondale Air Ride 109	—	400	—
SES Avondale Air Ride 109	—	400	—
SES Avondale Air Ride 109	—	400	—
SES Avondale Air Ride 109	—	400	—

Route operated
John F Kennedy Airport to Manhattan

United New York-New Jersey Sandy Hook Pilots Association
Sandy Hook, New Jersey, USA

High-speed craft operated

Type	Name	Delivered
MH Gladding-Hearn Shipbuilding Corp (C Raymond Hunt) 19.51m	*Sandy Hook*	1985

Washington State Ferries (Washington State Department of Transportation, Marine Division)
Colman Dock, Pier 52, Seattle, Washington 98104, USA

Telephone: (206) 464 7866

High-speed craft operated

Type	Name	Delivered
CAT Nichols Bros InCat	*Express* (ex *Glacier Express*, ex *Baja Express*)	15 September 1986

Route operated
Seattle-Bremerton, approx 35 min, weekdays only

Yukon River Cruises, Inc
Anchorage, Alaska, USA

High-speed craft operated

Type	Name	Seats
CAT 22m Nichols Bros InCat	*Klondike*	210

URUGUAY

Belt SA
Plaza Cagancha 1124

Telephone: (90) 5128/5063/4608/4668/2951/5987
Telex: 22133BELT UY

Juan Carlos Deicas, *Managing Director*

Annual traffic: 180 000 to 200 000 passengers

High-speed craft operated

Type	Name	Seats	Acquired
HYD Rodriquez RHS 140	*Tyrving*		1979
HYD Rodriquez RHS 140	*Colonia del Sacramento* (ex *Condor 3*)		1979
HYD Rodriquez RHS 140	*Farallón* (ex *Løberon '85*)	125	1985

Routes operated
Colonia to Buenos Aires
Montevideo to Colonia to Buenos Aires

VENEZUELA

Inversiones Turisticas Margarita CA (INTUMACA)
Coracrevi, Apartado Postal 101, Caracas, Venezuela

High-speed craft operated

Type	Name	Speed	Seats	Delivered
MH Swiftships 38.0m	*Gran Cacique I*	24 knots	300	1978
MH Swiftships 38.0m	*Gran Cacique II*	24 knots	300	1980
MH Swiftships 38.0m	*Gran Cacique III*	30 knots	300	1980

Route operated
Puerto La Cruz to Margarita Island

Gran Cacique I operating off the Venezuelan coast

Maraven SA
Apartado 809, Caracas 1010-A, Venezuela

Telex: 23535/23536/23227 CCAR

Rafael Pardo, *Director*
Carlos Borregales, *Exploration and Production Manager*
Hans Krause, *Exploration and Production Manager*

High-speed craft operated

Type	Yard no	Name	Seats	Delivered
SES Vosper Hovermarine HM 218	454	*Zumbador*	70	1979
SES Vosper Hovermarine HM 218	455	*Zumaya*	70	1980
SES Vosper Hovermarine HM 218		*Barroso*	70	1980

Operation
Support duties for oil production platforms on Lake Maracaibo

VIRGIN ISLANDS (US)

Nautical Trading Ltd
Transportation Services of St John
St John, US Virgin Islands

High-speed craft operated

Type	Name	Seats	Delivered
ALH Atlantic & Gulf	*Caribe Air Ride*	149	1987*
Boatbuilding Air Ride 65	(ex *Air Ride Express*)		
MH Equitable Shipyards 25.9m	*Caribe Tide*	232	1988

*Launched March 1983, originally delivered to South Florida Offshore Services Ltd, Plantation, Florida

Route operated
St John to St Thomas airport

YUGOSLAVIA

Atlas Pogon Hidrokrilnih Brodova
5001 Dubrovnik, Pile 1, Yugoslavia

Telex: 27515YU

Operator of Kometa hydrofoils

Kompas Touristik International
PO Box 307/IV, Pražakova 4, 61001 Ljubljana, Yugoslavia

Telex: 31209/32183 KOMPAS YU
Telefax: 061/319 888
Janez Pergar, *Director*

High-speed craft operated

Type	Name	Delivered
HYD S Ordzhonikidze Kometa	*Krila Pirana*	1979
HYD S Ordzhonikidze Kometa	*Krila Kornata*	1980
HYD S Ordzhonikidze Kometa	*Krila Briona*	1983
CAT Westamarin W100	*Poreč 1*	1982
CAT NQEA Wavepiercer InCat	*Prince of Venice*	1989

Routes operated
Poreč to Pula, Poreč to Umag, Poreč to Rovinj, Poreč to Portorož, Venice to Istria, Istrian coast to the Kornati islands, split to the islands of middle Dalmatia. Dubrovnik to the islands of southern Dalmatia and Montenegro.

The number of passengers carried by all vessels from June 1st to the end of August 1989 was 59 763.

Services are operated from April until October each year.

Kvarner Express
Maršala Tita 186, 51410 Opatija, PO Box 92, Yugoslavia

Telephone: (051) 711 111
Telex: 24174OPATUR YU/24379 KVEX YU
Telefax: (051) 711 549/721

Radomir Premuš, *Managing Director*
Aldo Simper, *Assistant Managing Director*

In 1985 Kvarner Express introduced high-speed daily ferry services from Opatija to the Island of Rab and to Venice. The company now operates a fleet of four 35-knot Kolkhida hydrofoil craft.

High-speed craft operated

Type	Name	Seats	Delivered
HYD S Ordzhonikidze Kolkhida	*Magnolija*	145	1985
HYD S Ordzhonikidze Kolkhida	*Kamelija*	145	1985
HYD S Ordzhonikidze Kolkhida	*Mirta*	145	1986
HYD S Ordzhonikidze Kolkhida	*Mimoza*	145	1986
MH Marinteknik Verkstads 42m	*Iris*	350	1989

Routes operated
Opatija to Rab, 50n miles, Mali Losin, 53 n miles
Opatija to Venice and in spring 1987 to Ancona and Rimini
Istrian Penisula to Venice, Kornati Islands, Rimini, Ravenna, Pesaro
Rab & Mali Losin to Venice, Rimini, Zadar
Rueica to Venice, Silba 7 Rimini
Zadar to Sirenic & Ancona

Kvarner Express *Iris*

Splosna Plovba Piran
Yugoslavia

High-speed craft operated

Type	Name	Delivered
CAT Westamarin W100	*Poreč*	January 1982

Union Dalmacija
Oour Flota, Kupalisni prilaz 12, 58000 Split, Yugoslavia

Telephone: (58) 513–066
Telex: 26102DALTUR YU

High-speed craft operated

Type	Name	Delivered
CAT Westamarin W86	*Mediteran*	June 1978
CAT Westamarin W86	*Marina I*	July 1978

Operation
Dalmatian coast

A Kompas Kometa at Venice, 1986

PRINCIPAL ENGINEERING COMPONENTS FOR HIGH-SPEED CRAFT

ENGINES
CANADA

PRATT & WHITNEY CANADA

1000 Marie-Victorin Blvd., Longueuil, Quebec
J4G 1A1, Canada

Telephone: (514) 677–9411 (514) 651–3633
(Industrial and Marine Division)

L D Caplan, *President and Chief Executive Officer*
G P Ouimet, *Executive Vice President*
R F Steers, *Vice President, Finance*
C J Pascoe, *Vice President, Counsel*
R C Abraham, *Vice President, Operations*
J B Haworth, *Vice President, Industrial and Marine Division*
R M Sachs, *Director of Marketing, Industrial and Marine Division*

In addition to its wide range of small gas turbine aero engines, Pratt & Whitney Canada also manufactures industrial and marine derivatives supplied by the Industrial and Marine Division. Engines are rated from 410kW (550 shp) upwards (see table) and are of the simple cycle, free-turbine type. They run on Nos 1 and 2 diesel or aviation turbine fuels.

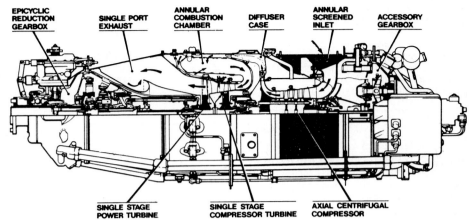

Main components of ST6

Typical marine applications are the ST6K-77 driving the auxiliary power unit on the Flagstaff 2 class hydrofoils built for the Israeli Navy, and the ST6T-76 Twin-Pac powering LACV-30 hovercraft built by Bell Aerospace Textron (now Textron Marine Systems) for the U.S. Army. Including aero-engine installations, more than 33 000 of Pratt & Whitney Canada's turbines have been delivered. Between them they have accumulated in excess of 175 million hours of operation.

ENGINE FEATURES: All ST6 engines have a single spool gas generator and a multi-stage compressor (3 axial plus one centrifugal stage) driven by a single-stage axial turbine. The larger models have cooled vanes. The radial diffuser incorporates Pratt & Whitney Canada patented diffuser pipes. The burner section has a reverse flow annular combustor. A single or two-stage free turbine provides a direct high-speed output or drives through a reduction gearbox.

Air intake is located at the rear of the engine and is through a screened annular inlet.

The ST6T-76 Twin-Pac is a dual version of the ST6 with two power sections mounted side-by-side coupled to a twinning reduction gearbox. The gearbox incorporates automatic clutches which permit emergency operation of one side independent of the other.

ST6 gas turbine

ST6 and SPW SERIES ENGINE DATA SUMMARY (GUARANTEED PERFORMANCE)
Sea Level Standard Pressure at 15°C Inlet Temperature

IMPERIAL MEASURE

Model	Maximum		Normal		Output Speed RPM		Length	Width	Height	Engine Dry Weight
					Direct Drive	Integral Gearbox	(in)	(in)	(in)	(lb)
	SHP	SFC	SHP	SFC						
ST6L-77	811	0.589	654	0.620	33 000	—	52.0	21.5	21.0	305
ST6J-77	750	0.608	550	0.660	—	2200	63.5	21.5	20.5	369
ST6K-77	690	0.620	550	0.660	—	6188	60.5	21.5	20.5	340
ST6L-79	944	0.582	862	0.586	33 000	1900*	46.0	22.0	22.0	306
ST6L-81	1182	0.551	1049	0.563	33 000	1700*	50.0	19.4	21.1	360
ST6T-76	1850	0.615	1440	0.650	—	6600	66.4	44.4	31.6	740
SPW901/1	1765	0.596	1642	0.596	24625	—	47	26	41.5	700
SPW124-2	2471	0.483	2125	0.505	20 000	1200*	60	26	33	660

METRIC MEASURE

Model	Maximum		Normal		Output Speed RPM		Length	Width	Height	Weight
					Direct Drive	Integral Gearbox	(mm)	(mm)	(mm)	(kg)
	kW	SFC	kW	SFC						
ST6L-77	605	0.358	488	0.377	33 000	—	1321	546	533	139
ST6J-77	560	0.370	410	0.401	—	2200	1613	546	521	168
ST6K-77	515	0.377	410	0.401	—	6188	1537	546	521	154
ST6L-79	704	0.354	643	0.356	33 000	1900*	1168	559	559	139
ST6L-81	881	0.335	782	0.342	33 000	1700*	1270	493	536	163
ST6T-76	1380	0.374	1074	0.395	—	6600	1687	1128	803	336
SPW901/1	1317	0.362	1225	0.362	24 625	—	1194	660	1054	318
SPW124-2	1843	0.294	1585	0.306	20 000	1200*	1524	660	838	300

Engine data shown is for direct drive
Engine data with integral gearbox available on request

SPW124–2

The SPW124–2 is an industrial and marine version of the PW124 aero turboprop. This engine benefits from the experience gained by its aero counterparts with 2 million hours of operation.
ENGINE FEATURES: The SPW-124 is a three shaft engine. The low pressure and high pressure centrifugal compressors (combined pressure ratio 15:1) are each driven independently by single-stage compressor turbines. This allows both compressors to operate at their optimum efficiencies without the need for complex variable geometry. Other features comprise Pratt & Whitney Canada patented pipe diffusers, reverse annular combus-tor, low pressure and high pressure stator cooling, and turbine blade cooling. The 2-stage power turbine retains the free turbine concept of the ST6 engine.

SPW901/1

This is a direct drive gas turbine of rugged design intended for industrial and marine use.
ENGINE FEATURES: A free turbine engine incorporating a cast aluminium air intake casing, centrifugal compressor, patented Pratt & Whitney Canada pipe diffusers, reverse flow annular combustor, single stage high turbine with cooled vanes and disk. The ball and roller bearings which support the gas generator rotor assembly and power turbine shaft have under-race lubrication. Thermal insulation blankets are selectively installed on the external surfaces of the engine to maintain surface temperature below 450°F.

PW901A

The PW901A is an auxiliary power unit which is fully marinised, lightweight and compact, delivering 551 lb/min of air at 54 lb/in² absolute. In addition it has provision to drive two 90 kVA electrical generators.

CHINA, PEOPLE'S REPUBLIC

CHENGDU ENGINE COMPANY

Please see United Technologies International Inc entry regarding forthcoming production of 24 609 kW FT8 marine gas turbine in China.

Marine FT8 propulsion unit will be packaged at a Navy facility near Harbin.

FRANCE

MOTEURS BAUDOUIN

165 Boulevard de Pont-de-Vivaux, BP 62, 13362 Marseilles Cedex 10, France

Telephone: (91) 83 85 00
Telex: 410944MOBOD F
Telefax: (91) 79 09 38

12 P 15.2 SR7

Fitted to the SBCN 38-metre patrol boat.
TYPE: A four-stroke direct injection diesel engine.
CYLINDERS: 12 cylinders, V-form, rigid wet type cylinder liners.
ASPIRATION: Turbocharged with air cooler.
COOLING: By water from closed circuit with fresh water/raw water heat exchanger integrated with engine.
LUBRICATION: Gear pump with full flow cartridge type oil filters.
INJECTION: Monoblock injection pump with mechanical governor.
TECHNICAL DATA
Swept volume: 31.8 litres
Compression ratio: 14.0:1
Max rating: 1030kW at 2000rpm
Mean effective pressure: 19.44 bar at 2000rpm
Fuel consumption: 265 litres/h
Dry weight, without gearbox: 3000kg

	A mm	B mm	C mm	D mm	E mm	Approx weight in kg without water or oil
12 P 15.2 SR7						3000
12 P 15.2 SRC IRS	355	1229	340	1084	165	3970
12 P 15.2 SRC IRX	488	1839	460	1356	226	5105
12 P 15.2 SRC RHS	355	1611	340	1084	165	3965
12 P 15.2 SRC RHX	488	2071	460	1356	226	5105

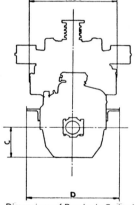
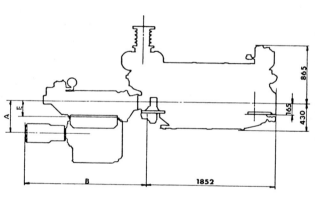

Dimensions of Baudouin Series 12 P 15.2 SR7 engines/gearboxes

Baudouin 12 P 15.2 SR7 marine diesel engine

BAUDOUIN VTi SERIES

A new series of diesel engines was announced in 1989, 4 stroke, direct injection, watercooled cylinders 6 or 12 in 90°V. Turbocharged with charge air intercooling.

V6Ti330
243kW at 3200 rpm; dry weight: 815 kg

V12BTi840
618kW at 3000 rpm; dry weight: 1360 kg

V12BTi1200
883kW at 2000 rpm; dry weight: 30020 kg

V12BTi1400
CHARACTERISTICS
1030kW at 2000 rpm for high-speed craft
Diesel engine, 4 stroke, direct injection turbocharged with charge air intercooling
Bore and Stroke: 150 × 150 mm

Number of cylinders: 12 in 90°V
Total sweep volume: 3181dm3³
Compression ratio: 14/1
Number of valves per cylinder: 4
Engine rotation to ISO 1204 standard: Counterclockwise
Idling speed: 700 min-1
Weight without water and oil: 3020 kg
Weight to power ratio (rating RP): 2.1 kg/HP

Baudouin V6 Ti330 243 kW

Baudouin V12 BTi1400 1030 kW

SOCIÉTÉ ALSACIENNE DE CONSTRUCTIONS MÉCANIQUES DE MULHOUSE (SACM)

DIVISION UNI diesel
1, rue de la Fonderie BP 1210
68054 MULHOUSE CEDEX
Telephone: (89) 46 01 08
Telex: 881699F
Telefax: (89) 56 52 76

DIVISION POYAUD
16, Avenue de la Gare BP 13, 17700 SURGERES
Telephone: (46) 07 62 10
Telex: 790 831F
Telefax: (46) 07 64 02

The SACM-M Company designs, manufactures and markets a range of modern high-speed diesel engines from 150 to 8000 kW. Over 25 000 engines have been supplied over 30 years under the trade names POYAUD, MGO, AGO and recently regrouped under the trade name UNI diesel. These engines are designed to meet sophisticated requirements for propulsion and power supply applications.

SACM-M UD33 V12 M7D 2020 kW engine

Type of engine	swept vol. l³	bore mm	stroke mm	rpm	kW	hp	length mm	width mm	height mm	Dry weight kg
UD18										
UD18 LO6 M5D					245	335	1530	850	1220	1100
UD18 VO8 M5D	1.8	135	122	2200	325	445	1400	1220	1290	1500
UD18 V12 M5D					490	665	1920	1340	1255	1900
UD23										
UD23 V12 M5D	2.6	142	166	1800	735	1000	1975	1380	1450	2650
UD33										
UD33 V12 M6D					1765	2400	2950	1700	2280	7500
UD33 V12 M7D					2020	2745	2950	1700	2280	7500
UD33 V16 M6D	5.5	195	180	1600	2355	3200	4030	1700	2280	9000
UD33 V16 M7D					2690	3660	4030	1700	2280	9000
UD45										
UD45 V12 M7D					2850	3875	3800	2000	2700	12 100
UD45 V16 M7D	10.2	240	220	1350	3800	5170	4400	2000	2700³	19 000
UD45 V20 M7D					4750	6460	6100	2000	2700	21 000

Rating at engine PTO fuel stop power according to ISO 3046.1

The SACM-M company ranks today among the world leaders for high performance vessel propulsion, heavy and armoured vehicle powering and nuclear plant safe-guard generator sets.

Over 5% of the turnover of SACM-M is devoted to R & D.

TECHNICAL CHARACTERISTICS
Compact through high integration of equipment.
Low operating costs:
  easy to maintain,
  low fuel consumption.
Performance range of engine adapted to particular resistance curves of various hulls.
Optimisation of propulsion line (engine-reversing-reducing gear-shaft line-propeller) in association with shipyards.
Calling on high-technology superchargers, a wide range of speeds, and a large degree of control over mechanical stresses, give these engines an extremely wide performance range.

SACM-M UD23 V12 M5D 735 kW engine
(*Phot'indus*)

TURBOMECA
64511 Bordes France

Telephone: (33) 59328436

S Meton, *President*
D Marchand, *General Director*
Y P François, *Land and Marine Turbine Department Manager*

Turbomeca had developed a new industrial gas turbine, which the company designates Makila T1, rated 1200 kW under ISO conditions and base load. Its modern design and the use of state-of-the-art technology have contributed to its 28% efficiency; exceptionally high for this class of prime mover.

This new industrial turbine is a derivative of the Makila turboshaft model and some 800 units have been built for the Super Puma helicopter manufactured by Aerospatiale. Consequently the reliability of all major components has been proven in several years of service.

At present, only the liquid fueled version of the industrial model is available, but the gas and dual fuel versions will soon be introduced. Plans are to continue development to increase machine performance until the year 2015 at least, when hopefully over 3000 units will be in operation for industrial amd marine applications.

The Makila T1 gas turbine comprises four main modules:

1) the auxiliary drive and air intake module incorporating three axial compressor stages with thick airfoils and fixed stators.

2) The gas generator module housing the centrifugal compressor stage, an annular combustion chamber for homogeneous temperature distribution and the two uncooled high pressure turbine stages with inset blades and nozzle guide vanes manufactured of refractory alloys.

3) The power turbine module including the two low pressure axial turbine stages and an integrated gearbox which reduces the power output speed to 22 000, 5000, 1600 and 1500 revs/min.

4) The dedicated electronic computer module, based on a multiprocessor and multilayered flexible card technology, performs start-up, control and regulation of the engine parameters. This module includes facilities for in-line auto-test and off-line failure detection and identification.

AT ISO conditions, under full load, the axial-centrifugal compressor section delivers 5.5 kg/s of air 9.9:1.0 pressure ratio.

The low pollution exhaust gas is discharged at 525°C. Specific fuel consumption is 300 g/kWh. The Makila T1 is intended for generator and mechanical drive applications such as railways, navy, cogeneration, oil and gas industry and is

Turbomeca Makila T1 industrial gas turbine rated 1200kW

specially protected for operation in marine environment.

MAIN CHARACTERISTICS:
- very low mass: 410 kg for 1200 kW–ISO
- high efficiency: over 28%
- reliability: derivative from 1000 engines produced for aviation and industrial applications (cogeneration, pumps, trains etc)
- small size: length × height × width = 1.9 × 0.7 × 0.7 metres
- free turbine type, particularly suited to drive waterjet units or surface piercing propellers

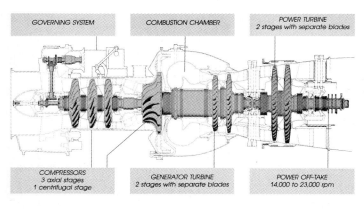

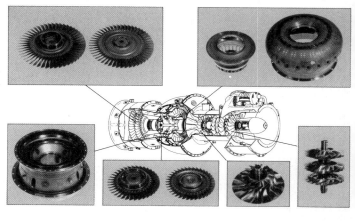

GERMANY, FEDERAL REPUBLIC

DEUTZ (KLÖCKNER-HUMBOLDT-DEUTZ AG)

Deutz Mülheimer Str 111, Postfach 800 509, D-5000 Cologne 80, Federal Republic of Germany

Telephone: (0221) 822 0
Telex: 88120
Telefax: (0221) 822 3525

Group companies:
Motoren-Werke Mannheim AG and MWM Diesel und Gastechnik GmbH,Carl-Benz-Str.5,Postfach 102 263, D-6800 Mannheim 1, Federal Republic of Germany

U K Subsidiary:
KHD Great Britain Limited, 2 St Martins Way, London SW17 0UT, England

Telephone: (081)946 9161
Telex: 8954136 KHDLON G
Telefax: (081)947 6380

KHD Deutz air-cooled engines of the 413F series have been in large-scale production for many years. Comprising 5- and 6-cylinder in-line and 6-, 8-, 10- and 12-cylinder 'V' engines, these naturally aspirated engines cover outputs ranging from 118kW to 441kW.

The 513 series is a further development of the 413F engine. The main feature of this new engine family is a completely re-designed combustion system. Other advantages include reduced exhaust gas emissions, electronically controlled cooling blower, and higher torque. In addition the same maximum power at 200rpm lower engine speed provides higher power at medium engine speeds and lower fuel consumption. Engines of the 513 series are available as 6-, 8-, 10- and 12-cylinder 'V' type, in naturally aspirated versions as well as 6-cylinder in-line and 8-, 10- and 12-cylinder 'V' type turbocharged or turbocharged/after-cooled versions. The power developed by this engine family covers a range from 141kW to 386kW, and for some applications extends up to 441kW flywheel net. The turbocharged/after-cooled 12-cylinder automotive version of the design offers the best power to weight ratio for that application.

KHD Deutz engines are installed in the following hovercraft: Griffon Hovercraft Ltd 1000 TD and 1500 TD powered by single BF6L 913C diesels, the 2500 TD by two BF6L 913Cs and the 4000 TD design by two BF8L 513s; Air Vehicles Ltd Tiger 16, Hovertrans PH 11 and Slingsby Aviation Ltd SAH 2200 are both powered by single BF6L 913Cs. Both Griffon Hovercraft Ltd and Air Vehicles Ltd have further models planned, using Deutz air-cooled engines. Four Deutz BF12L 513CP diesels are installed in the BHC AP1-88 general purpose hovercraft, two for lift and two for propulsion.

BF6/8/10/12L 513C

TYPE: Air-cooled four-stroke diesel with direct fuel injection naturally aspirated or turbocharged; BF12L 513C with air-charge cooling system.
CYLINDERS: Individually removable cylinders made in grey cast iron alloy, each with one inlet and one exhaust valve, overhead type. The valves are controlled via tappets and pushrods via a camshaft running in three metal bearings in the upper part of the crankcase. Camshaft is crankshaft driven via helical spur gears arranged at the flywheel end of the engine. Crankcase is grey cast iron. The main journals are supported after each throw in three metal bearings, one of which is designed as a locating bearing.
PISTONS: Each is equipped with two compression rings and one oil control ring and are force oil-cooled.

Deutz BF12L 513C air-cooled diesel as fitted to BHC and NQEA AP1-88 hovercraft

BHC AP1-88 powered by four 441 kW BF 12L 513 CP air-cooled diesels

COOLING SYSTEM: Air-cooled, mechanically driven axial type cooling air blower with optional load-dependent, electronic control.
LUBRICATION: Force feed by gear type pump. Oil is cleaned by full-flow paper filters. A centrifugal filter is installed in the fan hub as a high efficiency secondary flow filter.

BF12L 513C

Power, max (intermittent duty): 386kW at 2300rpm
Number of cylinders: 12
Bore/stroke: 125/130mm
Capacity: 19.144 litres
Compression ratio: 15.8:1
Rotational speed: 2300rpm
Mean piston speed: 9.96m/s
Specific fuel consumption (automotive rating flywheel net at max torque): 205g/kWh
Shipping volume: 3.16m³
DIMENSIONS
Length: 1582mm
Height: 1243mm
Width: 1196mm
USER: British Hovercraft Corporation AP1-88.

BF12L 513CP

This engine is a variant of the turbocharged and inter-cooled V12 which, by utilising a remotely mounted air-to-air inter-cooler raises the intermittent power to 441kW at 2300rpm.

This is used by BHC on their latest, well-deck version of the AP1-88 for lift and propulsion.

BF6L 913C

Built to the same specification as the 513, this 6-cylinder in-line engine is also available for hovercraft applications. It is fitted with an exhaust turbocharger and charge air-cooler.
Max (intermittent duty) power: 141kW at 2500rpm
Number of cylinders: 6
Bore/stroke: 102/125mm
Capacity: 6.128 litres
Compression ratio: 15.5:1
Rotational speed: 2500rpm
Mean piston speed: 10.4m/s
Specific fuel consumption (automotive rating at max torque): 214g/kWh
Shipping volume: 0.8m³
DIMENSIONS
Length: 1245mm
Height: 991mm
Width: 711mm
Weight: 510kg
USERS: Griffon Hovercraft Ltd 1000 TD, 1500 TD and 2500 TD, Air Vehicles Ltd Tiger 16, Slingsby Aviation Ltd SAH 2200. The BF6L 913 also powers the MARIC type 7210 and three are used in the MARIC type 716 II.

Please see MWM entry for details of Deutz MWM 234, 816 and 604B type engines.

DEUTZ MWM
Motoren-Werke Mannheim AG

Carl-Benz-Strasse 5, Postfach 102 263, D-6800
Mannheim 1, Federal Republic of Germany

Telephone: (0621) 384 0
Telex: 462341 D
Telefax: (0621) 384 328

Group Companies:
Klöckner-Humboldt-Deutz AG, Deutz-Mülhei-
mer-Str 111, Postfach 800 509, D-5000 Cologne,
Federal Republic of Germany

U K Subsidiary:
KHD Great Britain Ltd, 2 St Martins Way,
London SW17 OUT, UK

Telephone: (081) 946 9161
Telex: 8954136 KHDLON G
Telefax: (081) 946 9161

Following the merger in 1985 of Motoren-
Werke Mannheim AG and Klöckner-Humboldt-
Deutz AG, the company now offers a combined
range of medium-sized and large water-cooled
engines from 100 to 7250kW.

The principal engine ranges suitable for high-
speed surface craft and hovercraft are as follows:

Deutz MWM TBD 604B V12 diesel engine, 1440kW at 1800rpm

TBD 234

The 234 series is a modern high-power, high-
speed engine design offering decisive advantages
in power/weight ratio, power/space ratio, durability and fuel consumption. The engine is available in 60° V 6-, 8-, 12- and 16-cylinder versions,
either turbocharged and inter-cooled or naturally
aspirated. Power outputs are available from
100kW at 1500rpm up to 900kW at 2300rpm.
Examples of their application include a new series
of Spanish-built 14-metre customs launches, with
a maximum speed in excess of 55 knots. Each is
driven by twin TBD 234 V12 engines rated at
735kW at 2300rpm direct coupled to Riva Calzoni
waterjet units. Another application is the International Catamarans Pty 31-metre wave-piercing
catamaran *Tassie Devil 2001*, which is driven by
two TBD 234 V16 engines each rated continuous
at 755kW at 2200rpm.

BAM 816

The 816 series is a compact, low profile design.
The engine is available in in-line 6 and 8 cylinders,
together with 120° V 12- and 16-cylinder versions.
The power range available is from 100kW at
1000rpm to 1013kW at 1800rpm. Examples of
their application include the Westamarin W88
catamaran ferry *Haugesund* powered by twin
BAM 16M 816 each rated at 865kW at 1200rpm.

TBD 604B

Developed from the existing 603/604 engine
family, the new series 604B engine type is a
compact high-speed diesel engine incorporating
the very latest technology to give excellent pow-
er/weight ratios and a very favourable fuel consumption of only 190g/kWh. The engine is a four-
stroke, as are all Deutz MWM water-cooled diesel
engines, and is turbocharged and inter-cooled.
To give a power spread of 420kW (563bhp) at
1000rpm up to 1940kW (2601bhp) at 1800rpm,
the engine is available with an in-line 6-cylinder,
together with 90° V 8-, 12- and 16-cylinder
variants. The engine is fitted with an innovative
combustion system, the HALLO swirl, allowing
optimum combustion even under idling and other
low load conditions. Typical applications include
the FBM Marinteknik (S) Pte Ltd 35m mono-hull
ferries for Hong Kong, using twin TBD 604B V8
with an MCR of 840kW at 1800rpm, to give a
service speed of 25 knots. Also operating are
various units for International Catamarans Pty
and a 47-knot SES built by Brødrene Aå in

Deutz MWM TBD 604B V12 ,1460 kW at 1800 rpm

Norway, using two TBD 604B V12 at 1260kW at
1800rpm. Larger SESs are being built by the same
company using TB 604B V16 engines rated at

1690kW and with lift engines of type TBD 604B
V6 rated at 295kW.

MAN

MAN Nutzfahrzeuge GmbH

Nuremberg Works, PO Box 44 01 00, Franken-strasse 15, 8500 Nürnberg 44, Federal Republic of Germany

Telephone: (0911) 18–0
Telex: 622914–0 MN D
Telefax: (0911) 44 65 22

MAN GHH (Great Britain) Ltd, 4–5 Grosvenor Place, Hyde Park Corner, London SW1X 7DG, England
Telephone: 01–235 5011
MAN High Performance Diesels, 160 Van Brunt Street, Brooklyn, NY 11231, USA
Telephone: 718 935 1900
MAN GHH Australia Pty Ltd, MAN-Building, 275 Alfred Street, North Sydney, NSW 2060, Australia
Telephone: 2 922 7745
MAN B & W Diesel (Singapore) Pte Ltd, 29 Tuas Avenue 2, Singapore 2263, Singapore
Telephone: 862 1401

MAN marine diesel engines are blocked for different marine applications, rating 1 for displacement hulls, rating 2 for displacement and semi-displacement hulls and rating 3 for planing hulls. The kW or ps/hp rating given for the engine models featured in subsequent paragraphs is for rating 3.

D 0226 MLE

TYPE: Four-stroke diesel engine, 6-cylinder vertical in-line water-cooled with turbocharger and inter-cooler. Direct injection system. High unit output, low noise level and quiet running with low fuel consumption. Long service life and low upkeep and all ports to be serviced are readily accessible.

CRANKCASE AND CRANK ASSEMBLY: Cylinder block of grey cast iron, seven bearing crankshaft with integral forged balance weights, three layer type bearings and die forged connecting rods.

CYLINDER HEAD AND VALVE TRAIN: Double cylinder heads of grey cast iron, overhead valves, one inlet and one exhaust valve per cylinder, valve actuation via tappets, pushrods and rocker arms, four bearing camshafts.

LUBRICATION: Forced-feed lubrication-by-gear pump, oil-to-water oil-cooler, full-flow oil filter, changeover type optional.

FUEL SYSTEM: Bosch in-line injection pump with mechanical speed governor, fuel supply pump, fuel filter, changeover type optional.

INTAKE AND EXHAUST SYSTEM: Viscous air filter, water-cooled exhaust, manifold connected in engine cooling circuit.

SUPERCHARGING: Water-cooled exhaust turbocharger, seawater-cooled inter-cooler.

ELECTRICAL SYSTEM: Two-pole starter, 4kW, 24V and two pole alternator 28V, 35A.

APPLICATIONS: Work boats, customs and police patrol boats, yachts.

TECHNICAL DATA
Bore/stroke: 102/116mm
Swept volume: 5.691 litres
Compression ratio: 17:1
Rotation locking on flywheel; Anti-clockwise
Flywheel housing: SAE 3
Weight of engine dry, with cooling system: 545kg
Max rating 3: 154kW at 2800rpm
Mean effective pressure: 11.6 bar at 2800rpm
Torque: 525Nm at 2800rpm
Mean specific fuel consumption (+5%) at 2800rpm: 225g/kWh at 2800rpm

Model Summary

Model	No of cylinders/ configuration	Bore/ stroke in mm	Displacement in litres	Dry weight kg	Speed rpm	Rating ① kW	ps/hp	Rating ② kW	ps/hp	Rating ③ kW	ps/hp
D 0226 ME	6	102/116	5.69	520	1800	60	82	66	90	—	—
					2100	70	95	77	105	—	—
					2400	79	107	83	113	—	—
					2800	87	118	95	130	—	—
					3000	—	—	—	—	100	136
D 0226 MTE (T)	6	102/116	5.69	530	2600	110	150	121	165	—	—
					2800	—	—	125	170	135	184
D 0226 MLE (L)	6	102/116	5.69	545	2600	125	170	125	170	—	—
					2800	—	—	147	200	154	210
D 2866 E	6	128/155	11.97	985	1500	125	170	132	180	—	—
					1800	151	205	162	220	—	—
					2100	165	224	178	242	—	—
					2200	—	—	—	—	185	252
D 2866 TE (T)	6	128/155	11.97	1000	1800	190	258	206	280	—	—
					2100	—	—	227	300	—	—
					2200	—	—	—	—	235	320
D 2866 LE (L)	6	128/155	11.97	1035	1800	246	326	—	—	—	—
					2100	—	—	260	354	—	—
					2200	—	—	280	380	300	408
D 2848 LE	8	128/142	14.62	1200	2300	—	—	—	—	375	510
D 2840 LE (L)*	10	128/142	18.27	1350	1800	346	470	365	496	—	—
					2300						
D 2842 LE (L)*	12	128/142	21.93	1550	1800	420	571	441	600	—	—
					2300	—	—	—	—	559	760

T = Turbocharged model
L = Turbocharged and intercoded model
*From August 1987 the D 2840 LE was uprated from 635hp to 820hp and is known as the D 2840 LXE. Similarly, the D 2842 LE was uprated from 760hp to 900hp and designated D 2842 LXE. The existing models will be maintained in the sales programme. The dry weight of the D 2842 LXE is 1580kg.

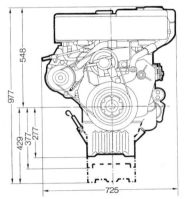
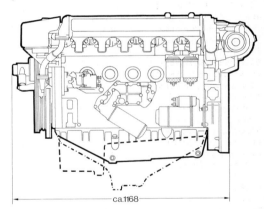

MAN Model D 0226 MLE dimensions (mm)

MAN Model D 0226 MLE marine diesel

D 2866 LE

TYPE: Four-stroke, direct injection.
CYLINDERS: 6 cylinder in-line, wet replaceable cylinder liners.
ASPIRATION: Turbocharged inter-cooled.
COOLING: Water circulation by centrifugal pump fitted on engine.
LUBRICATION: Force-feed lubrication by gear pump, lubrication oil cooler in cooling water circuit of engine.
GENERATOR: Bosch three-phase generator with rectifier and transistorised governor type K1, 28V, 35A.
STARTER MOTOR: Bosch solenoid operated starter type KB, 24V, 5.4kW.
TECHNICAL DATA
Bore/stroke: 128/155mm
Volume: 11.97 litres
Compression ratio: 15.5:1
Max rating 3: 300kW/402bhp at 2200rpm
Mean effective pressure: 13.7 bar at 2200rpm
Torque: 1302Nm at 2200rpm
Fuel consumption (+5% tolerance) at max rating 3: 214g/kWh at 2200rpm

D 2848 LE

TYPE: Four-stroke, direct injection.
CYLINDERS: 8 cylinders, V-form, wet replaceable cylinder liners.
ASPIRATION: Turbocharged, inter-cooled.
COOLING: Water circulation by centrifugal pump fitted on engine.
LUBRICATION: Force-feed lubrication by gear pump, lubrication oil cooler in cooling water circuit of engine.
INJECTION: Bosch in-line pump with mechanical Bosch speed governor fitted.
GENERATOR: Bosch three-phase generator with rectifier and transistorised governor type K1, 28V, 35A.
STARTER MOTOR: Bosch solenoid-operated starter, type KB, 24V, 6.5kW.
TECHNICAL DATA
Bore/stroke: 128/142mm
Volume: 14.62 litres
Compression ratio: 15.5:1
Max rating 3: 375kW at 2300rpm
Mean effective pressure: 13.4 bar at 2300rpm
Torque: 1559Nm at 2300rpm
Fuel consumption (+5% tolerance): 215g/kWh at 2300rpm

MAN Model D 2866 LE marine diesel

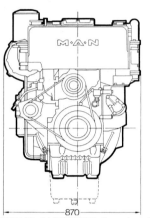
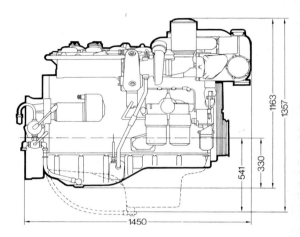

MAN Model D 2866 LE, dimensions (mm)

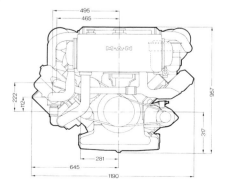

MAN Model D 2848 LE

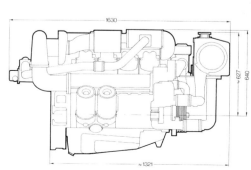

MAN Model D 2848 LE, dimensions (mm)

D 2840 LXE
(Supersedes D 2840 LE)

FEATURES: Four-stroke marine diesel engine, 10-cylinder, V-form, water-cooled with turbocharger and inter-cooler. Direct injection system.

CRANKCASE AND CRANK ASSEMBLY: Grey cast iron cylinder block, 6-bearing crankshaft with screwed-on balance weights, three-layer type bearings, die forged connecting rods. Replaceable wet-type cylinder liners.

CYLINDER HEADS AND VALVE TRAIN: Individual cylinder heads of grey cast iron, overhead valves, one intake and one exhaust valve per cylinder, valve actuation via tappets, push rods and rocker arms. Six-bearing camshaft, shrunk-fit valve seat inserts.

LUBRICATION SYSTEM: Force-feed lubrication by gear pump, oil-to-water oil cooler, full-flow oil filter, changeover type optionally.

FUEL SYSTEM: Bosch in-line injection pump with mechanical speed governor, fuel supply pump, fuel filter, changeover type optionally.

INTAKE AND EXHAUST SYSTEM: Viscous air filter, water-cooled exhaust manifold connected in engine cooling circuit.

SUPERCHARGING: Turbochargers, water-cooled in fresh water circuit, sea water-cooled inter-cooler.

ELECTRICAL SYSTEM: Two-pole starter, 6.5kW, 24V, two-pole alternator 28V, 120A, additional alternator 28V available with 35A, 55A or 120A on request.

APPLICATIONS: Yachts, customs and police patrol boats.

TECHNICAL DATA
Bore/stroke: 128/142mm
Volume: 18.271 litres
Compression ratio: 13.5:1
Rotation locking on flywheel: Anti-clockwise
Weight of engine, dry with cooling system: 1380kg
Speed: 2300rpm
Duty 3, max rating: 603kW/820hp
Mean effective pressure: 17.2 bar
Torque: 2504Nm
Mean specific fuel consumption (+5%): 220g/kWh

D 2842 LXE
(Supersedes D 2842 LE)

FEATURES: Four-stroke marine diesel engine, 12-cylinder, V-form, water-cooled with turbocharger and inter-cooler. Direct injection system.

CRANKCASE AND CRANK ASSEMBLY: Cylinder block of grey cast iron. Replaceable wet-type cylinder liners. Seven-bearing crankshaft with screwed-on balance weights, 3-layer type bearings, die-forged connecting rods.

CYLINDER HEADS AND VALVE TRAIN: Individual cylinder heads of grey cast iron, overhead valves, one intake and one exhaust valve per cylinder, valve actuation via tappets, push rods and rocker arms. Seven-bearing camshaft, shrunk-fit valve seat inserts.

LUBRICATION SYSTEM: Force-feed lubrication by gear pump, oil-to-water oil cooler, full flow oil filter, changeover type optionally.

FUEL SYSTEM: Bosch in-line injection pump with mechanical speed governor, fuel supply pump, fuel filter, changeover type optionally.

INTAKE AND EXHAUST SYSTEM: Viscous air filter, water-cooled exhaust manifold connected in engine cooling circuit.

SUPERCHARGING: Turbochargers, water-cooled in fresh water circuit, sea water-cooled inter-cooler.

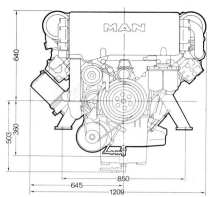
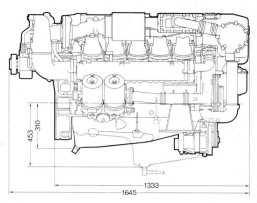

MAN Model D 2840 LXE, marine diesel, dimensions (mm)

MAN Model D 2842 LXE marine diesel

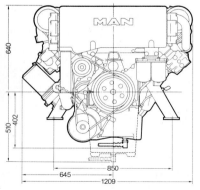

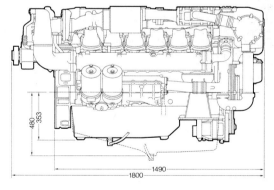

MAN Model D 2842 LXE, dimensions (mm)

ELECTRICAL SYSTEM: Two-pole starter, 6.5kW, 24V, two-pole alternator 28V, 120A, additional alternator 28V with 35A, 55A or 120A on request.

APPLICATIONS: Yachts, customs and police boats.

TECHNICAL DATA
Bore/stroke: 128/142mm
Volume: 21.931 litres
Compression ratio: 13.5:1

Rotation locking on flywheel: Anti-clockwise
Weight of engine, dry with cooling system: Approx 1580kg
Speed: 2300rpm
Duty 3, max rating: 662kW
Mean effective pressure: 15.7 bar
Torque: 2749Nm
Mean specific fuel consumption (+5%): 220g/kWh

MTU
Motoren-und Turbinen-Union Friedrichshafen GmbH

Olgastrasse 75, Postfach 2040, 7990 Friedrichshafen 1, Federal Republic of Germany

Telephone: (07541) 291
Telex: 734280–0 MT D

The MTU Group, formed by MTU Motoren-und Turbinen- Union München GmbH, MTU Motoren- und Turbinen-Union Friedrichshafen GmbH and their subsidiary companies, is a member of the Deutsche Aerospace A G, Munich.

MTU München plays a significant part in the field of advanced civil and military aviation engines. Repair and overhaul of civil aviation engines, industrial gas turbines and their sub-assemblies and components are the responsibility of MTU Maintenance Gmbh.

MTU Friedrichshafen is the development and production centre for high-performance diesel engines of Maybach and Mercedes-Benz origin and embodies the experience of these companies in diesel engine technology. In addition to diesel engines, MTU Friedrichshafen is responsible for industrial and marine gas turbine sales and application engineering.

In the field of hydrofoils, surface effect ships, catamarans and other high-speed craft MTU can draw from decades of experience with 600 engines having been supplied for the propulsion of hydrofoils and catamarans starting as early as 1955 when an MB 820 engine was delivered for the first PT 20 hydrofoil built by Cantiere Navale Rodriquez (nowadays Rodriquez Cantieri Navali SpA) in Messina.

Currently the 099, 783, 396 and 1163 engine families are offered for propulsion of these special types of craft. These engines cover a wide range of power. In the accompanying table the standard power outputs are listed; these, however, may have to be adjusted depending on the application, the power demand and the operating profile. The outputs are based on ambient conditions of 25°C air intake temperature and 25°C sea water temperature.

In addition to the delivery of the propulsion engine MTU can lay-out, design and deliver complete propulsion packages including the interface engineering and the technical assistance during installation and the start-up phase. An example is the re-engining task of the Kometa type hydrofoils where the original engines have been substituted by a powerpack consisting of two 8V 396 TB 83 engines with ZF gears.

MTU diesel engines for catamaran, hydrofoil and hovercraft propulsion and similar high-speed craft

Engine model		Engine speed rpm	Fuel stop power kW	hp (metric)	Engine dry weight kg
4R 099 AZ61	(OM 364)*	2400	52	71	460
6R 099 AZ 61	(OM 366)*	2400	80	109	580
6R 099 TA 61	(OM 366A)*	2400	108	147	600
6R 099 TE 61	(OM 366LA)*	2400	142	193	655
8V 183 AA 61	(OM 422)*	2100	171	233	1155
10V 183 AA 61	(OM 423)*	2100	214	291	1320
12V 183 AA 61	(OM 424)*	2100	253	344	1480
12V 183 TA 61	(OM 424A)*	2100	341	464	1530
12V 183 TE 61	(OM 424LA)*	2100	393	534	1590
8V 183 TE 61	(OM 442LA)*	2000	365	500	1500
12V 183 TE	(OM 444LA)*	2000	550	750	1770
8V 396 TE 74		2000	840	1140	2890
12V 396 TE 74		2000	1260	1710	3900
16V 396 TE 74		2000	1680	2280	5000
16V 396 TE 74L		2000	200	2720	5000
12V 1163 TB 73		1100	2760	3755	13 900
16V 1163 TB 73		1100	3680	5000	17 100
20V 1163 TB 73		1100	4600	6255	20 500

* original Mercedes-Benz designation on which types the corresponding MTU engines are based

MTU 12V 183 TE92

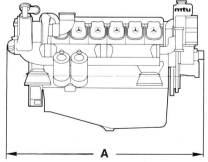

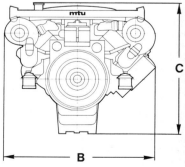

Engine model		A	B	C
6V 183 AA 61	(OM 421)*	1150	1180	1080
8V 183 AA 61	(OM 422)*	1310	1180	1055
10V 183 AA 61	(OM 423)*	1480	1180	1120
12V 183 AA 61	(OM 424)*	1630	1180	1135
12V 183 TA 61	(OM 424A)*	1660	1280	1170
12V 183 TE 61	(OM 424LA)*	7670	1280	1170
12V 183 TE 62	(OM 444LA)*	1720	1280	7350
8V 183 TE 62	(OM 442LA)*	1370	1280	1350

Main dimensions (mm) for Series 183 engine family

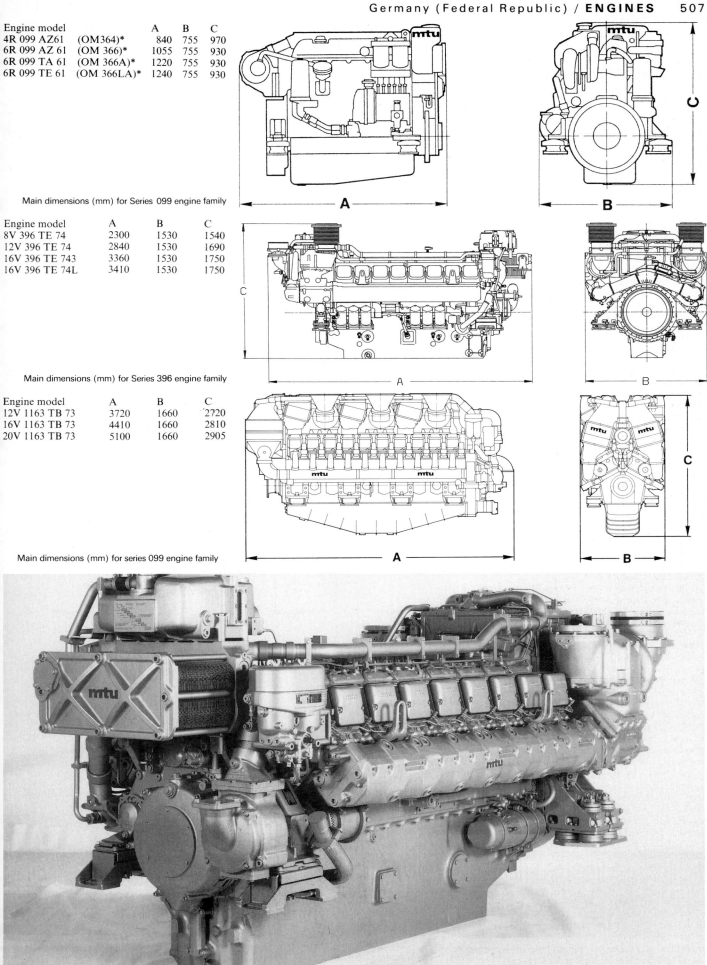

Engine model		A	B	C
4R 099 AZ61	(OM364)*	840	755	970
6R 099 AZ 61	(OM 366)*	1055	755	930
6R 099 TA 61	(OM 366A)*	1220	755	930
6R 099 TE 61	(OM 366LA)*	1240	755	930

Main dimensions (mm) for Series 099 engine family

Engine model	A	B	C
8V 396 TE 74	2300	1530	1540
12V 396 TE 74	2840	1530	1690
16V 396 TE 743	3360	1530	1750
16V 396 TE 74L	3410	1530	1750

Main dimensions (mm) for Series 396 engine family

Engine model	A	B	C
12V 1163 TB 73	3720	1660	2720
16V 1163 TB 73	4410	1660	2810
20V 1163 TB 73	5100	1660	2905

Main dimensions (mm) for series 099 engine family

MTU 16V 396 TE74

ITALY

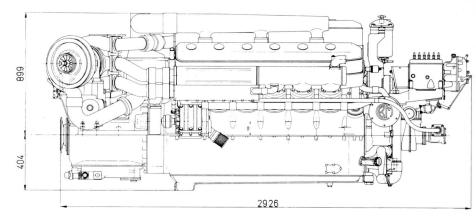

CRM MOTORI MARINI SpA

Head Office and Works: 21053 Castellanza, Via
Marnate 41, Italy

Telephone: (0331)501548
Telex: 334382 CREMME I
Telefax: (0331)505501

G Mariani, *Director*
Ing B Piccoletti, *Director*
Ing S Rastelli, *Director*
Ing G Venturini, *Director*

CRM has specialised in building lightweight
diesel engines for more than 30 years. The company's engines are used in large numbers of motor
torpedo boats, coastal patrol craft and privately-
owned motor yachts. The engines have also been
installed in hydrofoils (*Tehi*).

During the 1960s the company undertook the
development and manufacture of a family of 12-
to 18-cylinder diesel engines of lightweight high-
speed design, providing a power coverage of 600
to 1544kW.

These comprise the 12-cylinder 12 D/S and
12 D/SS and the 18-cylinder 18 D/SS, BR-1 and
BR-2. All are turbocharged with different supercharging ratios. The 12 cylinders are arranged in
two banks of six and the 18 cylinders are set out
in an unusual 'W' arrangement of three banks of
six.

All engines are available in non-magnetic versions; the perturbation field is reduced to insig-
nificant amounts when compensated with the
antidipole method.

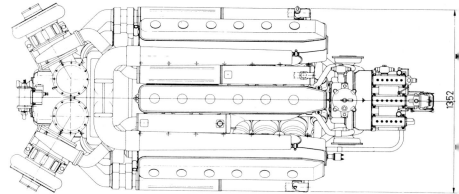

CRM 18-CYLINDER

First in CRM's series of low weight, high-speed
diesel engines, the CRM 18-cylinder is arranged
in a 'W' form. Maximum power is 1213kW at
2075rpm for the 18 D/SS ,1335kW at 2075rpm for
the BR-1 and 1544 kW at 2120 rpm for the BR-2

The following description relates to the
18D/SS,BR-1 and BR-2
TYPE: 18-cylinder in-line W type, four-stroke,
water-cooled, turbocharged with different supercharging ratios: 2.1 (18 D/S); 2.4 (18 D/SS) and
2.6 (BR-1).
CYLINDERS: Bore 150mm (5.91in). Stroke
180mm (7.09in). Swept volume 3.18 litres per cylinder. Total swept volume 57.3 litres. Compression ratio 14 : 1. Separate pressed-steel
cylinder frame side members are surrounded by
gas-welded sheet metal water cooling jacket
treated and pressure-coated internally to prevent
corrosion. Cylinders are closed at the top by a
steel plate integral with side wall to complete combustion chamber and chrome plated.Lower half
of cylinder is ringed by a drilled flange for bolting
to crankcase. Cylinder top also houses a spherical-
shaped pre-combustion chamber as well as inlet
and exhaust valve seats. Pre-combustion chamber
is in high-strength, heat and corrosion resistant
steel. A single cast light alloy head, carrying valve
guides, pre-combustion, chambers and camshaft
bearings bridges each bank of cylinders. Head is
attached to cylinder bank by multiple studs.
PISTONS: Light alloy forgings with three rings,
top ring being chrome-plated and bottom ring
acting as oil scraper. Piston crowns (hard anodised
top) shaped to withstand high temperatures
especially in vicinity of pre-combustion chamber
outlet ports.
CONNECTING RODS: Comprise main and secondary articulated rods, all rods being completely
machined I-section steel forgings. Big-end of each
main rod is bolted to ribbed cap by six studs. Big-
end bearings are white metal lined steel shells.
Each secondary rod anchored at its lower end to

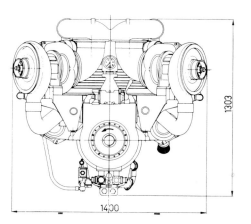

CRM 18 D/SS, BR-1

CRM 18 D/SS, BR-1

a pivot pin inserted in two lugs protruding from big-end of main connecting rod. Both ends of all secondary rods and small ends of main rods have bronze bushes.

CRANKSHAFTS: One-piece hollow shaft in nitrided alloy steel, with six throws equi-spaced at 120 degrees. Seven main bearings with white metal lined steel shells. Twelve balancing counterweights.

CRANKCASE: Cast light alloy crankcase bolted to bed plate by studs and tie bolts. Multiple integral reinforced ribs provide robust structure. Both sides of each casting braced by seven cross ribs incorporating crankshaft bearing supports. Protruding sides of crankcase ribbed throughout length.

VALVE GEAR: Hollow sodium-cooled valves of each bank of cylinders actuated by twin camshafts and six cams on each shaft. Two inlet and two outlet valves per cylinder and one rocker for each valve. End of stem and facing of exhaust valves fitted with Stellite inserts. Valve cooling water forced through passage formed by specially-shaped plate welded to top of cylinder.

FUEL INJECTION: Pumps fitted with variable speed control and pilot injection nozzle.

PRESSURE CHARGER: Two turbochargers, Brown Boveri type, on the 18 D/SS and BR-1.

ACCESSORIES: Standard accessories include oil and fresh water heat exchangers; fresh water tank; oil and fresh water thermostats; oil filters, fresh water, salt water and fuel hand pumps; fresh water and oil temperature gauges; engine, reverse gear and reduction gear oil gauges; pre-lubrication, electric pump and engine rpm counter. Optional accessories include engine oil and water preheater, and warning and pressure switches.

COOLING SYSTEM: Fresh water.

FUEL: Fuel oil having specific gravity of 0.83 to 0.84.

LUBRICATION SYSTEM: Pressure type with gear pump.

OIL: Mineral oil to SAE 40 HD, MIL-L-2104C.

OIL COOLING: By salt water circulating through heat exchanger.

STARTING: 24V 15hp electric motor and 85A, 24V alternator for battery charge, or compressed air.

MOUNTING: At any transverse or longitudinal angle tilt to 20 degrees.

REVERSE GEAR: Bevel crown gear wheels with hydraulically-controlled hand brake.

REDUCTION GEAR: Optional fitting with spur gears giving reduction ratios of 0.561 : 1, 0.730 : 1 and 0.846 : 1. Overdrive ratio 1.18 : 1.

PROPELLER THRUST BEARING: Incorporated in reduction gear. Axial thrust from 29.5kN to 39.5kN (3000 to 4000kgf).

CRM 12-CYLINDER

Second in the CRM series of low weight diesels, the CRM 12-cylinder is a unit with two blocks of six cylinders set at 60 degrees to form a V assembly. The bore and stroke are the same as in the CRM 18 series and many of the components are interchangeable including the crankshaft, bedplate, cylinders and pistons. The crankcase and connecting rod-assemblies are necessarily of modified design; the secondary rod is anchored at its lower end to a pivot pin inserted on two lugs protruding from the big-end of the main connecting rod. The fuel injection pump is modified to single block housing all 12 pumping elements located between the cylinder banks.

TYPE: 12-cylinder V type, four-stroke, water-cooled, turbo-supercharged with medium super-charging ratio (2.15 for 12 D/S) and light supercharging ratio (2.85 for 12 D/SS).

PRESSURE CHARGER: Two KKK type

	18 D/SS	BR-1	BR-2
DIMENSIONS			
Length:	2305mm	2305mm	2305mm
Width:	1400mm	1400mm	1400mm
Height:	1303mm	1303mm	1303mm)
Reverse gear:	621mm	621mm	621mm
WEIGHTS			
Engine dry:	1950kg	1950kg	1950kg
Reverse gear:	340kg	340kg	750kg
Reduction gear:	150 to 300kg	150 to 300kg	—
RATINGS (metric)			
Max power:	1213kW (1650hp) at 2075rpm	1335kW (1815hp) at 2075rpm	1544kW (2100hp) at 2120rpm
Continuous rating:	1103kW (1500hp) at 2020rpm	1213kW (1650hp) at 2020rpm	1403kW (1910hp) at 2050rpm
Specific fuel consumption:	0.224 ± 5% kg/kWh	0.230 ± 5% kg/kWh	0.240 ± 5% kg/kWh
Specific oil consumption:	0.002 ± 5% kg/kWh	0.002 ± 5% kg/kWh	0.002 ± 5% kg/kWh

End view of CRM 18 D/SS, BR-1

	12 D/S	12 D/SS
DIMENSIONS		
Length:	1909mm	2147mm
Width:	1210mm	1210mm
Height:	1204mm	1310mm
Reverse gear:	621mm	621mm
WEIGHTS, dry		
Engine:	1380kg	1560kg
Reverse gear:	340kg	340kg
Reduction gear:	150 to 300kg	150 to 300kg
PERFORMANCE RATINGS		
Max power:	687kW at 2075rpm	1010kW at 2075rpm
Continuous rating:	625kW at 2010rpm	918kW at 2020rpm
Fuel consumption:	0.227kg/kWh ± 5%	0.238kg/kWh ± 5%
Oil consumption:	0.002kg/kWh	0.002kg/kWh

FIAT AVIAZIONE SpA

Marine & Industrial Products Department, Via Nizza 312, P O Box 1389, 10100, Turin, Italy

Telephone: (011) 3302543/6931–1
Telex: 221320FIATAV I

The LM500 gas turbine is a compact high performance marine and industrial power unit in the 3000 to 6000 shaft horsepower class. General Electric's Marine and Industrial Engine Division and Fiat Aviazione SpA, in a co-operative undertaking, initiated the design programme in July 1978. In January 1980 the first engine began full load testing and the LM500 went into production.

The LM500 is a simple-cycle, two-shaft gas turbine engine with a free power turbine. It incorporates a variable stator compressor, with excellent stall margin capability, driven by an air-cooled, two-stage turbine. It is derived from the TF34 high bypass turbofan aircraft engine which was designed for marine operation in the US Navy's S-3A aircraft and later incorporated in the US Air Force's A-10 aircraft, with the same materials and marine corrosion protection as employed in the very successful LM2500 marine gas turbine. The LM500 incorporates the latest in proven design technology and corrosion-resistant materials to provide a mature design with maximum reliability, component life and time between inspections and overhaul. The LM500 demonstrates higher efficiency than currently available gas turbines in its class and is suited for marine applications requiring low weight and fuel economy.

General Electric Company and Fiat Aviazione SpA have designed the LM500 gas turbine to produce power for marine applications requiring significant fuel economy, compactness, light weight, minimum maintenance, high tolerance to fouling/deposits, and reliable operation. Such applications include military land craft, hydrofoils, air cushion vehicles, fast patrol boats, cruise power propulsion and on-board electric power generators.

LM500

The LM500 is a simple-cycle, two-shaft gas turbine engine. The single shaft gas generator consists of a 14-stage high pressure compressor with variable inlet guide vanes and variable stator vanes in the first five stages, an annular machined ring combustor with 18 externally mounted fuel injectors and an air-cooled, two-stage HP gas generator turbine. The free power turbine has four stages and the output shaft connecting flange is at the air inlet end of the engine.
AIR INTAKE: The LM500 offers, as optional equipment, an air inlet collector to guide the inlet air from the customer's intake ducting into the engine. The inlet duct is made from aluminium and provides the structural connection for the forward engine mounts or for the reduction gearbox containing the forward mounts.

An off-engine inlet screen is also offered to prevent objects from entering the compressor.
COMPRESSOR: The compressor is identical to the TF34 and consists of the front frame, accessory drive assembly, compressor rotor and case/vane assembly. The front frame is an uncomplicated four strut aluminium casting and is designed to provide the compressor inlet flowpath, the forward structural support for the engine, support the forward bearings and seals for the gas generator and power turbine rotors, and support the accessory gearbox.
COMBUSTOR: The LM500 combustor is of the TF34 flight engine design. It is an annular

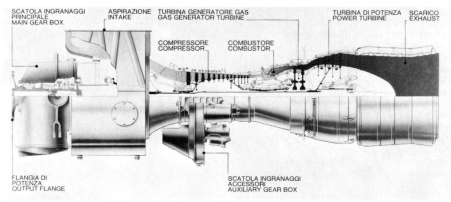

Cutaway of LM500

LM500

through-flow combustor using a machined ring liner construction for long life. Metered fuel is distributed and introduced through 18 central, individually replaceable injectors.
HIGH PRESSURE TURBINE: The LM500 high pressure turbine is a two-stage, fully air-cooled design, identical to the TF34 turbine except for minor changes to improve performance and meet the requirements for marine and industrial applications.
POWER TURBINE: The LM500 power turbine is a four-stage, uncooled, high performance design incorporating aerodynamic and mechanical features and materials identical to the TF34 low pressure turbine. The power turbine rotor structural components are made of inconel 718 material. The four turbine discs carry tip shrouded turbine blades that are attached to the discs with single tang dovetails. The blades are made of René 77 material with the first stage Codep coated. The durability of René 77 alleviates the need for coatings on the other stages. At operating gas temperatures 111°C less than the TF34, the LM500 blades have virtually infinite stress rupture life. The structural integrity of the power turbine rotor has been demonstrated to a speed of 9030rpm, 29 per cent over the normal rated speed of the LM500 engine.
LUBRICATION: The LM500 lubricating oil system provides the following functions: lubricates and cools the gas turbine main bearings; supplies hydraulic fluid for the variable geometry actuation system and fuel metering valve actuator.

The main engine bearings are lubricated from an accessory gearbox-driven lube pump. The scavenge circuit is based on a dry sump system and each bearing sump is scavenged by a separate pump or pump elements driven off the accessory gearbox. All scavenge oil is filtered (coarse screens) prior to entry into the pump elements.
FUEL: The LM500 is designed to operate with marine diesel, diesel, and JP fuels. The fuel system consists of on- and off-engine components. Filtered fuel is supplied by the customer to the fuel pump, which is mounted on the accessory gearbox, where the fuel pressure is increased by a centrifugal boost element and then ported externally to an on-engine last chance fuel filter. From the filter the fuel is routed to an off-engine fuel regulating assembly (FRA) which meters the engine fuel flow according to signals received from the off-engine main electronic control assembly (MECA). Also included in the FRA are two fuel shut-off valves mounted in series for redundancy which are used to shut off the fuel to the engine during normal shutdowns and automatic shutdowns. Fuel is then routed to the on-engine fuel distributor which divides the fuel through separate hose assemblies to 18 fuel injectors.

SPECIFICATION
BASIC ENGINE:
Length overall: 2184mm
Width: 864mm
Weight: 580kg
WITH OPTIONAL INLET AND AXIAL EXHAUST DUCT, STARTER KIT AND OUTPUT GEARBOX:
Length overall: 3307mm
Width: 1179mm
Weight: 1031kg

ISOTTA FRASCHINI SpA
Via Milano 7, 21047 Saronno, Italy

Telephone: (02) 9617.1
Telex: 332403BRIF I

Isotta Fraschini SpA is a company belonging to the Group Iri Fincantieri and owns two factories, one located at Saronno, 15 km north of Milan, and one at Bari. About 1000 people are now employed. Diesel engines are produced in the range of 200 to over 2500hp.

Current high-speed marine diesel engines are the Series ID 36 (6, 8, 12 and 16 cylinders), Series ID 38 (6 cylinders) and Series ID 32 (6 cylinders).

The engine type notation is defined as follows:
N naturally aspirated engine
S turbocharged engine
SS turbocharged and inter-cooled engine
6, 8, 12 and 16: Six, eight, twelve and sixteen cylinders respectively
V vee
P flat
L in-line
M special

ID 32 SERIES

Marine diesel.
CYLINDER NUMBER AND ARRANGEMENT: 6 in-line.
VERSION: Vertical (L).
INJECTION TYPE: Direct.
STROKE/BORE: 126/128mm.
DISPLACEMENT: 9.60 litres.
VALVES PER CYLINDER: 2.
MAIN BEARINGS: 7.
AIR FEEDING OPTIONS: N, S or SS.
COMPRESSION RATIO: 1:16.4 (N); 1:16.6 (S, SS).
DIRECTION OF ROTATION: Clockwise or anti-clockwise.
FUEL: A.S.T.M. No 2 (class A according to BSS)
LUBRICATION OIL: SAE 30 or 40/HD suppl. 3.
STARTING: Electric 24V dc.
COOLING: Water-cooling by means of heat exchangers.
OIL SUMP CONTENTS: 20kg.
ANGLE OF MAX TILT, REAR OR FRONT DOWN: 15°.

ID 32 6L (Vertical Engine)

| Engine type | Outputs according to ISO 3046/1 | | | | | | Weights |
| | A 2700rpm | | B 3000rpm | | C 3000rpm | | ±5% |
	kW	cv/hp	kW	cv/hp	kW	cv/hp	kg
ID 32 N 6L	132	180	154	210	162	220	705
ID 32 S 6L	176	240	198	270	213	290	725
ID 32 SS 6L	206	280	247	335	257	350	750

ID 32 SS 6LM (Vertical Engine)

| Engine type | Outputs according to ISO 3046/1 | | | | | | Weights |
| | A 2800rpm | | B 3000rpm | | C 3000rpm | | ±5% |
	kW	cv/hp	kW	cv/hp	kW	cv/hp	kg
ID 32 SS 6LM	228	310	266	362	294	400	750

Note: A = Continuous output for workboats
B = Continuous output for fast boats
C = Engine max nominal output

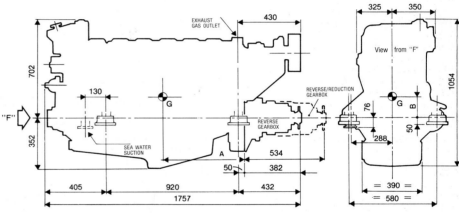

ID 32 diesel engines overall dimensions (mm)

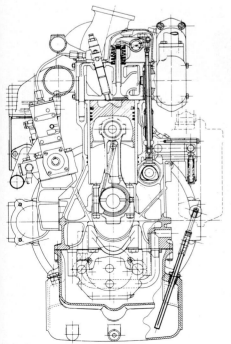

ID 32 SS 6L engine cross-section

ID 32 marine diesel engine

ID 36 SERIES

Marine diesel.

The ID 36 series are four-stroke direct injection diesels. There are 6- to 16-cylinder versions of this engine.

CRANKCASE: Single block cast iron.

CYLINDERS: Incorporated into the crankcase with wet type removable and replaceable centrifugal cast iron liners.

HEADS: Single type for each cylinder, in special cast iron with four valves (two intake and two exhaust) and inserted valve seats.

CRANKSHAFT: Alloy steel forged, normalised and hardened with nitrided journals and crank pins.

MAIN BEARINGS: Special steel coated with anti-friction alloy layer.

CONNECTING RODS AND CON-ROD BEARINGS: Side-by-side con-rod in high resistance alloy steel, special steel bushing coated with an anti-friction alloy layer, big-end bearings made of steel bushing coated with nickel-treated bronze.

PISTON: Light alloy type, oil-jet cooled.

TIMING SYSTEM: Gear driven and transmitted by means of satellites to various components (crankshaft, water pump, oil pump, injection pump etc).

INJECTION PUMP: Single block-type with variable delivery pumping elements driven by a mechanical speed governor. Feeding by gear pump.

LUBRICATION: Engine driven force-feed lubrication by means of two gear pumps. Each pump is equipped with a safety valve inside the engine.

WATER-COOLING: By means of gear driven centrifugal pump. The circuit is set to have an entry and an exit from the exchanger.

TURBOCHARGING AND INTER-COOLING: By means of two turbochargers activated by exhaust gases and two heat exchangers.

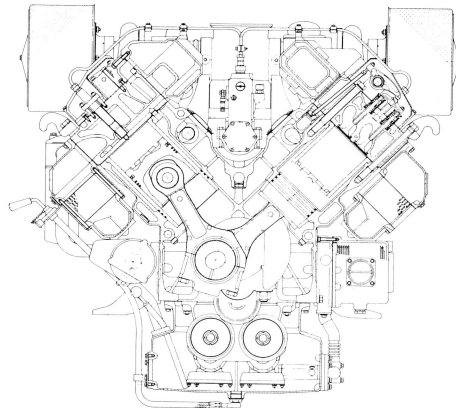

ID 36 series cross section

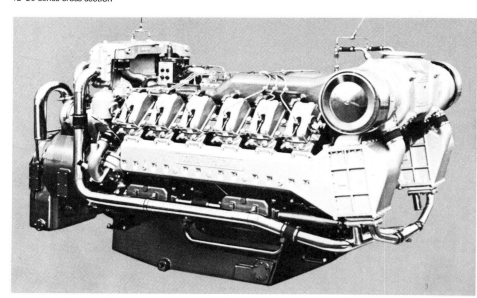

ID 38 series marine diesel

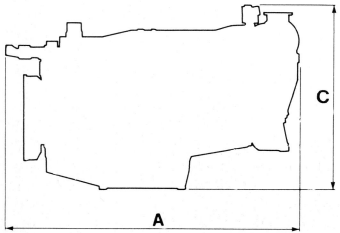

ID 36 series outline dimensions (mm)

In the hp/rpm table below, light duty refers to passenger craft, hydrofoil speed boats, supply vessels and light tug boats. Heavy duty refers to tugs, fishing vessels and dredgers.

ID 38 SERIES

Marine diesel.
TYPE: ID 38 6V.
CYLINDER NUMBER AND ARRANGEMENT: 6 V 90°.
INJECTION TYPE: Direct.
STROKE/BORE: 126/128mm.
DISPLACEMENT: 9.73 litres.
VALVES PER CYLINDER: 2.
MAIN BEARINGS: 4.
AIR FEEDING: N, S or SS.
COMPRESSION RATIO: 1:16.4 (N); 1:15.6 (S, SS).
DIRECTION OF ROTATION: Clockwise or anti-clockwise.
FUEL: A.S.T.M. No 2D (class A according to BSS).
LUBRICATING OIL: SAE 30 or 40 – HD suppl. 3.
STARTING: Electric 24V dc or by compressed air.
COOLING: Water cooling by means of radiator or heat exchangers.
OIL SUMP CONTENTS: 20kg.
ANGLE OF MAX TILT, REAR OR FRONT DOWN: 30°.
DRY WEIGHT: 780kg.

N-S-SS type engines

CRANKCASE: High tensile cast iron.
CYLINDER HEADS: 2 high quality cast iron.
PISTONS: Aluminium.
CONNECTING RODS: High tensile alloy steel.
FUEL INJECTION PUMP: Block type.
FUEL FEEDING PUMP: Diaphragm type.
OIL PUMP: Gear type.
OIL FILTER: 1 cartridge type.
AIR CLEANER: Dry type.
SPEED GOVERNOR: Mechanical type.
STARTING MOTOR: 1–6hp, 24V dc.
ENGINE WATER COOLING: By heat exchanger or radiator.
LUBRICATION: By oil-to-water heat exchanger.
ENGINE WATER PUMP: Belt driven type.
THERMOSTATIC VALVES: 2.
EXHAUST GAS MANIFOLDS: Water-cooled type.

S-SS type engines only

AIR CHARGING: By means of 2 turbochargers.

SS type engines only

CHARGING AIR INTER-COOLING: By means of air-to-water heat exchangers.

Optional equipment

Engine anti-vibration mountings
Flywheel housing
Instruments panel
Battery charger – 700W, 24V dc
Compressed air starting device
Sea water pump

Engine type	Workboats hp/rpm		Pleasure craft hp/rpm	Dimensions (mm)		
	light duty	heavy duty		A	B	C
ID 36 N 6 V	300/1650	300/1650	—	1400	1200	1467
ID 36 SS 6 V	660/1800	540/1800	800/1900			
ID 36 N 8 V	400/1650	400/1650	—			
				1605	1200	1478
ID 36 SS 8 V	880/1800	720/1800	1050/1900			
ID 36 N 10 V	500/1650	500/1650	—			
ID 36 SS 10 V	1100/1800	900/1800	1300/1900	1865	1200	1478
ID 36 N 12 V	600/1650	600/1650	—			
ID 36 SS 12 V	1320/1800	1080/1800	1600/1900	2285	1200	1529
ID 36 N 16 V	800/1650	800/1650	—			
ID 36 SS 16 V	1760/1800	1440/1800	2100/1900	3090	1380	1695

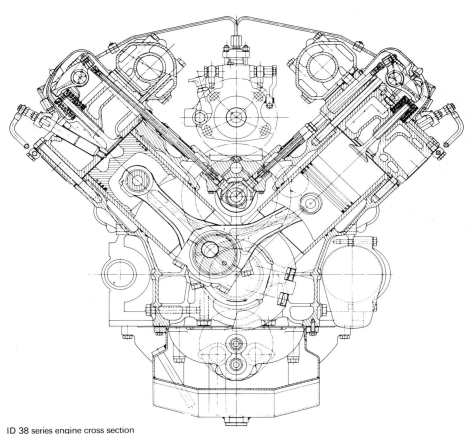

ID 38 series engine cross section

ID 36 series marine diesel

Notes
Types of service
C = Continuous unlimited service with blocked output.
D = Continuous service for fast military and pleasure craft without overload.
CONDITIONS
For continuous service C and D:-
Ambient air temperature: 27°C
Sea water temperature at heat exchanger inlet: 32°C
Relative humidity: 60%
DERATING
For air temperatures of 40°C consider a 6% derating.

Engine type	Outputs according to ISO 3046/1							
	Work C				Pleasure and Military D		Racing Applications	
	2700rpm		2900rpm		3000rpm		1150rpm	
	kW	hp	kW	hp	kW	hp	kW	hp
ID 38 N 6 V	132	180	143	195	331	450		
ID 38 SS 6 V	257	350	294	400				
Examples of application	Works and fishing boats, tugs and ferries				Fast craft, catamarans, hydrofoils, motor yachts and patrol boats			
ID 38 SS 6V SA							588	800

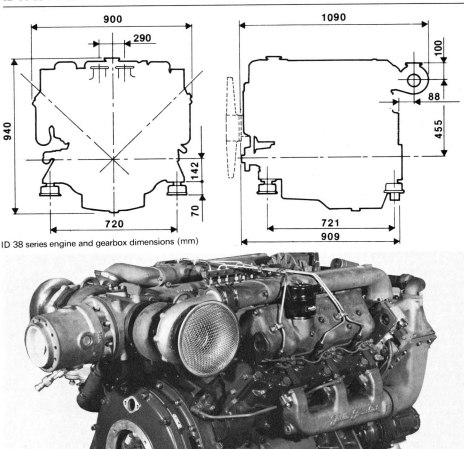

ID 38 series engine and gearbox dimensions (mm)

ID 38 SS 6V SA, 800hp at 3150rpm, for offshore racing applications

NORWAY

ULSTEIN TURBINE A/S

Ovre Maasan 10C, N-1370 Asker, Norway

Telephone: 2901810
Telex: 2901825
Telefax: 7011442

Jens Hetland, *President*

The Ulstein Group of Norway has purchased the technology and patents related to the unique engine design of the Radial Turbine operations which belonged to the former Kongsberg Vaapenfabrikk. Ulstein, a leading manufacturer of maritime machinery and equipment has seen a large potential for the new, high power density turbine engine design for high-speed surface transportation in general and marine propulsion in particular.

Ulstein is implementing its turbine development plans through a new company, Ulstein Turbine AS, situated in Oslo. Ulstein Turbine AS is structured as a design and development company with some 15 turbine engine experts employed.

The development programme leading up to a new propulsion engine for high-speed craft, such as catamarans and surface effect ships, has obtained Eureka status. Partners in the projects include leading international engine companies now interested in joint utilisation of the Norwegian engine concept.

When the new turbine engine is in production, it will have a positive effect on the more than 30 companies in the Ulstein Group, specially for Bergen Diesel A/S, the only remaining Norwegian owned diesel engine manufacturer.

The new turbine engine will have lower fuel consumption than any other turbine engine in its power range of 2 to 3MW. The engine will be compact and will only weigh some 10% of the light weight diesels now used for high-speed surface applications. Furthermore, the engine will be vibration free, have a very low noise level and most importantly, will satisfy the strictest exhaust emissions regulations.

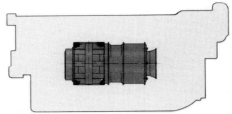

Relative sizes of the proposed Ulstein gas turbine and a light-weight diesel engine of the same power

SWEDEN

SAAB-SCANIA

Scania Division: S-15187 Södertälje, Sweden

Telephone: 75581000
Telex: 10200 SCANIAS
Telefax: 75583180

Scania marine diesels cover a range of 104kW (141hp) to 406kW (552hp). Power test codes are ISO 3406, DIN 6271, BS 5514 and SAE J 1349.

Scania marine engines have recently been radically redeveloped and constitute an almost new range, still, however, built for economical operation and long service life.

Scania claim that the excellent performance and low fuel consumption of their engines results from new injection equipment, carefully optimised turbochargers, and cylinder liners of a new design which improve performance and reduce lube oil consumption. The Keystone-type upper piston ring ensures a good seal and enables Scania engines to develop full power instantly without jeopardising engine life.

Turbocharged and intercooled models feature a new high efficiency charge-air cooler matched on marine engines to a two-compartment heat exchanger and effective gallery cooling of the piston crown. The crown is anodised for extended resistance to fatigue.

Marine diesel engines
RATINGS

Engine type		Turbo	Inter-cooled	Displacement dm³	Config-uration	Propulsion High-speed workboats, patrol, etc.[2] kW (hp) rpm	Specific fuel consumption[1] at 1500rpm g/kWh (g/hph)
Heat exchanger							
DN 11	(215)	—	—	11.0	6 L	158(215)2200	220(162)
DN 11	(330)	T	—	11.0	6 L	2439(330)2100	205(151)
DSI[1] 11	(387)	T	I	11.0	6 L	285(387)2100	200(147)
DS 14	(426)	T	—	14.2	V 8	313(426)2100	209(154)
DSI 14	(479)	T	I	14.2	V 8	352(479)2100	207(152)
DSI[1] 14	(552)	T	I	14.2	V 8	406(552)2100	208(153)
Keel cooling							
DN 9	(174)	—	--	8.5	6 L	128(174)2200	219(161)
DS 9	(224)	T	—	8.5	6 L	165(224)2200	207(152)
DS 9	(252)	T	—	8.5	6 L	185(252)2200	207(152)
DN 11	(215)	—	—	11.0	6 L	158(215)2200	220(162)
DS 11	(330)	T	—	11.0	6 L	243(330)2100	205(151)
DSI[1] 11	(367)	T	I	11.0	6 L	270(367)2100	203(150)
DS 14	(426)	T	—	14.2	V 8	313(426)2100	209(154)

[1] Continuous uninterrupted service.
[2] Intermittent service.

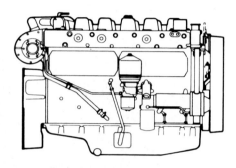

DS 9 Marine

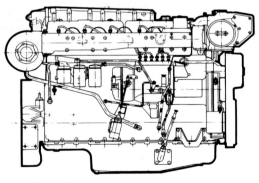

DSI 11 Marine

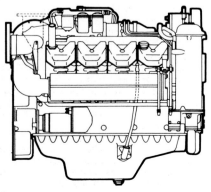
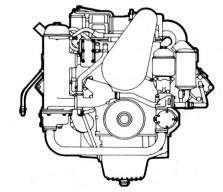

DSI 14 Marine

Saab-Scania marine diesel engines

WEIGHTS[5]

Engine type	Length	Max dimensions (mm) Width	Height	Weight dry (kg)
with heat exchanger				
DN 11	1461	744	1043	1085
DS 11	1551	744	1043	1110
DSI 11	151	744	1057	1115
DS 14	1314	1152	1165	1250
DSI 14	1314	1152	1165	1325
for keel cooling				
DN 9	1315	755	1008	860
DS 9	1315	755	957	875
DN 11	1395	701	1011	986
DS 11	1490	701	1057	1035
DS 14	1314	1152	1177	1180

[5] **Weights and dimensions.** Quoted are purely a guide; there are variations for each engine type. Weights exclude oil and water.

AB VOLVO PENTA
S-405 08 Gothenburg, Sweden

Telephone: (31) 235460
Telex: 20755PENTA S
Telefax: (31) 510595

The Board of Volvo Penta:
Pehr G Gyllenhammer, *Chairman*
Jan Walldorf, *President*
Olle Johansson, *Director*
Anders Lindström, *Director*
Ernst Knappe, *Director*
Hans Eric Ovin, *Director*
Union Group: Bengt Segeheden
    Sven Timm

Executive Marine Management:
Jan Walldorf, *President*
Leif Strand, *Director Marine*
Orvar Lundberg, *Director Parts*

AB Volvo Penta designs, manufactures and markets engines, transmissions, accessories and equipment for marine and industrial use.

Part of the Volvo Group, the sales of Volvo Penta engines account for around 4 per cent of sales within the transport equipment sector. The engines are used in ferries, pilot vessels, fishing boats and all types of leisure craft, as well as for industrial propulsion or power generation applications.

Production facilities are in the USA and Brazil plus four locations in Sweden. Volvo Penta products are sold in 130 countries world-wide. Approximately 2600 people are employed either directly or indirectly by Volvo Penta.

Volvo Penta diesels for commercial craft can provide up to 550hp. The company has updated the entire engine range covering two-, three- and four-cylinder commercially rated diesels as well as the in-line six series.

New to the range are the heavy diesels TAMD 162, TAMD 122 and TMD 102.

All eight units in the 31 and 41 series feature direct injection which reduces thermal stress, heat and pressure loss resulting in lower fuel consumption and longer life expectancy. Fuel consumption is around 15% less than with the equivalent pre-chamber ignition diesels. The new turbocharger is fresh water-cooled, and the pistons are oil-cooled to increase engine life.

Further up the power range are the 6- and 7-litre models TAMD 61 and TAMD 71. Both are turbocharged, after-cooled in-line, six diesels for which the latest three-dimensional computer techniques have been used as a means towards reducing engine weight and providing optimum rigidity.

Interesting design features of the new 16-litre in-line 6-cylinder diesel engine TAMD 162 include efficient cooling of the cylinder head with four

Volvo Penta TAMD 31 direct injection 3-litre engine

Volvo Penta TAMD 41

valves per cylinder, for high efficiency. The cylinder head is bolted to the block without gaskets for increased service life and low maintenance costs. A new fast injection pump on the cold side of the engine gives good economy and environmental properties in combination with a smoke limiter.

A responsive turbo and aftercooler with low internal resistance gives efficient combustion and cleaner exhausts, as well as increasing engine service life.

The new TAMD 122 has between four and seven per cent higher power output than the previous 121 generation.

The new technical features of the engine include new cylinder head and gaskets, new cylinder linings with flame barriers and improved sealing. The engine has a new injection pump with smoke limiter and new, five-hole nozzles for better combustion and less smoke.

The new 10-litre engine for workboats has the designation TMD 102. The power output in medium-duty operation has been increased by five per cent.

New technical features on the TMD 102 include reinforced engine block and new cylinder linings with improved sealing and cooling, together with new cylinder head with improved cooling and new piston rings to reduce oil consumption. The new five-hole nozzle gives better idling characteristics and less smoke.

Volvo Penta TAMD 61 in-line, six turbocharged and after-cooled 6-litre engine

VOLVO PENTA 3- TO 12-LITRE MARINE PROPULSION ENGINES

TAMD 31	hp	kW	rpm
Propeller shaft output ISO 3046,			
light duty:	124	91	3800
medium duty:	105	77	3250
Weight: 385kg including MS4 gearbox			
Displacement: 2.39 litres			

TAMD 41	hp	kW	rpm
Propeller shaft output ISO 3046,			
light duty:	192	141	3800
medium duty:	163	120	3250
Weight: 465kg including MS4 gearbox			
Displacement: 3.59 litres			

TAMD 61	hp	kW	rpm
Flywheel output,			
light duty:	306	225	2800
medium duty:	228	168	2500
Weight: 760kg excluding gearbox			
Displacement: 5.48 litres			

Volvo Penta TAMD 71 in-line, six turbocharged and after-cooled 7-litre engine

TAMD 71	hp	kW	rpm
Flywheel output,			
light duty:	357	263	2500
medium duty:	292	213	2500
heavy duty:	222	163	2000
Weight: 880kg excluding gearbox			
Displacement: 6.73 litres			

TMD 102	hp	kW	rpm
Flywheel output,			
medium duty:	272	200	2000
heavy duty:	238	175	1800
Weight: 1140kg excluding gearbox			
Displacement: 9.6 litres			

TAMD 122	hp	kW	rpm
Flywheel output,			
light duty:	450	331	2000
medium duty:	400	294	1900
heavy duty:	380	279	1800
Weight: 1300kg excluding gearbox			
Displacement: 11.98 litres			

Volvo Penta TAMD 122

Volvo Penta TMD 102

TAMD 162	hp	kW	rpm
Flywheel output,			
light duty:	551	405	1900
medium duty:	490	360	1900
heavy duty:	470	346	1800

Weight: 1705kg excluding reverse gear
Displacement: 16.12 litres

The following definitions define the duty ratings given in the accompanying table.

LD: Light Duty

Engines with this power setting are for applications where rated power for rated speed is utilised for short periods only, followed by cruising at reduced speed; also when operating time is short and does not exceed 500 hours per year.
Examples: Certain patrol boats, fireboats, rescue boats and charter craft.

MD: Medium Duty

Engines with this power setting are intended for applications where rated power at rated speed is utilised during part of the operating time only (up to ⅓), followed by cruising at reduced speed. Operating time should not exceed 2000 hours per year, or on average, one shift per working day.
Examples: Patrol boats, pilot boats, police boats and certain fishing vessels.

HD: Heavy Duty

Engines with this power setting are intended for applications where neither PD, LD nor MD applies and rated power at rated speed could be needed continuously. No interruption or load cycling is expected other than for service and maintenance.

Volvo Penta TAMD 162

Examples: Tugboats, ferries, fishing boats and most commercial applications in displacement vessels.

UNION OF SOVIET SOCIALIST REPUBLICS

A IVCHENKO (AI)

This design team, which was headed by the late A Ivchenko, is based in a factory at Zaporojie in the Ukraine, where all prototypes and pre-production engines bearing the 'AI' prefix are developed and built. Chief designer is Lotarev and chief engineer, Tichienko. The production director is M Omeltchenko.

First engine with which Ivchenko was associated officially was the 55hp AI-4G piston engine used in the Kamov Ka-10 ultra-light helicopter. He later progressed via the widely used AI-14 and AI-26 piston engines, to become one of the Soviet Union's leading designers of gas turbine engines.

Two AI-20s in de-rated, marinised form and driving two three-stage waterjets power the Burevestnik, the first Soviet gas-turbine hydrofoil to go into series production, and a single AI-24 drives the integrated lift/propulsion system of the Sormovich 50-passenger ACV. Two AI-20s, each rated at about 3600shp continuous, are also thought to power the Lebed amphibious assault landing craft.

IVCHENKO AI-20

The Ivchenko design bureau is responsible for the AI-20 turboprop engine which powers the Antonov An-10, An-12 and Ilyushin Il-18 airliners and the Beriev M-12 Tchaika amphibian.

Six production series of this engine had been built by the spring of 1966. The first four series, of which manufacture started in 1957, were variants of the basic AI-20 version. They were followed by two major production versions, as follows:

AI-20K. Rated at 3945ehp. Used in Il-18V, An-10A and An-12.

AI-20M. Uprated version with T-O rating of 4190ehp (4250ch e). Used in Il-18D/E, An-10A and An-12.

Conversion of the turboprop as a marine power unit for hydrofoil waterjet propulsion (as on the Burevestnik) involved a number of changes to the engine. In particular it was necessary to hold engine rpm at a constant level during conditions of varying load from the waterjet pump. It was

1750hp Ivchenko AI-23-CI marine gas turbine

also necessary to be able to vary the thrust from the waterjet unit from zero to forward or rearwards thrust to facilitate engine starting and vessel manoeuvring.

Constant speed under variable load was achieved by replacing the engine's normal high pressure fuel pump with a special fuel regulator pump. The waterjet pump was modified to have a variable exit area and was fitted with an air valve enabling a variable amount of air to be passed into the intake just ahead of the pump rotor. With less air passing through the waterjet, unit load on the engine increased, and vice versa if the air flow was increased by opening the air valve.

The fuel regulator pump was designed to maintain engine rpm constant and to regulate output while the AI-20 was driving the waterjet unit. Steady running conditions were shown to be satisfactorily maintained by the engine under all operating conditions-and rpm and turbine temperature were held within the limits laid down for the aircraft turboprop version: engine rpm did not fluctuate outside ±2.5% of its set speed when loading or unloading the waterjet unit.

During development of the marinised AI-20, the normal aircraft propeller and speed governor were removed and the turboprop was bench tested

over the full range of its operating conditions. This demonstrated stable engine performance throughout, from slow running to normal rpm. These tests were run initially using aviation kerosene Type TS-1 fuel, and then diesel fuel Types L and DS.

Following satisfactory results on the bench, the test engine was mounted on a self-propelled floating test bed equipped with a waterjet propulsion unit. Further tests with this configuration were also satisfactorily concluded, including starting checks with varying degrees of submersion of the pump section of the waterjet unit.

Electrical starting of the engine up to slow running speed (equal to approximately 25% of rated rpm) was shown to take 70 to 85 seconds. For starting and ignition at ambient conditions below 10°C, fuel pre-heating is employed and modified igniters are fitted. With this equipment, starts have been achieved down to minus 12°C.

Based on this experience, the marinised AI-20 for the twin-engined Burevestnik was rated at 2700hp at 13 200rpm. At this power output, the hydrofoil achieved speeds of up to 97km/h. Specific fuel consumption was 320–330g/hph.

Testing with the Burevestnik revealed a number

of operating characteristics: when the two AI-20s were running while the vessel was moored or manoeuvring, residual exhaust thrust from the turbines occurred and this is required to be balanced by a negative or reverse thrust from the waterjet by partially closing the unit's nozzle flaps. This increased the load on the engine, however, and caused a rise in fuel consumption.

Experience showed that with a normal start following a series of wet starts, any fuel which had accumulated in the jet pipe ignited. This resulted in a sharp rise in turbine temperature and back pressure, and flame emerged from the ejection apertures into the engine compartment and exhaust nozzle. To circumvent this, the ejection apertures were covered with a metal grid, and a spray of water is provided at the exhaust nozzle prior to starting.

Based on an overhaul life for the turboprop AI-20 of several thousand hours, special techniques have been applied to the marinised version to increase its service life. These include: the use of high quality assembly procedures for the engine; efficient design of the air intake and exhaust duct; adoption of appropriate procedures for starting and on-loading of the main and auxiliary turbines at all ambient temperature conditions; utilisation of highly-skilled servicing methods of the installation during operation.

The AI-20 is a single-spool turboprop, with a ten-stage axial-flow compressor, cannular combustion chamber with ten flame tubes, and a three-stage turbine, of which the first two stages are cooled. Planetary reduction gearing, with a ratio of 0.08732 : 1, is mounted forward of the annular air intake. The fixed nozzle contains a central bullet fairing. All engine-driven accessories are mounted on the forward part of the compressor casing, which is of magnesium alloy.

The AI-20 was designed to operate reliably in all temperatures from −60°C to +55°C at heights up to 10 000m. It is a constant speed engine, the rotor speed being maintained at 21 300rpm by automatic variation of propeller pitch. Gas temperature after turbine is 560°C in both current versions. TBO of the AI-20K was 4000 hours in the spring of 1966.

WEIGHTS
DRY
AI-20K: 1080kg
AI-20M: 1039kg
PERFORMANCE RATINGS
Max T-O:
AI-20K: 4000ch e
AI-20M: 4250ch e
Cruise rating at 630km/h at 8000m:
AI-20K: 2250ch e
AI-20M: 2700ch e
SPECIFIC FUEL CONSUMPTION
At cruise rating:
AI-20K: 215g/hph
AI-20M: 197g/hph
OIL CONSUMPTION
Normal: 1 litre/h

IVCHENKO AI-24

In general configuration this single-spool turbo-prop engine, which powers the An-24 transport aircraft, is very similar to the earlier and larger AI-20. Production began in 1960 and the following data refers to engines of the second series, which were in production in the spring of 1966.

A single marinised version, developing 1800shp, drives the integrated lift/propulsion system of the Sormovich 50-passenger ACV.

An annular ram air intake surrounds the cast light alloy casing for the planetary reduction gear, which has a ratio of 0.08255 : 1. The cast magnesium alloy compressor casing carries a row of inlet guide vanes and the compressor stator vanes and provides mountings for the engine-driven accessories. These include fuel, hydraulic and oil pumps, tacho-generator and propeller governor.

The ten-stage axial-flow compressor is driven by a three-stage axial-flow turbine, of which the first two stages are cooled. An annular combustion chamber is used, with eight injectors and two igniters.

The engine is flat-rated to maintain its nominal output to 3500m. TBO was 3000 hours in the spring of 1966.
LENGTH (overall): 2435mm
WEIGHT
Dry: 499kg
PERFORMANCE RATING
Max T-O with water injection: 2859ch e

KUZNETSOV
KUZNETSOV

NK-12M

The NK-12M, which powers the Aist amphibious assault ACV and is thought to power the Babochka and Sarancha hydrofoils, is the world's most powerful turboprop engine. In its original form it developed 8948kW. The later NK-12MV is rated at 11 033kW and powers the Tupolev Tu-114 transport, driving four-blade, contra-rotating propellers of 5.6m diameter. As the NK-12MA, rated at 11 185kW, it powers the Antonov AN-22 military transport, with propellers of 6.2m diameter.

The NK-12M has a single 14-stage axial-flow compressor. Compression ratio varies from 9:1 to 13:1 and variable inlet guide vanes and blow-off valves are necessary. A can-annular-type combustion system is used. Each flame tube is mounted centrally on a downstream injector, but all tubes merge at their maximum diameter to form an annular secondary region. The single turbine is a five-stage axial. Mass flow is 65kg/s.

The casing is made in four portions from sheet steel, precision welded. An electric control for variation of propeller pitch is incorporated to maintain constant engine speed.

NK-12MV

(Aviation International, Paris)

DIMENSIONS
Length: 6000mm
Diameter: 1150mm
WEIGHT
Dry: 2350kg

PERFORMANCE RATINGS
T-O: 11 033kW
Nominal power: 8826kW at 8300rpm
Idling speed: 6600rpm

SOLOVIEV

P A Soloviev, *Designer in Charge of Bureau*

SOLOVIEV D-30

This two-spool turbofan, in marinised form, is believed to provide the thrust power-augmented ram-wing project. It powers the Tu-134 twin-engined airliner and is derived from the D-20. Major portions of the core and carcass are similar, but the complete powerplant is larger, more powerful and efficient than the D-20.
TYPE: Two-shaft turbofan (by-pass turbojet).
AIR INTAKE: Titanium alloy assembly, incorporating air bleed anti-icing of centre bullet and radial struts.

FAN: Four-stage axial (LP compressor). First stage has shrouded titanium blades held in disc by pinned joints. Pressure ratio (T-O rating, 7700rpm, S/L, static), 2.65:1. Mass flow, 125kg/s. By-pass ratio, 1:1.
COMPRESSOR: Ten-stage axial (HP compressor). Drum and disc construction largely of titanium. Pressure ratio (T-O rating, 11 600rpm, S/L static), 7.1:1. Overall pressure ratio, 17.4:1.
COMBUSTION CHAMBER: Can-annular, with 12 flame tubes fitted with duplex burners.
FUEL GRADE: T-1 and TS-1 to GOST 10227–62 (equivalent to DERD. 2494 or MIL-F-5616).
TURBINE: Two-stage HP turbine. First stage has cooled blades in both stator and rotor. LP turbine also has two stages. All discs air-cooled on both sides, and all blades shrouded to improve efficiency and reduce vibration. All shaft bearings shock-mounted.
JET PIPE: Sub-sonic fixed-area type, incorporating main and by-pass flow mixer with curvilinear ducts of optimum shape. D-30–2 engine of Tu-134A fitted with twin-clamshell (Rolls-type) reverser.
LUBRICATION: Open type, with oil returned to tank.
OIL GRADE: Mineral oil MK-8 or MK-8P to GOST 6457–66 (equivalent to DERD 2490 or MIL-0–6081B). Consumption in flight is not more than 1kg/h.
ACCESSORIES: Automatic ice-protection

system, fire extinguishing for core and by-pass flows, vibration detectors on casings, oil chip detectors and automatic limitation of exhaust gas temperature to 620°C at take-off or when starting and to 630°C in flight (five minute limit). Shaft-driven accessories driven via radial bevel-gear shafts in centre casing, mainly off HP spool, accessory gearboxes being provided above and below centre casing and fan duct. D-30–2 carries constant-speed drives for alternators.

STARTING: Electric dc starting system with STG-12TVMO starter/generators.

DIMENSIONS
Overall length: 3983mm
Base diameter of inlet casing: 1050mm

WEIGHT
Dry: 1550kg

PERFORMANCE RATINGS
T-O: 66.68kN
Long-range cruise rating: 11 000m
Mach 0.75: 12.75kN

SPECIFIC FUEL CONSUMPTION
T-O: 17.56mg/Ns
Cruise as above: 21.81mg/Ns

D-30KU turbofan

SUDOIMPORT
5 Kaliayevskaya Str, Moscow 103006, USSR

Telephone: 2510505/299 52 14
Telex: 411272/387 SUDO SU

Soviet industry has developed a variety of marine diesel engines, selected models of which have been installed in the Krasnoye Sormovo series of hydrofoil craft. Most popular of these are the 1100hp M401 powering the Kometa hydrofoil, and the 1200hp M50 powering the Byelorus, Chaika, Meteor, Mir, Raketa, Sputnik, Strela and Vikhr hydrofoils. A third marine diesel engine is the 3D12 with a continuous rating of 300hp. A version of this engine is installed in the Nevka hydrofoil.

These and other marine diesels are available through Sudoimport, the USSR marine export, import and repair organisation.

TYPE M400
TYPE: Water-cooled, 12-cylinder, V-type four-stroke supercharged marine diesel engine.

CYLINDERS: Two banks of six cylinders set at 30 degrees, each bank comprising cast aluminium alloy monobloc with integral head. Pressed-in liner with spiral cooling passages comprises inner alloy steel sleeve with nitrided working surface, and outer carbon steel sleeve. Each monobloc retained on crankcase by 14 holding-down studs. Bore 180mm. Stroke 200mm. Cubic capacity 62.4 litres. Compression ratio 13.5 : 1.

SUPERCHARGING: Single-stage centrifugal supercharger, mechanically driven and providing supercharging pressure of at least 1.55kg/cm² at rated power.

CRANKCASE: Two-part cast aluminium alloy case with upper half carrying cylinder monoblocs, and transmitting all engine loads.

CYLINDER HEADS: Integral with cylinder monoblocs.

CRANKSHAFT: Six-crank seven-bearing crankshaft in nitrided alloy steel with split steel shells, lead bronze lined with lead-tin alloy bearing surface. Spring damper at rear end reduces torsional vibrations.

CONNECTING RODS: Master and articulated rods, with master connected to crankshaft by split big-end with lead bronze lining. Articulated rods connected by pin pressed into eye of master rods.

PISTONS: Forged aluminium alloy with four rings, upper two of which are of trapeziform cross-section. Alloy steel floating gudgeon pin. Piston head specially shaped to form combustion chamber with spherical cylinder head.

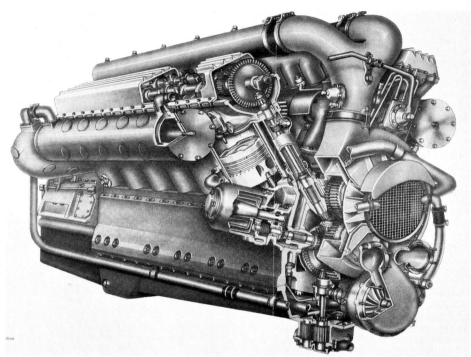
M400

CAMSHAFTS: Two camshafts acting direct on valve stems.

VALVES: Four valves in each cylinder, two inlet and two exhaust. Each valve retained on seat by three coil springs.

COOLING: Forced circulation system using fresh water with 1 to 1.1% potassium dichromate added. Fresh water pump mounted on forward part of engine. Fresh water and lubricating oil leaving the engine are cooled by water-to-water and water-to-oil coolers, in turn cooled by sea water circulated by engine-mounted sea water pump.

SUPERCHARGING: Single-stage centrifugal supercharger, mechanically driven and providing supercharging pressure of at least 1.55kg/cm² at rated power.

LUBRICATION: Comprises delivery pump together with full-flow centrifuge; twin-suction scavenge pump, double gauze-type strainers at inlet and outlet to oil system; and electrically-driven priming pump to prime engine with oil and fuel.

FUEL INJECTION: Closed-type fuel injection with hydraulically-operated valves, giving initial pressure of 200kg/cm². Each injector has eight spray orifices forming 140-degree conical spray. High pressure 12-plunger fuel injection pump with primary gear pump. Two filters in parallel filter oil to HP pump.

STARTING: Compressed air system with starting cylinder operating at 75 to 150kg/cm² two disc-type air distributors and 12 starting valves.

GOVERNOR: Multi-range indirect-action engine speed governor with resilient gear drive from pump camshaft. Governor designed to maintain preset rpm throughout full speed range from minimum to maximum.

EXHAUST SYSTEM: Fresh water-cooled exhaust manifolds fastened to exterior of cylinder blocs. Provision made for fitting thermocouple or piezometer.

REVERSING: Hydraulically-operated reversing clutch fitted to enable propshaft to run forwards, idle or reverse with constant direction of crankshaft rotation.

MOUNTING: Supports fitted to upper half of crankcase for attaching engine to bedplate.

DIMENSIONS
Length: 2600mm
Width: 1220mm
Height: 1250mm
PERFORMANCE RATINGS
Max: 1100hp at 1800rpm
Continuous: 1000hp at 1700rpm
FUEL CONSUMPTION
At continuous rating: Not over 193g/hph
OIL CONSUMPTION
At continuous rating: Not over 6g/hph

TYPE 3D12

TYPE: Water-cooled, 12-cylinder, V-type, four-stroke marine diesel engine.
CYLINDERS: Two banks of six cylinders in jacketed blocks with pressed-in steel liners. Bore 150mm. Stroke 180mm. Cubic capacity 38.8 litres. Compression ratio 14 to 15 : 1.
CRANKCASE: Two-part cast aluminium alloy case with upper half accommodating seven main bearings of steel shell, lead bronze lined type. Lower half carries oil pump, water circulating pump and fuel feed pump.
CYLINDER HEADS: Provided with six recesses to accommodate combustion chambers. Each chamber is connected via channel to inlet and outlet ports of cylinder bloc.
CRANKSHAFT: Alloy steel forging with seven journals and six crankpins. Pendulum anti-vibration dampers fitted on first two webs to reduce torsional vibration.
CONNECTING RODS: Master and articulated rods of double-T section forged in alloy steel. Master rod big-end bearings have steel shells, lead bronze lined. Small-end bearings of master rods and both bearings of articulated rods have bronze bushes.
PISTONS: Aluminium alloy.
CAMSHAFTS: Carbon steel camshafts with cams and journals hardened by high frequency electrical current.
COOLING: Closed water, forced circulation type incorporating centrifugal pump, self suction sea water pump and tubular water cooler.
LUBRICATION: Forced circulation type with dry sump, incorporating three-section gear pump, oil feed pump, wire-mesh strainer with fine cardboard filtering element and tubular oil cooler.
FUEL INJECTION: Rotary fuel feed pump, twin felt filter, plunger fuel pump with device to stop engine in event of oil pressure drop in main line. Closed-type fuel injectors with slotted filters. Plunger pump carries variable-speed centrifugal governor for crankshaft rpm.
STARTING: Main electrical starting system, with compressed air reverse system.
REVERSE-REDUCTION GEAR: Non-coaxial type with twin-disc friction clutch and gear-type reduction gear giving optional ratios, forwards, of 2.95 : 1, 2.04 : 1 or 1.33 : 1 and 2.18 : 1 astern.
DIMENSIONS
Length: 2464mm
Width: 1052mm
Height: 1159mm
WEIGHT
Dry fully equipped: 1900kg
PERFORMANCE RATING
Continuous: 300hp at 1500rpm
FUEL CONSUMPTION
At continuous rated power: 176g/hph
OIL CONSUMPTION
At continuous rated power: Not over 9g/hph

M401A

The M401A, fitted to the Voskhod and the latest variants of the Kometa and Raketa, is based on the M50. The new engine is more reliable than its predecessor and its development involved the redesigning of a number of units and parts, as well as the manufacturing of components with a higher degree of accuracy, which necessitated the

3D12

employment of the latest engineering techniques.

The engine is manufactured in left- and right-hand models. These differ by the arrangement on the engine housing of the fresh water pump drive and the power take-off for the shipboard compressor.
TYPE: Water-cooled, 12-cylinder, V-type four-stroke supercharged marine diesel.
CYLINDERS: Two banks of six cylinders set at 60 degrees. Monobloc is a solid aluminium casting. Pressed into monobloc are six steel sleeves with spiral grooves on the outer surface for the circulation of cooling water. Bore 180mm. Stroke 200mm. Compression ratio 13.5 : 0.5.
CRANKCASE: Two-piece cast aluminium alloy case with upper half carrying cylinder monoblocs and transmitting all engine loads.
CYLINDER HEADS: Integral with cylinder monobloc.
CRANKSHAFT: Six-crank, seven bearing crankshaft in nitrided alloy steel with split steel shells, lead-tin bronze lined with lead tin alloy bearing surface.
CONNECTING RODS: Master and articulated rods, with master connected to the crankshaft by split big-end, lined with lead tin bronze. Articulated rod connected to crankshaft by a pin pressed into its eye ring.
PISTONS: Forged aluminium alloy with five rings. Top two steel rings, one cast iron of rectangular section and the two bottom rings, in cast iron and steel, are oil control rings fitted in a common groove.
CAMSHAFTS: Two, acting directly on valve stems.
VALVES: Four in each cylinder, two inlet and

two exhaust. Each retained on seat by three coil springs.
SUPERCHARGING: Two, Type TK-18H superchargers, each comprising an axial-flow turbine and a centrifugal compressor mounted on a common shaft with a vane diffuser and volute. A silencer can be installed on the compressor air inlet. Turbine casing cooled with fresh water from the diesel engine cooling system.
GOVERNOR: Multi-range indirect action engine speed governor with resilient gear drive from pump camshaft. Designed to maintain pre-set rpm throughout full speed range.
LUBRICATION: Delivery pump with full-flow centrifuge, scavenge pump, double gauge strainers and electrically driven priming pump to power engine with oil and fuel.
COOLING: Double-circuit forced circulation system using fresh water with 1 to 1.1% potassium dichromate to GOST 2652–71. Fresh water pump mounted on engine. Fresh water and lubricating oil leaving engine are cooled by water-to-water and water-to-oil coolers in turn cooled by sea water circulated by engine-mounted sea water pump.
STARTING: Compressed air system with two disc-type air distributors and twelve starting valves.
REVERSING: Hydraulically operated reversing clutch to enable propeller shaft to run forwards, idle or reverse. Manual control available in emergency.
PERFORMANCE RATING
Rated power at ahead running under normal
  atmospheric conditions and at rated rpm:
  1000hp

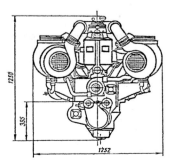

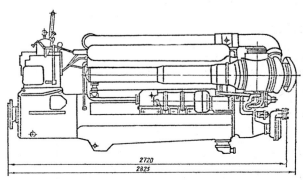

M401A

Rated rpm at ahead running: 1550
Max hourly power at max rpm: 1100hp
Max rpm at ahead running: 1600
Max power at astern running: 250hp
Minimum rpm at astern running (with the diesel
    engine control lever at reverse stop): 750
Max specific fuel consumption at rated power
    (with operating generator, hydraulic pump and
    the power take-off for compressor): 172g/ehp/h
    + 5%
Max specific oil burning losses at rated power:
    5g/ehp/h
FUEL
Diesel fuel Grade (GOST 4749–49) Oil
MC-20 (GOST 4749–49) with additive (GOST
    8312–57) 3% in weight
DIMENSIONS
Length: (with muffler at intake) 2825mm
Length: (without muffler at intake) 2720mm
Width: 1252mm
Height: 1250mm
WEIGHT
Weight (dry) with all units and pipe lines mounted:
    2000kg
PERFORMANCE
Sense of power take-off flange rotation (if viewed
from turbo-supercharger)
    of right-hand diesel engine: Clockwise
    of left-hand diesel engine: Counter-clockwise
Operating life (until major overhaul): 2500 hours

M503

M503A AND M504

The M503A is a multi-cylinder radial-type
diesel which was introduced on the Osa missile
fast-attack craft in the late 1950s and subsequently
installed in the Shershen and probably the Pchela
hydrofoil.

It is radically different from any other marine
diesel in use today because of its radial or 'star'
configuration, peculiar to aero-engines, and also
because of the number of cylinders incorporated
in the design.

The M503A has 42 cylinders in six seven-
cylinder blocks, but a more powerful version, the
M504, has 56 cylinders in eight seven-cylinder
blocks. M504, which develops 5000hp at 2000rpm,
powers the Osa II, Turya, Matka and Stenka.

A tropicalised version of the M504, derated to
4000hp, is installed in export Osa IIs and other
craft designed for these engines and destined to
operate in warm climates. Designation of the tropicalised M504 is M504T.

A twin-pack version, employing two M504s
with a common gearbox driving a single shaft,
is employed in the Nanuchka missile corvette.
Nanuchka has three M504 twin-packs, each developing 10 000hp, giving a total maximum output
of 30 000hp.

On the M504 the drive and reduction gear is
mounted directly on the engine, enabling the propeller shaft to run forwards or in reverse.
Lubricating and water-cooling systems are cooled
by sea water circulated under ram pressure when
making headway and pumped in when going
astern or when stopped. A supercharger is

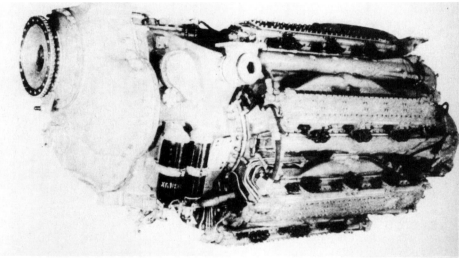

M503

mounted on the forward end of the engine and can
be powered either by drive from a main turbine or
mechanical transmission from the crankshaft.

The most economical operation of the engine is
attained at 1400 to 1700rpm, at which point the
specific fuel consumption is 160 to 165g/hph.
Economy at low power is achieved by cutting out
some of the cylinders. Running hours between
overhaul should be 1500 provided that the engine
is operated at maximum output for only 10 per
cent of that time.

The following details apply to the M504 only:

PERFORMANCE RATING
Max output: 5000hp at 2000rpm
CYLINDERS: Total 56, mounted in eight banks
of seven.
Cylinder diameter: 16mm
PISTON STROKE: 17mm
WEIGHT (including gearbox and drive): 7200kg
POWER TO WEIGHT RATIO: 1.44kg/hp
DIMENSIONS
Length: 4.4m
Width: 1.65m
Height: 1.64m

UNITED KINGDOM

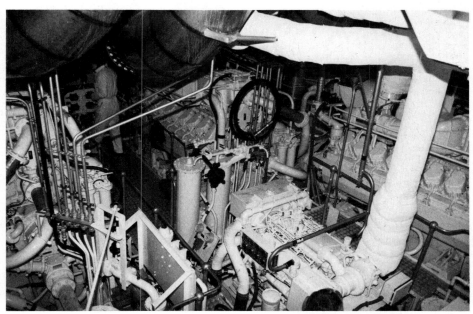

Valenta 16RP200–1–CM installations in Vosper Thornycroft ferries for Shun Tak Shipping, Hong Kong

PAXMAN

PAXMAN DIESELS LIMITED
(a management company of GEC Diesels Limited)

Paxman Works, Hythe Hill, Colchester, Essex CO1 2HW, England

Telephone: (0206) 575151
Telex: 98151 GENERAL G
Telefax: (0206) 577869

VALENTA RP200

TYPE: Direct injection, V-form, 8-, 12-, 16- and 18-cylinder, turbocharged and water-cooled, four-stroke engine.
OUTPUT: 1000–5000bhp, 1000–1600rpm.
BORE AND STROKE: 197 × 216mm.
SWEPT VOLUME (per cylinder): 6.57 litres.
HOUSING: High quality SG iron or fabrication
CRANKSHAFT AND MAIN BEARINGS: Fully nitrided shaft carried in aluminium tin pre-finished steel-backed main bearings. Engine fully balanced against primary and secondary forces.
CONNECTING RODS: Fork and blade type with steel-backed, aluminium tin-lined large end (forked rod) and steel-backed, lead bronze-lined, lead tin flashed bearings (blade rod).
PISTONS: Two-piece pistons, forged steel crown and forged aluminium skirt. Three compression rings in steel crown; one oil control in skirt.
CYLINDER HEAD: High grade casting carrying four-valve direct injection system.
LINERS: Wet type seamless steel tube, chrome plated bore and water side surface honeycombed for surface oil retention.
FUEL INJECTION: Single unit pumps. Pump plungers and camshaft lubricated from main engine pressure system. Feed and injection pump driven from engine drive and gear train; a fuel reservoir and air bleed system fitted. Multi-hole injectors spray fuel into the toroidal cavity in the top of piston. Injectors retained by clamp. Sleeved connection inside cover (Valenta).
GOVERNOR: Standard hydraulic 'Regulateurs Europa' unit with self-contained lubricating oil system; mechanical, electrical or pneumatic controls. Alternative makes available.
PRESSURE CHARGING AND INTER-COOLING: Water-cooled exhaust-gas-driven turboblowers mounted above engine. Air-to-water inter-cooler.
LUBRICATION: Pressure lubrication to all bearing surfaces; single pump system. Oil coolers mounted externally and integral with engine; sea water cooled (Valenta). Full flow single or duplex oil filter can be supplied.
FRESH WATER COOLING: Single pump at free end, shaft-driven from drive end gear train. Thermostatic control valve mounted above pump, giving quick warm-up and even temperature control of water; oil thermostat.
EXHAUST: Single outlet from turboblower; water-cooled manifolds.
STARTING: Air, electric or hydraulic starting.
FUEL: Gas oil to BS.2869–1988 Class A1 and A2 and ASTM D-975–88 No's 1 and 2D with Cetane No 45. Other classes of fuel subject to specification being made available.
LUBRICATING OIL: Oils certified to MIL-L-2104-E with a TBN of not less than nine).
OPTIONAL EXTRA EQUIPMENT: Gearboxes, starting control systems, and all associated engine ancillary equipment necessary for marine applications.

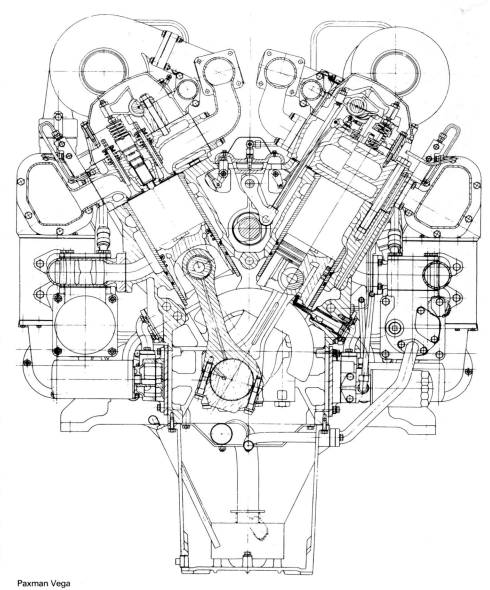

Paxman Vega

Applications

Recent applications of Valenta diesels in high-speed craft include the following:

Valenta 8RP200–1-CM Limbongan T patrol boat for Malaysian MoE

Valenta 12RP200–1-CM Brooke Marine patrol boat for Malaysian Customs

Valenta 12RP200–1-CM Brooke Marine patrol boat for Barbados

Valenta 16RP200–1-CM Karlskrona patrol boat for Trinidad and Tobago

Valenta 16RP200–1-CM Penang Yard patrol boat for Malaysian Police

Valenta 16RP200–1-CM MSE Yard patrol boat for Malaysian Customs

Valenta 16RP200–1-CM two Vosper Thornycroft ferries for Shun Tak Shipping (High Speed Ferries)

Valenta 16RP200–1-CM Picchiotti patrol boat for Seychelles

Valenta 16RP200–1-CM Bollinger Shipyard Island Class for United States Coast Guard

Valenta 18RP200–1-CM Vosper Thornycroft Province Class for the Sultanate of Oman

Valenta 18RP200–1-CM Vosper Thornycroft for fast strike craft

Vega12 Sheng Hsing Shipbuilding, Taiwan for Dragin Shipping Co

Vega12 Fairey Marinteknik Protector fast patrol boat for HM Customs and Excise

CATEGORY DEFINITION

(A) HIGH-SPEED CRAFT:Fast patrol craft, high-speed yachts, fast pleasure craft and similar applications

RATING DEFINITION

MARINE PROPULSION CATEGORY (A):The maximum rating is available for 30 minutes in each period of six hours operation at or below the continuous rating. If this time is exceeded it may be necessary to reduce the overhaul periods. The intermittent rating is available for one hour in each period of six hours operation at or below the continuous rating. If this time is exceeded it may be necessary to reduce the overhaul periods. The continuous rating is available for operating periods normally associated with high speed craft.

Paxman Vega 12.0.CM, 1074 kW at 1600 rpm (photo:copyright of Paxman Diesels Ltd)

ENGINE DATA

	ENGINE TYPE	CONFIG-URATION	BORE × STROKE mm	BMEP at max 'A' rating	MEAN PISTON SPEED AT 1600 rev/min m/s	LENGTH × WIDTH × HEIGHT mm	DRY WEIGHT kg
VEGA	12	12V	160 × 190	18.76	10.13	2350 × 1432 × 1700	3933
	16	16V	160 × 190	18.71	10.13	3155 × 1432 × 1850	4734
VALENTA	6	6L	197 × 216	19.20	11.52	2673 × 1219 × 1943	4363
	8	8V	197 × 216	21.33	11.52	2032 × 1460 × 2273	4617
	12	12V	197 × 216	22.68	11.52	2428 × 1530 × 2387	6671
	16	16V	197 × 216	22.68	11.52	2962 × 1530 × 2470	8963
	18	18V	197 × 216	22.66	11.52	3268 × 1460 × 2470	9371

RATING TO ISO 3046

ENGINE TYPE		MAXIMUM		INTERMITTENT		CONTINUOUS	
		UNITS kWb bhp CV, PS	SPEED rev/min	UNITS kWb bhp CV, PS	SPEED rev/min	UNITS kWb bhp CV, PS	SPEED rev/min

CATEGORY A

	ENGINE	MAXIMUM		INTERMITTENT		CONTINUOUS	
VEGA	12	1290 1730 1754	1800	1182 1585 1607	1750	1074 1440 1460	1700
	16	1716 2300 2332	1800	1575 2110 2140	1750	1432 1920 1947	1700
VALENTA	6	1007 1350 1370	1600	925 1240 1257	1550	835 1120 1135	1500
	8	1492 2000 2030	1600	1362 1825 1850	1550	1250 1675 1700	1500
	12	2440 3270 3315	1640	2215 2970 3010	1585	2015 2700 2735	1540
	16	3250 4360 4420	1640	2955 3960 4015	1585	2685 3600 3650	1540
	18	3655 4900 4965	1640	3325 4455 4516	1585	3020 4050 4105	1540

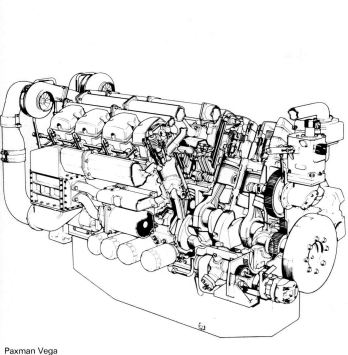

Paxman Vega

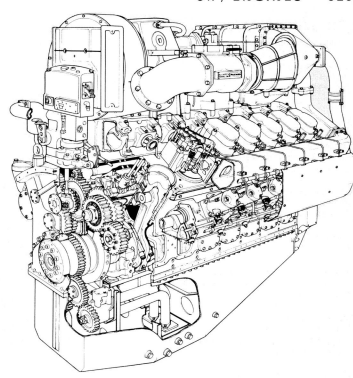

Paxman Valenta

PERKINS ENGINES (SHREWSBURY) LTD

Sentinel Works, Shrewsbury, Shropshire SY1 4DP, England

Telephone: 074352262
Telex: 35171PESL G

J A Gilroy, *Managing Director*
B J Willmott, *Director and General Manager*

Perkins marine diesel engines are built at the former Rolls-Royce diesel engine factory at Shrewsbury following its purchase in 1984.

CV 12 M 800Ti

A 12-cylinder, 800bhp turbocharged, charge-cooled marine diesel engine suitable for a wide variety of purposes. One application has been in the British Royal Navy Training Boats (20.0m, 32 tonnes standard displacement) for which they are rated at 611kW. More recently, a pair have been installed in the InCat *Bottom Time II*.
TYPE: 12 cylinders in 60° 'V' form, water-cooled.

BORE: 135mm.
STROKE: 152mm.
COMPRESSION RATIO: 14.5:1.
CAPACITY: 26.11 litres.
INDUCTION: Turbocharged, charge cooled.
ROTATION: Anti-clockwise viewed on flywheel.
NET DRY WEIGHT: 2800kg with Twin Disc MGN 332–1.
STANDARD FEATURES
Thermostatically controlled, pressurised, closed circuit coolant system with gear driven centrifugal fresh water pump
Fresh water heat-exchanger cooling with 'Gilmec' self-priming raw water pump
Fresh water-cooled exhaust manifolds and turbochargers
Charge-air coolers integral with induction manifolds
Dry type air-cleaners
Fresh water-cooled lubricating oil cooler, integral with three full-flow, spin-on element lubricating oil filters
Twin engine mounted fuel filters with spin-on elements

Fuel line water separator (loose)
Front and rear engine mounting brackets
Front power take-off facility
SAE No O Flywheel Housing
Flywheel suitable for marine reverse/reduction gears to SAEJ 620d size 18
24V, insulated return marine electrics with 35A alternator and associated electrical equipment, including battery master switch and start button
Instrumentation includes: Tachometer, ammeter, coolant temperature gauge, engine oil pressure gauge, oil pressure switch coolant temperature switch and engine hours counter
STANDARD FEATURES
Thermostatically controlled, pressurised, closed circuit coolant system with gear driven centrifugal fresh water pump
Fresh water heat-exchanger cooling with 'Gilmec' self-priming raw water pump
Fresh water-cooled exhaust manifolds and turbochargers
Charge-air coolers integral with induction manifolds

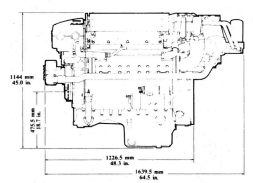

POWER RATINGS

	Max power	rpm	Fuel consumption
Pleasure:	600kW	2100	162.3 litres/h
Light dry commercial:	550kW	2100	149.1 litres/h
Heavy duty commercial:	455kW	1800	115.9 litres/h

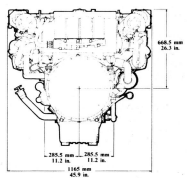

Perkins CV 12 M 800Ti

Perkins CV 12 M 800Ti

Dry type air-cleaners
Fresh water-cooled lubricating oil cooler, integral with three full-flow, spin-on element lubricating oil filters
Twin engine mounted fuel filters with spin-on elements
Fuel line water separator (loose)

Front and rear engine mounting brackets
Front power take-off facility
SAE No 0 Flywheel Housing
Flywheel suitable for marine reverse/reduction gears to SAE J 620d size 18
24V, insulated return marine electrics with 35A alternator and associated electrical equipment,

including battery master switch and start button
Instrumentation includes: Tachometer, ammeter, coolant temperature gauge, engine oil pressure gauge, oil pressure switch, coolant temperature switch, and engine hours counter.

ROLLS-ROYCE plc
(Industrial & Marine)
Ansty, Coventry, West Midlands CV7 9JR, England

Telephone: (0203) 624000
Telex: 31636 G
Telefax: (0203)624666

John Ferrie, *Director, Industrial and Marine and Repair*

Rolls-Royce offers a range of aero-derived industrial and marine gas turbines suitable for a wide variety of applications. Over 2550 marine and industrial gas turbines have been sold or are on order for operations around the world. Twenty five nations and a number of civil operators have selected Rolls-Royce engines.

MARINE GNOME
TYPE: Gas turbine, free-turbine turboshaft.
AIR INTAKE: Annular 15°C.
COMBUSTION CHAMBER: Annular.
FUEL GRADE
    DERD 2494 Avtur/50 Kerosene.
    DERD 2482 Avtur/40 Kerosene.
TURBINE: Two-stage axial-flow generator turbine and a single-stage axial-flow free power turbine.
BEARINGS: Compressor rotor has a roller bearing at the front and a ball bearing at the rear. Gas generator turbine is supported at the front by the compressor rear bearings, and at the rear by a roller bearing.
    Single-stage power turbine is supported by a roller bearing behind the turbine disc and by a ball bearing towards the rear of the turbine shaft.
JET PIPE: Exhaust duct to suit installation.
ACCESSORY DRIVES: Accessory gearbox provides a drive for : the fuel pump, the hydro-mechanical governor in the flow control unit, the centrifugal fuel filter, the dual tachometer and the engine oil pump.
LUBRICATION SYSTEM: Dry sump.
OIL SPECIFICATION: DERD 2487.
MOUNTING:
Front: Three pads on the front frame casing.
Rear: Mounting point is the rear flange of the exhaust duct centre-body.
STARTING: Electric.
DIMENSIONS:
Length: 1709mm
Width: 462mm
Height: 518mm
PERFORMANCE RATINGS:
Max: 1350bhp
Ratings are at max power turbine speed, 19500rpm.
SPECIFIC FUEL CONSUMPTION:
Max: 281g/bhp h
OIL CONSUMPTION:
0.28 litres/h
Power turbine: 0.84 litres/h

MARINE SPEY (SM2 and SM3)
Rolls-Royce produces two lightweight versions of the SM series of marine propulsion unit based on the Spey, a high efficiency fully marinised machine incorporating much of the state-of-the-art aerotechnology incorporated in the aero Tay.
    The two types are available for light craft, offering high thermal efficiency (in excess of 35%).

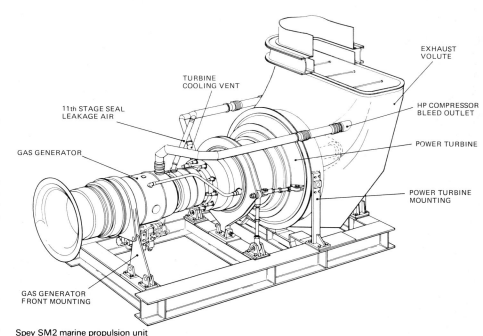

Spey SM2 marine propulsion unit

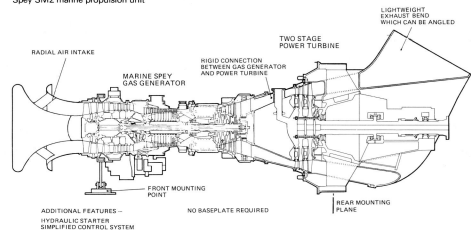

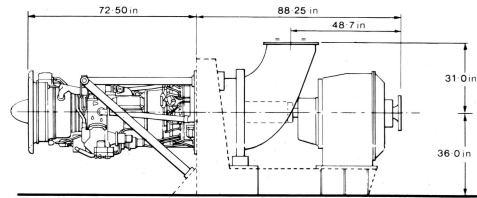

Lightweight Tyne RM2D with optional base frame

They are designed to provide high speed or cruising power for a wide range of present and future designs.
    For strike missile craft, corvettes or surface effect ships, a lightweight version, designated the SM2 is available.

A second variant, suitable for small craft, SWATH ships and hydrofoils is designated the SM3.
    The Spey gas turbine is a proven unit ordered by three navies for six ship classes. To date some fifteen Spey powered ships are at sea.

TYPE: Marine gas turbine incorporating two independently-driven compressors and a purpose-designed smoke-free power turbine.
GAS GENERATOR CHARACTERISTICS
AIR INTAKE: Direct entry, fixed, without intake guides.
LP COMPRESSOR: 5 axial stages.
HP COMPRESSOR: 11 axial stages.
COMBUSTION SYSTEM: Turbo-annular type with ten interconnected straight flow flame tubes.
TURBINES: Axial type, two HP and two LP stages.
EXHAUST: Fixed volume.
STARTING: Hydraulic or electric starting available.
FUEL SYSTEM: Fully integrated electronic control system with hydromechanical high pressure fuel system with automatic acceleration and speed control.
FUEL GRADE: Diesel fuel Grade 'A'. DEF 2402 or NATO F75.
LUBRICATION SYSTEM: Self-contained gear pump filters and chip detectors.
POWER TURBINE: Two-stage free axial-flow turbine.
DIMENSIONS:
SM2 UNIT:
Length: 6.096m
Width: 2.286m
Height: 2.794m
Weight: 15 tonnes
SM3 UNIT
Length: 6.544m
Width: 2.069m
Height: 2.352
Weight: 8.3 tonnes
GAS GENERATOR CHANGE UNIT: 1732kg
NOMINAL PERFORMANCE:
Max rating: 19500kW
*Specific fuel consumption: 0.226kg/kWh
*Based on LCV of fuel of 43125kJ/kg
No power take-offs
No intake or exhaust duct losses
Ambient air temperature of 15°C and an atmospheric pressure of 101.3kPA

MARINE TYNE (RM2D)

Rolls-Royce produces a lightweight version of the Tyne RM1C marine propulsion unit, an aero-derived high efficiency gas turbine.

This compact lightweight unit is ideal for hydrofoils, hovercraft, SES, SWATH ships and fast attack craft.

The Marine Tyne gas turbine is a well proven unit, 188 being in service with five navies in nine ship classes.
TYPE: Marine gas turbine incorporating two independently driven compressors and an integral free power turbine.
GAS GENERATOR CHARACTERISTICS:
AIR INTAKE: Direct entry, fixed with intake guide vanes.
LP COMPRESSOR: 6 axial stages.
HP COMPRESSOR: 9 axial stages.
COMBUSTION SYSTEM: Turbo-annular type with ten interconnected straight flow flame tubes.
TURBINES: Axial type, two HP and LP stages.
EXHAUST: Fixed volume.
STARTING: Hydraulic or electric starting available.
FUEL SYSTEM: Fully integrated control system with hydromechanical high pressure fuel system with automatic acceleration and speed control.
FUEL GRADE: Diesel fuel Grade 'A' DEF 2402 or NATO F75.
LUBRICATION SYSTEM: Self-contained gear pump filters and chip detectors
POWER TURBINE: Two stage free axial flow turbines

DIMENSIONS:Length: 4.083m
Width: 1.270m
Height: 1.70m
Weight: 2.76 tonnes
GAS GENERATOR CHANGE UNIT: 1208kg

NOMINAL PERFORMANCE:
Max rating 4000kW
  Specific fuel consumption: 0.286kg/kWh
  Based on LCV of fuel of 43124kJ/kg

No power take-offs
No intake or exhaust duct losses
Ambient air temperature of 15°C and an atmo-
spheric pressure of 101.3kPA

RUSTON DIESELS LIMITED
(A Management Company of GEC Diesels Limited)
Vulcan Works, Newton-le-Willows, Merseyside,
WA12 8RU, England

Telephone: (09252) 5151
Telex: 627131
Telefax: (09252) 22055

RK270

In late 1988 an order was announced by International Catamarans, Australia for the supply of
two 71 metre(later changed to 74 metre) 35 knot
wave-piercing catamarans for Sealink British
Ferries Ltd. Each vessel is to be powered by four
Ruston 16RK270 diesels with a maximum continuous rating of 3650kW at 750rpm and a continuous service rating of 3240kW at 720rpm. Each
engine will directly drive a KaMeWa water-jet
unit.

The Ruston RK270 is a development of the
successful RK engine with an increased bore providing an output of 1200 to 6000bhp at speeds
from 720 to 1000rpm, from a range of 6, 8, 12 and
16 cylinder engines. The RK270 is suitable for a
wide variety of applications including industrial
power generation, marine propulsion, marine
auxiliary power generation and rail traction
duties.

With appropriate de-rating the engine can
operate on residual fuels, and a spark-ignited
industrial version is also available.

BEDPLATE: The RK270 follows the proven
design features of the renowned RK range of
engines with the bedplate manufactured from a
high grade meehanite iron casting. Robust construction with transverse diaphragms for each
main bearing provides rigid support for the crankshaft. Angled joint faces ensure positive locking
of the main bearing caps in the bedplate.
CRANKSHAFT: The crankshaft is machined
from a single piece alloy steel forging produced
by the continuous grain flow method with bolted
on balance weights and an integrally forged coupling flange to which the flywheel is registered and
bolted. The camshaft drive gear is split to facilitate
replacement.
BEARINGS: The main bearings are pre-finished,
steel backed shells lined with high grade bearing
material having a lead-tin surface flashing to facilitate running-in. The bearings are retained in the
housings by caps drilled to direct oil to the bearings. These caps are located transversely in large
registers in the bedplate and held in position by
studs and nuts. The bearings are easily removable
through the crankcase doors.
CRANKCASE: The cylinder housing with integral air chest is machined from a rigid grey iron
casting having transverse diaphragms between
each cylinder to provide water compartments
around the cylinder liners. Detachable doors
facilitate access to the connecting rod and main
bearings and to the camshaft and governor drive
gear train.

Explosion relief valves are appropriately positioned on the crankcase doors and on the integrally cast charge airchest.
CYLINDER LINERS: Separate wet type liners
cast in alloy iron are flanged at their upper ends
and secured by the cylinder heads. The lower ends
of the liners are located in the crankcase and sealed
by synthetic rubber rings. The liners are machined
all over and the bore is hone finished to provide

Ruston 16RK270

good piston liner compatibility for long service
life.
CONNECTING RODS: A feature of the connecting rods is an oblique split large end with
the cap located by serrations on the joint face,
optimised to reduce bending and shear loads
across the joint. As a result, distortion of the large
end housing is minimised.

The small end features a stepped configuration
large diameter pin to distribute the load evenly
between piston and connecting rod, allowing
operation at very high firing pressures.
CYLINDER HEAD: Individual cylinder heads
are manufactured from iron castings. Each cylinder head carries two inlet and two exhaust valves
and a side entry air inlet port which is connected
to the crankcase air manifold.
PISTON: The standard piston is of single piece
aluminium alloy construction with a combustion
bowl of the Hesselman design. Cooling oil is fed
from the connecting rod, through the small end
bush and drillings in the gudgeon pin and piston
body to the cast-in cooling gallery. For some
duties, including heavy fuel operation, a steel
crown, aluminium skirt, 2 piece piston is used.
VALVE GEAR AND CAMSHAFT: Each pair
of valves is operated via short stiff pushrods and
conventional rockers. The pushrods are driven
from the side entry camshafts, one per bank of
cylinders via roller cam followers. Hardened steel
cams are used throughout.
CAMSHAFT: A single shaft for each cylinder has
few component parts and removal and replacement of cam clusters is simple and straight-
forward. The camshafts are side mounted in the
crankcase and can be easily inserted or removed
from the side of the engine.
CAMSHAFT DRIVE: The camshafts and auxiliary drive are driven through a train of hardened
and ground steel spur gears from the crankshaft
split gear.
FLYWHEEL: The mild steel flywheel, suitable
for mounting flexible couplings when required, is

fitted with a ring gear for starting and hand
barring and is statically balanced before bolting
to the integrally forged crankshaft flange.
GOVERNOR: A sensitive hydraulic governor is
bevel gear driven from the camshaft.

Overspeeding is prevented by a separate safety
trip mechanism which returns the control shaft to
the "NO-FUEL" position.

For Generator drive applications an electric
load-sensing governor is employed.
AUXILIARY DRIVES: Auxiliaries are driven
from the free end of the engine through a spring
drive and spur gears. The standard arrangement
includes one water pump for the jacket water,
one water pump for the charge air cooler and
lubricating oil cooler circuits and a gear type
lubricating oil pump.

An extension shaft may be fitted to allow power
to be taken from the free end of the engine.
INSTRUMENTATION: An engine mounted
instrument panel is provided to indicate:
  Engine speed
  Lube oil pressure and temperature
  Jacket water pressure
  Air chest pressure.

Engines are fitted with thermocouples for indicating cylinder exhaust outlet, turbine inlet and
outlet temperatures. A multi-point indicator with
compensating multi core cabling is supplied for
off engine mountings.
TURBOCHARGERS: Turbochargers and
charge air coolers are fitted as standard equipment. The standard location of the single turbocharger is at the free end of the engine. However,
a flywheel end mounted turbocharger may be
offered at customer's request. For rail traction
applications the turbocharger is mounted above
the alternator.

A high efficiency compressor is driven by an
axial flow exhaust gas turbine and delivers air to
the air chest through a charge air cooler. Lube oil
to the plain bearings and cooling water is provided
from the engine systems.

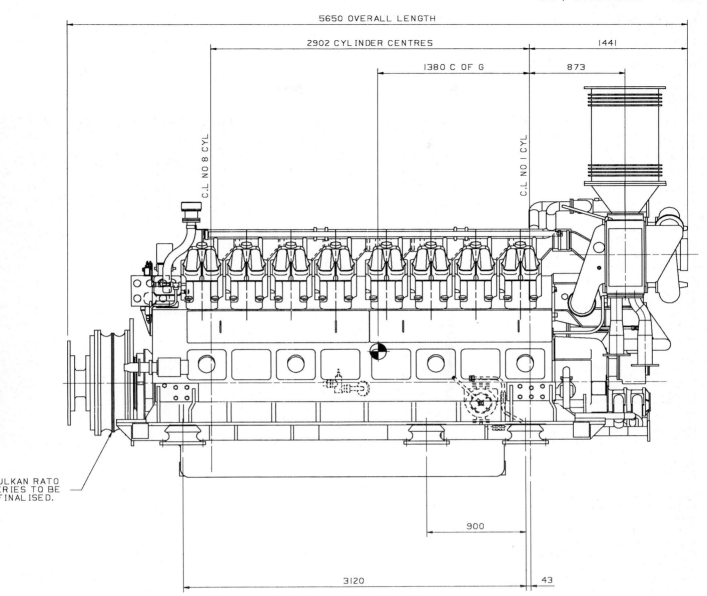

5650 OVERALL LENGTH
2902 CYLINDER CENTRES
1441
1380 C OF G
873
C.L NO 8 CYL
C.L NO I CYL
VULKAN RATO
SERIES TO BE
FINALISED.
900
3120
43

The Ruston 16RK270 diesel, 3650kW MCR, four of which power the Sealink Hoverspeed 74m, 35 knot InCat wave-piercing catamarans

By careful turbocharger matching, engine output is achieved with a favourable air/fuel ratio resulting in low thermal loading.

EXHAUST MANIFOLD: Exhaust manifolds, of cast iron construction, feature bolted flanges with heavy duty joints. Where required these are lagged with non-asbestos material, protected by a metallic skin.

LUBRICATING OIL SYSTEM: The system includes single or twin engine driven oil pumps, full flow filtration, thermostat and oil cooler. The oil pressure is controlled by one or two spring loaded relief valves.

COOLING SYSTEM: The jacket cooling system is thermostatically controlled and includes an engine driven water pump.

STARTING SYSTEM: Air or electric motor starting is standard, using one or two motors, operating via spur gears onto the flywheel ring gear which is also employed for hand barring.

FUEL INJECTION: The fuel injection system features individual pumps and injectors for each cylinder. Governing is by a Regulateurs Europa or equivalent unit, the governor drive being taken from the camshaft via bevel gears.

Number of cylinders		6	8	12	16
Cylinder configuration		In line	In line	45° vee	45° vee
Dry weight (with flywheel)	kg	12800	17200	21230	25820
Oil sump capacity	l	340	410	570	750
Length	mm	4020	4750	4785	5600
Width	mm	1325	1325	1830	1830
Height	mm	2490	2490	2400	2400
Turbocharger no. Position		One Free end	One Free end	One Free end	Two Free end & drive end
Charge cooler no. Position		One Free end	One Free end	Two Free end	Two Free end & drive end

TECHNICAL DATA
ENGINE TYPE: RK270
TYPE: Turbocharged and charge cooled diesel
CYCLE: 4-stroke
BORE: 270mm
STROKE: 305mm
Compression ration 12.8
MEAN PISTOL SPEED: 10.16m/s at 1000 rpm
STANDARD ROTATION: Counter clockwise
  looking on the drive end of the crankshaft

STANDARD EQUIPMENT
Flywheel
Air filter/silencer mounted on turbocharger
Air motor starting
Crankcase explosion relief valves
Water to air charge air coolers
Jacket water cooler
Lubricating oil cooler
Speed governor-type 1100
Lubricating oil pressure relief valve
Lubricating oil filter-
  simplex type for gen. sets
  duplex type for propulsion
Lubricating oil pressure pump engine driven
Fuel oil filter-duplex type
Pre-start lubricating oil priming pump
Engine cooling water pump-engine driven
Electric tachometer
Engine-mounted instrument panel
Remote exhaust temperature indicator
Charge air temperature alarm
Jacket water temperature alarm and shut down
Lubricating oil pressure alarm and shut down
Hand barring gear
Lagged exhaust manifold
Cylinder pressure relief valve/compression release
  valve and indicator (o kill type)
Exhaust silencer-non-spark arrester type
Exhaust uptake adaptor and bellous
Tools for routine maintenance

OPTIONAL EQUIPMENT
Auto starting
Reverse direction of rotation
Alternative type of speed governor
Power take off from free end of crankshaft
Sea water/secondary water pump-engine driven
Overload switch
Fuel limiter
Residual fuel build
Centrifugal bypass lubricating oil filter
Alternative exhaust silencer-eg spark arrester/
  improved attenuation
Turbocharger mounted at drive end (6, 8 and 12
  cylinder)
Handed engine control
Tools for engine overhaul

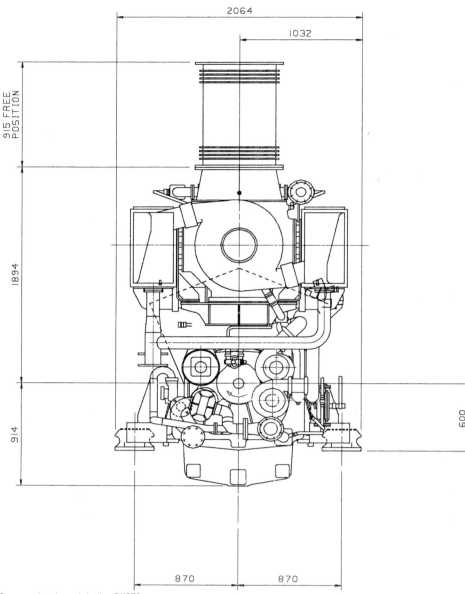

Cross section through in-line RK270

Marine unrestricted service power

Engine	Speed	Distillate		
	rev/min	Brakepower kW	hp	Electrical kW
6RK270	720	1410	1890	1350
	750	1440	1930	1380
	900	1620	2170	1550
	1000	1720	2305	1650
8RK270	720	1880	2520	1800
	750	1920	2575	1840
	900	2160	2895	2070
	1000	2300	3080	2200
12RK270	750	2820	3780	2700
	750	2880	3860	2760
	900	3240	4340	3100
	1000	3440	4610	3300
16RK270	720	3760	5040	3600
	750	3840	5150	3680
	900	4320	5790	4140
	1000	4600	6160	4400

Electrical power output will depend on actual generator efficiency

General performance data*

ENGINE TYPE		6RK270				8RK270				12RK270				16RK270			
Engine speed	rpm	720	750	900	1000	720	750	900	1000	720	750	900	1000	720	750	900	1000
BMEP	bar	22.40	22.03	20.64	19.72	22.40	22.03	20.64	19.75	22.40	22.03	20.64	19.72	22.40	22.03	20.64	19.75
	lb/in²	324.8	319.4	299.3	285.9	324.8	319.4	299.3	286.4	324.8	319.4	299.3	285.9	324.8	319.4	299.3	286.4
Mechanical efficiency	%	91.7	91.4	89.8	88.8	91.7	91.4	89.8	88.8	91.7	91.4	89.9	88.8	91.7	91.4	89.9	88.8
Brake thermal efficiency	%	42.52	42.52	41.47	41.27	42.52	42.52	41.47	41.27	42.52	42.52	41.47	41.27	42.52	42.52	41.47	41.27
Maximum cylinder pressure	bar	138	138	138	138	138	138	138	138	138	138	138	138	138	138	138	138
	lb/in²	2000	2000	2000	2000	2000	2000	2000	2000	2000	2000	2000	2000	2000	2000	2000	2000
Compression pressure	bar	100	98.5	97	97	100	98.5	97	97	100	98.5	97	97	100	98.5	97	97
	lb/in²	1450	1428	1407	1407	1450	1428	1407	1407	1450	1428	1407	1407	1450	1428	1407	1407
Charge air pressure	bar	2.2	2.15	2.1	2.1	2.2	2.15	2.1	2.1	2.2	2.15	2.1	2.1	2.2	2.15	2.1	2.1
	lb/in²	31.9	31.2	30.5	30.5	31.9	31.2	30.5	30.5	31.9	31.2	30.5	30.5	31.9	31.2	30.5	30.5
Air flow rate	kg/s	2.98	3.08	3.51	3.72	3.97	4.11	4.67	4.98	5.96	6.16	7.01	7.44	7.94	8.21	9.35	9.95
	lb/s	6.56	6.79	7.73	8.20	8.75	9.06	10.30	10.96	13.12	13.58	15.15	16.40	17.50	17.73	20.61	21.93
Exhaust gas flow rate	kg/s	3.06	3.10	3.60	3.82	4.08	4.21	4.79	5.11	6.12	6.32	7.20	7.64	8.15	8.43	9.60	10.22
	lb/s	6.74	6.83	7.94	8.42	8.98	9.10	10.57	11.27	13.48	13.65	15.86	16.84	17.96	19.09	20.31	22.52
Charge air temperature	°C	66	65	65	65	66	65	65	65	66	65	65	65	66	65	65	65
	°F	151	149	149	149	151	149	149	149	151	149	149	149	151	149	149	149
Turbine inlet temperature	°C	540	540	580	580	540	540	580	580	540	540	580	580	540	540	580	580
	°F	1005	1005	1075	1075	1005	1005	1075	1075	1005	1005	1075	1075	1005	1005	1075	1075
Turbine outlet temperature	°C	390	380	390	390	390	380	390	390	390	380	390	390	390	380	390	390
	°F	735	715	735	735	735	715	735	735	735	715	735	735	735	715	735	735
Fuel injection pressure	bar	1040	1055	1035	1120	1040	1055	1035	1120	1040	1055	1035	1120	1040	1055	1035	1120
	lb/in²	15100	15300	15000	16200	15100	15300	15000	16200	15100	15300	15000	16200	15100	15300	15000	16200
Lubricating oil consumption	l/hr	2.15	2.15	2.4	2.55	2.85	2.85	3.2	3.4	4.25	4.25	4.8	5.1	5.7	5.7	6.4	6.8
	pint/h	3.75	3.75	4.25	4.45	5.0	5.0	5.65	6.0	7.5	7.5	8.45	9.0	10.0	10.0	11.3	12.0

Heat dissipation and flow data*

ENGINE TYPE		6RK270				8RK270				12RK270				16RK270			
Engine speed	rpm	720	750	900	1000	720	750	900	1000	720	750	900	1000	720	750	900	1000
Heat dissipation to charge cooler	kW	525	542	600	636	699	723	799	851	1050	1084	1198	1272	1398	1445	1598	1702
	Btu/hx10³	1792	1849	2049	2171	2387	2967	2724	2905	3582	3699	4091	4341	4773	4630	5455	5805
Sec. water flow through charge cooler(s)-total**	m³/h	40.9	40.9	40.9	40.9	45.5	47.7	57.3	63.6	81.8	81.8	81.8	81.8	91.0	95.4	114.6	127.2
	gal/h	9000	9000	9000	9000	10000	10500	12600	14000	18000	18000	18000	18000	20000	21000	25200	28000
Heat dissipation to jacket water	kW	372	398	464	506	497	532	624	676	739	800	931	1012	992	1062	1240	1351
	Btu/hx10³	1268	1360	1584	1728	1696	1814	2129	2305	2522	2731	3178	3451	3386	3624	4230	4610
Jacket water flow rate	m³/h	45.5	47.7	57.3	63.6	45.5	47.7	57.3	63.6	91.0	95.4	114.6	127.2	91.0	95.4	114.6	127.2
	gal/h	10000	10500	12600	14000	10000	10500	12600	14000	20000	21000	25200	28000	20000	21000	25200	28000
Jacket water temperature into cooler	°C	82	82	82	82	82	82	82	82	82	82	82	82	82	82	82	82
	°F	180	180	180	180	180	180	180	180	180	180	180	180	180	180	180	180
Heat dissipation to lubricating oil	kW	178	191	219	231	239	255	292	310	354	384	436	464	475	509	582	619
	Btu/hx10³	608	653	747	789	814	871	996	1058	1207	1310	1488	1584	1621	1738	1986	2113
Lubricating oil flow through cooler	m³/h	32.7	32.7	32.7	32.7	37.0	37.0	37.9	37.0	50.9	50.9	50.9	50.9	61.4	61.4	61.4	61.4
	gal/h	7200	7200	7200	7200	8150	8150	8150	8150	11200	11200	11200	11200	13500	13500	13500	13500
Lubricating oil into cooler	°C	82	82	82	82	82	82	82	82	82	82	82	82	82	82	82	82
	°F	180	180	180	180	180	180	180	180	180	180	180	180	180	180	180	180
Heat to radiation (lagged exhaust manifold)	lcw	39	40	45	48	52	54	60	64	79	80	90	96	105	107	120	128
	Btu/hx10³	134	137	154	163	178	182	205	218	268	273	307	326	357	364	410	436

* At marine unrestricted service conditions of 45°C air intake and 32°C charge cooler water temperature.
Cooler design temperature-nominal setting of thermostatic valve is 77°C (170°F).
** Based on clean deep-sea water and A1-brass tubes.

Specific fuel consumption

Percent full load		110	100	75	50	25	110	100	75	50	25
	rpm	g/kW-h (brake)					il/bhp-h				
All **RK270**	720/750	204	202	201	209	228	335	332	330	343	375
	900	210	207	207	212	225	345	340	340	348	370
	1000	211	208	209	220	239	347	342	343	361	393
Tolerance		+5%					+5%				
LCV of fuel		42000kJ/kg					18060Btu/lb				

Fuel specification
Distillate. BSMA100. Class MI, M2 or equivalent specification
Residual. BSMA, 100 Class M4-M7 or equivalent specification having viscosities of 15, 25, 45, 75cst at 80°C (300, 600, 1500, 3500 Redwood No 1 at 100°F)

UNITED STATES OF AMERICA

ALLISON GAS TURBINE DIVISION
(General Motors Corporation)
General Offices: PO Box 420 SCU6, Indianapolis, Indiana 46206–0420, USA

Telephone: (317) 242 4151
Telex: 6876054
Telefax: 3172302900

Allison Gas Turbines has been active in the development of gas turbines for aircraft, industrial and marine use for many years. Production of the first Allison gas turbine began in the 1940s, when the company built the powerplant for the P-39, the first jet-powered aircraft to fly in the United States.

Later, the Allison T56 turboprop aircraft engine was developed. It demonstrated outstanding reliability and the same basic design has been adapted for industrial and marine applications. In the early 1960s, the first Allison 501-K gas turbine-powered electric powerplant went into service. Today, in excess of 1500 501-K industrial series engines are used not only in electric powerplants but also in industrial and marine applications. The two-shaft marine engine powers the Boeing/Kawasaki Jetfoil and is installed in the Israeli Shipyard Ltd M161 hydrofoil craft for primary propulsion.

Allison 501-KF

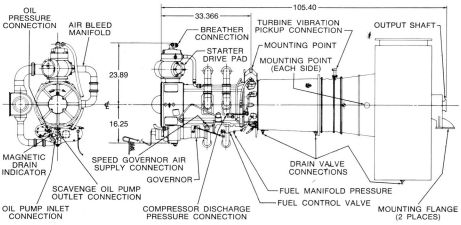

General arrangement of Allison 501-KF

ALLISON 501-K SERIES
The Allison 501-K series industrial gas turbine incorporates a 14-stage axial-flow compressor, with bleed valves to compensate for compressor surge.

Of modular design, it comprises three main sections: the compressor, combustor and turbine. Each section can be readily separated from the other. Modular design provides ease in handling and servicing of the engine.

The first stage of the four-stage turbine section is air-cooled, permitting the engine to be operated at higher than normal turbine inlet temperatures.

The combustor section of the 501-K consists of six combustion chambers of the through-flow type, assembled within a single annular chamber. This multiple provides even temperature distribution at the turbine inlet, thus eliminating the danger of hot spots.

The 501-K series engines are available in single-shaft or free turbine design.

The lightweight, compact size of the 501-K lends itself to multiple engines driving a single shaft through a common gearbox, or as a gas generator driving a customer-furnished power turbine.

The engine can be operated on a wide range of liquid fuels. Designation of the marine model is 501-KF, a brief specification for which follows.

ALLISON 501-KF
The marine version of the industrial 501-K engine at ISA, SL conditions:

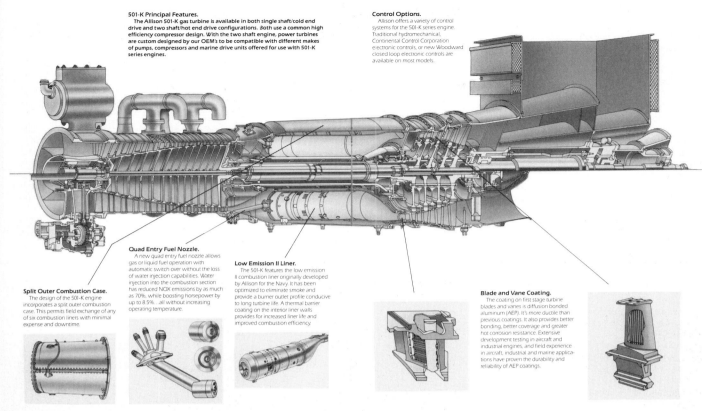

501-K Principal Features.
The Allison 501-K gas turbine is available in both single shaft/cold end drive and two shaft/hot end drive configurations. Both use a common high efficiency compressor design. With the two shaft engine, power turbines are custom designed by our OEM's to be compatible with different makes of pumps, compressors and marine drive units offered for use with 501-K series engines.

Control Options.
Allison offers a variety of control systems for the 501-K series engine. Traditional hydromechanical, Continental Control Corporation electronic controls, or new Woodward closed loop electronic controls are available on most models.

Quad Entry Fuel Nozzle.
A new quad entry fuel nozzle allows gas or liquid fuel operation with automatic switch over without the loss of water injection capabilities. Water injection into the combustion section has reduced NOX emissions by as much as 70%, while boosting horsepower by up to 8.5%...all without increasing operating temperature.

Split Outer Combustion Case.
The design of the 501-K engine incorporates a split outer combustion case. This permits field exchange of any of six combustion liners with minimal expense and downtime.

Low Emission II Liner.
The 501-K features the low emission II combustion liner originally developed by Allison for the Navy. It has been optimized to eliminate smoke and provide a burner outlet profile conducive to long turbine life. A thermal barrier coating on the interior liner walls provides for increased liner life and improved combustion efficiency.

Blade and Vane Coating.
The coating on first stage turbine blades and vanes is diffusion bonded aluminum (AEP). It's more ductile than previous coatings. It also provides better bonding, better coverage and greater hot corrosion resistance. Extensive development testing in aircraft and industrial engines, and field experience in aircraft, industrial and marine applications have proven the durability and reliability of AEP coatings.

Principal features of the Allison 501-K type engine

Continuous power: 3229kW
Weight: 1134kg
Length: 2667mm
Height: 1378mm
Calculated turbine inlet temperature: 982°C
Exhaust gas temperature: 534°C
Power turbine rpm: 13820
Specific fuel consumption: 305g/kWh
Dimensions in inches are shown on the accompanying general arrangement drawing.
Inlet air flow: 26 000ft³min
Exhaust air flow: 81 000ft³min
Engine jacket heat rejection: 6000 Btu/min

Lube heat rejection (Gasifier): 1270 Btu/min
Max liquid fuel flow: 6365 litres (360ghp)
Liquid fuel: DF-1, DF-2 per Allison EMS66
Lubricant: Synthetic oil per Allison EMS35 and 53
Required auxiliaries:
25hp starter
20–29V dc electrical power
Power take-off shaft and couplings
Temperature and speed controls from engine furnished signals
Oil cooler
Auxiliary lube pump

Compressor inlet sensor
Gauge panel, meters and associated components
Engine exhaust diffusing tailpipe

ALLISON 570-K

A 7000hp gas turbine designed as a prime mover in the industrial and marine fields, the 570 series is a front drive, two-shaft gas turbine. It entered production in 1978 and is in full operation. The model 570 represents General Motors' newest entry in the industrial and marine markets and is a derivative of the US Army's heavy lift helicopter (HLH) engine.

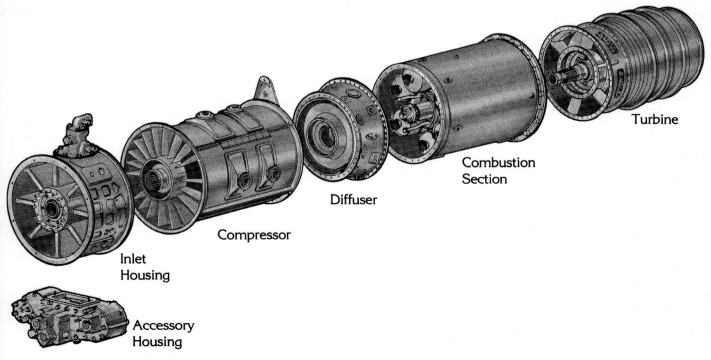

Inlet Housing
Compressor
Diffuser
Combustion Section
Turbine
Accessory Housing

The Allison 501-K is of modular design for ease of maintenance

The 570 engine uses a variable geometry, 13-stage, axial flow compressor with a compression ratio of 12.1:1; the inlet guide vanes and the first five stages of stators are variable. The compressor is directly coupled to a two-stage axial flow turbine and the vanes and blades of both stages are air-cooled. A power turbine drives the output shaft at the front end of the engine through a torque senser assembly located on the engine's centreline. The air foils of the power turbine are solid and do not require air cooling.

The 570 is operated by a full authority electronic control which features automatic starting sequence, speed governing, turbine temperature limiting, vibration sensing etc.

All production 570 engines are fully marinised using materials and coatings selected after more than ¼ million hours of marine experience with Boeing Jetfoils and DD 963 'Spruance' class destroyers.

The 570-K engine incorporates many technological advances and these have resulted in the unit having the lowest specific fuel consumption (sfc) of any turbine in its hp class. At maximum rated power of 7170hp, the engine's sfc is 0.46lb/hph. This low level is maintained over a wide range of output power and speed; at 50 per cent power the sfc increases by only 7 per cent.

The Allison 571, a larger version, designated the model 571-KF, entered production in mid-1985. A three-stage power turbine is used and the unit has a maximum power rating of 8288hp with an sfc of 246kg/kWh (0.405lb/hph). The engine is installed in the Swedish Stockholm Class fast patrol boats, yachts, and is awaiting installation in Canada's DDH-280 Trump destroyer programme as the cruise engine.

570-KF (two-stage) and 571-KF (three-stage) Gas Turbines

| | Maximum | | Continuous | |
	570-KF	571-KF	570-KF	571-KF
Power shp (kW)				
15°C (59°F)	7170 (5347)	8288 (6180)	6445 (4806)	7694 (5738)
26.7°C (80°F)	6610 (4929)	7602 (5669)	5890 (4392)	6908 (5151)
Fuel consumption 15°C (59°F)				
g/kW	282	246	280	249
lb/hph	0.462	0.405	0.46	0.408
Power turbine temperature				
°C	850	835	803	803
°F	1562	1535	1477	1477
Compression ratio	12.1	12.8	11.3	12.3
Corrected airflow				
kg/s	19.4	20.1	18.1	19.6
lb/s	42.8	44.2	40	43.3
Power turbine speed (rpm)	11 500	11 500	11 500	11 500
Weight				
kg	612	733	612	733
lb	1350	1615	1350	1615
Length				
metres	1.83	1.87	1.83	1.87
inches	72	74	72	74

Allison 570-KF

BRIGGS AND STRATTON CORPORATION

PO Box 702, Milwaukee, Wisconsin 53201, USA

Frederick P Stratton Jr, *President and Chief Executive Officer*
Laverne J Socks, *Executive Vice President*
L William Dewey Jr, *Executive Vice President*
George A Senn, *Executive Vice President*
Robert K Catterson, *Vice President, Engineering and Research*
J Byron Smith, *Vice President of Production*
James F Sullivan, *Vice President, Sales*
Michael D Hamilton, *Vice President, International*

Sales Representative and Central Service Distributor for Great Britain and Ireland:
Autocar Electrical Equipment Company Limited, 640 Ripple Road, Barking, Essex IG11 0RU, England

Briggs and Stratton Corporation is a major supplier of small two- and four-stroke petrol engines manufactured in the USA and at the Farymann Diesel factory in West Germany. Uses range from lawn and garden equipment to industrial and agricultural machinery. In accordance with US government regulations, Briggs and Stratton has introduced a range of 'quiet' engines and most recently an electric start system with a brake function to stop the engine when the operator leaves the controls. For industrial and other heavy-use applications, the I/C series was designed for prolonged life, low maintenance and general heavy-duty use.

With over 4.4 million square feet of manufacturing facilities and a new service parts distribution centre, Briggs and Stratton can produce custom-designed engines to more than 50 000 specifications. Central service distributors provide parts and technical training to 25 000 dealers around the world. Briggs and Stratton is one of the largest manufacturers of small engines in the world (more than 140 million since 1953).

Engines offered by Briggs and Stratton Corporation

Series No	Displacement in³/cc	hp	Net weight lb
Four-cycle aluminium alloy engines			
90700	9.02/147.9	3.5	20.75
91700	9.02/147.9	3.5	21.75
92900	9.02/147.9	3.5	19.75
94500	9.02/147.9	3	20.25
94900	9.02/147.9	3.5	20.75
110700	11.39/186.7	4	22
111700	11.39/186.7	4	22.5
110900	11.39/186.77	4	21
114900	11.39/186.7	4	24.75
112200	11.39/186.7	4	25.5
113900	11.39/186.7	4	21.5
130200	12.57/206	5	29.75
132200	12.57/206	5	29.75
130900	12.57/206	5	20.25
132900	12.57/206	5	20.25
132400	12.57/206	5	31.75
170400	16.79/275.1	7	44
171400	16.79/275.1	7	44
190400	19.44/318.5	8	44.5
195400	19.44/318.5	8	44.5
170700	16.79/275.1	7	43
190700	19.44/318.5	8	43.5
191700	19.44/318.5	8	48.5
221430	22.04/361.2	10	62
220700	22.04/361.2	10	55
252410	24.36/399.2	11	63.25
252700	24.36/399.2	11	59.25
253700	24.36/399.2	11	59.25
253410 (non-ducted)	24.36/399.2	11	63.5
253410 (ducted)	24.36/399.2	11	68.5
Four-cycle cast iron engines			
233400	22.94/376.5	9	92
243430	29.94/392.3	10	96
326430	32.40/530.9	16	106.5
Four-cycle twin-cylinder engines			
402707	40/656	16	98.25
402417 (non-ducted)	40/656	16	86.25

Series No	Displacement in³/cc	hp	Net weight lb
Four-cycle twin-cylinder engines (continued)			
402437 (non-ducted)	40/656	16	87.25
402417 (ducted)	40/656	16	99.75
402437 (ducted)	40/656	16	100.75
402707 (ducted)	40/656	16	98.25
422437 (non-ducted)	42.33/694	18	87.25
422437 (ducted)	42.33/694	18	100.75
422707 (ducted)	42.33/694	18	98.25
Twin cylinder			
402417	40/656	16	86.25
402417 (ducted)	40/656	16	99.75
402437	40/656	16	87.25
402437 (ducted)	40/656	16	100.75
402707 (ducted)	40/656	16	98.25
422437	42.33/694	18	87.25
422437 (ducted)	42.33/694	18	100.75
422707 (ducted)	42.33/694	18	98.25
Cast-iron cylinder series			
233400	22.94/376.5	9	92
243430	23.94/392.3	10	96
326430	32.4/530.9	16	106.5
Industrial/commercial series			
Vertical crankshaft			
131922	12.57/206	5	30.25
192700	19.44/319	8	48.5
193700	19.44/319	8	48.5
402707	40/656	16	98.25
422707	42.33/694	18	98.25
Horizontal crankshaft			
81232	7.75/127	3	24.5
131232	12.57/206	5	30
195432	19.44/318.5	8	46.5
221432	22.04/361.3	10	63.25
233431	22.94/376.5	9	92
243431	23.94/392.3	10	96
326431	32.40/530.9	16	106.5
402437	40/656	16	100.75
422437	42.33/694	18	100.75

CATERPILLAR TRACTOR CO INC

Marine Engine Division, 100 North East Adams Street, Peoria, Illinois 61629, USA

This company produces a wide range of high-speed diesel engines some of which have been used recently in various high-speed catamarans, engine types 3516 and 3512 powering the Nichols Bros. InCat *Catalina Flyer* and the Precision Marine *Equator Dream.*

Engine Designation	Power range (bhp)	bhp/cyl	Bore (mm)	Stroke (mm)	Rpm (mcr)	Bmep (kg/cm²)	Length (mm)	Width (mm)	Height (mm)	Wgt (tons)
3208	150–375	37	114	127	2800	10.61	1289(8)	962	1016	.85
3304	85–190	41	121	152	2200	9.78	1469(4)	881	1051	.83
3306	190–335	48	121	152	2200	11.42	1768(6)	933	1099	1.12
3406	250–540	67	137	165	2100	11.93	1878(6)	1092	1315	1.47
3408	402–585	63	137	152	2100	12.14	1692(8)	1230	1389	1.68
3412	503–1000	64	137	152	2100	12.24	2119(2)	1530	1621	2.46
3508	775–1150	125	170	190	1800	14.68	2454(8)	1703	2058	5.22
3512	1175–1750	125	170	190	1800	14.68	2994(12)	1703	2058	6.54
3516	1550–2250	125	170	190	1800	14.68	3540(16)	1703	2058	8.04
3406	275–310	39	137	165	1350	14.38	1878(6)	1092	1315	1.47
3408	318–394	49	121	152	1350	14.79	1692(8)	1230	1389	1.68
3412	425–475	40	121	152	1200	13.36	2119(12)	1530	1621	2.46
3508	600–820	103	170	190	1300	16.62	2454(8)	1703	2058	5.22
3512	900–1255	105	170	190	1300	17.03	2994(12)	1703	2058	6.54
3516	1200–1665	104	170	190	1300	16.93	3540(16)	1703	2058	8.04
3606	1700–2475	413	280	300	1000	20.4	4210(6)	1700	2612	15.6
3608	2250–3330	416	280	300	1000	20.4	5030(8)	1700	2612	19
3612	3400–4950	413	280	300	1000	30.4	4807(12)	1700	2626	22.7
3616	4500–6650	416	280	300	1000	20.4	5727(16)	1700	2626	27.5

Engine Model	D			E		
	kW	hp	rpm	kW	hp	rpm
3406B TA	366	490	2100	403	540	2100
3406 TA	—	—	—	—	—	—
3408B TA	—	—	—	—	—	—
3408B TA	399	535	2100	436	585	2100
3412 TA	—	—	—	—	—	—
3412 T	—	—	—	—	—	—
3508 TA	—	—	—	—	—	—
3412 TA	619	830	2100	641	860	2100
3508 TA	—	—	—	—	—	—
3412 TA	671	900	2100	746	1000	2100
3508 TA	—	—	—	—	—	—
3508 TA	858	1150	1800	—	—	—
3512 TA	—	—	—	—	—	—
3512 TA	—	—	—	—	—	—
3516 TA	—	—	—	—	—	—
3512 TA	—	—	—	—	—	—
3512 TA	1305	1750	1800	—	—	—
3516 TA	—	—	—	—	—	—
3516 TA	—	—	—	—	—	—
3516 TA	1641	2200	1800	—	—	—

D: For use in patrol, customs, police boats, and some fire boats. Also for bow/stern thrusters.

E: For use in pleasure craft with planning hulls, as well as for patrol, pilot ahd harbor master boats.

CUMMINS ENGINE COMPANY INC

Box 3005, Columbus, Indiana 47202–3005, USA

Telephone: (812) 377 5000

David Crompton, *Marine Marketing Manager*

Formed in 1919 in Columbus, Indiana, the Cummins Engine Company produces a wide range of marine diesel engines which are now manufactured and distributed internationally. In addition to manufacturing plants in the United States, the company also produces diesel engines in Brazil, India, Japan, Mexico, China and the United Kingdom. All these plants build engines to the same specifications thus ensuring inter-changeability of parts and the same quality standards. These standards meet design approvals for world-wide agency certification.

VTA-903-M

TYPE: Four-stroke cycle, turbocharged, after-cooled V-8 diesel engine.

AFTERCOOLER: Large capacity aftercooler plumbed for raw water cooling.

BEARINGS: Replaceable, precision type, steel-backed inserts. Five main bearings, 95mm diameter. Connecting rod bearings, 79mm diameter.

CAMSHAFT: Single camshaft precisely controls valve and injector timing. Lobes are induction hardened for long life. Five replaceable precision type bushings, 63mm diameter.

CAMSHAFT FOLLOWERS: Induction hardened, roller type for long cam and follower life.

CONNECTING RODS: Drop forged, I-beam section 208mm centre to centre length. Rifle drilled for pressure lubrication of piston pin. Rod tapered on piston pin end to reduce unit pressures.

COOLING SYSTEMS: Gear-driven centrifugal engine coolant pump. Large volume water passages provide even flow of coolant around cylinder liners, valves, and injectors. Modulating by-pass thermostat regulates coolant temperature. Spin-on corrosion resistor checks rust and corrosion, controls acidity and removes impurities.

CRANKSHAFT: Fully counterweighted and spin balanced high tensile strength steel forging with induction hardened fillets.

CYLINDER BLOCK: Alloy cast iron with removable wet liners. Cross bolt support to main bearing cap provides extra strength and stability.

CYLINDER HEADS: Alloy cast iron. Each head serves four cylinders. Drilled fuel supply and return lines. Valve seats are replaceable corrosion-

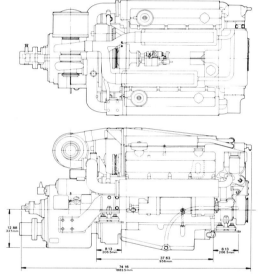

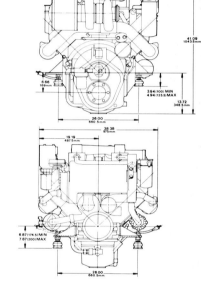

Cummins VTA-903-M turbocharged diesel engine

resistant inserts. Valve guides and cross head guides are replaceable inserts.

CYLINDER LINERS: Replaceable wet liners dissipate heat faster than dry liners and are easily replaced without reboring the block.

FUEL SYSTEM: Low pressure system with wear compensating pump and integral dual flyweight governor. Camshaft actuated fuel injectors give accurate metering and precise timing. Fuel lines are internal drilled passages in cylinder heads. Spin-on fuel filter.

GEAR TRAIN: Timing gears and accessory drive gears are induction hardened. Spur gears driven from crankshaft and located at rear of block.

LUBRICATION: Large capacity gear pump provides pressure lubrication to all bearings. Oil cooler and full-flow filters maintain oil condition and maximise oil and engine life.

PISTONS: Aluminium alloy, cam ground and barrel-shaped to compensate for thermal expansion, ensures precise fit at operating temperatures. One oil and two compression rings.

PISTON PINS: Full floating, tubular steel retained by snap rings, 44mm diameter.

TURBOCHARGER: Exhaust gas-driven turbocharger mounted at rear of engine. Turbocharging provides more power, improved fuel economy,

and lower smoke and noise levels.

VALVES: Dual 48mm diameter poppet-type intake and exhaust valves. Wear resistant face on exhaust valves.

POWER RATINGS

High output: 336kW

Rated rpm: 2600

Medium continuous: 283kW

Rated rpm: 2600

Continuous duty: 239kW

Rated rpm: 2300

Bore and stroke: 140 × 121mm

Displacement: 14.8 litres

Oil pan capacity: 19 litres

Net weight, dry*: 1660kg

*With selected accessories and Capitol HY-22000 marine gear.

6BT5.9-M

This engine is now replacing the VT-555-M type. Its compact size provides for ease of installation and easy access for routine maintenance. Fewer parts enables less inventory, faster maintenance and repair, and enables engines to be serviced and repaired with ordinary hand tools.

TYPE: Four-stroke cycle, turbocharged, direct injection, in-line, 6-cylinder diesel engine.

SKIRTED BLOCK: Cast iron with main bearing supports between each cylinder, for maximum strength and rigidity, low weight and optimum crankshaft support.
FUEL INJECTION SYSTEM: Direct, with high swirl intake ports for thorough mixing of air and fuel to provide low fuel consumption.
CRANKSHAFT: Forged steel with integral counterweights, allowing high power output from a compact size.
CONNECTING RODS: Forged steel, I-beam cross section, with angle split cap-to-rod interface and capscrew attachment for maximum structural strength and ease of service.
CAMSHAFT: Side-mounted gear drive for low engine height and minimum maintenance.
ALTERNATOR AND WATER PUMP DRIVE: Single-belt with self-tensioning idler for minimum belt maintenance.
CYLINDER HEAD: Single piece cross flow for short length and maximum structural stiffness of the block/head assembly and for fewer head gasket problems.
VALVES PER CYLINDER: Two with single valve springs for fewer parts.
TURBOCHARGER: Water-cooled exhaust manifold and water-cooled turbocharger can be configured for top-out or rear-out exhaust for added flexibility.
POWER RATINGS
High output: 157kW
Rated rpm: 2600
Medium continuous: 134kW
Rated rpm: 2500
Bore and stroke: 102 × 120mm
Displacement: 5.9 litres
Oil pan capacity: 14.2 litres
Net weight, dry: 579kg*
*Heat-exchanger-cooled and MG-502 marine gear.

6BTA5.9-M
As for 6BT5.9-M except:
TYPE: Four-stroke cycle, turbocharged, after-cooled, direct injection, in-line, 6-cylinder diesel engine.

JACKET WATER AFTERCOOLER: Mounted on top of intake manifold.
TURBOCHARGER: Water-cooled exhaust manifold and water-cooled turbocharger, configured for rear-out exhaust for lower profile.
POWER RATINGS
High output: 186kW (250bhp)
Rated rpm: 2600
Medium continuous: 164kW (220bhp)
Rated rpm: 2500
Bore and stroke: 102 × 120mm
Displacement: 5.9 litres
Oil pan capacity: 14.2 litres
Net weight, dry: 613kg*
*Heat-exchanger-cooled and MG-506A marine gear.

KTA19-M
TYPE: Four-stroke cycle, turbocharged, after-cooled diesel.
AFTERCOOLER: Large capacity aftercooler results in cooler, denser intake air for more efficient combustion and reduced internal stresses for longer life. Aftercooler is located in engine coolant system, eliminating need for special plumbing.
BEARINGS: Replaceable, precision type, steel backed inserts. Seven main bearings, 140mm in diameter. Connecting rod bearings 102mm in diameter.
CAMSHAFT: Single camshaft precisely controls valve and injector timing. Lobes are induction hardened for long life. Seven replaceable precision type bushings 76mm in diameter.
CAMSHAFT FOLLOWERS: Induction hardened, roller type for long cam and follower life.
CONNECTING RODS: Drop forged, I-beam section 290mm centre to centre length. Rifle drilled for pressure lubrication of piston pin. Rod is tapered on piston pin end to reduce unit pressures.
COOLING SYSTEM: Gear driven centrifugal pump. Large volume water passages provide even flow of coolant around cylinder liners, valves and injectors. Modulating by-pass thermostats regulate coolant temperature. Spin-on corrosion

resistor checks rust and corrosion, controls acidity and removes impurities.
CRANKSHAFT: High tensile strength steel forging with induction hardened fillets and journals. Fully counterweighted and dynamically balanced.
CYLINDER BLOCK: Alloy cast iron with removable wet liners. Cross bolt support to main bearing cap provides extra strength and stability.
CYLINDER HEADS: Alloy cast iron. Each head serves one cylinder. Drilled fuel supply and return lines. Valve seats are replaceable corrosion resistant inserts. Valve guides and cross head guides are replaceable inserts.
CYLINDER LINERS: Replaceable wet liners dissipate heat faster than dry liners and are easily replaced without reboring the block.
FUEL SYSTEM: Cummins PT self-adjusting system. Integral dual flyweight governor provides overspeed protection independent of main engine governor. Camshaft actuated fuel injectors give accurate metering and timing. Fuel lines are internal drilled passages in cylinder heads. Spin-on fuel filters.
GEAR TRAIN: Timing gears and accessory drive gears are induction hardened helical gears driven from crankshaft and located at front of block.
LUBRICATION: Large capacity gear pump provides pressure lubrication to all bearings and oil supply for piston cooling. All pressure lines are internal drilled passages in block and heads. Oil cooler, full-flow filters and by-pass filters maintain oil condition and maximise oil and engine life.
PISTONS: Aluminium alloy, cam ground and barrel shaped to compensate for thermal expansion assures precise fit at operating temperatures. CeCorr grooved skirt finish provides superior lubrication. Oil cooled for rapid heat dissipation. Two compression and one oil ring.
PISTON PINS: Full floating, tubular steel retained by snap rings, 61mm in diameter.
TURBOCHARGER: AiResearch exhaust gas driven turbocharger mounted on right side of engine. Turbocharging provides more power, improved fuel economy, altitude compensation, and lower smoke and noise levels.

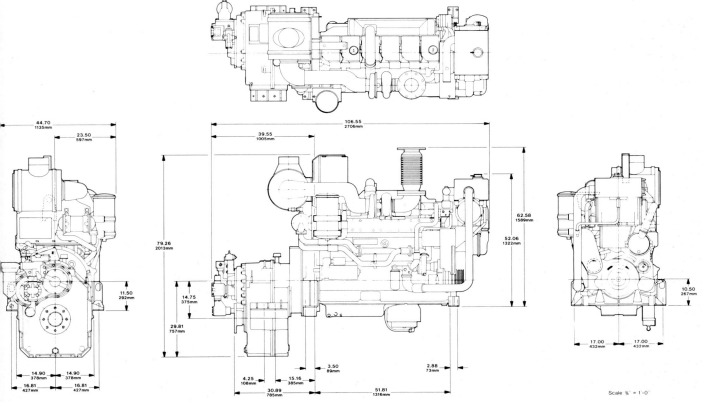

Cummins KTA19-M turbocharged after-cooled diesel engine

VALVES: Dual 56mm diameter poppet type intake and exhaust valves. Wear resistant face on exhaust valves.

POWER RATINGS
Continuous duty: 373kW

Rated rpm: 1800
Intermittent duty: 507.3kW
Rated rpm: 2100
Bore and stroke: 159 × 159mm
Displacement: 19 litres

Oil pan capacity: 38 litres
Net weight, dry: 3084kg*
*Heat-exchanger-cooled and MG-502 marine gear.

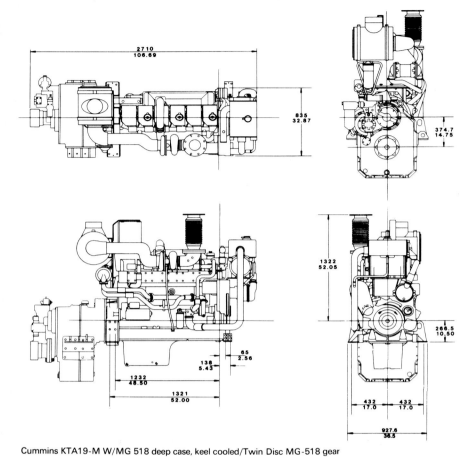
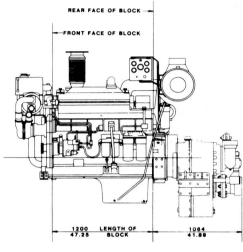

Cummins KTA19-M W/MG 518 deep case, keel cooled/Twin Disc MG-518 gear

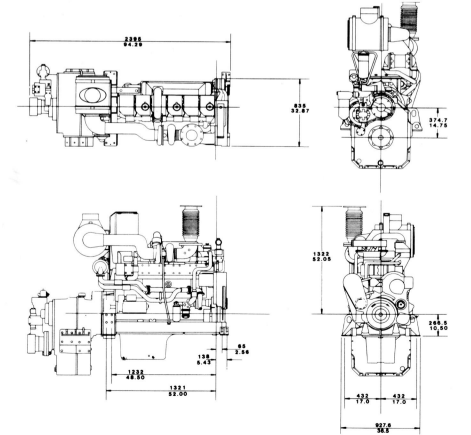
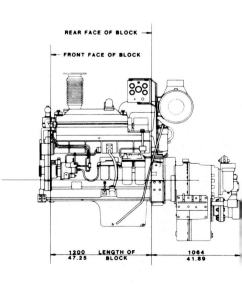

Cummins KTA19-M W/MG 518 deep case, heat-exchanger cooled/Twin Disc MG-518 gear

CUYUNA ENGINE COMPANY

1st Street SW, PO Box 116, Crosby, Minnesota
56441, USA

Telephone: (218) 546 8313
Telex: 757996CUYUNA ENG UD

Roger P Worth, *President*

The company manufactures a range of axial-fan-cooled single- and twin-cylinder engines, developing 20 to 40hp.

The engines are serviced through a network of 2000 independent service outlets and central distributors throughout the USA and Canada.

CUYUNA AXIAL-FAN SINGLE- AND TWIN-CYLINDER ENGINES

Models 215, 340 and 440

Features of this range include a standard mounting for all models to ease installation; low engine profile with built-in shrouding; lightweight

Cuyuna Model 250LC 214cc 25hp liquid-cooled marine engine

Cuyuna Model 430LC 428cc 40hp liquid-cooled marine engine

Cuyuna Model 500LC 428cc 50hp liquid-cooled marine engine

Single- and Twin-cylinder Axial-fan-cooled Engines

Model	215	340	440
Bore	67.51mm (2.658in)	60.00mm (2.362in)	67.51mm (2.658in)
Stroke	60.00mm (2.362in)	60.00mm (2.362in)	60.00mm (2.362in)
Displacement	214cc	339cc	428cc
Compression ratio	12.5 : 1		
Brake hp/rpm	20hp	32hp	40hp
	6500/7000rpm	6500/7000rpm	6500/7000rpm
Base mounting hole thread	$\frac{7}{16}$-14 UNC		
Cylinder	Aluminium with cast iron sleeve		
Connecting rod bearing upper	Needle		
Connecting rod bearing lower	Needle		
Connecting rod material	Forged steel		
Main bearings	2 heavy duty ball bearings (double row, PTO end)		
Lighting coil	12V, 150W		
Ignition setting before TDC	0.102in to 0.112in (cam fully advanced)		
Spark plug thread	14 × 1.25mm (0.75in) reach		
Gap	0.016in to 0.02in		
Type	Champion N-3		
Rotation	Counter-clockwise viewed from PTO end		
Fuel-oil mixture	40:1 (1 pint to 5 gallons)		
Lubrication	Premium Gasoline & Cuyuna 2 Cycle Engine Oil		
Starter	Rewind type, standard; electric, optional		
Rope material	Nylon		
Weight	86kg	137kg	137kg

Single- and Twin-cylinder Liquid-cooled Marine Engines

Model	250LC	430LC	500LC
Type	Single-cylinder	Twin-cylinder	Twin-cylinder
Bore	67.50mm (2.658in)		
Stroke	60.00mm (2.362in)		
Displacement	214cc (13in³)	428cc (26.10in³)	
Brake hp/rpm	25hp	40hp	50hp
	6500rpm	6250rpm	6500rpm
Power take-off shaft	30mm dia-10:1 Taper-$\frac{1}{2}$-20UNF		
Base mounting hole thread	4-$\frac{7}{16}$-14 UNC		
Cylinder	Aluminium with cast iron sleeve		
Connecting rod bearings	Needle		
Connecting rod and crankshaft material	forged steel		
Main bearings	Heavy duty ball bearings (double row, PTO end)		
Number of main bearings	4		
Ignition	Capacitor discharge (CDI)		
Alternator	12V, 150W ac output		
Carburettor	Downdraft with USCG approved flame arrestor		
Exhaust	Liquid-cooled manifold, elbow and tuning chamber		
Spark plug	Champion N3C or NGK BR8ES		
Cooling	Liquid-external supply		
Rotation	Counter-clockwise viewed from PTO end		
Fuel-oil mixture	40:1 (1 pint to 5 gallons)		
Starter	Electric		
Weight	28 to 30.87kg		

Horsepower ratings established in accordance with specifications SAE-J607.

construction to reduce overall vehicle weight and high interchangeability of all parts. Crankshafts, crankcases, blower assemblies, magnetos, recoil starters and hardware items are fully interchangeable, thus reducing spare parts inventory requirements and lowering maintenance costs. Specifications for the six standard productions are given in the accompanying table. Models 250LC, 430LC and 500LC are the marine engines.

Cuyuna engines can be fitted with the Nova Gear Mate reduction drive, and it is claimed that the drive is more efficient than belt drives. It also allows unrestricted airflows through the engine. Gear ratios are from 2.04:1 to 3.06:1. The unit can be ordered with an electric start, or an electric start can be added to an existing recoil start engine.

Users of Cuyuna air cooled engines with gearboxes are: Scat Hovercraft Inc, Miami, Florida; Hovercraft International, Inc, Atlanta, Georgia; Air Fun Inc, Clint, Texas; British American Hovercraft, Lake Elsinore, CA

Cuyana air cooled engine fitted with Nova Gear Mate reduction drive

DETROIT DIESEL CORPORATION

13400 Outer Drive West, Detroit, Michigan 48239–4001, USA
Telephone: (313) 592 5000
Telex: 4320091

A A Kozel, *Vice President, Marine Sales*

Detroit Diesel Corporation (formerly Detroit Diesel Allison Division of General Motors) is a joint venture company formed 1 January 1988 between General Motors Corporation and Penske Corporation. The new company is headquartered in Detroit, Michigan and has the design, manufacturing and sales responsibilities for all heavy-duty diesel engine activities formerly handled by Detroit Diesel Allison Division. In addition,

Detroit Diesel Corporation handles certain sales and service activities for the medium-duty diesel engine business which was retained by General Motors.

A range of marine diesel engines is available ranging in maximum shp from 240 to 2135. The following table gives the maximum marine ratings for these engines:

MODEL	MAXIMUM kW(bhp) @ rpm	kW(shp) @ rpm	LENGTH (mm)	WIDTH (mm)	HEIGHT (mm)	WEIGHT kg w/Marine Gear
8.2T	187(250) @ 3200	179(240) @ 3200	1245	802	802	798
6–71TI	362(485) @ 2500	351(470) @ 2500	1676	838	1118	1304
6V-53TI	298(400) @ 2800	285(382) @ 2800	1361	909	1097	1055
6V-92TA	410(550) @ 2300	399(535) @ 2300	1651	1041	1143	1500
8V-92TA	548(735) @ 2300	537(720) @ 2300	1753	1219	1245	1935
12V-71TA	671(900) @ 2300	649(870) @ 2300	2154	1263	1330	2458
12V-92TA	806(1080) @ 2300	776(1040) @ 2300	2337	1219	1295	2790
16V-92TA	1044(1400) @ 2300	1007(1350) @ 2300	2758	1247	1336	3538
16V-149TI	1641(2200) @ 2100	1593(2135) @ 2100	3727	1563	2135	6982

These ratings are applicable to installations in pleasure craft, fast patrol craft and fast ferries.

The most powerful engines are in the 16V-149 series (2135shp max).

The DDC range of high-speed diesel engines

Basic Engine	16V-149	16V-149T	16V-149TI
Model:	9162–7000	9162–7300	9162–7301
Description:	naturally aspirated	turbocharged	turbocharged inter-cooled
Number of cylinders:	16	16	16
Bore and stroke:	146 × 146mm	146 × 146mm	146 × 146mm
Displacement:	39.18 litres	39.18 litres	39.18 litres
Compression ratio:	17 : 1	16 : 1	16 : 1
Net weight (dry):	7258kg	5330kg*	5421kg*
Continuous,			
injectors:	120	140	140
rated gross power:	694kW at 1800rpm†	907kW at 1800rpm†	955kW at 1800rpm†
rated net power:	671kW at 1800rpm†	877kW at 1800rpm†	927kW at 1800rpm†
Intermittent,			
injectors:	130	140	150
rated gross power:	791kW at 1900rpm†	940kW at 1900rpm†	1130kW at 1900rpm†
rated net power:	765kW at 1900rpm†	910kW at 1900rpm†	1094kW at 1900rpm†
Max,			
injectors:	130	145	190
rated gross power:	791kW at 1900rpm†	1033kW at 1900rpm†	‡1343kW at 1900rpm†
rated net power:	765kW at 1900rpm†	1000kW at 1900rpm†	1302kW at 1900rpm†

* Weights shown are without marine gear
† Rating conditions of SAE: 77°F (25°C) air inlet temperature and 29.31 in Hg (99 kPa) Barometer (Dry)
‡ Preliminary data

Model 9162-7000   **16V-149**

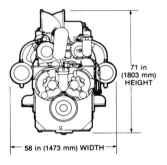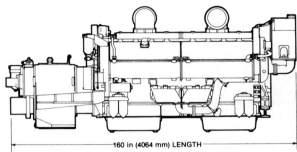

Model 9162-7300   **16V-149T**

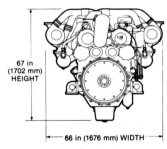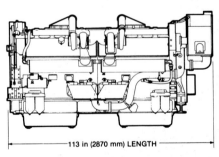

Model 9162-7301   **16V-149TI**

Principal dimensions of DDC 16V-149, 149T & 149TI series engines

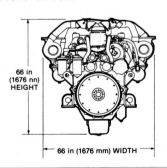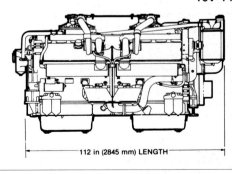

GENERAL ELECTRIC COMPANY
G E Aircraft Engines

1 Neumann Way, PO Box 156301, Mail Drop N87, Cincinnati (Evendale), Ohio 45215–6301, USA

Telephone: (513) 243 2000

Brian H Rowe, *Senior Vice President and Group Executive*

T R Boehm, *Vice President – Business Planning & Legal Operation*

General Electric Company's Dr Sanford A Moss operated the first gas turbine in the United States in 1903 and produced the aircraft turbo-supercharger, first flown in 1919 and mass-produced in the Second World War for US fighters and bombers.

The company built its first aircraft gas turbine in 1941, when it began development of a Whittle-type turbojet, under an arrangement between the British and American governments.

Since then General Electric has produced over 82 000 aircraft gas turbines for military and commercial aircraft, as well as aircraft derivative gas turbines for marine and industrial uses.

Six General Electric gas turbines have been marinised: the LM1500, the LM2500, the LM100, the LM500, the LM1600 and the LM5000. The LM2500 has been specified to power 33 classes of ships in 20 navies; the LM500 has been specified for the Danish Navy Stanflex 300 fast multi-mission patrol craft. In the 1960s 17 LM100 turbines powered Bell Aerosystems SK-5 hovercraft used by the US Navy, US Army and Oakland Port Authority.

LM2500

The LM2500 marine gas turbine is a two-shaft, simple-cycle, high-efficiency engine derived from the General Electric military TF39 and the commercial CF6 high by-pass turbofan engines for the US Air Force C-5 Galaxy transport and DC-10, 747 and A300 commercial jets. The compressor, combuster and turbine are designed to give maximum progression in reliability, parts life and time between overhaul. The engine has a simple-cycle efficiency of more than 36 per cent, which is due to advanced cycle pressures, temperatures and component efficiencies.

The LM2500 marine gas turbine provides foil-borne power for the US Navy PHM hydrofoils. The six PHM 'Pegasus' class vessels were built by the Boeing Company, Seattle, Washington. In addition to the Pegasus hydrofoils, GE LM2500 marine gas turbines propel over 260 ships. These ships include the Perry class FFG-7 frigates, Spruance class DD-963 destroyers, Kidd class DDG-993 destroyers, Ticonderoga class Aegis CG-47 cruisers, Burke class DDG-51 Aegis destroyers and the supply class AOE-6 auxiliary ships of the US navy.

In combination with diesels the LM2500 powers several classes of high speed patrol boats with top speeds of more than 40 knots. LM2500 diesel combinations also provide propulsive power for a broad cross section of vessels for 17 navies throughout the world, including aircraft carriers, cruisers, destroyers, frigates and corvettes.

Total operating time of LM2500 engines in all marine service is more than three million hours.
TYPE: Two-shaft, axial flow, simple cycle.
AIR INTAKE: Axial, inlet bellmouth or duct can be customised to installation.
COMBUSTION CHAMBER: Annular.

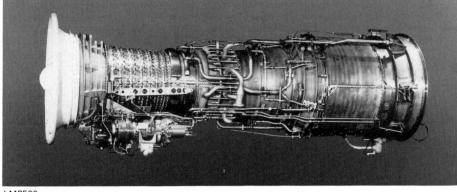

LM2500

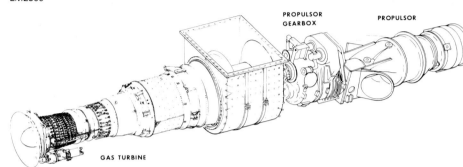

LM2500 installation aboard PHM 'Pegasus' class hydrofoil

FUEL GRADE: Kerosene, JP4, JP5, diesel, distillate fuels and natural gas.
TURBINE: Two-stage gas generator, six-stage power.
JET PIPE: Vertical or customised to fit installation.
OIL SPECIFICATION: Synthetic Turbine Oil (MIL-L-23699) or equal.
MOUNTING: At power turbine and compressor front frame.

STARTING: Pneumatic, hydraulic.
DIMENSIONS
Length: 6530mm
Width: 2240mm
PERFORMANCE RATINGS: 32 000bhp at 15°C at sea level
SPECIFIC FUEL CONSUMPTION: 0.171kg

TEXTRON LYCOMING
Stratford Division, Textron Lycoming, subsidiary of Textron Inc
550 Main Street, Stratford, Connecticut 06497, USA

Telephone: (203) 385 2000
Telex: 964242

John R Myers, *Vice President and General Manager, Lycoming Division*
Richard Ainsworth, *Vice President, Engineering*

Textron Lycoming, Stratford, is the turbine engine manufacturing subsidiary of Textron.

Textron Lycoming manufactures a wide range of gas turbine engines for helicopters, commuter jets, tanks and tracked vehicles, as well as for marine and industrial applications. The Marine versions of the large turboshaft and turbofan T55 family is designated the TF40.

TF40 and TF40B

The TF40 engine is a scaled-up TF25 with higher mass flow and a four-stage turbine section.

Both the JEFF(A) (Aerojet-General) and JEFF(B) (Textron Marine Systems) AALCs employed earlier model TF40s. JEFF(A) employed six, each developing 3350shp continuous. Four drive individual, steerable ducted propellers, and the remaining two drive separate centrifugal lift fans. In the case of JEFF(B), the six engines are arranged in two groups of three, located port and starboard. Each trio drives a single propeller and lift system through integrated gears.

An uprated version, the TF40B, is in production and provides the lift and propulsive power for the

TF25

US Navy's Landing Craft, Air Cushion (LCAC) built by Textron Marine Systems. The machinery arrangement is similar to that of JEFF(B) apart from the use of four engines instead of six.

AIR INTAKE: Side inlet casting of aluminium alloy housing internal gearing and supporting power producer section and output drive shaft. Integral or separately mounted gears are optional.

Provision for intake filters and/or silencers. Integral water-wash nozzles are provided.

COMPRESSOR: Seven axial stages followed by a single centrifugal stage. Two-piece aluminium alloy stator casing, with seven rows of steel stator blades bolted to steel alloy casing diffuser, to which combustion chamber casing is attached. Rotor comprises seven stainless steel discs and one titanium impeller mounted on shaft supported in forward thrust ball bearing and rear roller bearing. TF40 pressure ratio is 8.4:1.

COMBUSTION CHAMBER: Annular reverse flow type. Steel outer shell and inner liner. Twenty-eight fuel nozzles with downstream injection.

FUEL SYSTEM: Woodward fuel control system. Gear-type fuel pump, with gas producer and power shaft governors, flow control and shut-off valve.

FUEL GRADE: MIL-T-5624, JP-4, JP-5; MIL-F-16884 diesel, standard and wide-cut kerosene.

TURBINE: Two mechanically-independent axial-flow turbines. First turbine, with two stages, drives compressor. It has cored-out cast blades and is flange-bolted to outer coaxial drive shaft. Second two-stage turbine drives output shaft. It has solid blades and is mounted on inner coaxial drive shaft. (Other features include: integral cast cooled first turbine nozzle, cooled turbine blades in both first and second stages, second turbine vane cooling, and second turbine disc and blade cooling.)

EXHAUST UNIT: Fixed area nozzle, with inner cone, supported by six radial struts.

ACCESSORIES: Electric, air or hydraulic starter. High-energy ignition unit; four igniter plugs.

LUBRICATION: Recirculating type. Integral oil tank and cooler.

OIL GRADE: Synthetic base oils.

Cutaway of TF40 marine/industrial gas turbine rated at 2983 kW(4000shp) continuous,3430 kW(4600shp) 'boost' power

WEIGHT: 600kg
DIMENSIONS
Length: 1.32m
Width: 0.88m
Height: 1.11m
PERFORMANCE RATINGS
Max intermittent (at 15°C sea level): 4600shp
Max continuous (at 15°C sea level): 4000shp

FUEL CONSUMPTION
At max continuous rating: 0.54sfc 255 US gallons/h
OIL CONSUMPTION: 0.5pint/h

UNITED TECHNOLOGIES INTERNATIONAL INC
Turbo Power and Marine Systems Inc (TPM)

308 Farmington Avenue, Farmington, Connecticut 06032, USA

Telephone: (203) 678 9000
Telex: 221432TPM UTC

F L Bruno, *General Manager and Chief Operating Officer*
W H Day, *Director Industrial Gas Turbine Programmes*
R L Wheeler, *Director, Marketing/Sales*

United Technologies Power Systems Division (Turbo Power and Marine Systems Inc) designs and builds industrial and marine gas turbine powerplants and related systems employing the FT4 Modular Industrial Turbine. It also provides a systems support for each of its installations.

Canadian sales of the FT4 are handled by Pratt & Whitney Canada (qv) which also manufactures and sells the ST6 marine gas turbine.

Turbo Power and Marine efforts have resulted in over 1200 Modular Industrial Turbines supplied or on order in the USA and in 28 other countries. The turbines will supply more than 35 million hp for electric power generation, gas transmission and industrial drives as well as for marine propulsion.

FT4 MARINE GAS TURBINES

UTI's FT4 marine gas turbines were first used for boost power in military vessels, including two Royal Danish Navy frigates, 12 US Coast Guard 'Hamilton' class high endurance cutters and four Canadian Armed Forces DDH-280 'Iroquois' class destroyers. Another boost power application of the FT4 is in the Fast Escort and ASW vessel *Bras d'Or* also built for the Canadian Armed

Production model of FT4 with 38 600shp base load

Forces. Another application is for two new 12 000-ton Arctic icebreakers for the US Coast Guard. With three FT4 marine gas turbines, these vessels are capable of maintaining a continuous speed of 3 knots through ice 1.8m thick, and are able to ram through ice 6.4m thick.

UTI's marine gas turbines are used for both the main and boost propulsion in the four Canadian DDH-280 destroyers. These are the first military combatant vessels to be designed for complete reliance on gas turbine power.

FT4 gas turbines were also used initially as the main propulsion unit in the *Finnjet*, a high-speed Finnlines passenger liner which cut the Baltic crossing time in half, routinely maintaining 30 knots,with an engine availability of over 99 percent.

FT4 POWER PAC

Each FT4 Power Pac is built upon a rigid mounting frame and includes a housing and gas turbine mounting system, together with controls, accessory equipment, wiring and piping. A remote control system is also provided. Installation is simple. Since all the equipment is pre-tested at the factory before shipment, time required for checkout after installation is minimised.

The gas generator portion of the gas turbine is easily removed for servicing. With a spare gas generator to replace the one removed for servicing, the ship's powerplant can be changed in a matter of hours.

The FT4 gas turbine comprises the gas generator and the power (free) turbine. The independent power turbine accepts the kinetic energy of the gas generator and converts it to mechanical energy through a shaft which extends through the exhaust duct elbow.

GAS GENERATOR

TYPE: Simple-cycle two-spool turbine. A low pressure compressor is driven by a two-stage turbine and a high pressure compressor is driven by a single turbine. The burner section has eight burner cans which are equipped with duplex fuel nozzles.

AIR INTAKE: Cast steel casing with 18 radial struts supporting the front compressor bearing and equipped with a bleed air anti-icing system.

LOW PRESSURE COMPRESSOR: Nine-stage axial flow on inner of two concentric shafts driven by two-stage turbine and supported on ball and roller bearings.

HIGH PRESSURE COMPRESSOR: Seven-stage axial flow on outer hollow shaft driven by single-stage turbine and running on ball and roller bearings.

COMBUSTION CHAMBER: Eight burner cans located in an annular arrangement and enclosed in a one piece steel casing. Each burner has six duplex fuel nozzles.

TURBINES: Steel casing with hollow guide vanes. Turbine wheels are bolted to the compressor shafts and are supported on ball and roller bearings. A single-stage turbine drives the high compressor and a two-stage turbine drives the low compressor.

POWER TURBINE: The gas turbine is available with either clockwise or counter-clockwise rotation of the power turbine. Desired direction of rotation specified by customer. Power turbine housing is bolted to gas generator turbine housing. The three-stage turbine shaft assembly is straddle mounted and supported on ball and roller bearings. The output shaft is bolted to the hub of the power turbine rotor and extends through the exhaust duct.

BEARINGS: Anti-friction ball and roller bearings.

ACCESSORY DRIVE: Starter, fluid power pump, tachometer drives for low compressor, high compressor and free turbine.

LUBRICATION SYSTEM: Return system and scavenge pumps with internal pressure, 3.09kg/cm².

LUBRICATING OIL SPECIFICATIONS: Type 2 synthetic lube oil PWA-521.

MARINE APPLICATIONS: Meets installation, high shock and ships seaway motion requirements.

STARTING: Pneumatic or hydraulic.

DIMENSIONS
Length: 8788mm
Width: 2438mm
Height: 2794mm

FUEL SPECIFICATIONS
Light Distillate (Naptha): PWA-532(1)
Aviation Grade Kerosene: PWA-522(1)
Marine Diesel: PWA-527(1)
Heavy Distillate: PWA-539
(1) Covered by TPM-FR-1 for series engine
Treated crude and residual oil refer to manufacturer.

FT8 MARINE GAS TURBINE

United Technologies have recently introduced a new model, the FT8 marine gas turbine based on their JT8D aircraft engine, which will be available in 1990. The nominal 24609kW, 33000hp (33462 metric hp) size of the FT8 is expected to fit naval applications.

Derived from the Pratt and Whitney JT8D aircraft engine and the TPM FT4 industrial gas

UTI/PSD marine power pac with FT4 modular industrial turbine

FT4C-3F gas turbine

turbine, the FT8 has been launched with a collaboration programme between TPM and the China National Aerotechnology Import-Export Corporation (CATIC) of the People's Republic of China. Under this agreement, CATIC, which comes under the Ministry of Aviation and is responsible for China's domestic and international sales of the FT8, including marine engines, will purchase 30 FT8 gas turbines over a 10-year period and will produce some parts of the gas generator, the complete power turbine and some of the package components for the worldwide market.

The first gas generator will undergo testing at Pratt and Whitney's Willgoos Laboratories at the beginning of 1989. The first FT8 production unit is to be tested in 1990.

References: FT8: A High Performance Industrial and Marine Gas Turbine Derived from the JT8D Aircraft Engine, by William H Day, ASME Paper No 87-GT-242 presented at the Gas Turbine Conference and Exhibition, Anaheim, California, 31 May-4 June 1987.

FT8 production units to be available 1990 for utility and industrial use, by Victor de Biasi, Sas Turbine World, May-June 1988.

PERFORMANCE DATA: FT4 MARINE GAS TURBINE

Rating	Power Output *(1)*	Specific Fuel Consumption *(2)*
Max intermittent	36 018kW (48 300shp)	264g/kWh (0.435lb/hph)
Max continuous	32 662kW (43 800shp)	268g/kWh (0.440lb/hph)
Normal	28 784kW (38 600shp)	274g/kWh (0.450lb/hph)

(1) all ratings at 3600rpm shaft speed, 15°C (59°F) at sea level
(2) Based on fuel with LHV of 18 500 Btu/lb

SUMMARY OF PROPULSION ENGINE APPLICATIONS IN HIGH-SPEED CRAFT

ALH	Air-lubricated-hull craft
CAT	Catamaran
HOV	Amphibious hovercraft
HYD	Hydrofoil
MH	Mono-hull
SES	Surface-effect ship/sidewall hovercraft
SWATH	Small-waterplane-area twin-hull
WIGE	Wing-in-ground-effect craft

Engine manufacturer, engine principal designation, craft builder	Craft	Engine secondary designation	Craft name	Craft type
ALLISON GAS TURBINE DIVISION				
General Motor Corporation				
501-K				
Israel Shipyards Ltd	M161	F	—	HYD
Boeing Aerospace Company	Jetfoil 929–100	20A	—	HYD
Boeing Aerospace Company	Jetfoil 929–115	—	—	HYD
Boeing Aerospace Company	Jetfoil 929–115 Patrol	20A	—	HYD
570-KA				
F R Lürssen Werft (GmbH & Co)	46.60m yacht	—	—	MH
Bazan/CHACONSA	BES-50	KF	—	SEA
MOTEURS BAUDOUIN				
12 F 11 SRM				
International Catamarans Pty Ltd	20m	—	—	CAT
12 P 15.2 SR7				
Société Bretonne de Construction Navale (SBCN)	38m Patrol boat	—	—	MH
CATERPILLAR TRACTOR COMPANY, ENGINE DIVISION				
3208				
Jones Kirwan & Associates	Air Trek 140	—	—	HOV
Tjetty Marine	—	TA	*Jalesveva*	MH
3408				
RMI Inc	SD-60	DITA	*Halcyon*	SWATH
3412				
International Catamarans Pty Ltd	22m	TA	*Klondike*	CAT
CHINA, PEOPLE'S REPUBLIC				
12V 150 C				
	Type 717			
12150 CZ				
China Dagu Shipyard	Type 7203	—	—	SES
12180				
China Wuhu Shipyard	Type 719	—	—	SES
M50				
Hutang Shipyard	—	—	—	HYD
CRM MOTORI MARINI SpA				
CRM 18 D/SS-BR-1				
Azimut SpA	27m	—	*Atlantic Challenger*	MH
CUMMINS ENGINE COMPANY INC				
KTA-50-M (16 cylinder)				
Gulf Craft Inc		—	*Paula McCall*	MH
V-555-M (8 cylinder)				
Vosper Hovermarine	HM 216	—	—	SES
VT-8–370				
Helmut Kock		—	*Bolivia Arrow*	HYD
DETROIT DIESEL CORPORATION				
Division of General Motors				
6V-92				
Hovermarine Ltd	HM 221	TI	—	SES
Cheoy Lee	Air Ride 82	TA	—	ALH
8V-71				
Shinju Shipbuilding Co	—	N	*Kariushu*	MH
8V-92				
Vosper Hovermarine	HM 221	MTI	—	SES
Bell Halter	Model 720A	N	*Rodolph*	SES
Bell Halter	Model 212B	—		SES
International Catamarans Pty Ltd	20m	TI	—	
International Catamarans Pty Ltd	18m	TI	—	CAT
International Catamarans Pty Ltd	18m	TA	—	
Tjetty Marine	—		*Bima Express*	MH
Azimut SpA	AZ60	TI	—	MH
Vosper Hovermarine	HM 218	TI	—	SES
Boeing Aerospace Company	Jetfoil 929–320	TI	—	HYD

Engine manufacturer, engine principal designation, craft builder	Craft	Engine secondary designation	Craft name	Craft type
12V-71				
Korea Tacoma Marine Industries Ltd	21m	TI	—	SES
Chantiers Navals de l'Esterel SA	Esterel 26	TI	—	MH
Fairey Marinteknik (UK) Ltd	Tracker	TI	—	MH
Aluminium Boats Inc	Hargrave 23.78m	TI	*The Hope*	MH
Halter Marine Inc	Halmar 65	TI	—	MH
Halter Marine Inc	Halmar 101	TI	—	MH
Halter Marine Inc	Halmar 112	TI	—	MH
Halter Marine Inc	Halmar 122	TI	—	MH
12V-92 (with 145 type injection)				
Westport Shipyard Inc	Westfoil 80	TA	—	HYD
NQEA International Catamarans Pty Ltd	28m, 23m, 22m InCat	TA	*Spirit ofVictoria/ Spirit of Alderbrook*	CAT
SBF Engineering	—	—	*James Kelly II*	MH
Shinju Shipbuilding Co	—	TI	*Tropical Queen*	MH
Shinju Shipbuilding Co	—	TI	*Shimabara*	MH
Halter Marine Inc	Halmar 115	MTI	—	MH
Halter Marine Inc	—	—	*Sportsfisher*	SES
Precision Marine Holdings Pty Ltd	33m	TA	*Motive Explorer*	CAT
International Catamarans Pty Ltd	23m	—	—	CAT
Miwon Trading & Shipping Co Ltd	28m	—	—	MH
International Catamarans Pty Ltd	20m	TA	—	CAT
Cheoy Lee	Air Ride 82	TA	—	ALH
16V-92				
NQEA	InCat 28m/29m	TA	—	
NQEA	InCat 24m	TI	—	
Breaux's Bay Craft Inc	—	—	*Agathe*	MH
Magnum Marine Corp	Magnum 63	TI	—	MH
International Catamarans Pty Ltd	28m	TA	—	CAT
Cheoy Lee	Air Ride 87	A	—	SES
16V-149				
Brødrene Aa Båtbyggeri A/S	CIRR 105P Norcat	TIB	—	SES
Bell Halter Inc	212B	TIB	—	SES
Société Française de Constructions Navales (SFCN)	-	T	*Regina*	MH
Souter Shipyard Ltd	Wasp	TI	—	MH
Campbell Industries	Spalding 165	TI	—	MH
Sing Koon Seng	InCat	TI	*Ipo-Ipo 3001*	CAT
Textron Marine Systems	730A (SES-200)	TI	*Jaeger*	SES
International Catamarans Pty Ltd	37.2m	TIB	—	CAT
Mitsubishi Heavy Industries Ltd	26.03m	TI	—	MH
DEUTZ (KHD)				
BF6L 913				
Air Cushion Enterprises Pty Ltd	Surveyor 12 D	C	—	HOV
Air Vehicles Ltd	Tiger 16	C	—	HOV
Air Vehicles Ltd	Tiger 40	C	—	HOV
Dong Feng Shipyard	Type 7210	—	—	HOV
Griffon Hovercraft Ltd	1000 TD	C	-	HOV
Griffon Hovercraft Ltd	1500 TD	C	—	HOV
Griffon Hovercraft Ltd	2500 TD	C	—	HOV
Dong Feng Shipyard	Type 7210	—	—	HOV
Holland Hovercraft vof	Kolibrie 2000	C	*Capricorn 1*	HOV
Slingsby Aviation Ltd	SAH 2200	C	—	HOV
BF10L 413F				
Korea Tacoma Marine Industries	Turt IV	FC	—	HOV
BF12L 413				
Shanghai Hu Dong Yard	Type 716 II	FC	—	HOV
Korea Tacoma Marine Industries	Turt IV	FC	—	HOV
BF12L 513				
British Hovercraft Corporation plc	AP1–88/200 well-deck version	CP	—	HOV
NQEA	AP1–88	C	—	HOV
British Hovercraft Corporation plc	AP1–88	C	—	HOV
DEUTZ MWM				
TBD 234 V6				
Société Française de Constructions Navales (SFCN)	Marlin 21	—	—	MH
TBD 234 V12				
NQEA	22.0m, 24.0m	—	—	CAT
TBD 234 V16				
FBM Marine Ltd	28.8m	—	—	MH
International Catamarans Pty Ltd	30.0m	—	—	CAT
Brødrene Aa A.S.	18.0m CIRR 60P	—	*Harpoon*	SES
TBD 603 V16				
Vosper Private Ltd	—	—	*Jubail Fireboat*	MH
SBF Engineering	—	—	*Victory III*	CAT
TBD 604B V8				
FBM Marinteknik (S) Pte Ltd	35 MPV	—	—	MH
International Catamarans Pty Ltd	29m	—	—	CAT

Engine manufacturer, engine principal designation, craft builder	Craft	Engine secondary designation	Craft name	Craft type
TBD 604B V12				
NQEA	30.0m InCat	—	—	CAT
Brødrene Aa	—	—	*Ekwata*	SES
TBD 604B V12 (contd)				
Fjellstrand A/S	38.8m	—	—	CAT
Precision Marine Holdings Pty Ltd	33.4m	—	*Tropic Sunseeker*	CAT
TBD 604B V16				
Fjellstrand A/S	38.8m	—	—	CAT
International Catamarans Pty Ltd	—	—	*Tassie Devil 2001*	CAT
Brødrene Aa Båtbyggeri A/S	—	—	*Ekwata II*	SES
Aluminium Shipbuilders	49.0m WPC	—	*Condor 9*	CAT
BAM 16M 816				
Nichols Brothers Boat Building Inc	InCat	C	*Catamarin*	CAT
Westamarin A/S	W88	—	*Haugesund*	CAT
International Catamarans Pty Ltd	26m	—	—	CAT
Italthai Marine Ltd	27.4m	CR	—	MH
SBAM 12M 816				
Westport Shipyard Inc	27.4m	—	—	MH
SBA 16M 816				
Singapore Shipbuilding and Engineering Ltd	Patrol boat 22.7m	—	—	MH
FUJI PIELSTICK				
12 PA 4V 200 VGA				
Mitsui Engineering & Shipbuilding Co Ltd	CP30 Mk III	—	—	CAT
16 PA 4V 185-VG				
Mitsui Engineering & Shipbuilding Co Ltd	CP20HF	—	—	CAT
Mitsui Engineering & Shipbuilding Co Ltd	CP30	—	—	CAT
Mitsui Engineering & Shipbuilding Co Ltd	—	—	*Kotozaki*	SWATH
GENERAL ELECTRIC COMPANY				
LM 100				
Textron Marine Systems (formerly Bell Aerospace Canada Textron)	Voyageur 001	—	—	HOV
LM500				
Danish Navy Stanflex 300	Multi-mission Patrol	—	—	MH
LM2500				
Boeing Marine Systems	PHM	—	—	HYD
IKEGAI CORPORATION				
16V 190 ATC				
Mitsui Engineering & Shipbuilding Co Ltd	CP30 Mk III	—	—	CAT
Ikegai MAN 254 MLE V12				
Shinju Shipbuilding Co	—	—	*Lansing*	MH
ISHIKAWAJIMA-HARIMA HEAVY INDUSTRIES				
IM-100 (GE LM-100)				
Mitsui Engineering & Shipbuilding Co Ltd	MV-PP5	—	—	HOV
ISOTTA FRASCHINI SpA				
ID 32 SS 6				
A Fai Engineers & Shiprepairers Ltd	InCat 16m	LM	—	CAT
ID 36 6V				
Cantieri Navali Picchiotti 75	22.86m	SS	—	MH
Cantieri Navicelli	23.00m	SS	—	MH
A Fai Engineers & Shiprepairers Ltd	InCat 21m	SS	—	CAT
Oy Wärtsilä AB	PUC 22	S	—	HOV
ID 36 12V				
Feodosiya	Kometa	SS	—	HYD
Cantieri Navali Baglietto SpA	23m	—	—	MH
Navalmeccanica Belletti	27m	—	—	MH
Cantieri di Lavagna	32m	—	—	MH
ID 38 6V				
Fincantieri-Cantieri Navali Italiani SpA	Sparviero (auxiliary engine)	N	—	HYD
MAN NUTZFAHRZEUGE GmbH				
D 2540				
Wanganui	18m InCat	MLE	—	CAT
D 2542				
Hong Leong-Lürssen Shipyard Bhd	—	MLE	*Zaharah*	CAT
Versil Marine SA	—	—	*Challenger*	MH
Seaconstruct Pte Ltd	—	MLE	*Jetwise*, ex *Mariam*	MH
Gladding-Hearn Shipbuilding	19.15m C Raymond Hunt	—	*Sandy Hook*	MH
Shinju Shipbuilding Co	—	—	*Sea Angel*	MH
D 2840 (10 cylinder)				
Société Bretonne de Construction Navale (SBCN)	25m	LE	*Iles D'or XVIII*	MH
D 2842 (12 cylinder)				
Société Bretonne de Construction Navale (SBCN)	—	LE	*Atlante*	MH
Société Bretonne de Construction Navale (SBCN)	25m	LE	*Amiral de Joinville*	MH

Engine manufacturer, engine principal designation, craft builder	Craft	Engine secondary designation	Craft name	Craft type
MTU				
12V 93 TY 70				
Fjellstrand A/S	25.5m	—	—	CAT
8V 331				
Boeing Aerospace Company	PHM	TC 80	—	HYD
12V 331				
Rodriquez Cantieri Navali SpA	RHS 70	TC 82	—	HYD
Rodriquez Cantieri Navali SpA	RHS 150	TC 82	—	HYD
Hitachi Zosen	PTS 50 Mk II	TB 82	—	HYD
Cantieri Navale Italcraft Srl	M78	TC 82	—	MH
Vosper Private Ltd	SNV SEEB	TC 92	—	MH
Mitsui Engineering & Shipbuilding Co Ltd	CP20	TC 82	—	CAT
Swiftships Inc	125ft	TC 71	—	MH
12V 339				
Fjellstrand A/S	Alumaran 165 25.5m	TC 62	—	CAT
6V 396				
Marinteknik Verkstads AB	30MCB (CV900)	TC 82	—	MH
8V 396				
Korea Tacoma Marine Industries	26m	TB 83	—	SES
Wavemaster International Pty Ltd	Sea Raider	—	—	MH
Valmet Oy	Patrol craft 364–366	TB 83	—	MH
Westamarin A/S	S80	TB 83	*Vøringen*	MH
Oceanfast Pty Ltd	4000	TB 93	—	MH
Lantana Boatyard	Guardian	TB 93	—	MH
NQEA	22/23m InCat	TC 82	—	CAT
12V 396				
Marinteknik Verkstads AB	JC-F1	TC 82	*Aliterreno 1*	CAT
Marinteknik Verkstads AB	JC 3000	TB 83	—	CAT
Marinteknik Verkstads AB	Marinjet 33CPV (PV 2400)	TB 83	—	CAT
Marinteknik Verkstads AB	Marinjet 34CCB	TC 82	—	CAT
Vosper Hovermarine Ltd	HM 527 Series 1	TB 83	—	SES
USSR S Ordzhonikidze Shipbuilding & Repair Yard	Kolkhida	TC 82	—	HYD
Brødrene Aa Båtbyggeri A/S	25m	TC 62	*Hyen*	HYD
FBM Marinteknik (S) Pte Ltd	Marinjet 34CCB	TC 62	*Hakeem*	CAT
F R Lürssen Werft (GmbH & Co)	—	TB 83	*Shergar*	MH
Chung Wah Shipbuilding & Engineering Co Ltd	King Class	TB 83	—	MH
Scheepswerf Porsius BV	33m	TB 94	—	MH
Watercraft Ltd	P2000	TB 93	—	MH
Westamarin A/S	W88	TB 83	—	CAT
Fjellstrand A/S	31.5m	TB 63	—	CAT
Brooke Yachts Ltd	—	TB 93	*Virgin Atlantic Challenger II*	MH
Cantieri Navali Baglietto SpA	Seneca Megajet	TB 93	—	MH
16V 396				
SBF Engineering	—	TB 83	—	MH
Fjellstrand A/S	38.8m	TB 83	—	CAT
Marinteknik Verkstads AB	Marinjet 33CPV-D (PV 3100)	TB 83	—	CAT
Marinteknik Verkstads AB	Marinjet 34CCR (CV 3400)	TB 93	—	CAT
International Catamarans Pty Ltd	29.6m	TC 82	—	CAT
Fjellstrand A/S	38.8m	TB 63	—	CAT
Fjellstrand A/S	49.5m	TB 94	—	CAT
International Catamarans Pty Ltd	30.0m	TC 83	—	CAT
Sing Koon Seng Pte Ltd	InCat 29.0m	TB 63	—	CAT
Vosper Thornycroft Ltd	33.5m	TB 94	*Atlantic Challenger III*	MH
Westamarin A/S	W5000	TB 84	*Anne Lise*	CAT
Blohm & Voss	36.0m	TB 94	*Corsair*	SES
FBM Marine Ltd	37.0m	TB 84	*Patria*	SWATH/CAT
12V 493				
Rodriquez Cantieri Navali SpA	RHS 110	Ty 71	—	HYD
Rodriquez Cantieri Navali SpA	RHS 140	Ty 71	—	HYD
Rodriquez Cantieri Navali SpA	RHS 70	—	—	HYD
Rodriquez Cantieri Navali SpA	PT 50	Ty 71	—	HYD
Fjellstrand A/S	Alumaran 165 25.5m	Ty 70	—	CAT
Westamarin A/S	W86	Ty 70	—	CAT
Vosper Singapore Pte Ltd	PT 20B Mk II	Ty 70	—	HYD
Rodriquez Cantieri Navali SpA	PT 50 SL	Ty 70	—	HYD
16V 538				
Chantiers Navals de l'Esterel SA	Esterel 29 & 42	TB 92	—	MH
Italthai Marine Ltd	PGB 50.14m	TB 91	—	MH
12V 652				
Rodriquez Cantieri Navali SpA	RHS 200	TB 71	—	HYD
Supramar Hydrofoils Ltd	PTS 75 Mk III	—	—	HYD
Vosper	PT 75	—	—	HYD
12V 1163				
Westermoen Hydrofoil A/S, now Westamarin A/S	PTS 150 Mk III	TB 83	—	HYD

Engine manufacturer, engine principal designation, craft builder	Craft	Engine secondary designation	Craft name	Craft type
PAXMAN DIESELS LTD				
VEGA 12				
FBM Marine Ltd	26m Protector Class	—	—	MH
16RP 200–1-CM				
Vosper Thornycroft (UK) Ltd	62.5m	—	*Cheung Kong*	MH
	62.5	—	*Ju Kong*	MH
Bollinger Machine Shop and Shipyard Inc	33.0m Island Class	—	—	MH
Vosper Thornycroft (UK) Ltd	56m Province Class	—	—	MH
Vosper Thornycroft (UK) Ltd	Fast strike craft	—	—	MH
12 SET CWM				
Sheng Hsing Shipbuilding, Taiwan	Fast ferry	—	—	MH
FBM Marine Ltd	Protector fast patrol boat	—	—	MH
PERKINS ENGINES (SHREWSBURY) LTD				
CV 12 M 800				
Atlantic and Gulf Boat Builder Inc	24m InCat	—	—	CAT
T6				
Aluminium Shipbuilders Ltd	19m InCat	—	—	CAT
PRATT & WHITNEY CANADA				
ST6T				
Textron Marine Systems (formerly Bell Aerospace Canada Textron)	Model 7467 LACV-30	—	—	HOV
ST6T-76 Twin Pac				
Textron Marine Systems (formerly Bell Aerospace Canada Textron)	Voyageur 002 LACV-30	—	—	HOV
ROLLS-ROYCE plc				
Marine Gnome GN 1301GN 1051/1/GN 1452/GN1451				
British Hovercraft Corporation plc	SR.N6 Mk 6, 6C & 8	—	—	HOV
Marine Proteus				
Fincantieri-Cantieri Navali Italiani SpA	Sparviero	15M/553	—	HYD
British Hovercraft Corporation plc	SR.N4 Mk 3 (ex Mk 1)	15M/529	—	HOV
British Hovercraft Corporation plc	BH.7 Mk 5A	15M/549	—	HOV
RUSHTON DIESELS LTD				
16 RK 270				
International Catamarans Tasmania Pty Ltd	74.0m InCat	—	*Christopher Columbus*	CAT
SAAB-SCANIA				
Scania Division				
DSI 14				
Marinteknik Verkstads AB	41.9m	—	*Cinderella*	MH
Wico Boat, Finland	21.8m	—	—	MH
SACM				
M7 UD 33 V16				
Westamarin SES 4000	40.0m	—	*Super Swede* *Super Dane*	SEA
TEXTRON LYCOMING				
TF25				
Mitsui Engineering & Shipbuilding Co Ltd	MV-PP15	—	—	HOV
CHACONSA	VCA-36	—	—	HOV
Cougar Holdings Ltd/Commercial Marine Resources		—	*Pegasus*	CAT
TF40				
Textron Marine Systems	LCAC	B	—	HOV
Westamarin A/S	W100T	S	—	CAT
LTX101				
Günther W Jörg	18.0m Jörg V	—	—	WIGE
VOLVO PENTA				
AQAD 40/280B				
Korea Tacoma Marine Industries Ltd	12m	—	—	SES
MD 40A				
Korea Tacoma Marine Industries Ltd	12m	—	—	SES
TAMD 71				
Aluminium Shipbuilders Ltd	16.35m	—	*Daily Telegraph*	CAT
YANMAR				
6 LAAM				
Mokubei Shipbuilding Co	23.5m	UT 1	—	MH
12 LAAK				
Mokubei Shipbuilding Co	25.5m	UT 1	*Kaiyo*	MH

TRANSMISSIONS

BELGIUM

TWIN DISC INTERNATIONAL SA

Chaussée de Namur 54, B-1400 Nivelles, Belgium

Telephone: (067) 21 49 41
Telex: 57414 TWINSA B
Telefax: (067) 21 95 77

Ph Pécriaux, *Managing Director and Technical Director*

Ph Bronselaer, *Director, Finance and Administration*
K Sethi, *Marketing Director*
J Pierquain, *Marine Product Sales Manager*

During the Second World War Twin Disc Inc started manufacturing marine gears for landing craft. After the war production and development continued with marine gears for engine manufacturers and private boat builders. Twin Disc has manufacturing facilities in Racine, USA and Nivelles, Belgium.

The latest gearboxes are the MG 5050 series, MG 5060 series, MG 5061 series, MG 5090 and 5111 series and were introduced in October 1988 and it is intended that the new MG 5010 series will be introduced in January 1989. All these units can be provided with a live power take off and controlling valve.

Marine Transmissions Summary
Pleasure craft

		MG 5010A	MG 5021	MG 5050A	MG 5050	MG 5061A	MG 5061	MG 5071	MG 5071A	MG 5072	MG 5072A	MG 5090A	MG 5091	MG 5111A	MG 5111
Pleasure craft rating	hp	200	270	320	320	400	400	420	420	500	500	600	600	800	800
	rpm	@ 2800	@ 2800	@ 2800	@ 2800	@ 2800	@ 2800	@ 2300	@ 2300	@ 2300	@ 2300	@ 2300	@ 2300	@ 2300	@ 2300
Ratios		1.5	1.5	1.1	1.1	1.1	1.1	1.1	1.1	1.1	1.1	1.5	1.5	1.5	1.5
		2.0	2.0	1.5	1.5	1.5	1.5	1.5	1.5	1.5	1.5	2.0	2.0	2.0	2.0
		2.4	2.5	2.0	2.0	2.0	2.0	2.0	2.0	1.77	1.77	2.5	2.5	2.5	2.5
					2.5	2.5	2.5	2.5	2.5				3.0		3.0
					3.0		3.0	3.0	3.0						
Input housing		4, 3	3	1, 2, 3	1, 2, 3	1, 2, 3	1, 2, 3	1, 2, 3	1, 2, 3	1, 2, 3	1, 2, 3	1, 2	1, 2	1, 2	1, 2
Down angle or centre drop		10°	10°	10°	134mm	7°	144mm	Co-axial	7°	Co-axial	7°	7°	173mm	7°	190mm
V-drive			y	y		y							y		y
Power take-off		y		y	y	y	y						y	y	y
Cruise control		y		y	y	y	y	y	y	y	y	y	y	y	y
Weight (kg)		45	70	70	70	95	95	160	160	160	160	200	225	245	250

Twin Disc MG5111

Twin Disc MG5111 Deep Case

GERMANY, FEDERAL REPUBLIC

LOHMANN + STOLTERFOHT GmbH

Postfach 1860, D-5810 Witten, Federal Republic of Germany

Telephone: (2302) 877–1
Telex: 8229005
Telefax: (2302) 88148

Lohmann and Stolterfoht manufacture a range of gearboxes for torques ranging from 5kNm to 3580kNm for marine propeller transmissions.

Type	Torque	Reduction ratios available
Navilus GUU	5 to 16kNm	1.5 to 6.5:1.0
Navilus GUS	8.4 to 49kNm	2.0 to 6.0:1.0
Navilus GWC	15.5 to 190kNm	2.0 to 6.0:1.0
Navilus GCS/GUC	39.0 to 2200kNm	1.5 to 6.0:1.0
Navilus GUT	570.0 to 3580kNm	1.5 to 12.0:1.0
Navilus GVA/GVE	50.0 to 1620kNm	2.0 to 6.0:1.0
Navilus GVG	690 to 3580kNm	2.0 to 6.0:1.0

REINTJES
Eugen-Reintjes GmbH
P O Box 101344,D-3250 Hameln 1, Federal
Republic of Germany

Telephone: (05151) 104–0
Telefax: (05151) 104–300

UK representative: European Marine and
Machine Agencies, 22–26 Gore Road, New
Milton, Hampshire BH25 6RX

Telephone: (0425) 618704
Telex: 417170

Reintjes have specialised in the manufacture
of marine gears for harbour craft and sea-going
vessels for more than 50 years. The company has
produced over 60 000 gearboxes.

WVS GEARBOX

The WVS gearbox is specifically developed for
operational requirements that have weight saving
as a priority. The manufacturers claim that this
has been achieved with high efficiency, an aluminium housing giving a low power to weight
ratio, and smooth control with optimum quietness
when operating.

The gear range covers several sizes with a
maximum input torque of 51 600Nm at a power/
speed ratio between 0.09 and 4.411kW/rpm for
the offset version of the WVS gearbox. The torque
values for co-axial lightweight gears lie between
25 000Nm and 70 000Nm.

Gearboxes are fitted with a three-shaft arrangement. The output shaft is vertically offset below
the input shaft, the intermediate shaft is laterally
offset between both shafts. Clutch wheels on the
input and intermediate shafts are continually
washed. Both shafts have reduction pinions
driving the wheel mounted on the main shaft.
Full power can be transmitted in both directions,
ahead and astern, thus identical engines in multi-
engine layouts with contra-rotating propellers can
be used.

All WVS gearboxes can be supplied with trailing oil pumps, loiter drives, and power take-offs.

Applications
WVS 110 P: Installed in landing craft, input
power 300kW at 2800rpm, reduction ratio
2.28:1.0.
WVS 2232 IU: Installed in motor yachts, input
power 3460kW at 1850rpm, reduction ratio
3.95:1.0.
WAV 4942 SO: This gearbox has been installed
in the Peacock class of patrol boats built by Hall
Russell of Aberdeen, Great Britain. Input power
is 5220kW at 1000rpm.

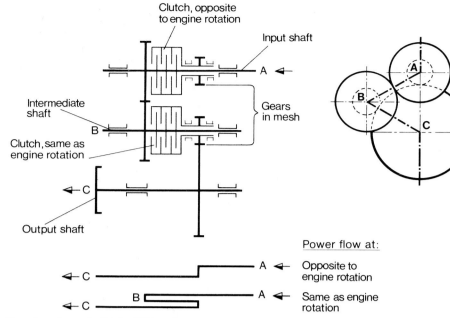

Power flow diagram for Reintjes WVS gearbox

Reintjes WVS 2232 U gearbox

VLJ 730–930 WATERJET DRIVES

Reintjes have developed a new gear design for waterjets. The gear unit can be used with either vertical or horizontally offset shafts rotating left- or right-handed. The reduction ratios meet the requirements for waterjets as they have a tolerance of ± 3%. These drives can also be fitted with a secondary drive for a hydraulic pump.

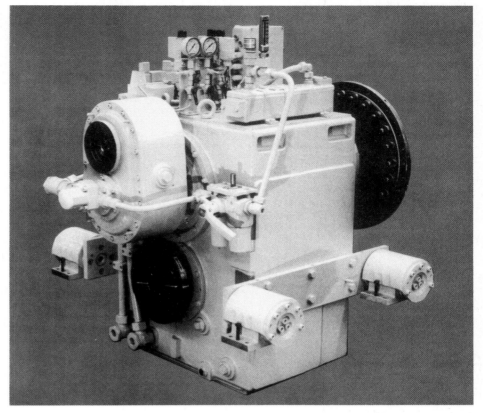

Reintjes VLJ 730–930 specially designed for high-speed craft

RENK TACKE GmbH

Augsburg Works, Postfach 102307, D-8900 Augsburg 1, Gögginger Strasse 73, Federal Republic of Germany

Telephone: (0821) 5700–0
Telex: 53781
Telefax: (0821) 5700460

Rheine Works, Rodder Damm 170, D-4440 Rheine, Federal Republic of Germany

Telephone: (05971) 790–1
Telex: 981637
Telefax: (05971) 790208

PLS AND PWS GEARBOXES

Renk Tacke's marine planetary gear units (PLS and PWS series) have been specifically developed for use in fast ships such as corvettes, speedboats,

Planetary marine gears

Type	Size	Reduction ratio (i)	kW/rpm	A i≤ 2.8	i> 2.8	B	C	D
PLS	12.5	1.5–4.8	1.7	850	750	730	890	400
PWS	12.5	1.5–4.8	1.7	970	870	730	900	400
PLS	18	1.5–4.8	2.4	900	800	820	920	450
PWS	18	1.5–4.8	2.4	1050	930	820	940	450
PLS	25	1.5–4.8	3.5	950	850	890	950	500
PWS	25	1.5–4.8	3.5	1130	1030	890	1000	500
PLS	35.5	1.5–4.8	5	1130	1050	1060	1040	580
PWS	35.5	1.5–4.8	5	1280	1150	1060	1100	580
PLS	50	1.5–4.8	7	1200	1100	1170	1140	650
PWS	50	1.5–4.8	7	1400	1250	1170	1150	650
PLS	60	1.5–4.8	8.4	1250	1150	1230	1150	690
PWS	60	1.5–4.8	8.4	1550	1400	1230	1180	690
PLS	71	1.5–4.8	10	1300	1100	1300	1200	710
PWS	71	1.5–4.8	10	1600	1500	1300	1200	710

Renk Tacke planetary gear unit during assembly

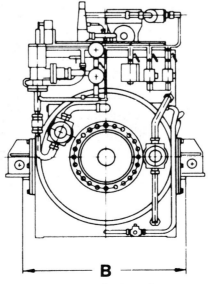
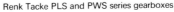
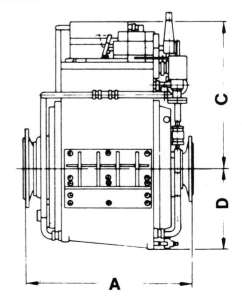

Renk Tacke PLS and PWS series gearboxes

minesweepers, minelayers, OPVs and IPVs. Designed for a performance range between 800 and 10 000kW, they cover a very wide range of applications. The specific characteristics and advantages of disconnectable planetary gear units (PLS) and planetary reversing gear units (PWS) are:

ratios 1.5 to 4.8

PWS series efficiencies 97.5 to 98%

PLS series efficiencies 98.5 to 99%

compact design, permitting favourable engine room concepts

low power-to-weight ratio of less than 0.5kg/kW co-axial input and output shafts for optimum power plant layouts

high shock resistance due to planetary design

insensitivity of transmission elements to hull distortion, providing high operational reliability even under extreme service conditions

high efficiency due to epicyclic concept

starboard and port gear units offer identical connection interfaces and with PWS units this means completely identical starboard and port gear units, even for multi-propeller ships

forward and reverse gears of PWS units are both designed for 100% loads, engines can therefore operate with the same direction of rotation without affecting the gear unit

on request, these gear units can be built under the supervision of any classification society. Anti-magnetic versions are available

high reliability

suitable for use with gas turbines

if required, low-speed gear can be provided

special design with vertically offset shafts for V drives

ZF

ZAHNRADFABRIK FRIECRICHSHAFEN AG

Postfach 2520, Löwentaler Strasse 100, D-7990 Friedrichshafen 1, Federal Republic of Germany

Telephone: (07541) 77–0
Telex: 734207–0 ZF D
Telefax: (07541) 772158

H Marschner, *Head, Marine Department*

ZF produces more than 10 000 units annually in their three plants in Friedrichshafen West Germany, Padua Italy, and São Paulo Brazil. Their range of reduction and reversing gears is from 75 to 4300kW for high-speed craft and 75 to 1000kW for work boats. All gears can be supplied with classification approval. ZF gears have been fitted in a large number of high performance, naval, commercial and pleasure craft throughout the world.

TYPE BW 460

A three-shaft reversing and reduction gearbox with offset input and output shafts, with one clutch on the input shaft and one on the reversing shaft. These gearboxes are suitable for fast leisure craft.

TYPE BW 190

A three-shaft marine reversing and reduction gearbox with offset input and output shafts, with one clutch on the input shaft and one on the reversing shaft. Suitable for fast crew boats.

TYPE BW 452–1

A reversing gearbox with a front-mounted helical gear reduction stage. The output shaft of the helical gear reduction stage is the input shaft of the reverse reduction stage. A multi-disc clutch is fitted to the input shaft and the reverse shaft. Suitable for heavy-duty work boats and fishing craft.

TYPE BW 1500

A three-shaft reversing and reduction gearbox with dual clutch on the input shaft. Fitted in fast patrol and strike craft.

TYPE MS 1000

A marine 15°-V reduction gearbox for high output installations with a gas turbine as the prime mover. Fitted in high-speed strike craft.

TYPE BW 250

A three-shaft reversing and reduction gearbox with dual clutch on the input shaft. Fitted in fast craft.

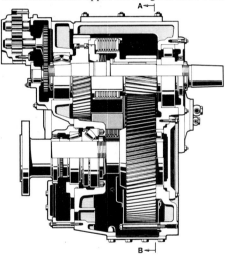

Type BW 460 ZF gearbox

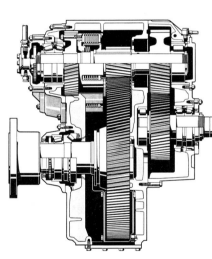

Type BW 452 ZF gearbox

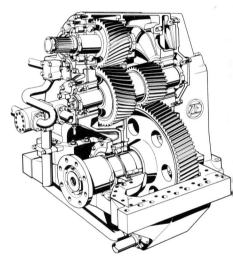

Type MS 1000 ZF gearbox

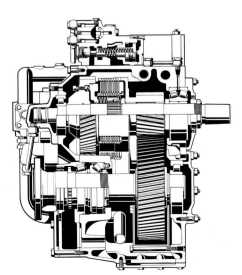

Type BW 190 ZF gearbox

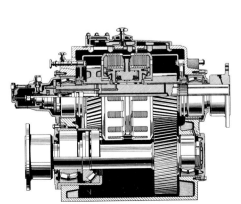

Type BW 1500 ZF gearbox

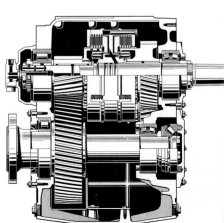

Type BW 250 ZF gearbox

TYPE BW 461

A three-shaft reversing and reduction gearbox with offset input and output shafts, with one clutch on input shaft and one on the reversing shaft. Installed in heavy duty work boats, and fishing craft.

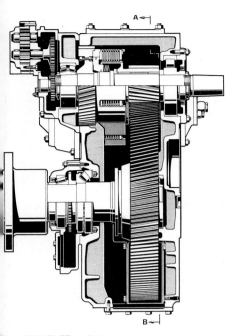

Type BW 461 ZF gearbox

MARINE RANGE

Details of the marine range of gearboxes for high-speed diesel engines are contained in the accompanying tables for power ratings of between 150 and 4300kW.

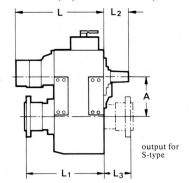

output for standard type

output for S-type

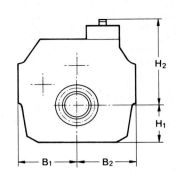

Type	Dimensions (mm)									Mass approx. kg
	A	B_1	B_2	H_1	H_2	L	L_1	L_2	L_1	
BW 160	200	305	305	200	487	517	385	99	—	263
BW 160S							—		95	255
BW 165	200	305	305	200	487	517	385	99	—	265
BW 165S							—		95	257
BW 161	365	355	355	340	652	517	390	99	—	568
BW 190	220	340	340	250	522	518	445	132	—	320
BW 190S							—		100	325
BW 195	220	340	340	250	522	518	445	132	—	322
BW 195S							—		100	330
BW 191	390	400	400	365	692	518	435	132	—	680
BW 250	235	340	340	250	572	616	565	151	—	437
BW 250S							—		100	462
BW 255	235	340	340	250	572	616	565	151	—	440
BW 255S							—		100	475
BW 251	360	375	375	395	697	616	625	151	—	870
BW 450–1	310	445	445	316	649	655	565	162	—	667
BW 450–1S							—		144	733
BW 460	310	445	445	316	649	655	565	162	—	672
BW 460S							—		144	738
BW 465	310	445	445	316	649	655	565	162	—	677
BW 465S							—		144	743
BW 451–1	460	465	465	439	799	655	638	162		1254
BW 461										1259
BW 750	340	500	500	348	694	759	600	146	—	880
BW 750S							—		120	910
BW 755	340	500	500	348	694	659	600	146	—	885
BW 755S							—		120	915

Main installation dimensions and weights for ZF gearboxes BW 160 to BW 755S (subject to technical modifications and valid for basic design of gearbox)

Types and capacities of ZF marine gearboxes

Type	kW range				
	1000	2000	3000	4000	5000
BW 160	▬				
BW 190	▬▬				
BW 250	▬▬				
BW 460	▬▬▬				
BW 750	▬▬▬				
BW 1200	▬▬▬▬				
BW 1500/2000	▬▬▬▬				

Types and capacities of ZF marine gearboxes

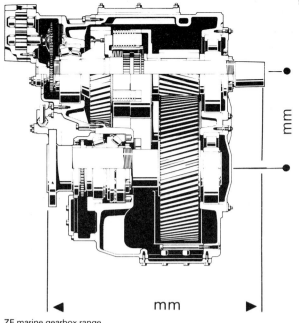

ZF marine gearbox range

		Marine Gears				
Type	Possible ratios	Input torque max. Nm		Input speed max min⁻¹	Length mm ◄ ►	Center distance ●mm●
		continuous*	intermittent*			
BW 160	1.1–3.0	1850	2100	2600	484	200
BW 165	1.1–2.5	—	2500	2600	484	200
BW 161	3.0–6.5	1850	—	2600	489	365
BW 190	1.1–3.0	2400	2800	2600	577	220
BW 195	1.1–2.5	—	3300	2600	577	220
BW 191	3.0–6.5	2400	—	2600	567	390
BW 250	1.1–3.5	3300	3750	2500	716	235
BW 255	1.1–2.5	—	4600	2500	716	235
BW 251	3.2–6.0	3300	—	2500	776	360
BW 460	1.2–3.5	5750	—	2300	727	310
BW 465	1.2–3.5	—	8250	2300	727	310
BW 451–1	3.5–5.6	4750	—	2000	800	460
BW 461	3.5–5.6	5750	—	2000	800	460
BW 750	1.2–3.2	7900	9400	2300	746	340
BW 755	1.2–3.2	—	11500	2300	746	340
BW 1200	1.9–3.6	—	16000	1900	1085	320
BW 1201	1.9–3.6	—	16000	1900	1085	450
BW 1203	3.3–5.6	—	16000	1900	1565	320
BW 1500	1.1–1.9	—	20000	1900	1085	320
BW 1501	1.6–3.2	—	20000	1900	1085	450
BW 1503	2.8–5.6	—	20000	1900	1565	320
BW 2000	Range on request					
*T max not applicable for entire reduction range.						

ITALY

MPM
MECCANICA PADANA MONTEVERDE SpA
Via Penghe n28, 35030 Caselle di Selvazzano,
Padova, Italy

Telephone: 049 8975599
Telex: 430320 MPM PD 1
Telefax: 049 8975598

V Rasera, *Chief Executive Officer*
M Contin, *Sales Manager – Marine Division*

Manufacturer of gearboxes for over 50 years.
MPM is now a full member of the ZF Group.

Type	Nominal ratio	Continuous		Duty service classification Intermediate duty		Pleasure		Max input rpm
		1800rpm bhp (kW)	2100rpm bhp (kW)	2100rpm bhp (kW)	2800rpm bhp (kW)	2300rpm bhp (kW)	2500rpm bhp (kW)	
IRM-41A/2–3	1.50/2.00	-	-	96 (71)	127 (93)	144 (106)	176 (129)	5000
IRM-50A/2–3	1.50/2.00	—	—	139 (102)	185 (136)	209 (154)	254 (187)	5000
IRM-220 A/V	1.23	130 (97)s	152 (114)s	197 (147)	263 (196)	263 (193)	320 (235)	4500●
	1.53	94 (70)s	108 (81)s	175 (131)	233 (175)	263 (193)	320 (235)	4500●
	2.05	94 (70)s	108 (81)s	175 (131)	233 (175)	263 (193)	320 (235)	4500●
	2.45	94 (70)s	108 (81)s	147 (110)	196 (147)	263 (193)	320 (235)	4500●
IRM-220	2.62	161 (120)s	188 (140)s	222 (166)	300 (224)	—	—	3200
	3.13	149 (111)s	174 (129)s	216 (161)	288 (215)	-	—	3200
	3.55	135 (101)s	157 (118)s	196 (146)	261 (195)	-	—	3200
	3.96	123 (92)s	143 (107)s	181 (135)	241 (180)	—	—	3200
	4.64	111 (83)s	129 (97)s	155 (116)	207 (155)	—	—	3200
IRM-301 AL-1	1.19/1.55	164 (122)	191 (142)	251 (187)	335 (250)	380 (284)	444 (331)	3000 +
	2.00/2.90	164 (122)	191 (142)	251 (187)	335 (250)	380 (284)	444 (331)	3000 +
IRM-301 PL-1	1.10/1.41	179 (133)	209 (155)	303 (223)	405 (298)	413 (309)	482 (360)	3000 +
	1.86/2.69	179 (133)	209 (155)	269 (201)	359 (268)	413 (309)	482 (360)	3000 +
IRM-301–1	3.13/3.55	229 (171)	267 (199)	346 (258)	461 (344)	—	—	2600
	3.96/4.64	194 (145)	226 (169)	295 (220)	393 (293)	—	—	2600
	5.0	169 (126)	197 (147)	270 (202)	360 (269)	—	—	2600
		1800rpm	**2100rpm**	**2100rpm**	**2400rpm**	**2300rpm**	**2500rpm**	
IRM-310 A	1.07	—	—	—	—	550 (410)	670 (492)	3000
	1.52					550 (410)	670 (492)	3000
	2.00					550 (410)	670 (492)	3000
	2.56					550 (410)	670 (492)	3000
IRM-310 PL	1.07	—	—	—	—	550 (410)	670 (492)	3000
	1.52	-				550 (410)	670 (492)	3000
	2.00	—	—	—	—	550 (410)	670 (492)	3000
	2.56	—	—	—	—	550 (410)	670 (492)	3000
IRM-320 A	1.55	322 (240)	376 (280)	463 (345)	529 (394)	650 (478)	715 (525)	3000◆
	2.08	322 (240)	376 (280)	463 (345)	529 (394)	650 (478)	715 (525)	3000◆
	2.52	322 (240)	376 (280)	405 (302)	463 (345)	490 (360)	557 (410)	3000◆
IRM-320 PL	1.05/1.48	322 (240)	376 (280)	463 (345)	529 (394)	650 (478)	715 (525)	3000◆
	2.14	322 (240)	376 (280)	463 (345)	529 (394)	650 (478)	715 (525)	3000◆
	2.51	322 (240)	376 (280)	405 (302)	463 (345)	490 (360)	557 (470)	3000◆

| Type | Nominal ratio | Continuous | | Duty service classification Intermediate duty | | Pleasure | | Max input rpm |
		1800rpm bhp (kW)	2100rpm bhp (kW)	2100rpm bhp (kW)	2800rpm bhp (kW)	2300rpm bhp (kW)	2500rpm bhp (kW)	
IRM-320	3.00	322 (240)	376 (280)	463 (345)	—	—	—	2100
	4.05	273 (203)	318 (237)	463 (345)	—	—	—	2100
	5.00	236 (176)	275 (205)	338 (252)	—	—	—	2100
IRM-350 PL	1.02/1.28	410 (301)	479 (352)	598 (440)	683 (502)	820 (603)	891 (655)	3000
	1.58/2.07	359 (264)	418 (307)	572 (420)	654 (481)	820 (603)	891 (655)	3000
	2.63/2.86	270 (198)	315 (231)	446 (328)	510 (375)	820 (603)	899 (655)	3000
IRM-350 A	1.28/1.58	410 (301)	479 (352)	598 (440)	683 (502)	820 (603)	891 (655)	3000
	2.07	359 (264)	418 (307)	572 (420)	654 (481)	820 (603)	891 (655)	3000
	2.63	270 (198)	315 (231)	446 (328)	510 (375)	820 (603)	891 (655)	3000
IRM-350	3.97/4.96	415 (304)	485 (356)	590 (434)	675 (495)	—	—	2200
	5.45	415 (304)	485 (356)	590 (434)	675 (495)	—	—	2200
	6.04	390 (287)	455 (334)	555 (408)	634 (465)	—	—	2200
	6.45	350 (257)	410 (301)	500 (367)	570 (419)	—	—	2200
BW-161	3.61 + , 4.00	507 (373)	592 (435)	592 (435)	676 (497)	-	—	2600
	4.53 + , 5.14	507 (373)	592 (435)	592 (435)	676 (497)	-	—	2600
	5.59 + , 6.12	468 (349)	546 (407)	—	—	—	—	2600
	6.48	468 (349)	546 (407)	—	—	—	—	2600

+ IRM-301AL/PL-1   Max continuous duty speed limit is 2600rpm
◆ IRM-320 A/PL   Max continuous duty speed limit is 2100rpm
● IRM-220/A/V   Diesel engine speed limit 4000rpm, and for gasolene engines - 4500rpm
s IRM-220   Max continuous duty speed limit is 3200rpm

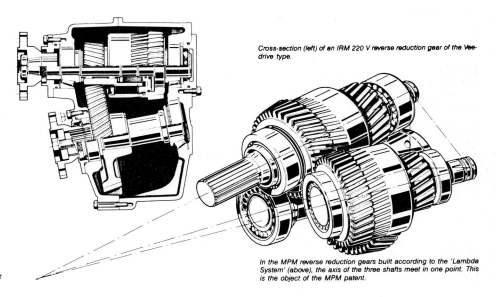

Cross-section (left) of an IRM 220 V reverse reduction gear of the Vee-drive type.

MPM IRM 220 V reverse reduction gear

In the MPM reverse reduction gears built according to the 'Lambda System' (above), the axis of the three shafts meet in one point. This is the object of the MPM patent.

REXROTH SpA

Hydrostatic transmission systems previously under this company heading are now under entry for Hydromarine SA.

HYDROMARINE SRL

I–20090 Cernusco S/N (MI), via Foscolo 11, Italy

Telephone: (02)9237863/9237607
Telefax: (02)9233221

Please see entry under Hydromarine SA, Switzerland, (the parent company of Hydromarine SRL) for details of this hydrostatic transmission development.

JAPAN

NIIGATA CONVERTER CO LTD

27–9, Sendagaya 5-chome, Shibuya-ku, Tokyo
151, Japan

Telephone: (03)3547111
Telex: 2323105 NICOTO J
Telefax: (03)3415365
Works: Kamo, Niigata Prefecture and Omiya,
Saitama Prefecture.

Niigata gearbox configuration

MARINE GEAR CAPACITIES FOR HIGH-SPEED MARINE CRAFT (PARALLEL SHAFT MODELS)

MODEL	SAE Hsg.	RATIOS	KW/RPM PC	MAXIMUM SPEED (rpm)	DRY WEIGHT (Kg)
MGN123	2. 1	1. 52, 1. 97, 2. 57	0. 134		
		3. 08	0. 126	3300	190
		3. 46	0. 118		
MGN133	2. 1. 0	1. 65, 2. 00, 2. 48	0. 178		
		2. 92	0. 173	2800	235
		3. 25	0. 168		
		3. 43	0. 164		
MGN173	1. 0	1. 53, 1. 97, 2. 44	0. 248		
		2. 93	0. 233	2600	300
		3. 54	0. 215		
MGN232E	1. 0	1. 29, 1. 50, 1. 76, 1. 96	0. 389	2600	360
		2. 48	0. 303		
MGN233E	1. 0	1. 57, 1. 79, 1. 97, 2. 52	0. 389		
		2. 96	0. 336	2600	410
		3. 52	0. 283		
MGN272	1. 0	1. 18, 1. 50, 1. 74, 2. 04	0. 479	2500	420
MGN273E	1. 0	1. 64, 1. 83, 2. 03, 2. 55	0. 479	2500	470
		3. 12	0. 414		
MGN332E	1. 0	1. 00, 1. 45, 1. 74, 2. 04	0. 621	2500	560
		2. 38	0. 567		
MGN433G	0	1. 18, 1. 53, 1. 73, 2. 06, 2. 52	0. 781	2500	900
MGN472	0	1. 55, 2. 09, 2. 52	0. 919	2100	1200

Marine gear capacities for high-speed marine craft

(DOWN ANGLE AND U-DRIVE MODELS)

MODEL	SAE Hsg.	RATIOS	KW/RPM PC	MAXIMUM SPEED (rpm)	DRY WEIGHT (kg)
MGNV172, C	1. 0	1. 55, 2. 03	0. 248	2600	330
		2. 34	0. 239		
MGNV232E, C	1. 0	1. 52, 1. 77, 1. 97	0. 389	2600	400
		2. 46	0. 281		
MGNV272E, C	1. 0	1. 66, 2. 06	0. 479	2500	500
		2. 48	0. 437		
MGNV332E, C	1. 0	1. 53, 1. 72, 1. 93	0. 621	2500	620
		2. 43	0. 567		
MGNV432, C	0	1. 54, 2. 06	0. 781	2500	1000
		2. 47	0. 628		
MGN472, C	0	1. 52, 1. 95	0. 997	2100	1450
		2. 46	0. 864		

PC : Pleasure craft rating

NORWAY

SERVOGEAR A/S

5420 Rubbestadneset, Norway

Telephone: (054) 27380
Telefax: (054) 27783

Servogear, established in 1973, produce light-weight gears to their own design which have in-built servo systems for controllable-pitch pro-pellers and hydraulic shaft clutches. Servogear gearboxes are specifically designed for high-speed craft where low weight and small size are par-ticularly important.

Since Servogear started production in 1975 over 650 gearboxes and propeller systems have been delivered of which more than 300 have been deliv-ered for high-speed craft with engines from 225kW to 2240kW and speeds from 20 to 40 knots

Servogear V-Drive Type VD 250B (746kW continuous at 2300 rpm)

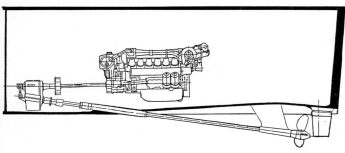

Servogear V-Drive Type VD 250A installation

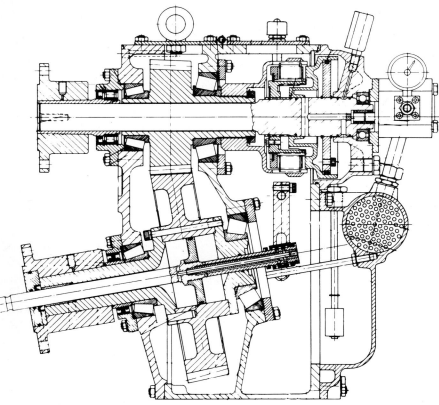

Section through a Servogear gearbox

SINGAPORE

NICO TRANSMISSION (S) PTE LTD

301 Jurong Town Hall Road, No 02–09, Singa-pore 2260

Telephone: 562 1100
Telefax: 563 6941

M Daley, *Managing Director*

Niigata Converter Company is licensed by Twin Disc, Inc of Racine, Wisconsin, USA for the pro-duction and marketing of marine reverse and reduction gears for high-speed engines.

Niigata Converter Company Ltd (NICO), well known for the manufacture and marketing of diversified lines of marine products, has a new series of marine reverse and reduction gears in lightweight and compact design utilising alu-minium alloy housings. Sixteen models in both of the standard and U-drive version are available in the 224 to 2165kW range. These marine gears are ideal for such vessels as pleasure craft, passenger ferries, patrol boats and crew boats for which the essential requirement is high speed.

Built-in hydraulic clutches, cooled by the same type of oil used in the engines, give the marine gears smooth and instantaneous shifting from ahead to astern and vice versa.

Standard equipment on all models includes filters, pump(s), temperature gauges, heat exchangers for salt or fresh water cooling, output companion flanges and manually actuated range selectors and control valves.

Optional equipment such as X-control or trailing pump is available on request.

SWITZERLAND

HYDROMARINE SA
Via Industrie, CH-6814 Lamone, Switzerland

Telephone: (091)505428
Telefax: (091)505429

POWER SHAFT HS-5000 HYDROSTATIC PROPULSION SYSTEM

Some of the first details of this power transmission system were given in the 1989 edition of this book and are repeated below. Using Rexroth hydraulic components the Hydromarine system is being marketed by the Hydromarine companies in Switzerland and Italy. The development of propellers for the system has been undertaken by Marintek in Trondheim, Norway, achieving an efficiency of 85% for the propeller component of the system.

The concept now developed is called Power Shaft HS-5000 and designs for units of four power levels are presently available from 350kW to 1050kW.

DESIGN PHILOSOPHY AND DESCRIPTION

With HYDROMARINE'S POWER SHAFT incorporated into the design of a high speed craft (semi-planing, hydrofoil, catamaran, SES, etc.), the following advantages are claimed over conventional propulsion systems:
—reduction in installed power
—increased carrying capacity
—lower fuel consumption
—higher average speeds in transit
—greater passenger comfort gained through drastic reduction in noise levels and improved seakeeping
—longer life of drive unit, and longer servicing intervals
flexibility of application and ease of installation given by mutual independence in positioning power shaft and diesel engine
—general improvements in structural design of craft, from the functional standpoint
—availability of spare parts worldwide
The revolutionary power shaft differs from all other conventional propulsion systems in terms of performance and novelty.

HORIZONTAL FIXED-PITCH TRACTOR PROPELLER

Propulsion is obtained using a tractor propeller, with correct alignment to the water flow. The propeller is driven by a high efficiency hydraulic motor installed within the power shaft, on which the rudder is also mounted.

Propeller cavitation problems are very greatly reduced by virtue of the fact that the propulsion stream is absolutely uniform and symmetrical about the rotation axis. In this way, the propeller enjoys ideal operating conditions, giving high efficiency and generating no vibration or noise at all through the vessel. The power shaft and its propellers have been optimised to give speeds of up to 50 knots.

The power shaft is flange-mounted to the bottom of the hull, selecting the most advantageous position in terms of hydrodynamics and propulsion.

Inside and outside the power shaft, hydraulic connections to the motor driving the propeller

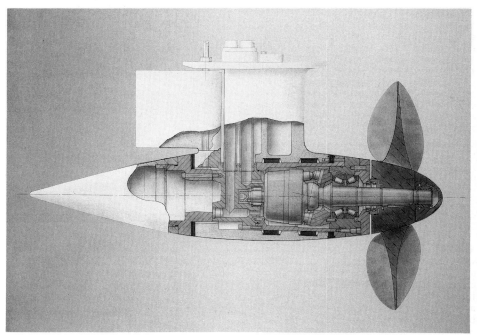
Longitudinal section of the POWER SHAFT

consist exclusively of hoses running from a hydraulic pump mounted direct to the diesel engine.

Both pump and motor are axial piston units manufactured by Mannesmann Rexroth; these are top quality components the reliability of which has been tried and proven since 1957 in many thousands of pieces in the most diverse marine applications throughout the world and further refinements have been made to ensure their complete suitability for marine propulsion.

HIGH OVERALL EFFICIENCY, EXTENSIVE POWER RANGE

Overall efficiency ratings of the power shaft system are high, better than those both of the water jet and of conventional mechanical drives with inclined axis and pusher propeller. More exactly, the fact of adopting tractor type propulsion in the power shaft signifies that the propeller operates in ideal hydrodynamic conditions; in addition, the pod-and-strut structure (which also carries the rudder and its actuator system) has been designed to recover a high percentage of the rotary kinetic energy generated by the propeller, in the form of thrust.

According to the applications, overall efficiency ratings including ratings of hydraulic transmission, propeller, power shaft (due to the water friction on its external surfaces) amounts to about 60%.

The power shaft also includes the rudder and its drive, and can be supplied for nominal powers from 350 to 2000kW (under development).

Dimensions and performance data are tabulated below.

SILENT, VIBRATIONLESS OPERATION, GREATER PASSENGER COMFORT

The design and positioning of the power shaft create particularly good hydrodynamic conditions for the propeller, with the result that overall propulsion noise is reduced to a level never achieved hitherto with propeller drives. In addition to the benefits attributable to improved hydrodynamics, there are those provided by the elastic suspension arrangement (patented) designed for the hydraulic motor and propeller drive assembly; vibrations generated by the motor and propeller are damped out by flexible components incorporated into the

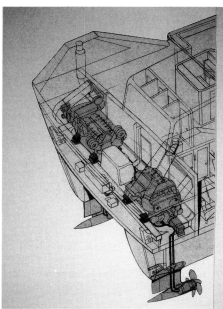
Simplified illustration of hydrostatic propulsion for a high-speed craft

mountings, and are thus prevented from being transmitted to the hull through the power shaft. Again, with hydraulic power supplied to the motor through hoses, further sound isolation is achieved.

An additional factor contributing to the reduction in noise and vibration is the distance which separates the propeller blades from the hull, with the propeller set well away from the structure of the vessel. Axial water inflow to the propeller eliminates the fluctuating forces that cause much of the vibration experienced with inclined shafts.

The final noise reduction expedient is that of suspending the diesel engine and pump equipment on anti-vibration mountings; the pumps can be either flange mounted direct to the engine or bolted to the same base plate. This type of installation can reduce vibration through the structure of the craft by as much as 20 dBA.

The fact that the engine and power shaft are connected by nothing other than a set of hoses brings the further advantage that the initial location of the engine unit can be selected to ensure minimum noise, for example, well aft.

POWER SHAFT AS TORQUE CONVERTER

The combination of variable displacement pump and fixed displacement motor provides a speed/torque converter (a detailed description follows).

Accordingly, the possibility exists of installing diesel engines with reduced power, size and weight specifications. With torque and speed thus variable the craft is able to accelerate and reach its cruising speed earlier, requiring significantly less time to plane, or to lift onto its foils in the case of a hydrofoil. Thus it emerges that the power shaft's fixed-pitch propeller, simple and economical in construction, functions substantialy as a variable pitch one. Another advantage of the transmission's flexibility in operation is that full power can also be extracted from the engine in taking craft to higher cruising speeds.

FAULTLESS BALANCE BETWEEN PROPELLER AND ENGINE SPEEDS

With mechanical transmission eliminated, the speed reduction from engine to propeller is no longer tied to fixed ratios specified by reduction gear manufacturers, but simply a matter of choice. Also provided is the highly desirable facility of adjusting the transmission ratio during operation to suit conditions of loading, or of the sea-state.

TOTAL ABSENCE OF MECHANICAL TRANSMISSION COMPONENTS

The fluid connection between hydraulic pump and motor eliminates a complete mechanical driveline incorporating speed reducing gears, shafting, bevel gears, reversing gears and clutches. Nor are there any problems arising from the close fit tolerances prescribed for mechanical components and their mounting to marine structures of limited rigidity. By contrast, the hydrostatic transmission effectively compensates for lack of rigidity.

PRECISION AND SPEED IN HANDLING

The operation of docking becomes especially swift and accurate thanks to the speed and precision with which the propeller can be controlled, reversing included; engine speed remains constant throughout all such manoeuvres.

REMOTE CONTROL

The running speed and direction of the propeller are controlled from the bridge. By shifting a handle connected to a potentiometer, a signal is produced that commands the pump servo control to produce a variation in flow, hence in the speed of rotation of the hydraulic motor.

Alternatively the same effect can be obtained

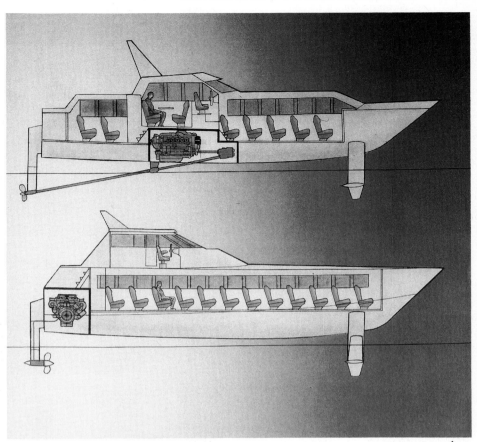
Layout advantages of the power shaft hydrostatic transmission

adopting a pneumatic remote control, likewise operated from the bridge.

LIGHTWEIGHT, COMPACT DRIVE

The POWER SHAFT brings advantages of weight and dimensions, especially when compared to water jet propulsion, as there is no heavy mass of water drawn into the craft through jet ducts.

FREEDOM IN DESIGN

Hydrostatic power transmission offers the naval architect a new sphere of freedom, as craft can at last be designed to suit the exact purpose for which they are intended, and at the same time, to prescribed specifications of seakeeping and hydrodynamic efficiency. In this 'new generation' of naval design, both the power shaft and the engine-pump unit can be located literally in any position that will best optimise the overall construction.

Looking at traditional ocean-going and high speed craft, there are many cases where it appears that the boat has been designed around the engine. This heavy compromise at the design level is dictated by the need to couple together a whole string of mechanical components including cardan shafts, gear pairs, engine units, reversing and speed reducing gears, and of course the propeller shaft, the latter, in most cases inclined to the water flow.

By adopting hydrostatic power transmission, a whole set of constructional expedients, aimed in particular at a successful insulation of the passenger saloon from the engine room environment, can be realised efficiently, simply, and with significant economies in weight and dimensions.

APPROVAL OF MARITIME INSURANCE AGENCIES

The following Agencies have expressed their approval of Hydromarine's power shaft propulsion system: Germanischer Lloyd, Det Norske Veritas, Bureau Veritas, Lloyd's Register of Ship-

ping, American Bureau of Shipping, Registro Italiano Navale.

MANNESMANN REXROTH HYDRAULIC COMPONENTS AND SERVICE WORLD-WIDE

Exclusive use is made of hydraulic components made by Mannesmann Rexroth, the world's biggest and most experienced manufacturer of such products; engineering and back-up services are guaranteed worldwide.

EASE OF SERVICING

The powershaft's rational design enables swift and simple removal and refitment of all component parts.

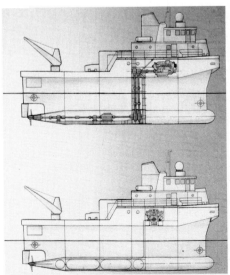
Simplicity of hydrostatic transmission for a SWATH installation

PRELIMINARY RESULTS

At the High-Performance Vehicle Conference, Shanghai, China, 2–5 November 1988, papers were presented giving details of a Rexroth hydrostatic transmission system fitted to a Rodriquez Supramar PT 20 hydrofoil. Trials started in June 1988 and finished in October 1988. Bench tests carried out on the prototype by Rexroth SpA have enabled the following efficiencies to be established:

hydraulic pump: 0.896
        piping: 0.966
hydraulic motor: 0.910
propeller: 0.72
pump coupler: 0.98
overall efficiency: 0.556

The efficiency levels for the original PT 20 single propeller inclined shaft drive system are:

gearbox: 0.98
shafting line: 0.979
inclined shafting line: 0.987
propeller: 0.65
overall efficiency: 0.606

Trials were run at various conditions, for example:

main engine rpm: 1500 (MTU MB 820 Db)
power (calculated): 937kW
overall propeller thrust: 3082 kg
vessel speed: 34.75 knots
hydraulic pump delivery pressure: 257 bar

Test installation on a PT20 hydrofoil

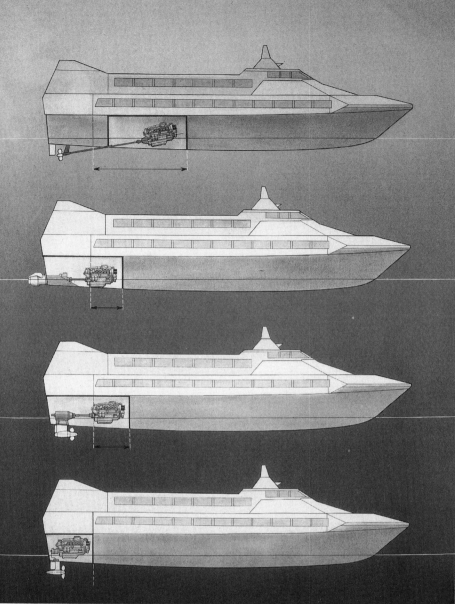

A suggested evolution of catamaran propulsion

hydraulic motor inlet pressure: 235 bar
calculated overall efficiency: 0.577

Some of the advantages of the total propulsion system that is made possible by the Rexroth hydrostatic transmission may be listed as follows:

freedom to optimise the powerplant in the logical optimum position (engine noise distanced from passengers), avoidance of "designing around the engine".

avoidance of inclined shaft hydrodynamic resistance

freedom to optimise passenger cabin layouts

compactness and flexibility of power transmission from engine to propeller

the ability to vary propeller speeds, quickly and accurately

variable speed ratio between engine and propeller enabling the full power of the engine to be used at low craft speeds

simple provision of neutral and reverse drive capability

MAAG GEAR-WHEEL COMPANY LTD

Hardstrasse 219, CH-8023 Zurich, Switzerland

Telephone: (01) 278 7878
Telex: 822 704 MZZ CH
Telefax: (01) 278 7880

The Maag Gear-Wheel Company designs and manufactures a wide range of marine gears and synchronous clutch couplings.

A recent application in the high-speed marine craft field was for the Blohm + Voss Corsair SES which was fitted with Maag reduction gear boxes driving Sulzer Escher Wyss 7-blade propellers at 940rpm.

UNITED KINGDOM

NEI ALLEN LTD
ALLEN GEARS

Atlas Works, Pershore, Worcestershire WR10 2BZ, England

Telephone: (0386) 552211
Telex: 337488
Telefax: (0386) 554491

D H Evans, *General Manager*
D E Yates, *Technical Manager*
H I Grant, *Sales and Marketing Manager*

Allen Gears first became associated with high-speed surface craft in the early 1950s when the Royal Navy commissioned two Vosper prototype aluminium hull vessels. Each triple-screw craft was powered by three Rolls-Royce Proteus gas turbines driving fixed-pitch propellers. The turbines had a rating of 3500hp at a speed of 11 600rpm, and an Allen epicyclic gear was incorporated to reduce engine speed to 5000rpm. The secondary reduction Allen gearbox consisted of bevel gears for a shaft angle of 15 degrees, driving into a double-train epicyclic reversing section. Since their introduction and subsequent uprating to 4250hp, over 260 primary gear sets have been supplied by Allen Gears to many of the world's navies.

C FORM GEARBOX

In 1978 Allen Gears fitted their C form gearboxes in a Don Shead-designed 29-metre, 45-knot, luxury yacht. The yacht cruises on two wing, diesel engine-driven jets and a gas turbine provides power for maximum speed. The turbine is a Textron Lycoming Super TF40 which produces 4600hp at 15 400rpm and drives a Rocketdyne jet pump running at 1664rpm. The gearbox has a C drive configuration, both input and output shafts are at the aft end, and consists of a primary epicyclic train with a single helical parallel-shaft secondary train. An idler is required to cover the necessary centre distance from the gas turbine to the Rocketdyne jet pump and also matches their standard rotations. The jet pump houses the main thrust bearing, therefore secondary gearbox bearings need only accommodate the thrust imposed by single helical gearing. A caliper disc brake is fitted to the free end of the secondary pinion enabling the main jet pump to be held stationary when using wing engine propulsion.

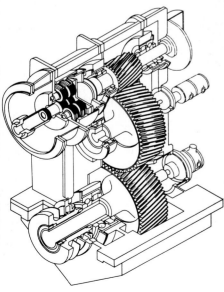

A section view of the Allen C form drive gearbox showing first and second stage reduction gears

The Allen five-shaft C form 12 000 to 681rpm reduction gearbox as fitted to a Fr Lürssen Werft luxury yacht, two 5406kW,(7250hp) gas turbines

Port and starboard multi-stage hovercraft propulsion gearboxes

FIVE-SHAFT C FORM DRIVE GEARBOX

As a follow-on from uprated gears for the Royal Navy, Allen Gears constructed a combined epicyclic and parallel-shaft C drive gearbox for a 46-metre, 45-knot luxury yacht built by Fr Lürssen Werft, Federal Republic of Germany. The yacht was powered by two Allison 570 gas turbines driving a KaMeWa waterjet. In addition there were two wing engines driving small waterjets of 1500hp. Total available power was 17 500hp. The gas turbines were positioned aft, driving forward into the gearbox. Each of the turbines has a maximum input of 7250hp at 12 000rpm giving an output speed to the waterjet unit from gearbox of 681rpm. A five-shaft configuration gearbox was adopted to accommodate the centre distance between the gas turbines and the output shaft. The input is taken from the primary epicyclic train

through quill-shafts, within the secondary pinion, to SSS self-synchronising clutches at the forward end of the gear case. This arrangement permits the second gas turbine to be introduced to the drive line or to be disconnected without interruption of power.

HOVERCRAFT TRANSMISSIONS

Allen Gears association with the Spanish Company CHACONSA and its VCA-36 craft has moved on to future developments with an overseas navy for a similar sized craft. This prototype vessel which has more than surpassed expectation on trials utilises Pratt and Whitney gas turbines for the lift system and Textron Lycoming for the propulsion system. In both cases the reduction gears are of Allen Gears light weight construction using the very latest gear technology. In order to achieve the best machinery layout and to meet the

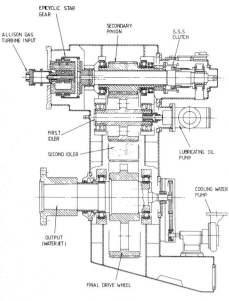

Sectioned view of one drive line of the five-shaft C form reduction gearbox

necessary weight targets Allen provided multi-stage parallel shaft gears in aluminium gear cases using gear components constructed according to proven aircraft methods. All techniques were fully tested with careful stress analysis in all areas prior to manufacture.

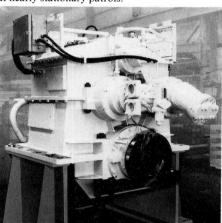

Gas turbine boost and diesel engine cruise gearboxes for 'Standard Flex 300'

CODAG PROPULSION SYSTEM

The first 7 ships of the Royal Danish Navy 'Standard Flex 300' multirole vessel programme use a 'CODAG' propulsion plant powered by MTU 16V396 TB94 diesels for cruise and a GE LM500 gas turbine for boost. The engines drive through Allen vertically-offset custom-engineered light-weight parallel shaft gearboxes with integral lubricating system. Each gear box is equipped with a hydraulic motor which forms part of a hydraulic system (powered by General Motors diesel) to meet the requirements of auxiliary propulsion during silent minehunting and economic loitering at nearly stationary patrols.

UNITED STATES OF AMERICA

THE CINCINNATI GEAR COMPANY

5657 Wooster Pike, Cincinnati, Ohio 45227, USA

Telephone: 5132717700
Telex: 21–4568

D R Bardill, *Marketing Manager*

The Cincinnati Gear Company was founded in 1907. Since the 1950s it has specialised in high performance parallel shaft and epicyclic marine drives. Successful installations include the Boeing Jetfoil craft series, the Textron Marine LCAC assault craft and the T-A0187 class oiler.

DETROIT DIESEL CORPORATION

13400 Outer Drive West, Detroit, Michigan 48239–4001, USA

Telephone: (313)592 5000
Telex: 4320091

Detroit Diesel Corporation provide a full range

of transmissions to give an optimum match for each DDC engine. These transmissions are manufactured by Twin Disc Corporation

DDC gearbox installation

DETROIT DIESEL MARINE TRANSMISSIONS

Engine Model	Configuration	Gear Ratios
8.2L	10° Down Angle	1.54, 2.00
6V-53	Inline & 7° Down Angle	1.10, 1.51, 1.77, 1.98
6-71	Inline & 7° Down Angle	1.10, 1.51, 1.77, 1.98
	Vertical Offset	1.45, 1.71, 2.04
6V-92	Vertical Offset	1.45, 1.71, 2.00, 2.04
	7° Down Angle	1.45, 1.73, 1.96
8V-92	Vertical Offset	1.50, 1.74, 2.04
	7° Down Angle	1.48, 1.92
12V-71	Vertical Offset	1.29, 1.50, 1.76, 1.96, 2.48
	10° Down Angle	1.52, 1.77, 1.97
12V-92	Vertical Offset	1.29, 1.50, 1.64, 1.76, 1.83, 1.96, 2.03, 2.48, 2.55
	10° Down Angle	1.52, 1.66, 1.77, 1.97, 2.06, 2.48
16V-92	Vertical Offset	1.00, 1.45, 1.74, 2.04, 2.55
	10° Down Angle	1.53, 1.71, 1.92, 2.38
16V-149	Vertical Offset	2.52

Detroit Diesel marine transmissions

TWIN DISC INC
Racine, Wisconsin 53403, USA

See entry under Twin Disc International SA, Belgium

AIR PROPELLERS

GERMANY, FEDERAL REPUBLIC

HOFFMANN PROPELLER
GmbH & Co KG

Postfach 265, Küpferlingstrasse 9, D-8200
Rosenheim 2, Federal Republic of Germany

Telephone: (08031) 32011
Telex: 525811HOCO D
Telefax: (08034) 15832

Richard Wurm, *Chairman*
Johann Sterr, *Managing Director*

Hoffmann Propeller GmbH & Co KG was
founded in 1955 by Dipl-Ing Ludwig Hoffmann
and Ing Richard Wurm and now employs about
70 people, divided into 15 clerical, 5 design, 5
inspectors and 45 in production. Of the three
design engineers, one is a licensed test pilot.

The company covers the following certification:
LBA I-EC 2 for design and development of aircraft propellers; LBA I-C 14 for production of
aircraft propellers and equipment; LBA II-A 35
for repair of aircraft propellers and governors
not of Hoffmann manufacture; FAA 810–3 F for
repair and overhaul of aircraft propellers and
accessories licensed by the US airworthiness authority; CAA Hovercraft Approval for design and
production of hovercraft propellers.

The total space is about 2600m² and this year
the factory will be enlarged with about 1800m² for
wood working and composite materials production.

Hoffmann Propeller has been involved in
research and development for the German Ministry of Research and Technology, the Ministry
of Transportation, the Ministry of Defence as well
as for major aircraft companies such as Mes-
serschmitt-Bölkow-Blohm, Dornier and others.

Propellers have been designed, constructed,
tested and produced from 6 to 6000shp. In the
latter case Hoffmann blades were installed in an
original British Aerospace Dynamics hub on the
German Military transport aircraft C-160 Trans-
all. The propeller received military certification.
Other developments were, for instance, the 5-
bladed shrouded propeller for the MBB/RFB
Fantrainer, this aircraft being produced under
licence in Thailand. Besides aircraft propellers,
blades for wind energy converters, blowers and
large fan blades for windtunnel application in the
automotive industry are in current production.
Propeller overhaul and service is provided for all
types of general aviation propellers and different
manufacturers.

Special hovercraft propellers have been manufactured as well as propellers for airboats. The
reason for this was the excellent erosion resistant
features of the composite materials which are
superior to aluminium alloy.

Recent installations (Hovercraft and
Airboat Propellers)

1960   Since 1960 smaller fixed-pitch and some
ground-adjustable and variable-pitch
propellers were constantly built for air-
propeller driven boats, snow sledges and
Hovercraft.
The Hovermarine Hovercat and earlier
Scorpion were the first hovercrafts for

Canadian Coast Guard BHC API-88 hovercraft propelled by Hoffman ducted propellers HO-V254

which Hoffmann built fixed-pitch propellers and electrically controlled variable and reversing pitch propellers. The
electric-controlled propeller was,
however, too slow in pitch change.

ca.   CHACONSA, VCA-2/3 small craft,
1970   2 propellers, free, driven by about
150kW, 2-bladed, ground adjustable, 2m
diameter. Propellers have been overhauled after 1000 hours in good
condition, replacements have been delivered.

1981   Wärtsilä *Larus*, 4 propellers, ducted,
driven by about 550kW, 4-bladed,
forward and reversing, 3m diameter,
hydraulically controlled by control valve.
This craft is currently with Arctic Transportation Ltd, Tuktoyaktuk, Northwest
Territories, Canada.

1982   BHC AP1–88, 2 propellers per craft,
ducted, driven by approx 370kW,
4-blade, ground adjustable, 2.75m diameter. Experience with these propellers is
increasing and the first propellers are
close to 5000 hours time since new. A
special polyurethane outer coating and
additional leading-edge protection gives
a service time for the blade between 1000
and 2000 operating hours before overhaul is considered necessary. The craft
are in service between Portsmouth and
the Isle of Wight, UK, between Denmark
and Sweden (Copenhagen to Malmö)
and in Australia.

1982   CHACONSA, VCA-36, 2 propellers,
free, one lefthand, one righthand
rotation, 1100kW, 5-blade, controllable
and reversing pitch propellers, 4m diameter, hydraulically controlled by control
valve.

1985   BHC AP1–88, 2 propellers, shrouded,
driven by approx 370kW, 4-blade, controllable and reversing, 2.75m diameter.
Blade design as for ground adjustable
propellers. Craft is in service in USA.

1985   Slingsby, Tropimere 6, 2 propellers,
ducted, 3-blade ground adjustable,
1.10m diameter.

Propeller used for 1988 project

1985   Slingsby SAH 2200 (ex 1500), 1 propeller,
ducted, 3-blade, 1.50m diameter, reversing.

1986   Marineswift Thunderbolt 30, 1 propeller,
ducted, driven by approx 200kW,
5-blade, 1.12m diameter, ground adjustable.

1987   USSR: 2 propellers, ducted, 4-blade,
257kW, 3m diameter, hydraulically controlled.

1988   5-bladed variable pitch ducted propeller,
2600kW, 4m dia., hydraulically controlled for 25m hovercraft; now in operation in Korea.

1989   Several new hovercraft propellers in
development.

MT-PROPELLER ENTWICKLUNG GmbH & Co KG

Postfach 0720, Airport D-8440 Straubing, Federal Republic of Germany

Telephone: 094291201/8111

Telex: 65599MTPRO D
Telefax: 094298432

Gerd Műhlbauer, *President*

This company was formed in 1982 and is mainly involved in the production of propellers for aircraft. It has developed a range of electric variable-pitch propellers and hydraulic constant-speed propellers. Some of the propellers are LBA approved. The largest diameter propeller built by the end of 1986 was 2.9m, for 800shp, but designs can be undertaken up to 3.5m, 2000shp, and above.

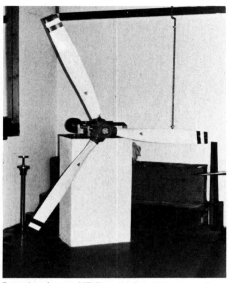

Examples of recent MT-Propeller Entwicklung propellers

UNITED KINGDOM

AIR VEHICLES LIMITED

Head Office and Factory: Unit 4, Three Gates Road, Cowes, Isle of Wight, Hampshire, England

Telephone: 0983293194
Telex: 86513HVWORK G
Telefax: 0983291987

C B Eden, *Director*

Air Vehicles Limited has been involved in hovercraft since 1968 and have manufactured centrifugal fans and propellers of various sizes for their own craft and others.

PROPELLERS: These are of the four-bladed, fixed-pitch, laminated-mahogany type and incorporate stainless steel leading-edge protection. Sizes from 0.61m to 1.83m diameter are manufactured.

PROPELLER DUCTS: Associated propeller ducts are also designed and manufactured. Various sizes and types have been designed for our own craft and others up to a propeller diameter of 3.6m and absorbing 2900hp.

FANS: Aluminium centrifugal fans of various sizes up to 0.915m are produced. They are of the reverse aerofoil type, using fabricated or extruded blades in marine aluminium giving a robust fan with a good fatigue life.

Air Vehicles duct installation fitted to an SR.N6 military craft

0.76m diameter aluminium fan produced by Air Vehicles Ltd

Air Vehicles-built, Robert Trillo-designed propeller on an AV Tiger 16

BRITISH AEROSPACE (DYNAMICS) LTD

Manor Road, Hatfield, Hertfordshire AL10 9LL, England

Telephone: 0707262300
Telex: 22324/5 G
Telefax: 0707261915

Norman Barber, *Managing Director*

For over 50 years British Aerospace (Dynamics) Ltd (formerly de Havilland Propellers Ltd) has been designing, developing and manufacturing propellers with their ancilliaries and control systems. British Aerospace has been responsible for providing the largest propellers for air cushion vehicles.

Recent installations (Air cushion vehicles)
British Hovercraft Corporation BH.7, 6.40m diameter, 4-blade, hydraulic pitch control with reversing, single propeller installation
SEDAM N 500, 6.40m diameter, 4-blade, hydraulic pitch control with reversing, triple propeller installation
British Hovercraft Corporation SR.N4, 5.76m diameter, 4-blade, hydraulic pitch control with reversing, four propeller installation, swivelling
British Hovercraft Corporation SR.N4 Super 4, 6.40m diameter, 4-blade, hydraulic pitch control with reversing, four propeller installation, swivelling
These propellers have the following design and construction features:
PROPELLER HUB: This is similar for both the

5.76m and 6.4m propellers, comprising a split barrel and a spider to which the blades are fitted and retained by lips on the barrel. Centrifugal loads are taken by single roller thrust bearings between the blade root flanges and the barrel lips. The spider mounts onto a modified SBAC splined engine shaft and is retained on the shaft by split front and rear cones and a retaining nut.

The hub is protected against the corrosive effects of salt water by epoxy type paint. The ingress of water is prevented by rubber water excluders around the blade shanks, a glassfibre excluder around the pitch change dome/barrel opening and by brushing sealant over all joint faces and fastenings.

The propeller blades on the 5.76m propeller are conventional aluminium alloy suitably anodised

One of the four composite-material blade propellers on the BHC SR.N4 Super 4 hovercraft

Erosion damage protection sheath, 0.914m length, for fitting to a 3.05m long glassfibre propeller blade

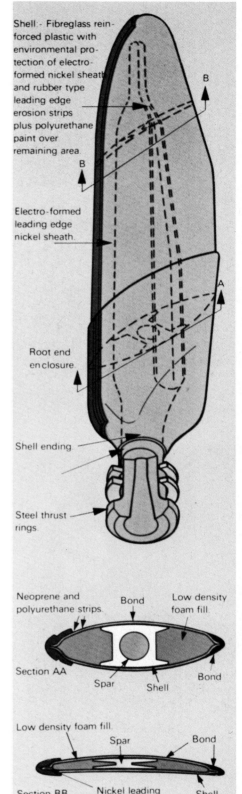

British Aerospace composite blade construction

and protected against erosion by rubber leading edge sheaths. The 6.4m propeller has composite construction blades consisting of an aluminium alloy spar, with a root end similar to the 5.76m and with a glassfibre blade shell. The shell is made by laminating glassfibre on a former having the specified shape and aerofoil section using a wet lay up process. The shell is then cured in an oven and bonded to the anodic protected spar. Foam is then introduced into the hollow cavities of the blade and the inboard end of the blade is sealed by glassfibre fairings. The leading edge of the blade is protected by an electro-formed nickel sheath and rubber erosion strip. The finished blade is then sprayed with special polyurethane paint.

PITCH CHANGE MECHANISM: Hydraulic oil is transmitted to the front or rear of a piston depending upon the requirement to alter the pitch angle of the blades. Motion of the piston is transmitted to the blade shank bevel gear by fixed rotating cylindrical cams. The piston and cams are housed in a dome which is fitted onto the front of the propeller hub and held by the dome retaining nut. The rate of change of blade angle is nominally 10° per second. The available range of blade angle can be altered to suit an application within the range −30° to +45° (at the 1.83m station on the blade) and with a feather angle of +90° nominal if desired.

PROPELLER CONTROL SYSTEMS: BAe (Dynamics) Ltd has produced both analogue and digital electronic control systems and the choice between these methods will depend upon the requirements of a particular application. A typical system is that provided for a large car/passenger carrying hovercraft.

In this hovercraft system the signal demanding blade pitch angle required by the pilot to carry out a particular manoeuvre is put into digital form and is then compared by standard mathematical techniques with the existing blade angle which is measured by an optical shaft encoder. The error signal so produced is modified by digital methods to obtain the required overall system response characteristics. The power stage of the electronics drives a stepper motor which controls the position of a single stage hydraulic control valve. According to the position of the valve, oil is directed through the bush and sleeve of a pitch control unit to the oil tubes which connect to the front and rear of the pitch change piston. The pitch control unit is mounted on a rear face of the propeller/engine gearbox and a mechanical blade angle feedback is provided through the movement

of the oil tubes which is sensed by the shaft encoder previously mentioned.

The ability to feather the propeller is independent of the control system, so that when a solenoid valve is energised a feathering pump moves oil to push the control valve spindle into the feather position, which in turn directs oil to the pitch change mechanism. A transmitter gives an output signal to an instrument on the flight deck indicating pitch angle and feather position.

WEIGHTS
6.4m diameter propeller (comprising hub, pitch change mechanism and blades): 812.83kg*
Oil in propeller: 33.11kg
Total 'on shaft' wet weight: 846kg
*Total weight subject to a production tolerance of +2.5%.
Polar moment of inertia: 998.7kg/m^2

EROSION/DAMAGE PROTECTION SYSTEM: The experience gained over many years of servicing glassfibre bladed 6.4m propellers on hovercraft in very severe operational and environmental conditions has enabled an Erosion/Damage Protection System (EDPS) to be developed and patented for blade leading edges. This system can be applied to any shape of component within the overall dimensions of a cylinder 2.44m long and 0.6m in diameter.

The breakthrough in technology which the EDP system offers, is the ability to plate a resilient substrate material with erosion-resistant nickel so that an integral molecular bond is formed which withstands erosion and impact or implosion damage. A further characteristic is that any cracks so caused to the nickel plating do not diminish the erosion properties of the system and neither do the cracks propagate to the main structure being protected. Experience in service, at rotational tip speeds of approximately 220m/s, has proved that the nickel plating, even though severely damaged, does not peel away from the substrate material.

The EDP system can be designed to give a predictable erosion life by varying the thickness of the substrate material and, more importantly, by changing the thickness of the nickel deposit locally, to adjust for varying erosion rates over the surface shape of the component being protected.

DOWTY ROTOL LIMITED
Cheltenham Road East, Gloucester GL2 9QH, England

Telephone: 0452712424
Telex: 43246G
Telefax: 0452713821

D G M Davis, *Technical Director*

J D Kemp, *Engineering Manager, Propulsion*
D Soley, *Project Engineer, Propulsion*
M B Kelly, *Sales and Marketing Director*
D S Russell, *Executive Director, Sales*
J H Clarkson, *Sales Engineer, Propulsion*

Dowty Rotol has been designing and manufacturing propellers for aircraft since 1937 and for over 26 years has been actively engaged in propulsion systems for air cushion vehicles.

The company is at present engaged in the production of propellers for the Textron Marine Systems LCAC vehicles. There is a repair, overhaul and assembly plant in the USA: Dowty Aerospace Corporation, PO Box 5000, Sully Road, Staverton West, Stirling, Virginia 22170.

Telephone: (703) 450 8200
Telex: 248212
Telefax: (703) 4309060

Shell:- Fibreglass reinforced plastic with environmental protection of electroformed nickel sheath and rubber type leading edge erosion strips plus polyurethane paint over remaining area.

Electro-formed leading edge nickel sheath.

Root end enclosure.

Shell ending.

Steel thrust rings.

Neoprene and polyurethane strips.
Bond
Low density foam fill.
Section AA
Spar
Shell
Bond

Low density foam fill.
Spar
Bond
Section BB
Nickel leading edge sheath.
Shell

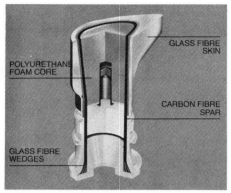

Dowty Rotol blade root retention features

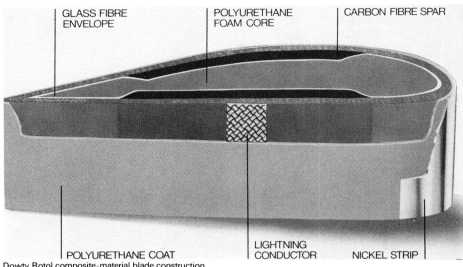

GLASS FIBRE ENVELOPE   POLYURETHANE FOAM CORE   CARBON FIBRE SPAR

POLYURETHANE COAT   LIGHTNING CONDUCTOR   NICKEL STRIP

Dowty Rotol composite-material blade construction

Hovercraft installations (Air cushion vehicles)

British Hovercraft Corporation SR.N5, SR.N6, 2.744m diameter, 4-blade hydraulic pitch control with reversing, single propeller installation, produced in aluminium alloy and composite material construction

British Hovercraft Corporation SR.N6 Mk 6, 3.049m diameter, 4-blade, hydraulic pitch control with reversing, 2-propeller installation, aluminium alloy blades

Mitsui PP15 3.201m diameter, 4-blade, hydraulic pitch control with reversing, single-propeller installation, aluminium alloy blades

Vosper Thornycroft VT 2 4.116m diameter, 7-blade, 2-propeller installation (ducted), composite-material blades

Textron Marine Systems LCAC 3.582m diameter, 4-blade, 2-propeller installation (ducted) composite material blades

Dowty Rotol ducted propeller installation on Textron Marine Systems LCAC

Dowty Rotol composite-material blade propeller for Textron Marine Systems LCAC

The extensive corrosion and erosion problems associated with air cushion vehicles led Dowty Rotol to develop composite blades with all-over erosion protection. These blades, the latest of which incorporate advanced technology aerofoil sections unique to Dowty Rotol, offer the following advantages: low weight combined with high strength, internal carbon fibre spars for high integrity, freedom from corrosion, easily repairable.

Dowty Rotol propellers for air cushion vehicles are designed to combine simple construction with safe operation. Techniques proven on ACVs have in turn been applied to and certificated on new generation general aviation, executive and commuter aircraft.

UNITED STATES OF AMERICA

ADVANCE RATIO DESIGN COMPANY, INC (ARDCO)

2540 Green Street, JEN Industrial Campus, Chester, Pennsylvania 19013, USA

Telephone: (215) 494 3200
Telefax: (215) 494 5079

David F Thompson, *President*

ARDCO specialises in composite airfoil blading and structures. The ARDCO team has designed and produced blades for turboprops, ducted propulsion fans, hovercraft compressors and helicopter main and tail rotors, also model blades for advanced unducted fan testing. Materials include glassfibre, graphite and/or Kevlar/epoxy, oriented linear-filament reinforced materials, compression moulded with low density cores of honeycomb or foam plastic and flush co-bonded metal leading edge erosion strips. ARDCO produces blades to fit existing hubs or complete rotor assemblies, as required. The company also uses resin transfer moulding (RTM) techniques where unusually massive (some hollow-ribbed) composite structures of hundreds of pounds weight are required, such as for marine propellers. Complete vehicle airframe structures are also custom-designed and fabricated.

HIGH-PERFORMANCE SURFACE-CRAFT PROPELLER

ARDCO is in the process of developing a specialised fan/propeller series useful for a variety of high performance surface craft which utilise ducted propulsion, such as hovercraft and airboats. The family of fan/propellers to be made available will offer a spread of characteristics approximately as follows:

Diameters: 914 to 1321mm
Number of blades:2,3,4,6,12 with equi-spaced patterns

Pitch angle: ground-adjustable pitch
Power input: to approximately 134 kW
Rotational tip speeds: 122 to 167 m/s

The objective for this propeller series is quiet operation while giving efficient performance and hence, operating at moderate tip speeds, these propellers require large blade area and/or a larger number of blades

The blades with relatively thin aerofoils are solid glass-filament epoxy, pressure-moulded and feature integrally-bonded stainless-steel leading-edge abrasion caps to protect against water spray environments.

The hub is pressure moulded in glass-fibre-reinforced composite material and features ground-adjustable blade pitch, allowing power absorption vs.rpm to be fine tuned.

The propeller is designed for long life and minimal maintenance in a marine environment and towards this end total elimination of metal-to-metal contact is embodied as well as minimisation of exposed metal surfaces.

ARDCO propeller rig tests

ARDCO all-composite surface-craft propeller

PACIFIC PROPELLER INC (PPI)
(Subsidiary of IMC Magnetics Corp)

5802 S 228th St, Kent, Washington 98032, USA

Telephone: (206) 872–7767
Telex: 32–0368
Telefax: (206) 872–7221

Charles W Johnson, *President*
Dennis Patrick, *Director of Engineering*

Roger Pearson, *Sales Manager*

Pacific Propeller manufactures, overhauls and sells propeller systems for aircraft and hovercraft use, having been in this business since 1946. PPI has manufactured over 10 000 metal propeller blades for single and multi-engine installations and is the current supplier of propellers for the Canadian Coast Guard SR.N5, SR.N6 and Voyageur hovercraft. In addition, PPI's designed and

manufactured propeller blades are the only current production units approved for installation on the US Army LACV-30 hovercraft.

HC200–1S PROPELLER BLADE

This is a hard alloy derivative of the AG-series blades manufactured for aircraft use. It is designed to be tougher and more erosion resistant to the effects of salt and sand spray. Typical hovercraft installations use the 3-bladed HSP 43D50 hub

coupled to the P&W ST6 TwinPac or the Rolls
Royce Gnome turbine engines. Propeller diameter
is 2.72m. This configuration has been tested in
excess of 1600 hp and is safe for operation up to
2300rpm. Each blade weighs 22.22kg and can be
overhauled using standard propeller overhaul
facilities.

LOW-SPEED AIRFOIL DESIGN

Efforts are currently under way to develop military and commercial applications of Pacific Propeller's proprietary low-speed airfoil technology.
This includes work for the US Army on the PPI
1300 blade design for application on the LACV-
30 and a similar commercial adaptation for the
Westfoil 25-metre hydrofoil craft. As a further
extension of the development work performed on
hovercraft, PPI has entered into an R&D contract
with the US Army to provide a ducted, low-speed
propulsion system to retrofit on the LACV-30.

Technicians preparing an instrumented PPI propeller for
testing on Canadian Coast Guard Voyageur

PPI 1300 low-speed experimental aerofoil propeller

MARINE PROPELLERS

AUSTRALIA

SS ENGINEERING (1984) PTY LIMITED

10 Ballantyne Road, Kewdale 6105, Western Australia, Australia
PO Box 5, Cloverdale, Western Australia, Australia

Telephone: (09) 3578388
Telefax: (09) 350 5302

Dennis Wade, *Manager*

Manufacturer of propellers from 250mm diameter to 2550mm in three-, four- or five-blade designs. Materials include 88/10/2 gunmetal, CX3 manganese bronze, AB2 aluminium bronze or CMAI bronze.

A recent installation of SS E and F propellers was on the 190-seat, 25-knot International Cata-marans *Thunderbird* built by Bulls Marine Industries at Metung, New South Wales. The propellers are 864mm in diameter, 812mm in pitch. They are also installed on the International Catamarans wave-piercing catamaran *Spirit of Victoria*.

Propellers can be supplied with up to 5, 6 or 7 blades and finished to ISO 484/2–1981 (E) to Class 2, 1 or S standards as required.

DENMARK

HUNDESTED MOTOR & PROPELLER FABRIK A/S

Skansevej 1, DK-3390 Hundested, Denmark

Telephone: (02) 337117
Telex: 40245HMF DK
Telefax: (02) 339902

Designers and manufacturers of controllable-pitch propellers since 1929. The 20-knot RMI SD-60 *Halcyon* SWATH vessel is fitted with Hundested 1143mm diameter fully-reversible (type FR-H) propellers.

Hundested type FR-H controllable-pitch propeller system as fitted to the RMI *Halcyon*

GERMANY, FEDERAL REPUBLIC

SULZER-ESCHER WYSS GmbH

Postfach 1380, D-7980 Ravensburg, Federal Republic of Germany

Telephone: (0751)830
Telex: 732901
Telefax: (0751)83 2396

Sulzer-Escher Wyss have a very considerable background in the design and production of controllable-pitch propellers, many supplied for frigates, corvettes, patrol boats, mine countermeasure vessels and special purpose vessels. A particularly interesting feature developed in 1970 by Sulzer-Escher Wyss for higher-speed propellers is an air ejection system to reduce the noise consequences of cavitation. Compressed air is led to channels in the leading edges of the blades and vented through a multiplicity of small holes at face and back, blade root and tip, and thus creates an air cushion over the blade. This air cushion considerably reduces the noise generated by a cavitating propeller. Over 100 propellers have been supplied with this system. A further promising development investigated by Sulzer-Escher Wyss is an increase in the number of blades to seven. Extensive model tests have shown that an interesting increase of the cavitation inception speed can be obtained without a penalty in efficiency: a disadvantage expected from the resultant slightly larger hub ratio is compensated by a reduction of the induction losses (approach to a propeller with an infinite number of blades). The mechanical hub design has been completed on the basis of the same loads and safety factors as have proven reliable in 5-bladed propellers.

A recent 7-blade controllable-pitch propeller design was supplied for the Blohm + Voss Corsair SES project. The propellers for this 52 land-vessel have the following characteristics:

1.2 metre diameter propellers for the Blohm + Voss 52 knot Corsair SES, capable of absorbing 2560kW each

Diameter: 1200mm
Hub ratio: 0.32
Design pitch ratio: 1.75

Maximum shaft power: 2560 kW
Rotational sped: 940 rpm

ITALY

BREDA MARINE SpA
[LEVI DRIVE UNITS]
Piazza S Ambrogio n16, Milan 20123, Italy

Telephone: (02) 4880790/4883032
Telex: 380283I
Telefax: 2–4880384

Ambrogio Caccia Dominioni, *Managing Director*
Renato Levi, *In charge Projects*
Ing Giovanni Patrone Raggi, *Sales and Marketing Manager*

LEVI DRIVE UNITS (LDU)

The Levi Drive Units are designed by Renato Levi, a designer of fast power boats over the past 30 years, a pioneer of the Deep-V hull and the Delta configuration. He sought to avoid appendage drag and towards the end of the 1960s he produced his Step-Drive system of propulsion which was first adopted on the 13.1m *Drago*, the world's fastest diesel production cruiser at that time. Since then he has designed over 50 craft employing the Step-Drive system. In seeking to improve this system he evolved the Levi Drive Unit offering the advantages of the conventional 'Z' drive with the increased performance of surface propulsion.

The engine may be fitted amidships or right aft without the added complication of a costly V-drive and transmission shaft. The tunnel rudders over the top half of the propellers have been employed to overcome some of the disadvantages of conventional rudders or propeller power steering. The two vertical rudder blades which are a continuation of the shroud act as side-walls, and, operating below the hull, give positive control as required as well as protecting the propeller in shallow water.

To enhance the reverse thrust capabilities of a fixed-pitch propeller Levi has devised a new blade section profile, giving on the back of the blade a concave area towards the trailing edge, producing improved section lift coefficients and hence thrust when in reverse rotation. The propeller incorporating this profile is called the Diamond Back® superface propeller and overcomes the poor astern thrust associated with surface propellers.

The present complement of Levi Drive Units covers a range from 50 to 4000hp (indicative power limits).

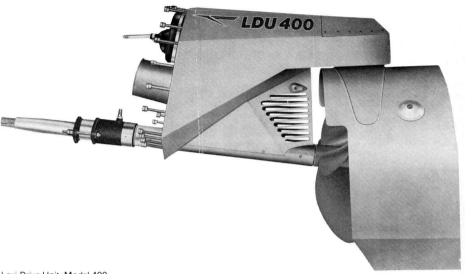

Levi Drive Unit, Model 400

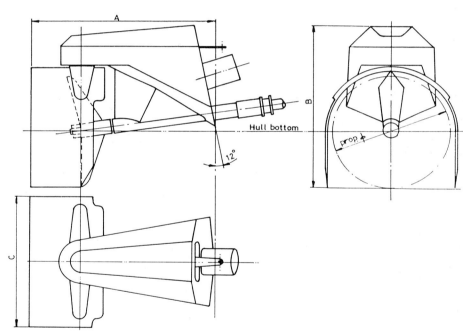

Levi Drive Unit, dimensions, see table

Diamond Back® surface propeller

LDU Model data

Model	LDU100	200PL	300	400	800
Max torque, shaft, kg.m:	45	105	175	205	360
Rpm/hp indicative limits:	120hp at 1950rpm to 292hp at 4760rpm	280hp at 1920rpm to 438hp at 3010rpm 2465rpm	380hp at 1554rpm to 600hp at 2460rpm	438hp at 1540rpm to 700hp at 2040rpm	650hp at 1330rpm to 1000hp at
Max torque, rudder stock, kg/m:	30	75	125	150	250
Exhaust, outside dia. mm:	120	75	168	160	200
Fitting to transom (studs):	22	22	22	22	24
Lubrication, linkage:	molybdenum grease				
Lubrication, shaft:	water				
Dimensions: A, mm:	806	878	1030	1117	1356
B, mm:	670	805	361.5	1019	1231
C, mm:	526	635	735	798	952
Weight, excluding propeller, kg:	85	140	240	265	500

Summary of features

Body of LDU: Monocoque structure in 316L stainless steel, welded and heat treated

Rudder: Of semi-circular design together with reinforcing plate and stock of 316L stainless steel plate and bar respectively

Rudder linkage: Consisting of yoke, dummy tiller and tie rod terminals in cast 316L stainless steel, or nickel-aluminium-bronze

Propeller shaft: Armco Aquamet 17–18–22 or monel k 500

Surface propeller: Four-bladed with Diamond Back sections cast in nickel-aluminium-bronze (NAB). For the Model 2000 and above the propellers are five-bladed

Shaft bearings: Water-lubricated in synthetic fibre

LDU Model data (contd)

Model	800PL	1000PL	2000	2400PL	3000PL
Max torque, shaft, kg.m:	550	470	850	850	1500
Rpm/hp indicative limits:	1200hp at 1600rpm to 1650hp at 2200rpm	700hp at 1070rpm to 1200hp at 1850rpm	1630hp at 1400rpm to 2330hp at 2000rpm	1200hp at 1010rpm to 2200ho at 1850rpm	2200hp at 1050rpm to 3500hp at 1650rpm
Max torque, rudder stock. kg.m	250	125	500	500	800
Exhaust, outside dia. mm:	200	200	300	300	460
Fitting to transom (studs):	24	22	24	22	24
Lubrication, linkage:	molybdenum grease				
Lubrication, shaft	water				
Dimensions: A, mm:	1356	1356	1596	1596	1995
B, mm:	1231	1231	1450	1450	1845
C, mm:	952	952	1130	1120	1400
Weight, excluding propeller, kg:	540	600	1000	1350	2200

COCO MOTORI

Via Aurelia Sud 137, 55044 Marina di Pietrasanta (Lucca), Italy

Telephone: (0584) 21611

Mario P Coco, *Proprietor*

Producer of Deltaprop 406mm diameter propellers for high-performance planing craft powered by Volvo Penta and BMW engines.

ELICHE RADICE SpA

Via Valtellina 45, 20092 Cinisello Balsamo, Milan, Italy
Telephone: (02) 6182548/6189348
Telex: 332352RADPRO I
Telefax: (02) 6127688

Alfredo Ridici
Carlo Ridici

Manufacture of fixed-pitch propellers for high-speed craft. Early Hovermarine HN2 craft were fitted with Ridici propellers in stainless steel.

Bronze propellers with two to five blades and diameters up to 3.5 metres can be supplied.

JAPAN

KAMOME PROPELLER CO LTD

690 Kamiyabe-cho, Totsuka-ku, Yokohama 245, Japan

Telephone: (045) 811 2461
Telex: 3822315KAMOME J

Design and manufacture of a wide range of controllable-pitch propellers from 300 , to 15 000hp. Recent installations have included 1750mm diameter, 1400mm pitch CPC-53F propellers on the Mitsui 20.5-knot *Kotozaki*, a 27m SWATH vessel.

THE NETHERLANDS

LIPS BV

PO Box 6, 5150 BB Drunen, Netherlands

Telephone: 416388115
Telex: 35185LIPS NL
Telefax: 416373162

F Bult

Lips was established in 1934 and are world leaders in the field of marine propellers, covering fixed-pitch, controllable-pitch, side-thruster and systems to their own design. Five hundred people are employed in the Netherlands company.

Lips provide a dealer network for Riva Calzoni. The company has provided propellers for a number of high-speed craft including Fjellstrand catamarans for Turkey and Norway and more recently for the FBM Marine FDC 400 fast displacement catamaran

Lips transcavitating CP propeller that was designed for the US Navy SAS *Sea Viking*

NORWAY

SERVOGEAR A/S
N-5420 Rubbestadneset, Norway

Telephone: (054) 27380
Telex: 40909N
Telefax: (054) 27783

Leif M Endresen, *Technical Manager*

Designers and manufacturers of controllable-pitch propellers (up to 2000hp) and drive systems. Servogear propellers are on a number of high-speed craft including the Westamarin S80 mono-hull vessel *Vøringen* and the Westamarin W95 *Sunnhordland*.

A new V-drive system, Type VD 250A, specifically for high-speed craft was announced in 1986. This unit has a built-in clutch and a servo for controllable-pitch propellers. The gearbox has the following characteristics:

max continuous power input: 590kW at 2300rpm
reduction ratio: 1.96:1
torque: 2500N
dry weight: 160kg

Servogear propellers are manufactured in

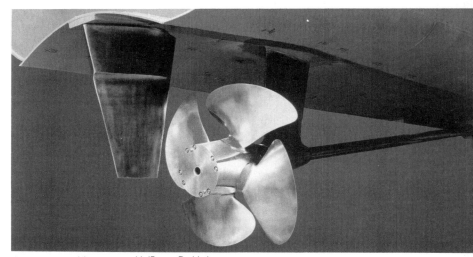
Servogear propulsion system with 'Power Rudder'

manganese bronze for the bosses and nickel-aluminium bronze for the blades, but other materials can be used if requested.

ULSTEIN INTERNATIONAL AS
Ulstein Propeller AS
Kjørpmannsgt 23, N-6025 Ålesund, Norway

Telephone: (071) 29929
Telefax: (071) 28561/28193

Designers and manufacturers of controllable-pitch propellers, tunnel thrusters, compass thrusters and the newly developed Speed-Z Propulsion System. The Speed-Z system is marketed in the output range of 700kW to 2800kW. Orders for the Speed-Z system have been received from the following shipyards: Westamarin A/S, Fjellstrand A/S, Broward Marine Inc and Baglietto Shipyard. High-speed applications have included a controllable-pitch installation on the Fjellstrand high-speed catamaran, *Asie III*, and two Liaaen Speed-Z 4-blade propulsion units, Type CPZ, for the Westamarin W5000 *Anne Lise*, 49.5m high-speed thermo-cargo catamaran, delivered June/July 1987. These units each absorb 2040kW and position the propellers in undisturbed free-stream flow. In comparison with conventional propeller systems an efficiency gain of 10% is claimed. The

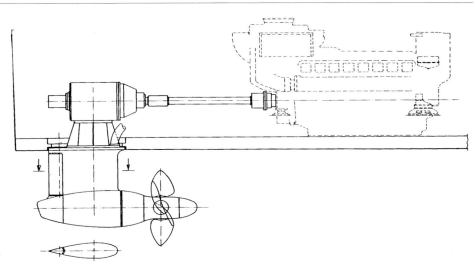
Layout of the Liaaen Speed-Z Propulsion System Type CPZ

Liaaen Helix Speed-Z Propulsion Systems Type CPZ 60/40–125 fitted to the Westamarin 5000 *Anne Lise*, 28-knot thermo-cargo catamaran
More recently Ulstein controllable pitch propellers have been fitted to the SWATH vessel *Navetek 1*

claimed. The system combines propulsion and steering functions. Other advantages of the Speed-Z propulsion system are reduced vibration and noise onboard, a cost efficient compact installation, effective load control for protection of the drive motors and good manoeuvring capability.

Since Speed-Z is a traction (pulling) propeller there are no appendages in front of it and therefore the propeller acts in a homogeneous velocity field. These are ideal conditions for efficiency and avoidance of damaging cavitation. This has been substantiated by cavitation tests and prototypes in operation which produce no noticeable noise or vibration in the hull.

Another major advantage is the right-angle drive which allows the propeller to be installed in line with the water flow. A conventional propeller installation is always a compromise between keeping the shaft angle low to avoid harmful root cavitation and ensuring sufficient clearance between the propeller and the hull to avoid noise and vibration from the high pressure pulses created by the propeller. The Speed-Z unit has, as mentioned, the best possible conditions of flow to the propeller giving stable cavitation conditions and minimal fluctuating forces.

A comparison has been made, based on model test tank results with the Speed-Z unit, with a conventional installation with sloping shaft, brackets, and rudder. The propeller on the conventional installation had a diameter of 1.6m with a maximum speed of 525rpm, while the Speed-Z unit has a diameter of 1.25m at 769rpm. Even though the Speed-Z unit is higher loaded, that is the power per unit area is greater, the propeller efficiency is 76% at an engine output of 2040kW and ship speed of 28 knots. The corresponding efficiency of a conventional installation is about 72%. When the resistance of the appendages was taken into account the improvement in efficiency was even more significant. The result of the model tests showed that the overall propulsive efficiency of the model fitted with the Speed-Z was 66% at 28 knots which compared with 58% for the conventional system as described above. In this case the new Speed-Z gave an improvement in efficiency of 8%, that is to say a saving in installed power of 13.8% to achieve the same speed.

Liaaen Helix Speed-Z Propulsion Unit showing the top reduction gear with clutch and the lower 90° reduction gear with rudder flap and propeller mounting

SWEDEN

J W BERG

S-43090 Öckerö, Gothenburg, Sweden

Telephone: (31) 781220
Telex: 89200868S

Telefax: (31) 783716

Design and manufacture of special types of propellers for high-speed craft.

KaMeWa AB

Box 1010, S-68101 Kristinehamn, Sweden

Telephone: 055084000
Telex: 66050KAMEWA S
Telefax: 055018190

Lars J Ohlsson, *Managing Director*
Ulf Athlei, *Sales Manager*

KaMeWa has accumulated experience from over 50 years of activity in the marine field. The company is also the only manufacturer of controllable-pitch propellers to possess a cavitation laboratory with comprehensive facilities for advanced testing of the various forms of marine propulsion device.

The KaMeWa design and manufacture of propellers for high-speed craft covers super-cavitating designs, super-cavitating designs modified to meet quiet and high-efficiency cruising conditions, wide-blade designs for these conditions, skewed wide-blade propellers for extremely quiet cruising and the same designs incorporating ventilated blades. These propellers are manufactured in either stainless steel or nickel-aluminium bronze.

The smallest propeller in the range is 710mm in diameter and is designed to absorb about 895kW (1200shp). These propellers are installed in fast patrol craft with speeds of up to 43 knots.

Propellers for patrol boats have been supplied over many years. One of the most powerful installations was in 1983 for the Swedish Navy Stock-

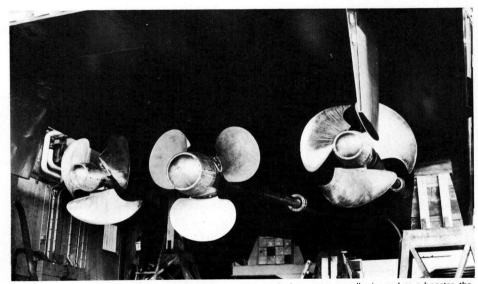

KaMeWa propeller installation on HMS *Stockholm*. The super-cavitating centre propeller is used as a booster, the highly-skewed wing propellers are for quiet running and cruising economy

holm, powered by two 1940kW diesels and a 4772kW gas turbine. Since then, a number of Spanish built patrol vessels have been fitted with KaMeWa propellers and in 1990 a Danyard patrol boat powered by two 3730kW diesels will be so equipped.

The waterjet unit is becoming an ever increasing alternative for high-speed craft propulsion especially for speeds beyond those of propeller driven craft. KaMeWa is leading also in this field; please see KaMeWa entry in Waterjet Unit Manufacturers section.

SWITZERLAND

ROLLA SP PROPELLERS SA

Via Silva 5, PO Box 251, Balerna 6828, Switzerland

Telephone: (091)439361
Telex: 842448 PROP CH
Telefax: (091)430653

Remo Cattaneo, *President*
Philip Rolla, *Managing Director*
Tobia Schnebli, *Director of Production*
Dipl Ing Piero Travi, *R&D Dept.*
Dipl Ing Marzio Porro, *R&D Dept.*
Dipl Ing John Rose, *Director of Rolla USA*

The company was founded in 1963 by Philip Rolla. The services, consultation and designs include: performance and power prediction for displacement and planing craft, propeller design, one-off propeller design, estimation of complete hydrodynamic characteristics of the propeller geometry and propeller cavitation characteristics, manufacturing of propeller models, model basin tests in the Berlin University cavitation tunnel, full-scale tests, propeller re-calculation and re-. design for existing vessels, designing and manufacturing of propeller prototypes and pre-series, designing of conventional and unconventional propulsion systems, consultation on propulsion problems. Surface-piercing, supercavitating, transcavitating and subcavitating propellers are designed and produced to any required geometry

and with up to eight blades. In general propellers are produced in high-tensile stainless steel (using investment casting and forging) for very high-speed craft and Nibral for commercial, military, work, luxury and pleasure boats up to 80 knots. The Rolla families of stainless steel and Nibral surface-piercing propellers include lines specifically designed for Árneson Drives, Levi Drive Units, T-Torque Drive System, Mondrive System and Trimax. Also interesting is the recent design and production of Rolla forged steel blades for controllable-pitch surface propellers for the new CPS surface drive units. The Rolla results obtained at the Technische Universitat Berlin constitute the first systematic series of surface propellers available in the world and permit Rolla to supply the torque and thrust coefficients and efficiency, horizontal and vertical force figures for different shaft inclinations and propeller immersions. The Rolla stainless steel propellers for stern drives include lines specifically designed for SF-MPM, Volvo Penta, MerCruiser, Kiekhaefer, Yamaha, OMC. The 1989 most important applications include:

Magnum, all of their production boats
Hatteras, all of their high-speed Fisherman craft
Tempest, all of their production boats
Mondo Rubber, all of their production boats
Magnum 70, 21.40m, 5-blade Rolla Surface Propellers, 50 knots
Hatteras 58,18 m,5-blade subcavitating propellers

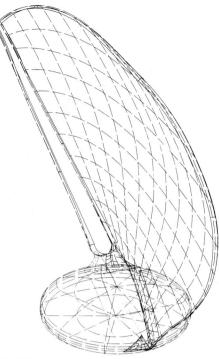

The Rolla blade, designed with Catia-Dassault Systems and manufactured in forged steel, for the new controllable-pitch surface drive units

Rolla REX P50/51 stainless steel surface-piercing propeller in worldwide use on luxury yachts

The 70 knot Vosper Thornycroft *Gentry Eagle* driven by one Rolla REX P5 propeller and two KaMeWa water-jet units

Rolla Nibral subcavitating propeller on the 26 m, 28 knot Costruzioni Navali di Lavagna *Admiral Santa Cruz*

Tempest 60, 18.50m, 4-blade Rolla surface propellers, 50 knots

Mondo Marine *Bugs* 20m, 4-blade Rolla transcavitating propeller, 38 knots

Vosper *Gentry Eagle* 33.5m, 5-blade Rolla surface propellers, 70 knots (transatlantic record at 48.32 knots

Brooke Yachts *G-Whiz* 33m, 5-blade Rolla surface propellers, 50 knots

Costruzione Navali di Lavagna *Admiral Santa Cruz*, 26m, 5-blade Rolla subcavitating propellers, 28 knots

Trinity Marine Group, Washington State Ferries, 33.5m, 4-blade Rolla subcavitating propellers, 29 knots

Knight and Carver 71, 22m, 5-blade Rolla surface propellers, 70 knots

Polyships R-56, 17m, 4-blade Rolla surface propellers, 65 knots

SBF Engineering, 28m, 4-blade Rolla surface propellers, 23 knots

Pacifica *Lookout*, 20m, 4-blade Rolla subcavitating propellers, 29 knots

Broward Marine *Motivation*, 35m, 5-blade Rolla subcavitating propellers, 20 knots

Magnum Marine 21.5 m, 50 knot motor yacht with Rolla 5-blade surface propellers

UNITED KINGDOM

BRUNTON'S PROPELLERS LIMITED

Station Road, Sudbury, Suffolk CO10 6ST, England

Telephone: 078773611
Telex: 98400PROPS G

Brunton's Propellers Ltd is a specialist in the design and manufacture of propellers for high performance craft such as patrol boats, surface effect ships, hydrofoils, catamarans etc, where the propellers have to work in very exacting conditions. The design requirements in such cases can be extremely critical and manufacturing to very close tolerances is required, ISO 484 Class 'S' and better. Brunton's parent company is Stone

1.0m diameter propellers (Dr Kruppa design) for HM527 surface effect ship

Brunton 5-blade propeller for twin-propeller 33.5m patrol boat

Manganese Ltd, designers and manufacturers of ship propellers.

As well as meeting commercial requirements, Brunton's Propellers Ltd supplies the British MoD and navies around the world.

Propellers may be manufactured in high-tensile manganese bronze, nickel-aluminium bronze, Novostron (a manganese-aluminium bronze alloy), Superstron 70 and gunmetal, though this last material is now seldom used.

Brunton's associated company, Stone Propellers Ltd, manufactures extremely accurate model propellers for test and research work in test tanks and cavitation tunnels.

STONE MANGANESE MARINE LIMITED

Dock Road, Birkenhead, Merseyside L41 1DT, England

Telephone: (051) 652 2372
Telex: 629270 SMMBH G
Telefax: (051)6522377

A member of the Langham Industries group

J M Langham, *Chairman*
J R Wilson, *Managing Director*
W J Teasdale, *Director*
B N Preston, *Director*
G Patience, *Technical Director*

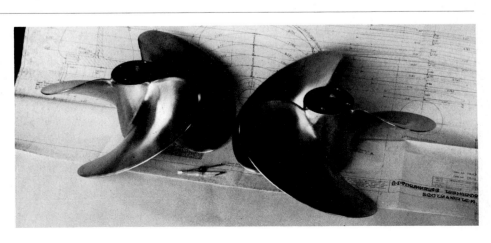

Stone Manganese Marine Ltd KCA design propellers for high-speed craft

Stone Manganese Marine has been manufacturing propellers for more than 100 years. The company and its associates operate ten manufacturing units throughout the world and the product range covers all sizes of fixed-pitch marine propellers for all types of ships, including high-speed marine craft.

The main factory is at Birkenhead, which includes the technical department, offering a comprehensive technical service to customers and the preparation of the company's proprietary Meridian design.

The company has a long established connection with the University of Newcastle upon Tyne, col-

laborating in the operation of the cavitation tunnel where the KCA design, specifically to suit high-speed craft, was developed and tested. The KCA design has been adopted for high-speed marine applications worldwide.

TEIGNBRIDGE PROPELLERS LIMITED

Decoy Industrial Estate, Newton Abbot, Devon TQ12 5NB, England

Telephone: (0626)333377
Telex: 42976 TEPROP G
Telefax: (0626)60783

D A Duncan, *Director*
D A Hunt, *Sales Director*
F R Phillips, *Director*

J Haines, *Commercial Sales*
G Paull, *Leisure Sales Manager*

The Teignbridge Propulsion Group comprises three separate manufacturing companies under one ownership. The companies, Teignbridge Propellers, Hamble Propellers and New Age Propulsion, combine to offer a comprehensive range of standard and special propellers. The Group specialise in designing and manufacturing propellers for high-speed craft such as catamarans, hydrofoils, surface effect ships and patrol boats.

The design parameters for propellers used on such vessels are extremely close, usually ISO 484 Class 'S'.

All Hi-Definition propellers manufactured by the Group are dynamically balanced and are manufactured from the materials to the highest specification, usually nickel-aluminium bronze.

The Group which has additional sales offices in Australia and The Netherlands also manufacture stern gear, rudders, shaft brackets, etc, offering craft builders a complete equipment package to the specialist field of high-speed propulsion.

Teignbridge propeller for a hydrofoil with MTU engines, 1530kW each at 2000rpm, gear ratio 2.028:1

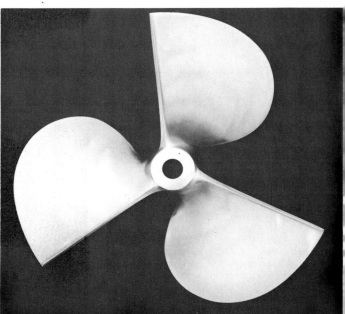

A Teignbridge surface-piercing propeller as fitted to a Bellamy surface drive, operating at speeds above 40 knots

UNITED STATES OF AMERICA

ARNESON MARINE INC

29485 Airport Road, PO Box 10605, Eugene, Oregon 97440, USA

Telephone: (503) 461 2223
Telefax: (503) 461 2224

Robert H Bolton, *President*
William G Bennett, *Director*
George W Laplante, Jr., *General Manager*

The Arneson Surface Drive system combines surface-piercing propeller technology with hydraulically actuated steering and trim control

effected through angular displacement of the propeller shaft. There is minimal underwater drag as drag of shafts, struts and rudders is eliminated.

A selection of surface-piercing propeller designs are available, manufactured in Nibral, stainless steel and manganese bronze.

Distributors have been appointed in Australia,

Model	ASD 6	ASD 7	ASD 8	ASD 10	ASD 12	ASD 14	ASD 16	ASD 18
Horsepower acceptance								
petrol:	to 450–550	to 730	to 1200	to be determined				
diesel:	to 235–300			to 3500 (subject to application)				
Unit weight, dry, with								
hydraulic cylinders (in-line):	61kg		129kg	189kg			900kg A	1769kg A
(drop centre):	72kg	147kg	220kg	272kg	352kg	515kg	1150kg B	2268kg B
Overall external length:	914–991mm	1114mm	1067mm	1270mm	1638mm	1805mm	2184mm	2896mm
Steering angle:	40°	40°	40°	40°	40°	40°	36°	36°
Trim angle (max travel inclusive):	15°	15°	15°	15°	15°	15°	15°	13°
Materials								
socket:	A or B	A or B	B	B	B	B	A or B	A or B
thrust tube:	A or B	A or B	B	B	B	B	A or B	A or B
ball:	B	B	B	B	B	B	A or B	A or B
propeller shaft:		Aquamet 17 stainless steel						

A-aluminium alloy
B-manganese bronze

Brazil, Japan, Kuwait, Scandinavia, Switzerland, Taiwan and Turkey. The Eastern Regional office is in North Miami Beach, Florida. The office which oversees Europe, the Middle East and Africa is in Viareggio, Italy.

Arneson Surface Drives combine proven surface-piercing propulsion technology with directed thrust, providing greater propulsion and manoeuvring effectiveness. In most applications, the elimination of the underwater drag of shafts, struts and rudders results in a marked improvement in vessel performance and efficiency.

The concept allows complete flexibility of engine location, weight placement and effective reduction of noise and vibration. With the hydraulic steering and propeller depth control, manoeuvrability is outstanding, and shallow

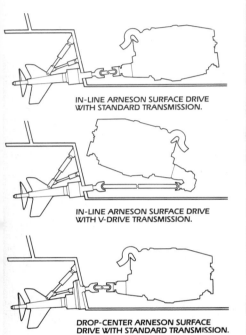

IN-LINE ARNESON SURFACE DRIVE WITH STANDARD TRANSMISSION.

IN-LINE ARNESON SURFACE DRIVE WITH V-DRIVE TRANSMISSION.

DROP-CENTER ARNESON SURFACE DRIVE WITH STANDARD TRANSMISSION.

Three possible layouts for Arneson Surface Drives

Arneson ASD 10 in-line unit

water capability becomes limited only by the draught of the vessel itself.

AMI currently manufactures fourteen models of Arneson Surface Drives, serving the commercial, military and pleasure craft market.

Differentiated by torque capacity, production ASD units are available for use with petrol, diesel and gas turbine engines up to approximately 5000hp.

Included among the many projects completed

in the past year are the supply of Arneson Surface Drives for a 17m passenger catamaran in Finland, a 12m patrol boat for Japan and a 16m high-performance offshore vessel for Canada, as well as numerous other pleasure and commercial

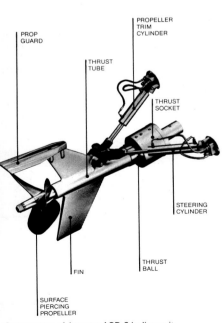

Components of Arneson ASD 6 in-line unit

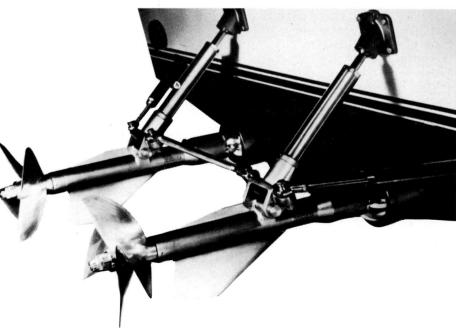

Arneson Surface Drive transmission arrangements

installations in the United States and overseas.

Recent applications of the larger Arneson Drive Units have included the following craft:

Huckins 78, 23.78m motor yacht *Princess Pat*, two ASD 14 units, 21 knots

Magnum Marine 19.21m pleasure yacht *Maltese Magnum*, two ASD 14 units, with two 18-cylinder CRM diesels giving an average speed of 51.0 knots when winning the Miami-Nassau-Miami sea race, 11 July 1987

Denison Marine 24.39m pleasure yacht *Haggis II*, two ASD 16 units, 45 knots

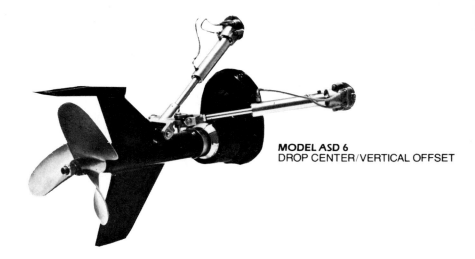

MODEL ASD 6
DROP CENTER/VERTICAL OFFSET

An Arneson Surface Drive installation

BIRD-JOHNSON COMPANY
Pascagoula Operations
3719 Industrial Road, Pascagoula, Mississippi 39567, USA

Telephone: (601) 762 0728
Telex: 589938
Telefax: (601) 769 7048

James W Elliot Jr, *Manager*

110 Norfolk Street, Walpole, Massachusetts 02081, USA

Telephone: (617) 668 9610
Telex: 6817294
Telefax: (617) 668 5638

Charles A Orem, *Chief Executive Officer and President*
Donald E Ridley, *Vice President, Regional Operations*

Gary W Dayton, *Director, Marine Marketing and Services*

Bird-Johnson Company is a leading supplier of fixed-pitch and controllable-pitch propeller systems for naval application. In-house capabilities include design, foundry, hand and NC finishing, assembly, test and repair. All products are backed by logistic support including a 24-hour emergency service network.

COLUMBIAN BRONZE CORPORATION
216 N Main Street, Freeport, New York 11520–2295, USA

Telephone: (516) 378 0470
Telex: 144550

Bill Bailey, *President*
Peter J Lapp, *Naval Architect*
William Thompson, *Chief Engineer*
James Burns, *Sales Engineer*

Designer and manufacturer of fixed-pitch propellers since 1901 in various alloys including manganese bronze, Nibral and stainless steel from 0.2m to 3.05m diameter. Standard catalogue styles are available in a wide range of sizes including the high-blade-area Crewboat/Mako style proven successful on many high-speed craft. Custom propellers also available to either in-house or customer design. Capability exists to manufacture to all tolerance levels and to dynamically balance up to 4.90m diameter. Recent applications include: custom 5-blade Nibral propellers for Nichols Bros *Hawaiian Express* and Gladding-Hearn *Mackinac*

Express high-speed catamarans; 1.07m 4-blade Nibral and stainless steel crewboat propellers for 36.6m Lantana Boat 30-knot patrol craft; custom 1.016m 3-blade Nibral 1.00 BAR propellers for US Coast Guard SES craft; custom 0.914m 4-blade Nibral props for 35-knot plus *Donzi*, 19.82m Sportfisherman and 40-knot plus Lydia Yacht 27.44m Sportfisherman *That My Hon*; 4-blade Mako style propellers for world class Burger Boat and Broward Marine yachts.

COOLIDGE PROPELLER GULF COAST

Now Bird-Johnson Company, Pascagoula Operations (see preceding entry).

KAHLENBERG BROS CO
Two Rivers, Wisconsin, USA

Telephone: (414) 793 4507
Telefax: 4147931346

K W Kahlenberg, *Executive Vice President*

Kahlenberg Bros Co was one of the pioneer internal combustion engine builders in the US and at the turn of the century it produced its first steel propellers. Of today's production of fixed-pitch propellers, 85% are in stainless steel but if requested, propellers may also be cast in manga-

nese bronze, cast iron or other alloys. Custom-built propellers up to 2.59m diameter and adjustable pitch propellers can be supplied. The company also manufacture air horns, air whistles, stuffing boxes, fog signal timers etc.

MICHIGAN WHEEL CORPORATION
1501 Buchanan Avenue SW, Grand Rapids, Michigan 49507, USA

Telephone: (616) 452 6941

Telex: 6877077MIMOT UW
Telefax: (616) 247 0227

William Herrick, *Director/Marketing Services*

Established in 1903, Michigan Wheel produces a wide range of fixed-pitch propellers, including

the Machined-Pitch type, diameter up to 2.44m, the Dyna-Foil type, diameter up to 2.44m, the Star, diameter up to 1.83m and the Super Crew Boat type, diameter up to 1.02m. These propellers can be made in manganese bronze alloy, nickle-bronze, aluminium bronze and stainless steel.

WATERJET UNITS

FINLAND

AB ALUMINA VARVET OY
Aurakatu 1C, 20100 Turku, Finland

Telephone: (921)502663
Telefax: (921)502673

Producer of water-jet units since 1985, Alumina Varvet Oy are marketing three models and have designs for units up to 2250kW.

FF-JET 310
Designed for planing boats up to 7 tonnes and displacement boats up to 12 tonnes. Power range: 40 – 300kW.

FF-JET 375
Designed for planing boats up to 11 tonnes and displacement boats up to 22 tonnes. Power range: 80 – 450kW.

FF-JET 450
Designed for planing boats up to 18 tonnes and displacement boats up to 35 tonnes. Power range 110 – 750kW.

ITALY

CASTOLDI SpA
Viale Mazzini 161, 20081 Abbiategrasso, Milan, Italy

Telephone: (02) 94821
Telex: 330236CAST I
Telefax: (02) 9460800

Dr Eng Andrea Tonti, *Export Sales Manager*

Castoldi SpA is associated with BCS SpA, the leading European manufacturer of self-propelled agricultural machines, and MOSA SpA, manufacturer of mobile electric welding machines. Development of Castoldi waterjet units started in 1958 and units are now available for fast craft in the range of 4 to 28m.

Castoldi manufactures a range of axial-flow waterjet units, the JET 03 for powers up to 40.5kW, the JET 05 for up to 130kW, the Turbodrive 238 for up to 184kW, the JET 06 for up to 266kW, The Turbodrive 337 for up to 405kW and the JET 07 for up to 883kW. All the Castoldi units feature a single stage axial-flow impeller; the casings are built in lightweight aluminium alloy which is very durable being hard anodised up to 80 microns. The impeller, the impeller shaft and many other parts are made in stainless steel.

The Castoldi drives (except for the JET 03) have several features that make them stand out from other waterjet units; a built-in gearbox for adapting the power and rpm characteristics of the engine to the Jet Drive, a positive clutch for engaging and disengaging the impeller, a remotely-operated movable weed rake for cleaning the water intake and other refinements. The Castoldi waterjet units are equipped with especially designed mechanical or electronic/hydraulic controls which make them extremely easy to operate.

Castoldi JET 07

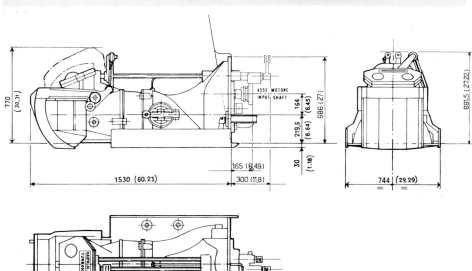

Castoldi Turbodrive 337 waterjet capable of absorbing up to 405kW

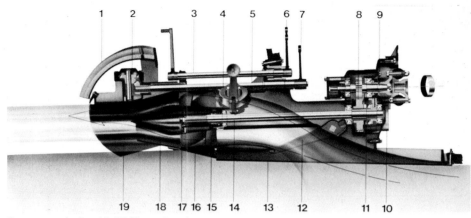

Components of a Castoldi JET 05 waterjet unit
(1) Deflector (2) Rudder control gears (3) Deflector control shaft (4) Inspection port (5) Rudder control shaft (6) Deflector control lever (7) Rudder control lever (8) Gear coupling (9) Primary shaft (10) Transmission box flange (11) Dog clutch (12) Movable grill (13) Body of unit (14) Impeller shaft (15) Impeller (16) Impeller shell (17) Impeller retaining bolt (18) Nozzle (19) Rudders

38 knot Italian Coast Guard vessel driven by two Castoldi 06 waterjet units

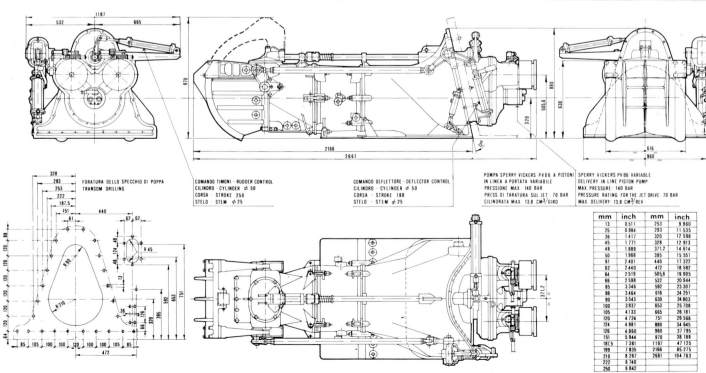

FORATURA DELLO SPECCHIO DI POPPA
TRANSOM DRILLING

COMANDO TIMONI – RUDDER CONTROL
CILINDRO – CYLINDER ⌀ 50
CORSA – STROKE 250
STELO – STEM ⌀ 25

COMANDO DEFLETTORE – DEFLECTOR CONTROL
CILINDRO – CYLINDER ⌀ 50
CORSA – STROKE 199
STELO – STEM ⌀ 25

POMPA SPERRY VICKERS PV B6 A PISTONI
IN LINEA A PORTATA VARIABILE
PRESSIONE MAX : 140 BAR
PRESS DI TARATURA SUL JET : 70 BAR
CILINDRATA MAX : 13,8 CM³/GIRO

SPERRY VICKERS PV B6 VARIABLE
DELIVERY IN LINE PISTON PUMP
MAX PRESSURE : 140 BAR
PRESSURE RATING FOR THE JET DRIVE : 70 BAR
MAX DELIVERY : 13,8 CM³/REV

mm	inch	mm	inch
13	0.511	253	9.960
25	0.984	293	11.535
36	1.417	320	12.598
45	1.771	328	12.913
48	1.889	371.2	14.614
50	1.968	395	15.551
61	2.401	440	17.322
62	2.440	472	18.582
64	2.519	505,6	19.905
66	2.598	532	20.944
85	3.346	592	23.307
88	3.464	616	24.251
90	3.543	630	24.803
100	3.937	653	25.708
105	4.133	665	26.181
120	4.724	751	29.566
124	4.881	880	34.645
126	4.960	960	37.795
151	5.944	970	38.188
187,5	7.381	1197	47.125
199	7.835	2166	85.275
210	8.267	2661	104.763
222	8.740		
250	9.842		

Castoldi 07 waterjet unit for powers up to 883kW

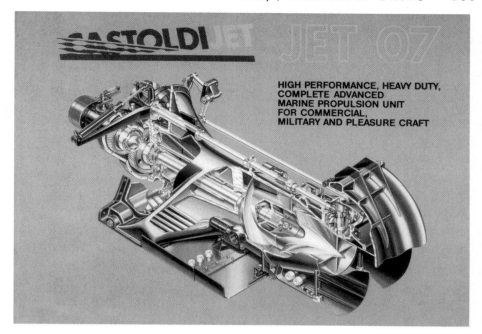

Components of a Castoldi 07 unit

RIVA CALZONI SpA
Via Stendhal 34, 20144 Milan, Italy

Telephone: (02) 41461
Telex: 332292 RIVAT I
Telefax: (02) 425749

Dr Ing Guido Ucelli, *General Manager*
Dr Bruno Ucelli, *Deputy General Manager*
Dr Ing Andrea Gasparri, *Manager Waterjet Department*

Riva Calzoni is a long-established major European designer and manufacturer with extensive experience of hydraulic machinery covering large water turbines, pumps, pump-turbines, governors for water and steam turbines, waterjet propulsion units, various types of hydraulic equipment, valves, gates and penstocks. Design techniques as well as laboratory and manufacturing facilities are being continually improved in order to cope with the increasingly demanding requirements of modern installations.

Riva was established in 1861, Calzoni in 1830. The first partnership between the two companies dates from 1922 and they merged in 1966 to form Riva Calzoni, which is privately owned and employs some 1200 personnel.

RIVA CALZONI WATERJETS
The very first waterjet, rated at 75kW, was designed, manufactured and tested by Riva Calzoni in 1932. Today Riva Calzoni is one of the leading manufacturers of waterjet propulsion units in the world, with a power range extending from 500 to over 50 000kW.

Riva Calzoni waterjets have been progressively known as IRC, which stands in Italian for 'Idrogetti Riva Calzoni'.

Riva Calzoni waterjets are optimised for each different application, to meet in co-operation with the designers and shipbuilders, optimum propulsive and hydraulic characteristics.

This optimisation is also possible due to the large quantity of data available through the

Riva Calzoni IRC 115 DX water-jet unit designed to absorb 5000kW

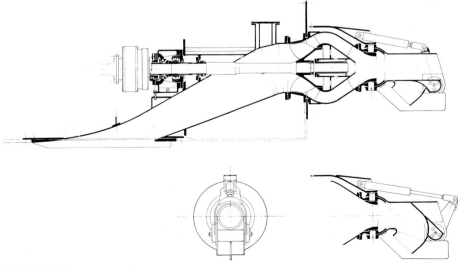

Riva Calzoni IRC type waterjet unit

studies and researches continuously carried out on pumps, turbines and waterjets in the Riva Calzoni hydraulic laboratory. Equipped with 13 testing rigs and including two special testing tunnels devoted exclusively to studies on waterjet propulsion systems.

The increase of specific power has led Riva Calzoni to use the Duplex type stainless steel for the rotor. This type of stainless steel combines optimum corrosion resistance with the mechanical characteristics typical of carbon steels. The adoption of this material has permitted Riva Calzoni to enhance further the avoidance of cavitation susceptibility by adopting ideal hydrodynamic profiles free of compromises that can occur with other materials.

A great effort has been made by Riva Calzoni in the design of the steering and reversing system. Riva Calzoni has two different families of deflectors. The conventional one, which has been developed in several steps, has a very simple and reliable design, which is also suitable for the control of very high flows of water. The other configuration allows a 360° rotating vectored thrust system, which is particularly suitable for slow speed applications and for specialised craft, such as minehunters.

Among recent orders for Riva Calzoni, it is worth mentioning those for a total of 12 waterjets type IRC 115 DX, rated at 3400 kW, for installation on the new 74m wave piercing catamarans.

Riva Calzoni waterjets are based on mix-flow pumps of proven reliability combined with high efficiency and excellent anti-cavitation characteristics, derived from Riva Calzoni's extensive experience in the field of hydraulic engineering.

Riva Calzoni waterjets are fabricated from AISI 316L stainless steel for low weight, high mechanical strength and corrosion resistance. They are equipped with two guide bearings, one inside the pump bowl, water lubricated, and one combined with the thrust bearing, located outside the inlet pipe. In this way the waterjet shaft is fully supported and the thrust bearing is easily accessible for maintenance. The steering and reversing deflectors are of special Riva Calzoni design and ensuring effective control of the craft. The water inlets can be incorporated into the waterjet body or they can be built as part of the craft by the shipyard. In the latter case, Riva Calzoni will provide the optimised hydraulic profile to the yard.

The control system, usually electro-hydraulic, can be supplied as a complete package with the

Riva Calzoni IRC 115 DX water-jet units for International Catamarans 74m Wave-Piercing catamarans. Input power 3860kW each. Steering and reversing systems on outboard units only

Riva Calzoni IRC DLX water-jet units; maximum input power: 2100kW each

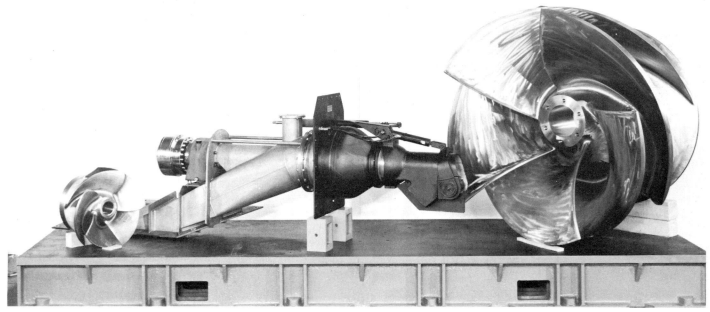

Left to right: Impeller for Riva Calzoni IRC 64 DL; waterjet unit IRC 41DL, complete with disconnecting clutch, impeller for waterjet unit IRC 190 DL, maximum input power 15 000kW

waterjet. Control logics of the analogue or digital type can also be supplied by Riva Calzoni.

Riva Calzoni has contributed considerably to the development of waterjet propulsion systems. As previously mentioned, the first Riva Calzoni waterjet dates back to 1932 when a 150 hp unit was successfully designed, manufactured and tested. The inlet shape and geometry was already the main purpose of the research, a philosophy of optimisation that is still valid and successful today.

Riva Calzoni has also introduced the concept of pump optimisation. Pump optimisation is not limited to the adjustment of the pitch or length of the impeller blades, but it includes the selection of the right pump, without compromises. It is for this reason that Riva Calzoni waterjets adopt various types of pump depending on the propulsive needs.

The systematic research on cavitation has given Riva Calzoni a recognised leadership in this field. The many direct drive installations and Azimut *Atlantic Challenger* are outstanding in this respect. The 27m Azimut *Atlantic Challenger*, in particular, was taken to plane easily, at 145 tons of displacement, by two Riva Calzoni waterjets each able to absorb the full power of 3700 hp at the speed of 25 knots, although these waterjets were designed for a maximum craft speed in excess of 50 knots.

Another contribution by Riva Calzoni to waterjet propulsion is the integral disconnecting clutch for direct drive applications. This disconnecting clutch, designed and manufactured by Riva Calzoni, allows a true neutral condition to be achieved without any residual thrust.

JAPAN

KAWASAKI HEAVY INDUSTRIES, LTD
Prime Mover Division
1–1, Higashi Kawasaki-cho 3-chome, Chuo-ku, Kobe, 650–91, Japan

Telephone: 078–682–5320
Telex: 5623–931
Telefax: 078–682–5500

Hisashi Ando, *General Manager*

Waterjet business of Rockwell International was transferred to Kawasaki in 1987. Now Kawasaki is manufacturing PJ-20 Waterjet Propulsors for Kawasaki Jetfoils and performing product support.

PJ-20
Specification of PJ-20 is the same as for the Rocketdyne Powerjet 20
Input horse power: 3800hp (metric)
Input shaft speed: 2060rpm
Flowrate: about 90kl/min
Weight (Dry): about 700kg

Kawasaki PJ-20 waterjet propulsor

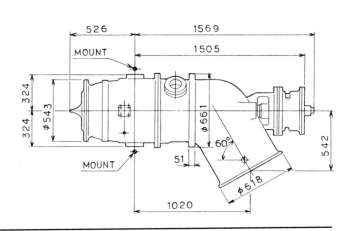

Dimensions (mm) of PJ-20

NEW ZEALAND

CWF HAMILTON AND COMPANY LIMITED

Annex Road, PO Box 709, Christchurch, New Zealand

Telephone: (3) 488 849
Telex: 4244HAMJET NZ
Telefax: (3) 480 725

Designers and manufacturers of waterjets since the mid-1950s, the company now offers models capable of absorbing up to 1119kW (1500shp). A large number of units have been installed around the world in many types of craft such as high-speed passenger ferries, police patrol craft, naval troop carriers, fishing boats, crew boats, rescue craft, pleasure cruises and fire boats. Current Hamilton waterjet models in production are the 770 Series, 1031, 271, 291, 361, 421 and 422.

MODEL 271

A smaller model of the proven 291 unit suitable for engine power levels between 150 and 240kW in small planing craft. In production from May 1987.
Impeller dia (9 configuration options): 270mm
Unit weight, less controls: 114kg
Thrust example
  max bollard pull: 1315kg at 225kW
  at 30 knots: 767kg at 225kW
Standard coupling: 120mm dia driveshaft flange
Intake screen: Heavy duty aluminium bar
Rotation: Clockwise looking aft

MODEL 291

Suitable for most high-speed marine diesel engines up to 300kW/3000rpm.
Impeller dia (6 configuration options): 290mm
Configuration: Single stage, axial flow
Thrust, max: 1300kgf
Casing material: LM6 aluminium alloy
Mainshaft: T316 stainless steel
Weight: 175kg
Steering: T3 single conical deflector with inboard tiller
Reverse: Twin duct deflector and HERC electro-hydraulic system

TYPICAL SINGLE 291 JET APPLICATION

Vessel: 10.4m aluminium fishing boat *Wiebbe Hayes*
Weight: 7 tonnes
Speed: 30 knots
Engine/propulsion: One Caterpillar 3208 TA directly driving jet unit 330shp (after ancillary pumps etc)
Owner: Phil McAuley, Geraldton, Western Australia

TYPICAL TWIN 291 JET APPLICATION

Vessels: Fleet of nine 11.35m Meriuisko assault troop carriers
Weight: 6.8 tonnes (light)
Speed: 37 knots
Engines: Two Volvo TAMD70E producing 221kW (300hp) at 2500rpm
Owner: Finnish Navy

TYPICAL TRIPLE 291 JET APPLICATION

Vessel: 20m VIP passenger launch *Jalesveva*
Weight: 20 tonnes
Speed: 26 knots (3 jets operating); 20 knots (2 jets operating); 12 knots (1 jet operating)
Engines/propulsion: Three Caterpillar 3208 TA directly driving jet units
Owner: Indonesian Navy

MODEL 361

The first of the new Hamilton Model 361 waterjets was completed in April 1986. The 360mm

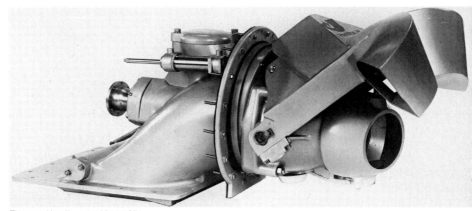
The new Hamilton Jet Model 271

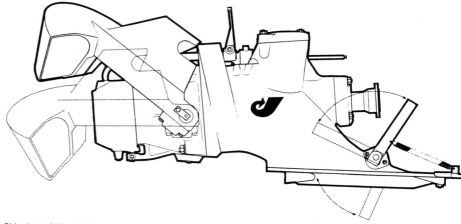
Side view of Model 271

8.8m *Rebel III* crayfishing boat (NZ) fitted with two Hamilton Jet 271 waterjet units giving 33 knots at 4.1 tonnes

One of nine Finnish Meriuisko troop carriers fitted with Hamilton Jet 291 units

diameter single-stage axial flow jets incorporate all the latest technological features such as: electronic reverse control (HERC) system, twin duct reverse deflector and T3 single piece steering deflector. These features combined give sensitive finger-tip control for in-harbour manoeuvrability. By working the reverse and steering deflectors in unison a resultant waterflow can be obtained in any direction giving a craft 360-degree thrusting.

A complete range of CAD (computer-assisted design) impellers are available for matching the 361 jet to a wide range of high-speed marine diesel engines from 300kW (2000rpm) up to 500kW (2300rpm). The performance of the 361 jet with various impeller options has been thoroughly tested and evaluated on Hamilton's water tunnel test facility. Precise performance and thrust data available from these tests enable accurate speed predictions to be made by comparing the 361 jet thrust with craft hull resistance data.

The versatility of the 361 jet and the absence of engine overloading (power demand depends on throttle opening only and is virtually independent of craft speed) makes them ideal for multiple speed craft. They can be used in conjunction with propeller drive systems or other waterjets, for either high-speed or loiter-speed operation. The flush-mounted 361 waterjet offers no drag when not driving and can contribute useful thrust at any speed.

An innovative feature of the 361 jet is the adjustable steering system which can be rotated 15 degrees to either port or starboard, allowing the 361 jet to be utilised for single, twin or triple installations in hulls with deadrise angles of up to 30 degrees. Installation kits supplied with each jet are available to suit aluminium, steel, grp and wooden hulls.

Typically a single 361 jet is designed for efficient propulsion of planing craft of up to 12 tonnes, and with limited input power, displacement craft up to 20 tonnes. Twin 361 jets are suitable for planing craft up to 26 tonnes and displacement craft up to 45 tonnes and triple 361 jets for craft up to 42 tonnes and 90 tonnes respectively.

Supplied as a complete factory tested package, the 361 jet includes integral steering and reverse systems. Installation is simple with no complicated alignment of components. With a minimum of preparation to the hull, the unit is simply lowered into place, bolted in, and steering, reverse controls and driveshaft coupled up. Installation studies of similarly sized Hamilton jet packages have shown savings of up to 40% in installation time when compared to the multiple job of installing a conventional propeller drive system of equivalent power.

Steering control supplied is a heavy duty manual hydraulic system complete with a stainless steel helm. Standard equipment with the 361 jet is Hamilton's latest HERC system which includes control lever, 12V or 24V dc hydraulic power unit, electronic control box, senders and hoses. The HERC system allows extremely fine control of the twin duct reverse deflector for excellent slow speed manoeuvrability. Each 361 jet package is assembled to order with an impeller and nozzle combination finely matched to the engine selection.

Other standard items with 361 jet include: transom seal assembly, intake block installation kit, all necessary nuts, bolts and fastenings, cathodic protection with anodes, coupling flange, water offtake for engine cooling system or wash down hose, owners manual, HERC manual and special tools kit. Optional accessories available to order with the 361 are: single lever reverse/throttle control, dual station steering and reverse controls, twin and triple jet reverse controls and an inspection hatch overflow preventer.

Impeller diameter (6 options): 360mm
Configuration: Single stage, axial flow
Thrust, max: 2100kgf
Casing material: LM6 aluminium alloy

Hamilton Jet 291

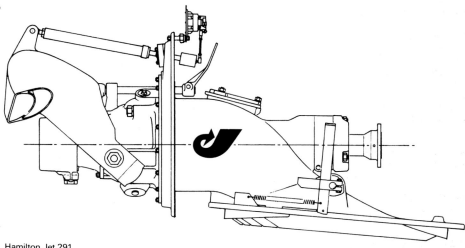

Hamilton Jet 291

Hamilton Jet 361

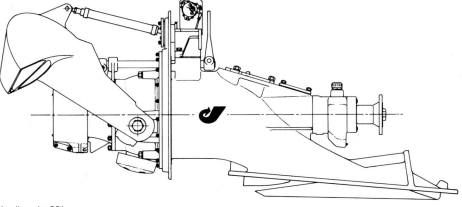

Hamilton Jet 361

Mainshaft: T316 stainless steel
Weight: 303kg
Steering: T3 single conical deflector with manual
    hydraulic cylinder and helm
Reverse: Twin duct deflector and HERC electro-
    hydraulic system
Certification available to: ABS, Lloyds, NKK

Hamilton Jet 421

TYPICAL PLANING CRAFT
APPLICATIONS FOR 361 JET UNITS
Single 361 Jet – Max 10 tonnes
Twin 361 Jets – Max 26 tonnes
Triple 361 Jets – Max 42 tonnes

MODEL 421
   Suitable for most high-speed marine diesel
engines up to 650kW (870hp), 2400rpm.
Impeller diameter (6 options): 400mm
Configuration: Single stage, axial flow
Thrust, max: 2750kgf
Casing material: LM6 aluminium alloy
Mainshaft: T316 stainless steel
Unit weight: 535kg
Steering: Twin balanced deflectors
Reverse: Twin duct deflector and HERC electro-
    hydraulic system
Certification available to: ABS, Lloyds, NKK

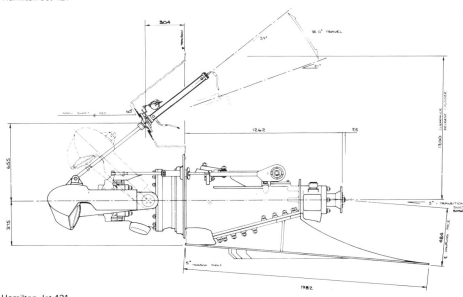

Hamilton Jet 421

TYPICAL SINGLE 421 JET APPLICATION
(Loiter Propulsion)
Vessel: 26m patrol craft
Weight: 80 tonnes
Speed (main propulsion): 24 knots
Speed, loiter propulsion (jet only): 7 knots
Engine driving 421 Jet: Mercedes OM402 145kW
    (195hp) at 2200rpm
Owner: Hong Kong Marine Police
Benefits of waterjet unit for secondary propulsion:
No drag at speed;
unloads main propulsion system;
360 degree thrusting ability for excellent slow
    speed manoeuvrability;
boosts top speed;
increases acceleration

TYPICAL TWIN 421 JET APPLICATIONS
A
Vessel: 25.6m high-speed passenger ferry *Atlante*
Weight: 31.6 tonnes (light)
Speed: 30 knots
Engines: Two MAN D 2842 LE each developing
    700hp
Owner: Vedettes de L'Odet Ferry Company,
    France

B
Vessel: 18.4m passenger ferry
Weight: 30 tonnes
Propulsion: Twin Hamilton Model 421 waterjets
Engines: Two V10 MAN 2840 MLE diesels, each
    producing 618hp
Top speed: 35 knots
Owner: Vainio Fleet, Helsinki

C
Vessels: Four new 28m passenger ferries – Choong
    Joo Dam Korea (Commissioned 20/8/86)
Weight: 35 tonnes
Propulsion: Two Hamilton Model 421 waterjets
Engines: Two GM 12V-71TI marine diesels each
    producing 870hp at 2300rpm (Int); 730hp at
    2180rpm (cont rating)
Top speed: 28 knots
Owner: Jung Ahang Express Company, South
    Korea

D
Vessel: 22m passenger ferry – Brittany, France
Weight: 45 tonnes laden
    37 tonnes light
Speed: 26 knots (light)
Propulsion: Two Hamilton Model 421 waterjets
Engines: Two MAN D 2842 LE marine diesels,
    each producing 760hp at 2300rpm

18m JMSA patrol boat fitted with two Hamilton Model 421 waterjet units giving 22 knots at 26.5 tonnes

Builder: Société Bretonne de Construction
    Navale, France

TYPICAL TRIPLE 421 JET APPLICATIONS
A
Vessel: 25.62m rescue/firefighting craft *Jetwise*, ex
    Miriam
Weight: 40 tonnes
Speed: 26 knots
Engines: Three MAN 12V D 2542 MLE marine
    diesel engines each producing 500hp at 2230rpm
Owner: Wijsmuller Salvage BV, Holland

B
Vessel: 25.6m high-speed passenger ferry
Weight: 54 tonnes (laden)
    42 tonnes (light)
Speed, light: 29.5 knots

Propulsion: Three Hamilton Model 421 waterjets
Engines: Three MAN D 2840 LE each producing
    630hp at 2300rpm
Builder: Société Bretonne de Construction
    Navale, France

MODEL 422
Impeller: 4- or 5-blade cast CF8M stainless steel
Unit weight, dry: 550kg
Entrained water weight: 110kg
Transition duct weight, steel: 300kg
    other materials: 140kg
Casings: Cast LM6 aluminium alloy
Standard coupling: GWB 587/50 250mm uni-
    versal driveshaft
Rotation: Clockwise looking aft
Thrust example: 3175kg at 1118kW at 40 knots
Astern thrust: Up to 55% of ahead thrust

SWEDEN

KAMEWA AB

A Vickers plc company
PO Box 1010, S-68101 Kristinehamn, Sweden

Telephone: (0550) 84000
Telex: 66050KAMEWA S
Telefax: (0550) 18190

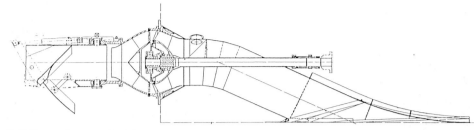

KaMeWa waterjet system, basic form

Since the beginning of this century KaMeWa in Sweden has designed and manufactured hydro-turbines and large pumps of various types. In the 1930s the first KaMeWa propeller of controllable-pitch type was delivered. A vast amount of experience in the marine propulsion field has since then been collected at KaMeWa. In the last two decades KaMeWa has been a major supplier of controllable-pitch propellers and thrusters. The company uses a well developed international network for sales and after sales service.

In the mid-1960s KaMeWa built two prototype jet-propulsion systems for small craft. The first larger units, however, were delivered in 1980 and since then KaMeWa has systematically established itself as the dominant producer of larger systems for waterjet propulsion.

An appreciable amount of research and development in hydrodynamics, mechanics and electronics constitutes the basis for the KaMeWa Jet-Propulsion System. Significant benefits for vessels with KaMeWa Jet-Propulsion Systems are high propulsive efficiency, even at part load; insensitivity to floating debris; suitability for shallow draught operation; good manoeuvrability; low hydro-acoustic and vibration levels; and low magnetic signature.

These features make waterjet propulsion suitable for example in medium and high-speed vessels such as corvettes, patrol boats, landing craft, passenger ferries, motor yachts and work boats.

DESIGN: Principally the waterjet consists of an inlet duct leading the water to the impeller, a pump casing and an outlet nozzle, forming the jet. Steering is accomplished by a steering nozzle, directing the jet ± 30 degrees which re-directs the jet of water issuing from the nozzle. Astern thrust is achieved by a reversing bucket incorporated in the steering nozzle.

The most effective propulsion will be with the jet just above the dynamic waterline. However, to secure priming of the pump at start-up, the pump shaft centre must not be higher than the waterline at rest.

INLET DUCT: In order to improve efficiency and to avoid excessive cavitation in the pump (the impeller and its casing), the velocity head of the inlet flow must be used to the largest possible extent. Thus, the inlet channel should lead the water to the pump with only small losses. Unsuitable inlet shapes not only cause losses but also result in choking, which can disturb the pump.

To be able to meet these demands, tests at correct cavitation numbers have been made in the KaMeWa Marine Laboratory with models of various inlet designs. Based upon these model tests the inlet duct can be given an efficiency of about 75–80% in relation to the inlet velocity head.

The inlet duct is preferably integrated into the hull and normally built by the shipyard according to KaMeWa drawings. The inlet at the hull surface is well rounded to avoid vortices entering the pump at low speeds. Debris is prevented from entering the inlet by a grid. Should the pump get clogged it can be cleaned through the inspection openings in front of the impeller. The inlet duct ends at the transom with a connecting flange for the pump.

PUMP: The pump is of the mixed flow type and the 6-blade impeller is bolted to a stub shaft carried in the stator hub by one radial and one axial roller bearing. The bearings are spherical

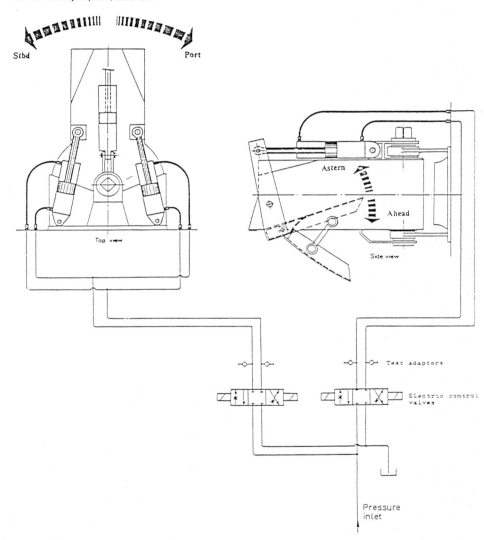

Main components of KaMeWa steering and reversing system

with the same centre of sphere, so that they are unaffected by minor deviations from the theoretically correct centre line of the pump shaft. Movements of an elastically-mounted prime mover will thus not affect the bearings.

The pump unit also contains the stationary guide vanes and the outlet nozzle forming the jet.

The thrust of the pump unit is taken up and transferred to the transom of the vessel.

The impeller hub is filled with oil to lubricate and cool the bearings. The thrust bearing also acts as a centrifugal pump circulating the oil within the hub. The temperature of the oil is thus kept within about 20°C above the water temperature without any extra oil cooler. To minimise the risk of water leakage into the hub, the oil pressure is kept above the water pressure by a gravity tank. For larger units the lubrication oil is slowly cir-

culated from the hub into the tank and back by a small electric driven pump. In this way a continuous monitoring of the oil with regard to flow and temperature is possible.

The pump unit as well as the pump shaft and the steering/reversing gear are made of acid-proof steel. Sacrificial zinc anodes are fitted within the space between the impeller chamber and the conical aft part of the inlet duct to protect the hull and inlet.

STEERING AND REVERSING GEAR: Steering forces are achieved by deflecting the jet sideways by turning the steering nozzle 30° port or starboard. The steering nozzle also incorporates the reversing device. Jet reversal is obtained by turning the bucket under the nozzle. It gradually enters the jet from below and finally gives full reverse thrust. By setting the bucket in inter-

Installation of KaMeWa 63S62/6 waterjet units on the Marinteknik 33 CPV *Ørnen*, in service with DSØ

Size	A	B	C	D	E	rF	G	H	rJ	K	L min	M min
40	1095	(2830)	440	300	20	75	415	480	790	(900)	480	2000
45	1400	(3350)	493	350	20	80	410	640	840	(1220)	540	2200
50	1520	(3750)	550	375	25	100	635	695	945	(1350)	600	2200
56	1670	(4200)	620	395	35	110	835	760	1030	(1510)	670	2500
63	1900	(4700)	695	465	35	120	675	860	1120	(1700)	760	2600
71	2115	(5300)	772	535	35	130	745	965	1280	(1900)	850	2900
80	2395	(5970)	875	535	40	140	810	1085	1450	(2140)	960	3300
90	2615	(6720)	972	630	30	165	1030	1185	1610	(2410)	1080	3500
100	3000	(7470)	1100	670	50	180	1020	1360	1820	(2680)	1200	4130
112	3360	(8360)	1230	750	60	200	1140	1520	2030	(3000)	1350	3620
125	3750	(9330)	1370	840	65	220	1270	1700	2270	(3350)	1500	5160

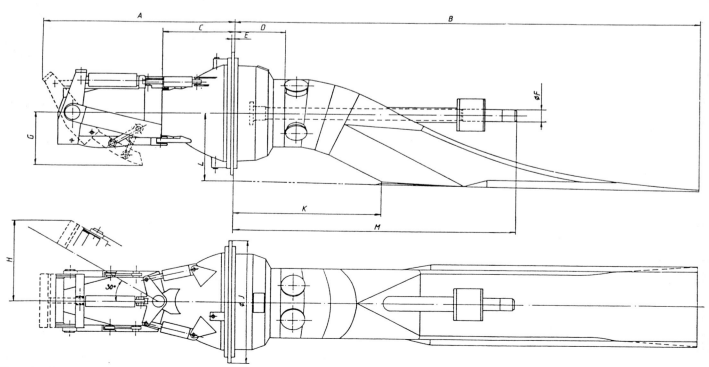

Size options for KaMeWa Type 62 waterjet units

mediate positions the thrust can be continuously and smoothly varied from zero to maximum ahead and astern.

The fact that the bucket is coming from under the jet means that a very low vibration level is achieved on the gear since only that part of the jet which needs to be deflected is affected while the remaining part of the jet is undisturbed.

The bearings for the steering as well as for the reversing bucket are of self-lubricating type. On top of the steering nozzle are two supports for the pivoted hydraulic cylinders for steering. The reversing bucket consists of an upper and a bottom part linked together by bearings at the aft end. The movement of the two parts is controlled by a yoke welded to the upper part and journalled in the steering nozzle. The bottom part is coupled to the steering nozzle by one link on each side of the nozzle. The yoke is connected to the pivoted hydraulic cylinder for reversing positioned on top of the steering nozzle. When reversing, the upper part closes the steering nozzle and deflects the jet down to the bottom part which further changes the jet direction to forward/down, resulting in astern thrust.

For feed-back and position indication, there are cables connected to the steering nozzle and to the reversing bucket. The cables are drawn through the transom and connected to potentiometers.

HYDRAULIC AND LUBRICATING SYSTEM: A separate hydraulic powerpack for each unit is used for manoeuvring. Normally the load compensated main pump is PTO-driven and for start and stand-by a small electric motor driven pump is used. The control valves are mounted on top of the powerpack.

For larger units, size 60 and above, a separate lubrication oil pack is delivered for each unit. A small electric motor driven pump is used for circulating the oil as well as to maintain a pressure higher than the waterhead outside the seal. The pack should be positioned above the waterline in order to keep a static head at stand still.

For smaller jet units only a gravity tank is used.

REMOTE CONTROL SYSTEM: Two standard electronic remote control systems are normally used. Either a steering wheel and one combined lever for control of engine speed and reversing bucket, or one combined lever for control of steering, engine speed and reversing bucket.

The two systems can be extended to include additional control stations, back-up control and electric shaft system.

Advantages and some installations

The KaMeWa waterjet units have the following advantages and characteristics:

Designed to give high performance at high ship speeds as well as at low cruising speed. The efficiency has been verified in a number of full scale installations.

For medium speed vessels, top speed 25–30 knots, the fuel economy is in general competitive with that achieved with propellers.

For fast patrol boats fuel economy may be improved compared with fixed-pitch propeller installation from top speed down to the 10–15 knots region.

The water inlets have a very low drag when idling during cruising which makes the KaMeWa waterjet units attractive as booster units, also in combination with propellers.

Comparison of KaMeWa impellers from Marinteknik *Apollo Jet* after 15 000 hours service with a new impeller, shown in the foreground

The thrust/weight ratios of the KaMeWa waterjet units are optimised for most common hull forms, ie planing and semiplaning hulls, catamarans and sidewall hovercraft (SES).

KaMeWa's modern Marine Laboratory provides the testing facility required for inlet design, cavitation and performance studies.

Fixed geometry inlets can be designed to operate satisfactorily at full engine load from low cruising speeds (when running on a reduced number of shafts) up to the top speed of the vessel.

The pump shaft speed is practically independent of ship speed at constant power output. This means that the waterjet unit will never overload a diesel engine as the power absorption always is approximately proportional to rpm^3. Reduced maintenance costs due to prolonged MTBO 'for the diesels may be achieved in certain installations.

Due to the absence of appendages and the rugged design of the KaMeWa waterjet units the costs for maintenance and off-hire time due to damages from floating debris can be reduced.

In multi-shaft installations CODAG/CODAD propulsion is possible without complex gearing and control systems. Full diesel power is always available irrespective of increased ship resistance due to bad weather, fouling etc or at extreme light displacements. This means increased top speed of the vessel.

The KaMeWa waterjet units are designed to simplify maintenance and overhaul. The units can be mounted and dismounted from outside the ship without docking of the vessel.

The KaMeWa waterjet installations are characterised by low noise and vibration levels.

Excellent manoeuvrability over the whole speed range of the vessel. Full engine torque is always available for manoeuvring and acceleration.

Years of operating in the debris-laden waters of the Hong Kong area have proven that the units are very reliable and insensitive to sand and floating debris in the water.

Sixteen units of 1645bhp each have been sold to catamaran ferries, of which eight are operating in Hong Kong. The vessels have a cruising speed of 30–34 knots depending on displacement. The first units delivered in 1980 to Hong Kong have been in daily service without any mechanical and hydrodynamic problems and are absolutely free from cavitation erosion.

A 77-tonne, 3-shaft planing craft uses two KaMeWa waterjet units for cruising. At full diesel power the cruising speed is about 25–26 knots. The wing units are also used in combination with a booster centre unit at about 50 knots. The units were delivered in 1981 and have functioned very satisfactorily.

The most powerful KaMeWa waterjet unit, absorbing about 10 000kW, was delivered to Fr Lürssen Werft NB 13503. The 230-tonne, 3-shaft vessel went on successful trials during July 1983. The vessel has two KaMeWa waterjet wing units, driven by diesel engines for cruising at about 15–16 knots. The centre KaMeWa waterjet unit is driven by two gas turbines (totalling 10 000kW). The top speed of the vessel is above 45 knots with all three waterjet units running. The diesel engines can deliver full power both at 15 and 45 knots without overload/overspeed.

APPLICATIONS: Following the first 250 and 480shp experimental units, KaMeWa delivered in 1980 two 1575bhp units for the first Marinteknik Jetcat JC-F1 catamaran ferry and the first such craft to use waterjet units. This installation represented a major move by KaMeWa into the field of waterjet propulsion, a step which has led to continuing orders for waterjet units in the 400 to 4500shp range and one of 13 900shp. The following table summarises these applications.

KaMeWa Waterjet Unit Deliveries 1988 Onwards

KaMeWa delivered its first major waterjet propulsion system in 1980. Two units, designed to take a shaft input power of 1160kW each were delivered to Marinteknik Verkstads AB for their first high-speed catamaran ferry, the JC-F1 *Jetcat*. This was the real beginning of a very large production of the units. By the end of 1987 deliveries had reached a figure of 247 units. Details of these deliveries are given in the 1989 edition and preceeding editions of this book.

KaMeWa Waterjet Unit Deliveries 1988 onwards

Delivery in	Name of ship	Type of ship	Owner	Shipyard	Yard No	Number of units	kW/ shaft	Size of unit
1988	—	Coastal-corvette	Swedish Navy	Karlskronavarvet AB Karlskrona, Sweden	424	3	2130	80S
1988	—	Coastal-corvette	Swedish Navy	Karlskronavarvet AB Karlskrona, Sweden	425	3	2130	80S
1988	Salten	Catamaran ferry	Saltens Dampskibsselskab, Bodö, Norway	Westamarin A/S, Norway	93	2	2040	63S
1988	Ofoten	Catamaran ferry	Ofoten, Norway	Westamarin A/S, Norway	94	2	2040	63S
1988	Vindile	Catamaran ferry	Nordstöm-Thulin, Sweden	Westamarin A/S, Norway	95	2	2040	63S

KaMeWa Water Jet Unit Deliveries 1988 onwards (continued)

Delivery in	Name of ship	Type of ship	Owner	Shipyard	Yard No	Number of units	kW/ shaft	Size of unit
1988	—	Motor yacht	—	Heesen Shipyard BV, Oss, The Netherlands	7441	2	1600	80S
1988	Catena	Motor yacht	—	Oceanfast Pty Ltd, Jandakot, Western Australia	92	2	980	66S
1988	—	Motor yacht	—	MCP, Brasilien	—	2	1090	63S
1988	—	Patrol craft	MSA, Japan	MHI Shimonoseki Shipyard, Shimonoseki, Japan	—	1	1839	80S
1988	Seacat	Passenger catamaran	—	A/S Fjellstrand Aluminium Yachts, Omastrand, Norway	1586	2	2040	71S
1988	Fjørtoft	Passenger catamaran	Fylkes, Norway	Brōdrene Aa Båtbyggeri, Hyen, Norway	196 E	2	1175	50S
1988	Santa Maria	SES	—	Brōdrene Aa Båtbyggeri, Hyen, Norway	199	2	1600	63S
1988	San Pawl	SES	—	Brōdrene Aa Båtbyggeri, Hyen, Norway	200	2	1600	63S
1988	Sant' Agata	SES	—	Brōdrene Aa Båtbyggeri, Hyen, Norway	201	2	1600	63S
1988	San Pietro	SES	—	Brōdrene Aa Båtbyggeri, Hyen, Norway	202	2	1600	63S
1988	Baraka 2	SES	—	Alfa Naval, La Seyne, France	27–02	2	1500	56S
1988	—	SES	—	Alfa Naval, La Seyne, France	27–03	2	1500	56S
1988	—	SES	—	Alfa Naval, La Seyne, France	27–04	2	1600	58S
1988	Jetcat	Passenger catamaran	—	Kvaerner Fjellstrand, Norway	1594	2	2040	71S
1988	Xin Ning	Passenger catamaran	Yuet Hing, Hong Kong	Precision Marine Holdings Pty Ltd, Jervoise Bay, WA, Australia	863	2	1680	71S
1988	Adaire	Passenger catamaran	Kuwait Public Transport	NQEA Australia, Pty Ltd, Cairns, Australia	156	2	725	50S
1988	Na'ayem	Passenger catamaran	Kuwait Public Transport	NQEA Australia, Pty Ltd, Cairns, Australia	157	2	725	50S
1988	Askepott	Monohull	—	Båtutrustning A/S, Rubbestadneset, Norway	87	2 1	730 730	40S 40S
1988	Quicksilver V	Passenger catamaran	Quicksilver Connections Ltd, Australia	NQEA Australia, Pty Ltd, Cairns, Australia	158	2	1650	63S
1988	Quicksilver VI	Passenger catamaran	Quicksilver Connections Ltd, Australia	NQEA Australia, Pty Ltd, Cairns, Australia	159	2	1650	63S
1988	Prince of Venice	Passenger catamaran	Quicksilver Connections Ltd, Australia	NQEA Australia, Pty Ltd, Cairns, Australia	160	2	1650	63S
1989	Quicksilver VII	Passenger catamaran	Quicksilver Connections Ltd, Australia	NQEA Australia, Pty Ltd, Cairns, Australia	161	2	1650	63S
1988	Shun Feng	Passenger catamaran	Yuet Hing, Hong Kong	Precision Marine Holdings Pty Ltd., Jervoice Bay, W Aus Australia	876	2	1680	71S
1988	Dae Won Catamaran	Passenger catamaran	Dae Won Ferry, S. Korea	Kvaerner Fjellstrand, Norway	1591	2	2040	71S
1988	—	Yacht	—	Heesen Shipyard BV, Oss, The Netherlands	7441	2	1600	80S
1988	—	Catamaran-yacht	—	Carrington Slipway Pty Ltd., Tomago, NSW, Australia	602200	2	660	45S
1988	—	Motorsailing yacht	—	Runmere Pty Ltd., Brisbane, Australia	21	2	1620	90S
1988	Akbarge	Air Cushion Vehicle	—	Mitsui Engineering & Shipbuilding Co Ltd. Tamano Shipyard, Ichikawa City, Japan	TH 1514	2	346	40S
1989	—	Sport-fisherman	—	Hakvoort B.V., Monnickendam, The Netherlands	202	2	2130	71S
1989	—	Motor yacht	—	Oceanfast Pty. Ltd., Henderson, W Aus, Australia	65	2	2090	80S
1989	—	Motor yacht	—	Oceanfast Pty Ltd., Henderson, W Aus, Australia	94	2	2090	90S
1989	—	Motor yacht	—	Oceanfast Pty Ltd., Henderson, W Aus, Australia	74	2	2090	80S
1988	Nordlicht	Catamaran	—	Kvaerner Fjellstrand, Norway	1592	2	1836	63S
1988	Nantucket Spray	Wave Piercing Catamaran	—	Nichols Bros. Boat Builders, Inc., Freeland, WA, USA	—	2	1743	63S
1988	Aquajet I	Catamaran	Kyodo Kisen, Kobe, Japan	Mitsui Engineering & Shipbuilding Co Ltd., Tamano Shipyard, Ichikawa City, Japan	TH 1613	2	1304	63S
1989	Aquajet II	Catamaran	Kyodo Kisen, Kobe, Japan	Mitsui Engineering & Shipbuilding Co Ltd., Tamano Shipyard Ichikawa City, Japan	TH 1614	2	1304	63S
1988	Frank Cook	Search & Rescue	—	NQEA Australia Pty Ltd., Cairns, Qld, Australia	171	2	1103	56S
1989	Metro Manhattan	SES	Tri-State Marine Transport, Inc	Avondale Industries, Boat Division, Harvey, LA, USA	—	2	1260	56S
1989	Vineyard Spray	Patrol	MSA, Japan	Hitachi, Japan	—	1	1443	80S
1989	—	Catamaran	Bay State Cruises, USA	Gladding Hearn Shipbuilding, Somerset, MA, USA	—	2	1680	71S
1989	—	Landing Craft	Singapore Navy	Singapore Shipbuilding & Engineering Ltd., Singapore	—	2	559	45S
1989	Yin Shan Yu	Catamaran Ferry	—	Wavemaster International Pty. Ltd., Henderson, W. Aus., Australia	—	2	1089	63S
1989	—	Passenger boat	Fuke Kaiun, Japan	Sanuki Zosen, Japan	—	2	1448	63S
1989	Jet Express	Catamaran	Put-in-Bay Boat Line	Gladding Hearn Shipbuilding, Somerset, MA, USA	—	2	1260	63S
1989	—	F.P.B.	—	Baglietto Shipyard S.p.A., Varazze, Italy	C33–24M/11 GC	2	1092	45S
1989	—	Motor yacht	Euro Canadian Marine Inc., Nassau, Bahamas	Denison Marine Inc., Forida, USA	003	2*	1200	63S
1989	Documen	Catamaran Ferry	Yuet Hing Marine Supplies, Hong Kong	Italthai Marine Ltd., Bangkok, Thailand	78	2	1250	63S
1989	Leopardo	Catamaran	Cat Lines SA, Spain	Kvaerner Fjellstrand, Norway	1593	2	1836	63S
1989	Eyra	Catamaran	—	Kvaerner Fjellstrand, Norway	1595	2	1836	63S
1989	Nam Hae Star	Catamaran	Nam Hae Express, S. Korea	Kvaerner Fjellstrand, Norway	1596	2	1836	63S

KaMeWa Water Jet Unit Deliveries 1988 onwards (continued)

Delivery in	Name of ship	Type of ship	Owner	Shipyard	Yard No	Number of units	kW/ shaft	Size of unit
1990	*Sognekongan*	Catamaran	Fylkkesbaatane i Sogn og Fjordane, Norway	Kvaerner Fjellstrand, Norway	1597	2	1836	63S
1989	—	Motor yacht	—	Derecktor, New York, USA	D156	2	2040	71S
1989	—	—	MSA, Japan	MHI Shimonoseki Shipyard, Shimonoseki, Japan	—	1	1443	80S
1989	—	SES	French Navy	C.M.N., Cherbourg, France	—	2	2510	71S
1989	—	SES	US Navy			2	2130	71S
1990	—	Motor yacht	—	Blohm & Voss AG, Hamburg, W. Germany	956	2 1	3680 13800	112S 1608
1990	—	Patrol craft	Finnish Frontier Guard	Hollming Ltd., Rauma, Finland	282	2	3130	90S
1989	*Shun Xing*	Catamaran Ferry	Yuet Hing Marine Supplies, Kong Kong	Italthai Marine Ltd, Bangkok, Thailand	80	2	1250	83S
1989	—	Motor yacht	—	Kees Cornelissen B.V., Oreumel, The Netherlands	—	2	1600	63S
1989	—	SES	—	Avondale Industries, Boat Division, Harvey, LA, USA	—	2	1680	63S
1989	—	Sport-fisherman	—	Meesen Shipyard B.V. Oss, The Netherlands	7629	2	1600	71S
1989	—	SES	—	Br. Aa Båtbyggeri A/S, Hyen, Norway	210	2	1600	63S
1990	—	SES	—	Br. Aa Båtbyggeri A/S, Hyen, Norway	212	2	1600	83S
1989	—	SES	—	Eikefjord Marine A/S, Eikefjord, Norway	211	2	1600	63S
1990	—	SES	—	Eikefjord Marine A/S, Eikefjord, Norway	213	2	1600	63S
1989	—	Catamaran	—	Catamaran Lines, Inc., Greenwich, CT, USA	—	2	2940	71S
1989	*Zhen Xing*	Catamaran Ferry	Yuet Hing Marine Supplies, Hong Kong	Wavemaster International Pty Ltd., Henderson, W. Aus., Australia	C22	2	—	63S
1989	—	Catamaran Ferry	The State Transit Authority, NSW, Australia	NQEA Australia Pty Ltd, Cairns, Qld, Australia	—	2	1680	63S
1990	—	Catamaran Ferry	The State Transit Authority, NSW, Australia	NQEA Australia Pty Ltd, Cairns, Qld, Australia	—	2	1680	63S
1990	—	Catamaran Ferry	The State Transit Authority, NSW, Australia	NQEA Australia Pty Ltd, Cairns, Qld, Australia	—	2	1680	63S
1990	*Murcury*	Catamaran	Far Eastern Shipping Co.	Kvaerner Fjellstrand, Norway	1598	2	2040	63S
1990	*Solovki*	Catamaran	Northern Shipping Co.	Kvaerner Fjellstrand, Norway	1599	2	2040	63S
1990	—	Catamaran	Black Sea Shipping Co.	Westamarin A/S, Mandal, Norway	103	2	—	71S
1990	—	Catamarin	Black Sea Shipping Co.	Westamarin A/S, Mandal, Norway	104	2	—	71S
1990	—	Catamaran	Black Sea Shipping Co.	Westamarin A/S, Mandal, Norway	105	2	—	71S
1990	—	Catamaran	Black Sea Shipping Co.	Westamarin A/S, Mandal, Norway	106	2	—	71S
1990	—	Motor yacht	—	Brooke Yachts International Ltd, UK	815	2 1	2000 2000	90S 80B
1990	—	Motor yacht	—	Astilleros MEFASA, San Juan de Nieva – Aviles, Spain	—	2	2705	80S
1989	—	Motor yacht	Oceanfast Pty. Ltd., Perth, Western Australia		94	1	1600	80S
1990	—	Mono hull	—	Miura, Japan	—	2	603	40S
1990	—	SES	Swedish Navy	Karlskronavarvet AB, Sweden	431	2	2040	63S
1990	—	Catamaran Ferry	—	NQEA Australia Pty Ltd, Cairns, Qld. Australia	170	2	1213	63S
1990	*Audubon Express*	Catamaran Ferry	New Orleans Steamboat Company, New Orleans, USA	Gladding Hearn Shipbuilding, Somerset, MA, USA	—	2	1194	63S
1990	—	Catamaran Ferry	Finnmark Fylkes, Norway	Kvaerner Fjellstrand, Norway	1600	2	2000	63S
1990	—	Catamaran Ferry	Dampskibsselskabet Øresund AS, Denmark	Kvaerner Fjellstrand, Norway	1601	2	2000	63S
1990	—	Catamaran Ferry	Dampskibsselskabet Øresund AS, Denmark	Kvaerner Fjellstrand, Norway	1602	2	2000	63S
1990	—	Catamaran Ferry	Indian Government	Tille Scheepsbouw B.V., The Netherlands	276	2	1150	63S
1990	—	Catamaran Ferry	Indian Government	Tille Scheepsbouw B.V., The Netherlands	277	2	1150	63S
1990	—	Sport boat	—	Derecktor Inc., USA	—	2	200	46S

MJP MARINE JET POWER AB

S-74063 Österbybruk, Sweden

Telephone: (0295) 20785
Telex: 76229FAGSTA S
Telefax: (0295) 21383

Gerard Törneman, *Managing Director*
Gunilla Törneman, *Director*
Paul Braums, *Export Manager*

Marine Jet Power AB is a relatively new company combining technical know-how, modern engineering and experience, set up to create advanced propulsion systems for commercial operation in vessels of various types and sizes, especially for high-speed surface craft such as mono-hulls, catamarans and SES.

During 1986 a series of advanced waterjets were developed, covering engine sizes from 300kW up to 3500kW and for cruising speeds from 15 knots to 60 knots.

MANOEUVRING CAPABILITY: The system includes jet propulsors, steering/reversing units, electro-hydraulic controls and a computerised remote control system (RMC) which is claimed to be the first digital control system in this field. With the computerised RMC the crew's learning period for advanced waterjet operation has been reduced to a minimum and the risk for mistakes in critical situations has been minimised. The RMC includes control levers for steering, speed/forward/reverse and a single combinator for cruising/harbour mode. Normally a twin installation of waterjets requires two combinators, one for each unit, but with the digital control system advanced manoeuvres are made with one single combinator. The combinator can be used in three ways:

1) at cruising for different speed setting on each unit, in harbour mode
2) lateral movement of the vessel without the need of bow thrusters

MJP delivery of two ship sets, J650R-DD to FBM Marinteknik Singapore, December 1988

MJP waterjet unit mounted on the 41m Marinteknik monohull ferry *Rosaria Lauro* operating between Naples and Ischia

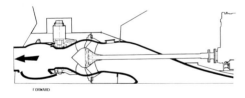
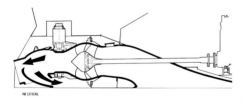
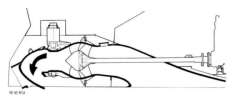

Mechanism of flow re-direction on MJP waterjet units

3) rotation around the vessel's centre of flotation.

The different settings of the waterjets ie forward/neutral/reverse, outward/inward inclination and speed are controlled by the computer and can be adjusted for different vessels and loading conditions by the crew.

For steering purposes hydraulic rotary actuators are used which allow full nozzle turning from one side to the other within 2.5 seconds. The feedback to the electro-hydraulic controls and the inclination to the mimic panel in the wheelhouse are done through double built-in electrical transmitters in the hydraulic actuators.

The complete steering and reversing unit is made of stainless steel castings and the reverser is

positively balanced, which allows a stepless re-direction of the jetflow from full speed ahead to full speed astern.

EFFICIENCY: To achieve predicted efficiency and speed a new type of mixed-flow pump was developed. The blade-to-blade flow analysis was carried out on a computer together with the finite element strength analysis of the impeller. This design technique is ensuring low drag and high freedom from cavitation.

To further increase the efficiency a new type of impeller bearing was designed including a continuous bearing monitoring system. This careful design also increases vessel comfort due to freedom from vibration of impeller and shaft.

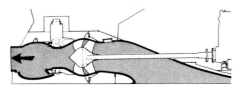
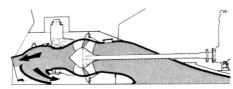
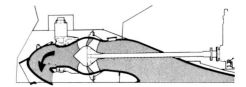

MJP waterjet forward to reverse thrust variation

OPERATING RELIABILITY: Many of today's high-speed surface craft are constructed in light alloy plate, and therefore a new type of intake including plastic parts was designed to avoid corrosion problems by insulating the stainless steel pump unit from the hull. All other components and materials are also chosen to avoid corrosion and mechanical wear in the demanding marine environment.

The monitoring system for the RMC has built in measuring points which give fast fault indication and in addition considerably shortens the servicing time.

RMC – DD
ADVANCED MANOEUVRING SYSTEM FOR WATERJETS

BACKGROUND: During the last two years, MPJ has delivered over 15 advanced manoeuvring systems installed in high speed catamarans and monohull ferries in the size of 33 to 42 metres length and speeds between 20 and 40 knots.

This system, 'Remote Manoeuvre Controller – Dual Drive' (RMC-DD) is unique on the market, having two preselectable modes of 'cruise' and 'harbour' for open sea and confined harbour operations respectively.

NEW GENERATION: The two separate combinator levers for direction and thrust control in the older system are now combined in one 2 – axis single combinator of joystick – type with some special mechanical tracking control facilities to give the operator an excellent feeling of having the ship's thrust and direction control in one hand during cruise as well as in confined harbour manoeuvres.

The other hand is to be free for steering control or to switch over to the auto pilot.

The auto pilot makes the harbour manoeuvres easier: By switching the auto pilot to control the steering in harbour mode during lateral (sideway) movement, the helmsman can leave the parallel steering control to the auto pilot.

In this case, the auto pilot will provide automatic parallel steering when leaving or approaching a pier in transversal direction.

By setting the auto pilot course parallel to the pier and activating the auto pilot, the helmsman needs only to concentrate his attention on controlling the sideway propulsive thrust and make required adjustment of the forward/reverse power that may be needed depending on current and wind affecting the movement, or when moving in diagonal fashion, still under 'parallelism' with the preset course. All these thrust control adjustments can now be done with the single hand combinator lever.

If the helmsman wants to take over the steering for a short adjustment or turning during the transversal movement, without switching the auto pilot control off, that can be done by overriding the auto pilot by turning the lever in the desired direction.

Re-transmitting the control to the auto pilot is done by setting the steering lever in Neutral Position (electrical auto pilot interface) or by letting go of the lever, if the auto pilot interface is driven by a friction coupled DC-motor directly on the steering lever shaft. (Alternative optional AP-interface.)

UPGRADING OF THE FIRST GENERATION OF RMC-DD: A retrofit kit for upgrading of the earlier deliveries of RMC-DD equipped with the older manoeuvring lever system is available on request.

FURTHER DEVELOPMENT OF SYSTEM OPTIONS: A Remote Manoeuvre Station (RMS) is under development and is expected to be ready in early 1990.

This RMS can be easily moved to different positions such as the bridge wing, the fly bridge or the aft deck if required.

The possibility to operate more than one RMS

with an advanced and safe 'take over' routine is incorporated in this development.

The RMS will be accumulator powered, and communicate with the main RMC-DD system by a non-galvanic ('contactless') adaptor to a simple communication net.

When not in use, the RMS unit(s) are connected to a charger, preferably placed on the main manoeuvre bridge.

A highly sophisticated internal self check and communication protocol and a very safe 'take over routine' assure safe handling and operation of the overall system.

Even the first generation of RMC-DD can be modified and upgraded with RMS units since they

are pre-adapted with input/output channels for that use.

MJP J450R, J550R, J650R and J750R

Four types of complete propulsion systems, single or double, including waterjets, hydraulics and computerised remote control system.
Output: 200–3500kW per unit
Speed range: 18–60 knots
Material: Stainless steel in waterjets
Weight: 600–2000kg
Manoeuvring: Electro-hydraulic servo system
Remote control: Computerised control including combinator for lateral movement and rotation

Size	A	B	ØC	ØD	E	F	G	Max power pending on speed
450								
500	640	1290	860	500	960	2050	3400	900 kW
550	695	1412	940	550	1050	2250	3790	1500 kW
650	830	1680	1120	650	1250	2675	4510	2100 kW
750	850	1900	1290	750	1440	3075	5180	2800 kW
850	930	2100	1460	850	1630	3430	5890	3700 kW
950	1090	2460	1640	950	1820	3910	6590	
1100	1190	2845	1895	1100	2110	4525	7630	
1250	1260	3230	2150	1250	2400	5140	8670	
1400								
1600								
1800								
2050								

ABOVE FIGURES ARE NOMINAL DIMENSIONS.
FINAL DIMENSIONS IN ACCORDANCE WITH
DETAILED PROJECT SPECIFICATION.

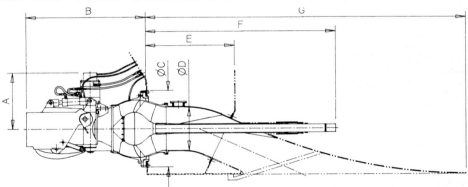

Dimensions of MJP waterjet units

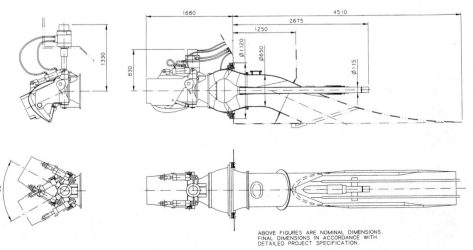

ABOVE FIGURES ARE NOMINAL DIMENSIONS.
FINAL DIMENSIONS IN ACCORDANCE WITH
DETAILED PROJECT SPECIFICATION.

Principal dimensions of MJP J650R

Units sold by January 1989
CINDERELLA: MJP P8601
Yard: Marinteknik Verkstads AB, B65
Vessel: 41m Monohull
Waterjets: J550R-DD, two 610kW, 24 knots
Delivery: 1987
Operator: City Jet Line, Stockholm, Sweden

GIUNONE JET: MJP P8702
Yard: Marinteknik Verkstads AB, B62
Vessel: 34m Catamaran
Waterjets: J650R-DD, two 1940kW, 43 knots
Delivery: 1988
Operator: Alilauro, Naples, Italy

NETTUNO JET: MJP P8703
Yard: Marinteknik Verkstads AB, B70
Vessel: 34m Catamaran
Waterjets: J650R-DD, two 1940kW, 43 knots
Delivery: 1988
Operator: Alilauro, Naples, Italy

ROSARIA LAURO: MJP P8710
Yard: Marinteknik Verkstads AB, B71
Vessel: 41m Monohull
Waterjets: J650R-DD, two 1050kW, 30 knots
Delivery: 1988
Operator: Alilauro, Naples, Italy

CAPRI JET: MJP P8706
Yard: FBM Marine Ltd, 1226
Vessel: 41m Monohull
Waterjets: J650R-DD, two 1050kW, 30 knots
Delivery: 1988
Operator: NLG, Naples, Italy

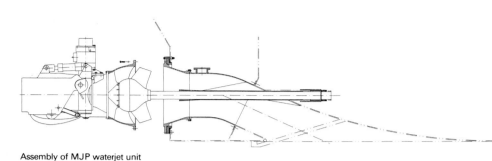

Assembly of MJP waterjet unit

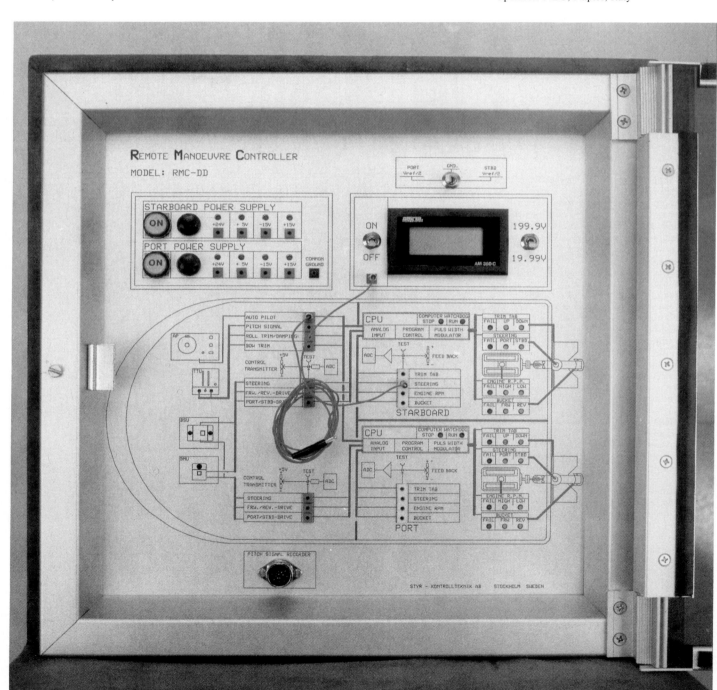

Computerised MJP Remote Control System

CRUISE MODE
POWER,DIRECTION and STEERING CONTROL

POWER CONTROL   **STEERING**

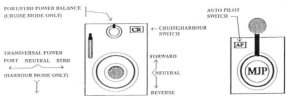

HARBOUR MODE
PORT TRANSVERSAL and COUNTER CLOCKWISE ROTATION

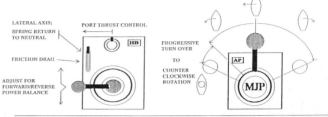

HARBOUR MODE
STARBORD TRANSVERSAL and CLOCKWISE ROTATION

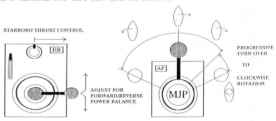

MJP Remote Control System Operating Modes

Bridge installation of Remote Control System

ÖREGRUND: MJP P8711
Yard: Marinteknik Verkstads AB, B74
Vessel: 41m Catamaran
Waterjets: J650R-DD, two 1940kW, 39 knots
Delivery: 1988
Operator: Hong Kong Macao Hydrofoil Co Ltd

CAMOES: MJP P8848
Yard: FBM Marinteknik, Hull 119
Vessel: 41m Catamaran
Waterjets: J650R-DD, two 1940kW, 39 knots
Delivery: 1989
Operator: Hong Kong Macao Hydrofoil Co Ltd

ESTRELLA DEL MAR: MJP P8848
Yard: FBM Marinteknik(S) Pte Ltd, Hull 120
Vessel: 41m Catamaran
Waterjets: J650R-DD, two 1940kW, 39 knots
Delivery: 1989
Operator: Hong Kong Macao Hydrofoil Co Ltd

ACAPULCO JET: MJP P8852
Yard: Marinteknik Verkstads AB, B69
Vessel: 34m Catamaran
Waterjets: J650R-DD, two 1940kW, 43 knots
Delivery: 1989
Operator: Alivit Due (Alilauro SpA), Naples, Italy

COSMOPOLITAN LADY: MJP P8712
Yard: Marinteknik Verkstads AB, B66
Vessel: 37m Monohull
Waterjets: J650R-DD, two 880kW, 25 knots
Delivery: 1989
Operator: Private Cruise, Oslo, Norway

CINDERELLA 2: MJP P8882
Yard: Marinteknik Verkstads AB, B72
Vessel: 41m Monohull
Waterjets: J650R-DD, two 1050kW, 30 knots
Delivery: 1989
Operator: City Jet Line, Stockholm, Sweden

IRIS: MJP P88100
Yard: Marinteknik Verkstads AB, B76
Vessel: 41m Monohull
Waterjets: J650R-DD, two 1050kW, 30 knots
Delivery: 1989
Operator: Kvarner Express, Opatija, Yugoslavia

NICOLAS BOUCHART: MJP P8852
Yard:Societe Bretonne de Construction, C116
Vessel: 32m Monohull
Waterjets: J550R-DD, two 880kW, 30 knots
Delivery: 1989
Operator: Navix, Paris, France

SORENTO JET: MJP P8712
Yard:FBM Marine Ltd, 1264
Vessel: 41m Monohull
Waterjets: J650R-DD, two 1050kW, 30 knots
Delivery: 1989
Operator: NLG, Naples, Italy

DISCOVERY BAY 19: MJP P8882
Yard:FBM Marine Ltd, Hull 122
Vessel: 35m Monohull
Waterjets: J550R-DD, two 815kW, 25 knots
Delivery: 1989
Operator: Hong Kong Resort Co, Hong Kong

1 FERRY: MJP P88100
Yard: Marinteknik Verkstads AB, B73
Vessel: 34M Catamaran
Waterjets: J650R-DD, two 1540kW, 36 knots
Delivery: 1990
Operator: Yasmin Line, Spain

CONDOR 9: MJP P8852
Yard:Aluminium Shipbuilders, 024
Vessel: 49m In Cat Wave Piercer
Waterjets: J650R-DD, four 1600kW, 35 knots
Delivery: 1989
Operator: Condor Ltd, Southampton, England

DISCOVERY BAY 20: MJP P8712
Yard: FBM Marine Ltd, Hull 125
Vessel: 35m Monohull
Waterjets: J550R-DD, two 815kW, 25 knots
Delivery: 1989
Operator: Hong Kong Resort Co, Hong Kong

CINDERELLA 3: MJP P8882
Yard: Marinteknik Verkstads AB, B78
Vessel: 41m Monohull
Waterjets: J650R-DD, two 1180kW, 28 knots
Delivery: 1990
Operator: City Jet Line, Stockholm, Sweden

1 FERRY: MJP P88100
Yard: FBM Marine Ltd
Vessel: 30m Catamaran
Waterjets: J650R-DD, two 1360kW, 35 knots
Delivery: 1990
Operator: Red Funnel, Southampton, England

1 FERRY: MJP P88100
Yard: FBM Marine Ltd
Vessel: 30m Catamaran
Waterjets: J650R-DD, two 1360kW, 35 knots
Delivery: 1990
Operator: Red Funnel, Southampton, England

UNITED KINGDOM

DOWTY HYDRAULIC UNITS LTD (DHU)
(An Ultra Group Company)

Arle Court, Cheltenham, Gloucester GL51 0TP, England

Telephone: (0242) 221155
Telex: 43176 G
Telefax: (0242) 533004

DHU, an Ultra Group Company is a high technology engineering company based in the UK with overseas representation in the USA and Canada.

D Burton, *Managing Director*
R J Scarborough, *Director*
C R G Ellis, *Sales Manager*

The product range of DHU includes waterjets, developed over 30 years' involvement in the marine field, starting with the Dowty Turbocraft jet boats of the 1950s. The current products, known as Dowty Hydrojets are among the most numerous water-jet units in the world

Hydrojets have been produced for defence markets and are principally designed to produce very high thrust at relatively low speed, without suffering from cavitation.

The basic component of the Hydrojet is an axial-flow impeller (single- or two-stage) made of stainless steel, set within a stainless steel reaction casing. The intake and outlet ducts are of cast aluminium.

The control mechanisms are simple and are designed to be robust and reliable. Both the steering and reversing actuator arms penetrate the transom plate and are readily adapted to match the boat's control systems. The zero thrust condition is achieved by the downward vectoring of the jet.

The control of the unit is identical to conventional rudder practice, requiring no retraining of crew. The jet can be directed 33° either side of the central position and the pivot arrangement ensures a high level of flow efficiency, in all conditions.

The components are all made from high quality materials and require minimal maintenance. Ingested debris can be cleared from within the boat by means of an access hatch, or simply discharged by back-flushing the unit.

Typical high speed craft utilising Dowty Hydrojets include combat support boats (bridge erection boats).

The Hydrojet 300 is installed in over 500 craft, including combat support boats for the USA, British, Greek, other NATO and Far Eastern

Dowty Hydrojet 300

armies. Versions of the basic unit have also been installed in army amphibious vehicles, where space constraints have dictated changes to the unit's layout.

The Dowty Hydrojet also has applications in the field of auxiliary or loitering propulsion for larger craft, such as patrol boats, where good manoeuvrability and slow speed economy are required.

Dowty is undertaking continuous development work on waterjet units. One such recent development is the rotating nozzle jet which is capable of

being directed through 360°. Another development utilises a high solidity stainless steel impeller which results in a 20% craft speed increase combined with smaller unit size and hence weight reduction.

Dowty offers purpose-built Hydrojets to meet customer requirements. Production has included 330mm and 440mm diameter units, capable of absorbing up to 600bhp and the company is prepared to investigate other sizes and powers to suit special applications. Development is proceeding on higher thrust Hydrojets.

PP JETS
R G PARKER (ENGINEERING) LTD

Units 5–7 Ailwin Road, Moreton Hall, Bury St Edmunds, Suffolk IP32 6DS, England

Telephone: (0284) 701568
Telex: 817670 ASABSE G
Telefax: (0284) 750545

R G Parker, *Managing Director*
H E Parker, *Secretary*

PP Jets offer a range of jet units up to their model PP 300 of 762mm impeller diameter suitable for powers up to 1500kW (2000hp).

PP Jets have for a number of years successfully

used glass-reinforced plastic for the major fixed components of their waterjet units. The range of jet units from model PP 115 upwards is now being built with a mixture of glassfibre, Kevlar and carbonfibre reinforcement. These materials are totally corrosion resistant and give excellent structural properties. All metal parts exposed to the water can be made in stainless steel or, for special applications, in more exotic materials eliminating problems associated with dissimilar metals in contact with salt water.

The method of construction allows the form of the jet to be made to match the hull contour with comparatively simple additions to the mould. Further, the moulded surface presents a highly polished finish for the water flow.

Canadian Coast Guard rescue boat *Hurricane* fitted with twin PP 140 waterjet units, driven by Caterpillar 375hp engines

An adjustable trim facility is available on most models giving up and down nozzle movement of ±10°.

PP 140
PERFORMANCE EXAMPLES
At max quoted power levels:
 Thrust at 10 knots, 400shp, 1650kg
 Thrust at 20 knots, 400shp, 1320kg
 Thrust at 40 knots, 400shp, 770kg

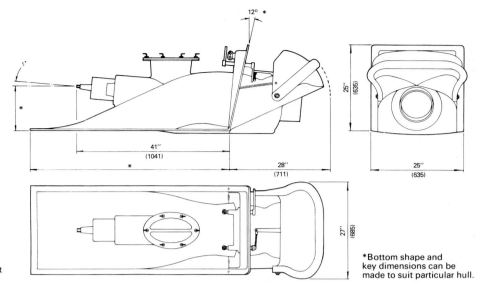

Model PP 140 waterjet unit

*Bottom shape and key dimensions can be made to suit particular hull.

PP type number	65	90 90G	115	140	170	210	250	300
Engine size (hp)								
Petrol	40–200	60–350	—	—	—	—	—	—
Diesel	10–50	40–250	70–400	100–600	200–900	400–3000	600–2000	1500–4000
Impeller dia at inlet (mm)	165	229	292	356	431	533	635	762
Materials								
Jet unit body	Aluminium LM25 hard anodised (PP 90G-GRP)		Composite materials					
Impeller	Aluminium bronze		Stainless 316/Superstron 70					
Weight (kg)	30	60 (PP 90G-70)	125	200	350	600	900	1500

AIR CUSHION SKIRT SYSTEMS

FRANCE

KLÉBER INDUSTRIE

4 rue Lesage-Maille, BP No 22, 76320 Caudebec lès Elbeuf, France

Telephone: (35) 81 00 99
Telex: 770438KLEBER F
Telefax: (35) 78 67 83

Michel Magnan, *Marketing and Sales Manager*

Kléber is one of Europe's major producers of coated fabrics and a principal supplier to inflatable boat and life raft manufacturers which involves conforming to rigorous technical standards. In addition, fabrics are produced for the construction of various forms of hovercraft skirt. Coatings are available in hypalon, neoprene and natural rubbers. Dependent upon the speci-

fication, a range of colours can be supplied. Materials are available in weights (total) ranging from $170g/m^2$ to $2500g/m^2$.

Kleber materials have been used in the UK on hovercraft produced by Air Vehicles Ltd and Griffon Hovercraft Ltd. The company is also involved in many aerospace and marine development and production programmes.

PENNEL ET FLIPO

384 rue d'Alger, 59052 Roubaix Cedex 1, France

Telephone: 20369260
Telex: 820373F
Telefax: 20245510

Philippe Lemyze, *Export Manager*

Pennel & Flipo, a subsidiary of Vev Prouvost, employs 600 people. This 60-year-old company has concentrated its considerable experience to develop a diverse range of products and coatings based on calendering and laminating of rubber, pvc and polyurethane.

Hypalon rubber-coated fabrics are produced for inflatable boats, either on a polyamide base

enka nylon or on a high-tenacity polyester trevira. A whole range of neoprene-coated fabrics have been produced for general use including hovercraft skirt applications. Finished weights for the various materials are in the range of $950g/m^2$ to $2500g/m^2$.

Polyurethane-coated fabrics are available from 145 to $1500g/m^2$.

SPAIN

NEUMAR SA

Head Office: La Rinconada, B-6, 28023-Madrid, Spain

Telephone: (1) 2071998/5636053
Telefax: (1) 5636113

M de la Cruz, *Technical Director*
J A Barbeta, *Manufacturing Manager*

Neumar SA specialises in research, develop-

ment and design of air cushion lift systems, and in the manufacture of flexible structures for hovercraft. The company was formed to bring together a group of engineers and technicians all of whom had previous experience in hovercraft technology; of this previous experience it is worth mentioning the research and development, design and manufacture of the hovercraft lift system and skirt for the company CHACONSA under a contract for the Spanish Ministry of Defence.

Neumar has developed a hovercraft lift system

that offers very high stability with low power requirements and reduced manufacturing and maintenance costs. It has been called an Automatic Transversal Air Distribution or ATAD lift system because of the main function it performs. Several two-dimensional models and two prototypes have been built and tested, with which the viability of this new lift system has already been demonstrated. The ATAD lift system is described in detail in the ACV Builders section under the Neumar SA entry.

Two views of the Neumar skirt system developed to secure high stability with low power requirements

---

UNION OF SOVIET SOCIALIST REPUBLICS

LISICHANSK INDUSTRIAL FABRICS PLANT

Lisichansk, Ukraine, USSR

Suppliers of rubberised fabric for Soviet air cushion oil rig platforms. The materials were developed in conjunction with the Rezi-

notekhnika Association which specialises in industrial rubber products and waterproofing fabrics.

UNITED KINGDOM

AIR CUSHION EQUIPMENT (1976) LIMITED

15/35 Randolph Street, Shirley, Southampton SO1 3HD, England

Telephone: (0703) 776468
Telefax: 0703 701202

J D Hake, *Chairman (USA)*
R C Gilbert, *Director*
R R Henvist, *Director*
G Westerling, *Director*

Air Cushion Equipment (ACE) specialises in the manufacture of flexible structures, mainly for the hovercraft industry. The company produces skirts for UK and US hovercraft manufacturers, for craft ranging from small two-seaters to large hoverbarges.

Because hovercraft skirts are an integral part of a system, the ACE design contribution varies from skirt design to full-scale development of the craft manufacturer's own design. In all cases, templates are produced and held by ACE. As a result of the company's long period of involvement with the hovercraft industry, it is able to advise on material suitability, manufacturing techniques and assembly methods.

The ACE factory in Southampton has equipment capable of making hot bonded (vulcanised) seams up to 5.18m long and bonding areas up to 2.44 × 1.22m in one operation. The workshops are fitted with an extraction system which allows large areas to be safely coated with adhesives associated with cold bonding. The company also possesses long-arm sewing machines and HF welding equipment. This equipment is in continuous use for the manufacture of flexible water tanks, mainly for sailing craft.

Stocks of material varying in weight from 170g/m² coated with pvc, hypalon, neoprene, natural rubber, polyurethane and nitrile/pvc, are held at the factory.

AVON INDUSTRIAL POLYMERS LIMITED (AIP)

Bumpers Way, Chippenham, Wiltshire SN14 6NF, England

Telephone: (0249) 444455
Telex: 444557G
Telefax: (0249) 444466

S J Willcox, *Managing Director*
M C Gillespie, *Asst Managing Director*
M R Shute, *General Manager/Director*
N Jobbins, *Technical Manager*
P S Smart, *Sales Manager*
P A England, *Manufacturing Manager*

Operating from its purpose-built factory in Chippenham, England, Avon Industrial Polymers (AIP) has facilities to provide comprehensive design, development, manufacture and material supply services to craft manufacturers and operators. Throughout its long involvement in this field, AIP has built up a world-wide reputation based on its quality of service and on the strength of its bonded materials. Avon is able to offer a wide range of coating weights, which in conjunction with particular weave types make skirts in these materials highly resistant to delamination.

The majority of air cushion skirt materials are coated with natural synthetic rubber blends or neoprene rubber calendered on to specially selected base fabrics. Avon can also provide plied materials from their range with two or more layers of base fabric to increase the mechanical properties to satisfy the requirements of certain components within the structure of the skirts.

Avon can offer special experience in the design of the attachment of skirts to craft and areas between flexible components. Mechanical fastenings for these purposes are stocked and can be offered when these form part of a seal. In the design of skirt components Avon recognise the need for rapid attachment and removal of all parts during maintenance periods.

Applications of Avon skirt materials include the following:

SR.N4 Mk II (BHC)

Avon has been sole supplier of fingers (segments) for the four SR.N4 Mk II craft, now operated by Hoverspeed, having first supplied to Hoverspeed's predecessors (Hoverlloyd and Seaspeed) in 1972. Avon also supplied and developed fingers for Hoverlloyd and Seaspeed SR.N4 Mk I craft dating back to 1969.

Avon's involvement over the years has led to major increases in finger life and has provided a high throughput test bed for the development of improved coated fabric materials and bonding systems.

Avon Industrial Polymers bow & stern seals in operation on the SES craft *Sant' Agata*

Avon has also supplied the material to BHC for the loop sections since 1973 and has manufactured finger attachment flaps, cones and loop sections since 1978.

SR.N4 Mk III (BHC)

Avon has been sole supplier of fingers to Hoverspeed for the SR.N4 Mk III since two craft were 'stretched' from the original Mark II craft in 1978. Avon was involved in the detailed design study for these components in 1976 and is involved in the continuing specification and manufacture of development fingers for these craft.

LCAC (Textron Marine Systems)

Avon is the only approved supplier of materials for the skirt system on this craft and has been heavily involved in the development components for all ship sets to date. Involvement started in 1980, at which time Avon had also carried out design studies for Rohr Marine Inc as an alternative prime LCAC contractor.

HM5/HM2 (Hovermarine International)

Avon developed the bow and stern seals for the four HM5 SES craft now operating on the route between Hong Kong and Macau. It also designed

and manufactured a special rear seal for the HM2 craft, which required no separate fan air supply.

LACV 30 (Textron Marine Systems)

In 1983 Avon manufactured a prototype spray suppression skirt as a direct contract for US Army. Avon has also supplied materials for these craft since 1979.

BH 110 SES-Bell Halter (now Textron Marine Systems)

Avon has been sole supplier of bow and stern seals for Bell Halter's BH 110 craft since development craft were produced and has also been manufacturing and developing components for the prototype since 1979 until the establishment of Bell Avon in the USA.

CIRRUS A/S (Brødrene Aa A/S)

The detailed design of seals for the *Norcat* fast ferry air cushion catamaran was undertaken in 1984 and included the geometric and structural design of the flexible components and of their attachments to the craft. Since then Avon has manufactured seals for all successive craft of this type designed by Cirrus A/S and has supplied seals to their customers for operation in various parts of the World.

Karlskronavarvet AB/Westamarin A/S

Avon was awarded a contract in 1987 for the design and supply of the skirt system for the two Jet Rider 3400 SES craft now in operation between Copenhagen and Helsingborg.

SES 4000 CRAFT

In 1988/89 design and supply of skirt seals

AP1–88 (BHC)

Avon has supplied all types of material for BHC for this craft since 1982.

SES SEASWIFT 23 (Royal Schelde)

In 1988/89 design & supply of skirt seals

CORSAIR (Blohm & Voss AG)

Design and supply of skirt seal system for SES test craft.

BRITISH HOVERCRAFT CORPORATION LIMITED (BHC)

East Cowes, Isle of Wight, PO32 6RH, England

Telephone: (0983) 294101
Telex: 86761 BHC G

For Directors see BHC entry in ACV Builders section

BHC has produced more than 90 hovercraft in various sizes covering seven basic types. These have together accumulated well over 500 000 hours of operation, and have involved a great deal of research particularly in the design and manufacture of flexible skirts. BHC has designed and manufactured skirts for other craft builders as well as for its own hovercraft. The result has been a progressive improvement in skirt performance, life and reliability and the build-up of experience and expertise. Much of this knowledge has been gained under extreme conditions in Scandinavia, the Middle East and Northern Canada.

In 1963, BHC granted a licence to Bell Aero-space (now Textron Marine Systems) and has, since then, been closely involved with that company's ACV programme. BHC was responsible for design and manufacture of the skirt for the Bell SKMR-1 and for the Bell Aerospace Canada Viking. The company was also retained to carry out research and development work for the skirt of the ARPA SEV designs, co-operated with Bell in the design of the 2K SES project skirt, and was consultant for the design of the JEFF(B) skirt. BHC also designed and manufactured skirts for LACV-30. The LCAC skirt was designed by BHC, and the company continues to be a major manufacturer of skirt systems under this programme.

As well as its unrivalled design experience, BHC has been continually improving its manufacturing techniques. The hot bonding process now used produces excellent integration. In the case of the LCAC skirt, bond strength has, under test, been proved to equal coating adhesion. Excellent flexibility is also achieved, giving the benefit of better fatigue life. Bonding adhesives are generally proprietary, being manufactured by FPT, a sister company of BHC, within Westland Aerospace.

A comprehensive description of BHC skirt production methods was given in the contributed paper of the 1986 edition of *High-Speed Marine Craft and Air Cushion Vehicles*.

A section of the LCAC skirt

BHC skirt fitted to Textron Marine Systems LCAC-1

Stern corner of BHC SR.N4 skirt

GREENGATE POLYMER COATINGS LIMITED (GPC)

Greengate Works, Manchester M3 7WS, England

Telephone: (061) 834 5652
Telex: 666706G
Telefax: (061) 834 1497

John Rogers, *Director and General Manager*
E J Thomas, *Sales Director*
R Wisner, *Manufacturing Director*
R W Collier, *Technical Manager*
A Yorke-Robinson, *Technical Sales Manager*

GPC manufactures many high-performance fabrics for hovercraft uses including buoyancy tubes, skirt, finger (segment) and ancillary applications.

Example materials:

GPC quality	Composition	Total weight (g/m²)	Breaking strength (kg/50mm width)	Tear strength (kg)
1188	Neoprene/Nylon	375	100	7.5
6816	Natural rubber/Nylon	620	250	20
2026	Neoprene/Nylon	1040	275	20
3144	Neoprene/Nylon	1200	450	35
3504	Hypalon/Nylon	1300	300	25

Tiger 4 hovercraft with GPC skirt

THE NORTHERN RUBBER COMPANY LIMITED

Retford, Nottinghamshire DN22 6HH, England

Telephone: (0777) 706731
Telex: 56417RUBBER G
Telefax: (0777) 709739

D E P Owen, *Managing Director*
W J Newbold, *Technical Director*
R Rawson, *Financial Director*
M J Thompson, *Sales and Marketing Director*
K D Bacon, *Commercial Manager and Overseas Sales*
S G Kenney, *National Sales Manager*
H T Brown, *Textile Division Production Manager*
G Surtees, *Sales*
D S Offord, *Business Development Manager*

The Northern Rubber Company has worked in co-operation with many major constructors of hovercraft around the world, supplying skirt materials, components and complete fabrications for lightweight sport vehicles to some of the largest craft currently in service.

Experience gained during initial development of skirt fabrics in the UK, together with continuing development closely matched to the requirements of constructors and operators, has led to an established range of materials used for the complete requirements of skirt structures, including fingers (segments), cones, loops, doublers, spray suppressors, anti-bounce webs etc.

Recent applications for Northern Rubber's materials include:

SR.N4 Series British Hovercraft Corporation (BHC)

Northern Rubber supplies materials used extensively on the above series, having been closely involved with BHC during the development of the skirt system for the SR.N4 Mk1 which came into service in 1969. Hoverspeed as operators continue to use Northern Rubber materials in the maintenance of these skirts.

SR.N6 Series (BHC)

Both civil and military variants of this series have incorporated skirt materials from the Northern Rubber range. The abilities of the materials to withstand the most rigorous operating conditions has contributed to the development of the SR.N6 Mk6 which features significantly enhanced all-weather performance and improved manoeuvrability partly due to skirt construction in which Northern Rubber materials feature.

Properties of Northern Rubber Skirt Materials

Number Reference	Materials Description	Total Weight/Unit Area (oz/yd²)	(g/m²)	Typical Use
NR-11310	Nylon coated both sides with equal weight of neoprene compound	8	271	Skirt and finger segments for use on sporting hovercraft. Segments for use on lower hover pellets
NR-11520	Nylon coated both sides 67% reverse 33% neoprene compound by weight	12	407	Skirt and finger segments for use on two- and four-seat hovercraft
NR-11846	Nylon coated both sides with equal weight of neoprene compound	18	600	Skirt and finger segments for use on lightweight hovercraft
NR-11323	Nylon coated both sides with equal weight of neoprene compound	28	950	Segment fabric for hovertrailers, also inflatable craft
NR-11111	Nylon coated both sides with equal weight of neoprene compound	40	1360	Finger segments for use on sidewall hovercraft
NR-C11569	Nylon coated both sides with equal weight of neoprene compound	40	1360	Skirt segments for hovercraft, water skates and heavy load trailers
NR-C11533	Nylon coated both sides with equal weight of neoprene compound	60	2040	Finger segments for sidewall hovercraft, also segments for water skates
NR-C10863	Nylon coated both sides with equal weight of neoprene compound	74	2515	Skirt and finger fabric for commercial passenger carrying vehicles
NR-11843	Nylon coated both sides with equal weight of natural rubber compound	83	2800	Skirt and finger fabric for commercial passenger carrying vehicles
NR-C11184	Nylon coated both sides with equal weight of neoprene compound	85	2890	Skirt and segment fabric for heavy-load transporters and passenger carrying vehicles
NR-C11828	Nylon coated both sides with equal weight of natural rubber compound	90	3000	Skirt and segment fabric for heavy-load transporters and passenger carrying vehicles
NR-C11748	Nylon coated both sides with equal weight of neoprene compound	95	3220	Segments for heavy-load transporters and passenger carrying vehicles
NR-C11549	Nylon coated both sides with equal weight of natural rubber compound	100	3400	Segments for heavy-load transporters and passenger carrying vehicles
NR-C11580	Nylon coated both sides with equal weight of natural rubber compound	110	3740	Segments for heavy-load transporters and passenger carrying vehicles

AP1–88 (BHC)

Northern Rubber currently supplies skirt component materials to the UK and overseas constructors and operators of the AP1–88.

HM5/HM2 Series (Hovermarine International)

Many of these craft are in service in the Far East with the Hong Kong and Yaumati Ferry

Company on routes to Macao and China, where Northern Rubber skirt fabrics perform under conditions of high utilisation.

PUC 22 *(Larus)* (Wårtsilä)

The complete skirt system for *Larus* was fabricated by Northern Rubber, and completed in a restricted period to schedule. On transfer to Canada, the craft underwent modification to allow operation in temperatures down to −50°C, temperatures which caused no detrimental effects on the skirt or the flexibility and integrity of its materials.

Other applications have included BHC BH.7, Manxcat, Finn-Leijo 378 and River Rover.

Two River Rover craft were used by the Joint Services Expedition to Nepal, where the turbulent white water along a 60-mile stretch of the Kali Gandaki River offered a severe test for both vehicles and their skirt systems, fabricated entirely from Northern Rubber materials. Originally constructed in 1978 one of the craft still operates in these arduous conditions.

MATERIALS: The range of composite flexible materials are manufactured in combinations of natural rubber or neoprene polymer and nylon substrates. All materials are tested in accordance with the highest standards covered by BS 4F100, but to demonstrate properly the adhesive properties of the hovercraft materials, Northern Rubber has developed a system of testing the materials which gives results related to closely monitored representative conditions.

Neoprene composite materials have outstanding oil and ozone resistance, and good low temperature flexibility down to −30°C. Natural rubber composite materials combine excellent abrasion resistance and lower temperature flexibility down to −51°C.

Craft employing Northern Rubber skirt materials: SR.N6 Mk6, BHC SR.N4 Mk3 and River Rover

UNITED STATES OF AMERICA

BELL AVON INC

1200 Martin Luther King Jr Blvd, Picayune, Mississippi 39466, USA

Telephone: (601) 799 1217
Telefax: (601) 799 1360

Malcolm Gillespie, *Vice President, Operations*
Keith D Smith, *General Manager*
P Gene Smith, *Production Manager*
Russell C McDermid, *Development Manager*
Arlene Davis, *Sales Administrator*

Bell Avon Inc is the Avon Industrial Polymers fabrications company in the USA and is a joint venture with Textron Marine Systems. Bell Avon was formed to meet the growing demand in the USA and Canada for high quality rubber-coated fabrics and hovercraft skirts. Backed by the parent company, Avon, it provides a comprehensive design, development and manufacturing service to many North American craft manufacturers and operators.

Bell Avon started operations in its new purpose-built, fully air-conditioned facility in Mississippi in April 1985, using specialised equipment and

procedures developed over the last two decades by Avon in England. Bell Avon is managed and operated by highly-trained technical, process and managerial personnel. The plant is currently undertaking ambitious expansion plans and expects to employ more than 100 personnel in a facility of 7435m² by 1991.

BONDING SYSTEMS AND MATERIALS

Bell Avon offers both "cold" and "hot" bonding techniques. Cold-bonding utilises air-drying cold adhesives, and is not generally appropriate for the harsh environments facing ACV and

SES skirts. Hot-bonding is accomplished using a range of specialised, proprietary hot-vulcanised Avon adhesives, which are not usually available to unaffiliated companies. After appropriate surface preparation, the adhesive is applied to the surfaces to be bonded. The surfaces are then joined under high pressure and temperature conditions. This process results in an extremely well-integrated composite structure, and the very thin adhesive layer provides considerably better flexural fatigue properties than hot-bond tapes or adhesives available from rubber companies for less aggressive applications.

Bell Avon is able to offer customers the full range of Avon coated fabrics, either in roll form, or in fabricated structures for hovercraft skirts and other applications. The ten major types of rubber-coated fabric are stocked at the company's Mississippi location, offering North American customers significantly reduced lead times. Special run or non-stock fabrics can normally be obtained in 10–15 weeks, depending on the type required.

DESIGN CAPABILITY

Bell Avon maintains an in-house pre-production engineering capability, which is coupled with a process of continuous value engineering to offer customers major benefits in terms of improved cost and enhanced operational skirt performance. Bell Avon's programme team works with a customer's design engineers to obtain an acceptable compromise between theoretical design and final cost.

This detail design input is utilised by customers for virtually every "original equipment" proposal or contract received by Bell Avon. On less frequent occasions, customers may require major design engineering input, and Bell Avon can obtain backup for service of this type from the British parent company, Avon Industrial Polymers Ltd. Avon's design capability has included full skirt design, involving stress analysis, design appraisal and reduced or full-scale model testing. Like the parent company, Bell Avon utilises CAD and other sophisticated computer-aided techniques in developing skirt configurations.

REFURBISHMENTS

Traditionally, many ACV and SES craft operators have accomplished skirt repairs using crude 'bolt-on' patches. Avon initially developed a bonded panel-replacement system for SES bow fingers, and subsequently became the sole source of supply for this service to Bell Halter and their SES customers such as the US Coast Guard.

Bell Avon's US location has permitted the company to extend this service to other SES craft, and refurbishment has now been accomplished on SES skirts used by the US Coast Guard, the US Army Corps of Engineers, the US Navy, and Tidewater Marine Service Inc.

More significantly, Bell Avon now offers an unparalleled skirt repair and refurbishment capability for the more complicated ACV skirts. Such skirt components as LCAC keel systems, spray suppressors and even an entire craft set, have been inspected and rebuilt to operational condition in the Mississippi facility. This repair work is carried out to factory standards at a small fraction of the cost of providing new components.

Service begins with a thorough inspection of all seams and doubler areas. A report is issued to the client showing damage or abrasion. An important bonus to this approach has been that a significant and reliable database of common repair types has been accumulated, highlighting areas for possible re-design. Bell Avon's report includes repair detail and a firm cost proposal, assessing both the financial and structural viability of such work, pointing out key parameters the client might consider in deciding whether to proceed with refurbishment.

LCAC

The LCAC skirt comprises more than 80 dif-

Avon bow skirt on Bell Halter US Coast Guard vessel *Dorado* (WSES 1)

Textron Marine Systems Landing Craft, Air Cushion (LCAC) for which Bell Avon has now become a major supplier of skirt systems and components

Textron Marine Systems LACV-30 for which Bell Avon have developed a new stern seal skirt configuration

ferent components, and is supplied to the craft manufacturers as assembled segments for ease of installation. The skirt is developed from the conventional bag-and-finger design, using lockbolts to facilitate the changing of worn or damaged components. The skirt design uses seven different weights of rubber-coated fabrics and calendered sheet to arrive at the optimum combination of weight, flexibility and operational life. The coated fabric weights vary between $1390g/m^2$ and $3050g/m^2$, and both natural and synthetic types of rubber are used, compounded and processed to meet the unusual environmental and operating conditions which will face this craft.

Bell Avon has rapidly become a major supplier of original equipment for this programme. In 1988, Textron awarded Bell Avon ten craft sets, which, coupled with other competitively-bid spares contracts, resulted in a total sub-contract of $5 million, believed to be the world's largest ever hovercraft skirt contract. Bell Avon is the major supplier of operational spares for the LCAC programme.

Bell Avon's increasing involvement has enabled the company to offer a complete service to LCAC craft manufacturers and the US Navy. Spares requirements can often be met from Bell Avon stock. The company also offers a flexible rapid response scheduling service to meet customer requirements, quoting a maximum four weeks lead time for routine components. The company has also refurbished many LCAC skirt components and subsystems worn or damaged in use, resulting in a reduction in the overall operating costs of these craft.

BELL HALTER SES CRAFT

The surface effect ship (SES) concept utilises full height bow fingers, some facets of which are patented by Bell Halter. The stern seal of this craft is a well-proven two-lobe system, giving excellent operational life. Several different weights of coated fabric are used, varying between $2375g/m^2$ for small craft up to $4340g/m^2$ on some parts of the larger craft. All craft currently utilise synthetic rubber compounds, specially developed for abrasion, flexural and environmental resistance.

Bell Avon is the sole supplier of skirts for Textron Marine SES craft. Bow finger and stern seal components manufactured and assembled by Bell Avon have been installed on Bell Halter commercial craft in Egypt, on US Coast Guard craft in Key West, Florida, on the US Navy's SES 200 and on the US Army Corps of Engineers survey boat, *Rodolph*.

SERVICES

MARINE CRAFT REGULATORY AUTHORITIES

ARGENTINA
Prefectura Naval Argentina
  Avenida Madero 235,
  Buenos Aires,
  Argentina

AUSTRALIA
ACVs and Hydrofoils
Covers interstate and international voyages.
Smaller craft come under jurisdiction of state or
local authorities.
Department of Transport
  Maritime Safety Division,
  GPO Box 594,
  Civic Square ACT 2601,
  Australia
Telephone: 062 67 9811
Telex: 61680 AA

New South Wales
The Maritime Services Board of NSW
  Maritime Centre,
  207 Kent Street,
  Sydney,
  New South Wales 2001,
  Australia
  or
  PO Box 32 GPO,
  Sydney,
  New South Wales 2001,
  Australia
Telephone: (02) 364 2111
Telex: 24944 MSBSY AA
Telefax: (02) 364 2064

Northern Territory
Department of Ports and Fisheries
  PO Box 390,
  Darwin,
  Northern Territory 5794,
  Australia
Telephone: (089) 81 6701
Telex: 85605 AA

Queensland
Department of Harbours and Marine
  GPO Box 2595,
  Mineral House,
  George Street (Cnr Margaret Street),
  Brisbane,
  Queensland 4001,
  Australia
Telephone: 224 2111
Telex: 40760 HARBS AA

South Australia
Department of Marine and Harbors
  PO Box 19,
  Port Adelaide,
  South Australia 5015,
  Australia
Telephone: (08) 47 0611
Telex: 82525 AA
Telefax: (08) 47 0605

Tasmania
Navigation and Survey Authority of
Tasmania
  1 Franklin Wharf,
  GPO Box 202B,
  Hobart,
  Tasmania 7001,
  Australia
Telephone: (002) 34 7122
Telex: 58319 AA
Telefax: (002) 31 0693

Victoria
The Port of Melbourne Authority
  World Trade Centre,
  GPO Box 4721,
  Melbourne,
  Victoria 3001,
  Australia

Western Australia
Department of Marine and Harbours
  1 Essex Street,
  PO Box 402,
  Fremantle,
  Western Australia 6160,
  Australia
Telephone: 09 335 0888
Telex: SMHFRE 94784
Telefax: (09) 335 0850

BELGIUM
Ministry of Communications
  Administration de la Marine et de la Navigation
  Intérieure
  rue d'Arlon 104,
  B-1040 Brussels,
  Belgium
Telephone: 02/233 12 11
Telex: 61880 VERTRA B

CANADA
Transport Canada
  Special Ships-Ship Safety Branch,
  Canadian Coast Guard,
  Canada Building,
  344 Slater Street,
  11th Floor,
  Ottawa,
  Ontario K1A 0N7,
  Canada
Telephone: (613) 998 0660
Telefax: (613) 998 5670
Official: R G Wade, *Superintendent*
  Design approval and safety certification of all
craft covered by the IMO Code of Safety for
Dynamically Supported Craft and licensing of
maintenance personnel.

DENMARK
Danish Maritime Authority
  Vermundsgade 38C,
  DK-2100 Copenhagen Ø,
  Denmark
Telephone: (45) 1 27 15 15
Telex: 31141 SOFART DK

EGYPT
ACVs
The Arab General Organisation for Air Transport
  11 Emad El Din Street,
  Cairo,
  Egypt

FIJI
Director of Marine
  Marine Department,
  Government Buildings,
  PO Box 326,
  Suva,
  Fiji

FINLAND
Board of Navigation
  Vuorimiehenkatu 1,
  PO Box 158,
  SF-00141 Helsinki,
  Finland
Telex: 12–1471

FRANCE
Secrétariat d'Etat auprès du Ministre des Trans-
ports, Chargé de la Mer
  3 Place de Fontenoy,
  75700 Paris,
  France
Telephone: 273 55 05
Telex: 250 823 (Mimer Paris) F

THE GAMBIA
Gambia Ports Authority
  Wellington Street,
  PO Box 617,
  Banjul,
  The Gambia,
  West Africa

GERMANY, FEDERAL REPUBLIC
See-Berufsgenossenschaft
  Ships Safety Department,
  Reimerstwiete 2,
  2000 Hamburg 11,
  Federal Republic of Germany

GHANA, REPUBLIC OF
The Shipping Commissioner
  Ministry of Transport and Communications,
  PO Box M.38,
  Accra,
  Ghana

GREECE
Ministry of Mercantile Marine
  Merchant Ships Inspectorate,
  Palaiologou 1 str,
  Piraeus 185 35,
  Greece
Telephone: 411 1214
Telex: 212581 GR

HONG KONG
Director of Marine
  Marine Department,
  Harbour Building,
  38 Pier Road,
  GPO Box 4155,
  Hong Kong
Telephone: (852) 4512
Telex: 64553 MARHQ HX
Telefax: (852) 5 449241

HUNGARY
General Inspection for Transport
  PO Box 102,
  1389 Budapest 62,
  Hungary

ICELAND
Directorate of Shipping
  PO Box 7200,
  Hringbraut 121,
  IS-127 Reykjavik,
  Iceland
Telex: 2307

INDIA
Directorate General of Shipping
  Bombay,
  India

INDONESIA
Department of Transport, Communications and
  Tourism
  8 Medan Merdelka Barat,
  Jakarta-Pusat,
  Indonesia

IRELAND
Department of the Marine
  Leeson Lane,
  Dublin 2,
  Ireland
Telephone: 785444
Telex: 618214

ISRAEL
Ministry of Transport
  Administration of Shipping and Ports,
  102 Ha'atzmauth Road,
  PO Box 33993,
  Haifa,
  Israel
Telephone: (4) 520241
Telex: 46632

ITALY
Ministero della Marina Mercantile
  Ispettorato Tecnico,
  Viale Asia,
  00100 Rome,
  Italy

IVORY COAST
Ministère des Travaux Publics et des Transports
  BP V6,
  Abidjan,
  Ivory Coast

JAMAICA
The Marine Board
  c/o The Port Authority,
  15–17 Duke Street,
  Kingston,
  Jamaica
Telephone: 92 20290/8

JAPAN
Japanese Ministry of Transportation
  2-1-3 Kasumigaseki,
  Chiyoda-ku,
  Tokyo,
  Japan

KOREA, SOUTH
Bureau of Marine Transportation
  Ministry of Transportation
  1 3 Do Dong,
  Choong-ka,
  Seoul,
  South Korea

KUWAIT
Department of Customs and Ports
  PO Box 9,
  Kuwait

LEBANON
Ministère des Travaux Publics
  Direction des Transports,
  Beirut,
  Lebanon

LUXEMBOURG
Service de la Navigation
  Ministère des Transports,
  19–21 boulevard Royal,
  L-2938 Luxembourg
Telephone: 4794–336
Telex: 1465 CIVAIR LU

MADAGASCAR
Ministère de l'Amina
  Jement du Territoire,
  Anosy,
  Antananarivo,
  Madagascar

MALAWI
Ministry of Transport and Communications
  Private Bag 322,
  Capital City,
  Lilongwe 3,
  Malawi
Telephone: Lilongwe 730122

MALAYSIA
The Ministry of Transport
  Wisma Perdana,
  Jalan Dungun,
  Damansara Heights,
  Kuala Lumpur,
  Malaysia
Telephone: 948122
Cables: MINCOM, KL
Telex: 30999 MA

MEXICO
Departamento de Licencias
  Direction de Marina Mercante,
  SCT,
  Luerpo A,
  2 Piso,
  Mexico 12,
  Mexico

MOROCCO
Ministère de l'Equipement
  Direction des Affaires Techniques,
  Rabat-Chellah,
  Morocco

NETHERLANDS
Ministerie van Verkeer en Waterstaat
  Directoraat-Generaal Scheepvaart en Maritieme Zaken,
  Bordewijkstraat 4,
  Postbus 5817,
  2280 HV Rijswijk,
  Netherlands
Telephone: 070 949420
Telefax: 070 996274

NEW ZEALAND
Maritime Transport Division
  Ministry of Transport
  1st Floor, Transport House
  271–281 Upper Cuba St
  PO Box 27006
  Wellington
  New Zealand
Telephone: (04) 828 198
Telefax: (04) 829 065
  Hydrofoils and surface effect ships are subject to the Ship Construction and Safety Equipment (Code of Practice for Hydrofoil Ships and Surface Effect Ships) Notice 1989. The Hovercraft Act 1971 is administered by the Division but no regulations have been enacted to date to give effect to the Act.

NORWAY
Sjrartsdirektoratet
  Norwegian Maritime Directorate,
  Thv Meyersgt 7,
  PO Box 8123-Dep,
  0032 Oslo 1,
  Norway
Telephone: 02–35 02 50
Telex: 76997 SIDR N

SOUTH AFRICA
Department of Transport
  Private Bag X193,
  Pretoria 0001,
  South Africa

SPAIN
Dirección General de la Marina Mercante
  Ruiz de Alacron No 1,
  Madrid 14,
  Spain

SWEDEN
The National Maritime Administration
  Sjöfartsverket,
  601 78 Norrköping,
  S-601 78 Sweden
Telephone: (11) 191000
Telex: 64380 SHIPADM S

SWITZERLAND
Lake Constance
Schiffahrtskontrolle des Kantons Thurgau
  Bleichestrasse 42,
  CH-8280 Kreuzlingen,
  Switzerland
Telephone: 054 79111
Strassenverkehrs und Schiffahrtsamt des Kantons
  St Gallen
  Abr. Schiffahrt,
  9400 Rorschach,
  Switzerland
Kantonale Schiffahrtskontrolle
  Rosengasse 8,
  CH-8200 Schaffhausen,
  Switzerland
Telephone: 053 80601

Lake Geneva
République et Canton de Genève
Service des automobiles et de la navigation
  Service de la navigation   6 rue du 31-Décembre,
  CH-1207 Genèva,
  Switzerland
Telephone: (022) 27 27 54

Lake Lucerne
Strassenverkehrsamt des Kantons Luzern
  Schiffsinspektorat,
  Postfach Obergrund,
  6000 Luzern 4,
  Switzerland

Lake Lugano and Lake Locarno
Ufficio Cantonale della Circolazione
  Servizio Navigazione,
  CH-6528 Camorino,
  Switzerland

Lake Neuchatel
Departement de Police
  CH-2000 Neuchatel,
  Switzerland

Lake Thoune, Lake Brienz and Lake Biel
Strassenverkehrs-und Schiffahrtsamt
des Kantons Bern
  Schermenweg 5,
  Postfach,
  3001 Bern,
  Switzerland

Lake Zürich
Seepolizei Kantonspolizei Zürich
Schiffahrtskontrolle
  Seestrasse 87,
  CH-8942 Oberrieden,
  Switzerland
Telephone: 01 720 70 21

TURKEY
T C Ulastirma Bakanligi
  Deniz Ulaştirmasi Genel Müdürlügü,
  Ankara,
  Turkey
T C Ulastirma Bakanligi
  Marmara Bolgesi Liman ve Denizisleri Müdürlügü,
  Karaköy-Istanbul,
  Turkey

UNITED KINGDOM
Civil Aviation Authority
Hovercraft-Certification, Issue of Type, Safety, Experimental and Export Certificates. Approval of persons or organisations from whom the CAA may accept reports on the design, construction, maintenance or repair of hovercraft or elements thereof. Approval of hovercraft items and equipment. Publication of 'British Hovercraft Safety Requirements'
Technical enquiries to:
A C G Seal,
  Head,
  Hovercraft Department,
  Airworthiness Division,
  CAA Safety Regulation Group,
  Aviation House,
  Gatwick South,
  Gatwick,
  West Sussex RH6 OYR,
  England
Telephone: 0293 573294/5
Telex: 878753
Telefax: 0293 573999

Publications:
Civil Aviation Authority
  Printing and Publication Services,
  Greville House,
  37 Gratton Road,
  Cheltenham,
  Gloucestershire GL50 2BN,
  England
Telephone: 0242 35151

Department of Transport
Hovercraft Operating Permits, Registration and the Certification of High Speed Marine Craft
Department of Transport
  Marine Directorate,
  Sunley House,
  90 High Holborn,
  London WC1V 6LP,
  England
Telephone: 01 405 6911
Telex: 264084 MARBOT G

UNITED STATES OF AMERICA
Cdr R B Meyer
Department of Transportation
Commandant (G-MTH-4/13)
  US Coast Guard,
  Washington DC 20593–0001,
  USA
Telephone: (202) 267 2997

VENEZUELA
Ministerio de Transporte y Comunicaciones
  Dirección General Sectorial de Transporte Acuatico Dirreccion de Navegacion Acuatico,
  Caracas,
  Venezuela

YUGOSLAVIA
Yugoslav Federal Economic Secretariat
  Transport Department,
  Bulevar AVNOJ-a 104,
  Belgrade,
  Yugoslavia

CONSULTANTS AND DESIGNERS
AUSTRALIA

CROWTHER MULTIHULLS PTY LTD

PO Box 35, Turramurra (Sydney), NSW 2074, Australia

Telephone: (02) 94 6988
Telefax: (02) 949 3271

Lock Crowther, *Proprietor*

Lock Crowther is a long-established designer of multi-hull sail, motor and motor/sail craft.

The Crowther design office is an Australian Government-approved research organisation and manufacturers are eligible for Government grants (in Australia) on research and development work carried out by the office.

Designs of recent years from the Crowther office have included:

DMB. A 22.4m ketch rigged pearling/diving catamaran (design no 73) of exceptional performance under sail and power.
TAFUA. Four 18m luxury charter motor sailers (design no 58).
SOUTHERN SPIRIT. A 29.9m luxury motor sailer/yacht, (design no 96 Mk II).
OCEAN SPIRIT. A 32m tourist motor sailer yacht, (design no 126).
SUNBIRD, SUNSEEKER. and *QUICKCAT.* Three 34m high-speed passenger ferries, (design nos 109, 117 and 132).
KIMBERLEY EXPLORER. A 34m mini passenger liner catamaran, (design no 120).

XIN NING and *SHUN FENG* (lines, powering and developmental design for Precision Marine Holdings) two 39.7m 36 knot waterjet passenger ferries (design no 155) for China.
MELANESIAN DISCOVERER. 35m mini passenger liner catamaran for Papua New Guinea.
REEF ADVENTURER II. 33m high speed ferry. (design no. 136).
CAPRICORN REEFSEEKER. 35m high speed passenger ferry. (design no 142).
MAJISTIC. 25m 28 knot water jet luxury motor sailer (design no 161 Mk II).
EQUATOR DREAM. 35.6m 25 knot luxury cruise cat (design no 160) for Singapore.
PRINCESS OF RHODES. 35.6m 33 knot high speed ferry (design no 157) for Greece.

PHIL CURRAN DESIGN

Philip E Curran Pty Ltd
Lot 300 Sparks Road, Henderson 6166, Western Australia, Australia

Telephone: (09) 410 2988
Telex: 94110 FILCO AA
Telefax: (09) 410 2553

Phil Curran, *Director, Naval Architect*
Gordon Blaauw, *Design Manager, Naval Architect*

Phil Curran designs range from 6-metre vessels to high-speed private luxury yachts of over 65 metres, having produced nearly 500 designs since first commencing business some 12 years ago.

Commercial and pleasure craft are designed in all forms of construction, Phil Curran Design specialising in modern 'high-tech' construction materials such as aluminium, composites, foam sandwich, carbon fibre and Kevlar.

Our designs have included the following craft:
CUSTOMISED A 21m, 38-knot, 15-tonne planing vessel with waterjet propulsion.
PM 17. Built by Precision Marine Holdings Pty Ltd. This 17m power boat design has received numerous orders and has won the '1986 and 1988 Power Boat of the Year' awards and the Australian Design Award. With a 24-tonne displacement the boat is capable of 40 knots.
PM 40. Precision Marine 40' sports fisherman. This production vessel is capable of 35 knots and has proved a very successful design with 37' and 43' vessels soon to be added to the range.
Numerous high speed fishing vessels with speeds ranging from 20 to 50 knots built of aluminium and composites.
OCEANFAST 2800 *MERCEDES.* A 27m, 30 knot luxury motor yacht with twin waterjets, operating out of Florida waters.
OCEANFAST 3000 *NEVER SAY NEVER.* A 33.3m, 30-knot luxury charter vessel now operating in the Caribbean.

OCEANFAST 3000/2 *ANTIPODEAN.* A magnificent sistership to Oceanfast 3000, '*NEVER SAY NEVER.*

OCEANFAST 4000 *PARTS VI.* A 46.69m, 30-knot, 150 tonnes (light ship) luxury motor yacht used by the Royal Perth Yacht Club as their flagship during the 1986/87 America's Cup Regatta in Fremantle, Western Australia.

OCEANFAST 5000 *MYSTIQUE.* A 49.5m, 34-knot, 180 tonne, planing vessel with waterjet propulsion operating out of New York waters.

SUN GODDESS. A 200-seat, 34.0m, 25-knot ferry, the second to be built for Ansett Transport Industries, Hayman Island, Queensland, Australia.

SUNDANCER. A 145-seat, 27.5m, 34-knot ferry with waterjet propulsion built by SBF Engineering.

WILDERNESS SEEKER. A 100-seat, 19.95m, 30-knot ferry with waterjet propulsion, built for Gordon River operations in Tasmania.

CANADA

D F DICKINS ASSOCIATES LIMITED

Suite 503A, 21 Water Street, Vancouver, British Columbia V6B 1A1, Canada

Telephone: (604)684 0516
Telex: 0454247
Telefax: (604)684 2357

D F Dickins, *President*

DF Dickins Associates Ltd is actively involved in Arctic marine transportation studies. The company provides route evaluation, conceptual, design and testing for Arctic air cushion vehicles. DF Dickins offers a range of consulting expertise through affiliations with specialists in hovercraft skirt systems, naval architecture and propeller design.

From 1981 to 1984 Dickins Associates provided technical direction of Sohio Petroleum Company's hovercraft research. This involved the co-ordination of an international design team to develop the concept for a 1000-ton ACV. In the last year of the Sohio programme, Dickins Associates directed the testing of the 200-ton JEFF(A) at Prudhoe Bay.

A recently completed project for Gulf Canada Resources involved the conceptual design of a series of large self-propelled hovercraft up to 845 tonnes gross weight. The project included a complete economic evaluation of capital and operating costs in comparison with a Boeing 234 helicopter, and existing hovercraft capable of operating over rough ice with obstacles over 2.5m in height.

Current programmes include the evaluation of air cushion vehicles as high-speed platforms for spraying chemical dispersants on oil slicks at sea. The Canadian Coast Guard Vancouver Search and Rescue base provided an SR.N6 for preliminary trials during the summer of 1986.

In April 1989 Dickins Associates completed an economic and technical evaluation of air cushion vehicles to resupply an oil installation offshore Alaska.

Recent publications are included in the bibliography section of this edition. David Dickins has also contributed a chapter entitled Arctic Transportation in a new book *Hovercraft Technology, Economics and Applications*, J R Amyot, editor, Elsevier Science Publishers B V.

Another paper has been recently published: *An Economic Evaluation of Air Cushion Vehicles in Support of Arctic Offshore Oil Development*: Proceedings 1988 International Conference on Air Cushion Technology, Annapolis, Md.

FINLAND

MXA-CONSULTING LTD OY

It Pikäkatu 3a D, SF-20520 Turku, Finland

Telephone: (921) 333881

Telex: 62004 TURKU SF
Telefax: (921) 331934

Matti Ahtikari

Designer of the MXA 1700 catamaran and a range of high-speed catamaran ferry types now being marketed in the United States of America

FRANCE

BERTIN ET CIE

BP 3, 78373 Plaisir Cedex, France

Telephone: (1) 34818500
Telex: 696231F

Eric Barsalou, *President, Director General*
Georges Mordchelles-Regnier, *Director General*

Bertin et Cie has been engaged in developing the

Bertin principle of separately fed multiple plenum chambers surrounded by flexible skirts since 1956. A research and design organisation, the company employs a staff of more than 500, mainly scientists and design engineers who are involved in many areas of industrial research, including air cushion techniques and applications.

SEDAM was originally responsible for developing the Naviplane and Terraplane vehicles but this responsibility has now passed to IFREMER

(see later entry). The Bertin principle of multiple air cushions has also led to the development of the Aérotrain high-speed tracked transport system and to numerous applications in the area of industrial handling and aeronautics. These applications, developed by Bertin, are described in the sections devoted to *Air Cushion Applicators, Conveyors and Pallets* and *Air Cushion Landing Systems* in *Jane's Surface Skimmers 1980* and earlier editions.

INSTITUT FRANÇAIS DE RECHERCHE POUR L'EXPLOITATION DE LA MERS (IFREMER)

Centre de Brest, BP 70, 29263 Plouzane, France

Telephone: (98) 224040
Telex: 940627OCEAN F

Philippe Marchand

IFREMER was formed in 1984 from the merger between CNEXO (National Centre for Sea

Development) and ISTPM, Scientific and Technical Institute for Sea Fisheries. IFREMER is commissioned by the French Government to conduct studies for the evaluation of unconventional ships, eg amphibious hovercraft, surface effect ships, hydrofoil craft, catamarans and SWATH vessels and may participate in any development of these concepts. Test facilities are located at Brest in Brittany. The largest part of the unconventional ship research programme of IFREMER is concerned with air cushion technology and the relevant patents have been acquired from the former SEDAM company. Since 1985 IFREMER has been mainly involved in the design of the ADOC 12 hovercraft and the NES 24 surface effect ship.

ADOC 12

Full details of this 14-seat craft are given in the Société Aeroplast entry in the main Air Cushion Vehicle Builders section of this edition. In 1986 IFREMER conducted complete performance tests on the craft from their establishment at Brest. In 1988 the craft was improved with diesel engines and a new propulsion system for better manoeuvrability.

NES 24

A 22m surface-effect ship project which has been studied in collaboration with French shipyards (see DCN entry in Air Cushion Vehicles section). Final design and construction had been started by the end of 1988.

GERMANY, FEDERAL REPUBLIC OF

MTG MARINETECHNIK GmbH

Wandsbeker Konigstrasse 62, P.O.Box 70 12 49, D-2000 Hamburg 70, Federal Republic of Germany

Telephone: 040 65830
Telex: 215200
Telefax: 040 6583392

Franz-Josef Gorgen, *Managing Director*
Werner Kutz, *Commercial Director*

MTG Marinetechnik GmbH was founded in 1966 at the instigation of the Federal German MoD as a central Planning and design office for naval systems, especially naval surface craft, and general naval technology. Its shareholders are major shipyards and electronics companies. MTG designs naval systems, prepares tender documents for naval projects and is involved in all project development phases with particular emphasis on

the early planning stages. The company is staffed by some 200 employees, the majority of whom are technical/scientific engineering graduates. MTG is renowned for its competence and impartial consulting services.

For several years now MTG has been working on the design of unconventional marine platforms. Initial basic studies have led to the design of the Fast Test Craft SES 700 and a SWATH design for a research vessel.

Over the past five years a design study for naval fast test craft has been worked on in the Federal Republic of Germany. The selected vessel is a large steel-hulled surface effect ship, with a full load displacement of 720 tonnes and a maximum speed in excess of 50 knots. The design study was managed by MTG Marinetechnik GmbH in Hamburg, on behalf of the German Ministry of Defence in close co-operation with the US Naval Sea System Command under a Data Exchange Agreement. Extensive model tests were performed

at the David Taylor Model Basin (DTRC). MTG integrated into the overall design, contributions from Maritime Dynamics Inc. for a seal and lift system design and a ride control system.

During the last few years extensive investigations have been performed by MTG on SWATH technology leading to the design of a Naval Research Vessel. This design is intended to replace the 2000 tonne conventional monohull *Planet* which is currently in operation for the German Navy. The SWATH 3200 tonne, 13 to 15 knot vessel has been designed to meet the operational requirements of the German MoD for the tasks which are anticipated in the field of naval research in the year 2000. The basic missions and tasks are related to: underwater acoustics, maritime geology and geophysics, and meteorology and aerology. MTG has developed a high standard of expertise in the design of unconventional craft which can be readily exploited for a wide range of naval and commercial applications.

THE NETHERLANDS

WIJSMULLER ENGINEERING BV

Sluisplein 34, 1975 AG Ijmuiden, The Netherlands
PO Box 510, 1970 AM Ijmuiden, The Netherlands

Telephone: 02550 62666

Telex: 41914 MM NL
Telefax: (0) 2550 62761

Consultants to the marine industry.

Feasibility studies, conceptual and final design,

writing of tender specifications, bid evaluation, contract negotiations, building supervision, surveys, maintenance and repair co-ordination, training and development of marine management information systems.

NORWAY

CIRRUS A/S

Vakleiva 133, P O Box 130, 5062 Bones, Bergen, Norway

Telephone: 475 124550
Telex: 40422CIRR N
Telefax: (05)124565

Atle Ulvesaeter, *Managing Director*
Dick Vinkler, *General Manager*

Cirrus A/S has been responsible for the design of the first Norwegian SES, the CIRR 105P *Norcat*, which in conjunction with the builders Brødrene Aa A/S, led to the development of a sister vessel followed by the now well established

and larger CIRR 120, a 330 passenger SES, built by both Brødrene Aa A/S and Eikefjord Marine A/S of Ulstein International. Another Cirrus design, the CIRR 60 has taken their SES experience up to speeds of 52 knots and the latest project, the CIRR 200 has extended their range of SES designs to over 60 metre vessels.

OTTO L SCHEEN JR A/S

Holterteigen 5, N-1440 Drøbak, Norway

Telephone: (09) 930775/930341
Telefax: (09) 930775

Otto L Scheen, Jr *Principal*

Designers of high-speed mono-hull vessels for a wide variety of applications, many in the range of 15 to 20m.

Otto Scheen has been responsible for the design of nearly one hundred mono-hull fast craft up to 20 metres in length with speeds of 39 knots; a considerable number of these have been passenger or ambulance boats. Brødrene Aa have built over 70 of these designs with many diverse yards building the others. Recent designs have included the 20m, 37 knots *Sea Princess*, a 77 passenger vessel, and the 19.2m, 35 knot *Delphin Jr II*.

TEKNISK MODELL-SENTER A/S

6780 Hyen, Nordfjord, Norway

Telephone: (057) 69805/(090) 70027
Telefax: (057) 69925

Ola Lilloe-Olsen, *Proprietor*

Design consultants with a 47 metre towing-tank facility, established 1979. Designers of a large number of high-speed mono-hull ferries, since 1985 some twenty passenger, ambulance and multi-purpose boats have been designed, all with speeds in the range of 27 to 47 knots.

Current designs and investigations are concerned with mono-hull craft in the 50 to 120 passenger range and speeds of around 45 knots. Teknisk Modell-Senter is also engaged in SES development with systematic model testing and full-scale measurement work for vessels with 60 knot cruise capability. In addition, larger mono-hull designs of between 45 and 60 metres are under investigation for providing cost-effective evaluations for the carriage of limited volumes of cargo in the most remote areas of operation. Such vessels might carry 300 tonnes of cargo at 22 knots with 5200kW, or 200 tonnes at 26 knots.

Patrol craft concepts have also been developed; the TMS Mission Cruiser is a 30 to 40 knot design with 4500kW (6000 bhp). TMS is engaged on development programmes for high-speed car ferries, of catamaran and mono-hull form and is participating in SES development by the Ulstein group which includes the SES building companies, Brødrene Aa and Eikefjord Marine A/S.

SINGAPORE

VOSPER NAVAL SYSTEMS PTE LTD

A member of the Swan Hunter Group

232 Tanjong Rhu Road, Singapore 1543

Telephone: 3449388
Telex: 21219 RS
Telefax: 3446642

J.H. Cars, *Managing Director*
Teo Yeow Soon, *Financial Controller*

Michael Lew, *Logistic Support Manager*
S.Y. Seeto, *Technical Manager*

This company has a history in Singapore going back to 1923. The company specialises in the following fields: logistic support and supply, planned maintenance systems, international procurement, general marine services, design of high performance naval vessels, design of quasi military craft for Police and Customs duties, technology transfer using designs based on a range of model tested hull forms. Complete materials packages together with production supervision and other technical assistance can be provided.

Together with the parent company in the U.K. there is experience of a complete range of warships from small patrol boats to frigates and aircraft carriers. In addition the company has facilities to design and build landing craft and fleet auxiliary vessels of all types from 30 to 300m long.

Over the years vessels have been supplied to government organisations in 15 countries in the Middle and Far East as well as many commercial companies in the region.

SWITZERLAND

DR ING E G FABER

Gratstrasse 20, CH-8472 Seuzach, Switzerland

Telephone: (052) 53 30 40
Telex: 78670DATAG CH

Consultant in marine engine plant planning, marine engineering and marine technology, with special emphasis on high-speed and hydrofoil craft, feasibility studies, cost estimates, specifications, plant descriptions, speed estimates and hydrodynamic problems.

DIPL ING E SCHATTÉ

Amlehnstrasse 33, CH-6010 Kriens (Luzern), Switzerland

Telephone: 041412794

Consulting in hydrodynamics, aerodynamics and marine technology, especially high-speed craft.

SUPRAMAR HYDROFOILS AG

Ausserfeld 5, CH-6362 Stansstad, Switzerland

Telephone: (041) 61 31 94
Telex: 866274SUPR CH
Telefax: 8142441

Dipl Ing Volker Jost, *President*
Dipl Ing Harry Trevisani, *General Manager*

Dipl Ing Eugen Schatté, *Research and Development*
Dr Ing Herrmann de Witt, *Hydrodynamics*
Dr Ing Otto Münch, *Stabilisation and Control*
Jürg Bally, *Board Member*

Supramar was founded in Switzerland in 1952 to develop on a commercial basis the hydrofoil system introduced by the Schertel-Sachsenberg Hydrofoil Syndicate and its licensee, the Gebrüder Sachsenberg Shipyard.

Since its foundation, Supramar has provided a world-wide consultancy service, covering not only its hydrofoil vessels but also other aspects of fast marine transport. Its scientists have delivered papers to most of the world's leading professional bodies.

The company has been under contract to many governments and military services.

UNITED KINGDOM

AIR CUSHION EQUIPMENT (1976) LIMITED

15–35 Randolph Street, Shirley, Southampton, Hampshire SO1 3HD, England

Telephone: (0703) 776468
Telefax: 0703 701202

J D Hake, *Chairman (USA)*
R C Gilbert, *Director*
R R Henvest, *Director*

G Westerling, *Director*

Air Cushion Equipment (1976) Ltd is the largest supplier of skirts for medium size passenger hovercraft in the world. It has been in business for 20 years. ACE can offer experience of designing skirts and associated parts for a variety of air-propelled passenger craft from 2-seat leisure craft to the 32-seat Griffon 2500 craft operated at Expo 86 in Vancouver.

ACE also has designed many industrial and non-passenger carrying applications of the fluid cushion principle.

These include: water skate heavy load moving system, tank moving equipment and heavy lift platforms and trailers.

ACE can provide a complete consultancy design and manufacturing service on all aspects of ACV design and performance as well as inflatable or flexible structures.

AIR VEHICLES LIMITED

Head Office and Factory: Unit 4, Three Gates Road, Cowes, Isle of Wight, England

Telephone: (0983) 293194
Telex: 86513HVWORK G
Telefax: (0983) 291987

C B Eden, *Director*

Air Vehicles Limited, formed in 1968, has a wide experience of all types of hovercraft and hovercraft operations and can offer a full range of services as consultants. Particular fields where Air Vehicles Limited has specialised knowledge are in the design of hovercraft up to 20 tonnes payload, the design and manufacture of propeller duct systems and installations up to 3.6m diameter and the design and manufacture of lift fans.

Approved by the Civil Aviation Authority, the company can design and undertake modifications to existing craft. Typical of this work is the conversion of SR.N5 and SR.N6 to flat deck layout for logistic operations, the addition of high speed, dunking hydrographic equipment to SR.N6 and Tiger 12 craft and various modifications for seismic surveying operations. The company also has hovercraft available for charter.

Air Vehicles Limited also undertakes feasibility studies and was responsible for an original design concept leading to the AP1–88, 80-passenger diesel craft operated by Hovertravel Limited and undertook the detail design for this craft.

A G BLYTH

2 Aubrey Villas, Green Lane, Warsash, Southampton SO3 9JJ, England

Telephone: (0489) 574432
Telefax: (0489) 578862

Andrew G Blyth, *Principal*

Naval architecture services for high-speed and unconventional surface craft.

Design, evaluation and feasibility studies for high-speed marine vehicles, especially surface effect ships, mono-hulls and catamarans, from a background of practical shipyard design experience allied to experimental and theoretical research and development work.

Consultant to EEL Ltd (Test Facilities) (UK) for technical direction of a major research programme into the ultimate stability boundaries of surface effect ships, funded by the UK Department of Transport and the United States Coast Guard. This six-year-long fundamental research project has established a new and more comprehensive understanding of the on-cushion stability limitations of this type of vessel.

Consultant to Civil Aviation Authority (UK), for developing theoretical methods of evaluating the on-cushion roll stability of surface effect ships, and determining suitable criteria for safe operation, in a seaway and in high-speed turns.

Consultant to SSPA Maritime Consulting AB (Sweden), for surface effect ship design, development and experimental evaluation and techniques.

Work undertaken includes seal and lift system design and modelling, self-propelled model tests with waterjets, and development of full-scale design based on model tests and theoretical data.

Particular expertise in parametric comparative studies, powering and performance predictions including model testing, SES lift and skirt system development, design and execution of complete theoretical and experimental investigations in the field of high-speed vessel naval architecture, as well as conducting conventional conceptual, preliminary and production design work. Included in this work has been the development of General Arrangement and Lines Plans, structural and stability calculations, preparation of specifications and co-ordination of input of other professional engineers.

BMT FLUID MECHANICS LIMITED

Orlando House, 1 Waldegrave Road, Teddington, Middlesex TW11 8LZ, England

Telephone: (01) 943–5544
Telex: 263118 MARFEL G
Telefax: (01) 943–5347 or 977–3622

Dr M E Davies, *Managing Director*

Formed in 1985 by the merger of the National Maritime Institute and the British Ship Research Association, The British Maritime Technology Group (BMT) is one of the largest independent maritime consultancy organisations in Europe. BMT Fluid Mechanics, one of eight subsidiary companies in the Group, offers extensive services in consultancy centred mainly on its capabilities in the fields of physical and mathematical modelling.

The Company has two large towing tanks, one equipped with a wavemaker, and five wind tunnels, one of which is the most sophisticated of its kind in Europe. Hydrodynamic and aerodynamic studies are undertaken for clients in the field of high-speed craft, ferries, small craft and ships. Wind engineering experiments are undertaken for a variety of clients including those involved with the design of buildings, bridges and Formula 1 racing cars.

Major tank testing studies have been undertaken for the Department of Transport Marine Directorate into ship safety (notably that of ro-ro passenger ferries) and the RNLI for the design of new high-speed lifeboats. Resistance, propulsion, seakeeping and manoeuvring experiments are offered as a standard service and the Company has a long history of such work for high-speed planing and semi-displacement craft. The well known NPL Round-Bilge Displacement craft series stems from a fore-runner of the Company.

Recently work has been carried out for sailing yachts, mainly in connection with the America's Cup and this, in common with many studies carried out by the Company, has been accomplished with a blend of physical and mathematical modelling, allied to design expertise.

Mathematical models relating to resistance, seakeeping, propeller design and manoeuvring simulation are available to clients, supported by CAD systems which are compatible with those used in the high speed and small boat industry.

The Company, being part of a larger Group, can help clients by allowing them access to the wider expertise, ranging from environmental studies in the sea and air to CAD/CAM, available throughout the Group.

HOVERCRAFT CONSULTANTS LIMITED (HCL)

Chinook, Nash Road, Dibden Purlieu, Southampton, Hampshire SO4 5RS, England

Telephone: (0703) 843178
Telex: 477580HOVCON G
Telefax: (0703) 846417

J E Rapson, *Managing Director*
P J Rapson, *Director*
S M Rapson, *Secretary and Director*
M J Cox, *Associate*

Hovercraft Consultants Limited (HCL) offers a comprehensive advisory service to the hovercraft and related industries. Since HCL has no affiliation with any manufacturer or operator, it is able to provide unbiased appraisals of existing and projected craft. The suitability of such craft for particular routes and duties is assessed both technically and economically. The company keeps extensive and up to date records of both the technical and commercial aspects of high-speed, waterborne transport. This information, which includes details of craft, operations, manufacturers, routes and traffic, can be made available to its clients.

HCL specialises in the design of cushion and skirt systems and has designed skirts for a hoverplatform to carry payloads of 300 tons in the Arctic for the Sohio Petroleum Company. This programme involved extensive model work over water and simulated ice surfaces as well as the construction of a full scale box test rig in conjunction with Avon Industrial Polymers operating at pressures greater than the full scale cushion pressure.

The company has recently been involved in the design of an amphibious hovercraft to be built in Asia. For this contract HCL was required to design and construct a 2.5m model which was tested in a wind tunnel and a testing tank and was then converted for radio controlled tests on open water.

HCL has built on its existing experience in skirt design and has completed over twenty full-scale skirt designs, covering all sizes of craft, since 1982. One such project included the design and supervision of the building of a small recreational hovercraft for the American market. The craft has a low profile and streamlined shape compared with other small craft and has set new standards of quietness, controllability and safety. The company also undertakes research and development in connection with improving the economics and the general efficiency and controllability of all types of hovercraft.

HCL is headed by John Rapson, who has been involved with hovercraft technology since 1956. Formerly with Hovercraft Development Limited as Technical Director and Chief Engineer, he has advised government departments and official committees on design, operational requirements and safety of hovercraft.

HOVERCRAFT SALES AND MARKETING (HOVSAM)
PO Box 7, Sarisbury Green, Southampton SO3 6YS, England

Telephone: (042 121) 3547
Telex: 477164HOVSAM G

G A Gifford, *Managing Director*

Hovercraft Sales and Marketing (HOVSAM) undertakes general hovercraft consultancy work, specialising in the recommendation of various amphibious and non-amphibious hovercraft for particular routes and applications. In the ½ to 7 tonne payload range of amphibious hovercraft, HOVSAM acts as consultant to Griffon Hover-

craft Ltd. For the Surface Effect Ship (SES) range of craft, HOVSAM is consultant to Hovermarine International Ltd. Graham Gifford has placed many hovercraft and SES into various countries around the world and will advise on route feasibility and economics, and the suitability of both commercial and military hovercraft for particular areas and applications.

HOVERWORK LIMITED
12 Lind Street, Ryde, Isle of Wight, Hampshire PO33 2NR, England

Telephone: (0983) 65181
Telex: 86513(A/B Hoverwork Ryde)
Telefax: (0983) 65181

C D J Bland, *Managing Director*

E W H Gifford, *Director*
A C Smith, *Director*
R G Clarke, *Director*
G M Palin, *Secretary*

Hoverwork Limited, formed in early 1966, is a wholly owned subsidiary of Hovertravel, the Solent ferry company, which has been operating hovercraft longer than any other company in the world. In addition to its fleet of SR.N6 type craft

it now has access to Hovertravel's new, much larger, AP1-88, also fully amphibious and with approximately the same performance capability.

The company specialises in chartering craft for seismic and other survey work, crew change operations and other related operations within the oil industry in shallow water areas and terrain difficult for other forms of transport.

The company also offers a route feasibility investigation service.

LORNE CAMPBELL
The Powerboat Compound, 14 West Quay Road, Poole, Dorset BH15 1JD England

Lorne F Campell, *Principal*

Design, naval architecture and consultancy in the area of high speed power craft.
The principal, Lorne Campbell, has been working in the area of high speed marine craft for twenty five years. He started as an apprentice at Vosper (now Vosper Thornycroft) in 1965. Since then he has worked on the design of hovercraft, fast patrol boats, pleasure cruisers, landing craft, rescue craft, and racing powerboats as well as slower craft such as displacement harbour launches and motor yachts.
Much experience has been gained in the design of high speed offshore racing powercraft and numerous successes have been gained over the years with monohull, hydroplane, catamaran and trimaran configurations. Racing achievements include:

1971 World offshore powerboat speed record (85.6mph) held until 1979
1976 4 litre (modified) class National championship
1980 The first offshore powerboat to be timed at over 100mph (102.45mph)
1984 & 1985 2 litre class National Champion
1986 4 litre class European Champion
1987 National and World 2 litre class Champions
1988 World, National and South African 4 litre class Champions
1989 World, European and National 4 litre class Champions and world speed record for electric boats
Much has been learned from the racing side about the complicated aero and hydrodynamic interaction affecting high speed craft working close to the air/water interface, and the design and handling of craft which have to maintain high speeds in rough water.
The company can offer a unique blend of practical and theoretical experience in the design, performance and naval architecture of high speed

craft for both calm and rough conditions. Both wind tunnel and free running scale models are used during the design of craft which have no previous 'parent' form to work from. Considerable experience has been gained in the area of propulsion systems in general and surface propellers in particular. Propellers have been designed in house where nothing suitable has been available.
A service is offered ranging from concept design and preliminary investigation through general arrangement, layout and styling, resistance, propulsion and stability, up to overseeing of construction, liaison and trials.
The variation on projects undertaken is shown by the present preliminary investigation into a fast diesel/waterjet powered aluminium alloy catamaran to carry 12 sea anglers up to 40 miles offshore at speeds approaching 40 knots, and the design of the hydroplane with which Lady Arran obtained the world speed record for electric boats in November 1989 at 50.825mph.

NIGEL GEE AND ASSOCIATES
26 Montague Road, Bishopstoke, Eastleigh, Hampshire SO5 6AG England

Telephone: (0703) 643948
Telefax: (0703) 643949

Nigel Gee, *Senior Partner*
John R Bonafoux, *Partner*

Nigel Gee and Associates are a group of naval architects and marine design consultants specialising in particular in the design of high-speed marine craft and surface effect ships. Since its

formation in 1986, the company has undertaken a variety of SES contracts, ranging from the design of a small pleasure craft to an assessment of three ocean-going craft designed to a NATO specification.
Senior partner, Nigel Gee, has 21 years experience in SES design and production. Partner, John Bonafoux, is also a high-speed marine specialist. Since 1986, the partners have, with a team of specialist engineers and draughtsmen, undertaken a wide variety of high-speed marine craft work including several SES design and consultancy contracts, as well as advanced catamaran and monohull designs.
Nigel Gee and Associates are an independent

consultancy with no commerical ties with any shipbuilder or manufacturer. The company is approved by the UK Civil Aviation Authority for the design of SES. The company work from their own 1600 sq ft offices located in Eastleigh, Hampshire, close to motorway, rail and air links. The offices include a well equipped modern drawing office and in-house computing facilities. The company uses commercial hydrostatics and stability software on their own computer and have their own programs for performance and stability analysis. The company has a large date base of information on SES and other comparable high speed craft designs.

P N STRUCTURES LIMITED
Marine and Engineering Division
5 Vigo Street, Piccadilly, London W1X 1AH, England
Telephone: 01–734 2578
Telex: 884392G
Telefax: 01–434 3465

Theo Pellinkhof, *Chairman*

Karin M Adeler, *Director*
Henk J Wimmers, *Associate (The Netherlands)*
Dolf Le Comte, *Associate (The Netherlands and USA)*
David J Rimmer, *Secretary*

Consultancy in the fields of marine transport systems for: economic commercial use, effective surveillance duties, and leisure.

Consultancy includes selection of hydrofoils, air cushion vehicles or any other type of surface effect ships and the full range of the more conventional craft varying from the planing hull to the full displacement type.
Consultancy also covers marine engineering and materials handling (air cushion platforms).
A wide area of industrial and technological resources can be made available to clients.

SKIMA HOVERCRAFT LIMITED

6 Hamble Close, Warsash, Hampshire SO3 6GT, England

Telephone: (04895) 3210

M A Pinder, *Director*

In 1972 Pindair Limited was set up by M A Pinder who developed the Skima range of inflatable and semi-inflatable hovercraft which the company manufactured and sold to 70 countries. In 1982 Skima Hovercraft Limited was formed as a separate development company with Pindair Ltd concentrating on manufacturing and marketing. In 1983 it was decided to subcontract or licence

manufacture and Pindair Limited was wound up. The Skima 4 hovercraft is now marketed by Air Vehicles Ltd. Skima Hovercraft Limited is continuing the design and development programme on this craft. Details of Skima hovercraft types are given in *Jane's High-Speed Marine Craft and Air Cushion Vehicles 1986*.

ROBERT TRILLO LIMITED (RTL)

28a St Thomas St, Lymington, Hampshire SO4 9NE, England

Telephone: (0590) 675098
Telex: 47674MATCOM G
Telefax: (0590) 672720

Eur Ing Robert L Trillo, *Managing Director*
Ann U Alexander, *Director and Secretary*

Registered office: The Homestead, Broadlands, Brockenhurst, Hampshire, SO42 7SX, England.
Telephone: (0590) 22220

An independent firm formed in 1969, since when consultancy has been undertaken in many countries throughout the world

Feasibility study expertise is available to shipbuilders, ferry operators and component suppliers covering market characteristics and technology developments in the high-speed vessel field; in addition technical and market evaluation for potential investors in new projects is undertaken.

RTL engages principally in consultancy and design work on all forms of high-speed waterborne transport, amphibious vehicles and low-speed aerodynamics. Specific areas include: conceptual studies, investigative analysis, propulsion (water, amphibious, air) with extensive expertise in the design of ducted air propellers, ten hovercraft types now employing RTL designs.

Investigations have also been undertaken in Wing-in-Ground-Effect craft and airship propulsion and resistance. Thrust devices have been designed for amphibious vehicle swamp pro-

pulsion and various designs for advanced agricultural vehicles using air cushion systems have been undertaken.

Work has continued on the RTL minimum-wash high-speed river craft concept especially conceived and optimised for relatively calm and shallow-water operations in city and urban transport areas. This concept has been taken up by FBM Marine Ltd as the RTL Hydrocat and also has been utilised in the design of three vessels built for Golden Mile Marine, Brisbane for service on the Brisbane River, Queensland.

RTL holds extensive statistics and information on the high-speed ferry business and has conducted many world-wide surveys for clients.

The principal has been engaged as an expert witness on arbitration cases and is author of the book *Marine Hovercraft Technology*.

WOLFSON UNIT FOR MARINE TECHNOLOGY AND INDUSTRIAL AERODYNAMICS, UNIVERSITY OF SOUTHAMPTON

Southampton, Hampshire, SO9 5NH, England

Telephone: (0703)585044
Telefax: (0703)671532

W J Allday, *(Director)*

The Wolfson Unit is the Industrial Advisory Unit of the Department of Ship Science at the University of Southampton. The Unit was established in 1967 to provide a comprehensive consultancy service in marine technology and industrial aerodynamics. It is staffed by full time

qualified consulting engineers, with a wide range of academic and industrial experience. It is also able to draw on the experience of academic staff and other consulting engineers throughout the university to widen the scope of consultancy.

The work of the unit includes development work for clients on powered craft of all types from ships and coasters to high-speed catamarans and fast patrol boats. Much of this work takes place in the towing tank including the measurement of resistance and the study of ship motions and seakeeping in head seas. The wind tunnel is used to study air flow over superstructures, aerodynamic forces on high-speed craft, and flow into propellers. Radio controlled models are used in the study of seakeeping and of manoeuvring.

Recent work has included resistance and seakeeping tank tests on FBM Marine Fast Displacement Catamaran and the comparison of two

high-speed craft under survival conditions in breaking waves in the tank.

The Unit does not work only with models. Using portable computerised data acquisition systems, trials data have been collected from as far away as the Grand Banks and the Barrier Reef. With many ferry operators evaluating high-speed catamarans for their routes, this has included comparing the seakeeping ability and passenger comfort of these craft with existing ferries.

The Wolfson Unit sells a wide range of computer programs to naval architects, including hydrostatics and stability, ship motions, manoeuvring and powering. These programs have been sold worldwide to customers from small design offices to government organisations such as the Department of Transport. They also run a bureau service, including stability booklets for fast ferries.

UNITED STATES OF AMERICA

AEROPHYSICS COMPANY

3500 Connecticut Avenue NW, Washington DC 20008, USA

Telephone: (202) 244 7502

Dr Gabriel D Boehler, *Chairman*

Carl W Messinger Jr, *President*
William F Foshag, *Chief Engineer*

Founded in 1957, Aerophysics Company has undertaken research and development work in all phases of ACV design. Dr Boehler had previously

performed feasibility studies with ACV pioneer Melville Beardsley. Although still interested in the complete vehicle, Aerophysics has recently concentrated on lift systems. Termination of the US Navy's 3K SES halted Aerophysics' full-scale fan development.

BAND, LAVIS & ASSOCIATES, INC

900 Ritchie Highway, Severna Park, Maryland 21146, USA

Telephone: (301) 544 2800, (301) 261 1030
Telefax: (301)647 3411

Edward G U Band, *Chief Executive Officer*
David R Lavis, *President*

Shirley A Wilson, *Vice-President*
Brian G Forstell, *Research Director*
Daniel L Wilkins, *Research Director*
John L Allison, *Chief Engineer*
Daniel G Bagnell, *Chief Naval Architect*

Band, Lavis & Associates, Inc (BLA) was established in 1977 to work on all aspects of advanced marine vehicles. The firm now has twenty-one full-time employees. BLA has worked on all major advanced ship programmes in the USA from the 3KSES programme to the LCAC and large strategic sealift SES. BLA is especially capable in conceptual designs of new ships and craft, in conducting model test programmes and in analysing model and full-scale test results. BLA has been involved in analysis of ship motions and in the design of equipment to facilitate ship operations (such as helicopter landings on frigates and offloading containers from a moored ship to an ACV lighter) in higher sea states than have been possible before. BLA is involved in a number of programmes which relate to Logistics-Over-The-Shore operations.

BLA, Inc offers particular expertise in the design of ACVs and SES. Since 1977 the company has been developing a comprehensive range of computer software to support this capability including procedures for the design of hull structure, propulsion and lift systems and the analysis of craft resistance, stability, seakeeping and manoeuvrability etc. The company has also developed two extensive computer-aided design-synthesis models, one for SES and one for ACVs, both of which permit whole-ship design trade-offs to be examined with respect to cost and mission performance. Ship designs and detailed hardware designs are developed on the BLA CAD system. The Company has a library containing over 10 000 documents which is one of the most extensive computer-catalogued repositories of reference material on advanced marine vehicles.

BLA is working for the U.S. Army on a number of projects aimed at improving the Army's capability to off-load vehicles and cargo over undeveloped shorelines during amphibious operations. These projects include:

The design and development of a Portable Air-Cushion Kit (PACK) that can be rapidly deployed around platforms formed of standard 40' × 8' pontoons. The PACK system provides the platform with an amphibious capability. Model tests were completed in 1989 and full-scale trials are planned for 1990. In support of this, and other projects, BLA has designed and model-tested in the company's test facility, a high-capacity, high pressure lift fan whose characteristics are suitable for various applications.

The design, development and test of a platform equipped with a gantry crane, to facilitate the off-loading of containers from container ships to LACV-30 lighters. The LACV-30 flies onto the platform where it can be straddled by the gantry so that off-loading operations can continue in higher sea states than has previously been possible. This system, called HISEAC-OTS, will be subject to subsystem tests in 1989 and full-scale trials in 1991.

The design and development of a fly-on, fly-off (FO/FO) platform to enable the Navy LCACs and the Army air-cushion vehicles to load rolling stock cargo which is transported in RO/RO ships and off-loaded in the stream via RO/RO Discharge Facility platforms. A full-scale technology demonstration of the concept is scheduled for 1990.

In addition to work for the U.S. Department of Defense, BLA has become increasingly involved in the last few years in overseas SES and ACV projects in West Germany, France, Italy, Norway, Singapore and Japan.

DAI INC
451 Hungerford Drive, Suite 700, Rockville, Maryland 20850, USA

Telephone: (301) 424 0270

William B Humphrey, *President and Technical Director*

Ronald G Bryant, *Vice President and Controller*

Dai Inc, formerly Doty Associates, is a privately-owned, small business firm founded in 1968. The firm specialises in financial management, project control, weapons system analysis, test planning and evaluation, operations research, cost and economic analyses for Department of Defense and other government and state agencies.

Since its foundation, the firm has provided engineering services to the US Navy on a number of high technology programmes. These programmes include both the 2K and 3K Surface Effect Ship (SES) designs, the PHM hydrofoil, the Sea Control Ship and the Vertical Support Ship (VSS). In addition, the firm has been involved in Naval V/STOL aviation studies.

FRYCO
7107 Silver Leaf Lane, Houston, Texas 77088, USA

Telephone: (713) 931 8932
Telex: 493–7128 FRYCO
Telefax: (713) 931 5168

Edward D Fry, *Principal*

Edward Fry established FRYCO in 1978 after 22 years building experience. Fry has supervised the design and construction of over 700 commercial, military and pleasure craft including: US Navy high-speed combatants for Navy SEAL Teams, catamarans for commercial and US Army use, mono-hull yachts up to 50 knots, and rig service vessels up to 30-knot speed. He has also conducted scale model tests at various institutions and has data available for design study, designed equipment and wrote training manuals for oil pollution recovery equipment at five major ports and supervised Middle East licensee shipyard for US builder for 4 years.

FRYCO designs vessels up to 50 metres and specialises in high-speed craft. Experienced in gas turbine engine packaging and installation as well as diesel and petrol engines. Computer models are used for speed prediction and hydrostatics. Hulls are created with computer graphics making fully developed offsets available to the builder for auto-matic CAD/CAM cutting. Fry's building background assures practical, economic designs with emphasis placed on reliability and serviceability.
Recent projects
1986 Design, scale model test, styling model, specifications for 50-knot, gas turbine powered 31.10m high-speed yacht.
1986 Design, computer modelling and construction details for 19.82m passenger catamaran, diesel powered, USCG certified, 30-knot speed in Sea State 4.
1987 Design, computer modelling, computer lines and offsets for 35.06m rig service vessel, diesel powered, 30-knot service speed in Sea State 3.

GIBBS & COX, Inc
119 West 31st Street, New York, New York 10001, USA
Telephone: (212) 613 1300
Richard M Ehrlich
Arlington Office: 1235 Jefferson Davis Highway, Arlington, Virginia 22202, USA

Telephone: (703) 979 1240

Bath, Me. Office: 1116 Church Road, Brunswick, Maine 04011, USA

Telephone: (207) 729 2950

Project management, co-ordination and consultation on conceptual and preliminary designs, contract drawings and specifications and construction drawings for commercial or naval ships of the SES/ACV or submerged hydrofoil systems, destroyers, escorts, frigates, corvettes and VTOL/Helo carriers.

KINETICS GROUP INC (KGI)
PO Box 1071, Mercer Island, Washington 98040, USA
&
1315 NW Mall Street, Suite C, Issaquah, Washington 98027, USA

Telephone: (206) 392 7267

J F Sladky, *Principal*
P M Ressler, *Principal*

Kinetics Group Inc has been established to engage in the management of technology develop-ment with particular expertise being available in marine vehicle design, combustion processes, signature reduction and propulsion systems. KGI is interested in bringing about technology transfer and helping negotiate technical teaming and co-operative agreements.

TIMOTHY GRAUL MARINE DESIGN
211 North Third Avenue, PO Box 290, Sturgeon Bay, Wisconsin 54235, USA

Telephone: (414) 543 5092

Timothy Graul, *Principal*

Timothy Graul Marine Design was established in 1981 to provide naval architecture, consulting and design services to owners, builders and vessel operators. The principal, Timothy Graul, has over 25 years experience in design of patrol boats, ferries, tugs, fireboats, military vessels, research boats, passenger craft and river towboats and barges. Graul is a graduate of the University of Michigan, a Registered Professional Engineer, and previously worked for Grafton Boat Co., Inc. and Peterson Builders, Inc. He is a member of SNAME and its Small Craft Committee and is Vice Chairman of Panel SC-5 (Small Passenger Vessels) and is also a member of RINA. He is the author of numerous papers and articles on planing craft, towboats, steering systems and aluminium boat design and construction.

Timothy Graul Marine Design is qualified and capable of designing craft up to about 60 metres in length. Because staff members are experienced in vessel construction and operation as well as design, they emphasise practical solutions to design problems. The firm uses modern design techniques, including a complete AutoCAD system new in 1989, and applies them whenever feasible, but only within the context of reliability and production constraints. Timothy Graul Marine Design stresses the importance of practical, serviceable vessels which perform efficiently at minimum cost and highest levels of dispatch availability.

Major vessels completed in 1989 include three passenger/vehicle ferries: 29.27m, 30.49m, 32.93m in length and several excursion vessels.

Other projects completed include fishing boats, yachts, a survey boat, fast patrol craft, several passenger/sightseeing and restaurant boats and consulting work for re-powering, lengthening, cost estimating, load line and stability. The firm has developed a speciality of preparing pre-construction cost estimates.

J B HARGRAVE NAVAL ARCHITECTS INC

205½ Sixth Street, West Palm Beach, Florida 33401, USA

Telephone: (407) 833 8567
Telefax: (407) 833 7791
Cable: HARGRAVE

J B Hargrave, *President*

Designers of a range of medium- to high-speed mono-hull ferry boats. Currently on the boards is a design for a 32m mono-hull passenger ferry with a speed of 30 knots for Shepler's Inc. This will be the sixth design for the Shepler fleet.

A 39.5m yacht is now under construction in Australia for an American client. Designs for a 32m yacht for a Canadian client and a 43m yacht for another American client are in the preliminary stages.

J B Hargrave, Naval Architects, Inc have been designing a wide variety of passenger vessels, commercial vessels and yachts for 30 years ranging from 5.5m runabouts to a 190.5m chemical tanker.

JOSEPH FOLE

4833 Santa Monica Boulevard No 7784, Ocean Beach, California 92107, USA

Telephone: (619) 223 4212

Naval Architect, Marine Engineer and Consulting Associates since 1978 specialising in large high-speed yachts with capabilities in all aspects of naval architecture and marine engineering with craft built and in service. Design of yachts 30m and larger with many smaller yachts also completed. This includes power, sail, hydrofoil and large motor-sailor capabilities. Specialising in composite construction, along with aluminium, steel and wood. Propulsion systems include diesel, waterjet, FPP, CPP, gas-turbine, etc.

Complete design including structure, systems, propulsion and aesthetics for the ultimate yacht, specialised craft, patrol boats or other marine craft.

Recent projects include current design of a 52m, 50 knot waterjet Mega yacht, composite construction; a 33m, 38 knot waterjet yacht, aluminium construction, built by Broward Marine Inc., Florida, 1988; a 32m, 22 knot F.P.P. yacht, aluminium construction *Starlight* launched September 1986, Broward Marine Inc; a 27m, 30 knot tunnel-drive yacht, composite construction, launched April 1988; a 30m, 40 knot waterjet-drive yacht, composite construction, completed 1988.

HOVER INC

4112 Victoria Blvd, Hampton, Virginia 23669, USA

Telephone: (804) 722 6994

Ronald Gorton, *President*
Simon T Gorton, *Vice-President*
Steven G Doleac, *Project Manager*

Hover Inc has been established to aid in the development of the market for air cushion technology. As a service company, it performs consulting, marketing and sales functions for various industry participants. The company utilises a marketing approach rather than the traditional engineering approach and serves suppliers, manufacturers, sellers, resellers and buyers within the industry. Each of these participants have separate identifiable needs which Hover Inc addresses.

Hover Inc offers suppliers and manufacturers: new product analysis; market analysis and evaluation; and advertising and promotional programmes for new or existing products. Hover Inc provides support system programmes to resellers of this technology. Such programmes are similar to those listed above but are tailored to meet the needs of the seller rather than the manufacturer.

The company also serves the needs of buyer groups interested in air cushion technology. It provides information about products available from the industry along with the associated regulations. Hover Inc also puts together buyer and seller of this technology recommending manufacturers and/or craft for various applications and markets.

C RAYMOND HUNT ASSOCIATES INC

69 Long Wharf, Boston, Massachusetts 02110, USA

Telephone: (617) 742 5669
Telefax: (617) 742 6354

John H Deknatel, *President*
Winn Willard, *Manager Commercial and Military Projects*
Peter S Boyce
John C Kiley
Stephen M Weld
Craig J Obara

Colin Rees
Robert P Provencal
Ann W Crosby, *Office Manager*

C Raymond Hunt Associates created the deep-V hull design in 1959 and have been refining the concept since. Specialising in the design of deep-V fast yachts and commercial and military craft, Hunt Associates' in-house capabilities include the full range of design and engineering services. The present staff of nine includes naval architects and engineers with expertise in all construction materials and methods of propulsion. A recent commercial application of the Hunt deep-V design philosophy is the 22m, 24knot *Medora* motor yacht, the result of a collaborative effort between Burger Boat Co. of Manitowoc, Wisconsin and Hunt Associates.

Other commercial applications of the Hunt deep-V concept have included; *SANDY HOOK*. A 20m, 24-knot, aluminium pilot boat for Port of New York-New Jersey built by Gladding-Hearn Shipbuilding Corp.
P-150. A 24m 27-knot frp patrol vessel for Western Australia syndicate, now a fisheries patrol vessel in the Solomon Islands.
TPB-86. A 26m, 30-knot frp waterjet patrol vessel built in Thailand by Technautic Co Ltd.
1988. Study for Massachusetts Port Authority concerning water transportation in Boston Harbor and Logan Airport focusing on high-speed ferry.

PERSONAL WATERCRAFT DEVELOPMENT (PWD)

8255 S.W. 94 Street, Miami, Florida 33256, U.S.A.

Telefax: (302)598 2033

Kevin D Bedsworth, *President*
William E Flett, *Marketing Director*

PWD was developed to fill a need in the marketplace for groups with good ideas on how to capitalise on the rapidly expanding personal watercraft market. Specialising in prototype development and production implementation on a subcontract basis, PWD's personnel have been responsible for the design and production phase of products such as the Scat Hovercraft line, the Wildcat Jet Scooter, the Maui Marine outboard runabout, as well as other important marine products.

Experts in design and development of marine leisure products, our group is capable of providing a wide range of services including design and construction of: foam-injected cavities for enhanced flotation and structural stiffness, tooling for materials such as fibreglass and thermoformed sheet goods, remote control models for prototype testing.

MARITIME DYNAMICS, INC. (MDI)

Route 4, Box 424X, Lexington Park, Maryland 20653, USA

Telephone: (301) 863 5499
Telex: 6714380MARYUW
Telefax: (301) 863 2054

Clarence A Lysdale, *President*

John D Adams, *Vice President*
Mark E Lindler, *Director of Operations*

Maritime Dynamics, Inc. (MDI) was founded in 1972 by technical and management personnel with unique experience in the fields of advanced marine vehicles. MDI has eighteen years' experience as a prime contractor and subcontractor in the design, development, testing, operations, and maintenance of surface effect ships (SESs), air cushion vehicles (ACVs), and related subsystems. Corporate experience includes the following surface effect ships: USN SES-100A, USN XR-1D, USCG WSES, USN SES-200, and the CIRR-120P class of SES ferries designed by Cirrus and built by Brødrene Aa of Norway. Air cushion vehicle corporate experience includes: USN AALC JEFF-A and JEFF-B, USN LCAC, and US Army LACV-30. The company staff of approximately 40 persons includes experienced naval architects; marine, mechanical, and electrical engineers; field engineers; designers; drafters; programmers; mechanical and electronic technicians; and technical writers.

For eleven years, the company has designed, developed, and manufactured microprocessor-based motion control systems for advance marine vehicles, including SES ride control systems (RCSs) and ACV manoeuvring control systems. This capability includes the analysis and simulation of ship motions and their impact on overall mission capability, detailed design, software development, hardware fabrication, installation, and crew training. MDI is recognised as a leader in the application of motion control systems for SES and has ride control systems in operation on the following vessels: USN SES-200, USCG WSES, and the CIRR 120P class of passenger ferries.

MDI has established analytic techniques, computer simulations, and a body of model and full-scale trials data that predict the performance and seakeeping characteristics of SESs and ACVs. These are used to provide design engineering services in support of SES/ACV conceptual, preliminary, and detailed design. The company can provide integrated designs for the SES air cushion system. This includes performance predictions, seakeeping predictions, arrangements, hull lines and offsets, seal (skirt) geometry, lift system design, lift fan design, and ride control system design.

RIDE CONTROL SYSTEMS

Maritime Dynamics, Inc. (MDI) manufactures ride control systems (RCSs) for air cushion supported craft that provide habitability improvement, motion control, and real-time data for optimisation of overall craft performance. Operational systems are currently installed on the USN SES-200, the USCG SEABIRD-class WSES, and on the CIRR 120P class of SES ferries designed by Cirrus and built by Brødrene Aa in Norway.

The RCS offers a means of minimising wave-induced pressure changes in the air cushion; the system reduces craft motions caused by waves pumping the cushion volume. The resulting attenuation of the vertical accelerations can significantly reduce fatigue and discomfort during moderate-to-high speed cushion-borne operations. This reduction is accomplished by using an electronic control unit (ECU) in conjunction with cushion vent valves or variable flow fans to regulate net airflow to the cushion.

Components for a typical RCS installation consist of pressure, attitude, and motion sensors; a microprocessor-based ECU with applicable control algorithms; a hydraulic system; and a set of air valves that are connected to the ship's air cushion (vent valves) and/or to lift fan inlets (guide vanes or variable geometry sleeves). Each vent valve or inlet guide vane assembly consists of several louver vanes driven by a small servo-controlled hydraulic actuator.

The MDI RCS uses a 32-bit micro-processor to perform sampled data control algorithm using ship motion feedback signals and to transmit control signals to each vent valve or inlet guide vane selected for active control. Fault monitoring of the system's electronic, hydraulic, and mechanical components is performed between each control algorithm computation. RCSs installed by MDI on SES operating in the 35- through 45-knot range reliably and consistently achieve a 50 percent reduction in vertical accelerations and have demonstrated reductions as high as 70 percent.

The ECU also provides a menu-driven real-time display of measured craft parameters relating to air cushion and craft operating conditions (e.g., means and standard deviations of trim, roll, cushion pressure, vent valve position, vertical acceleration, etc.). This data display has proven to be extremely valuable to the SES operator for optimising overall vessel performance while underway under various speed/seaway conditions.

The ECU can be used on any SES/ACV craft equipped with either vent valves or variable-flow fans by programming it with appropriate control algorithms. MDI has developed a systematic technique for deriving these control algorithms based on classical and optimal control theory plus experimental testing.

M ROSENBLATT & SON INC

350 Broadway, New York, New York 10013, USA

Telephone: (212) 431 6900

Lester Rosenblatt, *Chairman and Chief Executive Officer*
P W Nelson, *President*
A M Stein, *Vice President, Operations*
S Halpern, *Vice President and Manager, Western Division*
N M Maniar, *Vice President and Technical Director*
Z Awer, *Vice President and Head, Mechanical Section*
D M Krepchin, *Vice President and Manager, San Diego Branch*
A Baki, *Vice President and Manager, Washington DC Area Branch*
C Laviola, *Vice President & Design Manager, Eastern Division*

M Rosenblatt & Son Inc is an established naval architectural and marine engineering firm with over 40 years of proven experience in all phases of ship and marine vehicle design.

With offices in 11 US cities and abroad, the firm is close to the entire shipbuilding community and has a thorough understanding of its problems and

needs. Its experience covers programme management and inspection of construction, as well as design.

A major portion of the company's design activities has been and is for the US Navy. Completed assignments are of the broadest possible variety covering research and development, feasibility studies, and conceptual and detail design for all classes of major combatants, auxiliaries, and high performance craft. In addition, the company has provided extensive design services for the conversion, overhaul, and repair of naval combatants, auxiliaries, submarines, amphibious warfare supply and landing craft.

The service to the maritime industry includes a wide variety of tasks covering the new and modification design of oceanographic ships, containerships, tankers, general cargo ships, dredges, bulk carriers, drilling platforms and ships, survey vessels, pipe-laying barges, and a great variety of supporting craft.

Typical high-speed marine craft and ACV assignments have included:
Concept designs of a 20 ton Wheeled ACV and a 60 ton Wheeled Hydrofoil for the US Army.
Preliminary and detail design of a 30m combat hydrofoil for a foreign army.
Steering and manoeuvring system design for a tracked ACV for Bell Textron.

Surface Effect Ship Advanced Design and Technology handbook for US Navy.

ARPA Advanced Surface Effect Vehicles

Conceptual studies, parametric studies and propulsion machinery analysis for phase 'O' studies of Advanced Surface Effect Vehicles for Advanced Research Project Agency. Work performed for American Machine and Foundry Company.

JSESPO Surface Effect Ship Test Craft

Conceptual and feasibility design studies of candidate SES vehicles for the JSESPO sizing study for second generation SES test craft in the 1000- to 3000-ton range. The work included studies of various candidate versions of SES to identify and evaluate their unique operational and design capabilities; technological assessment of various structural materials and systems; preparation of a proposed development programme with required supporting research and development. Work performed for Joint Surface Effect Ship Program office.

AAAAV(P) Advanced Assault Amphibious Vehicle Personnel

The company is assisting FMC corporation with alternative concepts for proposal to the US navy.

SRI INTERNATIONAL
(formerly the Stanford Research Institute)
333 Ravenswood Avenue, Menlo Park, California 94025, USA

Telephone: (415) 326 6200
Telex: 334486

Telefax: (415) 326 5512

William F Miller, *President and Chief Executive Officer*

SRI employs about 3000 staff in offices and laboratories in North America, Europe, East Asia

and the Middle East. Each year it undertakes several hundred research projects for the public and private sectors on a wide variety of interests and issues. Overall, SRI's research operations divide into four programme groupings: management and economics, the sciences, engineering and world business.

STEVENS INSTITUTE OF TECHNOLOGY DAVIDSON LABORATORY

Castle Point Station, Hoboken, New Jersey 07030, USA

Telephone: (201) 420 5345

Dr D Savitsky, *Director*

Organised in 1935 as the Experimental Towing Tank, the Laboratory is active in basic and applied

hydrodynamic research, including smooth water performance and manoeuvrability, seakeeping, propulsion and control of marine vehicles including ACV, SES, hydrofoil craft, planing craft etc. Special model test facilities are available to investigate the dynamic behaviour of all types of vessels and platforms in smooth water and waves.

TRACOR HYDRONAUTICS INC

7210 Pindell School Road, Howard County,

Laurel, Maryland 20707, USA

Telephone: (301) 604 4300
Telex: 87585
Telefax: (301) 604 4395

Robert F Weiland, *President*
Eugene R Miller Jr, *Technical Director*
Brian L White, *Director, Experimentation and Simulation Dept.*
Stephen D Clark, CPA, *Treasurer and Contracting Officer*

The company was founded in July 1959, and

has undertaken research, development and design of air cushion vehicles, hydrofoil craft and surface effect ships as well as advanced propulsion systems, under US Government and industrial contacts. Tracor Hydronautics has its own ship model basin and high-speed water channel suitable for the evaluation of air cushion vehicles and hydrofoils.

WHEELER INDUSTRIES INC

Corporate Headquarters: 2611 Jefferson Davis Highway, Suite 1200, Arlington, Virginia 22202, USA

Telephone: (703) 418 1500
Telex: 904084
Telefax: (703) 685 1897
110 Marter Avenue, Moorestown, New Jersey 08057, USA
Telephone: (609) 778 7161
1816 Old Mobile Highway, PO Box 126, Pascagoula, Mississippi 39567, USA
Telephone: (601) 769 6321
4 Industrial Drive, Brunswick, Maine 04011, USA
Telephone: (207) 725 4566
PO Box 433, Wayland, Massachusetts 01778, USA
Telephone: (617) 358 2721

Fred L Thomas, *Chairman, Chief Executive Officer and President*
E Joseph Wheeler Jr, *Vice Chairman and Treasurer*
Bruce L Valley, *Vice President and Director of Operations*
Delia G Lagman, *Vice President, Finance and Administration*
Louis P Rossi, *Manager, Advanced Craft Programmes*

Wheeler Industries Inc is a privately-owned, small disadvantaged business firm, founded in 1966, which specialises in systems engineering for ship, air, electronic, and deep ocean systems, as well as oceanographic and environmental research. Since its establishment the company has continuously provided technical, engineering and management support, primarily in ship acquisition areas, to the US Navy. This support has encompassed a wide range including top level management plans; ship acquisition plans; tech-

nology assessments and forecasts; sub-system analysis and trade-offs; development and acquisition requirements and specifications; programme budgeting; development of hydrofoil design data; and hydrofoil strut/foil hydrodynamic load criteria and data. The company employs experienced professionals capable of providing engineering, technical, design and management services associated with hydrofoils, air cushion vehicles and surface effect ships.

The technical and operational functions and capabilities are co-ordinated by the Director of Operations. Permanently assigned Project Managers (for ship, electronic and oceanographic systems) form engineering task teams for the duration of a contract or included task(s). They are assisted as necessary by technical support (clerical, graphics, editorial and reproduction) personnel. This approach allows maximum management visibility and control over each task, and provides optimum response to customers while minimising costs.

ASSOCIATIONS AND CLUBS INVOLVED WITH HIGH-SPEED CRAFT

AUSTRALIA

HOVER CLUB OF AUSTRALIA
GPO Box 1882, Brisbane, Queensland 4001, Australia
H B Standen, *Hon Secretary*

BELGIUM

HOVERCLUB AND ASSOCIATION OF BELGIUM
Bld St Michel 78, 1040 Brussels, Belgium

CANADA

CANADIAN AIR CUSHION TECHNOLOGY SOCIETY (CACTS)
Canadian Aeronautics and Space Institute
222 Somerset Street West, Suite 601, Ottawa, Ontario K2P 2G3, Canada

Telephone: (613) 234 0191

Carson Payne, *Chairman*
A J S Timmins, *Executive Director*

The Canadian Air Cushion Technology Society (CACTS) is a constituent society of the Canadian Aeronautics and Space Institute (CASI). It is devoted to the development and application of air cushion technology, principally with regard to the transportation domain, but also in industry and in other fields where this technology may be of benefit. The goal of the society is to keep its members abreast of developments in the field through information dissemination and exchange. This is done through periodic conferences to which participants from various countries involved in air cushion technology and hovercraft are invited.

EUROPE

EUROPEAN HOVERCRAFT FEDERATION
24 rue Louis Dardenne, 92170 France

Franz Berndt, Senior (Germany), *President*
Louis Le Chevalier (France), *Secretary*
Francois Porot (France), *Treasurer*

This is a Federation of all the European national governing bodies for the sport of hovercraft. The Federation has an annual delegate meeting for the formation of regulations and its prime objective is to promote the annual European Hovercraft Racing Championships. This consists of a series of race meetings held in some of the participating countries.

Present Members of the Federation
Hoverclub of CSSR
Ing Villiam Teply
Jesenskeho 12, 81102 Bratislava, Czechoslovakia
Federation Francaise des Clubs d'Aeroglisseurs
Louis Le Chevalier
12 rue Beranger, F-92100 Boulogne BT, France

Hoverclub von Deutschland
Frantz Berndt Senior
Lechfeldstrasse 2, 8905 Mering, Federal Republic of Germany
Hoverclub of Great Britain
HCGB, 12 Mount Pleasant, Bishops Itchington, Warwickshire CV33 0QE, England
Hoverclub of Holland
Hans Peerenboom
Uiterdijksehof 5, Nederhorst Den Berg, Netherlands
Italian Hoverclub
Sandro Scanavino
Via Medail 87, 10052 Bardonecchir, Torino, Italy
The Hover Club of Sweden
Manfred Schneider
Ollonvagen 17, 18400 Akersberga, Sweden

FRANCE

FFM AÉROGLISSEURS
49 rue de Boulainvilliers, 75016 Paris, France

Telephone: (1) 45256176

Louis de Santis, *President*
J Beaudequin, *Founder and Honorary President*
Gabriel J Vernier, *President Commission Aeroglisseurs*
Jacqueline Tretout, *Secretary*

Member Clubs:
CLUB AEROGLISSEURS DE L'OISE
2 Rue Malmaire, 60610 La Croix St Ouen, France
B Raynal, *President*
AEROGLISSEURS BEAUCE AND SOLOGNE
11 Grand Rue, 41290 Oucques, France
J Bonnet, *President*
AEROGLISSEURS D'AQUITAINE
Chez R. Favart, Mairie D'Arbis, 33760 Loupiac, France
R Favart, *President*
AEROGLISSEURS D'ILE DE FRANCE
15 rue de Vaugirard, 75291 Paris CX 06, France
M Soulabail, *President*
AEROGLISSEURS D'OC
51 Avenue Louis Abric, 34400 Lunel
Guy Ackerman, *President*
AEROGLISSEURS PARIS EST
4 Allee d'Orgemont, Le Clos, 77200 Torcy, France
J P Noel, *President*
AEROGLISSEURS VAL DE METZ
18 rue des Prés, Argancy, 57640 Vigy, France
M Lallier, *President*
ANJOU AEROGLISSEURS
La Grosse Pierre, 49220 Le Lion D'Angers, France
J P Godicheau, *President*
AERO COTE DE LUMIERE
12 Rue Torterue, 85800 St Gilles Croix De Vie, France
Alain Trolle, *President*
CLUB AEROGLISSEUR HOULGATAIS
4 Impasse des Marguerites, 14510 Houlgate, France
Marcel Romano, *President*
RHONE ALPES AEROGLISSEURS
Sillans, 38590 St Etienne De St Geoirs, France
Gerard Schenkl, *Secretaire*

ASSOCIATION PONTA LOISIRS
5 Rue Sisley, 29200 Brest, France
D Hascoet, *President*
AEROGLISSEURS DU CENTRE OUEST
1 Place Gambetta, 17580 Le Bois En Re, France
L Leruste, *President*
AERO-LOIRE
42 Grande Rue – Oison, 45170 Neuville Au Bois, France
P Branchu, *President*

GERMANY, FEDERAL REPUBLIC

HOVERCLUB OF GERMANY
c/o Helgrel Ruft, AM Clockenbach 10, D-8000, Munich, Federal Republic of Germany

JAPAN

HOVER CLUB OF JAPAN
Information from Masahiro Mino, Senior Director, Aerodynamics Section, Nihon University at Narashino, 7–1591 Narashinodai, Funabashi, Chiba-Ken, Japan

NEW ZEALAND

HOVERCRAFT CLUB OF NEW ZEALAND
22 Puriri Road, Manurewa, Auckland, New Zealand
Tel: 2669188
H Stockley, *President*
R Armstrong, *Hon Secretary*

SWEDEN

SWEDISH HOVERCLUB
(Svenska Svävarklubben)

Ollonvägen 17, S-184 00 Åkersberga, Sweden
Tel: 0764 23431
Manfred Schneider, *Treasurer*

UNITED KINGDOM

THE HOVERCLUB OF GREAT BRITAIN LIMITED
The National Organisation for Amateur Hovercraft
10 Long Acre, Bingham, Nottinghamshire, England

Mrs B Kemp, 10 Long Acre, Bingham, Nottingham, *Secretary*
Mrs D Naylor, 12 Mount Pleasant, Bishops Itchington, Leamington Spa, Warwickshire
(Tel: (0926) 613180)

J Kemp, 10 Long Acre, Bingham, Nottingham, *Chairman*
(Tel: (0949) 37294)
A Bliault, Askeveien 3, Lura, 4300 Sandnes, Norway, *Chief Scrutineer*
(Tel: 4 678343)

As Britain's national organisation for light hovercraft, the Hoverclub exists to encourage the construction and operation of light, recreational hovercraft by private individuals, schools, colleges, universities and other youth groups. The main role of the Club over the last few years has been the organisation of a series of race meetings, at sites throughout Britain for a National Championship. At these events, which are held at stately homes or lakes and pastures, craft will race over a land and water course. It is possible that up to 100 racing hovercraft may attend the meetings. The Hoverclub is a founding member of the European Hovercraft Federation, which organises an International Race series every year.

A growing activity within the Hoverclub has been the development of recreational use in the form of organised river and coastline cruises and also Hover Holidays where members meet for a weeks' camping in an area where there is plenty of opportunity to use their craft. One such event is held in the Loire region of France every year.

The Hoverclub provides a technical advice service for members through a Scrutineering Committee and can arrange insurance for racing and recreational use.

PUBLICATIONS
Light Hovercraft A monthly magazine for Club members with race reports, news, comment, technical articles and children's pages.
Light Hovercraft Handbook The prime reference book for the design and construction of small recreational and competition hovercraft.
Guide to Model Hovercraft An introduction to small models ranging from rubber band to radio controlled.
Design, Construction and Safety Requirements for:
 Racing Hovercraft
 Cruising Hovercraft
 Utility Hovercraft
Three separate and detailed regulations governing how a craft should be built. Compliance to these regulations is checked by scrutineers at events.
Competition Rules These are regulations used for the running of all National and International races.

CHILTERNS
K Dymond,
Hillside, Akeley, Nr Buckingham, Buckinghamshire
Tel: (02806) 209

EAST ANGLIA
B Hill,
10 Fenland Road, Reffley Estate, Kings Lynn, Norfolk

MIDLAND HOVERCLUB
Mrs B Kemp,
10 Long Acre, Bingham, Nottingham
Tel: (0949) 37294

NORTH WEST
Rev W G Spedding,
26 Milverton Close, Lostock, Bolton BL6 4RR
Tel: (0204) 41248

SOUTH EASTERN HOVERCLUB
G L Parson, *Secretary,*
64 Hawthorn Avenue, Rainham Mark, Gillingham, Kent MF8 6TS
Tel: (0634) 35197

SOUTHERN HOVERCLUB
R Henvist,
37 Fox Hills, Totton, Southampton, Hampshire
Tel: (042129) 2521

WELSH
Robert Lansdown,
13 Dovedale Close, Lady Mary Estate, Cyncoed, Cardiff
Tel: (0222) 484788

INDEPENDENT CLUB

ESSEX
E W Sangster,
53 Elm View Road, Benfleet, Essex SS7 5AR

THE HOVERCRAFT SOCIETY (THS)

24 Jellicoe Avenue, Alverstoke, Gosport, Hampshire PO12 2PE, England

Sir Christopher Cockerell, *President*
R L Wheeler, *Vice President*
J E Rapson, *Vice President*
W F S Woodford, *Vice President*
B J Russell, *Chairman*
W Jacobs, *Secretary*
B J Russell, *Editor, Hovercraft Bulletin*

Formed in 1971, the Hovercraft Society was the UK constituent member of the 'International Air Cushion Engineering Society'. Membership is open to persons engaged in hovercraft related fields and to those having a bona fide interest in hovercraft in the UK and overseas. Current membership is drawn from ACV manufacturers, ferry operators, design groups, government departments and agencies, financial and insurance organisations, consultants, journalists and universities.

THS organises regular meetings at which talks are given on the technical, commercial and military, design and operating aspects of hovercraft and air cushion devices. Many of these lectures have been taken from proceedings written for THS and are available to members. THS also produces a monthly *Hovercraft Bulletin* containing the latest information on hovercraft activities throughout the world. Occasionally, THS arranges visits and social events for its members.

A collection of books, periodicals, papers and reports on the subject of hovercraft have been accumulated by the Society. These are housed at 15 St Marks Road, Alverstoke, Hampshire; access by arrangement with the secretary.

HOVERMAIL COLLECTORS' CLUB

Highlights, Down Road, Tavistock, Devon PL19 9AQ, England

John L Hobbs, *Chairman*
J K Pemberton, *Editor, Slipstream*

The Hovermail Collectors' Club arranges and provides souvenir carried covers for collectors and organises occasional auctions. *Slipstream*, a monthly newsletter, advises members on new material available and provides details of new developments in the hovercraft transport industry.

UNITED STATES OF AMERICA

THE HOVERCLUB OF AMERICA INC

Box 216, Clinton, Indiana 47842–0216, USA

Jeff Nicholson, *President*
Terry Chapman, *Vice President*
Sara Mahler, *Secretary*
Kerry Tracy, *Tresurer*
Al Mahler, *Editor, Hovernews*

Membership of the Hoverclub of America Inc costs $25, US dollars only, per annum.

Following a general meeting of the members of the American Hovercraft Association in May 1976, it was agreed to reorganise the Association into the Hoverclub of America Inc. The Hoverclub of America was incorporated under the State Laws of Indiana in 1976.

In the USA the Hoverclub of America Inc organises rallies and other events for members and also publishes a newsletter, *Hovernews*.

To locate other Club members and/or Chapters in your region please contact the Hoverclub at the above address. The Hoverclub of America Inc holds the Hoverally during the month of June in the midwestern United States. The Hoverclub of Great Britain will host the WHF Championship in 1991.

THE INTERNATIONAL HYDROFOIL SOCIETY

PO Box 51, Cabin John, Maryland 20818, USA

IHS Board of Directors:
1987–90
William Ellsworth
Robert Johnson
Lanny Puckett
Phil Yarnall

1988–91
Ron Adler
Mark Bebar
Raymond Hoop
John King(*Treasurer*)

1989–92
Capt.William Erickson
John Meyer(*Vice President*)
John Monk
James Wilkins(*President*)
Patsy N Jackson,(*Recording Secretary*)

BIBLIOGRAPHY

In general, only papers specifically concerned with high-speed marine craft and air cushion platforms are included in this bibliography. In a few instances some of the papers listed may not be available in published form.

All papers prior to 1986 have been deleted from this edition but may be referred to in the 1987 to 1989 editions.

SECTION 1 contains references of separate papers which have been published from 1986 onwards.

SECTION 2 contains references of papers given at conferences specifically concerned with high-speed craft and published in bound proceedings.

SECTION 3 covers reference publications, books and periodicals.

Key to principal coverage

ALH	Air-lubricated-hull craft
CAT	Catamaran
DISP	Displacement hull vessel
GEN	Generally applicable
HOV	Amphibious hovercraft
HYB	Hybrid craft
HYD	Hydrofoil craft
LSACP	Low-speed air-cushion platform
MH	Mono-hull
PAR	Power-augmented ram-wing craft
PLA	Planing craft
SES	Surface effect ship (sidewall hovercraft)
SHYD	Sailing hydrofoil
SWATH	Small-waterplane-area twin-hull vessel
WIGE	Wing-in-ground-effect craft

SECTION 1

PAPERS PUBLISHED 1986 TO EARLY 1990

New Developments in Amphibious Warfare Vessels and Equipment of the US Navy, A Preston. RINA Warship 86 Symposium, London, 19–22 May 1986.

Further Discussions on the Dynamic Instability of Small High-Speed Craft, S H Cohen, D L Blount and J Zseleczky. Presented at the SNAME 1987 Power Boat Symposium.

Design Studies for an Arctic Heavy Lift Air Cushion Vehicle, Robert F Tangren and D F Dickins Associates Ltd. Accepted for presentation at the Offshore Mechanics and Arctic Engineering Symposium, Tokyo, Japan, April 1986.

The Design, Construction and Operation of Light Air Cushion Vehicles, H S Fowler. Canadian Air Cushion Technology Society, Ottawa, Canada, 1982.

Small Water Area Twin Hull (SWATH) Vessels For Offshore, A Eyres (Eyretechnics Ltd, Dartmouth, Nova Scotia). Canadian Offshore Resources Exposition Conference, Halifax, Nova Scotia, 7–9 October 1986.

Recent Developments in Waterjet Propulsion, R Svensson (KaMeWa AB, Sweden). Shipbuilding Technology International, 1986. Sterling Publications Ltd, London.

SWATH Developments and Comparisons with Other Craft, T G Lang and J E Sloggett (Semi-Submerged Ship Corporation, Solana Beach, California, USA). RINA International Conference on SWATH Ships and Advanced Multi-Hulled Vessels, London, April 1985.

Replacement of the University Research Fleet and a 2500-Ton SWATH Ship Candidate, R P Dinsmore and T G Lang. AIAA 8th Advanced Marine Systems Conference, San Diego, California, USA, 22–24 September 1986.

SSP *Kaimalino*: Conception, Development, Hurdles, Success, T G Lang. ASME Winter Annual Meeting, Anaheim, California, USA, 9 December 1986.

Influence of the Moment of Equilibrium on the Powering Characteristics of Planing Craft including Hydrofoils, F Van Walree and E Stierman (Maritime Research Institute, Netherlands). RINA Warship '86 Symposium, London, 19–22 May 1986.

Air-Cushion Vehicles for Amphibious Assault - The Next Generation, D R Lavis and E Band (Band, Lavis Associates Inc, New York). RINA Warship 86 Symposium, London, 19–22 May 1986.

Development of the Turt 4 Diesel-Powered Amphibious Hovercraft, S Lee, C Lee and S Kim (Korea Tacoma Marine Industries Ltd). RINA Warship 86 Symposium, London, 19–22 May 1986.

Diesel Engines Specially Designed for Fast Patrol Boats, B Gondouin (Alsthom Groupe Diesel). RINA Warship 86 Symposium, London, 19–22 May 1986.

The Use of Amphibious Hovercraft for Assault Purposes, G Elsey (British Hovercraft Corporation). RINA Warship 86 Symposium, London, 19–22 May 1986.

Design of Cored Laminates for Chines in FRP Boat Hulls, J J Seidler and R P Reichard. Presented at the SNAME 1987 Power Boat Symposium.

An Approach to Computer-Aided High-Speed Propeller Design, P G Kozhukharov and V H Hadjimikhalev. International Symposium on Propellers and Cavitation, China, 1986.

Notes on the Propulsion of Fast Craft and CRM Engines, G Venturini (CRM Motori Marini). Milan, Italy, 1986.

Development of the BR – 1/2000 High-Speed Marine Diesel Engine, G Venturini (CRM Motori Marini). Milan, Italy, 1986.

Planing-Hull Resistance, G Venturini (CRM Motori Marini). Milan, Italy, 1986.

A Method for Estimating the Resistance of Catamarans, Huang Wulin and Zhang Surong. Ship Engineering No 1, 1987, The Chinese Society of Naval Architecture and Marine Engineering.

Amphibious Assault Hovercraft, R L Wheeler (British Hovercraft Corporation). RINA Warship Symposium 86, London, 19–22 May 1986.

The Take-Off Characteristics of Hydrofoil Craft Calculated by Means of a Newly Developed Prediction Method, F van Walree (Maritime Research Institute, Netherlands). RINA Warship Symposium 86, London, 19–22 May 1986.

The Equation of Cushion Pressure for Air-Cushion System, He Zhifei and Xing Shengde (China Ship Scientific Research Centre, China). RINA Warship Symposium '86, London, 19–22 May 1986.

Motion Characteristics of the Kaiyo, M Saeki (Japan Marine Science and Technology Center) and H Nakamura (Mitsui Engineering & Shipbuilding Co Ltd). Presented at OCEANS '86, Washington DC, USA, 23–25 September 1986.

Resistance Predictions and Parametric Studies for High-Speed Displacement Hulls, Siu C Fung. *Naval Engineers Journal*, Vol 99, No 2, March 1987.

Application of Harmonic Capstan to Air-Cushion Platform, Wong Huilin. Ship Engineering, The Chinese Society of Naval Architecture and Marine Engineering, No 1, 1988.

High-Speed Marine Diesel Engines, B Feurer, MTU Friedrichshafen GmbH, West Germany. Shipbuilding Technology International Review, 1988.

High-Speed Marine Engines for Naval and Commercial Vessels, W J Gardner, Caterpillar Inc. Shipbuilding Technology International Review, 1988 (Sterling Publications, London).

AERODYNAMICS	AIR LUBRICATION	ARCTIC, ANTARCTIC APPLICATIONS	COMMERCIAL APPLICATIONS/OPERATIONS	CONTRACTS	DESIGN	DEVELOPMENT	DYNAMICS/SEAKEEPING	ECONOMICS	ENVIRONMENTAL ASPECTS	FANS	HYDRODYNAMICS	ICE BREAKING	LEGISLATION	LIFT-AIR SYSTEMS	MILITARY/NAVAL APPLICATIONS	PERFORMANCE/DRAG	POWER PLANTS	POWER TRANSMISSION	PRODUCTION	PROPULSION	SAFETY	SKIRTS/SEALS	STABILITY AND CONTROL	STRUCTURE/MATERIALS	TEST FACILITIES	TRIALS
															HOV											
						PLA																				
		LSACP			LSACP																					
					HOV																			HOV		
					SWATH																					
																				GEN						
							SWATH																			
			SWATH																							
					SWATH	SWATH																				
																PLA										
																HYD										
															HOV											
						HOV																	HOV			
																	PLA									
															HOV											
																								PLA		
																				GEN						
																	GEN									
																	GEN									
											PLA					PLA										
																CAT										
															HOV											
																HYD										
															HOV		HOV									
							SWATH																			
																DISP										
			HOV																							
																	GEN									
																	GEN									

SECTION 1 CONTINUED

Waterjet Propulsion for Ferries, R Svensson (KaMeWa AB, Sweden). Shipbuilding Technology International Review, 1988 (Sterling Publications, London).

The Hamilton Waterjet Concept for Work Boats, G H Davison (C W F Hamilton & Co Ltd, New Zealand). Shipbuilding Technology International Review, 1988 (Sterling Publications, London).

Noise Control Program for the USCG 100-Foot Patrol Boats – A Case History, R W Fischer. Paper presented at the SNAME Spring Meeting/Star Symposium, May 1987, USA.

Why the GNI Doesn't Plane – Computer-Aided Diagnosis, P S Glandt. Paper presented at the SNAME Spring Meeting/Star Symposium, 27–30 May 1987, Philadelphia, USA.

Research Plan for the Investigation of Dynamic Instability of Small High-Speed Craft, S H Cohen (US Coast Guard Headquarters, Washington, DC) and D L Blount (Naval Sea Combat Systems Engineering Station, Norfolk, VA, USA). SNAME Annual Meeting, New York, 19–22 November 1986. Paper No 7.

SSP *Kaimalino:* **Conception, Developmental History, Hurdles and Success,** T G Lang (Semi-Submerged Ship Corporation, Solana Beach, CA, USA). ASME Winter Annual Meeting, Anaheim, California, 7–12 December 1986.

Replacement of the University Research Fleet and a 2500 ton SWATH Ship Candidate, R P Dinsmore and T G Lang. AIAA 8th Advanced Marine Systems Conference, San Diego, CA, 22–24 Sept 1986.

On a Programme for the Study of Dynamic Ice Rupture by Hovercraft, M Shinbrot (M Shinbrot Mathematical Consulting Inc), Transport Canada Transportation Development Centre, TP 7857E, 1986.

SWATH Feasibility Study, T W Edwards, D J Hussey and JF Mitchell (Eyretechnics Ltd). Transport Canada Transportation Development Centre, TP 7419E, 1986.

Parameters Analysis of Air-Cushion Vehicle Responsive Skirt Characteristics, Zhou Weilin. Ship Engineering (Chinese SNAME) No 5,1987.

A Case Study of Dynamic Instability in a Planing Hull, L Codega and E Lewis. SNAME, Hampton Roads Section, USA, April 1986.

Recent Research into the Ultimate Stability of Surface Effect Ships, A G Blyth. RINA International Conference on Ship Stability and Safety, London, June 1986.

The Roll Stability of an SES in a Seaway, A G Blyth. 4th International Hovercraft Conference, Southampton, May 1987.

The Contribution of the Progetto Finalizzato Trasporti in the Field of the Sea Transport, L Bianco (Progetto Finalizzato Trasporti, Consiglio Nazionale delle Ricerche, Italy) 1987.

Design Studies for a Diesel-Powered Heavy Lift Vehicle, D Dickins. 5th International Offshore Mechanics and Arctic Engineering Symposium, Tokyo, April 1986.

Development of the BR-1/2000 High-Speed Marine Diesel Engine, G Venturini (CRM, Milan) 1987.

Hovercraft, Waterborne Ambulance for the Future, Lt Col H C Cook (Maryland Natural Resources Police, USA) 1987.

Stability Analysis and Prediction of Performance for a Hydrofoil Sailing Boat Part 1. Equilibrium Sailing State Analysis, Y Masuyama (Kanazawa Institute of Technology, Ishikawa, Japan). International Shipbuilding Progress, Vol 33, No 384, August 1986.

Stability Analysis and Prediction of Performance for a Hydrofoil Sailing Boat Part 2. Dynamic Stability Analysis, Y Masuyama (Kanazawa Institute of Technology, Ishikawa, Japan). International Shipbuilding Progress, Vol 34, No 390, February 1987.

Stability of Hydrofoil Sailing Boat in Calm Water and Regular Wave Condition, Y Masuyama (Kanazawa Institute of Technology, Ishikawa, Japan). 3rd International Conference on Stability of Ships and Ocean Vehicles, STAB '86, Gdansk, Poland, September 1986. Paper 4.7.

Hydrofoil: High-Speed Control and Cleanup of Large Oil Spills, M Vacca-Torelli (Italian Navy, Ret, Operational Center for Emergency at Sea, Department of Civil Protection, Rome) and A L Geraci and A Risitano (Machinery Institute, Department of Engineering, University of Catania, Italy) 1987. Publ Rodriquez Cantieri Navali, Messina, Italy.

The Evolution of Round Bilge Fast Attack Craft Hull Forms, A Steven Toby (Princeton University, USA). *Naval Engineers Journal,* November 1987.

Air-Cushion Transport Technology in Brazil - The "Projecto VCA" Experience, M H de Souza Oliveira, MA de Rezende Veiga, P J Bandeira de Mello and R R de Araujo (University of Brasilia, Brazil). International Society for Terrain Vehicle Systems 9th International Conference, Barcelona, Spain, 31 August-4 September 1987.

Recent Developments of 4-Stroke Medium and High-Speed Engines for Marine Applications, V Drei (Diesel Ricerche, Italy). CETENA International Symposium on Advanced Research for Ships and Shipping in the Nineties, Genoa, Italy, 1–3 October 1987.

Advanced Marine Vehicles: A Critical Review, P van Oossanen (MARIN, The Netherlands). CETENA International Symposium on Advanced Research for Ships and Shipping in the Nineties, Genoa, Italy, 1–3 October 1987.

Deep V Hull-Form Design. A Model Experimental Investigation on Resistance and Propulsive Performances, A Colombo, I Elice, A Coscia and M Parodi (Fincantieri CNI, Italy). CETENA International Symposium on Advanced Research for Ships and Shipping in the Nineties, Genoa, Italy, 1–3 October 1987.

AERODYNAMICS	AIR LUBRICATION	ARCTIC, ANTARCTIC APPLICATIONS	COMMERCIAL APPLICATIONS/OPERATIONS	DESIGN	DEVELOPMENT	DYNAMICS/SEAKEEPING	ECONOMICS	ENVIRONMENTAL ASPECTS	FANS	HYDRODYNAMICS	ICE BREAKING	LEGISLATION	LIFT-AIR SYSTEMS	MILITARY/NAVAL APPLICATIONS	PERFORMANCE/DRAG	POWER PLANTS	POWER TRANSMISSION	PRODUCTION	PROPULSION	SAFETY	SKIRTS/SEALS	STABILITY AND CONTROL	STRUCTURE/MATERIALS	TEST FACILITIES	TRIALS
																		GEN							
																		GEN							
								PLA																	
										PLA															
						GEN																			
				SWATH	SWATH																				
				SWATH	SWATH																				
								HOV																	
				SWATH																					
						HOV															HOV				
						PLA																			
						SES																SES			
						SES																SES			
			GEN																						
				HOV																					
																GEN									
				HOV																					
															SHYD							SHYD			
															SHYD							SHYD			
						SHYD																SHYD			
			HYD																						
										PLA															
				HOV																					
																GEN									
				GEN																					
										PLA					PLA										

SECTION 1 CONTINUED

Wave Loads Experienced by SWATHS in Waves, W G Price, P Temarel and Tongshu Wu (Brunel University, UK). CETENA International Symposium on Advanced Research for Ships and Shipping in the Nineties, Genoa, Italy, 1–3 October 1987.

NES 200L – The French SES programme, Yann Pivet (Constructions Mecaniques de Normandie, Cherbourg, France). 6th WEMT Symposium, Lubeck-Travemunde, West Germany, 2–5 June 1987.

Optimisation of a CRM 18D/SS BR-1 Engine and Waterjet Package for a 1200kW Propulsion System, G Venturini (CRM Motori Marini, Milan, Italy). 6th WEMT Symposium, Lubeck-Travemunde, West Germany, 2–5 June 1987.

Air-Cushion Vehicles: Any Potential for Canada?, J E Laframboise, Transport Canada, Transportation Development Centre. Canadian Aeronautics and Space Journal Vol 33 No 3, September 1987.

Investigations of the Dynamics of Large Air Cushions, P A Sullivan, M J Hinchey, T A Graham, J E Byrne, A Dupuis, N Milligan and C Walsh (Institute for Aerospace Studies, University of Toronto). TP 7560E, August 1986. Prepared for Transport Canada.

Project "Frigonav" Hovercraft Type 140 Operating Experience, February-March 1987, D Jones (Ice Control Enterprises Inc, Hamilton, Ontario). Report (with French summary) prepared for Transport Development Centre, Montreal, TP 8432E, April 1987.

Experimental Study of Wing-in-Ground-Effects in the Afit 5-foot Tunnel, L C Edwards (Air Force Flight Dynamics Laboratory, Wright-Patterson Air Force Base, Ohio) 1987.

FT8: A High-Performance Industrial and Marine Gas Turbine Derived from the JT8D Aircraft Engine, W H Day (Turbo Power and Marine Systems Inc, Farmington, USA). Presented at the Gas Turbine Conference, Anaheim, California, 31 May-4 June 1987. Publ The American Society of Mechanical Engineers, New York. 87-GT-242.

Design and Operation of ACV Lightering Barges, S V Yakonovsky (Leningrad Central Project and Design Bureau, USSR). Paper presented at 1987 CACTS International Conference on Air-Cushion Technology, Canada.

Rotating Stall in Centrifugal Fans – A Cure in Sight, A N Bolton (Fluids Division, National Engineering Laboratory, East Kilbride, Glasgow, Scotland). CME, January 1988.

Compact Gas Turbine Power for Fast Ships, T B Lauriat (AVCO Lycoming Textron). SAE Technical Paper 861211, 1986.

Investigations of the Dynamics of Large Air Cushions, P A Sullivan, M J Hinchey, T A Graham, J E Byrne, A Dupuis, N Milligan and C Walsh (University of Toronto Institute for Aerospace Studies). Prepared for Transportation Development Centre. TP 7560E, August 1986.

Investigations of the Dynamics of Large Air Cushions, by P A Sullivan, M J Hinchey, T A Graham et al., University of Toronto, Institute for Aerospace Studies, 1986. TP 7560E.

Introduction to Vistar im 301 Night Vision System, by P Matthews (McClennan Marine Ltd). Paper presented to Joint Meeting of The Institute of Navigation and The Hovercraft Society, School of Navigation, Warsash, UK, 12th February 1987. THS 14/87. ISSN 0144 8161.

NES 200L – The French SES Programme, by Y Pivet. 6th WEMT Symposium, Travemund, June 1987 (West European Conference on Marine Technology).

A Complete Linearized Theory for the Analysis and Design of Two-Dimensional Hydrofoils near a free surface, by P. Piperni. UTIAS Technical Note No 264. CN ISSN 0082–5263. October 1987. University of Toronto, Institute for Aerospace Studies, Canada.

Twenty-three years of the Application of Aerospace Techniques to Advanced Marine Vehicles, KAI Ketron Annapolis Inc., Stevensville Md., USA, January 1988.

Controllable Pitch Propellers for High-Speed Boats, by R. Havre. High-Speed Surface Craft, January/February 1988.

Experience from compilation of Global Wave Statistics, by N. Hogben (Consultant, British Maritime Technology Ltd). Ocean Engineering, Vol. 15 No. 1, 1988, p. 1–31.

History of Coast Guard Surface Effect Ship Performance Improvements, by G Larimer, J B McCollum, B Schaub, D Van Liew and C Whipple. Lecture given at ASNE Day 1988.

Patrol Boat Habitability Noise Control, by R Fischer. Naval Engineers Journal, May 1988, p 73–89.

The Effect of Surface Roughness on the Rollup Process of TIP Vortices on a Rectangualr Hydrofoil, by J Katz and J B Galdo (The Johns Hopkins University, Baltimore, MD., USA) AIAA-88–3743. AIAA/ASME/ASCE/SIAM/APS 1st National Fluid Dynamics Congress, Cincinnati, Ohio, 25–28 July 1988.

Extreme and Climatic Wave Spectra for use in Structural Design of Ships, by W H Buckley. Naval Engineers Journal, September 1988, p 36–58.

The R T L Hydrocat, A Minimum-Wash River, Lake and Harbour Craft Concept, by R L Trillo. Lecture given at the International Marine Transit Association Conference, Boston, USA, 19–22 September 1988.

On the Analysis and Evaluation of the marine Transport System of the Hellenic Islands, by Y Agapoulakis, A Papadopoulos and P Stolakis (MARTEDEC, Greece). Paper presented at Nav '88 – WEMT '88 Symposium "Advances in Ship Operations", Trieste, 12–14 October 1988, CETENA SpA, Genoa, Italy.

Air-Cushion Vehicles for Arctic Operation, by J Koleser and D R Lavis. Paper presented at 24th Annual Symposium of the Association of Scientists and Engineers of the naval Sea Systems Command. Naval Engineers Journal, November 1988, p 59–71.

AERODYNAMICS	AIR LUBRICATION	ARCTIC, ANTARCTIC APPLICATIONS	COMMERCIAL APPLICATIONS/OPERATIONS	DESIGN	DEVELOPMENT	DYNAMICS/SEAKEEPING	ECONOMICS	ENVIRONMENTAL ASPECTS	FANS	HYDRODYNAMICS	ICE BREAKING	LEGISLATION	LIFT-AIR SYSTEMS	MILITARY/NAVAL APPLICATIONS	PERFORMANCE/DRAG	POWER PLANTS	POWER TRANSMISSION	PRODUCTION	PROPULSION	SAFETY	SKIRTS/SEALS	STABILITY AND CONTROL	STRUCTURE/MATERIALS	TEST FACILITIES	TRIALS
						SWATH																			
				SES																					
																GEN			GEN						
			HOV																						
						HOV																			
											HOV														
WIGE																									
																GEN									
		LSACP	LSACP																						
									GEN																
																GEN									
						HOV																			
						HOV																			
			GEN																						
				SES																					
										HYD															
										GEN															
																			GEN						
								GEN																	
					SES										SES										
								SES / GEN																	
										HYD															
								GEN																	
				CAT						CAT															
							GEN																		
		HOV																							

SECTION 1 CONTINUED

Recent Developments in the Research of Coastal Morphology, by P de Wolf (Belgian Ministry of Public Works), A Grobben and J Van Rensbergen (Eurosense-Belfotop, Belgium). Paper presented at Oceanology International, Brighton, UK, 1988.

BEASAC – A Survey Hovercraft for Observing the Beaches and Offshore Areas near the Belgian Coast. Paper presented at Oceanology International '88 Conference, Brighton, UK, 8–11 March 1988. The International Hydrographic Review, January 1989, p 53–60.

Concept Design and Optimisation of a SWATH Passenger/Car Ferry, by A Papanikolaou et al (NTUA, Greece and TU, Berlin). Paper presented at IMAS '89, 4th International Maritime and Shipping Conference, Athens, Greece, 24–26 May 1989. Sponsors: The Institute of Marine Engineers, UK and IMarE/RINA Greek Joint Branch.

Overview of Surface Piercing Propellers and the Future, by J C Rose (Rolla SP Propellers, Balerna, Switzerland). Paper Presented to the VE.GA. Conference, Genoa, 2nd March 1989.

High-Speed Cargo and Passenger Catamaran, by Fjellstrand A/S, Omastrand, Norway. Shipbuilding Technology International 1989, p 42–44.

SECTION 2

PAPERS PRESENTED AT CONFERENCES SPECIFICALLY COVERING HIGH-SPEED CRAFT (INCLUDING SOME LOW-SPEED AIR CUSHION VEHICLES) 1986 TO 1990

Papers presented at the American Society of Naval Engineers (Flagship Section) and US Coast Guard Technical Symposium Patrol Boats 86, Arlington, Virginia, USA, 13–14 March 1986.

Development of a Hydrofoil Combatant, Preliminary Design, D S Olling.

The Combat Patrol Boat, Topside Design, P E Law, Jr, S Kuniyoshi and T Morgan.

US Coast Guard Conceptual Design of an Offshore Patrol Boat, S Cohen.

A Patrol Boat Hybrid Concept for the Coast Guard, J R Meyer.

Nasty Patrol Boats, J Stebbins.

AMPB-Advanced Multi-Mission Patrol Boat, L R Sheldon and T Sauer.

Patrol Boat Design Considerations, H Winters.

USN Sea Viking Design Development Highlights, C M Lee.

Compact Diesel Engines for Patrol Boats, V Jost.

Gas Turbines for Patrol Boat Power, J E Roberts.

Design, Development and Application of Diesel Engines for High Performance Patrol Craft, K Hosking.

Papers presented at the Royal Institution of Naval Architects International Symposium on Coastal Defence and Assault Vessels and Systems, Warship 86, London, 19–22 May 1986.

Influence of the Moment of Equilibrium on the Powering Characteristics of Planing Craft Including Hydrofoils, F Van Walree and E Stierman (Maritime Research Institute, Netherlands).

Air Cushion Vehicles for Amphibious Assault-The Next Generation, D R Lavis and E Band (Band, Lavis Associates Inc, USA).

Development of the Turt 4, Diesel Powered Amphibious Hovercraft for the Amphibious Warfare Role, S Lee, C Lee and S Kim (Korea Tacoma Marine Industries Ltd, Korea).

Diesel Engines Specially Designed for Fast Patrol Boats, B Gondouin (Alsthom Groupe Diesel, France).

The Use of Amphibious Hovercraft for Assault Purposes, G Elsley, UK.

Design, Construction and Operational Experience of High-Speed Aluminium Patrol Craft for the Finnish Coast Guard, O Ostring (Valmetin Laivateollisuus OY, Finland).

Diesel Engine Design, MTU (Motoren und Turbinen-Union Friedrichshafen GmbH), Federal Republic of Germany.

Catamarans Versus Single-Hull Concepts. A Study of Stability, Powering and Seakeeping Qualities, O Rutgersson (SSPA Maritime Consulting AB, Sweden).

The Dynamic Response of Surface-Effect-Ships in Regular Head Seas using Model Simulations, B R Clayton and R Webb (Dept of Mechanical Engineering, University College, London).

AERODYNAMICS	AIR LUBRICATION	ARCTIC, ANTARCTIC APPLICATIONS	COMMERCIAL APPLICATIONS/OPERATIONS	DESIGN	DEVELOPMENT	DYNAMICS/SEAKEEPING	ECONOMICS	ENVIRONMENTAL ASPECTS	FANS	HYDRODYNAMICS	ICE BREAKING	LEGISLATION	LIFT-AIR SYSTEMS	MILITARY/NAVAL APPLICATIONS	PERFORMANCE/DRAG	POWER PLANTS	POWER TRANSMISSION	PRODUCTION	PROPULSION	SAFETY	SKIRTS/SEALS	STABILITY AND CONTROL	STRUCTURE/MATERIALS	TEST FACILITIES	TRIALS
			HOV																						
			HOV																						
			SWATH	SWATH																					
																			GEN						
				CAT																					
					HYD									HYD											
				PLA										PLA											
			PLA																						
				PLA																					
					PLA									PLA											
														PLA											
					PLA									PLA											
														SES											
																PLA									
																PLA									
																PLA									
															PLA										
															HYD										
														HOV											
														HOV											
																PLA									
														HOV											
														PLA											
																GEN									
						CAT GEN									CAT GEN								CAT GEN		
						SES																			

SECTION 2 CONTINUED

Papers presented at the High-Speed Surface Craft and Shipping News International 5th International High-Speed Surface Craft Conference, Southampton, England, 7–8 May 1986.

Meeting the Channel Tunnel Challenge, D Meredith (Hoverspeed).

Regression Analysis of Gawn-Burrill Series for Application in Computer-Aided High-Speed Propeller Design, Dr P G Kozhukharov (Bulgarian Ship Hydrodynamics Centre).

ADOC 12: A Light Utility Air Cushion Vehicle, B de Lagarde (IFREMER).

SWATH Seakeeping in the Presence of Control Fins, Dr J -Y Wu and Dr R C McGregor (Department of Naval Architecture and Ocean Engineering, University of Glasgow).

Successful High-Speed Fleets Prove Viability of Waterjet Propulsion, J Seastrom (North American Marine Jet).

Experience with Jet-Propulsion Systems in Various Types of Craft, R Svensson (KaMeWa AB).

Fast Ferry Potential in the United States, W Wohleking (Advanced Marine Systems Associates).

A Numerical Method for Calculating Hydrodynamic Characteristics of a Hydrofoil with Arbitrary Planform, L Baiqi (China Ship Scientific Research Center).

The Development of the Wave-Piercing Catamaran, P Hercus (International Catamarans).

Hovercraft Design with an Automatic Transversal Air Distribution Lift System, M de la Cruz and J M Berbiela (Neumar).

Advanced Composite Structures for High-Speed Surface Craft, A Marchant (Marchant Filer Dixon).

Papers presented at the Urban Waterborne Mass Transportation Symposium, Miami, Florida, 26 April 1986, sponsored by The Marine Council and The Southeast Section, The Society of Naval Architects and Marine Engineering.

Development of a Series of Fast Passenger Catamarans in Australia, Mathew Nichols.

Surface-Piercing Hydrofoil Application to Ferry Missions, Trial Program, James H King and John R Meyer.

A Total Approach to Rapid Waterborne Transportation, Donald E Burg.

Three Years of Coast Guard Operation Experience in Relation to Mass Transportation Needs, Cmdr Paul C Jackson.

The Operations and Economics of Marine Transit: Comparative Studies by Computer, Edward C Hagemann.

Assessing the Market and Financial Feasibility of Waterborne Transportation Systems, John F DiRenzo.

Papers presented at the 1986 CACTS International Conference on Air Cushion Technology, arranged by the Canadian Air Cushion Technology Society of the Canadian Aeronautics and Space Institute in co-operation with The Hovercraft Society and the US Hovercraft Society. Held in Toronto, Ontario, 16–18 September 1986.

Design Criteria for Light High Speed Desert Air Cushion Vehicle, B E Abulnaga (McGill University, Montreal, Canada).

Preliminary Testing of Linear Propellers over Water, C Ives (Hudex International Consultants Ltd, Montreal, Canada).

Some Tests at IMD on High-Speed Hovercraft Icebreaking, J Whitten, M Hinchey (Memorial University of Newfoundland) and B Hill, S Jones (Institute of Marine Dynamics, St John's, Newfoundland).

Flow Visualization and Ducted Propellers on the LACV 30, P E Robertson (X-Aero, USA).

Bertelsen Research on Sliding Seals for an Air Cushion Crawler Tractor, W R Bertelsen (Bertelsen Inc, USA).

The High Speed Performance Vehicle in Anti-Submarine Warfare, M Reid (Defence Programs, External Affairs, Canada).

Diesel Engine Concepts for Hovercraft, H Evans (InTech International Inc, Spokane, Washington, USA).

Propagation of an ACIB Air Cavity Under a Floating Ice Sheet, M J Hinchey (Memorial University of Newfoundland).

Performance Criteria for Air-Cushion Heave Dynamics, J R Amyot (National Research Council of Canada, Ottawa).

A Proposed Laboratory Method to Determine Propeller Foreign Object Damage, D J Vitale (US Naval Sea Systems Command).

The Experimental Investigation of the Bounce Characteristics of an ACV Responsive Skirt, W L Zhou and T Ma (Marine Design and Research Institute of China).

The Improvement of the ACV Skirt Test Facilities, N Zheng and Y Hua (Marine Design and Research Institute of China).

Hovercraft in Law Enforcement – Part 2, H C Cook (Department of Natural Resources, State of Maryland, USA).

The LACV 30 in Service, R G Helm (Bell Aerospace Textron, USA).

AERODYNAMICS	AIR LUBRICATION	ARCTIC, ANTARCTIC APPLICATIONS	COMMERCIAL APPLICATIONS/OPERATIONS	DESIGN	DEVELOPMENT	DYNAMICS/SEAKEEPING	ECONOMICS	ENVIRONMENTAL ASPECTS	FANS	HYDRODYNAMICS	ICE BREAKING	LEGISLATION	LIFT-AIR SYSTEMS	MILITARY/NAVAL APPLICATIONS	PERFORMANCE/DRAG	POWER PLANTS	POWER TRANSMISSION	PRODUCTION	PROPULSION	SAFETY	SKIRTS/SEALS	STABILITY AND CONTROL	STRUCTURE/MATERIALS	TEST FACILITIES	TRIALS
			HOV																						
																			GEN						
				HOV																					
						SWATH																			
																			GEN						
																			GEN						
			GEN																						
										HYD															
					CAT																				
													HOV									HOV			
																							GEN		
					CAT																				
			HYD																						
	ALH SES		ALH SES			ALH SES																			
			SES																						
							GEN																		
							GEN																		
				HOV																					
																			GEN						
											HOV														
																			HOV						
																					HYB		HYB		
														GEN											
															HOV										
											LSACP														
						HOV																			
								HOV											HOV						
						HOV																HOV			
																						HOV		HOV	
			HOV																						
														HOV											

SECTION 2 CONTINUED

Papers presented at the AIAA 8th Advanced Marine Systems Conference, San Diego, California, USA, 22–24 September 1986.

Ride Quality Criteria of Assessment for Advanced Marine Vehicles, W E Farris (Boeing Marine Systems, Seattle, Washington, USA). Paper AIAA-86–2360.

Linear Analysis of Heave Dynamics of a Bag and Finger ACV Skirt, T Mar and P A Sullivan (University of Toronto, Canada). AIAA-86–2361.

Analysis and Prediction of Flat Bottom Slamming Impact of Advanced Marine Vehicles in Waves, P Kaplan (Virginia Polytechnic Institute and State University, Blacksburg, Virginia, USA). AIAA-86–2362.

Innovation in SWATH, T A Schmidt (Lockheed Advanced Marine Systems, Santa Clara, California, USA). AIAA-86–2363.

Progress in the Development of the Surface Effect Catamaran Hull Form, J M Durkin and N M Paraskevas (David W Taylor Naval Ship R&D Center, Bethesda, Maryland, USA). AIAA-86–2364.

Ram Air Catamaran (RAC) Vehicle Concepts, R W Gallington (Science Applications International Corp, Seattle, Washington, USA). AIAA-86–2365.

Worldwide Study on High Speed Waterborne Transportation, W G Wohleking (Advanced Marine Systems Associates, Gaithersburg, Maryland, USA). AIAA-86–2366.

High Speed Catamarans, M Nichols (Nichols Boat Builders, Freeland, Washington, USA). AIAA-86–2367.

The Mitsui Sea Saloon 15 *Marine Wave*, K Nishimura (Mitsui Engineering & Shipbuilding Co Ltd, Tokyo), H Nakamura (Mitsui Engineering & Shipbuilding Co Ltd, Ichihara, Japan) and M Komoto (Mitsui Zosen (USA) Inc, New York). AIAA-86–2368.

Hydrofoil Operations, L Rodriquez (Rodriquez Cantieri Navali, Messina, Italy). AIAA-86–2369.

The SWATH Ship *Halcyon* Operations, R Cramb (RMI Inc, National City, California, USA). AIAA-86–2370.

A High Productivity Waterborne Rapid Transport System, D E Burg (Air Ride Craft Inc, Miami, Florida, USA). AIAA-86–2371.

The Surface Effect Ship Special Warfare Craft (SWCM), C Lee (RMI Inc, National City, California, USA). AIAA-86–2372.

The Arctic ACV Program, J Koleser (Naval Sea Systems Command, Washington DC, USA). AIAA-86–2375.

Preliminary Design of an Air-Cushion Crash Rescue Vehicle (ACCRV), R Brown (AFWAL/FIEMB Wright-Patterson Air Force Base, Ohio) and R Thom (Bell Aerospace Textron, Buffalo, New York, USA). AIAA-86–2377.

Replacement of the University Research Fleet and a SWATH Ship Candidate, R P Dinsmore (Woods Hole Oceanographic Institution, Woods Hole, Massachusetts, USA) and T G Lang (Semi-Submerged Ship Corp, Solana Beach, California, USA). AIAA-86–2378.

Arctic Operations of *Larus*, E Makinen (Wärtsilä Arctic Inc, Vancouver BC, Canada). AIAA-86–2380.

Development of HYCAT, D E Calkins (University of Washington, Seattle, Washington, USA). AIAA-86–2381.

New Small Waterplane Area Ship Concept, W C O'Neill (Newton Square, Pennsylvania, USA). AIAA-86–2382.

The Wavestrider Family of Planing Boats, P Payne (Ketron Inc, Annapolis, Maryland, USA). AIAA-86–2383.

SWATH T-AGOS: A Producible Design, P M Covich (Naval Sea Systems Command, Washington DC, USA). AIAA-86–2384.

Large SWATHs: A Discussion of the Diminishing Returns of Increasing SWATH Ship Size, C B McKesson and T R Cannon (NAVSEA, Baltimore, Maryland, USA). AIAA-86–2385.

Air-Cushion Equipment Transporter (ACET), G R Wyen (AFWAL Wright-Patterson Air Force Base, Ohio, USA) and R Helm (Bell Aerospace Textron, Buffalo, New York, USA). AIAA-86–2386.

Papers presented at The Hovercraft Society Fourth International Hovercraft Conference, Southampton, England, 6–7 May 1987.

The Development of the Current Range of Griffon Hovercraft, J Gifford (Griffon Hovercraft Ltd, UK).

The Tiger 40 Hovercraft, C B Eden (Air Vehicles Ltd, UK).

AP1–88 Operating Experience, M D Mant (British Hovercraft Corporation, UK).

The United Kingdom Trials of the SES 200, B J W Pingree, B J Russell and J B Willcox.

The Roll Stability of an SES in a Seaway, A G Blyth (UK).

Coupled Roll and Heave Motions of Surface Effect Ship in Beam Seas, L Yun, T F Wu and Y N Cheng (Shanghai, China).

Experimental Investigation of Bounce Feature of ACV Bi-Bag Skirt, W L Zhou and T Ma (Marine Design and Research Institute of China).

The Hovercraft Doctor Service, M Cole.

AERODYNAMICS	AIR LUBRICATION	ARCTIC, ANTARCTIC APPLICATIONS	COMMERCIAL APPLICATIONS/OPERATIONS	DESIGN	DEVELOPMENT	DYNAMICS/SEAKEEPING	ECONOMICS	ENVIRONMENTAL ASPECTS	FANS	HYDRODYNAMICS	ICE BREAKING	LEGISLATION	LIFT-AIR SYSTEMS	MILITARY/NAVAL APPLICATIONS	PERFORMANCE/DRAG	POWER PLANTS	POWER TRANSMISSION	PRODUCTION	PROPULSION	SAFETY	SKIRTS/SEALS	STABILITY AND CONTROL	STRUCTURE/MATERIALS	TEST FACILITIES	TRIALS
						GEN																			
						HOV															HOV				
						GEN																	GEN		
				SWATH	SWATH																				
					CAT																				
					SES																				
				CAT																					
				WIGE																					
			GEN																						
				CAT	CAT																				
				SWATH																					
			HYD																						
				SWATH																					
				ALH																					
				SES																					
														SES											
		HOV																							
					HYB																				
			SWATH																						
		HOV																							
					CAT																				
					HYD																				
				SWATH	SWATH																				
				PLA		PLA																			
														SWATH			SWATH								
				SWATH																					
														LSACP											
				HOV	HOV																				
					HOV																				
			HOV																						
														SES											
																						SES			
						SES																			
						HOV															HOV				
			HOV																						

SECTION 2 CONTINUED

The Static Formation Calculation of ACV Bi-Bag Skirts on the Water Surface, N Zheng, T F Wu and Y Hua (Marine Design and Research Institute of China).

ACVPP – A Computer Application for Air-Cushion Vehicle Power Prediction, F J Steele, Jr (University of Michigan, Ann Arbor, USA).

The Deep Cushion SES Concept, E G Tattersall (Hovermarine International Ltd, UK).

The Use of Hovercraft in the Defence of the Home Base, B J Russell (Ministry of Defence, UK).

Papers presented at The Royal Aeronautical Society, London, Ram Wing and Ground Effect Craft Symposium, 19 May 1987.

Taking Advantage of Surface Proximity Effects with Aero-Marine Vehicles, Robert L Trillo (Robert Trillo Limited, Lymington, Hampshire).

Ram Wings – A Future? J M L Reeves (Naval Air Development Center, USA).

Power Augmentation of Ram Wings, R W Gallington (Science Applications International Corporation, USA).

History and Development of the ''Aerodynamic Ground Effect Craft'' (AGEC) with Tandem Wings, G W Jorg (West Germany).

On the Design of Stable Ram Wing Vehicles, R W Staufenbiel (Institute of Aerospace Engineering, West Germany).

A Possible Maritime Future for Surface Effect Craft in the UK, C B Betts and B R Clayton (University College, London).

Papers presented at the American Society of Naval Engineers ASNE Day 1987 and published in the Naval Engineers Journal (ASNE) Vol 99 No 3, May 1987, USA.

The Effect of Stern Wedges on Ship Powering Performance, G Karafiath and S Fisher.

The Deep-Vee Hull Form – Improves Seakeeping and Combat System Performance, J W Kehoe, Jr (USN, Ret), K S Brower and E H Serter.

The History of Aluminium as a Deckhouse Material, R A Sielski.

T-AGOS 19: An Innovative Program for an Innovative Design, P Covich.

Papers presented at the 1987 CACTS International Conference on Air-Cushion Technology, Montreal, Canada, 22–24 September 1987. Sponsored by Transportation Development Centre, Transport Canada. Presented by the Canadian Air-Cushion Technology Society with the co-operation of the US Hovercraft Society and The Hovercraft Society.

Planning Surface Transportation in Northern Canada, V Hume (Indian and Northern Affairs, Canada).

Tractive Requirements for Off-Road ACVs, R N Young and P Bonsinsuk (McGill University, Montreal).

Air-Cushion Assisted Airport Rescue vehicle, D J Perez (Wright-Patterson Air Force Base, USA).

GPC: A Device for Easy Control of a Small ACV, B de Lagarde (IFREMER, France).

Development of Hovercraft Skirt for Desert Operation, B E Abulnaga (American University, Cairo, Egypt).

Industrial Applications of Air-Cushion and Fluid Jets by Bertin & Cie, J Cayla (Bertin & Cie, France).

Ice Management Chicoutimi Harbour with an ACV, G Desgagnes (Chicoutimi Port) and D Jones (Ice Control Enterprises, Canada).

Critical Speed Data for a Floating Model Ice Sheet, M J Hinchey (Memorial University of Newfoundland, Canada).

Requirements for ACV Operations in Antarctica, J S Dibbern (US Army, Charlotteville, VA, USA).

Design and Operation of ACV Lightering Barges, V A Galistsky (Leningrad Central Project and Design Bureau, USSR).

Specification and Acquisition of AP1.88 by the CCG, T F Melhuish (Canadian Coast Guard).

Design of Canadian Coast Guard AP1.88, J Leonard (British Hovercraft Corporation, UK).

Initial Operating Experience with the CCG AP1.88, G Moore (ACV Base, Canadian Coast Guard, Montreal).

Operational Costs and Requirements for the AP1.88, D Marshall (SRO-KMA Consultants Inc, Montreal).

Engineering Development and Service Experience of the Amphibious ACV *Gepard*, I A Martynov (Neptun Central Design Bureau, Moscow, USSR).

Hovercraft Water/Land Ambulance Service, H Cook (Maryland Natural Resources Police, USA).

Design and Test Results of Air-Cushion Vehicles Built by A M Gorki Institute, S F Kirkin (Mariiskiy Polytechnic Institute A M Gorki, USSR).

Design Criteria for Hovercraft Propellers: US Army LACV-30 Case Study, R J Gornstein (Pacific Propeller Inc, Kent, WA, USA).

Horizontal Launch System for Transatmospheric Vehicles, M D Chawla (Wright-Patterson Air Force Base, USA).

AERODYNAMICS	AIR LUBRICATION	ARCTIC, ANTARCTIC APPLICATIONS	COMMERCIAL APPLICATIONS/OPERATIONS	DESIGN	DEVELOPMENT	DYNAMICS/SEAKEEPING	ECONOMICS	ENVIRONMENTAL ASPECTS	FANS	HYDRODYNAMICS	ICE BREAKING	LEGISLATION	LIFT-AIR SYSTEMS	MILITARY/NAVAL APPLICATIONS	PERFORMANCE/DRAG	POWER PLANTS	POWER TRANSMISSION	PRODUCTION	PROPULSION	SAFETY	SKIRTS/SEALS	STABILITY AND CONTROL	STRUCTURE/MATERIALS	TEST FACILITIES	TRIALS
																					HOV				
															HOV										
				SES		SES																			
														SES											
														HOV											
ACV			GEN																						
WIGE			WIGE																						
			WIGE																						
WIGE															WIGE										
					WIGE										WIGE										
					WIGE																	WIGE			
														SES											
										PLA					PLA										
										PLA				PLA											
						PLA																	GEN		
				SWATH																					
		GEN																							
															HOV										
															HYB										
			HOV																						
			HYB																						
																						HOV			
								HOV													HOV				
GEN										GEN															
											HOV														
											HOV														
	HOV																								
	HOV		HOV																						
				HOV																					
				HOV																					
			HOV																						
			HOV				HOV																		
			HOV	HOV	HOV																				
			HOV																						
				HOV											HOV										HOV
																			HOV						
WIGE																									

SECTION 2 CONTINUED

Hovercraft Dynamics Modeling: A Review of Current Techniques, P Taylor (US Navy Ocean Engineering, MIT) and D D Moran (David Taylor Naval Ship R&D Center, USA).

Papers presented at the 12th Annual Conference of the International Marine Transit Association, Taormina, Sicily, 28–30 September 1987.

Possible Improvements in Semi-Conventional Fast Marine Craft, A Magazzu (Palermo University, Italy).

The Competitivity of the Offer on the Market of Fast Ships, C Sicard (Organisation Claude Sicard).

The future for Composite Materials in Marine Transportation, A Marchant (Marchant Filer Dixon, UK).

Development of High Velocity Marine Vehicles for Passenger Transportation in Mediterranean Area, B Della Loggia (CETENA, Italy).

Self Propulsion Tests with Waterjets, V Ruggiero (University of Genoa) and G Venturini (CRM, Milan, Italy).

AP1.88 Operating Experience, M D Mant (British Hovercraft Corporation, UK).

Papers presented at IMAEM '87, IV Congress of the Bulgarian Ship Hydrodynamics Centre, Varna, Bulgaria, 25–30 May 1987.

Influence of Skirt Parameters on Hovercraft Transverse Stability Characteristics, E Brzoska, L Kobwlinski and M Krezelewski (Ship Research Institute, Technical University of Gdansk, Poland).

Some Features of Computerized High-Speed Propeller Design Based on Data from Systematic Tests of Cavitating Propeller Series, P Kozhukharov and V Dimitrov (Bulgarian Ship Hydrodynamics Centre, Varna).

Experimental Investigation of Propulsive Characteristics of Ships with Waterjet Propulsion Systems, S Lazarov (Bulgarian Ship Hydrodynamics Centre) and K Varsamov (Higher Institute of Machine and Electrical Engineering, Sofia, Bulgaria).

Papers presented at the 6th International High-Speed Surface Craft Conference, London, 14–15 January 1988. Proceedings published by Hawkedon International Ltd, Chipping Norton, England. ISBN 1 869894 08 1.

Fast River Ferries, R M Mabbott (Thames Line, England).

The Design and Construction of a Stolkraft High-Speed Passenger Ferry, J A Lund (Stolkraft International, Australia).

The Servogear High Performance Propulsion System, L M Endresen (Servogear A/S, Norway).

The Influence of Shaft Inclination on the Relative Merits of Propellers and Waterjets, A G Blyth (Consultant, UK).

The Development of SES Jet Rider, O Gullberg (Karlskronavarvet AB, Sweden).

Model Tests – A Powerful Design Tool in SES Development, L Ronnquist (SSPA Maritime Consulting, Sweden).

Evaluation of a Ride Control System for SES, B R Clayton and R Webb (University College, London).

The Role for Composite Materials in Future Marine Transportation, A Marchant (Marchant Filer Dixon, UK) and R F Pinzelli (Du Pont de Nemours, Switzerland).

Flexural Fatigue Properties of Advanced Marine Composites, R J Rymill and J E Course (Lloyd's Register of Shipping) and R F Pinzelli (Du Pont de Nemours, Switzerland).

High Performance Composites and their Effectiveness in Sandwich Panels, H G Allen and K Raybould (Southampton University, UK).

The Powering Characteristics of Hydrofoil Craft, F van Walree (Maritime Research Institute, Netherlands).

A New Generation of Marine Engines with Very Low Mass/Power Ratios and Their Application on Fast Craft, G Venturini (CRM Design Office) and V Ruggiero (Genoa University, Italy).

The Influence of High-Speed Powerboat Design on Commercial and Military Operations, J P Sutcliffe (Cougar Holdings Ltd, UK).

Drag Estimation for Hovercraft, Y Wang (Dalian Institute of Technology, China).

On the Design Technology of SWATH Ship for High-Speed Coastal Passenger Vessel, K-Y Lee and D-K Lee (Korea Institute of Machinery and Metals) and E-S Kim, J-G Kim and J-H Kim (Hyundai Heavy Industries, Korea).

Wigfoil Interface Craft Concept, Y Manor (Manor Engineering Products, Israel).

Papers presented at the 1988 Joint International Conference on Air-Cushion Technology, Annapolis, Maryland, USA, 27–29 September 1988.

Developments of the US Army's Pontoon Air Cushion Kit (PACK), D Wilkins (Band, Lavis & Associates,, Inc., Severna Park, MD).

An Update on SES Design Techniques and their Application to Repowering the USCG SES-110 and the USN SES-200, R Church (David Taylor Research Center, Bethesda, MD).

Computer Aided Conceptual Design of Surface Effect Ships, D R Lavis and B G Forstell (Band, Lavis & Associates Inc).

AERODYNAMICS	AIR LUBRICATION	ARCTIC, ANTARCTIC APPLICATIONS	COMMERCIAL APPLICATIONS/OPERATIONS	DESIGN	DEVELOPMENT	DYNAMICS/SEAKEEPING	ECONOMICS	ENVIRONMENTAL ASPECTS	FANS	HYDRODYNAMICS	ICE BREAKING	LEGISLATION	LIFT-AIR SYSTEMS	MILITARY/NAVAL APPLICATIONS	PERFORMANCE/DRAG	POWER PLANTS	POWER TRANSMISSION	PRODUCTION	PROPULSION	SAFETY	SKIRTS/SEALS	STABILITY AND CONTROL	STRUCTURE/MATERIALS	TEST FACILITIES	TRIALS
						HOV																		HOV	
										GEN					GEN										
			GEN																						
																							GEN		
			GEN		GEN																				
																			GEN						
			HOV																						
																					HOV	HOV			
															GEN				GEN						
															GEN				GEN						
			CAT																						
				ALH																			ALH		
																	GEN								
																	GEN		GEN						
					SES																				
										SES														SES	
						SES																			
																							GEN		
																							GEN		
																							GEN		
										HYD					HYD										
																GEN									
			PLA											PLA											
															HOV										
															SES										
				SWATH																					
				WIGE																					
					LSACP									LSACP											
				SES																					
				SES																					

SECTION 2 CONTINUED

Jetrider SES 250 Passenger Ferry Development, by O Gullberg (Karlskrona Varvet, Karlskrona, Sweden).

Cushion Damper for Air-Cushion Vehicles, J Bellemare (US Coast Guard Research Center, Groton, CT).

Some Thoughts on ACV Structural Impact Design Requirements, R G Wade (Ships Safety, Canadian Coast Guard, Ottawa).

Development of Responsive Bag-Finger Skirts, T Ma and P A Sullivan (University of Toronto, Canada).

The Static Formation of ACV Three-Dimensional Bag-Finger Skirt, Y N Xie and N Zheng (Marine Design and Research Institute of China, Shanghai).

The US Naval Landing Craft Air Cushion LCAC 008: Cold Weather Tests, J Ehrhardt, (NAVSEA, Washington, DC).

Economics of Air-Cushion Vehicles in Support of Arctic Offshore Oil Development, D F Dickins (D F Dickins Associates Ltd., Vancouver, BC).

Computer Integrated Manufacturing (CIM) Technology Trends: Reducing the Cost of Air-Cushion Development, C R Payne (Hovercraft Fabrics Ltd., Oakville, Ontario).

SEAOPS Manual, Navy Hovercraft Operations, D C Braa and J T Easley (Naval Coastal Center, Halifax Engineering, USA).

Hovercraft Support in Antarctica, H C Cook (Frank W Hake Inc., Eddystone, PA).

The Waterjet Propulsion of the Inland Sidewall Craft, J Z Zhu (Marine Design and Research Institute of China, Shanghai).

Linear Propellers: Tires and Tracks that Produce Waterjet Thrust, C Ives (Hudex Ltd., Hudson Heights, Quebec).

Papers presented at The Chinese Society of Naval Architecture and Marine Engineering International High-Performance Vehicle Conference, Shanghai, 2–5 November 1988.

Development of a Craft for Supercritical Operation in Rough Seas, H Walderhaug and A Jaeger, (Norwegian Institute of Technology).

Improvement of Comfortability in Design of High-Speed Craft, K Kihara, (Mitsubishi Heavy Industries Ltd., Japan).

Assistance of Marine Radar to Sea State Monitoring, R Hososa, K Ikeda (University of Osaka Prefecture), Y Kunitake (Mitsui Engineering and Shipbuilding Co. Ltd.) M Koga (Japan Weather Association) and S. Yamashita (Nippon Telegraph and Telephone Corporation) (Japan).

Combined Propulsion Systems of Fast Vessels with Jet Turbine Engines, A Churchalis, (Naval Academy, Gdynia, Poland).

Structural Considerations for the Survivability of Advanced Marine Vehicles in Ice-Infested Waters, M R Steinhilber (US Coast Guard) and A Moshaiov (Department of Ocean Engineering, MIT).

Development of Air-Cushion Vehicles in China in the Last Three Decades, L Yun and Y Q Sun (MARIC, Shanghai, China).

The Application of Waterjet Propulsion in High-Performance Vehicles in China, P Z Jin and L X Wang.

Design and Development of the Power Plant of the 65-ton Class Model 722 Prototype Landing Air-Cushion Vehicle, J Zhu and Y Shen (MARIC, China).

An Experimental Study on the Performance Characteristics of Partially Submerged Propeller, S Liu and H Zhu (China Ship Scientific Research Center, Wuxi, China).

Waves Generated by a Moving Disturbance in a Shallow Channel, D Wu and X Cui (Harbin Shipbuilding Engineering Institute, China).

Design and Testing of a Gas Turbine Powerplant for a Hovercraft, N Wang and P Chen (Marine Boiler & Turbine Research Institute, Harbin, China).

Motion Control and Analysis of SES and ACV, B R Clayton and R Webb (University College, London).

Computerized Design of Air-Cushion Vehicles and Surface Effect Ships, E G U Band and D R Lavis (Band, Lavis & Associates, Inc., Severna Park, MD., USA).

Skirt Systems for Amphibious Craft and Air-Cushion Catamarans-Current and Future Needs, P Inch (Avon Industrial Polymers, UK).

Responsive Skirt-Its Effect on Stability and Ride Quality of Hovercraft, T Ma and W L Zhou (MARIC, China) and P A Sullivan (UTIAS, Toronto, Canada).

Design Features of the Model 716II Air-Cushion Vehicle, R Zheng and X Jiang (MARIC, China).

Amphibious Air-Cushion Vehicle Designed by Marine Polytechnic Institute A M Gorki, S F Kirkin (Marine Polytechnic Institute A M Gorki, USSR).

SES Stability in Turns-the Influence of Sidewall Shape, A G Blyth (Southampton, UK).

The Design of Jet-Propelled Surface Effect Passenger Craft of Ming River and Chong Qing, Z L Lin (MARIC, China).

New Conceptual Design of Hydrofoil Catamarans, H Miyata, Y Tsuchiya and M Kanai (University of Tokyo, Japan).

AERODYNAMICS	AIR LUBRICATION	ARCTIC, ANTARCTIC APPLICATIONS	COMMERCIAL APPLICATIONS/OPERATIONS	DESIGN	DEVELOPMENT	DYNAMICS/SEAKEEPING	ECONOMICS	ENVIRONMENTAL ASPECTS	FANS	HYDRODYNAMICS	ICE BREAKING	LEGISLATION	LIFT-AIR SYSTEMS	MILITARY/NAVAL APPLICATIONS	PERFORMANCE/DRAG	POWER PLANTS	POWER TRANSMISSION	PRODUCTION	PROPULSION	SAFETY	SKIRTS/SEALS	STABILITY AND CONTROL	STRUCTURE/MATERIALS	TEST FACILITIES	TRIALS
					SES																				
						SES HOV																			
																							HOV		
																					HOV				
																					HOV				
	HOV							HOV							HOV										
	HOV						HOV																		
																		HOV			HOV				
														HOV											
	HOV																								
																			SES						
																			HOV						
						PLA																			
						PLA																			
								GEN																	
																GEN									
	GEN							GEN															gen		
			GEN		GEN																				
																			SES						
																HOV									
																			GEN						
										GEN															
																HOV									
						HOV SES																			
				HOV SES																					
																					HOV SES				
						HOV															HOV	HOV			
				HOV																					
				HOV																					
				SES																			SES		
				SES															SES						
				HYD CAT																					

SECTION 2 CONTINUED

Investigation of Longitudinal Motion Dynamics of Surface Piercing Hydrofoil Type Kometa, P Bogdanov and P Kozhukharov (Bulgarian Ship Hydrodynamics Centre, Varna, Bulgaria) and A Y Panov (Gorki Polytechnic Institute, USSR).

Experiment and Analysis of Shallow Water Effect on Hydrofoil Boat, S Lan, D Zhang and W Rui (China Ship Scientific Research Center, Wuxi).

A New Computational Tool to Estimate the Resistance of SWATH Ships, H H Chun, A M Ferguson and R C McGregor (University of Glasgow, UK).

A Practical Method for Wave Resistance Prediction for SWATH Ships, V Bertram and G Jensen (Institut fur Schiffbau, Hamburg, Federal Republic of Germany).

Some UK Developments in SWATH Design Research, C V Betts (University College London, UK).

Comparative Study of SWATH Seakeeping, R C McGregor, E K Arthur, E Djatmiko, L H Drysdale and X Zheng (University of Glasgow, UK).

A Computer Augmented Procedure for SWATH Configuration Development, J R MacGregor, R C McGregor (University of Glasgow) and N S Miller (YARD Ltd., Glasgow, UK).

Experimental Study on Spray of SWATH Strut at High Speed, B Zhu and W Ge (China Ship Scientific Research Centre, Wuxi).

The Study and Development of Swath in China and the Project of Multi-Purpose SWATH Vessel, Y Cao (MARIC, China).

The Design of a 500-Passenger SWATH for Service Between Dalian and Yantai, D Yuan and L Bo (Wuhan Ship Design and Development Institute, Wuhan, Hubei, China).

On the Determination of Sizes of Stabilizing Fins for SWATH Ships, D Huang (Dalian University of Technology) and X Li (Shanghai Ship and Shipping Research Institute, China).

Wake Shapes Behind Planing Hull Forms, D Savitsky (Davidson Laboratory, Stevens Institute of Technology, Hoboken, N.J., USA).

Effect of Stern Trimming Plate on Speed Performance of Semi-Displacement Craft, Z Dong and Z Shao (Naval Academy of Engineering, China).

Hydrodynamic Lift of Craft with Two Wedges, C Zhang (Hudong Shipyard, Shanghai, China).

Analysis on the Resistance and Propelling Force of Stepless Planing Boat AO, Q Meng (Wuhu Shipyard, China).

Catamaran Inland River Passenger Ship-A Ship Form Worth to Develop, B Cheng, W. Pan, S. Shao and Y Wang (Shanghai Jiao Tong University, China).

The Research of Wave Element for a High-Speed Catamaran in the Inland River, G Song, S Du and D Chen (China).

Development of an Amphibian Wing in Ground Effect Craft, A Hu (MARIC).

The 902 Single-Sear Ram Wing Surface Effect Craft, S Li and K Li (China Ship Scientific Research Center, Wuxi).

Airfoil Technique Explained on X 113 and X 114, H Fischer (RFB, Federal Republic of Germany).

The Study and Development of High-Speed Craft in Poland, E Brzoska, L Kobylinski, M Krezelewski and A Rogalski (Ship Research Institute, Technical University of Gdansk, Poland).

The Hull Form and Stability of Air-Cushion Barge, Y Su and X Huang (Harbin Shipbuilding Engineering Institute, China).

The Developed Heilongjiang Air-Cushion Barges by Applying the Principle of Air-Cushion for Reducing Resistance, H Fan (Heilongjiang Research Institute of Watertransport Science, China).

On the Design and Trial of a Self-Propelled Hoverplatform and its Application, G Tang (MARIC).

Hydrostatic Power Transmission: A new Hydrofoil Design for the Nineties, G Falzea and D di Blasi (Rodriquez Cantieri Navali) and H Speich (Rexroth, Milan, Italy).

On the Measurements of Towing Force Acting on an ACV Model Over Land in a Yawed State, R Murao (Aoyama Gakuin University, Tokyo, Japan).

Papers presented at the RINA 2nd Conference on SWATH Ships and Advanced Multihull Vessels, London, 28–30 November 1988:

The Design of Compensators for Control of SWATH Motions, F Caldeira-Saraiva and D Clarke (British Maritime Technology).

Development of a SWATH Structural Design Procedure for Royal Naval Vessels, A G Stirling, G L Jones and J D Clarke (Ministry of Defence, UK).

The Catsemi, a New Advanced Multihull Vessel, G J Schepman (Marine Structure ConsultantsBV, The Netherlands).

Stability and Survivability of Passenger Catamaran Vessels, B Matthewson (Australian Department of Transport) and S A Roberts (Vosper Thornycroft (UK) Ltd).

AERODYNAMICS	AIR LUBRICATION	ARCTIC, ANTARCTIC APPLICATIONS	COMMERCIAL APPLICATIONS/OPERATIONS	DESIGN	DEVELOPMENT	DYNAMICS/SEAKEEPING	ECONOMICS	ENVIRONMENTAL ASPECTS	FANS	HYDRODYNAMICS	ICE BREAKING	LEGISLATION	LIFT-AIR SYSTEMS	MILITARY/NAVAL APPLICATIONS	PERFORMANCE/DRAG	POWER PLANTS	POWER TRANSMISSION	PRODUCTION	PROPULSION	SAFETY	SKIRTS/SEALS	STABILITY AND CONTROL	STRUCTURE/MATERIALS	TEST FACILITIES	TRIALS
						HYD																			
										HYD															
										SWATH															
										SWATH															
				SWATH																					
						SWATH																			
				SWATH																					
				SWATH						SWATH															
				SWATH																					
			SWATH	SWATH																					
																						SWATH			
										PLA															
										PLA				PLA											
										PLA															
			CAT							CAT															
				CAT																					
										CAT															
					WIGE																				
					WIGE																				
WIGE					WIGE																				
				PLA HOV GEN HYD																					
																						LSACP			
										LSACP				LSACP											
			LSACP											LSACP											LSCAP
														GEN HYD											
														HOV											
					SWATH																				
														SWATH									SWATH		
			CAT																						
					CAT																CAT		CAT		

SECTION 2 CONTINUED

Some Design Approaches for Reducing the Structural Weight of SWATH Hulls, J P Sikora (David Taylor Naval Ship Research & Development Center, USA).

SWATH Ship Motion Stabilisation Using Linear Quadratic Theory of Optional Control, E E Zarnick (David Taylor Naval Ship R&D Center, USA).

On the Design Technology of High Speed Passenger SWATH Ships, K Uy-Yeul Lee and D K Lee (Korea Institute of Machinery and Metals) and B-S Kim, J-G Kim and J-H Kim (Hyundai Heavy Industries Ltd (South Korea).

Small Model Experiments of SWATH Concept at Ship Research Institute, M Grygorowicz and L Kobylinski (Technical University, Gdansk, Poland).

Slamming Experiments with a Radio-Controlled SWATH Model, R Graham (Defence Research Establishment Atlantic, Canada).

Assessment of the Prediction of SWATH Ship Motions in Waves, R J Scrace (Ministry of Defence, UK).

Design and Assessment of a Single-Mission ASW SWATH Frigate, T R Cannon and J A Peters (Naval Sea Systems Command, USA).

Wavemaking Characteristics of SWATH Ships, H Chun and A M Ferguson (University of Glasgow, UK).

An Extended SWATH Concept Exploration Model, A Koops (MARIN, The Netherlands) and W C E Nethercote (DREA, Canada).

SWATH-UK MOD Design and Assessment Programme, J D Coles, P A Oliver and S A Harris (Ministry of Defence, UK).

A Review of Recent SWATH Developments, C V Betts (University College London, UK).

Rational Structural Design of SWATH, J F Garside, J J Dowling and P K Das (British Maritime Technology, UK).

Prediction of SWATH Manoeuvring Characteristics in the Design Stages, O M Khattab (British Maritime Technology, UK).

Papers presented at The High-Speed Marine Craft Conference, 4–6 May 1988, Kristiansand, Norway, arranged by the Norwegian Society of Chartered Engineers.

Tools for Predictions of Motions and Seakeeping Qualities of SES and Catamarans, O M Faltinsen (Norwegian Institute of Technology, Trondheim).

Needs Within the Norwegian Navy/NATO Towards the Year 2000. Are We Heading for a New Speed Dimension? S G Oystein Rrnning (Naval Material Command, Norway).

Propulsion Systems for High-Speed Marine Craft, K J Minsaas (Marintek A/S, Trondheim Norway).

How to Choose a Concept for High-Speed Marine Craft, K R Johnsen (Batservice Verft A/S, Norway).

Today's and Tomorrow's Materials for High-Speed Marine Craft, A Marchant (Cetec A/S, Norway .

Power and Seakeeping Performance of High-Speed Marine Vehicles, P Werenskiold (Marintek A/S, Trondheim, Norway).

Market Needs and Potential for High-Speed Marine Transport, E G Tattersall (Hovermarine International Ltd., UK).

The World Market Place and the High-Speed Marine Craft Industry-an Overview, P O Brett (Det norske Veritas Classification A/S, Norway).

Marintek High-Speed Craft Research Programme, K O Holden (Marintek A/S, Trondheim, Norway).

High-Speed Commercial Craft in Coastal Waters-Economical Aspects, B Elvestad (SINTEF, Norwegian Institute of Technology).

Evaluation of Materials for High-Speed Marine Craft within the Norwegian Navy, O Rrnning (Naval Material Command, Norway).

Total Transportation Concept Sea/Land/Air-How Will High-Speed Marine Craft Compete? J-E Wahl (IKO Logistikk A/S, Oslo, Norway).

How can the Military and Commercial Needs Be Combined? Co-operation in Development, S G O Rrnning (Naval Material Command, Norway).

Status of SES Technology, W A Crago.

Fast Method for Determining and Checking the Main Dimensions of a Waterjet, V Ruggiero (Genoa University) and G Venturini (CRM Design Office, Milan, Italy).

AERODYNAMICS	AIR LUBRICATION	ARCTIC, ANTARCTIC APPLICATIONS	COMMERCIAL APPLICATIONS/OPERATIONS	DESIGN	DEVELOPMENT	DYNAMICS/SEAKEEPING	ECONOMICS	ENVIRONMENTAL ASPECTS	FANS	HYDRODYNAMICS	ICE BREAKING	LEGISLATION	LIFT-AIR SYSTEMS	MILITARY/NAVAL APPLICATIONS	PERFORMANCE/DRAG	POWER PLANTS	POWER TRANSMISSION	PRODUCTION	PROPULSION	SAFETY	SKIRTS/SEALS	STABILITY AND CONTROL	STRUCTURE/MATERIALS	TEST FACILITIES	TRIALS
				SWATH																			SWATH		
						SWATH																			
				SWATH																					
										SWATH														SWATH	
						SWATH				SWATH															
						SWATH																			
				SWATH										SWATH											
										SWATH															
				SWATH																					
				SWATH										SWATH											
					SWATH																				
																							SWATH		
																						SWATH			
						SES CAT																			
														GEN											
																		GEN							
			GEN																						
																							GEN		
						GEN								GEN											
			GEN																						
			GEN																						
			GEN											GEN						GEN					
							GEN																		
														GEN									GEN		
			GEN		GEN	GEN																			
			GEN											GEN											
				SES		GEN								GEN SES							SES				
																			GEN						

SECTION 3

REFERENCE PUBLICATIONS, BOOKS AND PERIODICALS

LEGISLATION
INTERNATIONAL
Code of Safety for Dynamically Supported Craft, London 1978, Resolution A 373(X), International Maritime Organisation (IMO).

CANADA
Standards relating to Design, Construction and Operational Safety of Dynamically Supported Craft in Canada, Vol 1, Air Cushion Vehicles; Vol 2, Registration and Certification of Dynamically Supported Craft asnd Dynamically Supported Craft Operations, Transport Canada, Ship Design and Construction Division, Ship Safety Branch, Canadian Coast Guard, Ottawa, December 1985.

NORWAY
Rules for Classification of High-Speed Light Craft, 1985, Det norske Veritas (Veritasveien 1, N-1322 Norway). Effective 1 January 1985.

UK
British Hovercraft Safety Requirements, Airworthiness Division, Civil Aviation Authority (Brabazon House, Redhill, Surrey RH1 1SQ, UK.

BIBLIOGRAPHIES AND GLOSSARIES
Glossary for High-Speed Surface Craft, The Society of Naval Architects and Marine Engineers (1 World Trade Center, Suite 1369, New York, NY 10048, USA).

Bibliography on Hovercraft (ACV), Compiled by H G Russell, TIL Reports Centre, UK, September 1968. TIL/BIB/101.

ITTC Dictionary of Ship Hydrodynamics, Maritime Technology Monograph No 6, 1978. The Royal Institution of Naval Architects, London, August 1978.

Bibliography and Proposed Symbols on Hydrodynamic Technology as Related to Model Tests of High-Speed Marine Vehicles, SSPA Public Research Report No 101, 1984. (SSPA, PO Box 24001, S-40022, Gothenburg, Sweden.)

High-Speed Waterborne Passenger Operations and Craft: Bibliography, US Department of Transportation, Urban Mass Transportation Administration, Washington DC, USA. UMTA-IT-32–0001–84–2, August 1984.

Jane's High-Speed Marine Craft and Air Cushion Vehicles 1987. Contains a bibliography of 186 papers prior to 1980. ISBN 0 7106 0837 3.

GENERAL INTEREST BOOKS
Hovercraft and Hydrofoils, Roy McLeavy. Blandford Press Ltd.

Hovercraft and Hydrofoils, Jane's Pocket Book 21, Roy McLeavy. Jane's Publishing Company.

The Interservice Hovercraft (Trials) Unit, B J Russell. Hover Publications, 1979, ISBN 0 9506 4700 4.

The Law of Hovercraft, L J Kovats. Lloyd's of London Press Ltd, 1989.

Amazon Task Force, Peter Dixon. Hodder and Stoughton, London, UK, 1981, ISBN 0 340 32713 8 and 0 340 34578 0 Pbk.

The Great Himalayan Passage, Adventure Extraordinary by Hovercraft, Michel Peissel. William Collins Sons & Co Ltd, London, UK, 1974, ISBN 0 00 211841 6

Hydrofoils and Hovercraft, Bill Gunston. Aldous Books, London, UK, 1969, ISBN 490 00135 1 and 490 00136 X.

An Introduction to Hovercraft and Hoverports, Cross & O'Flaherty. Pitman Publishing/Juanita Kalerghi.

Light Hovercraft Handbook, (ed) Neil MacDonald. Hoverclub of Great Britain Ltd (available from 45 St Andrews Road, Lower Bemerton, Salisbury, Wilts), 1976.

Hover Craft, Angela Croome, 4th edition, 1984 Hodder and Stoughton Ltd, ISBN 0–340–33201–8, ISBN 0–340–33054–6 Pbk.

Twin Deliveries, J Fogagnolo. International Catamarans Pty Ltd, Hobart, Tasmania. Paperback, 1986.

Ships and Shipping of Tomorrow, Rolf Schonknecht, Jurgen Lusch, Manfred Schelzel, Hans Obenaus, Faculty of Maritime Transport Economics, Wilhelm-Pieck University, Rostock, German Democratic Republic. MacGregor Publications Ltd, Hounslow, England, 240pp, 1987.

Power Boat Speed, Racing and Record-Breaking: 1897 to the Present by Kevin Desmond. Conway Maritime Press Ltd, London, 1988. ISBN 0 85177 427 X.

TECHNICAL BOOKS
High-Speed Small Craft by P du Cane. Temple Press Books Ltd, London, 3rd edition 1964.

Jane's Surface Skimmers (annual 1967–1985) editor: Roy McLeavy, published by Jane's Publishing Company.

Jane's High-Speed Marine Craft (annual, 1986 onwards) editor: Robert L Trillo, published by Jane's Information Group.

Hovercraft Design and Construction, Elsley & Devereax. David & Charles, Newton Abbot, UK, 1968.

Dynamics of Marine Vehicles, by Rameswar Bhattacharyya (US Naval Academy, Annapolis, Maryland, USA). John Wiley & Sons, 1978. ISBN 0 471 07206 0.

Air Cushion Craft Development (First Revision), by P J Mantle (Mantle Engineering Co, Inc, Alexandria, Virginia, USA). David W Taylor, Naval Ship Research and Development Center DTNSRDC-80/012, January 1980.

Transport Ships on Hydrofoils, by Blumin, Massejef and Ivanof Isdatelstvo Transport, Basmannij Tupik, D 6a, Moskowsaja Tipografija Nr 33, Glawpoligrafproma, Moscow, USSR, 1964.

Marine Hovercraft Technology, by Robert L Trillo, 1971. ISBN 0 249 44036 9. Available from Robert Trillo Ltd, Lymington, Hampshire, UK.

Resistance and Propulsion of Ships, by Sv Aa Harvald (The Technical University of Denmark). John Wiley and Sons, 1983. ISSN 0275 8741.

Industrial Fans-Aerodynamic Design, Papers presented at a seminar organised by the Fluid Machinery Committee of the Power Industries Division of the IMechE, held London, 9 April 1987. Published: MEP Ltd.

Global Wave Statistics, N Hogben (British Maritime Technology Ltd). Unwin Brothers Ltd, Woking, UK, 1987, 656pp, £295.

Fibre Reinforced Composites 1986, Institution of Mechanical Engineers publication 1986. ISBN 0 8529 8589 4/297, 262pp.

Encyclopaedia of Composite Materials and Components, (ed) M Grayson, 1983. 1100pp. Avail: AIAA, order number 57–8. ISBN 0 471 87357 8.

Marine Gas Turbines, J B Woodward. Wiley-Interscience (1–95962–6) 1975. 390pp.

The Marine Encyclopaedia Dictionary (2nd Edition), E Sullivan. May 1988. ISBN 1 85044 180 4. 468pp.

Design of High-Speed Boats. Vol 1 Planing, P R Payne. Fishergate Inc, Annapolis, MD, USA. 244pp. 1988. ISBN 0 942 720 06 07.

Hovercraft Technology, Economics and Applications. Editor: J R Amyot, Elsevier Science Publishers BV, 1989. ISBN 0–444–88152–2 & 0–444–41872–5. 770 pp. Dfl.395.00

Mechanics of Marine Vehicles, B R Clayton and R E D Bishop, Gulf Publishing Company, Houston, USA (not available in Bangladesh, Europe, Ireland or The United Kingdom).

PERIODICALS
Fast Ferry International, (10 issues annually) High-Speed Surface Craft, Ltd, 69 Kings Road, Kingston upon Thames, Surrey KT2 5JB, UK.

Hovercraft Bulletin, (monthly) The Hovercraft Society, 24, Jellicoe Avenue, Alverstoke, Gosport, Hampshire, PO12 2PE

Light Hovercraft, (monthly) The Hoverclub of Great Britain Ltd, 45 St Andrews Road, Lower Bemerton, Salisbury, Wilts.

Work Boat World, (monthly) Baird Publications Pte Ltd, 190 Middle Road, Unit 15–07 Fortune Centre, Singapore 0718
and
PO Box 460, South Yarra 3141, Australia.

Ship and Boat International, (ten times a year) 10 Upper Belgrave Street, London SW1X 8BQ, England.

Small Ships, (bi-monthly) International Trade Publications Ltd, Queensway House, 2 Queensway, Redhill, Surrey RH1 1QS, England.

ADDENDA

AUSTRALIA

ADVANCED MULTI-HULL DESIGNS

66 Grandview Street, Pymble, Sydney, New South Wales 2073, Australia

Telephone: (02) 488 9877
Telefax: (02) 488 8144 Administration/(02) 488 8466 Technical

Max Martin, *Managing Director*
Allen J Soars, *Technical Director*
John C Szeto, *Engineering Director*
Bahram Ossivand, *Company Secretary, Financial Controller*

Advanced Multi-hull Designs is a new design group, the formation of which was announced in January 1990. The company has stated its intention to engage in the design of conventional fast catamarans, wave-piercing catamarans and foil-assisted multi-hull craft and has licensed two builders, FBM Marine Ltd in England and Carrington Slipways Pty Ltd in Australia to produce their designs.

AIRLIFT MARINE PTY LTD

69 Coal Point Road, Toronto 2283, New South Wales, Australia

Telephone: (049) 595489
Telefax: (049) 595489

Ross McLeod, *Managing Director*
Kuini Tuato, *Director*

Airlift Marine Pty Ltd was formed in late 1989. Main aims of the company are as follows:
Firstly, to offer a design consultancy service covering all aspects of air cushion vehicle design in the small to medium craft size ranges.
Secondly, to manufacture 3 models of light hovercraft, namely the Airdash 1 (1 or 2 seat), the Airdash 2 (2 or 3 seat) and the Hoverute (5 or 6 seat utility craft).

AIRDASH 1

A two seat sports hovercraft. Airdash 1 Mk1 as built by Hovercraft Manufacturers is the current model and has updated styling and some minor mechanical changes.
LIFT AND PROPULSION: Integrated system powered by single two cylinder two-stroke motor producing 35kW. Power is transmitted via a reduction gearbox mounted directly to the back of the engine to a 900 mm diameter ducted fan. Fuel is carried in a portable tank of approx. 20 litres.
HULL: Monocoque construction of vacuum formed FRP and PVC foam with deck, cockpit, seat locker and duct system moulded in one piece. The hull base is moulded separately and is bonded to the top to form a buoyant one piece structure. Replaceable wear pieces are fitted to strategic points of the hull. Features of this structure type are: very light weight, high strength and stiffness, good impact resistance, easily and quickly repaired.
CONTROLS: Triple rudders controlled by handlebars with twist grip throttle.
SKIRT: Fully segmented type in Urethane or neoprene coated nylon. Segments individually replaceable using quick release clips and nylon ties.
DIMENSIONS
Length: 3.35m
Width: 1.78m
PERFORMANCE
Max recorded on land: 85 km/h

Max recorded on water: 70 km/h
Normal cruising speed on water: 40 km/h

AIRDASH 2

A two-to-three seat sports hovercraft, the Airdash 2 is a stretched version of the Airdash 1.
LIFT AND PROPULSION: An option of a 35kW or a 48 kW engine is available. An integrated system similar to Airdash 1 is employed with an adjustable lift-to-thrust ratio in the peripheral air-dividing ducting. Fuel is carried in two portable tanks of approx. 20 litres each.
DIMENSIONS
Length: 4.15m
Width: 1.78m
PERFORMANCE: (48kW engine)
Max recorded on land: 90 km/h
Max recorded on water: 77 km/h
Normal cruising speed on water: 48 km/h

HOVERUTE

A four-to-five-passenger (or 500 kg payload) plus one crew hovercraft, the Hoverute has been designed primarily for commercial operators in rugged remote areas. To enable operation in extreme conditions and or continued operation in harsh environments particularly where maintenance is difficult to perform, the craft has been designed with large performance reserves and is extremely simple mechanically for easy servicing. The craft is designed to Australian Marine Survey standards (USL) and may be built to survey for commercial personnel transport if required.
The Hoverute can be adapted for a range of applications including surveying, water taxi, commercial fishing, recreational use, patrol, etc. Interest in the craft has been strong in environmentally sensitive areas. The craft has a large cockpit with a flat floor that allows several seating or seating and freight configurations, or the mounting of any special equipment as required for commercial or military operations.
Normally the craft is supplied with a wraparound windscreen and open cockpit; a fabric top is available if required. A custom-built trailer is also available allowing the craft to be either driven or winched on or off for complete one person craft operation if required. The trailer has a moulded deck and hot dipped galvanised steel frame.
LIFT AND PROPULSION: Lift is provided by a single-cylinder air-cooled motor mounted directly driving the lift fan in the lift duct at the front of the craft. The lift fan and motor assembly

is concealed beneath a cover with forward facing air intake vents providing protection, sound absorption and more attractive styling. The lift fan blades are replaceable fixed-pitch moulded polypropylene and glass. Thrust is provided by choice of engines ranging from a two cylinder two-stroke water-cooled engine mounted directly in the thrust fan housing driving the thrust propeller through a reduction gearbox to a four-cylinder four-stroke engine driving the thrust propeller via a flexible coupling and belt. The thrust engine is encased in an FRP cover providing streamlined acoustic isolation and weather protection. The adjustable-pitch propeller blades are pressure moulded using epoxy resin, glass, polyaramid fibre and high-density PVC foam. A single engine integrated lift and thrust version of the craft will be offered in 1991 pending customer demand. Fuel tanks are portable for non-surveyed craft and fixed for surveyed craft, capacity variable upon requirement.
HULL: Foam sandwich, glass and polyaramid fibre reinforced plastic, vacuum formed into a female mould. This method of construction is lightweight while retaining excellent strength, stiffness and good absorption characteristics. The hull is built in two parts and bonded together with sealed buoyancy compartments for maximum safety. Hull lifting and towing points are provided as well as a landing pad system.
CONTROLS: Craft direction is controlled from the front of craft by a handwheel linked to aerodynamic rudders mounted behind the operators side. All engines may be started and stopped from the operators position. Full instrumentation is provided.
SKIRT: A full tapered pressurised bag and finger system is fitted to give optimum stability and handling.
DIMENSIONS
Length overall: 5.5 m
Width overall: 2.35 m
Cushion height: 350mm front to 320mm rear
Cockpit length: 2.8m
Cockpit width: 1.5m
WEIGHTS
Payload: 500 kg
PERFORMANCE
Max Speed: 70km/hr + (38 knots)
Cruising speed: 35km/hr to 50km/hr (20 to 30 knots)
N.B. Performance varies considerably with engine and equipment options chosen.

INTERNATIONAL CATAMARAN DESIGNS PTY LTD

1 Mafeking Avenue, Lane Cove, Sydney, NSW, Australia 2066

INTERNATIONAL CATAMARANS (TASMANIA) PTY LTD

18 Bender Drive, Moonah, Tasmania, Australia

CHRISTOPHER COLUMBUS

Due to enter service with Hoverspeed on 14 June 1990 between Portsmouth and Cherbourg, this 74m InCat wave-piercing catamaran was launched in Hobart on 28 January 1990. See main entry on page 226 for International Catamarans Tasmania Pty Ltd for details. During the final stage of the delivery voyage from Hobart, Tasmania to Portsmouth, an attempt will be made for the Blue Riband Atlantic crossing record.

The 74m InCat wave-piercing catamaran *Christopher Columbus* just after launching in Hobart, Tasmania, 28 January 1990

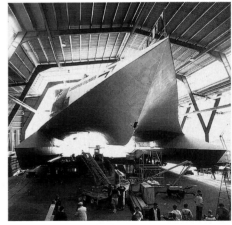

InCat *Christopher Columbus*, just prior to launching

InCat *Christopher Columbus*, superstructure not fitted.   (photo: Ruston Diesels)

DELTA HOVER PTY LTD
25 Sara Street, Toronto, NSW 2283, Australia

Telephone: (049) 504144

RANGER 2000
See also main entry on page 3.

Ranger 2000 instrumentation

Ranger 2000 powered by a Cummins 6CTA 224kW water-cooled diesel engine

CANADA

HIKE METAL PRODUCTS LTD
Box 698, Wheatley, Ontario, Canada

Andrew G Stanton *President*

Builder of aluminium law enforcement vessels and other types of multi-purpose vessels of lengths up to 35 metres and speeds up to 35 knots.

Hike Metal Products yard showing a 35 knot, 34.75 trimaran under construction

CHINA, PEOPLES REPUBLIC OF

CHONG-QING COMPANIES

INTRODUCTION OF MARIC
AMPHIBIOUS HOVERCRAFT AND SES
OPERATIONS ON PASSENGER ROUTES IN
CHINA

The upstream region of the Yang Tze River
named the Chuang Jiang River is located in Shi
Chuan Province and is particularly dangerous for
navigation. The total length of the Chuang Tiang
is about 1044 km (from Yi Chang city of Wu Bei
Province in the east to Yi Bin city of Shi Chuan
Province in the west). Some areas of the river beds
are steep and narrow, where large numbers of
boulders and small rocks are distributed causing
fast-flowing river stretches to form with shallows
and swirling vortices. Progress upstream can
therefore be very difficult for conventional ships;
the SES type shows to advantage in these conditions.

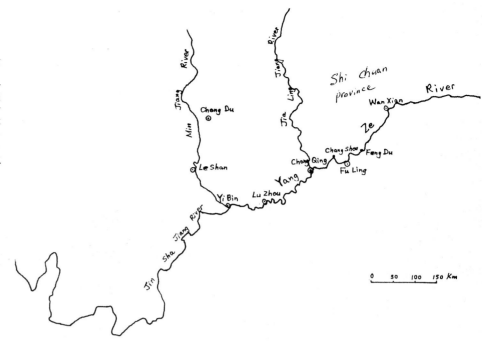

The river routes operated by the Chong-Qing companies.

CI XI NAVIGATION
COMPANY/MARIC/CACTEC
JOINT VENTURE

Shanghai is located on the north side of the
Hang Zhou Gulf and Ning Bo and Ci Xi are on
its south side. The south beach of the gulf is piled
up with sand and mud and extends to a very
large area. It is therefore very difficult to construct
harbours and wharfs in this area.

In 1989 the Ci Xi Navigation Company,
MARIC and CACTEC (see main entry on page
8) established a joint venture, signing a contract
to develop a passenger/car ferry route crossing the
Hang Zhou Gulf from Jin Shan (Shanghai) to Ci-
Xi city of Zhe Tiang Province.

The hovercraft serving the route is a MARIC
716 II named *Ci Ping*. Operations started in
January 1989 and the trip takes 30 minutes.

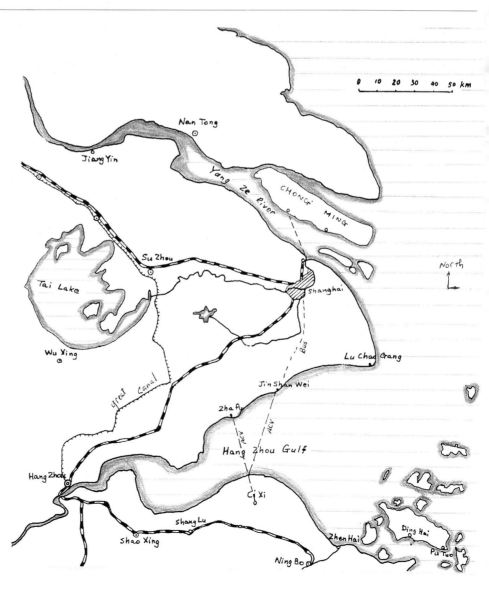

Routes operated by the Ci Xi Navigation Company in
conjunction with MARIC & CACTEC.

FINLAND/USA

SCANDINAVIAN INTERNATIONAL INC
1640 W Oakland Park Boulevard, Suite 301, Fort Lauderdale, Florida 33311, USA

Telephone: (305)731–6199
Telefax: (305)731–6055

Egil Lepsoe, *President*

This company is licensed to build the catamaran design of MXA-Consulting Ltd OY, Finland.

Please see main entry for details of MXA catamaran projects on page 242.

FRANCE

CONSTRUCTIONS MÉCANIQUES DE NORMANDIE
51, Rue de la Bretonnière, BP No 539, 50105 Cherbourg, France

Telephone: 20 12 50
Telex: 170 507 F
Telefax: 44 01 09

AGNES 200
See main entry on page 20 for further information.

Fore structure of AGNES 200 (250 Tonne SES) before turning right way up (CMN April 1990)

Fore structure of AGNES 200 on keel before assembling to the main blocks (CMN April 1990)

INTERNATIONAL MARINE SERVICES (IMS)
Le Pin Rolland, 83430 Saint Mandrier, France

Telephone: (91)330807
Telex: 404619
Telefax: (91)330875

TRANSMED 2000
This 35 knot planing ferry designed by Mauric Design has been built to operate between Marseille and Calvi in Corsica. The vessel is powered by three high-speed diesel engines, the central one employed as a 'booster'

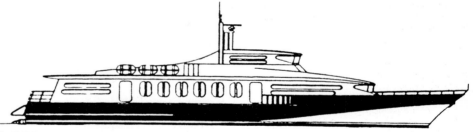

The IMS Transmed 2000

PRINCIPAL PARTICULARS
Hull: aluminium alloy
Length, overall: 36.90m
Beam, max: 7.50m
Engines: three DDC 16V 149 TIB 1540kW each

PROPULSION: three Riva Calzoni IRC 76 DLX water jet units
ACCOMMODATION: 250 passengers
SPEED, DESIGN: 35 knots

GERMANY, FEDERAL REPUBLIC

BLOHM + VOSS AG

857/8 Herman-Blohm Str., 2000 Hamburg 11, Federal Republic of Germany

CORSAIR
See main entry on page 23 for further information.

Blohm + Voss Corsair

Blohm + Voss Corsair

KÖNIG MASCHINENBAU GmbH

Sophienstrasse 52–54, D-6330 Wetzlar, Federal Republic of Germany

AIR RIDER BOOSTER
This craft is now certificated by the USCG and NMMA.

AIR RIDER WILDCAT
This luxury craft has been changed from a three-seater to a four-seater and will be available from September 1990. Details additional to those in the main entry on page 140 are:
Beam: 2.50m
Height: 1.80 m
Engine: BMW M20 BZMi, 125 kW
Speed: 110 km/h

The König Air Rider Booster

ITALY

SOCIETA ESERCIZIO CANTIERI (SEC)
Via dei Pescatori 56 Viareggio, Italy

Telephone: (0584) 3801
Telex: 500369 SEC I
Telefax: (0584) 384559

Registered Office:
Largo Toniolo 10, Rome

Dr Renzo Pozzo, *Managing Director*
Dr Ing Claudio Pesce, *Sales*
Dr Ing Leonardo Auoiarri, *Technical*

SEC an Italian naval shipbuilder has been building ships for over 10 years including trawlers, tugs, supply vessels, gas carriers, and chemical carriers.

SEC yard no's 774/778/779
SEC has signed a contract with Sea Searchers Sud Srl for three SES ferries to be used for services to Mediterranean Islands. Construction of the first vessel will start in June 1990 to be followed by launching in October 1991, sea trials in March 1992 and delivery in June 1992. Classification of these vessels will be by ABS and RINA.
PRINCIPAL PARTICULARS
Hull: High tensile steel
Superstructure: Aluminium alloy
Length, overall: 67.00m
Beam, overall: 21.00m
Depth, overall: 8.30m
Draught, on cushion: 0.60m
    off cushion: 3.60m

Artists impression of the SEC SES passenger car ferry for delivery in June 1992

ENGINES: Two GE LM 1600 gas turbines
PROPULSION: Two waterjet units
LIFT: Four fan systems
SKIRT SYSTEM: Segmented bow skirt, lobe type stern seal

AUXILIARY POWER: Two 600kW generators
PAYLOAD: 350 passengers and 90 cars
PERFORMANCE
Speed, max (Sea State 0): 52 knots
Endurance: 15h at 40 knots

JAPAN

AWASHIMA KISEN CO. LTD
1–67 Iwafuneminato-machi, Murakami-shi Niiga-ken 958, Japan

See main entry, page 464. A second craft entered service in 1989:

Route operated
This vessel operates on the same route as the company's other mono-hull, *Iwayuri*, from Awashima to Iwafune.

High-speed craft operator

Type	Name	Speed	Seats	Delivered
MH Sumidagawa Zosen Co. Ltd.	*Asuka*	24 knots	173	May 1989

Asuka delivered to Awashima Kisen Co. Ltd. in May 1989

SOUTH KOREA

KOREA TACOMA MARINE INDUSTRIES LIMITED

Main office and shipyard:
P O Box 339, 974–15 Yang duk-dong, Masan 630–728, South Korea

Telephone: Masan (051) 55–1181/8, 93–2181
Telex: 53662 KOTAMAN K
Telefax: (0551)94–9449

Jong-Nak Kim, *Chairman*
Jung-Tae Kim, *President*
Sung-Jin Lee, *Executive Managing Director*
Mu-Ryong Bae, *Executive Managing Director*

Seoul office:
CPO Box 4296, Seoul, South Korea

Telephone: (02)777–0901/5
Telex: 27351 KOTAMI
Telefax: (02)757 0884

A four-engine 25m amphibious hovercraft designed for navy landing craft operations (similar to the LCAC type) has been completed and has engaged in trials. The craft is powered by two 2600 kW Textron Lycoming gas turbines driving two 4 metre ducted propellers for propulsion. Two Pratt and Whitney gas turbines power the lift system.

See also main entry on page 30.

THE NETHERLANDS

TILLE SCHEEPSBOUW BV
Balkwar 10, Post Box 8, 9288 ZG Kootstertille, The Netherlands

Telephone: (05)121 2300
Telefax: (05)121 2395

Reim Amels, *Managing Director*

This company is one of eight yards in the Conoship Shipbuilding Group.

ILES DE LERINS
Delivered to Mr Coopamat, France

PRINCIPAL PARTICULARS
Length, overall: 25.00m
Breadth, moulded: 8.50m
Depth: 2.70m
Draught, max: 1.80m
Accommodation: 220 passengers
Engines: Two DDC diesels, each 478kW at 2300 rpm
Speed: approx 20 knots

Iles de Lerins

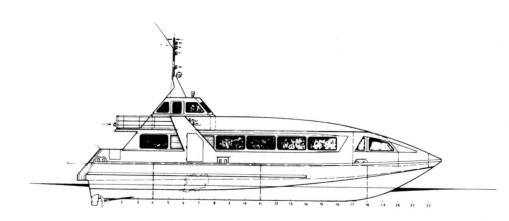

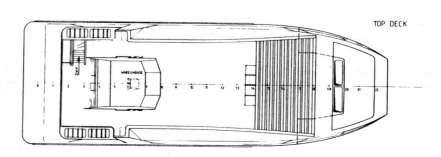

Iles de Lerins

38 KNOT CATAMARAN

(Yard No's. 276 and 277) Based on the company's experience building the catamaran *Iles de Lerins*, the Indian Government placed an order with the yard in 1989 for two 360-passenger high-speed catamarans for inter-island passenger services in the Lakshadweep area of South West India. The vessels designed by Mulder Design of Gorinchem, are powered by two Deutz MWM 12V 604B diesels, 1242kW each, driving through ZF gearboxes KaMeWa 63S water-jet units.

Auxiliary power is provided by two Cummins 6B5.9G S 4kW auxiliary engines with two Newage Stamford MHC-234 61kVA generators.

DIMENSIONS
Length, overall: 31.75m
Length,p p: 28.85m
Beam, moulded: 9.40m
Depth: 3.30m
Draught: 1.40m

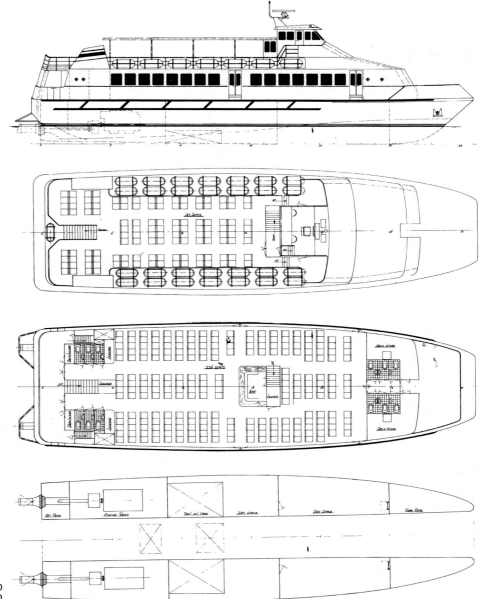

General arrangement of Tille Scheepsbouw 38 knot, 360 passenger catamaran

NORWAY

BÅTSERVICE INDUSTRIER

Mandal, Norway

Ole Guttorme, *Production Manager*

BÅTSERVICE MARINE

N-4500 Mandal, Norway

Telephone: (43) 61011
Telex: 21862 YARD N
Telefax: (43) 64580

SES MINE COUNTERMEASURE VESSELS

Under a $280 million contract, Båtservice Marine is to deliver to the Royal Norwegian Navy four minehunters and five minesweepers between 1992 and December 1995 with an option on a tenth. The vessels will replace the present class of

Model of a 55m mine counter-measures SES, nine of which will be built for the Royal Norwegian Navy.

28 METRE CATAMARAN

Early in 1990 Rogaland Traffikkselskaps of Stavanger took delivery from Båtservice of a 150 passenger, 37 knot catamaran. The first of two to be delivered, the vessel is powered by two 1490 kW diesel engines, driving propellers. Service speed 35 knots. The craft will operate on the routes Stavanger to Jørpeland, Sauda to Sand, Vikeda to Sandeid and Hjelmeland.

eight US-built 1950's MSC-60 coastal mine-sweepers/hunters and trials of the first one are expected in 1991.

The Kvaerner Group will provide engineering support, quality assurance services and financial assistance. Brødrene Aa has already built and tested a full-scale hull section.

Båtservice Marine was formed in 1989 under the joint ownership of Båtservice Verft and Moss Rosenberg/Kvaerner to build the MCRVs and a new yard has been constructed for the purpose at Sismerøya.

PRINCIPAL PARTICULARS
Length: 55.00m
Beam: 13.00m

Engines, propulsion: Two 2192kW diesels
      lift: Two 1387kW diesels
Propulsion: Two KaMeWa water jets
Speed: 22 knots, transit
Crew: 37
Displacement: 375 tonnes

HARDING VERFT A/S
Box 55, N-5470 Rosendal, Norway

Telephone: (054)81322
Telefax: (054)81934

Kjartan Stensønes, *Managing Director*

Harding Verft A/S was established in 1989. The history of the yard reaches back to 1855 and over the years a great number and range of ships have been built and launched: ferries, research vessels, inspection craft, naval vessels, special tankers, fishing vessels, chemical tankers, life-boats, ice-breakers, tugs and mine-layers for the Royal Norwegian Navy.

With 30 years of experience in building with aluminium the yard stated in 1986 with a sub-contract for Fjellstand A/S. The work included complete production of five 38.8m passenger Catamarans for delivery in Turkey.

In 1989, Harding Verft A/S delivered the first Harding 26m Catamaran to owner S. Møkster, Norway. The vessel's name was *Havstril*.

The design of the Harding 28m Catamaran was based on experience with *Havstril* and a great deal of research. A complete new hull was designed based on extensive model tank tests in order to provide improved passenger comfort, low fuel consumption and high manoeuvrability. A service speed of 32.5 knots, fully loaded and at 85% MCR, is now quoted for this vessel.

In 1990, Harding Verft A/S will deliver the first Harding 28m catamaran to owner Rederij Doeksen, Holland. The vessel's name will be *Stuifdijk*, she will be delivered in June, and will be classified DnV, 1A1 light craft passenger cata-maran (R 20, E0).

The next 28m catamaran will be delivered in November 1990, to the Norwegian owner Nesodden-Bundefjord D/S.

See also main entry on p. 257.

The Harding 26m *Havstril* (photo:Fotograf Løtvedt)

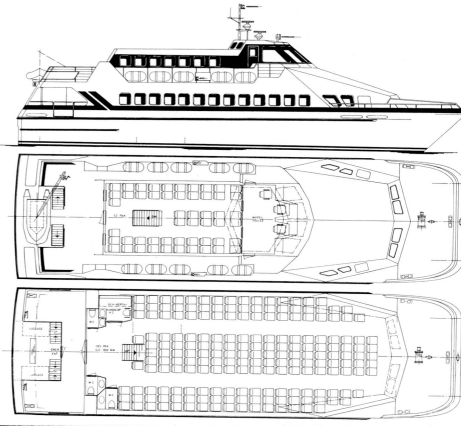

Harding 28m catamaran as supplied to Rederij Doeksen

A model of the Harding Verft 250 passenger catamaran *Stuifdijk*, to be delivered to Rederij Doeksen in June 1990.

KVAERNER FJELLSTRAND A/S

N–5632 Omastrand, Norway
MERCURY (Yard No. 1598)
SOLOVKI (Yard No. 1599)

The *Murcury* and the *Solovki* are both 38.8 metre catamarans. *Mercury* was delivered on 1 March 1990 to the Far Eastern Shipping Company, Vladivostock, USSR, and *Solovki* on 15 March 1990 to the Northern Shipping Company, Archangelsk, USSR.

See also main entry on p. 257.

CLASSIFICATION
USSR Register of Shipping (RS) KM * 11 ⁅2⁆ A3
PRINCIPAL PARTICULARS (see main entry)
GRT: 431
NRT: 102
Main engines: two MTU 16 V 396 TB84, 2040 kW each, at 100% output, 1940 rpm
Auxiliary engines: MTU GR 099 TA 31
Propulsion: two KaMeWa 63S 11 water-jet units
Speed, max: 39 knots.
   service: 34.6 knots at 27 413 kg load, *Solovki*
          34.7 knots at 28 679 kg load, *Mercury*
Noise levels *Solovki*: lounge, main deck: 72 dBA
                lounge, upper deck (middle 65 dBA
                wheelhouse: 56 dBA
Accommodation: 230 passengers, *Solovki*
              252 passengers, *Mercury*

The Fjellstrand 38.8m catamaran *Solovki* for service in the White Sea between Archangelsk and the Solovetskiy islands.

WESTAMARIN AS

4501 Mandal, Norway
KRYMSKAYA STRELA (Yard No. 103)

The first of four Westamaran 4100S 42.50m catamarans purchased by AKP Sovcomflot/Black Sea Shipping Co., USSR andc delivered in March 1990.

See also main entry on page 48.

CLASSIFICATION
USSR Register of Shipping (RS) KM * ⁅2⁆ 11 A3 pass. CAT
PRINCIPAL PARTICULARS (see main entry)
GRT: 493
NRT: 148
Main engines: two MTU 396 V 16 TB 84, 2040 kW each, at 1940 rpm
Fuel consumption: 916 kg/h at 100% MCR
Auxiliary engines: two Daimler Benz OM 366A

The Westamarin 4100S 42.50 metre catamaran

SWEDEN

BOGHAMMAR MARINE AB
Nysätravägen 6–8, 18160 Lidingö, Sweden

Telephone: (08)766 0190
Telex: 14149 BOGBOAT 5
Telefax: (08)766 1855

GRIPSHOLM (Yard No. 1148)
    A 120 seat, 34 knot monohull ferry built 1989 for Rydstafors AB, Mariefred. Length, overall: 26.50m beam: 5.60m GRT 110, NRT 30 engines: two MAN D2842, 850 kW

UNITED KINGDOM

RUSTON DIESELS
Vulcan Works, Newton-le-Willows, Merseyside, WA12 8RU, England

    See also main entry on page 528.

One of the four 3650 kW Ruston 16 RK 270 diesels being installed in the first International Catamarans (Tasmania) 74m wave-piercing catamarans for the Hoverspeed Portsmouth to Cherbourg service this year
(photo: Ruston Diesels)

International Catamarans (Tasmania) 74m passenger/car ferry showing form of the central bow hull   (photo: Ruston Diesels)

UNITED STATES OF AMERICA

BERTRAM YACHT

3663 NW 21st Street, Miami, Florida, 33142, USA

Telephone: (305) 633 8011
Telefax: (305) 635 1388

G Robert Smith, *President*
Jim Krueger, *Vice President of Sales*

Bertram Yacht was established in 1960 with the introduction of the famous 31-foot Moppie deep-V yacht. Currently, the company builds yachts from 8.54m (of which over 1,500 have been launched), through 33, 37, 43, 50, 54 and the new 60 Convertible, plus the 72 Convertible which is flexible in its interior layout. The Bertram 72 was launched in December 1989.

BERTRAM 72
PRINCIPAL PARTICULARS
Hull: vacuum bagged Baltek polymer-coated AL-600 balsa is used extensively. Decks have carbon-fibre reinforcement
Length, overall: 22.10m

Beam, max: 5.61m
Draft: 2.06m
Height above waterline, max: 6.03m
Cockpit area: 17.93m^2
Displacement, cruise: 54.42 tonnes
Engines: two MTU 12V 396 TB93 1DS,1454 kW each
Gear (with MTU): MGNV433 1.53:1
Speed: 35 knots
Fuel capacity, total (label cap) standard: 9727 l
Fresh water capacity, total, standard: 1136 l

BURGER BOAT COMPANY INC

808 North Dixie Highway, Lantana, Florida 33462, USA

Telephone: (407)533 3600
Telefax: (407)586 1256

MEDORA
Built in welded aluminium at the construction yard at Manitowoc, Wisconsin, *Medora* was designed by C Raymond Hunt Associates, Inc., which is an exception for the very many motor yachts built by the Burger Boat Company
PRINCIPAL PARTICULARS
Length, overall: 22.15 m

Medora

Length, waterline: 20.00 m
Beam: 5.79 m
Draught: 1.75 m
Displacement: 45.71 tonnes

Engine: MAN D2842LE V12 567kW Gearbox: ZF BW165 2.0:1.0
Speed, cruising: 18 to 20 knots
    max: 24 knots

ELLIOTT BAY DESIGN GROUP LIMITED

5301 Shilshole Ave. N.W. Seattle, Washington
98107, USA

Telephone: (206) 782–3082
Telefax: (206) 782–3449

John W Waterhouse, *President*
Kenneth R Lane, *Vice President*
Christopher Barry, *Project Manager*
Brian King, *Project Manager*
Annette Grimm, *Business Manager*

Elliott Bay Design Group is a firm dedicated to providing naval architecture and marine engineering services. Using microcomputer technology and an extensive reference library, the company offers a wide range of services, from concept design of high-speed hulls to numerical lofting of structure. The full time staff of nineteen includes four naval architects, three marine engineers, and two electrical engineers.

As the successor to Nickum & Spaulding Associates, the staff experience is focused on commercial workboats and passenger boats. High-speed vessel designs up to 45m and 50 knots have been prepared using both high-speed diesels and gas turbines. The firm has worked on hydro-foils, catamarans, planing hulls and SWATHs. The staff is familiar with the requirements of various regulatory bodies including USCG, ABS, IMO, and DNV.

Projects undertaken within the past two years include: the design of a 18.6m aluminium pilot boat, performance analysis of a 12.8m high-speed survey boat, design of a harbour service craft with fire fighting and oil spill recovery capabilities, and a ferry transportation study for Cook Inlet, Alaska. The company has also lofted a variety of hulls from other designers including a 76.5m tuna seiner, a 17.7m high-speed limit seiner, a 39.6m steel crab boat, and a 6.7m aluminium seine skiff.

LACE EXPRESS YACHTS

850 N E 3rd Street, Suite 207, Dania, Florida 33004, USA
MIDNIGHT LACE 68'
A 22 knot motor yacht designed by Tom Fexas and built in Divinycell PVC cored foam and uni-directional fibre glass reinforcement

PRINCIPAL PARTICULARS
Length, overall: 20.88 m
Beam: 5.95 m
Draught, keel: 1.07 m
Displacement: 25.40 tonnes

TEXTRON MARINE SYSTEMS

600 Plaza Drive, New Orleans, Louisiana 70127–2596 USA

Telephone: (504)245 6600

LCAC

On 8 February 1990, Textron Marine Systems announced a contract for a further 9 LCACs valued at US $121 million, bringing the total to 45 since the spring of 1981.

SES 200

On 11 April 1990, Textron Marine Systems announced the award of a US $1,858,744 contract by the US Army Corps of Engineers for the conversion, modification and upgrading of the propulsion system and hull structure of the 48.78m SES 200.

The conventional propellers and existing 16V 149 TI diesel engines and gearboxes will be replaced by two MTU 16V 396 TB 94 diesel engines using two ZF BW 755 gearboxes driving KaMeWa 71 S62/6–SII waterjet systems. Following the conversion, which will increase the propulsion power from 2386 kW to 4265 kW, the SES 200 is expected to achieve speeds in excess of 40 knots in calm water, have greater manoeuvrability, produce lower in-water noise emission, and be able to operate in shallower waters.

To conduct the conversion/re-powering work, the SES 200 was lifted from the water at the Textron Marine Systems shipyard, transported 160 metres overland and brought into position in a high-bay construction building.

After successfully completing acceptance trials in the Gulf of Mexico, the SES 200 will return to its home port at the David Taylor Research Center (DTRC), located at the Naval Air Station, Patuxent River, Maryland on the Chesapeake Bay. The DTRC, the Navy's laboratory for advanced naval vehicle development, will deploy the craft in evaluation programmes.

Textron Marine Systems 48.78m SES 200

LCAC–24 shown during builder's trials on Lake Borgne

The SES 200, weighing 162 long tons, lifted from the water and being lowered onto a transporter at the Textron Marine Systems shipyard in New Orleans

VIKING YACHTS
Garden State Parkway, New Gretna, NJ 08224

Telephone: (609)296 6000
Telefax: (609)296 3956

VIKING 72′
A high performance motor yacht available 1990
PRINCIPAL PARTICULARS
Length, overall: 22.00 m
Beam: 5.30
Draught: 1.42 m
Displacement: 36.36 tonnes
Fuel capacity: 5564 l
Water capacity: 1325 l

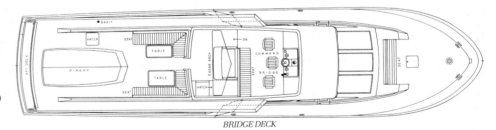

BRIDGE DECK

UPPER LEVEL: Widebody Layout

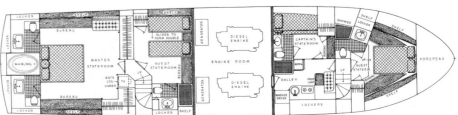

Deck arrangements of Viking 72′

LOWER LEVEL

Viking 72' motor yacht

INDEX OF ORGANISATIONS

Please note that late Addenda entries are not included in the indexes

INDEX OF CRAFT TYPES

INDEX OF ENGINE TYPES

INDEX OF CRAFT NAMES